George D. Grant
1708 Manning Street
Phila. 3, Pa.
Tel. - PE 5-5648

» TEXTBOOK OF CHEMISTRY «

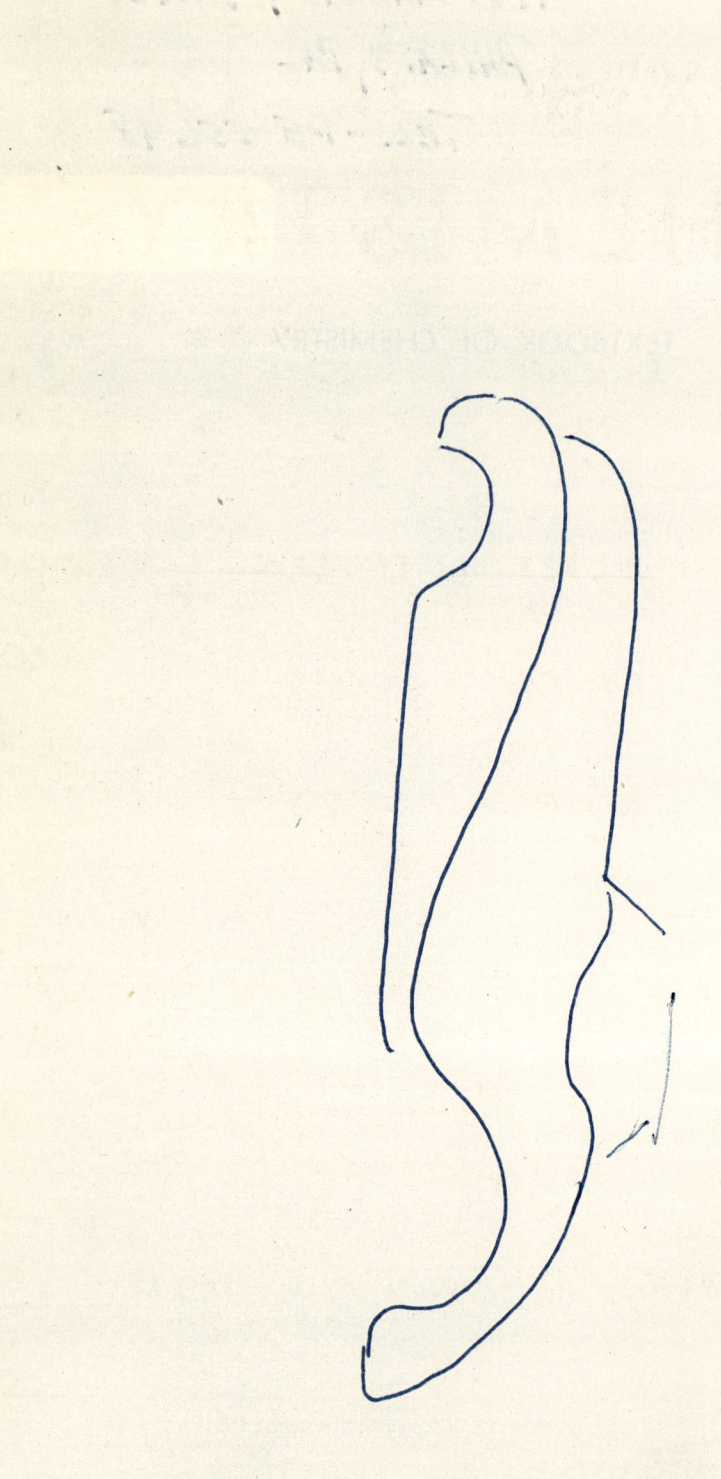

INTERNATIONAL ATOMIC WEIGHTS

	Symbol	Atomic No.	Atomic Weight
Molybdenum	Mo	42	95.95
Neodymium	Nd	60	144.27
Neon	Ne	10	20.183
Nickel	Ni	28	58.69
Nitrogen	N	7	14.008
Osmium	Os	76	190.2
Oxygen	O	8	16.0000
Palladium	Pd	46	106.7
Phosphorus	P	15	30.98
Platinum	Pt	78	195.23
Potassium	K	19	39.096
Praseodymium	Pr	59	140.92
Protactinium	Pa	91	231
Radium	Ra	88	226.05
Radon	Rn	86	222
Rhenium	Re	75	186.31
Rhodium	Rh	45	102.91
Rubidium	Rb	37	85.48
Ruthenium	Ru	44	101.7
Samarium	Sm	62	150.43
Scandium	Sc	21	45.10
Selenium	Se	34	78.96
Silicon	Si	14	28.06
Silver	Ag	47	107.880
Sodium	Na	11	22.997
Strontium	Sr	38	87.63
Sulfur	S	16	32.066
Tantalum	Ta	73	180.88
Tellurium	Te	52	127.61
Terbium	Tb	65	159.2
Thallium	Tl	81	204.39
Thorium	Th	90	232.12
Thulium	Tm	69	169.4
Tin	Sn	50	118.70
Titanium	Ti	22	47.90
Tungsten	W	74	183.92
Uranium	U	92	238.07
Vanadium	V	23	50.95
Xenon	Xe	54	131.3
Ytterbium	Yb	70	173.04
Yttrium	Y	39	88.92
Zinc	Zn	30	65.38
Zirconium	Zr	40	91.22

TEXTBOOK OF CHEMISTRY

REVISED EDITION

By

ALBERT L. ELDER
Director of Research,
Corn Products Refining Co.

EWING C. SCOTT
Associate Professor of Chemistry,
Syracuse University

FRANK A. KANDA
Assistant Professor of Chemistry,
Syracuse University

NEW YORK
HARPER & BROTHERS PUBLISHERS

TEXTBOOK OF CHEMISTRY, REVISED EDITION

Copyright, 1941, 1948, by Harper & Brothers
Printed in the United States of America

All rights in this book are reserved.
No part of the book may be reproduced in any manner whatsoever without written permission except in the case of brief quotations embodied in critical articles and reviews. For information address Harper & Brothers

G-Y

CONTENTS

Preface		vii
1. Introduction		1
2. Methods Used in the Discovery of the Elements		6
3. The Particle Nature of Matter		17
4. The Kinetic Molecular Theory of Gases		26
5. The Electrical Nature of Matter		50
6. Electron Arrangement in Atoms and Valence		64
7. The Periodic System		79
8. Names and Formulas of Compounds		91
9. Types of Chemical Reactions		101
10. Oxygen		115
11. Ozone and the Peroxides		131
12. Hydrogen		138
13. Properties of Liquids and Solids		161
14. Solutions		172
15. Water, Acids, and Bases		190
16. Properties of Ions. Salts		201
17. Chemical Equilibria		221
18. Electricity as a Tool of the Chemist		246
19. The Atmosphere		270
20. Water—Its Purification and Uses		284
21. Colloids		298
22. Alkali Metals and Halogens and Their Compounds. Products of the Salt Industry		310
23. Sulfur, Selenium, and Tellurium		361
24. Nitrogen and Its Compounds		394
25. Phosphorus and Its Compounds		422
26. Arsenic, Antimony, and Bismuth		437
27. Silicon and Its Compounds		453
28. Boron and Its Compounds		478
29. Characteristics of the Metals		487
30. The Alkaline Earth Metals; Aluminum		502
31. Zinc, Cadmium, Mercury, Tin, and Lead		536

32. Copper	570
33. Silver and Gold	581
34. The Platinum Metals	594
35. Iron	599
36. Metals Used in the Steel Industry	613
37. The Less Familiar Metals	638
38. Nuclear Chemistry	646
39. Carbon and Its Compounds	660
Appendix	733
Index	737

» PREFACE «

TO THE STUDENT

This book was written for students who expect to make some branch of science their life work. This implies (which is not always true) that you have a good background in mathematics and a genuine interest in science. Your success in chemistry will be limited unless you can multiply, divide, subtract, solve proportions, and otherwise do accurate work in mathematics. It is expected that you will enjoy laboratory work—that you like to do things for yourself—that you have an inquiring mind.

It is quite probable that your chemistry course will consist of lectures and demonstrations, recitations, and laboratory work. Learn to use your textbook as a reference guide in the laboratory. Read over the topic for lecture before going to class, and the topics pertaining to the laboratory work before going to the laboratory. Make notes in your textbook, underscore points that are not clear, and in every way possible use the printed page as an aid to your progress in the course. As soon as possible after each lecture, read over your lecture notes, and if there is any point which you do not understand, look it up in the text. Use the index to find where other phases of the subject may be discussed; special pains have been taken to provide an unusually complete index to make this easy for you. Do not hesitate to ask your instructor for help if any point is still not clear. *You cannot do yourself justice in chemistry if you skip over such points, for they may have an important bearing on later subject matter.*

There is no attempt to tell the whole story of chemistry in this one book, for this is impossible in so few pages. By the time this book reaches you many new discoveries will have been made. Furthermore, current research may prove incorrect some statements that appeared true when they were written here. Your instructor can help you keep up to date with the progress of science. The lists of references at the end of the chapters are not long; they usually refer to articles which contain numerous references to earlier literature. Spend one evening each month in the library reading these references and you will become more interested in chemistry. During the year you should read at least one popular book on chemistry such as *Crucibles* by Jaffe. Weeks' *The Discovery of the Elements* is a truly great book; throughout the course you should read chapters in it which pertain to the topics under discussion. Manufacturers issue many pamphlets, booklets, and periodicals that will add to your knowledge of chemistry. Ask your instructor where you can obtain them. Two of the popular handbooks of chemistry—Lange's *Handbook of Chemistry* and the *Handbook of Chemistry and Physics*—contain many tables and other factual material you will need. If you are undecided about majoring in Chemistry, read a series of articles on the chemist at work, published in 1938 in the *Journal of Chemical Education*.

TO THE INSTRUCTOR

The authors recognize that each teacher finds some method and order of presenting material best adapted to the type of student, aim of the course, equipment available, and his own individuality. This book is intended for students desiring a good foundation in general chemistry, irrespective of their previous training in the subject. Each new concept is accordingly presented with a complete explanation which does not imply any prior knowledge of chemistry, and each technical word is thoroughly defined and its use illustrated.

We feel strongly that a student should know something about the nature of matter before beginning to study the chemical properties of particular substances. We therefore prove the reality of molecules by citing the most modern experiments, and proceed immediately to develop the kinetic theory. The existence of atoms is proved by Avogadro's Law, and their electronic structure is described in simple terms and related to the periodic table. The student is then ready to understand the nature of chemical change with a completeness of comprehension impossible to one who starts to study oxygen before he knows what makes the difference between a free and a combined element. This thorough foundation puts the beginning student on a level with the student who took chemistry in high school. At the same time it offers interestingly new material to the latter, and enables him to maintain that interest by presenting all the descriptive (as well as the theoretical) material on a distinctly college level.

Carbon and its compounds are discussed in the last chapter but may be introduced between Chapters 26 and 27 if desired. Your suggestions for improvements and changes in this book will be gratefully received.

ACKNOWLEDGEMENT

The authors are appreciative of the efforts of those who have assisted in the preparation of this book. The General Chemistry staff at Syracuse University has cooperated in every way; their help and criticisms have been invaluable. Great assistance has been rendered by the helpful criticisms of the many users of the first edition. Several companies and publishers have provided photographs for reproduction, and the authors wish to express to them their gratitude.

ALBERT L. ELDER
EWING C. SCOTT
FRANK A. KANDA

» TEXTBOOK OF CHEMISTRY «

» 1 «

INTRODUCTION

The time has passed when man is content to adapt himself to the shortcomings of materials which he finds in nature. Today, if no known material has exactly the needed properties, chemistry may create a new one which does have them. Anciently used substances are improved almost beyond recognition. Processes are developed which put former rarities within the reach of everyone. You are surrounded not merely by objects, but by *substances* which George Washington never knew. It would be hard indeed to name a single article in use in which chemistry has not played an important part.

Since substances and processes, diet and disease, matter and energy are no longer taken for granted but are the object of man's active study and intervention, some knowledge of the facts and principles which govern them must be gained by anyone who wishes to consider himself educated. A course in general chemistry furnishes an excellent survey of these for the student, and is a definite necessity to all students of the sciences, pure or applied.

Chemistry is the study of the nature of substances, the changes which they undergo, and the energy which is produced or which vanishes during these changes. It is one of the *exact* sciences. Philosophical speculation fumbled almost fruitlessly along chemical lines for two thousand years, but modern chemistry really began when Lavoisier, martyr of the French Revolution, introduced the use of the balance. Only by continuous recourse to every exact method of measurement and observation offered by the laboratory has the science confuted false hypotheses, amplified inadequate ones, and confirmed the theories based on true insight.

Research workers in all branches of science, everywhere, use the metric system of measurements in making and recording their observations. They do this because of the convenience afforded by the simple interrelationships between its various kinds of units and by its use of decimal multiples and subdivisions, but even more because it is truly international. The metric system is used exclusively throughout Europe, Siberia, and South America and is becoming increasingly popular elsewhere. In the United States the units of the English system are legally defined in terms of metric standards which are kept in the Bureau of Standards in Washington.

Units of Measure

The metric unit of length is the meter (m.). It was intended to be one 10,000,000th of the earth's quadrant. It is 39.37 inches, or approximately 1.1 yards. Commonly used subdivisions of the meter are the centimeter (cm.), 0.01 meter, and the millimeter (mm.), 0.001 meter. The centimeter is about two fifths of an inch; the millimeter, one twenty-fifth of an inch.

The liter (l.) is the metric unit of capacity; it is a little more than a quart. The most commonly used subdivision of the liter is the milliliter (ml.), 0.001 liter, which is roughly a quarter teaspoonful.

The unit of mass is the gram (g.). It is rather small; three aspirin tablets weigh about a gram; a nickel weighs 5 grams. A kilogram (kg.), 1000 grams, is about 2.2 pounds.

The mass of a body is the quantity of matter it contains, expressed in a suitable unit. The weight of a body is the force with which the earth attracts the body. Since the latter varies inversely as the square of the distance from the center of the earth, the weight of a given mass on the surface of the earth is greater than the weight of the same mass at a higher altitude. For any one place, weight is always proportional to mass and the two terms may be used interchangeably.

Convenient relationships exist between units of the metric system. Within ordinary limits of accuracy it is true that 1 cubic centimeter of water occupies 1 milliliter and weighs 1 gram. For other units of the metric system and for conversion factors, consult the Appendix.

Temperature

The centigrade temperature scale is regularly used in scientific laboratories. It is so called because it divides into 100 parts the distance between the two major calibration points upon which it is based. That is, the centigrade scale is defined by stating that the freezing point of water is 0° C. and its boiling point (under standard pressure) is 100° C. These two temperatures are 180° apart on the Fahrenheit scale; hence Fahrenheit degrees are smaller. Nine Fahrenheit degrees equal five centigrade degrees. A Fahrenheit temperature cannot be converted into the equivalent centigrade temperature simply by multiplying it by 5/9, because the zeros on the two scales are different. However, − 40° F. is the same temperature as − 40° C.; so by counting from this common point instead of from the differing zeros conversion in either direction is very simple. The rule is: Add 40°, multiply by the ratio 5/9 or 9/5 (as the case requires) and subtract 40°. There will be no difficulty in deciding which form of the ratio to use if you remember that Fahrenheit degrees are smaller and therefore more numerous than centigrade degrees.

Another temperature scale, the use of which is confined to scientific measurements, is called the absolute centigrade scale and differs from the centigrade scale only in having its zero 273° lower. That is, 0° C. = 273° A. (The

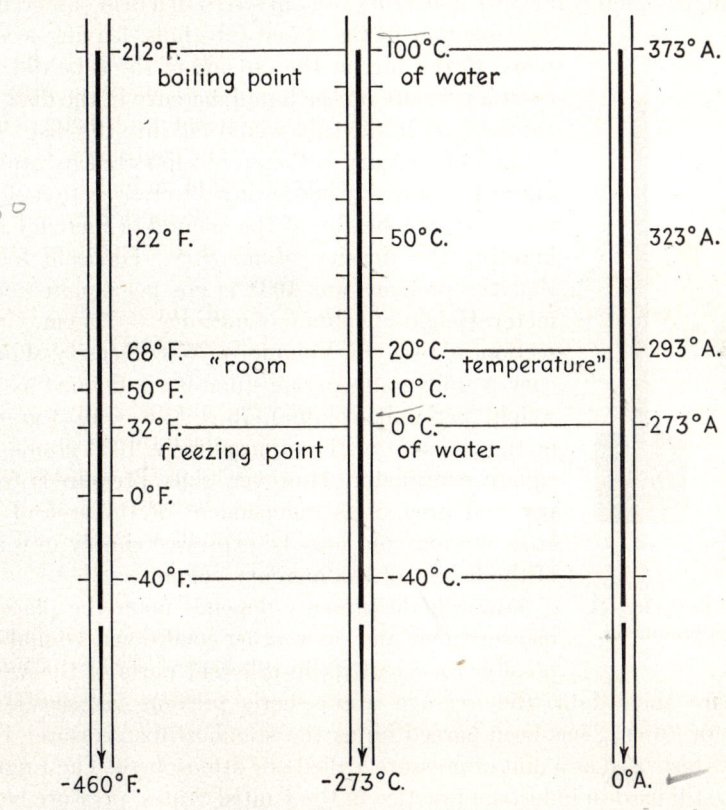

Fig. 1.1. Fahrenheit, centigrade, and absolute centigrade temperature scales.

absolute scale is also called the Kelvin scale, in honor of the great British physicist.) The necessity for the absolute scale will be discussed on page 33.

Fig. 1.1 shows these three scales. Note that 0° C. = 32° F. = 273° A.; 100° C. = 212° F. = 373° A. The English "room temperature" of 68° F. = 20° C. In the United States "room temperature" is more commonly taken to be 77° F. = 25° C.

Pressure

Soon after Galileo proved that air had weight, Torricelli, a pupil of his, set about to prove that if air had weight, it should exert a pressure upon the earth. The barometers used in most laboratories today are patterned after the one devised by Torricelli. Fig. 1.2B shows the Torricelli type, and Fig. 1.2A a modification of it which is more popular because less mercury is required to fill it.

In the Torricelli barometer, a glass tube at least a meter in length is closed at one end, completely filled with mercury, and inverted in a dish of mercury. The mercury in the closed tube falls, leaving a vacuum. If the air on the outside of the tube did not exert a pressure on the liquid mercury in the dish, all the mercury in the tube would fall into the dish. The column of mercury is therefore supported by atmospheric pressure. By measuring the cross section of the tube and the height of the column of mercury and knowing the density of mercury, Torricelli found that the pressure was 1033 grams per square centimeter. Height of column of mercury = 76 cm. Cross section = 1 sq. cm. Volume = 76 cc. Density of mercury = 13.6 grams per ml. (density is defined as the weight per unit volume). 76 × 13.6 = 1033 grams, or the pressure of the atmosphere is 1033 grams per square centimeter. However, since pressure is force per unit area, it is independent of the area of the cross section, and may be expressed simply in terms of the height of the mercury column.

FIG. 1.2. A, common type of barometer; B, Torricelli barometer.

Atmospheric pressure depends upon the place of measurement and on weather conditions. To make it possible for scientists in different parts of the world to compare their data, the average atmospheric pressure at sea level, 760 mm. or 76 cm., has been agreed on as the standard for pressure. This pressure is also used as a unit of pressure, called one atmosphere. The English system is still used in industrial practice in the United States, pressure being recorded as pounds per square inch. Atmospheric pressure is equivalent to about 15 pounds per square inch.

QUESTIONS AND PROBLEMS

1. Look in yesterday's paper for the local temperature and express it in degrees centigrade. Change the Fahrenheit temperature recorded for the past week to centigrade and plot a curve of ° F. and ° C. against days of the week.
2. Express your weight in kilograms and your height in meters and centimeters.
3. What was the average barometric pressure at your college for the past week?

INTRODUCTION

4. A "cup," in recipe parlance, is ½ pint; a tablespoonful is ½ fluid ounce; 3 teaspoonfuls make a tablespoonful. Express these volumes in milliliters.
5. Find which of your fingernails is 1 cm. wide. Find the place at which the palm of your hand is 10 cm. across.
6. Does a half dollar weigh as much as two quarters? Weigh some on the laboratory balance and see how many run to the hundred grams. Weigh a nickel.

» 2 «

METHODS USED IN THE DISCOVERY
OF THE ELEMENTS

Most of the substances you see about you will break down under the action of heat or an electric current, yielding two or more simpler substances. Some of these decomposition products can in turn be broken down into still simpler substances. When chemists determined to see how far this process could be pursued, they found that it soon came to an end, with substances which they could not decompose by any chemical process. These simple, undecomposable substances are called *elements*. Fewer than a hundred of them exist. They are of exceptional interest because all other substances can be made from them. The elements combine in definite proportions to form *compounds*; most natural substances are mixtures of these compounds.

Early in the 16th century Paracelsus stated that the true aim of alchemy should be the preparation of medicines, not gold. The study of substances led during the next century or so to the discovery that while most substances could be decomposed into simpler substances, there were some that could not. In 1661 Robert Boyle, the first real chemist, concluded that these undecomposable substances were that way by nature, and that all other substances were composed of combinations of a relatively small number of these elements. "I mean by elements," he wrote, "certain primitive and simple, or perfectly unmingled bodies; which not being made of other bodies or of one another, are the ingredients of which all those perfectly mixed bodies are immediately compounded, and into which they are ultimately resolved."

Under Boyle's influence the study of substances took on an *analytical* nature. Analysis is still one of the fundamental techniques used by the chemist in studying matter. To analyze a substance, a chemist must convert it into simpler substances and then isolate and identify each substance. He can limit himself to this, in which case the analysis is merely qualitative; or he can determine the relative amounts of the substances, making the analysis quantitative. Synthesis, the opposite of analysis, involves the building of a substance from simpler units. It is another of the fundamental techniques of chemistry, but in chemistry as elsewhere, it is usually easier to tear down than to build up. It takes a long time to build a home, but one bomb will destroy it. It is easy to decompose sugar into carbon (charcoal) and water by heat, but to synthesize sugar in the laboratory is a different story. It is natural that the first chemists were analysts.

Classification of Substances

In choosing substances to analyze in order to test Boyle's ideas, common sense led to the rejection of those that were obviously mixtures. It doesn't take a chemist to separate meat from raisins in a mince pie; Jack Horner sufficed. Heterogeneous mixtures, then, were rejected or separated mechanically. It may be noted here that experience has shown an easy test for detecting heterogeneity in fluids. If a liquid or a gas is muddy-looking, or white, or even hazy, it is heterogeneous; it contains suspended particles far larger than molecules, which will in time settle out under the influence of their weight. Conversely, if the fluid is clear and transparent, regardless of color, any substance which it contains in admixture is molecularly dispersed and will never settle out. The fluid will remain homogeneous permanently. In the case of solids it is frequently more difficult to detect inhomogeneity. Homogeneous substances gradually were found to fall into two classes, now familiar to us as *pure substances* and *solutions*. If a substance has variable composition it is of course a mixture; but if it is also homogeneous it is given the special name, solution. It must be understood that although the composition may vary from one solution to another, it is constant in any one solution. A pinch of salt in a glass of water would make one homogeneous solution; a spoonful of salt in a glass of water would make another.

The Laws of Definite and Multiple Proportions

From the above you have doubtless deduced that we define a pure substance as one that has a fixed, definite composition. This was first definitely set forth by J. L. Proust in 1801 as the Law of Definite Proportions. Not everyone accepted it at first. Wasn't it obvious that different kinds of water had slightly different colors, tastes, and smells, for example? And didn't it stand to reason that if one heated iron with a *large* excess of sulfur in making iron sulfide, the resulting product would be at least a *little* richer in sulfur? But, as always, the truth emerged from the laboratory. By careful distillation, portions may be collected from each of the different waters which are simply *water*, and identical. Increasingly accurate analyses always found the same percentage of sulfur in iron sulfide.

In the course of these investigations the curious fact came to light that from the same pair of Boyle's elements it was sometimes possible to make, not a compound with a little extra proportion of one element, but two entirely different compounds. And it was found that *if two or more elements combine to form more than one compound, the weights of one which combine with a definite weight of the other can be represented by a ratio of small whole numbers.* This is called the Law of Multiple Proportions.

One compound of mercury and oxygen was red and another was brownish black. Likewise two compounds of copper and oxygen were known. One of these copper compounds, called an oxide, was prepared by heating copper in a stream of air or, even better, in pure oxygen. A black substance was obtained. The other oxide (red in color) was more difficult to prepare, but by following "cookbook directions" one could make it in the laboratory.

If samples of these copper oxides are analyzed, we find that for each gram of copper in the black oxide there is 0.251 g. of oxygen. In the red oxide, each gram of copper is combined with only 0.125 g. of oxygen. There is just twice as much oxygen, $\frac{0.251}{0.125} = 2$, per gram of copper in the black oxide as there is in the red one; in other words, the weights of one which combine with a definite weight of the other can be represented by a ratio of small whole numbers. When such data as these were tabulated for several compounds, it was clear that the law of multiple proportions was an accurate statement of the existing facts.

Table 2.1. Data Required to Substantiate the Law of Multiple Proportions

Elements in the Compound	One Gram of the First Element Combines with x Grams of the Second	Ratio of Weights of Second Element per Gram of the First Element in the Two Compounds
Cu, O	.251	$\frac{.251}{.125} = \frac{2}{1}$
Cu, O	.125	
C, O	1.33	$\frac{1.33}{2.66} = \frac{1}{2}$
C, O	2.66	
Hg, Cl	.16	$\frac{.16}{.32} = \frac{1}{2}$
Hg, Cl	.32	

How were the elements discovered? Was it the result of an organized effort on the part of an individual or a group? Was it mere luck? Was a great knowledge of chemistry the prerequisite for discovery? Was complicated and expensive equipment necessary? These are questions frequently asked by the beginning student in chemistry.

The methods used in the discovery of most of the elements were not particularly complicated. The real secret of discovery in most cases was to obtain a *pure sample* of the substance containing the element. The elements were not discovered in the order of increasing difficulty in getting them from

METHODS USED IN THE DISCOVERY OF THE ELEMENTS

their compounds. Many were discovered accidentally. Moreover, in certain cases the discovery of one element led to the search for other elements with similar chemical and physical properties. In her book, *The Discovery of the Elements*, Weeks traces the life of the discoverer of each element and the technique used in isolating the element. (After you have learned formulas and equations you should read this fascinating book; it also contains many interesting photographs.)

The discoverers of some elements—carbon, sulfur, and gold, for example—are unknown. The general procedures used in discovering elements are as follows:

1. Heating of a compound of the element.
2. Heating of a compound of the element with one substance:
    a. With carbon,
    b. With hydrogen,
    c. With sodium or potassium.
3. Heating of a compound of the element with several substances.
4. Use of an electric current.
5. Use of the spectroscope.
6. Separation of the gaseous elements by chemical and physical methods.
7. Use of the radioactive properties of elements.
8. Nuclear research methods.

Two types of *changes* called *physical* and *chemical* are involved in the methods just cited. Observations as to the density of a substance, its color, odor, taste, ductility, and conduction of electricity pertain to its physical properties. The solubility of substances should be classed as chemical or physical, depending upon the presence or absence of chemical transformation. The dissolving of sugar in water is listed as a physical change because no chemical change takes place. If you spill some of the solution from the storage battery of an automobile on your clothes, it will destroy the cloth or "eat" a hole in it. This is a chemical change.

Thus, chemical changes pertain to the capacity of substances to be transformed into other materials and are frequently accompanied by measurable gains or losses of energy. The burning of wood is a chemical change and heat is produced. Iron rusts in moist air and a red deposit forms; bright shiny copper telephone wires soon darken, silverware tarnishes, milk sours, and toast burns. These are all chemical changes. It is difficult at times to measure the heat change (gain or loss of energy) in a chemical reaction, but it can always be proved that some change does occur.

The discovery of many of the elements has been in reality a verification of the Law of Definite Proportions. Suppose that you had been living 150 years ago and had carefully analyzed a certain rock and knew its composition, and that some other person analyzed a material which *looked like* the sample you had but an analysis did not show the same percentage composition. What would you do? You would look for some other substance in the sample. Often these new substances eluded chemists for years. They knew that they were present, but no methods for separating the constituents could be found. Pure limestone, whether found in New York State or England, is composed of 40 per cent by weight of calcium, 12 per cent carbon, and 48 per cent oxygen. Any other percentage composition would indicate either

Ewing Galloway

FIG. 2.1. Michael Faraday washing apparatus for Sir Humphry Davy.

an error in analysis or impurities in the sample. Finely powdered sand and sugar look alike. Sugar contains carbon, hydrogen, and oxygen. Sand contains silicon and oxygen. If the two were mixed, the analysis would show that the sample was neither pure sugar nor pure sand. Could you prove, without analysis, that the powdered white substance was a mixture? How would you do it? Simple tests no more difficult than this illustration were used in the discovery of some elements. Important discoveries were made with very poor equipment (Fig. 2.1). Compare the apparatus of the modern chemical laboratory with that used by Faraday and Davy.

Ancient Discoveries

In very early writings the word "element" had a broad meaning. About four centuries B.C. Empedocles thought of the world as being composed of four elements: the earth, air, water, and fire. Each of these elements was defined in terms of qualities pertaining to touch. Thus the earth was cold and dry, air was warm and moist, fire was dry and warm, and water was moist and cold. The descriptive adjectives used were cold, moist, warm, and dry. We do not consider any of these four "elements" as elements today. Far from it; the earth is extremely complex and contains hundreds of compounds from which nearly all the elements can be obtained. Even pure water can be decomposed into the two elements hydrogen and oxygen. Water as the ancients knew it contained many elements in the form of compounds dissolved in it. Air, a mixture of gases containing both elements and compounds, is composed of nearly 80 per cent nitrogen and 20 per cent oxygen. Traces of hydrogen, helium, neon, argon, krypton, xenon, and radon are also present. (These last six gases are called the inert gases.) Fire as we think of it today is a mixture of incandescent substances. It is hard for us to believe that great debates were once held as to whether or not these four substances were elements.

There is ample evidence that the ancients definitely identified twelve of the elements.

Elements Known to the Ancients

Antimony	Copper	Lead	Sulfur
Arsenic	Gold	Mercury	Tin
Carbon	Iron	Silver	Zinc

No one knows who first isolated any of these elements, for some of them are found free in nature and their discovery depended only upon finding a deposit. All the others can be obtained quite easily by either heating a compound containing the element or heating a compound with a very common substance, carbon. The compounds of course must have been found in nature in a fairly pure state; otherwise the pure elements could never have been obtained by such a simple process. Since such deposits do exist, their discovery appears to have been only a matter of chance. Some postulate that the discovery of iron resulted from a fire being built on a deposit of hematite, an ore containing iron. The hot carbon reacted with the ore, and after the fire was out someone may have stirred the ashes and found a lump of material which was not there before the fire was built. The discoverer had to be endowed with what we call today *the power of scientific observation*, or the change would have gone unobserved.

There is an ore of arsenic, realgar, from which the silver-white arsenic can be obtained by heating with coal or carbon. Likewise, antimony, bismuth, copper, lead, silver, tin, and zinc could have been obtained from their ores. Cinnabar, an ore of mercury, yields the element when it is heated.

If you have ever visited any of the larger museums, you have probably seen gold ornaments found in Egyptian tombs. There are numerous Biblical references to the use of gold as a medium of exchange. Since gold is found widely distributed throughout the world in the free state as grains and nuggets, the only refining necessary was mechanical separation.

Apparently the use of silver is of later origin, probably because of the fact that it occurs free less often in nature. The wide distribution of silver and its early use, however, are shown by Biblical references. During the ancient Peruvian civilization silver utensils were common. Although it is hard to imagine, historians claim that when the Phoenicians first sailed to Spain they found silver so common that they substituted it for lead in weighing their wooden anchors.

Ancient Egyptians apparently found deposits of pure copper in the free state, for some of the articles found in the tombs have proved on analysis to be nearly pure copper. The prophet Ezra mentions "vessels of fine brass, precious as gold." The ore malachite is easily converted into copper by being heated with carbon.

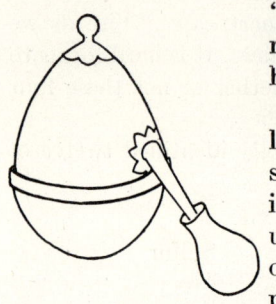

Numerous Biblical references are also made to lead. Because of the ease with which it can be scratched, inscriptions have been found engraved on it. The Romans made water pipes of lead and also used it for cooking utensils. Because of the solubility of lead in water and its toxicity many people were poisoned by its continued use; even today lead poisoning is not uncommon.

FIG. 2.2. Ancient mercury still.

Mercury has been found in ancient Egyptian tombs. It can be obtained by simply heating mercuric oxide, which breaks down into mercury and oxygen. An ancient mercury still is shown in Fig. 2.2. One of your first laboratory experiments will probably be to heat mercuric oxide in a test tube. The shiny droplets of metallic mercury will deposit on the walls of the test tube. The red compound will disappear. The gas coming from the test tube will cause a glowing splint to burn brightly. Today our explanation for this simple chemical change is that the red oxide is composed of two elements, mercury and oxygen. On being heated, the two elements separate and the oxygen escapes as a gas. The mercury also becomes a gas, but it quickly liquefies in the cooler portion of the test tube. Mercury boils at 357° C. The ancients used to purify mercury by squeezing it through a leather bag.

For centuries tin has been used in making tin bronzes, and coatings of this metal were used then as now to protect copper from corrosion. Tin was recognized as having properties differing from those of lead.

An ancient vase now in the Louvre has been found on analysis to consist of nearly pure antimony. The ore, a compound of antimony and sulfur, decomposes in the presence of carbon to produce the element.

Some believe that the art of obtaining zinc from its ores was first developed in the Orient, probably in India. Thence it was carried to China. Early Portuguese traders were known to have brought it from the Orient and introduced it into European civilization.

Impure carbon found in the form of coal or obtained by heating wood must have been known for many centuries. Pure carbon in the form of diamonds is mentioned in the Bible, but there is nothing in these references which indicates whether it was known that carbon could occur either as coal or as the clear diamond. In 1797 an English chemist, Smithson Tennant, proved that a diamond was pure carbon by burning it and identifying the product as carbon dioxide.

Some very pure deposits of uncombined sulfur are found scattered throughout the world. The deposits in Italy and Sicily contained sulfur which could be chipped out in blocks.

All the discoveries just mentioned required little knowledge of what is today called chemistry. As more facts were brought to light, the study of the properties of matter became more and more a specialized field. The subject of chemistry now takes in such a broad field of knowledge that the chemist of today can at best specialize only in one or two branches of chemistry.

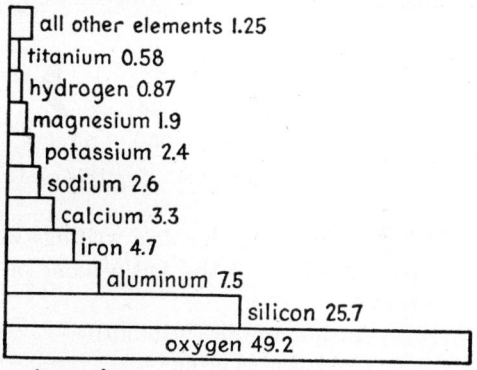

Fig. 2.3. Percentage of elements in the earth's crust, including the ocean and atmosphere.

Abundance of the Elements

The composition of the earth's crust including the ocean and atmosphere has been subjected to careful estimates. The composition of the atmosphere and ocean waters is nearly constant throughout the world. Inland lakes and streams vary in mineral constituents depending upon the rock and soil formation which the water has traversed.

The percentage of elements in the earth's crust including the ocean and atmosphere is shown in Fig. 2.3. The ten most abundant elements in order are oxygen, silicon, aluminum, iron, calcium, sodium, potassium, magnesium, hydrogen, and titanium. These ten make up 98.75 per cent of the earth's crust; 1.25 per cent is made up of all the other elements. Such important elements as chlorine (0.19 of 1 per cent), phosphorus (0.11 of 1 per cent), carbon (0.08 of 1 per cent), sulfur (0.06 of 1 per cent), and nitrogen (0.03 of 1 per cent) are present in small amounts in terms of the total, yet we do not think of these as being rare. Air is about 80 per cent nitrogen; salt deposits containing chlorine as chlorides are well distributed throughout the world;

the plant kingdom is rich in carbon; phosphorus is found in the form of compounds called phosphates; and sulfur is obtained as the element in large deposits and is also present in many compounds.

Shorthand for Writing the Names of the Elements

In the early days during what is called the period of alchemy each of the elements known to the alchemists was assigned the symbol of a heavenly body. Fig. 2.4 shows a few of these symbols. However, this system of symbols soon became inadequate because of the discovery of compounds of the elements, and today these symbols are unintelligible to most of us.

FIG. 2.4. Symbols used by the alchemists.

Many of the early chemical writings were in Latin, and the initial letter or a pair of letters of the Latin name of the element was usually used for the symbol.

Antimony, Sb (Stibium)
Gold, Au (Aurum)
Iron, Fe (Ferrum)
Lead, Pb (Plumbum)
Potassium, K (Kalium)
Silver, Ag (Argentum)
Sodium, Na (Natrium)
Tin, Sn (Stannum)
Mercury, Hg (Hydrargyrum)

The symbols for the elements discovered since that period consist of the first letter of the English name, with an additional letter if necessary. An exception is tungsten, discovered fairly recently, which gets its symbol, W, from the German name of the element, wolfram. The German name came from that of the ore wolframite; the English name, from the Swedish name for another ore, tungsten (heavy stone).

In learning the symbols for the elements, you will find it convenient to make a chart, listing in one group those just mentioned whose symbols differ from the name of the element; in a second group list those with only one letter for the symbol; in a third, those with the first two letters of the name; put all the other elements in a fourth group. Make this chart at once and fill it in as rapidly as new elements are introduced, for you can no more expect to make progress in the study of chemistry without learning the symbols than you can expect to read a foreign language without learning the equivalent of the English words. Spend a few minutes each day studying your chart.

QUESTIONS AND PROBLEMS

1. Define the following: element; compound; pure substance.
2. Classify the following changes in three groups, physical, chemical, or doubtful (as far as you know):

Boil water	Melt glass
Char sugar	Dry paint
Digest food	Cure hay and tobacco
Soften water with soap	Dissolve salt in water
Melt butter	Use a flashlight
Break glass	

3. Suggest a method for separating the following mixtures:
    - Salt and pepper
    - Sugar and flour
    - Sand and iron filings
    - Salt, carbon, and sulfur
    - Gasoline and lubricating oil
    - Gold amalgam (mercury and gold)
4. Which of the substances in Question 3 are elements? Compounds?
5. What is the minimum number of elements required to form a compound?
6. Is there an important mine near your home? Have you ever visited a mine? Was the substance mined a mixture or a pure compound?

REFERENCES[1]

Titles of publications are abbreviated in the references at the end of the chapters. A few of the more common ones are:

J. Chem. Ed.	*Journal of Chemical Education*
J.A.C.S.	*Journal of the American Chemical Society*
Ind. and Eng. Chem.	*Industrial and Engineering Chemistry*
Chem. and Met. Eng.	*Chemical and Metallurgical Engineering*
Met. and Alloys	*Metals and Alloys*
C. and E. News	*Chemical and Engineering News*

Books

Chemistry in Life. Arrhenius, S. A. D. Van Nostrand & Company, Inc.
History of Chemistry. Moore, F. J. McGraw-Hill Book Company, Inc.
Creative Chemistry. Slosson, E. E. D. Appleton-Century Company, Inc.
Crucibles. Jaffe, B. Tudor Publishing Company.

[1] The librarian will be able to tell you the standard abbreviations for journals and show you how to look up articles in *Chemical Abstracts*. This journal abstracts articles in all the other chemical journals. If you wish to find the latest information on a chemical subject, look in *Chemical Abstracts* under the title or topic, turn to the pages referred to, read the abstracts, and, if the article appears interesting, ask the librarian to help you find the original article. DO NOT UNDERESTIMATE THE IMPORTANCE OF LEARNING HOW TO USE THE LIBRARY WHILE IN COLLEGE.

Man in a Chemical World. Morrison, A. C. Charles Scribner's Sons.
Atoms, Rocks and Galaxies. Allen, J. S., and others. Harper & Brothers.
Drama of Chemistry. French, S. J. University Society.
The Discovery of the Elements. Weeks, M. E. Mack Printing Co.

Articles

"Naming Elements." Ewing, M. A. *J. Chem. Ed.* **15,** 123–126 (1938).
"Symbols of Alchemy." Davis, T. L. *J. Chem. Ed.* **15,** 403–410 (1938).
"Present Trends in Geochemistry." Wells, R. C. *J. Chem. Ed.* **15,** 524–532 (1938).

» 3 «

THE PARTICLE NATURE OF MATTER

The scientist devotes much of his energy to attempting to answer such questions as "What will happen under certain conditions?" "What is it?" "How does it act?" He does not attempt to answer the question "Why?" If you persist in asking this question, you must expect nothing more for an answer than "I don't know."

The chemist is interested in studying the composition of matter. What is air? What is a liquid? What is a rock? What can be done with the things we find out about? The unraveling of these mysteries is told in countless thrilling stories.

If you pick up a rock and break it into two pieces, each can be identified as a fragment of the rock. Suppose each piece is broken into two parts again and again until only very small particles of dust remain. It is still the same rock, only in smaller states of subdivision. Is there a limit to the number of times the rock can be subdivided? What do you think about it?

Logic and analogy can be called upon to answer the question either way. For example, a herd of cattle is obviously not infinitely subdivisible. Early subdivisions simply produce smaller herds of cattle, but eventually the fractions are individual cows. Further subdivision produces something quite different, beef. On the other hand, it is impossible to think of a distance so small that one cannot conceive of half of it. Obviously the question is one of fact, to be settled by experiment, not argument. The obviousness, however is evident only to the modern mind, conditioned as it is by experience with the scientific method. Two thousand years of inconclusive argument on the subject preceded the appeal to the laboratory.

Molecules, the Units of Substances

The now thoroughly proved answer is, "No, matter is not continuous, but discrete." We have adopted the word *molecule* to describe the smallest particle into which a substance can be dispersed without turning it into a different substance. (Molecule, derived from the Latin, is merely the diminutive of a word meaning particle.) It has been found that a substance is separated into molecules[1] when it evaporates and also when it dissolves in a solvent. The molecules which have actually been separated from their neighbors are found to range in size from about one ten-millionth of a millimeter almost into the range of the ultramicroscope, perhaps a thousandfold range of diameters. They may be spherical, triangular, pyramidal, threadlike, be shaped like dumbbells or rings, or have more complicated forms.

The properties of any substance are those of its molecules. This is true just as it is true that the properties of a group are the properties of the component individuals. If the individuals are singers, the group is a chorus; if they are soldiers, it is an army. In every case where it is possible to change the molecules in any way, the new molecules are found to be molecules of a different substance. When a molecule is broken into two parts, the parts are still molecules, but not necessarily identical with each other and certainly not with those of the original substance. Two or more molecules may be made to join together. The resulting particle is still a molecule, just as a train made by joining two trains together is still a train, but it is a molecule of a different substance.

Detection of Individual Molecules

Since molecules are too small to see, even with the most powerful microscope, how can we prove that they actually exist? One way is to make them move quickly enough so that their energy is appreciable, even if their size is not. An object half an inch in diameter and a couple of inches long would be invisible to an aviator flying a thousand feet above it; but if you fire a stream of them at him from a .50-caliber machine gun, and if one punctures his gasoline tank, he will not doubt their reality. Give even the smallest molecule sufficient speed and it too will have energy enough to produce visible results. Of course a lot more speed will be necessary, but fortunately the energy of a particle increases with the square of its speed. A molecule moving with 10,000 times the speed of a machine-gun bullet will have 100,000,000 times as much energy in proportion to its mass. Such cases actually exist in nature.

The Spinthariscope

It has been found that the gas *helium* is continually produced from radium. The rate of production is slow, but enough has been collected to be measured and identified by ordinary methods. At the moment of production each molecule is hurled forth with such velocity that it can penetrate several centimeters of air or even a thin layer of metal foil. The initial speed ("muzzle

---

[1] When these particles are electrically charged, as occurs in the case of salts, they are called *ions*. See p. 21.

velocity," so to speak) is 10,000 miles per second. Although it weighs less than a billionth of a billionth of a milligram, a helium molecule at such speed has enough energy to produce a visible flash of light when it strikes a crystal of zinc sulfide. If a small enough speck of the radium compound is held far enough from the crystal, only a few molecules of helium will strike it each second and the individual flashes can be seen through a lens.[2] A device for observing this phenomenon is the *spinthariscope* (Greek, spark-seer) and is available in most physics departments. By counting the flashes over a period of time, and from consideration of the geometry of the apparatus, it is possible to compute the number of helium molecules produced by a given quantity of radium in any specified time. When the helium is actually collected and measured and the number of molecules present is calculated by theoretical means, the same result is obtained.

The Geiger Counter

Another instrument that can detect individual high-speed molecules is called the Geiger counter,[3] from the name of its inventor. In speeding through air at such a high velocity these particles render air momentarily a conductor of electricity. If one particle passes through a Geiger counter, this enables a tiny pulse of current to flow between a pair of high-voltage electrodes. This is amplified enough by means of a simple radio circuit to make a telegraph sounder click. By combining a spinthariscope and a counter it can be confirmed that the latter clicks every time a helium molecule makes a flash on the zinc sulfide. This, then, is a second instrument capable of observing the effects of single molecules.

The Geiger counter is frequently used to find lost radium in hospitals. In one instance a tiny tube containing a small fraction of a gram of radium bromide (but worth over $1000) was thrown away with some dressings. The loss was not discovered until after the trash had been burned in the furnace and the ashes taken to the city dump. A Geiger counter was sent for and carried back and forth over the most likely part of the dump. Only a few hours passed before it began to click. When it came closer to the radium the rate of clicking increased; the valuable ashes were soon localized, shoveled up, and sent to the refiner for reworking.

The Wilson Cloud Chamber

The operation of the Geiger counter depends upon the fact that the speeding particle electrifies the gas molecules through which it shoots, leaving a trail of *ions* behind it. (An ion is an electrically charged molecule; how a molecule can become charged will be explained later.) In a sufficiently damp

[2] If there is more radium and it is closer to the zinc sulfide crystal, the flashes merge into a general glow, like the Milky Way. Luminous paint for watches and airplane instrument dials is made by mixing a small amount of a radium compound with ground zinc sulfide and a binder.

[3] *Life*, **20**, 103 (1946).

atmosphere myriads of microscopic drops of water will condense upon these ions. Under strong transverse illumination the track of the particle will be visible as a sharp line of mist. The Wilson ray-track apparatus (Figs. 3.1, 3.2) is a device for producing the required atmospheric conditions repeatedly in a convenient chamber. When an *alpha particle* (the high-speed helium mole-

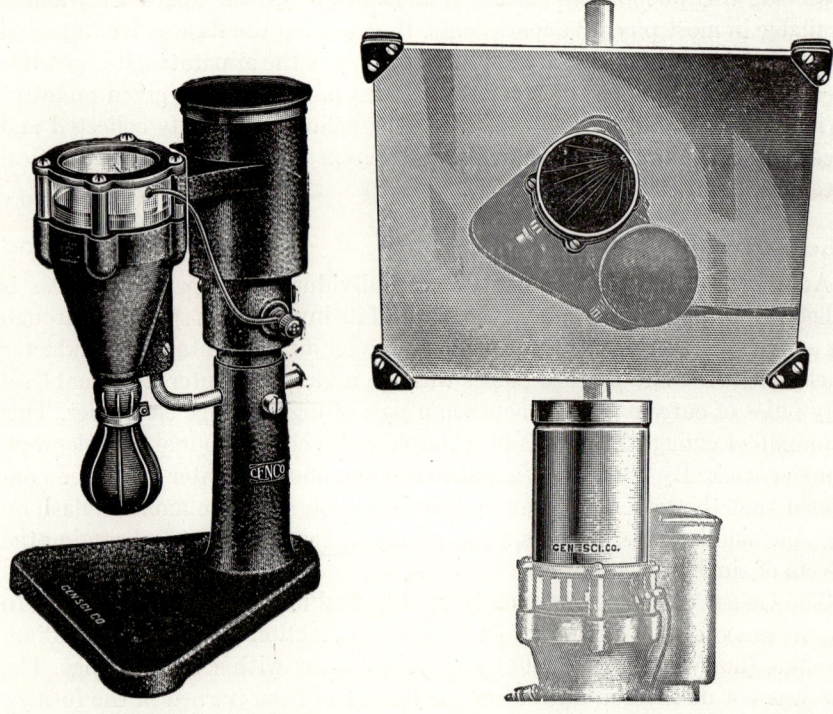

Fig. 3.1. Alpha ray-track apparatus. (Courtesy, Central Scientific Co.)

Fig. 3.2. Reflecting apparatus for alpha ray-track apparatus. (Courtesy, Central Scientific Co.)

cules from radium were so named before their nature was known, and the name is still used for brevity) makes a head-on collision with a molecule of one of the gases of the air, it is deflected sharply to one side. Dr. W. D. Harkins, of the University of Chicago, took a photograph (Fig. 3.3) showing such tracks and, in addition, a heavier track going on a short distance from the point of the angle in the helium track. The latter was caused by the nitrogen molecule which was struck by the alpha particle and recoiled from the collision with sufficient velocity so that it itself produced ionization.

The Mass Spectrograph

The spinthariscope, the Geiger counter, and the Wilson ray-track apparatus are applicable only to molecules in extraordinarily *rapid* motion, because

THE PARTICLE NATURE OF MATTER

in each case it is necessary to detect a single molecule. But if all molecules are in continual motion (and in the next chapter this will be proved to be the case) we ought to be able to plan an experiment in which a vast number of molecules, doing the same thing one after another, will produce a cumulative result large enough to see. For example, molecules of a gas confined in a chamber with a tiny hole in it will slowly leak out. Since molecules are moving in all directions at random, bumping into each other continually, some moving in the right direction will be sure to strike the hole from time to time.

If molecules emerging from the hole are not to be lost in the crowd outside, there must be no crowd outside. In other words, the gas chamber must be in an evacuated apparatus. Molecules escaping through an oblong slit of appreciable dimensions will diverge somewhat, like light shining through a window. If, however, another slit is mounted parallel to the first at a little distance from it, only the molecules that happen to be heading straight down the line joining them can get through both. The result, beyond the second slit, is a ribbon-shaped beam of molecules. If this beam strikes a bit of photographic film, the molecular bombardment presently renders it developable. A narrow black line is found on the film, after it is developed, where the beam played upon it. Only a few million molecules are needed to produce a visible trace.

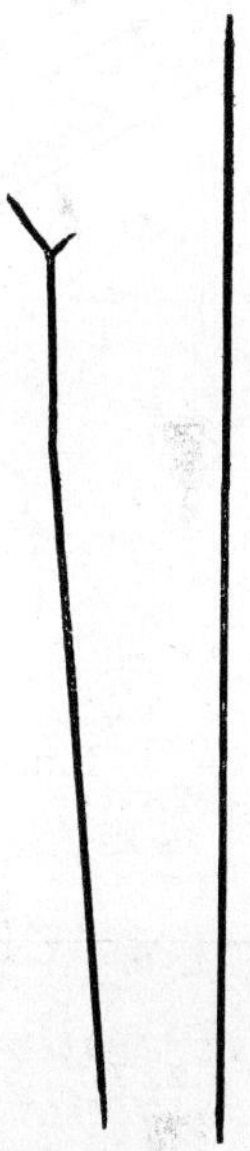

In the experiment just described it was shown that a gas actually behaves just as we would expect it to if composed of moving elastic particles. But one successful experiment does not prove a theory, any more than one robin makes a summer. A beam of light shining through the slit would have produced exactly the results observed. But it is possible to electrify molecules in such a beam. These *ions*[4] (charged molecules) can be deviated from their normal path by an electric or a magnetic field and made to strike the film in a different place. Light is unaffected by such treatment, but electrified particles big enough to be seen behave exactly like our ions; so we feel that the theory has received convincing support.

FIG. 3.3. Cloud chamber tracks of two α-particles and recoil track of a nitrogen atom. (After Harkins' photograph.)

Moving at the same speed, light molecules would be forced much farther out of line than heavy ones. A bowling ball of the right size can be painted so as closely to resemble a volley ball. But imagine yourself standing halfway down a bowling alley and giving each ball a sideways kick as it passed. A kick that would barely alter the course of the heavy bowling ball would send the light volley ball off the alley. Or compare the effect of a side wind on tennis balls and baseballs.

[4] The fact that it is possible to impart motion to these charged particles by means of such a field is the reason they were named "ions." "Ion" is Greek for "going."

F. W. Aston used electric and magnetic fields to impart the "sidewise kick" required to deflect a charged particle. Fig. 3.4 is a diagram of the mass spectrograph shown in Fig. 3.5. The ribbon beam of charged particles enters a combined electrostatic and magnetic field immediately upon emerging from the second slit (S_2). The electrostatic field and the magnetic field (H_1) are so adjusted that only particles having the same velocity emerge from slit S_3. These particles represent all the masses present in the original mixture.

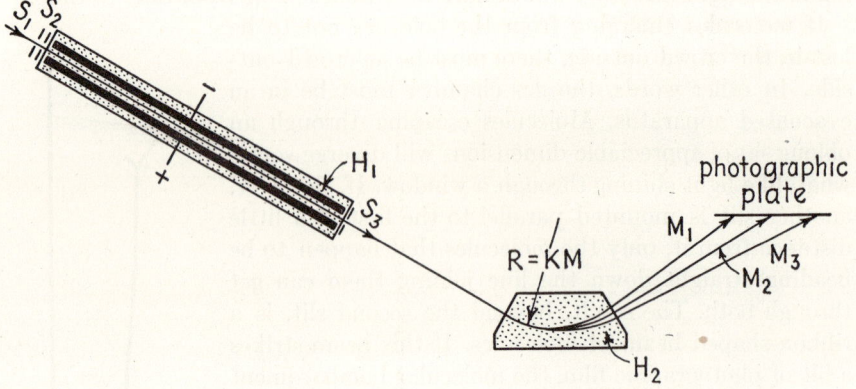

Fig. 3.4. A diagram of the mass spectrograph shown in Fig. 3.5.

Fig. 3.5. A mass spectrograph. (Courtesy, E. B. Jordan)

THE PARTICLE NATURE OF MATTER

Particles possessing velocities different from those of the particles emerging from S_3 are deflected in the combined electrostatic and magnetic fields and therefore are not in line with slit S_3 and cannot emerge through it.

The beam of particles of constant velocity enters a second magnetic field H_2 where only mass will account for differences in momentum of the various particles. The particles having the greatest momentum, therefore the greatest mass (M_3), are deflected the least. The radius of curvature of the particles emerging from the magnetic field H_2 is proportional to the mass. The resultant photograph will show a row of images corresponding to the slit. This row of images (Fig. 3.6) is called a spectrum.

FIG. 3.6. Mass spectrum; lines of NH and CH$_3$, difference 0.01256 mass units. (Courtesy, E. B. Jordan)

Different colors of light can also be separated into a spectrum, the deviation in this case being produced by a prism instead of a field. The instrument by means of which light spectra are photographed is called a spectrograph (Fig. 22.7). Bunsen and Kirchhoff, German chemists, invented the original form of it in 1860. Since the mass spectrograph produces spectra by separating the ions passing through it according to their masses, you can see the logic in calling it the mass spectrograph.

Molecular Weight Determination

From the geometry of the apparatus and the known laws of physics, the actual weight of the individual molecules in question can be calculated. The accuracy of molecular weight determination with this instrument has now reached the remarkable figure of ± 1 in 100,000. Furthermore, by measuring the density (= opacity) of the lines on the film, it is possible to estimate quite accurately the relative numbers of molecules of various weights present in a mixture. This enables the *average* weight of the molecules in a mixture to be calculated. By heating the gas container sufficiently, it is possible to gasify many substances which are ordinarily solids, and so determine their molecular weights. As a research instrument the mass spectrograph produced information of enormous scientific value, even in the original crude form invented by Sir J. J. Thomson in 1911. In 1943 the mass spectrometer, an instrument based upon the same principle, entered commercial laboratories as a means of analyzing the complicated mixtures of gases used in the manufacture of synthetic rubber and high octane gasoline. In the mass spectrometer, the field is progressively altered so as to cause ions of first one weight, then the next, to fall successively upon a fixed collector, where their quantity is measured and recorded by electrical amplifying equipment. When the relative numbers of ionized fragments of various weights produced by the electron bombardment of molecules of the different substances involved have been determined experimentally, the composite spectrum of a mixture can be unraveled. This method gives in minutes the percentage composition of a mixture whose analysis would have required days by older methods, and gives it more accurately. The mass spectrometer, originally invented merely to satisfy a researcher's curiosity, actually had much to do with the success of our gigantic synthetic rubber and high octane gasoline programs by shortening the time lag in composition control.

QUESTIONS AND PROBLEMS

1. See if you can match the names of the following substances with the descriptions of their molecules. The descriptions are not listed in the same order as the substances.

    Substances
    a. Hydrogen gas.
    b. Nylon.
    c. Rubber.
    d. Iso-octane (important constituent of aviation gasoline).
    e. Iron.
    f. Sugar.

    Descriptions
    a. Small, heavy; has strong attraction for its own kind.
    b. Slender, flexible, straight, and indefinitely long.
    c. Lightest and smallest of all molecules; has extremely little attraction for its neighbors.
    d. Shaped like a compact bunch of grapes; has moderate attraction for its neighbors.
    e. A neat hexagon with a short handle; has strong attraction for water molecules.
    f. Slender, flexible, indefinitely long, and very kinky.

2. Try to explain the behavior of the spinthariscope, the Geiger counter, the Wilson ray-track apparatus, and the mass spectrograph on the assumption either that matter *is* infinitely subdivisible or that it is continuous.

3. The mass spectrograph shows that the gas, hydrogen chloride, is composed 77.15 per cent of molecules weighing 36.01 atomic weight units each, and 22.84 per cent of molecules weighing 38.01 atomic weight units each. Calculate the average molecular weight (i.e., the average of the weights of the

molecules). Considering that 0.01 of 1 per cent of the molecules are not accounted for, how many figures in your answer have any real significance?

REFERENCES

Books

For more description of the Wilson ray-track apparatus, or Wilson Cloud Chamber, as it is frequently called, see *Atomic Physics*. Physics Staff of the University of Pittsburgh. Wiley, pp. 228–231 and Fig. 2, p. 258. See also *The Particles of Modern Physics*. Stranathan. Blakiston, pp. 408–409.

Articles

"The Mass Spectrometer as an Analytical Tool." Washburn, H. W., Wiley, H. F., and Rock, S. M. *Ind. and Eng. Chem., Anal. Ed.* **15,** 541, (1943).
"New Horizons in Modern Science." Wiswesser, William J. *J. Chem. Ed.*, **24**:25, Figs. 20–25 (1947).

» 4 «

THE KINETIC MOLECULAR THEORY OF GASES

When the word gas is mentioned, one usually thinks of air, oxygen, hydrogen, helium, carbon dioxide, or gases used in war. Actually many substances can be converted into the gaseous state. If the temperature is high enough, the pressure low enough, and a substance sufficiently stable, it may be obtained as a gas. Even metals meet these prerequisites. Table 4.1 gives the boiling points of a few metals, which at first we might never think of as capable of existing in the gaseous state.

TABLE 4.1. BOILING POINTS OF METALS IN °C.

Aluminum, 1800	Gold, 2500	Silver, 1950
Chromium, 2200	Iron, 2450	Tin, 2270
Copper, 2310	Platinum, 3910	Zinc, 930

Substances which are liquids at room temperature have boiling points much lower than do the metals just listed. In converting a liquid such as petroleum into the gaseous state, several different gases are obtained. Such liquids can be separated into fractions richer in a given constituent by using the differences in the boiling points of the individual compounds. As the gases obtained from petroleum cool, they again liquefy; hence the change is not permanent. (Distillation of crude petroleum will yield some substances which remain gases at room temperature.)

To say that iron is odorless because it is a solid is incorrect. Iodine, camphor, and mothballs are all solids at room temperature, and a bottle containing any of these has an odor. But we could not detect any odor any more than we could if the bottle contained iron filings if these substances did not have one characteristic. This is the tendency of molecules to escape from the solid state to the gaseous state; it is called the *vapor pressure* of a substance. Some molecules of camphor must strike the olfac-

THE KINETIC MOLECULAR THEORY OF GASES

tory organs if the compound is to be detected by the sense of smell. Therefore some camphor molecules must escape from the solid state.[1]

The reverse of the procedure of converting solids into liquids and liquids into gases is also possible.

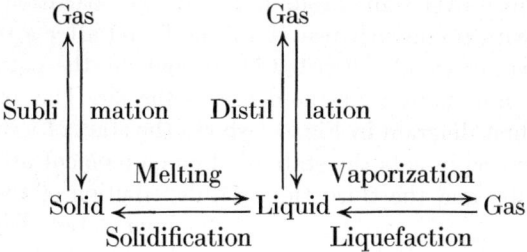

All the known gases have been liquefied, and most of them can be changed into the solid state. There are several laws which in general apply to the behavior of gases. This chapter will discuss the *physical behavior* of gases.

Qualitative Observations of the Characteristics of Gases

Cylinders filled with helium, hydrogen, oxygen, and carbon dioxide demonstrate the fact that a large amount of gas can be confined in a small space under pressure. Automobiles rest on air under pressure in automobile tires.

The opposite is also true; gases will expand indefinitely unless confined in a suitable container. Open the valve on a tank of carbon dioxide and the gas escapes; puncture an automobile tire and it quickly becomes flat. Qualitatively then, an increase in pressure decreases the space occupied by a gas; a gas expands as the pressure is decreased. Liquids and solids also change in volume with a change in pressure, but the change is very small.

More automobile tires blow out on warm days than in cold weather. This is due not to changes in the strength of the rubber and fabric but to the fact that a gas at constant volume exerts a pressure in proportion to the temperature. Increase in temperature causes an increase in pressure if the gas is kept at constant volume. If a tire containing 30 pounds per square inch air pressure at $-10°$ F. is heated to $115°$ F., the pressure exerted by the air may be more than the fabric and rubber can withstand.

Another experiment which illustrates the effect of pressure may be demonstrated with a thin-walled gallon can. If a little water is put into the

---

[1] A good sense of smell is a valuable asset to an experienced chemist. Chemists who specialize in the manufacture of perfumes can identify many compounds by their odor. Students in general chemistry who do laboratory work can usually identify twenty to forty compounds by smell alone at the close of the course. Chemistry professors are always on the alert for escaping toxic gases in the building. Practice in identifying compounds by their odor may prove a lifesaver to you, as in detecting gas leaks around the kitchen stove, a leak in the electric refrigerator, or the presence of spoiled food. Some gases such as carbon monoxide, oxygen, nitrogen, and hydrogen are odorless. Most hydrogen explosions are due to someone's lighting a match to see whether any of the gas is present.

can and it is placed on an asbestos mat and heated until the water boils, the can contains only steam. If the can is quickly stoppered and cooled under the tap, the steam condenses and greatly decreases the pressure within the can. The external pressure is sufficient to cause its sides to cave in.

If air is confined over some bromine gas and the partition between them is slipped out with no disturbance, it will be found after a reasonable time that both gases are evenly distributed throughout the entire space, even though the bromine is $5\frac{1}{2}$ times as dense as the air. This process is called *diffusion*. The first diagram in Fig. 4.1 shows the start of a diffusion experiment, the second represents the state of affairs a moment after the removal of the glass plate, and the third the even distribution of the two gases an hour later. Diffusion of two liquids which will mix is much slower than it is with two gases, and diffusion of two solids is extremely slow.

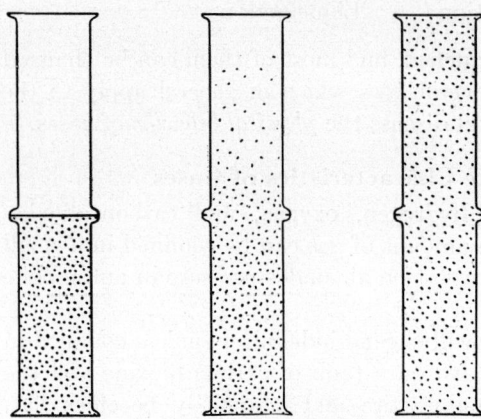

Fig. 4.1. Diffusion of bromine in air.

A pure homogeneous gas has no tendency to settle. The use of toxic gases in chemical warfare depends upon the gas being heavier than air so that the rate of diffusion upward will be slow. Gases used to disinfect the holds of ships, if heavier than air, must be removed by forced ventilation before another cargo is loaded on board. Any container, irrespective of size, will eventually contain in all its parts gas of the same composition.

These qualitative observations of the *homogeneity, compressibility, diffusibility*, and *exhaustibility* of gases have also been made quantitatively.

Only within comparatively recent times have gases been commonly recognized as being really substances. Except when in rapid motion, even air was not considered material. The air was a region rather than a substance. Some two centuries ago, however, men began to recognize the individuality of some of the commoner gases and to prepare them in the pure state. Furthermore, the idea of making quantitative experiments had begun to take root. As a result, a remarkable series of coincidences in the behavior of different gases was discovered. In order to explain them, the *kinetic molecular theory* of the structure of matter was put forth, and it did explain the experimental observations. Belief in the reality of molecules thus became universal among chemists long before any direct evidence of their individual existence was known.

THE KINETIC MOLECULAR THEORY OF GASES

Basic Assumptions of the Kinetic Molecular Theory

According to the kinetic molecular theory as at present accepted, gases are composed of molecules moving rapidly about in a relatively large amount of otherwise empty space. These molecules move in straight lines until they collide with other molecules, whereupon they rebound elastically. In the case of ordinary gases under ordinary conditions, their volume is less than a thousandth part of the total volume occupied by the gas. The molecules have a slight but measurable attraction for one another. The number of molecules in a given volume is independent of their nature. In the following paragraphs the application of this theory to the experimentally known facts about gases will be shown.

Explanation of Pressure

Any quantity of gas, however small, will distribute itself evenly throughout any container into which it is introduced, and will exert pressure upon the walls of it. In terms of the theory, the molecules travel in straight lines until they reach the walls of the container and rebound. Collisions with one another will gradually send them in all possible directions and they will become evenly distributed throughout the space. The pressure exerted by the gas is due simply to the myriad blows struck by the molecules. It is constant rather than fluctuating, because the individual blows are tiny and the number of blows per second upon any appreciable area is enormous.

Explanation of Temperature

When a hot gas is brought into contact with a cold gas under conditions such that rapidly moving molecules collide with slower ones, with resulting equalization of energy, the two gases come to the same temperature. Whenever work is done upon a gas, as by stirring, so that the energy of the molecules is increased, the gas is found to be hotter than before. The increase in temperature is proportional to the amount of energy expended upon it. It is concluded, therefore, that temperature is a measure of the energy of motion possessed by molecules. When the energy of a given molecule is increased, its velocity is increased. There will be more blows per second upon the walls of the container, and they will be harder ones; hence the pressure will be higher. If the volume is kept constant, the increase in pressure will be proportional to the increase in temperature. The preceding sentence sums up the results of actual measurements of several gases made by the distinguished French chemist Gay-Lussac at the beginning of the 19th century. Since similar measurements of many additional gases lead to the same conclusion, we assume that the statement has general validity and we call it a natural *law*.

Boyle's Law

Gases are highly compressible. An oxygen cylinder such as you have seen a welder use furnishes two hundred times its own volume of oxygen to the flame. In 1660 Robert Boyle, a pioneer investigator in both chemistry and physics, made some careful measurements of the compressibility of air. He found that when the temperature is the same at the end of the experiment as it was at the beginning, *the volume of a gas varies inversely with the pressure.* Of course it is assumed that no gas is added or allowed to escape, that is, that the weight remains constant.

This relationship between the pressure exerted by a gas and the volume occupied by it is shown in Fig. 4.2. The temperature is assumed to remain constant during the experiment, as is the weight of gas in the cylinder. Imagine the cylinder to be closed by a weightless, freely movable piston, with nothing to keep the gas from pushing the piston out of the top except a weight or weights which are placed upon it. If the quantity of gas is small, say 0.05 g., a weight of 1 kg. may confine it to a volume of 4 l. The volume of the gas will vary with any change in pressure. If you add the weight of your finger to the top of the weight, the piston will sink, and you can feel the increasing pressure of the gas as its volume is reduced. *The gas exerts its pressure equally in all directions.* If the weight is doubled to 2 kg., the pressure exerted on the gas is doubled and the pressure exerted *by* the gas is also doubled. In other words, the greater the pressure applied to a gas, the greater will be the pressure which it exerts upon the walls of a container. But by the time the pressure of the gas has doubled to withstand the doubled weight on top, its volume has decreased to half the original volume. If the weight is increased to 4 kg., the volume will be reduced to 1 l. A weight of 8 kg. will reduce the volume to half a liter, or $\frac{1}{8}$ of the original volume. Note that in every case the product of any pressure and the corresponding volume has the same numerical value, i.e., is a constant. Pressure is expressed in terms of force per unit area. In this case, for convenience, we shall take the unit area as that of the piston; the pressures will then be numerically equal to the respective weights. Thus:

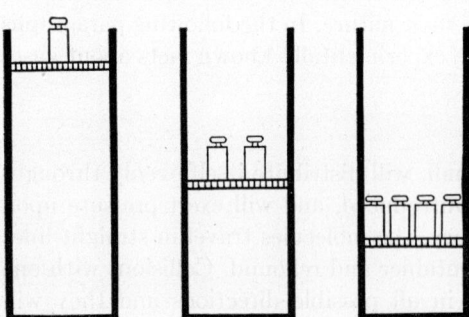

FIG. 4.2. The volume of a gas varies inversely with the pressure (Boyle's Law).

$$4 \times 1 = 4; \quad 2 \times 2 = 4; \quad 1 \times 4 = 4; \quad \tfrac{1}{2} \times 8 = 4$$

The constant for this particular experiment is 4. At any other temperature the constant will be some other number, but any number of pressures each multiplied by the corresponding volume will still give the new constant. In an experiment with a different weight of the gas there will be still a different constant. The use of different units of measurement will also give new numerical values to the constant; but with the conditions and units for any given

THE KINETIC MOLECULAR THEORY OF GASES

experiment once set, the constant will remain a constant, in spite of any changes in the pressure and volume relationships.

A typical apparatus used for measuring the volume of a gas and illustrating Boyle's Law is shown in Fig. 4.3. The stopcock at the top of the graduated tube makes it possible to fill the tube with different gases. The liquid usually used in the leveling arms is mercury, although saturated salt solution can be used with fair results. The liquid should have little tendency to go into the gaseous state. The gas being measured should neither react with the liquid in the leveling bulb nor be soluble in it.

The following data are taken from a student's notebook in general chemistry at Syracuse University. This student first recorded the volume of air in the tube in ml. at atmospheric pressure, that is, with the liquid in both sides of the leveling bulb at the same height. The leveling bulb was raised, and the new volume and difference in height of mercury were recorded. The leveling bulb was lowered, and another set of data was recorded. The volumes measured by the student agree closely with the predictions of Boyle's Law, as shown in Table 4.2.

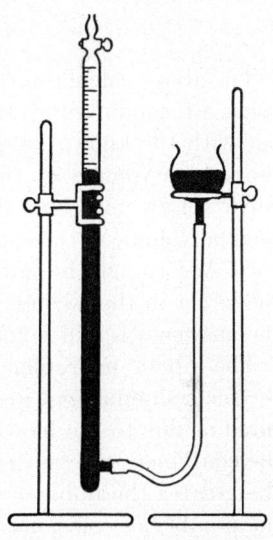

FIG. 4.3. Apparatus used to illustrate Boyle's Law.

TABLE 4.2. STUDENT DATA ON BOYLE'S PRESSURE LAW

	Reading in mm. on Meter Stick		Pressure in mm.	Volume of Enclosed Gas in ml.	
	Gas Side	Open Side		Observed	Calculated from Boyle's Law
Mercury levels the same	350	350	(1) 745	10	
Mercury in the leveling bulb high	352	407	(2) 745+(407−352)=800	9.30	9.31
Mercury in the leveling bulb low	348	303	(3) 745−(348−303)=700	10.60	10.64

(1) Barometer reading that day.
(2) Reading (1) + difference in mercury levels.
(3) (1) − difference in mercury levels.

His calculations were as follows:

$$\text{New volume} = 10.00 \text{ ml.} \times \frac{745 \text{ mm.}}{800 \text{ mm.}} = 9.31 \text{ ml. (first part)}$$

$$\text{New volume} = 10.00 \text{ ml.} \times \frac{745 \text{ mm.}}{700 \text{ mm.}} = 10.64 \text{ ml. (second part)}$$

Check: $PV = 7450$ (original measurements)
$PV = 7448$ (at end of first part)
$PV = 7448$ (at end of second part)

The above calculations were made by applying common sense, rather than using a formula.[2] Since the student wanted volume for an answer, he started out with the known volume. In order to get the new volume he multiplied the known volume by the ratio of the pressures. Qualitative application of Boyle's Law told him that the new volume had to be smaller than the original volume at the end of the first part, and larger at the end of the second part. Accordingly he put the smaller pressure on top in the first ratio, and the larger in the second. Since the units of pressure cancel out of this ratio, the answer was still volume, and in the same units with which he started.

The kinetic molecular theory offers a perfectly reasonable explanation of the facts summarized in Boyle's Law. If we remember that pressure is pictured as due to the blows struck by colliding molecules against the walls of the container, we can easily see that the greater their *concentration* (that is, the greater the number of molecules per unit volume), the greater will be the number of collisions against the wall. The pressure will then rise as the molecular concentration is increased by diminishing the volume. The pressure will also rise if the concentration of the molecules is increased by putting more molecules into the same space. This is what happens when a tire is inflated. The possibility of either much or little of a gas occupying the same space is explained by the statement that there is a relatively large amount of empty space between the molecules.

Charles' and Gay-Lussac's Laws

In 1802 Gay-Lussac published an article in which he stated that in 1787 Charles (also French) had found that different gases expand equally between 0° C. and 80° C. Gay-Lussac, continuing the investigation, found that the expansion between 0° C. and 1° C. was $\frac{1}{273}$ of the volume at 0° C., and that for any other 1° rise in temperature the expansion was the same. In the light of the kinetic molecular theory, this follows directly from what we have learned. If heating a fixed volume of gas increases the pressure by speeding up the molecules, the pressure can be brought back to the original pressure by permitting a compensating increase in the volume, giving the molecules more space in which to move.

When equal increments in one variable—temperature in this case—produce equal increases in another (volume in the case of Charles' Law, and pressure in the case of Gay-Lussac's Law) a direct proportionality exists between the two. At constant volume the pressure of a gas is proportional to

[2] "Why Solve for X?" Scott, E. C., *J. Chem. Ed.* **15**, 342 (1938).

THE KINETIC MOLECULAR THEORY OF GASES

the temperature. There is, however, an interesting detail to be attended to before these statements can be applied mathematically. To illustrate the point in question, consider the similar statement that railroad fare is proportional to the distance. New York City is twice as far from Albany as Poughkeepsie is. Does this mean that a ticket from Montreal to New York will cost twice as much as one from Montreal to Poughkeepsie? Obviously we must measure from where the trips start if the fares are to be proportional. Similarly, if pressures or volumes are to be proportional to temperatures, we must measure from their beginning. Zero pressure and zero volume are simple enough ideas, but zero temperature is not. In fact, we are familiar with *two* temperature zeros, and neither of them is the bottom! The Centigrade zero is merely the freezing point of ice. Dr. Fahrenheit took as his zero the lowest temperature in his home town of Danzig in the winter of 1709 during which he invented the mercury thermometer.

Absolute Zero

If pressure is due to the kinetic energy of molecules, the starting point must be zero kinetic energy. It is not easy to see what might be the limit to coldness, but zero kinetic energy is a perfectly simple idea. It means, simply, no motion. Less than no motion is as obviously impossible as a negative volume, so this zero is called *absolute* zero. From the rate at which pressure changes with the temperature this zero has been calculated to be $-273.1°$ C. Since many thermometers are not accurate to a tenth of a degree, the fourth figure is usually neglected. Centigrade degrees are always used in measuring absolute temperatures on the absolute centigrade scale. $0°$ C. is thus $273°$ A., and any other centigrade temperature can be converted into the corresponding absolute temperature by adding $273°$ to it. Instead of A., K. is also used to designate the centigrade scale of absolute temperatures; K. stands for the name of Lord Kelvin, noted for low-temperature research.

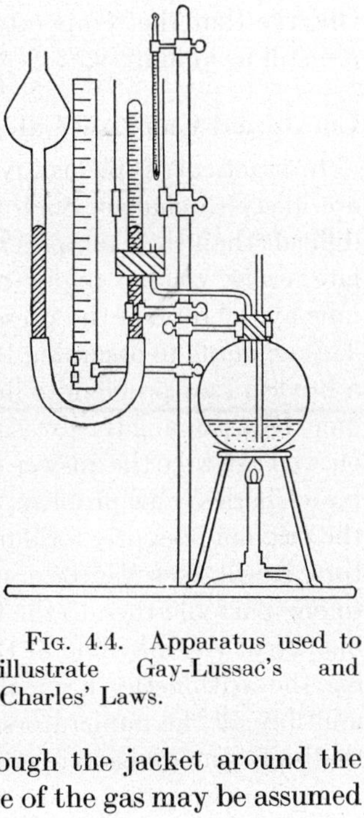

Charles' Law Calculations

An apparatus which can be used to illustrate both Gay-Lussac's and Charles' Laws is shown in Fig. 4.4. A definite volume of gas is measured at room temperature and atmospheric pressure. Water in the flask is heated to

FIG. 4.4. Apparatus used to illustrate Gay-Lussac's and Charles' Laws.

boiling, and the steam generated passes up through the jacket around the enclosed gas. After a few minutes the temperature of the gas may be assumed to be the same as that recorded by the thermometer. The mercury in the leveling arm is lowered until the two levels are the same, and the new volume is recorded. From these data Charles' Law can be confirmed.

A problem based on Charles' Law will illustrate the proper handling of the temperatures:

100 ml. of gas at 20° C. will have what volume at 90° C. if the pressure remains constant?

A tabulation may conveniently be set up for the data:

	Initial Conditions	Final Conditions
Temperature	20° + 273° = 293° A.	90° + 273° = 363° A.
Volume	100 ml.	unknown

If we want to find the unknown volume, we must start with the known volume and multiply it by the ratio of the temperatures. Since the gas is heated during the experiment, the molecules are moving faster at the end and striking harder blows. If the pressure is to remain constant, the volume must become larger so that the molecular blows are less frequent. The way to make the final volume larger than the initial one is to multiply the latter by a ratio greater than 1; so we put the larger temperature on top.

$$\text{New volume} = 100 \text{ ml.} \times \frac{363° \text{ A.}}{293° \text{ A.}} = 123.8 \text{ ml.}$$

Observe that the temperature units cancel out and the units of the answer are still in milliliters.

Combined Gas Law Calculations

In practical problems involving the use of the gas laws, *all* the conditions are likely to change. Such problems may be solved in steps, each no more difficult than the examples already given. For example, if you want to calculate a new volume under changed conditions, multiply your original volume by the ratio of the pressures and then by the ratio of the temperatures. This amounts to assuming the temperature to remain constant while you do a Boyle's Law problem to find the effect of the pressure change upon the volume. By assuming the pressure to remain constant at the new value from then on, you can take the answer to the Boyle's Law problem as the starting volume for a Charles' Law problem. Similarly, if you want a new pressure, start with the original pressure; for a new temperature, start with the original temperature. It will, however, be a waste of time actually to work out the answer first to one part and then to the next; for if the multiplications and divisions are indicated, you may find at the end that some terms cancel out, thus simplifying the arithmetic. Even if no cancellations are possible, you can always multiply all the numerators together and all the denominators together so that only one division operation is necessary.

To illustrate the saving in time, calculate the volume which a gas will

THE KINETIC MOLECULAR THEORY OF GASES

have at 50° C. and 750 mm. pressure, if the volume was 100 ml. at 20° C. and 790 mm. pressure.

Initial Conditions	Final Conditions
$V_1 = 100$ ml.	$V_2 =$ unknown
$T_1 = 20° + 273° = 293°$ A.	$T_2 = 50° + 273° = 323°$ A.
$P_1 = 790$ mm.	$P_2 = 750$ mm.

The general rule for working the problem is: The original volume times the temperature ratio times the pressure ratio equals the new volume. A temperature change from 293° A. to 323° A. is an increase and this causes an increase in volume. Therefore the temperature ratio must have the larger number in the numerator. A pressure change from 790 mm. to 750 mm. is a decrease and this causes an increase in volume. Therefore the larger of the two pressure terms must be in the numerator:

$$100 \text{ ml.} \times \frac{323° \text{ A.}}{293° \text{ A.}} \times \frac{790 \text{ mm.}}{750 \text{ mm.}} = V_2 = \text{answer} = \text{approximately 116 ml.}$$

You are urged to reason problems through rather than memorize formulas; it takes only clear thinking to set up the calculation just indicated. If you prefer to memorize formulas, Charles' Law $V_2 = \frac{T_2 V_1}{T_1}$ and Boyle's Law $V_2 = \frac{P_1 V_1}{P_2}$ can be combined into one expression, $V_1 \times \frac{P_1}{P_2} \times \frac{T_2}{T_1} = V_2$, as follows:

Solve Boyle's Law for V_2 and insert this value for V_1 in Charles' Law:

$$V_2 = \frac{T_2 \frac{P_1 V_1}{P_2}}{T_1} = V_1 \times \frac{P_1}{P_2} \times \frac{T_2}{T_1}$$

The same equation is obtained by solving for V_2 in Charles' Law and inserting it for V_1 in Boyle's Law:

$$V_2 = \frac{P_1 \frac{T_2 V_1}{T_1}}{P_2} = \frac{V_1 \times P_1 \times T_2}{P_2 \times T_1}$$

If we solved the problem in two steps, the part to which Boyle's Law applies would be:

$$V_2 = \frac{P_1 V_1}{P_2} = \frac{790 \text{ mm.}}{750 \text{ mm.}} \times 100 \text{ ml.} = 105.33 \text{ ml.}$$

This answer becomes the V_1 in the Charles' Law equation:

$$V_2 = \frac{T_2 V_1}{T_1} \text{ or } V_2 = \frac{323° \text{ A.}}{293° \text{ A.}} \times 105.33 \text{ ml.} = \text{approximately 116 ml.}$$

Standard Conditions

We have just seen that a given quantity of a gas may occupy almost any volume, depending upon the temperature and pressure. For convenience in making statements about gases comparable, a standard temperature, 273° A. (0° C.), and a standard pressure, 760 mm. (1 atm.), have been universally adopted. The results of experiments are regularly recalculated to these standard conditions.

Deviation of Real Gases from the Gas Laws

The gas laws, in the simple form in which we have stated them, depend upon the molecules having negligible volume and negligible attraction for one another. In ordinary cases the molecules are so far apart and moving so rapidly that the error caused by neglecting intermolecular attraction is of the order of 1 per cent. Because measurements of gases are difficult to make with great accuracy, this amount of error may often be neglected. The assumption that the whole volume of a gas is free space results in the actual pressure being greater than the calculated pressure by a fraction of 1 per cent. Since the effect of attraction is to make the actual pressure less than the calculated pressure, these two sources of error produce a combined effect equal only to their difference. For nitrogen and oxygen, the chief gases in the air, and for hydrogen and helium and many other less familiar ones, the net inaccuracy of the gas laws is less than the probable error of measurement, as long as the temperature and pressure are within limits conveniently obtainable in the laboratory. Thus the most convincing proof offered by the behavior of gases that the molecular picture has objective reality is furnished, interestingly enough, by the failure of the gas laws in certain cases. This is because these failures are exactly what our picture leads us to expect under extreme conditions.

Molecular Volume

Our picture of the molecular structure of gases leads us to predict that at extremely high pressures Boyle's Law cannot possibly continue to be obeyed. Increasing pressure does not compress the molecules of a gas; it merely brings them closer together, squeezing out the empty space, so to speak. When the empty space is gone, further compression requires tremendous pressures. But the failure of Boyle's Law appears long before this point. A liter of a typical gas may, under ordinary conditions, contain 1 ml. of gas molecules and 999 ml. of empty space. If the pressure is doubled, the concentration of the molecules will be doubled; there will be 1 ml. of molecules to $499\frac{1}{2}$ ml. of empty space, and the new volume will be $500\frac{1}{2}$ ml. This is 0.1 of 1 per cent greater than that predicted by Boyle's Law, which is practically perfect agreement. But suppose the initial pressure was 100 atm. instead of 1. The gas would have a volume of 11 ml., composed of 1 ml. of molecules (as before) and 10 ml. of empty space. If the pressure is doubled and the empty space correspondingly halved, the new total volume is $1 + 5 = 6$ ml. This is 9 per cent greater than the prediction by Boyle's Law. If the pressure is raised to 400 atm. the error will be 27 per cent. Under such conditions the law is worthless.

Intermolecular Attraction

According to Charles' Law, the volume of a gas should be zero at 0° A. According to the kinetic molecular theory, this can never happen, even if the molecules come completely to rest. Only the empty space will disappear; the molecules themselves will retain their original volume. As a matter of fact, it is by no means necessary to deprive the molecules of all kinetic energy in order to get rid of practically all the empty space. All gases, if sufficiently cooled, will condense into liquids because of the attraction of their molecules for one another. The liquid has a volume less than a thousandth that of the original gas, and it is practically incompressible; hence we believe that the molecules are nearly or actually in contact with one another. Like Boyle's Law, Charles' Law begins to be inaccurate long before it fails completely. As soon as a gas is cooled enough so that the kinetic energy of the molecules is no longer large in comparison with the attractive force between them, the volume begins to diminish more rapidly than the law predicts. The deviations from the law at any given temperature are larger the higher the pressure; for the closer the molecules are to one another, the more they are affected by their mutual attraction.

Formation of Liquids

Many gases can be liquefied at room temperature simply by increasing the pressure. Among these are steam, carbon dioxide, chlorine, and butane (pyrofax). But there is a limit to the effectiveness of pressure in bringing molecules closer together. Therefore the effectiveness of their mutual attraction can be increased by pressure only up to that limit. If, when the molecules have been brought practically into contact with one another, the attractive force is still insufficient to overcome the kinetic energy, they will escape from each other at every collision. The gaseous condition still exists. The essential feature of a liquid is not the nearness of the molecules, but their inability to leave each other as shown by the existence of a free top surface.

When a gas has been liquefied by pressure at constant temperature, nothing has been done to diminish the kinetic energy of the molecules. The molecules of a liquid have just as much energy as do those of any gas at the same temperature. The difference between a liquid and a gas is simply that the molecules of the former have too great mutual attraction for this energy to overcome. If the attraction between molecules is so low that no amount of pressure can liquefy a particular gas, it is necessary to decrease the energy of the molecules by cooling the gas until the attraction *can* overcome it.

Critical Temperature

Since the attraction between different kinds of molecules varies greatly, the amount of cooling necessary for liquefaction at average atmospheric pressure ranges from 4° A. (helium) to some 3500° C. (carbon). If the experiment is carried out at extreme pressure (molecules in contact) but is begun at such a high temperature that the substance is still a gas, equally widely differing amounts of cooling may be necessary, depending upon the nature of the substances. Liquefaction may occur while the temperature is still above red heat, or it may be necessary to cool the gas to as low as 5.2° A. (helium again). This characteristic temperature above which liquefaction is impossible, no matter how great the pressure, is called the *critical temperature* of a substance. At the critical temperature the pressure must be great enough to produce molecular contact in order to liquefy the gas. The pressure which will just suffice to do this is called the *critical pressure*, and is also characteristic of the particular substance. As the temperature is lowered, less and less pressure is required for liquefaction. Why?

Van der Waals' Law

The so-called *perfect* or *ideal* gas is one in which there would be no attraction between molecules at any temperature or pressure. Such a gas does not exist. An equation which satisfactorily describes the behavior of real gases, even when they are near enough to the liquefaction point to be quite "imperfect," was developed by van der Waals. Starting out with the simple equation given on page 35, he introduced a term to correct the pressure for the way in which intermolecular attraction overcomes it with diminishing volume, and another term to correct the total volume for the volume of the molecules. Both of these terms are different for each individual gas, whereas the perfect gas law pays no attention to the nature of the gas. Since van der Waals was the first to take mathematical account of the attractive forces between molecules, these are usually called "van der Waals forces." The success of these kinetic molecular theory considerations in explaining quantitatively the deviations between the behavior of real gases and that predicted by the gas law long ago convinced chemists and physicists that the picture they gave of the structure of matter was essentially true and real. It was no accident that the very "imperfections" in the behavior of gases were the means of bringing additional knowledge. On the contrary, every annoying irregularity in the application of a general principle, every "defect" in a law, may be confidently regarded as the outcropping of a new vein of knowledge, a challenge to the researcher or the theorist.

Graham's Law

In 1833 Graham reported that the rate of diffusion of a gas is inversely proportional to the square root of its density. The usual apparatus for demonstrating that gases diffuse at different rates is shown in Fig. 4.5. A porous porcelain cup is fitted with a 1-hole stopper; a glass tube through it serves as a manometer. If a beaker is inverted, filled with hydrogen gas, and lowered over the porcelain cup, hydrogen gas diffuses into the cup faster than air diffuses out. This increases the number of molecules within the cup and therefore the pressure; and this increase in pressure forces some water from the manometer. Graham was not so fortunate as to have porous cups available; he made his own from plaster of Paris.

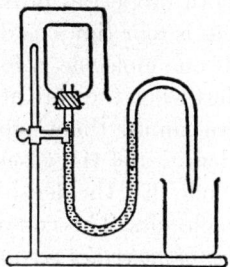

Fig. 4.5. Diffusion of hydrogen through a porous cup.

The experiment just described is qualitative only, but a more quantitative one can be done as shown in Fig. 4.6. A long tube is suspended between two ring stands and a wad of cotton is put in each end of the tube to decrease air currents. By means of a pipette 1 ml. of a solution of hydrogen chloride is placed inside the cotton at one end of the tube, and a similar amount of a solution of ammonia at the other. After a few minutes a white ring forms where the two gases meet. The white smoke is the salt, ammonium chloride, formed by their reaction when they meet. The relative distances traveled by the gases are proportional to their relative rates of diffusion. The distances which they should travel according to Graham's Law can be calculated as follows:

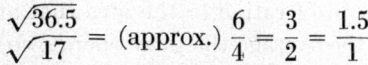

$$\frac{\text{Rate of diffusion of ammonia}}{\text{Rate of diffusion of hydrogen chloride}} = \frac{\sqrt{\text{density of hydrogen chloride}}}{\sqrt{\text{density of ammonia}}} =$$

$$\frac{\sqrt{36.5}}{\sqrt{17}} = (\text{approx.}) \frac{6}{4} = \frac{3}{2} = \frac{1.5}{1}$$

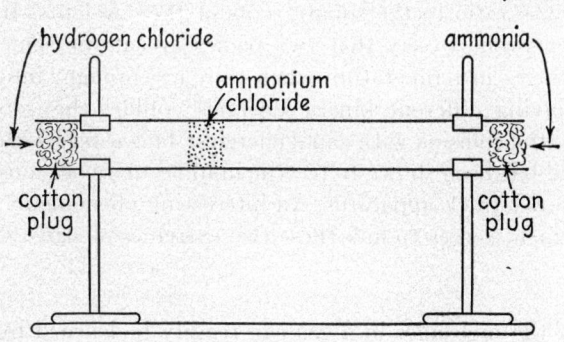

Fig. 4.6. Relative diffusion of hydrogen chloride and ammonia.

In expressing density of gases the unit volume chosen (see the definition of density on page 4) is 22.4 liters and the weights given are those which that volume of each gas would have if measured at 0 °C. and 1 atmosphere pressure. This volume and these conditions are chosen for reasons of convenience which will be appreciated later, but any change of conditions will affect both gases proportionately and the *ratio* will keep the same value.

Avogadro's Law

According to the kinetic molecular theory, the rate of diffusion of a gas is proportional to the speed of its molecules. Experimental measurements of both properties prove this to be true. Other experiments show that if one gas is four times as dense as another it diffuses half as fast (Graham's Law). If one molecule is four times as heavy as another it will move just half as fast when they are at the same temperature and so have equal energies. Thus we can use the weights of the individual molecules interchangeably with the densities of the gases in calculating the rate of diffusion. From this we conclude that the densities of gases must be proportional to the weights of their molecules. This can only be true (and it *is* true) if *all gases have the same number of molecules per unit volume under the same conditions*. The italicized statement is called Avogadro's Law. It is not merely an inescapable conclusion of logic but an experimentally proved fact.

It may seem curious at first consideration that there should be the same number of helium molecules (wt. = 4 atomic weight units), nitrogen molecules (wt. = 28 atomic weight units), or chloroform molecules (wt. = 111 atomic weight units) in a liter of each gas at the same temperature and pressure. Actually, it follows logically from what has been stated about temperature and pressure. At the same temperature all molecules have the same average energy. If pressure is caused by the blows of these molecules on the walls of the container, it will take the same number of blows of equal energy to produce the same pressure, hence there must be the same concentration of molecules.

In view of the importance of the subject, it may be well to give further consideration to the idea that at a given temperature all molecules have on the average the same energy, so that light molecules move more rapidly and heavy ones less so, in inverse ratio to the square roots of their weights. It should be acceptable to everyone to say that two bodies are at the same temperature if neither changes in temperature when they are brought into contact. But if objects having different kinetic energies collide, they do change in energy and leave the collision with equal energies. This is true with objects of ordinary size and has been shown to be true in molecular collisions as observed by the Wilson ray-track apparatus. An interesting phenomenon known as Brownian movement serves to link these two extremes of size.

Brownian Movement

The average velocity of the molecules in a gas can readily be learned by determining the velocity of transmission of sound through it, since sound waves are actually propagated by molecular motion. The velocity of a hydrogen molecule (1 mile per second) is too great to permit the molecule to be seen even if it were big enough to reflect light. Larger molecules should move more slowly, but practically none of them reach even the lower limit of visibility in the ultramicroscope,[3] which is at about a millimicron in diameter. However, according to Avogadro's Law, size and weight should have nothing to do with the continued equal sharing of energy. If a particle composed of thousands of molecules is suspended freely in a gas and is being knocked about by collisions with the molecules of the gas, it should still have the same average energy as any *one* of them. Such a particle 0.2 micron in diameter would be a thousand times as large as a hydrogen molecule, would have a billion times its volume, and might easily have 37 billion times its weight. Remembering that its energy is the same as that of the hydrogen molecule, we can easily see that its velocity must be correspondingly less. The velocity would, in fact, be that of the hydrogen molecule divided by the square root of 37 billion, which amounts to about 1 cm. per second. Such a size and velocity are within the range of visual measurement. Particles of about that size are found in smoke, fogs, and dust clouds;[4] and when observed in the ultramicroscope they are actually seen to be in continuous zigzag motion of just the velocities that correspond to their weights. The Scottish botanist Brown, who first observed this motion in 1827, did not realize that the jerky changes in motion[5] of the visible particles were due to the impacts of invisible molecules.

Thus we see that all molecules at the same temperature must and do have the same average kinetic energy, regardless of the differences in velocity that are needed to compensate for differences in their weights. A given number of them, whether light or heavy or of different weights, will therefore produce the same pressure in a given volume at a given temperature. This last statement is simply a rephrasing of Avogadro's Law. The importance of this to the chemist is enormous. For one thing, it means that by merely measuring the volumes of gases which react with each other chemically, he can determine the relative numbers of the different kinds of molecules involved.

Gay-Lussac's Law of Combining Volumes

Avogadro's hypothesis was originally advanced to explain Gay-Lussac's Law of Combining Volumes. In 1808 Gay-Lussac had announced, as the result of many experiments, that when two or more gases are used up or produced in a chemical reaction, the relationship between their volumes can be expressed in terms of small, whole-number ratios. For example, 10 ml. of hydrogen will combine with 5 ml. of oxygen, the volume ratio being 2:1. The product is water; and if the experiment is begun and finished at room temperature, no gas will take the place of those disappearing. If, however, the initial and final temperature are above the boiling point of water (100° C.), the water produced will remain in the form of the gas steam, and its

---

[3] *Encyclopedia Americana*, **27**, 204–205 (1941 ed.).

[4] They may also be found at times in liquids. Particles large enough to be visible in the ultramicroscope but small enough so that their temperature motions keep them from settling to the bottom are called *colloidal* particles.

[5] See the diagram of the path of one such particle, Fig. 21.6.

volume will be 10 ml. The volume of the hydrogen is to the volume of the oxygen as 2 is to 1; the volume of the hydrogen is to that of the steam as 1 is to 1; the volume of the oxygen is to that of the steam as 1 is to 2. Of course, in the experiment at the higher temperature fewer molecules will be present in the same volumes, but the ratios will be the same.

Belief in the molecular theory was already fairly general in Gay-Lussac's time, because it explained the gas laws as nothing else could. Avogadro explained the facts summarized in Gay-Lussac's Law in terms of the molecular hypothesis, thus: If molecules exist, any reaction between two substances must be between molecules of two kinds. One molecule should be able to react with one or two or three of another kind, but not with 1.036 molecules, or any other odd fraction. Since we expect whole-number molecular ratios and actually find whole-number volume ratios, what more natural than to conclude that these are the same? That is, a milliliter of any one gas contains the same number of molecules as a milliliter of any other gas at the same temperature and pressure. This conclusion has since been justified by many diverse and independent experiments and lines of reasoning, and is now regarded as a fundamental law.

The Weights of Molecules

The acceptance of Avogadro's Law gave chemists a way of measuring the weights of molecules long before physicists had developed the mass spectrograph or, indeed, any means of handling individual molecules. Chemists deal only with enormous numbers of molecules; but if they can be counted, there is nothing to prevent the determination of their individual weights. A person needs only to divide the weight of any quantity of material by the number of molecules in it. This can be illustrated by a case which is more easily imagined because it deals with familiar things. Suppose a sealed freight car is known to contain a shipment of 2000 sacks of flour, and you want to know the weight of each sack. You can have the car shunted onto the track scales and weighed to the nearest ton. Suppose that after the weight of the car is subtracted from the total weight, the result is 24 tons. The weight of one sack of flour is then $\frac{24}{2000}$, or 0.012 ton. Of course this answer is ridiculous, even though true, on account of the disproportion between the object and the size of the unit used to express its weight. In order to change the weight into an appropriate unit we must multiply by the number of pounds in a ton. The problem then takes the form:

$$\frac{24 \text{ tons total weight} \times 2000 \text{ lbs. per ton}}{2000 \text{ sacks}} = \frac{24 \times 2000}{2000} = 24 \text{ lbs. per sack}$$

Note how much the arithmetic is simplified by the fact that the number of sacks weighed was the same as the number of pounds in a ton.

Similarly, to determine how much a carbon dioxide molecule weighs, we

THE KINETIC MOLECULAR THEORY OF GASES

need only weigh a convenient quantity of the gas and divide this weight by the number of molecules present. The weight should be in atomic weight units in order to avoid having a long string of zeros between the decimal point and the first significant figure. Laboratory scales are calibrated in grams; so the weight of the carbon dioxide must be multiplied by the number of atomic weight units in a gram. The letter N is commonly used for this number. Just as it was arithmetically convenient to have as many flour sacks as there are pounds in a ton, so in this case it will be much less work if we have as many carbon dioxide molecules as there are atomic weight units in a gram. Then we have:

$$\frac{\text{Wt. in g. of carbon dioxide} \times \text{N at. wt. units per g.}}{\text{N carbon dioxide molecules}} = \text{Wt. of 1 molecule}$$

That is, one molecule weighs as many atomic weight units as N molecules do grams. N molecules of carbon dioxide weigh 44 g.; hence one molecule of carbon dioxide weighs 44 at. wt. units.

The Volume of N Molecules

Notice that if you have any way of being sure that the amount of gas you measure contains N molecules, it is not even necessary to know the numerical value of N. Actually the atomic weight unit was so defined as to make it very easy to measure out N molecules. In choosing a new unit of weight it was not necessary for it to bear any particular relationship to the gram, any more than to the pound or to any of the other multifarious units of weight men have invented. It was only necessary that it should be of the same order of magnitude as the objects which were to be weighed in terms of it, namely, molecules. It was thus perfectly feasible to define the atomic weight unit in terms of the weight of some particular molecule, and leave to future generations the task of finding out, if they wanted to, how many of these units there are in a carat or grain or gram. For reasons of convenience it was finally decided that the atomic weight unit should weigh $\frac{1}{32}$ of the weight of an oxygen molecule.

How are we to go about weighing N molecules? Very simply. If 1 molecule of oxygen weighs 32 atomic weight units, N molecules will weigh 32 g. But if 32 g. of oxygen contains N molecules, we need only to measure the volume it occupies and then measure this same volume of any other gas, in order to have N molecules of that gas. The weight in grams of that volume of any gas will then be numerically equal to the weight in atomic weight units of an individual molecule of that gas.

The Gram-Molecular Weight, or Mol

N, the number of atomic weight units in a gram, is called Avogadro's number. N molecules are called a *gram-molecular weight*. This term refers to the fact that N molecules of a substance weigh as many grams as the weight of an individual molecule in atomic weight units. The rather awkward expression is sometimes shortened to gram molecule, but the usual term now is *mol*. A mol of a substance is the practical chemical unit quantity of that substance. It contains the same number of molecules (N) as a mol of any other substance, but the weights differ in the same ratio as the weights of the individual molecules. This statement may be thought of in terms of an analogy: A dozen is the commercial unit quantity for eggs; it contains the same number of eggs (12), regardless of the kind, but a dozen ostrich eggs

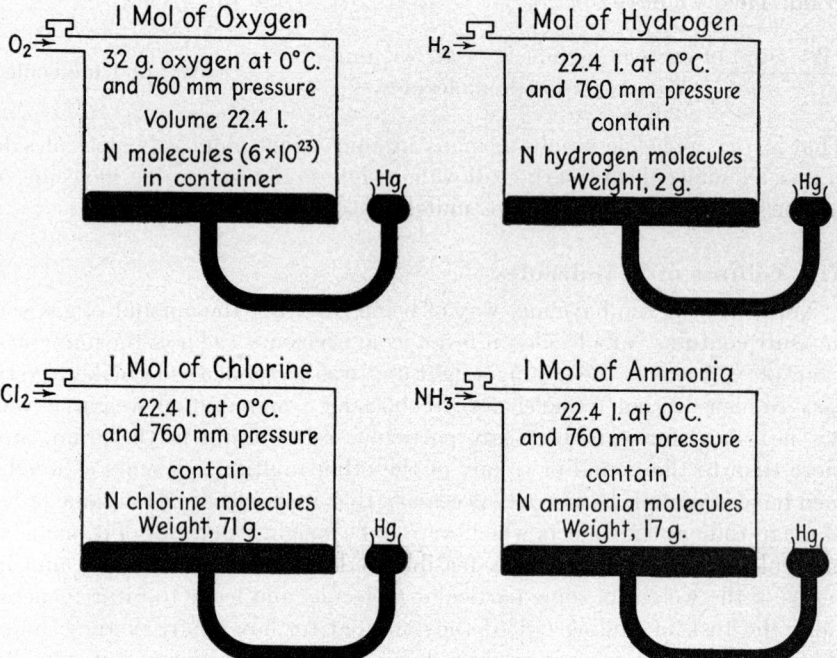

FIG. 4.7. Equal volumes of all gases under the same conditions of temperature and pressure contain the same number of molecules.

will weigh more than a dozen hummingbird eggs, in the same ratio as the weight of the individual eggs.

At standard temperature and pressure (S.T.P.) N molecules of oxygen occupy 22.4 l. (a trifle less than a cubic foot). So a mol of *any other gas* (namely, N molecules of it) will occupy the same volume, 22.4 l., under standard conditions. This volume is therefore called the gram-molecular volume or, more briefly, the *molar volume*. Few arbitrary numbers in chemistry need to be committed to memory, for they can be found in reference books when needed. But because of the incessant usefulness of the mol, you should learn the following by heart: One mol of any gas contains N molecules and occupies the molar volume of 22.4 l. under standard condition of 760 mm.

THE KINETIC MOLECULAR THEORY OF GASES

(=1 atm.) and 273° A. (=0° C.). It is not necessary for a chemist to remember the numerical value (6.023·10²³) Avogadro's number, N.

Finding the Molecular Weight

The average weight of the molecules of a substance is called the molecular weight of that substance and is regularly expressed without labeling it with the name of the weight unit. Thus an oxygen molecule weighs 32 at. wt. units; a mol of oxygen weighs 32 g. Both statements are implied when one says that the molecular weight of oxygen is 32.

To find the molecular weight of any gaseous substance it is only necessary to find the volume occupied by some weighed quantity of it under known conditions of temperature and pressure. If this volume is then calculated to standard conditions, the weight of 22.4 l. under the same conditions can easily be obtained from it. Of course 22.4 l. of a gas at S.T.P. is a mol, and its weight in grams is the molecular weight.

Suppose, for example, that we learn by experiment that an evacuated 100-ml. bulb increases in weight by 0.0688 g. when filled with ammonia at 22° C. and 745 mm. pressure. It is convenient to set up a table of data as follows:

	Initial Conditions	Final Conditions
Volume	100 ml.	x (= vol. at S.T.P.)
Pressure	745 mm.	760 mm.
Temperature	22° C. = 295° A.	273° A.

Then $x = 100 \text{ ml.} \times \dfrac{745 \text{ mm.}}{760 \text{ mm.}} \times \dfrac{273° \text{ A.}}{295° \text{ A.}} = 90.2$ ml.

The weight of a mol of ammonia is given by:

$$x = 0.0688 \text{ g.} \times \frac{22{,}400 \text{ ml.}}{90.2 \text{ ml.}} = 17.0 \text{ g.}$$

In the first part of the calculation we write both ratios with the small figure on top, because the volume is reduced both by raising the pressure to standard pressure and by lowering the temperature to standard temperature. In the second calculation we start with the weight because we want weight for our answer. The larger volume goes in the numerator of the fraction because a large volume of gas must weigh more than a small volume *at the same temperature and pressure*. Note that the units in which the molar volume is expressed have been changed from liters to milliliters. This is done so that the units will cancel out. Of course the volume of the gas, 0.0688 g., could just as well have been expressed as 0.0902 l. The important thing is that in each ratio both quantities should be expressed in the *same* units. Always check this. Changing the temperature from the centigrade to the absolute scale was not optional, but absolutely necessary. See what happens if you try to use both temperatures centigrade!

The use of an algebraic formulation of the gas laws, such as the one mentioned on page 35, or one of the equivalent forms frequently seen in high-school texts, in making calculations such as this is perfectly possible but is not recommended.

Significant Figures

The calculation could have been carried out to a second decimal place, yielding 16.98 g. Only the first three figures in this result are *significant*, however, since even the third figure is somewhat uncertain, first, because any figure obtained by the use of logarithms or a slide rule is likely to be in error by a unit or two in the last place, and second, because, as previously explained, the gas law is inaccurate to the extent of 0.1 of 1 per cent or more. Thus even if we made the unjustifiable assumption that the experimental results were perfectly accurate, the true value for the molecular weight might just as well be 16.95 or 17.01. But the experimental data do not even pretend to be perfectly accurate. It is an accepted scientific convention to use one uncertain (but probable) figure in recording results. Hence the statement that the volume is 100 ml. means that it is probably between 99 and 101 ml. When the temperature is given as 22° C., the implication is that the thermometer has not been calibrated accurately enough to make its readings trustworthy to a tenth of a degree; however, the temperature was probably nearer 295° A. than 294° or 296°. Similarly, the pressure, 745 mm., definitely does not mean 745.0 mm. The latter would claim a probable accuracy of 0.1 mm., or 0.015 of 1 per cent, whereas the actual claim admits a possible error of 1 mm., or 0.15 of 1 per cent. This, added to the possible 1 per cent error in the volume and the possible 0.34 of 1 per cent error in the temperature, makes an uncertainty of 1.5 per cent in the experimental data, or nearly 0.2 g. in the weight of a mol. Accordingly the calculated 16.98 g. is rounded off to 17.0 g., in which the final .0 expresses the opinion that the result is reliable to one or two tenths of a gram. The actually accepted value, the result of much more careful experiments, is 17.03 g.

Splitting Molecules by Chemical Reactions

When various examples of the Law of Combining Volumes were studied in the light of Avogadro's Law, it became evident that molecules are frequently split into two or more parts by chemical reactions. Consider, for example, the reactions of hydrogen with chlorine and with oxygen, as shown in the accompanying diagram. In accordance with Avogadro's Law, each unit volume is diagramed as containing the same number of molecules. Now count the number of hydrogen molecules, and then the number of hydrogen chloride molecules. There are twice as many of the latter as of the hydrogen, and yet all the hydrogen chloride molecules are alike and all contain hydrogen.

THE KINETIC MOLECULAR THEORY OF GASES

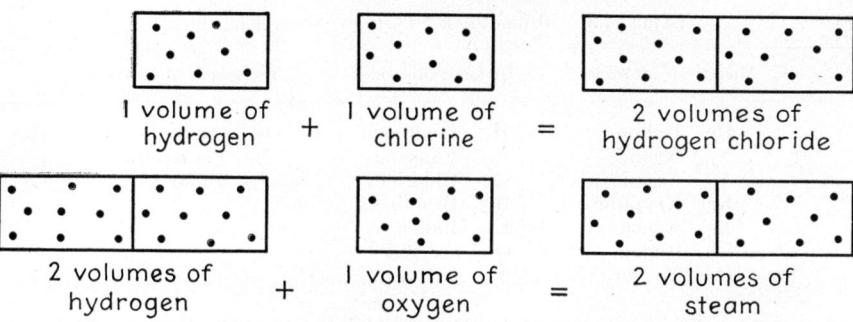

Evidently each hydrogen molecule has split into two parts, one of which goes into the formation of each molecule of hydrogen chloride. The same statements that have been made about hydrogen hold true for chlorine. Our conclusion is that the net result of a collision between a hydrogen molecule and a chlorine molecule is that each breaks in two and each half-molecule of hydrogen unites with a half-molecule of chlorine to make a hydrogen chloride molecule.

The second part of the diagram shows that oxygen molecules are also divisible into two parts, and that a water molecule contains one of these, together with both parts of a hydrogen molecule. Other experiments show that other molecules can be broken during chemical reactions into even more than two identical pieces. One milliliter of ozone (p. 120) will react with three of hydrogen, and if the entire experiment is carried out at 110° C., the product will be 3 ml. of steam (gaseous water). Since all water molecules are alike, each ozone molecule must have split into three parts, each identical with half an oxygen molecule. One of these must have joined with each of three hydrogen molecules to form that number of water molecules. The phosphorus molecule can be split into four identical parts. On the other hand, some molecules cannot be split by any reaction whatever. Helium, neon, argon, and mercury belong to this class.[6]

Atoms

Since molecules which can be split by chemical reactions into two or three or four identical parts can never be split into any larger number of parts by collisions of whatever violence with molecules of whatever kind, the parts are appropriately called *atoms* (Greek, not cut). Atoms, then, are the building blocks of molecules. Atoms bear the same relation to molecules as rooms to houses or cars to trains. Just as a house may have one or many rooms, and a train may consist of a single Diesel-motored unit or of many cars, so a molecule may be monatomic or polyatomic. If a diatomic molecule is broken into

[6] These substances are present in the familiar "neon" sign light tubes. The yellow ones contain helium, the orange ones neon, and the blue both argon and mercury. An excess of the mercury beyond what can remain in the form of a gas at the working temperature can usually be seen in horizontal portions of blue light tubes as drops of liquid metal.

TABLE 4.3. MOLECULAR STATE OF SOME ELEMENTS

Monatomic Molecules		Diatomic Molecules		Polyatomic Molecules	
He	Helium	H_2	Hydrogen	O_3	Ozone
Ne	Neon	F_2	Fluorine	P_4	Phosphorus
A	Argon	Cl_2	Chlorine	S_8	Sulfur
Kr	Krypton	Br_2	Bromine		
Xe	Xenon	I_2	Iodine		
Rn	Radon	O_2	Oxygen		
Hg	Mercury	N_2	Nitrogen		

NOTE: The subscript following the symbol for the element tells how many atoms there are in the molecule. If there is no subscript, 1 is understood.

two separate atoms by a violent collision (i.e., by high temperature), these two atoms are two new and different molecules as long as they remain separate particles.

The number of different kinds of molecules is enormous. Even those whose structure is accurately known are numbered by the hundred thousand. If each of these had to be studied without relation to any of the others, the task would be Herculean, like learning to read Chinese, where each word has a separate ideogram. Fortunately, the task is like learning to read English, where half a million words are all composed of only 26 letters, for in all the different kinds of molecules of which the earth is composed, only 96 chemically different kinds of atoms have been found.

QUESTIONS AND PROBLEMS

1. At 20° C. the pressure in a steel cylinder of oxygen is 100 atm. What will it be if the cylinder stands in the sun until its temperature is 37° C.?
2. At what temperature will the pressure in the cylinder in problem 1 fall to 95 atm.?
3. The walls and top of a gas tank such as those in which city gas is stored are movable and counterbalanced in such a way that a constant pressure is maintained upon the stored gas regardless of volume changes. If the gas in such a tank occupies 100,000 cu ft. at 0° C., what will the volume be if the temperature rises to 17° C.? What fraction of the total weight of the gas will still be in the original 100,000 cu. ft.?
4. To what temperature will it be necessary to cool the gas in problem 3 in order to reduce its volume to 95,000 cu. ft.? By what fraction will the density of the gas then exceed the original density?
5. Suppose that 75 ml. of air are confined over the mercury in the apparatus shown in Fig. 4.3. What volume of mercury will have to be forced into space now occupied by air in order to increase the pressure from 750 mm. to 800 mm.? (If the pressure is increased suddenly the work done upon the gas in compressing it will raise its temperature a little, but this must not be con-

sidered in solving this problem. Temperature is not mentioned in the problem; *therefore it is assumed to be constant.* Simply imagine that you have waited long enough for the air to return to its original temperature before making the final measurement. In all problems, assume that any factor not specifically mentioned is constant.)

6. The molecular weight of chlorine is 70.9. At what temperature will 141.8 g. of it exert a pressure of 5.00 atm. in a steel cylinder having a volume of 10.50 l.? Notice that the statement about the molecular weight contains within itself a complete set of initial data for the problem. If you don't obtain the correct answer of 47° C., go back over your work and see if you did not at some point forget that your x was temperature.
7. What weight of hydrogen will fill a balloon of 100,000 cu. m. capacity if the temperature is 27° C. and the barometer reads 735 mm.?
8. The average molecular weight of air is 29. How many times heavier is any volume of air than the same volume of hydrogen under the same conditions? What is the gross lifting power of the balloon in the preceding problem? What will it be if helium is used instead of hydrogen?
9. From a steel cylinder of compressed nitrogen 112 g. of the gas was allowed to escape. What volume did the expanded gas occupy if it was at 17° C. and 757 mm. pressure?

REFERENCES

Articles

"Liquid Air," Cady, H. P. *J. Chem. Ed.* **8**, 1027–1043 (1931).

» 5 «

THE ELECTRICAL NATURE OF MATTER

In the two preceding chapters we have seen that substances can be separated into molecules by such a simple process as evaporation, and that molecules can be split into atoms by chemical reactions. How about atoms? Can they in turn be split up into smaller pieces? In 1803 Dalton, called the Father of the Atomic Theory, thought not. Toward the end of the 19th century, however, there began a series of epoch-making experimental discoveries which proved that an atom is a fairly complex structure. But just as innumerable molecules are composed of atoms of fewer than a hundred elements, so we find that all atoms are apparently composed of no more than three kinds of particles. These three are called *electrons*, *protons*, and *neutrons*. These are the *ultimate units of matter*, probably capable of no further subdivision. They are considered to be composed of energy itself rather than of other particles.

Fundamental Particles

The weight of an electron is negligible compared with that of even the lightest atom, namely, about 0.0005 at. wt. units. It has, or perhaps *is*, a unit electrical charge; a current of electricity in a wire is nothing more or less than a stream of electrons moving from atom to atom in it. Since the charge is *negative*, the symbol ⊖ may be used for an electron. (An electron has been shown by the physicists to behave also as a magnet.)

The proton is a particle weighing close to 1 at. wt. unit. It bears an electrical charge equal to that of the electron, but opposite in sign; hence ⊕ is an appropriate symbol for it.

A neutron has approximately the same weight as a proton but, as the name indicates, has no charge. It may be symbolized by Ⓝ.

Although protons and neutrons are approximately 1840 times as heavy as electrons, they are far smaller. Two hundred or more of them can be clustered together in a space no larger than the volume of a single electron. In an atom all the protons and neutrons are actually thus clustered into what is called the *nucleus*. The total diameter of an atom is roughly 10,000 times the diameter of its nucleus.

The General Structure of an Atom

Since matter as a whole is electrically neutral, atoms must consist of equal numbers of protons and electrons. The *atomic number* of an electrically neutral atom designates the number of protons and electrons in its structure. An atom consisting of ten protons and ten electrons has therefore an atomic number of 10.

The electrons are effectively segregated from the protons in an atom. As pointed out above, the protons are centrally located in the nucleus of the atom, whereas the electrons revolve about the nucleus in orbits. Electrons, being negative, are attracted by the positively charged nucleus. They are kept from falling into it by centrifugal force generated by their rotation about it. The greater the energy of rotation of an electron, the greater will be its average distance from the nucleus. Only certain energies are possible for electrons revolving in orbits;[1] therefore only certain orbits are possible. The groups of orbits in which electrons have about the same average distance from the nucleus are said to constitute a "shell" or "layer." These various features of atomic structure are represented in Fig. 5.1, showing one of the smaller atoms, that of magnesium. It is impossible to draw such a diagram to scale, for the nucleus would be invisible and the layers of electrons would be inconveniently spread over the entire page.

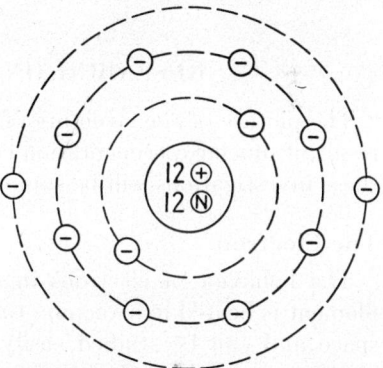

Fig. 5.1. Structure of a magnesium atom. Atomic number, 12; atomic weight, 24.

It must also be remembered that the diagram shows the cross section of a three-dimensional structure. The dashed circles do not show the paths of the electrons, but merely indicate the individual shells making up the extra-nuclear structure. The circle bounding the nucleus is purely imaginary, put there to help keep the eye from confusing the nuclear particles with the electrons; actually, no skin or sheath surrounds the nucleus. The number of protons in the nucleus is equal to the atomic number of the element represented; it will be shown presently how this can be determined experimentally.

[1] Electrons are believed to have a wave nature in terms of which this curious fact can be explained by means of a complex branch of higher mathematics called *wave mechanics*. This explanation is beyond the scope of this book.

The number of neutrons is obtained by subtracting the atomic number of an atom from its atomic weight. The nucleus of an *ordinary* hydrogen atom consists of a single proton; it is the only one containing no neutrons. Nuclei of other light atoms have about the same number of neutrons as protons. As the atomic number increases, the number of neutrons increases faster and eventually reaches a figure 60 per cent larger than the number of protons.

The nucleus is not affected by ordinary chemical changes,[2] nor are the inner layers of electrons. The chemical properties of atoms depend primarily upon the number of electrons in the outer layers and to some extent upon the size of the atom. The atomic number sets the number of electrons in an atom, and this in turn fixes the number of outer electrons and the size of the atom, determining all the chemical properties. Now we can understand how an element can be defined with perfect precision as *a substance whose atoms all have the same atomic number*.

RESEARCH ON ATOMIC STRUCTURE

The picture of the structure of atoms which has just been outlined is the result of much experimentation combined with brilliant deduction. Some of these investigations will be summarized in the following sections.

The Electron

The behavior of electrons in atoms is complicated, but when a metal filament is heated in a vacuum tube electrons "evaporate" out of it into free space and can be studied easily. A positively charged plate draws these electrons toward itself with an acceleration which proves them to be very light in proportion to their charge. A magnetic field forces them into a circular path, the small radius of which proves that they are not heavy. The actual size of the charge was measured by Millikan in his oil-drop experiment which won the Nobel prize.[3] This enabled the weight to be calculated as $\frac{1}{1838}$ of an atomic weight unit.

A conductor from which electrons are being emitted is called a cathode. The positively charged conductor which receives the electrons is called an anode. If there is a high voltage difference between them, a stream of very fast electrons will result. High-speed electrons produced in this way were called cathode rays before their nature was understood. A fast electron striking an atom may knock out an electron from the atom just as a marble may knock another marble out of a ring. The electron which has been knocked out of the atom joins the other electrons in their race toward the anode. The remainder of the molecule necessarily has an excess positive charge and

[2] By ordinary chemical change we exclude the possibilities of chemical reactions brought about by means of bombarding atomic nuclei with atomic projectiles or due to naturally occurring unstable nuclei such as those of radium. Any reference to chemical properties and reactions will hence forth refer to the *ordinary* type.

[3] *Encyclopedia Americana*, **10**, 203-204 (1941 ed.).

THE ELECTRICAL NATURE OF MATTER 53

is, in fact, a positive ion. Positive ions are drawn toward the cathode. If the cathode is pierced by a small hole or canal, the positive ions may shoot right through it as a beam of "positive rays" or "canal rays." Such a stream of positive ions is, in fact, exactly what is used in the mass spectrograph (p. 20), and this instrument enables us to analyze the positive rays and learn what elements are present. It was in 1891 that Sir J. J. Thomson showed by this means that electrons could be knocked out of the molecules of any gas. Since they could also be obtained from all the metals he used for cathodes, he rightly concluded that electrons are a constituent of all substances.

The Proton

The lightest atomic nucleus ever identified by the mass spectrograph is that of ordinary hydrogen, which weighs 1.008 atomic weight units. When the weights of all other muclei proved to be very close to whole numbers on the same scale, it revived Prout's hypothesis, an old speculation that all the elements might somehow be composed of the first element, hydrogen. The hydrogen nucleus, when thought of as a component unit of other nuclei, was called the proton. The theory was confirmed by Rutherford's discovery that certain unstable nuclei emitted high-speed hydrogen nuclei. The identity of the ejected particles was proved by measurements of their mass and charge made in Wilson cloud chambers (p. 19). The unstable nuclei which eject protons from themselves were produced by bombarding stable nuclei with alpha particles or with projectiles of even higher speed and smaller size produced by means of apparatus like the cyclotron (Chapter 38).

The Neutron

In 1920 Rutherford proposed the neutron to explain the fact that the weights of most atomic nuclei were greater than the sum of their protons. Chadwick, in 1932, actually obtained neutrons from unstable nuclei produced, as described in the preceding paragraph, by bombardment. Having no charge, neutrons produce no measurable ionization and cannot be detected by either the cloud chamber or the Geiger counter. The mass of the neutron was eventually determined by observing in the cloud chambers the extent of recoil of atoms struck by the neutron, as well as the velocity of protons ejected from the atoms by the recoil collisions. By means of appropriate interpretation of the experimental results and the application of the laws of momentum and of conservation of energy the mass of the neutron was determined. Chadwick received the Nobel prize for his efforts in solving the problem of the mass of the neutron. Since they do not lose energy in producing ionization, high-speed neutrons can penetrate feet of steel or concrete, in great contrast to rays of charged particles which are stopped by a few centimeters of air or a sheet of glass. Neutrons which collide with the actual nuclei of atoms are likely to be absorbed, and the resulting new nuclei are usually unstable, i.e., *radioactive*.

Other Fundamental Particles

Names of other subatomic fundamental particles may be more or less familiar to you, such as positron, mesotron (or meson or barytron), neutrino, and photon. The first is like an electron, but positive in charge. The second has the charge of an electron but has some 200 times its weight. Neither of these has an existence longer than a tiny fraction of a second. The neutrino is an uncharged particle with the weight of an electron. A pulse of electromagnetic radiation (e.g., light, X rays, gamma rays, cosmic radiation) behaves to some extent like a particle. This is particularly noticeable if the vibration frequency, and therefore the energy, are high. If the particle nature rather than the wave nature of the light-pulse is being discussed, it is frequently called a photon.

None of these last-mentioned particles need to be considered in studying the relationship of atomic structure to chemical behavior. Furthermore, these particles need not be thought of as affecting the physical characteristics of the atom such as mass, since they apparently arise from the particles we have already shown to be present in the atom; e.g. a positron (e+) can be postulated as coming from a proton, which upon losing its positive charge becomes a neutron:

$$\oplus \longrightarrow \text{\textcircled{N}} + e^+$$

Atomic Numbers

In 1895 Roentgen found that if a piece of metal was struck by a stream of cathode rays (electrons) it emitted a previously unknown type of radiation, which he called X rays (Fig. 5.2). In the course of years X rays were shown to be a kind of light with very short wave length, which means they have a very high frequency. Their generation is due to displacement of electrons from some inner shell of the structure of the bombarded element to an outer shell or even entirely outside the structure. Electrons immediately "fall back into" the inner shell, emitting energy in the form of light. If the electrons involved in this process are in the shell nearest the nucleus, X rays having the highest energy and therefore the highest frequency are emitted. This phenomenon is analogous to that observed and explained by Bohr for visible light emitted by atoms as a result of electron displacement of higher-energy electrons (i.e., electrons in shells far from the nucleus). The British physicist, H. G. J. Moseley, observed that the frequencies of the highest-energy X rays emitted by various target elements

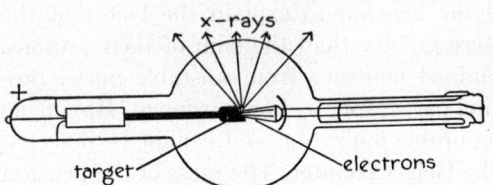

Fig. 5.2. X ray tube produces short electromagnetic waves.

bore a simple relationship to whole ordinal numbers. This is shown in Fig. 5.3. His discovery can be summed up mathematically as follows:

$$f = k(N - a)^2$$

k = a constant f = the frequency of vibration
a = a constant N = atomic number

The atomic numbers in Fig. 5.3 were the whole ordinal numbers discovered by Moseley. His conclusion, which has been thoroughly confirmed, was that the atomic number is equal to the positive charge on the nucleus of the atom. Thus the simplest atom is hydrogen (A.N. 1), the next simplest is helium (A.N. 2), the next lithium (A.N. 3), and so on progressively up to curium (A.N. 96).

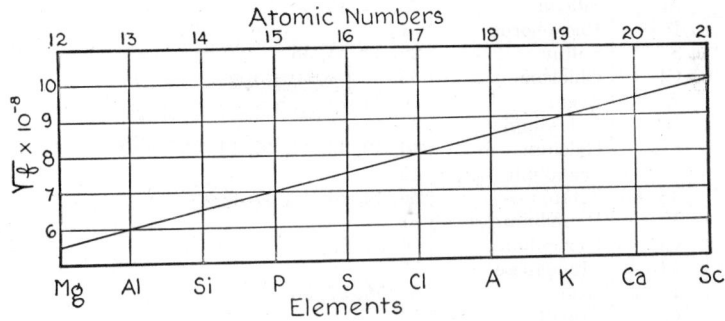

FIG. 5.3. Relation between frequency of vibration and atomic number.

The Locality of Particles in the Atom

Prior to 1911 there was no evidence as to how the charge and weight of an atom were distributed. Was the mass of the atom evenly distributed? Were the positive and negative charges scattered all through it like raisins in a plum pudding? Or were they localized in distinct regions of the atom? These questions were answered by the researches of Rutherford and Bohr.

Rutherford proved in 1911 that the positive charge and practically all the mass of an atom were concentrated in a tiny region at its center which he called the nucleus. He did this by directing alpha particles against gold leaf. Most of them went straight through the thin foil, but a few were deflected at considerable angles or even reflected. Evidently most of the atom was empty space. The positive charge and the mass had to be concentrated in an extremely small amount of space in order to explain the high-angle scattering and reflection of the alpha particles that sometimes occurred.

In 1913 Bohr, in explaining how electrons kept from falling into the nucleus, advanced the theory that they moved in orbits. He supported this

TABLE 5.1. THE STABLE[a] ISOTOPES OF THE ELEMENTS

Atomic Number	Symbol	Name	Mass Numbers of the Isotopes (The most abundant is in bold-face type)
1	H	Hydrogen	**1**, 2
2	He	Helium	3, **4**
3	Li	Lithium	6, **7**
4	Be	Beryllium	**9**
5	B	Boron	10, **11**
6	C	Carbon	**12**, 13
7	N	Nitrogen	**14**, 15
8	O	Oxygen	**16**, 17, 18
9	F	Fluorine	**19**
10	Ne	Neon	**20**, 21, 22
11	Na	Sodium	**23**
12	Mg	Magnesium	**24**, 25, 26
13	Al	Aluminum	**27**
14	Si	Silicon	**28**, 29, 30
15	P	Phosphorus	**31**
16	S	Sulfur	**32**, 33, 34, 36
17	Cl	Chlorine	**35**, 37
18	A	Argon	36, 38, **40**
19	K	Potassium	**39**, 40, 41
20	Ca	Calcium	**40**, 42, 43, 44, 46, 48
21	Sc	Scandium	**45**
22	Ti	Titanium	46, 47, **48**, 49, 50
23	V	Vanadium	**51**
24	Cr	Chromium	50, **52**, 53, 54
25	Mn	Manganese	**55**
26	Fe	Iron	54, **56**, 57, 58
27	Co	Cobalt	**59**
28	Ni	Nickel	**58**, 60, 61, 62, 64
29	Cu	Copper	**63**, 65
30	Zn	Zinc	**64**, 66, 67, 68, 70
31	Ga	Gallium	**69**, 71
32	Ge	Germanium	70, 72, 73, **74**, 76
33	As	Arsenic	**75**
34	Se	Selenium	74, 76, 77, 78, **80**, 82
35	Br	Bromine	**79**, 81
36	Kr	Krypton	78, 80, 82, 83, **84**, 86
37	Rb	Rubidium	**85**, 87
38	Sr	Strontium	84, 86, 87, **88**
39	Y	Yttrium	**89**
40	Zr	Zirconium	**90**, 91, 92, 94, 96
41	Cb	Columbium	**93**
42	Mo	Molybdenum	92, 94, 95, 96, 97, **98**, 100
43	(Tc)	(Technetium)[b]	—
44	Ru	Ruthenium	96, 98, 99, 100, 101, **102**, 104
45	Rh	Rhodium	**103**
46	Pd	Palladium	102, 104, 105, **106**, 108, 110
47	Ag	Silver	**107**, 109
48	Cd	Cadmium	106, 108, 110, 111, 112, 113, **114**, 116

[a] Half lives greater than 100,000 years.
[b] Names in parentheses are not official.

THE ELECTRICAL NATURE OF MATTER

TABLE 5.1. THE STABLE ISOTOPES OF THE ELEMENTS (*Continued*)

Atomic Number	Symbol	Name	Mass Numbers of the Isotopes (The most abundant is in bold-face type)
49	In	Indium	113, **115**
50	Sn	Tin	112, 114, 115, 116, 117, 118, 119, **120**, 122, 124
51	Sb	Antimony	**121**, 123
52	Te	Tellurium	120, 122, 123, 124, 125, 126, 128, **130**
53	I	Iodine	127
54	Xe	Xenon	124, 126, 128, 129, 130, 131, **132**, 134, 136
55	Cs	Cesium	133
56	Ba	Barium	130, 132, 134, 135, 136, 137, **138**
57	La	Lanthanum	139
58	Ce	Cerium	136, 138, **140**, 142
59	Pr	Praseodymium	141
60	Nd	Neodymium	**142**, 143, 144, 145, 146, 148, 150
61[c]	—	—	—
62	Sm	Samarium	144, 147, 148, 149, 150, **152**, 154
63	Eu	Europium	151, **153**
64	Gd	Gadolinium	152, 154, 155, 156, 157, **158**, 160
65	Tb	Terbium	159
66	Dy	Dysprosium	158, 160, 161, 162, 163, **164**
67	Ho	Holmium	165
68	Er	Erbium	162, 164, **166**, 167, 168, 170
69	Tm	Thulium	169
70	Yb	Ytterbium	168, 170, 171, 172, 173, **174**, 176
71	Lu	Lutecium	**175**, 176
72	Hf	Hafnium	174, 176, 177, 178, 179, **180**
73	Ta	Tantalum	181
74	W	Tungsten	180, 182, 183, **184**, 186
75	Re	Rhenium	185, **187**
76	Os	Osmium	184, 186, 187, 188, 189, 190, **192**
77	Ir	Iridium	191, **193**
78	Pt	Platinum	192, 194, **195**, 196, 198
79	Au	Gold	197
80	Hg	Mercury	196, 198, 199, 200, 201, **202**, 204
81	Tl	Thallium	203, **205**
82	Pb	Lead	204, 206, 207, **208**
83	Bi	Bismuth	209
84	Po	Polonium	—
85	(At)	(Astatine)	—
86	Rn	Radon	—
87	(Fr)	(Francium)	—
88	Ra	Radium	—
89	Ac	Actinium	—
90	Th	Thorium	232
91	Pa	Protactinium	—
92	U	Uranium	234, 235, **238**
93	(Np)	(Neptunium)	**237**
94	(Pu)	(Plutonium)	—
95	(Am)	(Americium)	—
96	(Cm)	(Curium)	—

[c] Formerly known as Illinium. No new name proposed yet, but this element has been reported as an unstable isotope obtained by the researches of the Manhattan Project.

theory by showing mathematically that an electron falling from an outer orbit to one closer to the nucleus necessarily releases energy in the form of light. The amount of energy in each photon can be calculated from its frequency as measured by a spectroscope. Bohr calculated the energies for a set of hydrogen orbits and found that their differences corresponded to many of the frequencies of light actually observed to be emitted by hydrogen. With the mathematics of that day he was able to calculate only the simplest type of orbit, and only cases in which the atom had but a single electron, namely, H and He^+ (the helium atom with one electron stripped from it). Present-day wave mechanics makes possible the calculation of orbital energies which check perfectly with spectroscopic observations even in complex cases.

Isotopes

The number of protons in a nucleus does not determine the number of neutrons it contains. On the contrary, a given number of protons may be associated with several different numbers of neutrons in atomic nuclei. All these atoms, having the same atomic number but different numbers of neutrons, will be atoms of the same element. They will have the same number of electrons and the same size, but different masses; therefore they will have the same chemical properties. Atoms that differ only in mass are called *isotopes*.

Table 5.1 lists the stable isotopes of the elements. It will be noted that they are more numerous for heavy than for light elements, and for even than odd atomic numbers. Some odd-numbered elements, in fact, have no stable isotopes; many consist entirely of a single isotope; and none has more than two. The number of protons plus the number of neutrons is called the *mass number* of an isotope. Above atomic number 7 (nitrogen), even mass numbers do not appear to be stable in combination with odd atomic numbers. The atomic weights of the elements are the statistical averages of the weights of their isotopes. Thus chlorine has the atomic weight 35.457 because 24.6 per cent of the atoms have a weight of 37, and the rest have a weight of 35. Bromine has nearly a whole-number atomic weight because its two isotopes, differing in mass number by 2, are about equally abundant.

Separation of Isotopes

Isotopes of a given element can be separated into pure fractions by means of a mass spectrograph, because of their difference in mass. In an ordinary mass spectrograph the amounts thus separated are infinitesimal. During World War II gigantic mass spectrographs were built under the direction of University of California scientists and used for the separation of important quantities of the famous isotope of uranium, U^{235}. (The superscript 235 is the mass number.) These oversized mass spectrographs are known as calutrons.

Enrichment of an element with respect to heavier or lighter isotopes can also be accomplished by taking advantage of differences in rates of diffusion, evaporation, adsorption on charcoal, or various chemical reactions. Most of these separations are tedious and incomplete.

If two isotopes of an element are formed by the decay of two different radioactive elements, they may be found separate in nature. For example, Theodore W. Richards of Harvard, famous for his atomic weight determinations, found that lead from uranium ores had an atomic weight of 206.05. This lead is produced, through many intermediate unstable stages, by the radioactive decay of the common uranium isotope, U^{238}. Ordinary lead, a mixture of isotopes from many sources, has an atomic weight of 207.21.

Heavy Water

Only in the case of hydrogen is the percentage difference in weight between two isotopes great enough to make separation relatively easy. In 1934 Dr. Urey (Fig. 5.4), then at Columbia University, received the Nobel prize for his discovery of heavy hydrogen. He found that the purest water ever prepared contained besides hydrogen and oxygen another substance like hydrogen but with an atomic weight of 2. The substance, an isotope of hydrogen, is now called deuterium (D), and it combines with oxygen to form D_2O. Deuterium is prepared by electrolysis of water. The hydrogen ion is converted into hydrogen gas more easily than is the deuterium ion, for a higher voltage is required to free deuterium than hydrogen. Therefore, if a large volume of water is electrolyzed, the remaining water becomes richer and richer in D_2O. Heavy water boils at a higher temperature than H_2O and the two may be separated to some extent by fractional distillation. Even with still-columns 30 to 40 feet in height, the process of concentration by distillation is very slow.

© *Bachrach*

Fig. 5.4. Harold C. Urey.

Oxygen has three isotopes; hence it is possible to write several formulas for water: H_2O, D_2O, HDO, H_2O^{17}, D_2O^{17}, HDO^{17}, H_2O^{18}, D_2O^{18}, etc.

D_2O has some surprising physiological effects. It appears to be inert and useless as far as its effect on plant and animal life has been studied. Seeds do not sprout in it. Rats given it to drink will die of thirst; but apparently it is not toxic, for if the rats are given H_2O soon enough they recover and show no ill effects.

Heavy hydrogen gives the physiological chemist a new tool with which to study the fate of organic compounds in the human body. By substituting deuterium for hydrogen in an organic molecule he attaches a label to the molecule which makes it possible to find the molecule again. A comparison of some of the properties of H_2O and D_2O is given in Table 5.2.

TABLE 5.2. PROPERTIES OF H_2O AND D_2O

	H_2O	D_2O
Density	1.0000	1.0790 ± 0.00005
Temperature for maximum density	4.0°	11.6°
Molar volume at temperature of maximum density	18.015 cc.	18.140 cc.
Molar volume of the ices at 0°	19.65 cc.	19.32 cc.
Viscosity (millipoises) 30° C.	8.0	9.72
Melting point	0.0	3.802
Boiling point	100.	101.42
Heat of fusion per mol	1436 cal.	1510 cal.
Heat of vaporization per mol	10,484 cal.	10,743 cal.
Ionization constant	1.04×10^{-14}	0.33×10^{-14}

Crystal Structure and the Size of Atoms

It has been found that atoms and ions are arranged in crystals in a definite orderly fashion. If one could place himself in the center of a crystal he would see row upon row of atoms or ions in any direction selected. This is the same

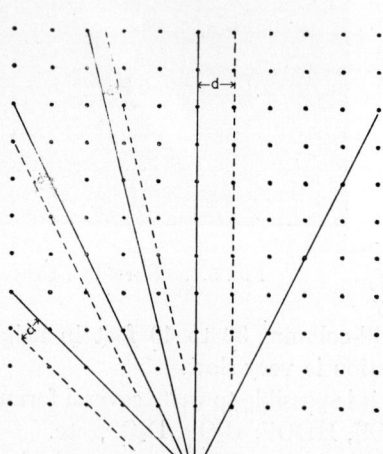

FIG. 5.5A. Rows of corn viewed from one place in a cornfield.

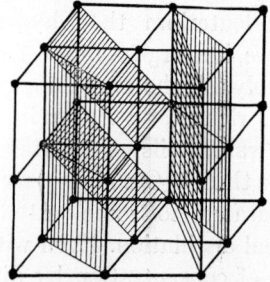

FIG. 5.5B. Some planes in a crystal. (Such a crystal extends far beyond the limits of this figure so that the number of possible sets of parallel planes becomes very large.)

as standing in the midst of a cornfield. No matter in which direction one may look, he can see rows of corn running in that direction (Fig. 5.5A).

Von Laue suggested in 1912 that such an orderly arrangement should allow for *diffraction* of X rays. Diffraction phenomena were known at that time in connection with visible light. If parallel scratches are ruled on a glass plate and visible light is directed at an angle against these scratches, the light rays are bent (or diffracted) and leave the glass in a series of light bands corresponding to the different wave lengths making up the original beam of light. As the distances between the parallel scratches are decreased, shorter wave lengths are found to respond to the diffraction phenomenon. The rows of atoms in crystals should lie close enough together to behave as a ruled line grating for diffraction of very short light waves (X rays) (Fig. 5.5B).

The invisible rays affect a photographic plate, and thus a record of the diffraction can be obtained. Von Läue proved this experimentally and Sir William Bragg followed it up by giving the mathematical relationships involved for crystal diffraction (Fig. 5.6).

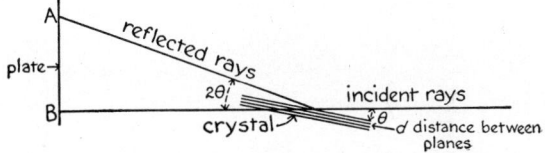

FIG. 5.6. Darkening at B on the plate is due to the part of the incident beam which passes unscattered through the crystal. Darkening at A is produced by the scattered or reflected beam. The Bragg equation, $n\lambda = 2d \sin \theta$, is used in determining interplanar spacing in crystals. Distance from crystal to plate, distance BA, wave length λ are known; angle θ can be calculated, and hence the distance, d, between the planes.

Since von Laue's initial researches, refinements in techniques and interpretations of diffraction phenomena have been devised which allow crystal analysts to interpret crystal structure accurately. X-ray diffraction pictures such as those in Fig. 5.7 now lead to knowledge about the positions of atoms or ions in the crystal, distances between neighboring units, and the manner in which they are joined together chemically.

One of the most important contributions made in this field of scientific research is the accurate knowledge of the size of atoms and ions. It is indeed a remarkable feat to measure, with such a relatively high degree of precision, something which cannot be seen.

QUESTIONS AND PROBLEMS

1. List the fundamental particles of matter according to (a) charge, (b) mass, (c) location in the atom.
2. Define (a) atom, (b) isotopes.
3. Are the masses of the fundamental units of matter determined by weighing? Explain.

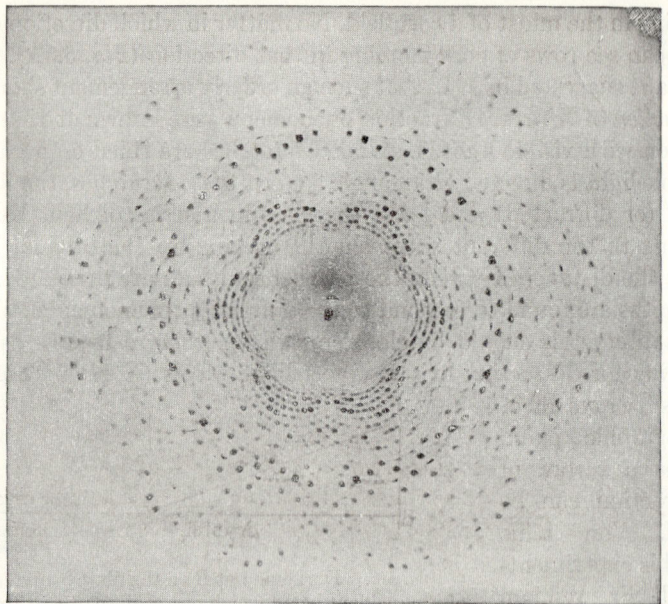
Typical Laue photograph.

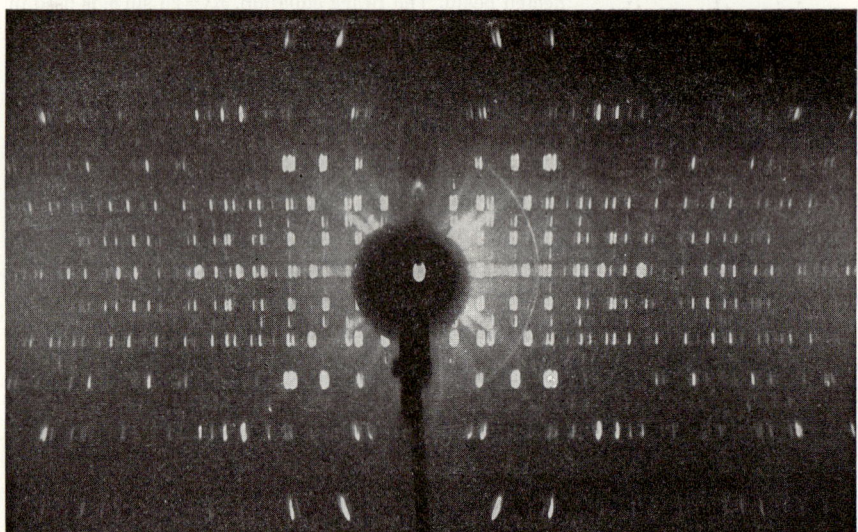
Typical rotation photograph. Bragg method.

Typical powder photograph of sodium chloride.

Fig. 5.7. Typical X ray photographs. (From W. L. Bragg, *Atomic Structure of Minerals*, Cornell University Press.)

4. What did scattering experiments prove about the structure of the atom? Who was responsible for these experiments?
5. What contribution did Bohr make to our knowledge about atomic structure?
6. Of what importance are X rays in acquiring knowledge of atomic structure?
7. Discuss some methods by which isotopes can be separated.

» 6 «

ELECTRON ARRANGEMENT IN ATOMS AND VALENCE

The chemical behavior of the atom (i.e., its reaction with other atoms to form molecules) depends upon the number, arrangement, and properties of its electrons. For a generation now, chemists and physicists and, more recently, mathematicians have vied with one another in elucidating the behavior of the electrons of an atom. Since these three independent methods of approach have led to conclusions which are in full agreement with each other, we are confident of their essential truth.

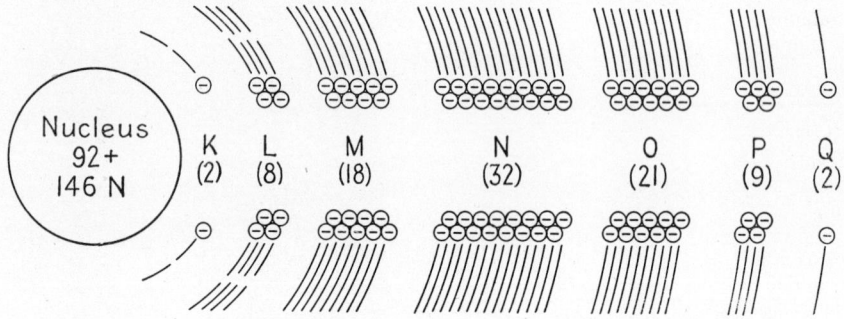

FIG. 6.1. Showing the complete electronic structure of the uranium atom (A.N. 92).

Energy Levels and Orbits

The preceding chapter contained a diagram of the magnesium atom in which the electrons were shown to be arranged in shells or energy levels. These energy levels are usually represented as circles about the nucleus. This is merely a diagrammatic means of distinguishing any one energy level from its neighbors. It is impossible to show by a diagram the actual distribution of electrons in an energy level because each energy level beyond the one nearest the nucleus is made up of a system of several orbits possessing a

ELECTRON ARRANGEMENT IN ATOMS AND VALENCE

TABLE 6.1. ARRANGEMENT OF ELECTRONS IN THE ENERGY LEVELS OF ATOMS OF THE ELEMENTS

Element	Atomic Number	K	L	M	N	O	P	Q	Element	Atomic Number	K	L	M	N	O	P	Q
Hydrogen	1	1							Indium	49	2	8	18	18	3		
Helium	2	2							Tin	50	2	8	18	18	4		
Lithium	3	2	1						Antimony	51	2	8	18	18	5		
Beryllium	4	2	2						Tellurium	52	2	8	18	18	6		
Boron	5	2	3						Iodine	53	2	8	18	18	7		
Carbon	6	2	4						Xenon	54	2	8	18	18	8		
Nitrogen	7	2	5						Cesium	55	2	8	18	18	8	1	
Oxygen	8	2	6						Barium	56	2	8	18	18	8	2	
Fluorine	9	2	7						Lanthanum	57	2	8	18	18	9	2	
Neon	10	2	8						Cerium	58	2	8	18	19	9	2	
Sodium	11	2	8	1					Praseodymium	59	2	8	18	20	9	2	
Magnesium	12	2	8	2					Neodymium	60	2	8	18	21	9	2	
Aluminum	13	2	8	3					———	61	2	8	18	22	9	2	
Silicon	14	2	8	4					Samarium	62	2	8	18	23	9	2	
Phosphorus	15	2	8	5					Europium	63	2	8	18	24	9	2	
Sulfur	16	2	8	6					Gadolinium	64	2	8	18	25	9	2	
Chlorine	17	2	8	7					Terbium	65	2	8	18	26	9	2	
Argon	18	2	8	8					Dysprosium	66	2	8	18	27	9	2	
Potassium	19	2	8	8	1				Holmium	67	2	8	18	28	9	2	
Calcium	20	2	8	8	2				Erbium	68	2	8	18	29	9	2	
Scandium	21	2	8	9	2				Thulium	69	2	8	18	30	9	2	
Titanium	22	2	8	10	2				Ytterbium	70	2	8	18	31	9	2	
Vanadium	23	2	8	11	2				Lutecium	71	2	8	18	32	9	2	
Chromium	24	2	8	13	1				Hafnium	72	2	8	18	32	10	2	
Manganese	25	2	8	13	2				Tantalum	73	2	8	18	32	11	2	
Iron	26	2	8	14	2				Tungsten	74	2	8	18	32	12	2	
Cobalt	27	2	8	15	2				Rhenium	75	2	8	18	32	13	2	
Nickel	28	2	8	16	2				Osmium	76	2	8	18	32	14	2	
Copper	29	2	8	18	1				Iridium	77	2	8	18	32	17	0	
Zinc	30	2	8	18	2				Platinum	78	2	8	18	32	17	1	
Gallium	31	2	8	18	3				Gold	79	2	8	18	32	18	1	
Germanium	32	2	8	18	4				Mercury	80	2	8	18	32	18	2	
Arsenic	33	2	8	18	5				Thallium	81	2	8	18	32	18	3	
Selenium	34	2	8	18	6				Lead	82	2	8	18	32	18	4	
Bromine	35	2	8	18	7				Bismuth	83	2	8	18	32	18	5	
Krypton	36	2	8	18	8				Polonium	84	2	8	18	32	18	6	
Rubidium	37	2	8	18	8	1			Astatine	85	2	8	18	32	18	7	
Strontium	38	2	8	18	8	2			Radon	86	2	8	18	32	18	8	
Yttrium	39	2	8	18	9	2			Francium	87	2	8	18	32	18	8	1
Zirconium	40	2	8	18	10	2			Radium	88	2	8	18	32	18	8	2
Columbium	41	2	8	18	12	1			Actinium	89	2	8	18	32	18	9	2
Molybdenum	42	2	8	18	13	1			Thorium	90	2	8	18	32	19	9	2
Technetium	43	2	8	18	14	1			Protactinium	91	2	8	18	32	20	9	2
Ruthenium	44	2	8	18	15	1			Uranium	92	2	8	18	32	21	9	2
Rhodium	45	2	8	18	16	1			Neptunium	93	2	8	18	32	22	9	2
Palladium	46	2	8	18	18	0			Plutonium	94	2	8	18	32	23	9	2
Silver	47	2	8	18	18	1			Americium	95	2	8	18	32	24	9	2
Cadmium	48	2	8	18	18	2			Curium	96	2	8	18	32	25	9	2

variety of orientations about the nucleus. An orbit is the path generated by an electron about the nucleus of an atom. It is now known that each orbit can never have more than two electrons in it. Each electron is a magnet as well as an electric charge. The two electrons in a given orbit are so arranged that their magnetic fields neutralize each other. In referring to this relation between two electrons in a given orbit we say that they are *paired* or *coupled*.

Fig. 6.1 is a diagrammatic representation of these facts. The energy levels are indicated by the letters K, L, M, N, O, P, and Q. The system of orbits in each level is indicated by the circular segments, and two electrons are shown in each of these possible orbits. Uranium was purposely selected because it illustrates all the known energy levels.

In showing the structure of atoms in a general chemistry course it is sufficient to represent the electron configurations in terms of shells rather than orbits as was done in the case of the magnesium atom in the preceding chapter. However, it is well to keep in mind that the shell has a detailed structure of orbits. It will be necessary to refer occasionally to the orbital structures when discussing certain properties and relationships elsewhere in the text.

Table 6.1 gives the electron configurations of all the elements in order of increasing atomic number. Each successive atom has one more proton and electron than the atom immediately preceding it.

Stable Electron Configurations

Theoretical physicists have shown that certain numbers of electrons in definite energy levels are required to build an atom which is chemically stable. A stable atom is one which has no stray magnetic fields created by its electrons. The physicists have shown that all generated magnetic fields are neutralized or "coupled" by the following total numbers of electrons: (a) 2, (b) 10, (c) 18, (d) 36, (e) 54, (f) 86.

TABLE 6.2

	A. N.	K	L	M	N	O	P
He	2	2					
Ne	10	2	8				
A	18	2	8	8			
Kr	36	2	8	18	8		
Xe	54	2	8	18	18	8	
Rn	86	2	8	18	32	18	8

This is borne out by experimental proof. It has been observed in chemistry that the elements having the above atomic numbers, and therefore the above number of electrons, are chemically unreactive. These are the so-called *inert gases* and are listed in Table 6.2 with their known electron configurations.

It is apparent from studying Table 6.2 that in all these gases but He (which requires only two electrons for perfect coupling) the outermost energy level has 8 electrons in it. This arrangement can be shown mathematically to be conducive to excellent coupling.

Further experimental evidence of the stability of the inert gas structures is furnished by a study of the ionization potentials of elements. It is seen in Fig. 6.2 that the ionization potentials of the inert gases are exceptionally high. This means that it is more difficult to knock an electron off of any one of these atoms than from atoms with slightly greater or slightly smaller atomic numbers than those of the inert gases.

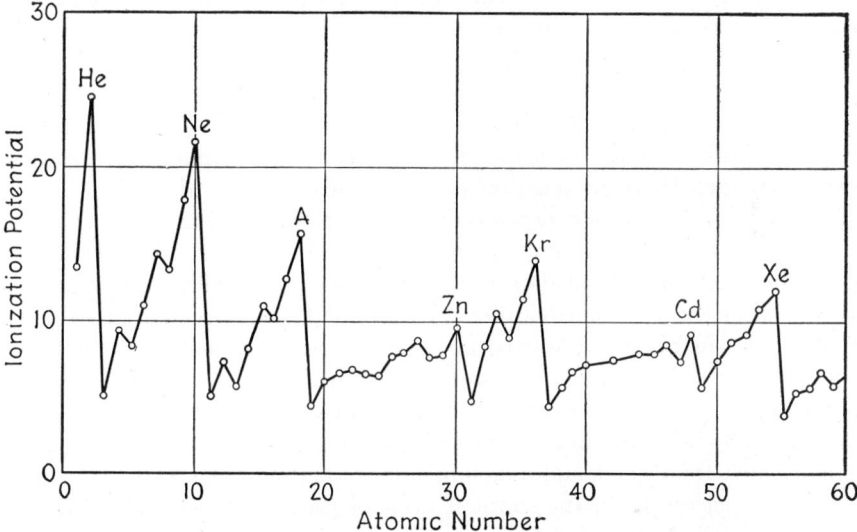

FIG. 6.2. Ionization potentials, in volts, of the first 60 elements.

Filling of Electron Shells

Study of Table 6.1 will show the way in which electrons fill shells as the elements increase in atomic number. Hydrogen has its lone electron in the K shell. Helium, with 2 electrons, has both of them in the K shell. Two electrons fill this shell; therefore lithium, the next element, has its third electron in the L shell. The eight elements, lithium through neon, progressively fill the L shell with electrons. Neon with 8 electrons in this shell has a stable configuration, as indicated previously. Eight electrons is the maximum number this shell can hold; hence sodium has to start the M shell with its eleventh electron. Electrons are now added to the M shell successively until argon is reached, when again the outermost shell has 8 electrons in it and there is thus another stable configuration. The next element, potassium, has a nineteenth electron to add to this stable configuration and this electron starts the N shell. You may well wonder why this shell was started when the M shell is capable of holding 18 electrons. The answer lies in the fact that even though the N level is a higher energy level than the M level, one of the orbits in the N level actually has a lower orbital energy than several of those in the M level. All the orbits in a given energy level do not have the same orbital energy. The differences in the orbital energies are due to variations in the complexities or geometrical shapes of the orbits. The more orbits there are in a given level, the greater will be the complexities of some of these orbits. Thus it is found that there is an "overlap" of orbital energies between the most complex orbits in the M level and the simplest in the N level. The nineteenth electron of potassium therefore goes into one of the simpler orbits (lower energy) in the N level rather than into a more complex orbit (higher energy) in the M level. Calcium has its nineteenth and twentieth electrons in the simplest orbit in the N level. Scandium, the next element, has its twenty-first electron in one of the more complex orbits of the M level since no vacancies of low enough orbital energies are left in the N level; i.e., all the remaining orbits in the N level (after the first orbit is filled) have higher orbital energies than the remaining complex orbits of the M level.

The overlap of orbital energies is even greater between the N and O levels, since the N level has the greatest number of orbits and hence presents the greatest variety of orbital shapes. Again and again, therefore, a new shell is started when the preceding one is only partly full. It will be seen from Table 6.1 that a new shell is never started above an incomplete shell until the latter contains the stable configuration of 8 electrons. Thus the element sodium, following neon, starts filling the M shell; potassium, following argon, starts filling the N shell; rubidium, after krypton, starts the O shell; cesium, after xenon, starts the P shell, and francium, after radon, starts the Q shell. Usually there are 2 electrons in the simplest orbit of the outermost shell while the shell below it is being filled from 8 to 18; and there are 9 in the next to the outer shell while the second from the outside shell is being filled from 18 to 32. Exceptions (e.g., chromium and copper in Table 6.1) require detailed explanations beyond the scope of this book. This should not disturb you, because the electrons most recently added to an atom are frequently so similar in orbital energy as to be indistinguishable by chemical means.

Valence—Metals and Non-Metals

We can now divide all atoms into two classes. One is a small class, the inert gases, representing thoroughly coupled structures or stable configurations. None of the remaining elements which form the other class have stable configurations. These atoms will undergo chemical reactions to acquire stable configurations. A study of Fig. 6.3 shows what electron changes the atoms in the figure would have to undergo to acquire inert gas electron configurations.

The series of atoms illustrated in order of increasing atomic numbers (A.N.) is bracketed by two inert gases, helium (He) and neon (Ne). Every one of the elements listed between these inert gases could acquire the He electronic structure by giving up the electrons in the L shells. Likewise they all could

ELECTRON ARRANGEMENT IN ATOMS AND VALENCE 69

acquire the neon structure by building up their respective L shells to an 8-electron shell.

Two questions are immediately suggested. (1) Do atoms actually make such changes in their electron configurations? (2) If they do, which of the above two processes do they follow?

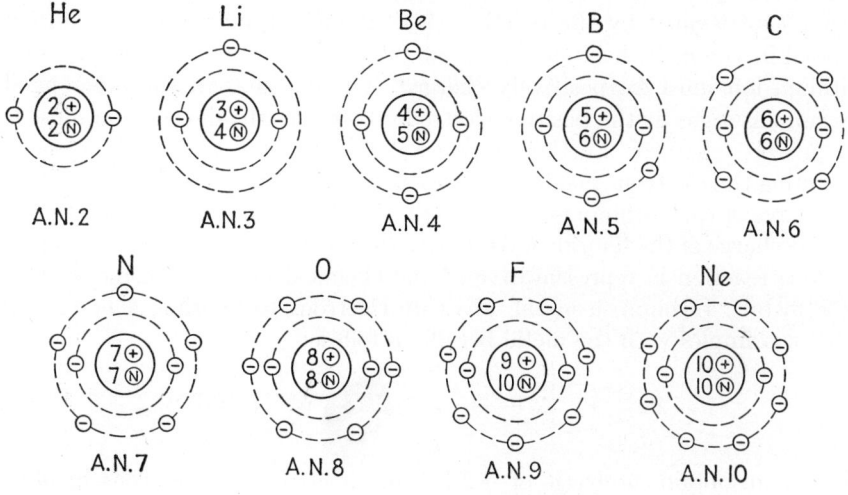

Fig. 6.3.

There is much chemical evidence to the effect that when atoms of elements react with each other they create stable configurations for themselves. For instance, when Li and F are put together, a violent, quick reaction takes place. If Li lost 1 electron it would have 2 left and would have the He electronic structure. F on the other hand could acquire the Ne structure by gaining 1 electron. In other words, 1 atom (Li) wants to get rid of 1 electron, and 1 atom (F) wants 1 electron; therefore we should expect these two atoms to react when brought together, mutually accommodating each other to acquire stable configurations. We shall summarize this by means of the following diagram:

This reaction can also be written by means of Lewis' electronic formulas, in which the symbol of the element represents the *atomic kernel* which is everything but the outermost shell.

$$Li \cdot + \cdot \ddot{\underset{\cdot\cdot}{F}} : \longrightarrow \overset{+}{Li} + : \ddot{\underset{\cdot\cdot}{F}} : ^{-}$$

The positively charged lithium ions and the negatively charged fluoride ions formed through this reaction would be expected to attract each other and "hold together" because of the electrostatic attraction of opposite charges.

Proof that these ions exist is furnished by the fact that the product of this reaction when fused (melted) conducts electricity. The fact that 1 electron was given by a lithium atom to a fluorine atom is proved in this way: If the compound formed by the reaction (LiF) is melted and two electrodes are placed in the melt, lithium collects at the negative electrode; therefore the lithium ion must be positively charged. The fluorine, on the other hand, escapes as a gas at the positive electrode; therefore the fluoride ion must be negatively charged. Furthermore, we have accurate electrical means of counting the electrons passing through a circuit and it can be shown that the discharge of each lithium ion is due to the acquisition of one electron, whereas the discharge of the fluoride ion is due to the stripping of one electron from it.

This reaction is representative of the chemical behavior of metals with non-metals. Lithium, a metal, gives up electrons to fluorine, a non-metal. Other examples with the metal beryllium follow:

$$Be + 2\,:\!\ddot{F}\!: \longrightarrow Be^{++} + :\!\ddot{F}\!:^{-} + :\!\ddot{F}\!:^{-}$$

Beryllium obtains a charge of $+2$ because it gives up 2 electrons in order to acquire the helium electronic configuration.

$$Be + :\!\ddot{O}\!: \longrightarrow Be^{++} :\!\ddot{O}\!:^{=}$$

The oxygen ion, with a charge of -2, has the neon electronic configuration.

Electrovalence

It is apparent from these illustrations that the outermost shell is involved in the chemical reaction. Obviously, then, this shell is very important in dictating the chemical properties of the element. For this reason it is referred to as the *valence* shell, and the electrons in it are valence electrons. If atoms lose electrons in reactions they are designated as displaying a positive valence of a numerical magnitude equal to the number of electrons lost. Thus lithium has a positive valence of 1. This is also referred to as an electrovalence of $+1$. The same idea holds for atoms that gain electrons except that the valence is negative; thus fluorine displays an electrovalence of -1.

In chemical reactions that actually involve the transfer of electrons the phenomenon known as *oxidation and reduction* is taking place. Any atom which *loses* electrons during reaction is said to be *oxidized*, whereas any atom *gaining* electrons is said to be *reduced*.

The Sharing of Electrons. Covalence

When atoms need electrons to fill a shell up to a stable configuration of 8 electrons they may acquire them in two ways. One of these, as already shown,

ELECTRON ARRANGEMENT IN ATOMS AND VALENCE

is through electron transfer, in which the number of electrons needed is obtained outright from some other atom or atoms. The other way this may be accomplished is by *sharing* electrons. Consider fluorine. This atom needs an electron to complete its valence shell octet. If two fluorine atoms are brought together, each will need an electron and they can accommodate each other by sharing an electron apiece between them.

$$:\!\ddot{F}\!\cdot\ +\ \cdot\ddot{F}\!: \longrightarrow\ :\!\ddot{F}\!:\!\ddot{F}\!:$$

It can be seen that the donation of *one electron* by each fluorine atom results in an *electron pair* being shared between the two fluorine atoms. For this reason we say that an *electron pair bond* or a *covalent bond* exists between the two atoms and each atom is described as exhibiting a *covalence* of 1. An electron pair is required for each covalent bond. Neither the bond nor the stable 8-electron configuration can exist if the atoms are separated. The product of this reaction is a diatomic molecule, F_2.

Note the difference between this case, and that of $Li^+:\ddot{F}:^-$. After reaction, lithium and fluoride ions may be separated, but the stable configurations created by the electron transfer will still exist for each.

When electrons are shared between atoms the coupling of magnetic fields in each individual atom is not as good as when the atom actually obtains an octet completely for itself. It is for this reason that the F_2 molecule has stray magnetic fields and will react chemically with an atom or atoms of a different element so that each atom of fluorine will acquire its *own* electrons to *complete its own octet*. Now we may write the reaction between lithium and fluorine more exactly:

$$Li\cdot\ +\ Li\cdot\ +\ :\!\ddot{F}\!:\!\ddot{F}\!: \longrightarrow Li^+\ +\ Li^+\ +\ :\!\ddot{F}\!:^-\ +\ :\!\ddot{F}\!:^-$$

which obviously is the same as:

$$2\ Li\cdot\ +\ :\!\ddot{F}\!:\!\ddot{F}\!: \longrightarrow 2\ Li^+\ +\ 2:\!\ddot{F}\!:^-$$

When atoms lack two or more electrons for a complete octet they share an appropriate number of electron pairs.

Nitrogen atoms lack three electrons for a stable octet and therefore share three electron pairs.

$$:\!N\!\cdot\ +\ \cdot N\!: \longrightarrow\ :\!N\!:\!:\!:\!N\!:$$

Each nitrogen atom displays a covalence of 3. For experimental evidence that like atoms combine to form diatomic or even polyatomic molecules, see pages 46–48.

Covalence in Molecules of Dissimilar Atoms

Since identical atoms lacking electrons for a stable configuration can combine by covalent processes to form molecules, we should expect two or more dissimilar atoms which lack electrons for a stable configuration to combine by the same process.

Hydrogen, which needs one electron to acquire the helium electronic configuration, can share a pair of electrons with fluorine to form the compound *hydrogen fluoride*.

$$\text{H:H} + \text{:}\ddot{\text{F}}\text{:}\ddot{\text{F}}\text{:} \longrightarrow 2\,\text{H:}\ddot{\text{F}}\text{:}$$

Each atom displays a covalence of 1.

Nitrogen needs three electrons, so it shares three pairs of electrons with three hydrogen atoms to form a molecule of the compound *ammonia*.

$$3\,\text{H:H} + \text{:N:::N:} \longrightarrow 2\,\text{H:}\ddot{\text{N}}\text{:} \begin{array}{c} \text{H} \\ \\ \text{H} \end{array}$$

In this compound the nitrogen displays a covalence of 3 and each hydrogen a covalence of 1.

Carbon has only four valence electrons, but by offering one electron to each of four fluorine atoms it completes their octets and simultaneously its own, forming four covalent bonds. The compound formed is carbon tetrafluoride.

$$\cdot\dot{\text{C}}\cdot + 2\,\text{:}\ddot{\text{F}}\text{:}\ddot{\text{F}}\text{:} \longrightarrow \begin{array}{c} \text{:}\ddot{\text{F}}\text{:} \\ \text{:}\ddot{\text{F}}\text{:C:}\ddot{\text{F}}\text{:} \\ \text{:}\ddot{\text{F}}\text{:} \end{array}$$

The covalence of carbon in CF_4 is 4; that of fluorine, 1.

Coordinate Covalence; the Dative Bond

One atom may serve as the sole donor of the shared pair of electrons while the other atom or atoms act as parasites, sharing electrons without donating any. Let us consider the possible combinations between sodium (Na·), chlorine (:C̈l:), and oxygen (:Ö:).

$$\text{Na}\cdot + \text{:}\ddot{\text{Cl}}\text{:} \longrightarrow \text{Na}^+\text{:}\ddot{\text{Cl}}\text{:}^-$$

The chloride ion has a complete octet and carries a charge of -1. It is found that the chloride ion will share one or more of the four pairs of its outer-shell electrons with oxygen. This is known as *coordinate covalence* and the bond between the chloride ion and the oxygen is called a *dative bond*.

ELECTRON ARRANGEMENT IN ATOMS AND VALENCE

In all the following diagrams each electron pair between oxygen and chlorine comes from the chloride ion.

$$Na^+\left[:\ddot{\underset{..}{Cl}}:\ddot{\underset{..}{O}}:\right]^-$$ Sodium *hypochlorite*

$$Na^+\left[\begin{array}{c}:\ddot{Cl}:\ddot{\underset{..}{O}}:\\:\ddot{\underset{..}{O}}:\end{array}\right]^-$$ Sodium *chlorite*

$$Na^+\left[\begin{array}{c}:\ddot{\underset{..}{O}}:\ddot{Cl}:\ddot{\underset{..}{O}}:\\:\ddot{\underset{..}{O}}:\end{array}\right]^-$$ Sodium *chlorate*

$$Na^+\left[\begin{array}{c}:\ddot{\underset{..}{O}}:\\:\ddot{\underset{..}{O}}:\ddot{Cl}:\ddot{\underset{..}{O}}:\\:\ddot{\underset{..}{O}}:\end{array}\right]^-$$ Sodium *perchlorate*

Note that in all cases the oxygen atoms are attached to the chlorine by means of the dative bond and that the electron which produces the negative charge of −1 for each negatively charged ion came from the sodium atom.

Electronegativity of Atoms

Atoms which gain electrons to complete the valence octet differ in the vigor with which they do so. In general, the closer the valence electrons are to each other the stronger is the tendency to complete the octet. This tendency to gain electrons is called *electronegativity*. A very electronegative atom may also be said to be highly *electrophilic*.

A high electron concentration in the valence layer is primarily the result of an atom's possessing a large number of valence electrons, and it is also true that a given number of valence electrons will be closer together in a small layer (such as the L) than in a large one (such as the O). Thus, the most electrophilic of all the elements is fluorine with the electron configuration 2–7. Next to fluorine, however, comes oxygen (2–6), not chlorine (2–8–7). The small size of the oxygen atom concentrates its 6 valence electrons to more than make up for the 7 valence electrons of the larger chlorine. Chlorine and nitrogen (2–5) are about equally electrophilic. The elements with high electronegativity are those which take electrons vigorously from the metals and, in the absence of metals, complete their valence octets by sharing electrons with each other in covalent bonds. They are, in fact, the nonmetals.

The metals are the elements that are so slightly electrophilic that they not only fail to complete the octet but instead lose valence electrons. An atom that is large enough may be somewhat metallic even if it has 6 valence electrons; only when the atom has 7 valence electrons is even the largest one a non-metal. This explains why there are many more metals than non-metals.

Transition Elements

Elements in which an inner layer of electrons is being filled (i.e., undergoing a "transition" from one stable number to another) are called *transition* elements. All of them have a few loose electrons and are therefore metals when in the free state. The positive ions formed when the loosest electrons are lost do not have inert gas structures and therefore are surrounded by magnetic as well as electrical fields. As a result they have two types of chemical reactivity not possessed by such ions as Na^+, K^+, or Ba^{++}. In the first place they can lose more electrons beyond those in the valence shell, acquiring additional electrovalences. Thus we have Cu^+ and Cu^{++}, Fe^{++} and Fe^{+++}, and many others. In the second place the combination of electric and magnetic fields enables them to acquire dative bonds from many kinds of neutral molecules or negative ions with an unshared electron pair to offer. A whole valence layer may thus be acquired by sharing electron pairs donated by water, ammonia, fluoride ion, and cyanide ion, $:C:::N:^-$, to name a few of the most common cases.

These elements cannot complete a valence layer by an outright gain of electrons because any ion so formed would have the impossible charge of -6 or -7. In this respect they differ from the typical non-metals we have described. After they have lost two or three electrons, however, they can form *complex ions* by dative bonding which will have only a moderate $+$ or $-$ charge, or perhaps even be electrically neutral. Examples are:

$$Cu^{++} + 4\ NH_3 \longrightarrow Cu(NH_3)_4^{++}$$
$$Ni^{++} + 4\ CN^- \longrightarrow Ni(CN)_4^{--}$$
$$Mn^{+++} + 4\ Cl^- \longrightarrow MnCl_4^{-}$$
$$Hg^{++} + 2\ H_2O + 2\ Cl^- \longrightarrow Hg(H_2O)_2Cl_2\ \text{(uncharged)}$$

The charge on the complex ion is simply the algebraic sum of the charges of its component parts, and in turn is its electrovalence.

When the number of electrons lost by a transition metal atom is large, even the attachment of 4 oxide ions does not result in too high a negative charge. Thus we have the chromate ion, CrO_4^{--}, in which the Cr may be thought of as having lost 6 electrons to the 4 oxygens, which need a total of 8 electrons to complete their octets but have already acquired 2 (the $--$ charge of the ion) from some other source, e.g., two sodium atoms. The same logic can be applied to the permanganate ion, MnO_4^-, in which the manganese has lost (but partially regained) 7 electrons. Such compounds are similar in structure and properties to the corresponding compounds of the typical non-metals sulfur (SO_4^{--}) and chlorine (ClO_4^-). The central elements in them are definitely behaving as non-metals.

Oxidation Numbers

In any covalent bond between two atoms of unequal electronegativity the electrons are nearer the more electrophilic atom most of the time. If the difference is extreme, the electrons become entirely the property of one atom and we have independent ions instead of a covalent bond. If the two atoms are identical, the bond is entirely covalent, but most covalent bonds have a more or less ionic character. Electrovalence is a property of ions, whether they are monatomic or polyatomic; an atom in a polyatomic ion cannot have an electrovalence of its own. But since most bonds are partly ionic, it is possible to speak of the valence which a covalently bound atom *would* have if all the bonding electrons belonged completely to the more electrophilic atoms. The charge ascribed to an atom in this way is called its *oxidation number*. For monatomic ions the electrovalence and the oxidation number are of course the same. When the valence of an atom is mentioned without any qualifying adjective, it is usually the oxidation number that is meant. If you are asked what is the state of oxidation of an element in a given compound, the oxidation number is the expected answer. The manganese in the permanganate ion is in the $+7$ state of oxidation. Thus we describe the chlorines in the ions shown on page 73 as having the following oxidation numbers: $+1$ in ClO^-; $+3$ in ClO_2^-; $+5$ in ClO_3^-; and $+7$ in ClO_4^-. Since oxygen is more electrophilic than any other element except fluorine, its oxidation number is regularly -2. It will be noted that the algebraic sum of the oxidation numbers of the atoms gives the charge on the resulting ion or neutral molecule, just as was the case when a complex was formed from actual ions capable of independent existence.

Atomic Size and Its Effect on Valence

Thus far it has been apparent that atoms display a definite tendency to create stable configurations for themselves through chemical reactions. The few illustrations using metals showed that they got rid of electrons, thereby destroying what had been their outermost shell and making the shell underneath it the outermost one. In all cases illustrated this resultant configuration represented that of an inert gas. *This is a general tendency of the metals; and in all cases, with the exception of boron, an element with three or less electrons in its outer shell is a metallic element.* There are a very few metals, however, with more than three electrons in the outer shell.

Let us consider the mechanism whereby an element gets rid of its valence electrons. First there must be an atom or atoms to take on the electrons. The ease with which the electrons will be released and transferred depends upon (1) the attractive force of the non-metal atom for the electrons, and (2) the attractive force of the metal atom for its electrons. The closer the positive nucleus of the non-metal atom can get to the transferable electrons the greater will be the electrostatic force of attraction for the electrons. Thus fluorine is found to add an electron to itself more readily than iodine because it has a smaller atomic diameter. The atomic diameters of elements increase with each new shell added, and decrease as a shell is being filled. Thus (see Fig. 6.3) lithium with 1 electron in the L shell is largest, and neon with 8 electrons in this shell is smallest. You will see from Fig. 6.2 that it is increasingly more difficult to knock a single electron as we go, for example, from A.N. 3 toward 9. Furthermore, it is more difficult to remove the second electron, and still more difficult to remove the third one. It is for these reasons that boron holds on to its three external electrons and shares them through covalence in forming chemical compounds. By comparison (see Table 6.1) aluminum is the next element with a 3-electron valence shell, but this element has one more shell than boron and therefore a larger atomic diameter. The electrons should not be held as strongly by aluminum as by boron and we see that it has a lower ionization potential to substantiate this. Aluminum forms a trivalent ion (Al^{+3}) and also some covalent compounds.

The covalent character of the metals in chemical combinations becomes more apparent as the atomic numbers of the metals increase. Again the effect of the size of the metallic atom is important in deciding just how the metal may behave in valence phenomena. Since we associate the gaining of electrons with non-metals and since this process is more efficient the smaller the diameter of the atom, it is not strange that there is a scarcity of non-metals from elements with A.N. 19 to 96 (see Table 6.1). In fact, the only true chemically active non-metals in this series of elements are numbers 33, 34, 35, 53, and possibly 85. Only 33 adds three electrons and 34 two electrons, whereas 35, 53, and 85 each add one electron to acquire *stable octets with completely filled inner shells*. A definite tendency not to add electrons is displayed as we progress up this series of atomic numbers. Inspection of Fig. 6.2 shows this clearly. The inert gas ionization potentials decrease as the atomic numbers increase, indicating that electrons are more loosely held in Xe, for example, than in Kr.

Obviously loosely held electrons can be stripped more easily from atoms than strongly held electrons. But even in these large atoms it becomes increasingly more difficult to remove additional electrons after the first. If a covalent bond should form between a large-diameter metal atom and a small-diameter non-metal atom it is perfectly logical that the electrons offered by the metal for sharing with the non-metal would be more closely associated with the non-metal because of the greater attractive force or proximity of its nucleus to the shared pair. In other words, this covalent bond approaches the electrovalent condition and hence we say that a certain amount of ionic character is exhibited by the bond. These and other facts are illustrated below. Let us consider manganese and its variety of valences. Mn has the electron configuration 2-8-13-2. To acquire a stable configuration (an outer octet of 8) it would have to add 6 electrons to the outer shell, or lose the outer 2 and 5 from the 13-electron shell. Obviously this latter process is very improbable, in view of the discussion above.

ELECTRON ARRANGEMENT IN ATOMS AND VALENCE

The addition of 6 electrons to the N shell is also as improbable as the stripping out of several electrons. But if manganese rearranged its configuration to 2–8–8–7, as a result of the influence of a highly electrophilic reactant, then only one electron would need to come from an outside source to complete the external octet. The electrons will not stay in this arrangement unless something holds them in this shifted pattern, and this can only be done by atoms bonding covalently with manganese and sharing these electrons; in other words, coordinate covalence must be displayed. Suppose manganese acquired 1 electron from sodium to complete its octet and oxygen atoms were covalently bonded to the four pairs of manganese electrons to maintain the electron shell shift mentioned above.

$$Na^+ : \overset{\displaystyle :\ddot{O}:^-}{\underset{\displaystyle :\ddot{O}:}{\ddot{O}:Mn:\ddot{O}:}}$$

The compound is sodium permanganate and the ion MnO_4^- acquires its single negative charge from sodium through electrovalence. The oxygens, being small in diameter and therefore highly electrophilic compared to manganese, exert quite an attractive force for the shared electrons, and hence these electrons are considered to be more closely associated with the oxygens than with the manganese; therefore manganese is said to have an oxidation number of $+7$ in this compound—i.e., the 7 manganese electrons plus 1 from the sodium effectively but not entirely (they are still shared) belong to the oxygens.

Many complexities in valence phenomena result from shifts in electron positions, as in the case of manganese. A variety of such shifts may be possible for a given atom and may give rise to several valences. These shifts are especially noticeable when the shell immediately underlying the valence shell is in the process of being built up to its full complement of electrons, e.g., for elements number 21–29, 39–46, 57–79, and 89–96.

Any metallic atom will also undergo a reaction to rid itself of the electrons in the valence shell. If these electrons total 4 or more, covalent bonding will take place, with the shared electrons situating themselves in closer association with the more electrophilic of the atoms entering into the union (i.e., those of the non-metal). This gives these bonds some ionic character; e.g., tin can form $SnCl_4$ because of the 4 electrons in the valence shell of tin. The bonds between tin and chlorine are actually covalent but have much ionic character, and so we say that tin in this compound displays an oxidation number of $+4$.

Complexities which arise in valence studies will be dealt with in the chapters devoted to the various elements in such detail as is allowable in an elementary course.

QUESTIONS AND PROBLEMS

1. Distinguish between energy levels and orbits.
2. What is meant by "coupling of magnetic fields"?
3. What is meant by a "stable electron configuration"? What elements exhibit such configurations? How can atoms not have stable configurations? Illustrate.
4. Draw the complete electronic structures and show the Lewis symbols of atoms with atomic numbers 1, 3, 5, 6, 7, 12, 13, 15, and 17.
5. Which of the atoms in question 4 are metals? Non-metals?
6. Using any of the atoms in question 4, illustrate with Lewis symbols (a) electrovalence, (b) covalence, (c) coordinate covalence.
7. What is meant by the "overlap of orbital energies"? How is this reflected in the process of filling successive electron shells?
8. Correlate ionization potentials to (a) inert gases, (b) metals, (c) non-metals, (d) atomic diameters, and (e) the electrophilic nature (electronegativity) of atoms.
9. How is the electrophilic nature of an atom related to its atomic diameter and the number of valence electrons?
10. What is a complex ion? What class of elements form them?
11. Distinguish between oxidation number and electrovalence. When are they the same thing?
12. Assuming the oxidation number of oxygen (O) is -2, what are the oxidation numbers of the other elements in the following ions: MnO_4^-, ClO_3^-, CO_3^{--}, $Cr_2O_7^{--}$, SO_4^{--}?
13. Assuming the following elements have the oxidation numbers given— O^{-2}, Mn^{+6}, S^{+4}, and Cl^{+5}—what will be the valences of the following ions: MnO_4, SO_3, ClO_3?

REFERENCES

Books

Mr. Tompkins Explores the Atom. Gamow, George. Macmillan.

» 7 «

THE PERIODIC SYSTEM

As has been shown in the preceding chapter, chemical reactions of elements consist in the gaining, losing, or sharing of electrons. Only those electrons take part in these reactions which are in the outer layer or are among those most recently added to an inner layer which is in the process of filling up. Whenever the atoms of two elements have a similar arrangement of outside electrons their chemical properties will be fundamentally similar, but will differ in the intensity with which they are manifested on account of the different distances between the nuclei and the reacting electrons. Because of the principles of electron arrangement which have just been discussed, these similarities do occur, time after time, though at intervals which increase in the rather curious manner we have described. It is possible, therefore, to divide the elements into families each of which exhibits a characteristic set of properties to a degree which varies regularly from element to element in the family.

Chemical and physical resemblances of certain elements to each other were obvious to the chemist before the structure of the atom was known. Knowledge of the structure of an atom allows us to interpret the "whys" and "hows" of these resemblances but is not necessary for observing these resemblances in the laboratory.

Early History of the Periodic System

In 1829 the first attempt to classify the elements was made by Döbereiner. He observed three groups of elements which have been called "Döbereiner's triads." These three groups had many similar chemical properties. Many other elements were known at that time, but their properties were not so classified that the similarities were obvious.

The next significant announcement was made in 1864 by an English chemist, John Newlands, with his so-called octave classification of the ele-

TABLE 7.1. DÖBEREINER'S TRIADS

Element	Atomic Weight	Element	Atomic Weight	Element	Atomic Weight
Calcium (Ca)	40.1	Sulfur (S)	32	Chlorine (Cl)	35.5
Strontium (Sr)	87.6	Selenium (Se)	79.2	Bromine (Br)	79.9
Barium (Ba)	137.4	Tellurium (Te)	127.5	Iodine (I)	126.9

ments. He observed that a periodicity in the properties of elements was apparent if they were arranged in order of increasing atomic weights. He submitted a brief paper on this theory to *Chemical News*, but it was returned to him, labeled "Not adapted for publication in the Society's Journal." He presented a more complete paper on his observations before the English Chemical Society in 1866, but he was so far ahead of his time that his paper was coldly received. He is said to have been nearly heart-broken because his paper was the subject of so much scorn. Some even derided him by suggesting that he arrange the elements alphabetically and again list their properties. His classification started as follows:

Li	Be	B	C	N	O	F
Na	Mg	Al	Si	P	S	Cl
K	etc.

He presented the paper in the hope that someone could suggest why the series did not continue to check with all the elements. No help was forthcoming. However, in 1882 the Royal Society awarded him the Davy medal and thus acknowledged their error in judgment.

The world had to wait only seven years for the correct answer as to why Newlands' classification broke down. Newlands had no trouble in his classification with the first two rows or *periods* across his periodic table, but in the third period his chart was not consistent with the known facts. Two men solved this problem at about the same time, each working independently. One was the German scientist, Lothar Meyer. Since his published work was not well understood at the time, he is usually not given the credit which he deserves.

Our present periodic classification of the elements bears the name of the great Russian scientist, Mendeléeff. Dimitri Ivanowitch Mendeléeff (Fig. 7.1) was born on February 7, 1834, in Tobolsk, Siberia. His early life was so full of hardship and sorrow that it seems incredible that he could have stayed at his work; but he lived to reap in some measure the satisfaction of work well done.

He studied in France and Germany, but not until he returned to the University of St. Petersburg as a professor of chemistry did he begin to arrange the data which he had accumulated. Only 63 elements were known at that time, and he is said to have gathered together all the known data

THE PERIODIC SYSTEM

regarding them on sixty-three cards. He listed such facts as atomic weight, color, density, state, and activity. We could today make the same observations as he made. For example, some metals are liquids, some are solids, etc.; mercury is a liquid and iron is a solid at room temperature; lithium is lighter than water, osmium has a density of 22.48; potassium will ignite and burn in the air, gold is very stable; many of the metals are silver color but copper is not. After making sure that all his data were correct (later improvements in experimental techniques resulted in corrections of much of the data used by Mendeléeff), he arranged the cards into piles according to characteristics of the elements, placing them in order of increasing atomic weight *providing the characteristics justified doing so*. This was Newlands' mistake. When the cards were thus arranged, Mendeléeff had seven stacks. He found that the very active metals—lithium, sodium, potassium, rubidium, and cesium—all fell in one group. So did a group of elements which were called the halogens and belong to the class of elements called *non-metals*. Although little was known regarding fluorine, he placed it in the halogen group. When he had finished his classification he was able to state that *the properties of the elements* are *periodic functions of their atomic weights*.

Photograph by Brown Brothers

FIG. 7.1. Dimitri Ivanowitch Mendeléeff.

Mendeléeff had courage; if the atomic weight of the element did not coincide with the properties, he boldly predicted that a mistake had been made in determining the atomic weight. When gold and platinum were found to be out of place, he urged that the atomic weights be checked again; and sure enough, he was right. Every time anyone suggested a mistake in his classification, he countered with a suggestion for a recheck of what were supposed to be accurate data. That he was a real prophet is indicated by one of his far-reaching predictions.

He left blank spaces in the periodic table for elements which he predicted would be discovered and which would have certain chemical and physical properties. He predicted that an element, eka-boron, would be discovered with properties similar to those of boron; he also predicted the discovery of eka-aluminum and eka-silicon. From the characteristics of known elements it was clear that the properties of an undiscovered element should be between those of the element just below and above it in the same group. To illustrate how accurately this could be done, note the verification for eka-silicon; Mendeléeff's list of properties for this element, now called germanium, are extremely accurate.

TABLE 7.2. THE PERIODIC ARRANGEMENT OF THE CHEMICAL ELEMENTS (WITH ATOMIC NUMBERS AND ELECTRON CONFIGURATIONS)

Period	Levels being filled	VIIIA Inert Gases	IA	IIA	IIIB	IVB	VB	VIB	VIIB	VIIIB			IB	IIB	IIIA	IVA	VA	VIA	VIIA	VIIIA Inert Gases
1	K		1 H 1																	2 He 2
2 elements																				
2	L 0→8	2 He 2	3 Li 1 2	4 Be 2 2											5 B 3 2	6 C 4 2	7 N 5 2	8 O 6 2	9 F 7 2	10 Ne 8 2
8 elements																				
3	M 0→8	10 Ne 8 2	11 Na 1 8 2	12 Mg 2 8 2											13 Al 3 8 2	14 Si 4 8 2	15 P 5 8 2	16 S 6 8 2	17 Cl 7 8 2	18 A 8 8 2
8 elements																				
4	M 8→18 N 0→8	18 A 8 8 2	19 K 1 8 8 2	20 Ca 2 8 8 2	21 Sc 2 9 8 2	22 Ti 2 10 8 2	23 V 2 11 8 2	24 Cr 1 13 8 2	25 Mn 2 13 8 2	26 Fe 2 14 8 2	27 Co 2 15 8 2	28 Ni 2 16 8 2	29 Cu 1 18 8 2	30 Zn 2 18 8 2	31 Ga 3 18 8 2	32 Ge 4 18 8 2	33 As 5 18 8 2	34 Se 6 18 8 2	35 Br 7 18 8 2	36 Kr 8 18 8 2
18 elements																				

Transitional Elements

GROUP NUMBERS

THE PERIODIC SYSTEM

Main table

		36 Kr 2,8,18,8	37 Rb 1,8,18,8,2	38 Sr 2,8,18,8,2	39 Y 2,9,18,8,2	40 Zr 2,10,18,8,2	41 Cb 1,12,18,8,2	42 Mo 1,13,18,8,2	43 Tc 1,14,18,8,2	44 Ru 1,15,18,8,2	45 Rh 1,16,18,8,2	46 Pd 18,18,8,2	47 Ag 1,18,18,8,2	48 Cd 2,18,18,8,2	49 In 3,18,18,8,2	50 Sn 4,18,18,8,2	51 Sb 5,18,18,8,2	52 Te 6,18,18,8,2	53 I 7,18,18,8,2	54 Xe 8,18,18,8,2
5	N 8→18, O 0→8																			
18 elements																				
6	N 18→32, O 8→18, P 0→8	54 Xe 2,8,18,18,8,2	55 Cs 1,8,18,18,8,2	56 Ba 2,8,18,18,8,2	*Rare Earths	72 Hf 2,10,32,18,8,2	73 Ta 2,11,32,18,8,2	74 W 2,12,32,18,8,2	75 Re 2,13,32,18,8,2	76 Os 2,14,32,18,8,2	77 Ir 17,32,18,8,2	78 Pt 1,17,32,18,8,2	79 Au 1,18,32,18,8,2	80 Hg 2,18,32,18,8,2	81 Tl 3,18,32,18,8,2	82 Pb 4,18,32,18,8,2	83 Bi 5,18,32,18,8,2	84 Po 6,18,32,18,8,2	85 At 7,18,32,18,8,2	86 Rn 8,18,32,18,8,2
32 elements																				
7	O 18→25, P 8→9, Q 0→2	86 Rn 2,8,18,32,18,8,2	87 Fr 1,8,18,32,18,8,2	88 Ra 2,8,18,32,18,8,2	**Actinides															
10 elements																				

*RARE EARTHS (Lanthanides)

57 La 2,9,18,18,8,2	58 Ce 2,9,19,18,8,2	59 Pr 2,9,20,18,8,2	60 Nd 2,9,21,18,8,2	61 Pm 2,9,22,18,8,2	62 Sm 2,9,23,18,8,2	63 Eu 2,9,24,18,8,2	64 Gd 2,9,25,18,8,2	65 Tb 2,9,26,18,8,2	66 Dy 2,9,27,18,8,2	67 Ho 2,9,28,18,8,2	68 Er 2,9,29,18,8,2	69 Tm 2,9,30,18,8,2	70 Yb 2,9,31,18,8,2	71 Lu 2,9,32,18,8,2

**ACTINIDES

89 Ac 2,9,18,32,18,8,2	90 Th 2,9,19,32,18,8,2	91 Pa 2,9,20,32,18,8,2	92 U 2,9,21,32,18,8,2	93 Np 2,9,22,32,18,8,2	94 Pu 2,9,23,32,18,8,2	95 Am 2,9,24,32,18,8,2	96 Cm 2,9,25,32,18,8,2

1871 Eka-silicon Predictions by Mendeléeff		1886 Germanium Data Obtained by Winkler
72	Atomic weight	72
Dirty gray	Color	Grayish white
5.5	Density	5.47
Slight	Effect of acids	None by hydrochloric acid
Less than 100° C.	Boiling point of chloride	86.5° C.

He predicted many other properties of the compounds of germanium, but these few tell the story of his accuracy. Why did he not predict the inert gases, the elements which are now placed in the zero group of the periodic table? He did not realize that any of them existed.

The Mendeléeff table (back cover) has the elements arranged essentially as originally proposed by Mendeléeff. Of course more elements are now known and included in this table than were known in his time. The table is read like a page of a book, from left to right and downwards. By thoroughly "reading" through the table you will notice that argon (A) which precedes potassium (K) is actually heavier than potassium. This same thing is observed for Co and Ni and for Te and I. If Mendeléeff's original statement of the periodic law is correct, either these elements are in reverse order or the atomic weights are wrong. Moseley clarified this puzzle with his discovery of atomic numbers (these are the small numerical superscripts at the left of each symbol). As a consequence of Moseley's work we know now that the periodic law is correctly stated as follows: The chemical properties of the elements are a periodic function of their atomic numbers. You will note that the arrangement of the elements follows a regular progression, the atomic number increasing by one for each successive element.

Each vertical column is called a *group*. Groups I–VII consist fundamentally of two *subgroups* each. These subgroups bear certain similarities to each other. Resemblances within a particular subgroup are strong and for that reason it is called a *family*. Thus Cu, Ag, and Au make up one subgroup (family) of Group I, whereas Li, Na, K, Rb, Cs, and Fr make up the subgroup (family) known as the *alkali metals*.

The numbered horizontal rows are called *periods*. The periods vary in length, some—e.g., period 4—requiring two crossings of the table to complete them.

Several variations of the Mendeléeff table have been proposed. One of these (Table 7.2) has the advantage of having the periods in one continuous line, except for the rare earths and actinides. It separates the subgroups from each other and makes a distinct separation of the metals and non-metals. The following discussions refer to this arrangement of the elements.

General Aspects of the Periodic Chart

This chart, like all the others, represents an arrangement of the elements according to their atomic numbers. We cannot hope that all physical and chemical characteristics of the elements can *absolutely* be treated in generalizations and related to positions of the elements in the chart. Frequently factors other than atomic numbers affect the properties of the elements to a greater or lesser extent, e.g., atomic size. Some indications of this have been given in the preceding chapter. Nevertheless it is helpful to learn generalizations about properties, especially in relation to the periodic chart, in order to simplify the study of the elements. Any divergences from a general rule are usually considered later in the book when the particular elements involved are discussed.

The elements are listed according to their atomic numbers (the numbers above each symbol). The corresponding electron shell configurations (the small numbers to the left of each symbol) are also given. The Roman numerals above each vertical column of elements (*group*) indicates the group to which the elements belong. The Arabic numerals vertically at the left of the chart indicate the *period* to which a particular horizontal row of elements belong. The letters in the column next to the period numbers indicate which electron levels are being filled in that particular series as we progress from left to right. The zigzag heavy line which descends the chart toward the right separates the non-metals (to the right of it) from the metals (to its left). the rare earths and the actinides are shown separately below the chart but belong in group III B, as indicated. The inert gases are listed at the beginning as well as at the end of each period for convenience in comparing their electronic structures to those of the elements in that period.

Electron Configuration and Period Relationships

It will be noted that the filling of electron shells follows a particular scheme within the periods. For period 1 the outermost shell is the only shell and thus only two elements can exist in this period. In period 2 the second shell is being filled; and since this requires 8 electrons eight elements are necessary (you will count nine across the period because the inert gases are counted twice). This scheme of *eight electrons* being required to fill the *outer shell* is observed in *every period*, and *the elements involved in progressively filling the outer shell are in the A subgroups*. Periods 4 and 5 contain elements which, in addition to the electron filling mentioned above, are also filling the *next to the outer shell from 8 to 18 electrons*. The elements in periods 6 and 7 are filling in addition the second from the outermost shells from 18 to 32 electrons. (Period 7 is incomplete and therefore the elements which are present are not sufficient in number to attain the filling of shells from 8 to 18 or from 18 to 32.)

This process of filling an inside shell up to 18 or 32 electrons is known as a *transition* and it is for this reason that we call the elements involved in these transitions the *transitional elements*. Note that they all fall in subgroups III B– VIII B.

The elements in groups I B and II B do not belong to the transition class because their inner shells are as completely filled, as is allowable for the particular period in which they belong. They do not belong to the A subgroups either because their outermost shells have not added any more electrons than are already found in the outer shells of the group II A elements preceding them. The first elements after group II A that have more electrons in the outer shell than group II A does are the elements found in group III A.

Group Numbers and Valence

A simple relationship exists between the group number and the valence. It can be seen that groups I (A and B), II (A and B), III A, IV A, V A, VI A, and VII A have valence electrons in the external shell corresponding in number to the group number. From these group numbers we can postulate the valences of the elements. Lithium was shown to lose one electron and display a valence of $+1$ to acquire the helium structure, and it will be noted that all the other elements in group I A can acquire inert gas electron structures by means of the same process. This is also true of group II A elements which show a valence of $+2$ by losing two electrons, and of group III A with a valence of $+3$ by losing three electrons, except for boron as noted in the preceding chapter. The non-metals can acquire directly or share sufficient electrons to complete their external octets.

The negative electrovalence of these non-metals is readily obtained by adding the group number to -8. Thus fluorine and all the other elements in group VII A display a negative electrovalence of -1 from the operation $7 - 8 = -1$. Similarly the non-metals in group VI A show a valence of -2, since $6 - 8 = -2$; for group V A non-metals, $5 - 8 = -3$, and so on. If the non-metal atom is combining with another atom or atoms by covalence, the algebraic sign of the valence is dropped. Thus two fluorine atoms each donate one electron to a pair shared between them and display a covalence of 1. Two nitrogen atoms share three pairs of electrons between them and each displays a covalence of 3.

Both the metals and the non-metals in these higher groups may be assigned positive valences (oxidation numbers) corresponding to the group number. Thus Mn, a metal, and Cl, a non-metal, both in group VII, display a valence of $+7$. Bi in group V A has a valence of $+5$ and S in group VI A a valence of $+6$. These high positive valences are actually not true electrovalences but are similar to the case discussed for Mn (see p. 77).

The negative valence obtained by adding the group number to -8 and the positive valence corresponding to the group number represent the two valence extremes of the atom. In addition to this, other valences may be possible. (See p. 73, where the intermediate valence states of chlorine are illustrated.)

Elements in Groups III B, IV B, V B, VI B, and VII B may also acquire stable configurations by displaying positive valences corresponding to the group number. This readily happens for elements in Group III B, including the rare earths and the actinides. (Note that these elements all have a 9–2 electron configuration in the last two levels which becomes 8–0 when a valence of +3 is exhibited.) The elements in groups IV B through VII B may readily combine with other elements in the same manner as Mn (see p. 77) when displaying these high positive valences (oxidation numbers).

The valences of elements in group VIII B cannot be predicted by the group number. These elements display valences of +2 and +3, as well as several other valences which vary within the group. In general, elements in the B subgroups (except III B) may display several additional valences which cannot be determined by means of the simple relationships discussed above. In some instances these additional valences may be the most important, e.g. group I B ions, Cu^{++} and Au^{+++}.

Hydrogen can be classified in either group I A or VII A since it is found readily to lose an electron and to display chemical behavior similar to the metals in I A, as well as to gain one electron through covalence or electrovalence just like the halogen elements (group VII A). It is classified as the head of group VII A merely by choice to separate the non-metals completely from the metals.

Ionization Potentials and the Periodic Chart

By comparing the data in Fig. 6.2 with the periodic chart it can be seen that *in general* the ionization potentials decrease as we progress down a group. This difference in tendency to hold on to or give up electrons is reflected in the chemical behavior of the elements. Lithium has a higher ionization potential than cesium, hence lithium will not get rid of its valence electron as readily as cesium; and we find that in chemical reactions cesium reacts more readily than lithium. We should of course expect No. 87 (Fr) to react even more readily than cesium. This tendency to show an increasing metallic nature in chemical behavior as we progress down a group of elements is, in general, observed for any group elements. Since, in the same manner, the ionization potential of $F > Cl > Br > I >$ (very probably) At, the chemical activities of these elements should follow the same order since these are non-metals and, therefore, electron acceptors. Thus, *for this series*, F is the most reactive nonmetal (most electrophilic) and we would predict that At would be the least reactive (least electrophilic). We observe too that except for minor differences, the chemical behavior of the elements within a period bears a close relationship to the ionization potentials. It can be seen that the ionization potentials show a tendency to increase as we go from left to right across a period. Thus the elements showing the least tendency to hold on to electrons (therefore the most active metals) are on the left side of the chart and the elements showing the greatest tendency to hold on to electrons (non-metals) are on the right side. In accordance with the relationships discussed above, the most chemically active metal is No. 87 (Fr) and the most active nonmetal is No. 9 (F).

According to the appropriate interpretation of the ionization potentials there should be a gradual gradation horizontally from the metallic to the non-metallic state. This is found to be true. The zigzag line which was mentioned as separating the metals from the non-metals must be looked upon as representing an approximation in this separation. In fact, elements on either side of this line are classed as *amphoteric*, meaning that they display both metallic and non-metallic characteristics. The farther we go to the right of this dividing line the more non-metallic the elements become and, conversely, the farther to the left of it the more metallic they become. Similarly it should be obvious from what has been said above that the farther we go below this line the more metallic are the elements.

Comparisons of A and B Subgroups

The elements in the A and B subgroups of a given group usually bear only weak resemblances to each other. This resemblance is generally shown in only one valence state, the group number valences. Table 7.3 shows some of these resemblances by valences in formulas of similar compounds. These and other resemblances will be more clearly understood when family chemistry is discussed in later chapters, for we can then relate such factors as size of ions and atoms and incomplete electron shells to the properties observed for the comparable elements in the various subgroups.

TABLE 7.3

Elements Compared	Group Number	Subgroup A	Subgroup B
Li—Ag	I	$Li^{+1}Cl$	$Ag^{+1}Cl$
Ca—Zn	II	$Ca^{+2}SO_4$	$Zn^{+2}SO_4$
Al—Sc	III	$Al^{+3}Cl_3$	$Sc^{+3}Cl_3$
Sn—Ti	IV	$Sn^{+4}O_2$	$Ti^{+4}O_2$
P—V	V	$H_4P_2^{+5}O_7$ ($P^{+3}Cl_3$)	$H_4V_2^{+5}O_7$ ($V^{+3}Cl_3$)
S—Cr	VI	$H_2S^{+6}O_4$	$H_2Cr^{+6}O_4$ (-2 valence does not exist
Cl—Mn	VII	$KCl^{+7}O_4$	$KMn^{+7}O_4$ (-1 valence does not exist

Stability of Compounds

Compounds within a given subgroup bear interesting relationships to each other, and again atomic (and ionic) size plays an important part. The salts, combinations between metals and non-metals, are found to be increasingly stable as we progress down a metal family. Thus, NaCl is more stable than LiCl. This is due to the fact that sodium gives up an electron more easily than lithium (see ionization potentials); hence it is more difficult for sodium to take back an electron than it is for lithium. LiF is more stable than LiI. By a similar analogy, (F^-) has a greater affinity for its electron than (I^-), and therefore it is easier to decompose the compound LiI than LiF, making I⁻ return its gained electron to Li⁺.

Similarly, going across a period we would expect SrO to be more stable than CdO since Sr gives up its electrons more readily than Cd according to the ionization potentials.

Working against these stability relationships is the effect of ionic radii. The smallness of radii of oppositely charged ions leads to stability because the positive nucleus of the positive ion may be close enough to the negative charge of the negative ion to hold on to it strongly. Thus, LiF is more stable than CsF, even though Cs loses its electron more readily than Li. The small Li⁺ ion is held more strongly by the F⁻ ion than is the much larger Cs⁺ ion. Ionic radii increase as we go from top to bottom and right to left in the chart.

Other Generalizations

Many references will be made to the periodic chart during the course. In this chapter we have merely scratched the surface in pointing out some of the *basic* generalizations. You should learn these as a start and gradually accumulate more of such associations between properties and arrangements of elements in the chart as they are pointed out to you.

QUESTIONS AND PROBLEMS

1. Why didn't Mendeléeff predict the discovery of the inert gases?
2. Why are fractional atomic weights listed in the periodic table?
3. Do the alkali metals become more or less active as you go from top to bottom of the periodic table? How about non-metals? Explain.
4. How can you tell the valence of a metal from its place in the periodic system? To what extent does your rule apply to the B subgroup metals?
5. Devise a rule that will give the valence of monatomic non-metallic ions from their periodic table group numbers.
6. What atomic weights would you predict for elements 85 and 87?
7. What error did Mendeléeff make in stating the periodic law?
8. What is meant by "transition element"?
9. If enough transuranium elements are discovered to complete the actinide group, how many of them will there be?
10. How do you account for fifteen elements being required to fill the lanthanide group?
11. What is the derivation of the name "actinide"?
12. Relate ionization potentials to the elements in a given group and a given period.
13. Relate monatomic radii in general to elements in a given period. What is the explanation of this?
14. Relate the metallic and non-metallic nature of elements to progression through a period. Through a group containing both. Explain.
15. Compare A and B subgroups of a given group electronically.

REFERENCES
Articles

"Periodic Tables. Graphic Classifications of the Elements." Quam, G. N., and Quam, N. B. *J. Chem. Ed.* **11**, 27–32 (1934).

A number of modifications have been published since this review was written. Look for them in the index of this journal.

"Periodic System and Atomic Structure." Wiswesser, W. J. *J. Chem. Ed.* **22**, 314–320, 370–379, 418–426 (1945). (Note the list of references on page 379.)

» 8 «

NAMES AND FORMULAS OF COMPOUNDS

Many names of elements and compounds have been mentioned in these opening chapters, most of them unfamiliar. There will be a constant succession of them throughout the book. No progress can be made in chemistry without mastering its vocabulary, so all these names must be learned. If each substance had an individual name independent of the others the task of learning all their names would be appalling. Before chemistry became a science the names of substances bore little if any relation to their composition and were completely without system; but as chemistry opened a Pandora's box of new elements and compounds it became clear that this would not do. A comparison of the old and new names for the few compounds listed below will make plain the advantages of systematic nomenclature.

Old Name	Chemical Name	Formula
Salts of tartar	Potassium carbonate	K_2CO_3
Soda ash	Sodium carbonate	Na_2CO_3
Precipitated chalk	Calcium carbonate	$CaCO_3$
Witherite	Barium carbonate	$BaCO_3$
Dry-bone ore	Zinc carbonate	$ZnCO_3$

No one could tell from the old names that the above substances were closely related in formula; furthermore, each of the old names required an individual effort of memory, whereas the chemical names fit into a framework which is an effective aid to memory.

A large proportion of the compounds dealt with in an elementary chemistry course have two parts, one with a positive, the other with a negative oxidation number. All such compounds have a double name, consisting of the name of the positive part followed by the name of the negative part. Since these parts can in most cases be recombined in all imaginable combinations, learning the names of some fifty *radicals*, as they are called, will enable you to name some six hundred of their compounds. You should therefore memorize the names of the most common radicals immediately, and learn others as fast as possible.

Names of Positive Radicals

A radical is an atom or group of atoms which can be transferred as a unit from compound to compound. In many cases the positive and negative radicals of a compound are independent ions that attract each other electrically but are not bound together by a covalent bond. *Salts* are compounds composed of ions.

Most positive radicals are simple, monatomic metallic ions (Li^+, Ca^{++}, Al^{+++}). A positive ion, because it is attracted to a *cathode* (a negative electrode), is frequently called a *cation*. The name of a monatomic positive radical is in most cases merely the name of the element. When an element has more than one valence its name is modified to distinguish between the different valence states. This is done by adding the termination "ic" for the higher valence, and "ous" for the lower valence, usually to the Latin rather than the English name of the element, e.g., ferrous ion, Fe^{++}, and ferric ion, Fe^{+++}, from iron. Look for other cases in the list of positive ions on page 98.

Few positive radicals are polyatomic, but one, namely NH_4^+, is very common and very important. It behaves much like a metal ion and its name, ammonium ion, intentionally sounds like the name of a metal. The termination "um" or "ium" has been given to all metallic elements discovered since the latter part of the eighteenth century. (Unfortunately a few non-metals have the same ending, namely helium, selenium, and the border-line element tellurium.)

Names of Negative Radicals

Most negative radicals can be independent ions, and when in combination with metals are regularly so. Since they are attracted to a positively charged electrode, or *anode*, negative ions are commonly called *anions*. The most familiar anions are composed of a single atom of a non-metal, either alone or in combination with various amounts of oxygen. Examples already given include Cl^-, F^-, ClO^-, ClO_4^-. They are named for the characteristic non-metal they contain, but since each non-metal may form several ions a number of prefixes and suffixes are required. These are applied to a stem consisting usually of the first syllable or two of the element's name, as follows:

1. If the ion contains no oxygen, the termination "ide" is used. Examples: F^-, fluoride; O^{--}, oxide; Cl^-, chloride; S^{--}, sulfide. Special cases: OH^-, hydroxide; CN^-, cyanide.

2. If the anion is polyatomic and contains oxygen, the *commonest* of the oxygen-containing anions formed by a given non-metal is chosen as a reference point and is given the termination "ate." Examples: NO_3^-, nitrate; SO_4^{--}, sulfate; ClO_3^-, chlorate; IO_3^-, iodate. Special cases: $C_2H_3O_2^-$, acetate; CNO^-, cyanate.

3. If an oxygen atom is added to an "ate" ion, the prefix "per" is added to its name. Examples: ClO_4^-, perchlorate; IO_4^-, periodate.

4. When an anion has one less oxygen atom than the commonest ion, the "ate" is replaced by "ite." Examples: NO_2^-, nitrite; ClO_2^-, chlorite; SO_3^{--}, sulfite. Do not confuse these with the names of *minerals*, most of which have this "ite" ending but are not derived from the names of these ions.

5. If an oxygen atom is taken away from the "ite" ion, the prefix "hypo" is added to its name. Example: ClO^-, hypochlorite.

Names of Neutral Molecules

Many neutral molecules may be thought of as formed from two radicals and are named in the same way. Frequently, however, non-metals have too many positive oxidation numbers to be taken care of by the "ous" and "ic" terminations. In these cases the Greek prefixes for the subscript numerals in the formula may be used to distinguish various compounds of the same elements. These are:

$$\begin{array}{ll} \text{mono} = 1 & \text{tetra} = 4 \\ \text{sesqui} = 1\tfrac{1}{2} & \text{penta} = 5 \\ \text{di} = 2 & \text{hexa} = 6 \\ \text{tri} = 3 & \text{hepta} = 7 \end{array}$$

Examples: MnO, manganous oxide or manganese monoxide; Mn_2O_3, manganic oxide or manganese sesquioxide; MnO_2, manganese dioxide; MnO_3, manganese trioxide; Mn_2O_7, manganese heptoxide; CO, carbon monoxide; CO_2, carbon dioxide; Cl_2O, chlorine monoxide; I_2O_5, iodine pentoxide; N_2O, nitrous oxide; NO, nitric oxide; NO_2, nitrogen dioxide; N_2O_3, nitrogen trioxide.

Since there are two oxides of manganese ending in O_3, the only way to distinguish between them by name is on the basis of the ratio of oxygen atoms to manganese atoms. In Mn_2O_3 the ratio is $1:1\tfrac{1}{2}$, and in MnO_3 it is $1:3$; therefore the former is called manganese sesquioxide and the latter is manganese trioxide.

Acids. Hydrogen is one of the less electrophilic non-metals. In combination with other non-metals it is always assigned the oxidation number $+1$. We may therefore call the compound HCl hydrogen chloride; H_2S, hydrogen sulfide; HPO_4^{--}, monohydrogen phosphate; and $H_2PO_4^-$, dihydrogen phosphate. But the hydrogen compounds of the more electrophilic elements have an interesting set of properties in common which causes them to be classified together as *acids*. Leaving the discussion of the properties of acids to later chapters, we shall here tell how to name them. The name of an acid may be derived from the name of the anion with which the hydrogen is combined, by the following rules:

1. If the anion name ends in "ide," change the termination to "ic" and add the prefix "hydro" to this name. Examples: HCl, hydrogen chloride, is hydrochloric acid; HCN, hydrogen cyanide, is hydrocyanic acid; H_2S, hydrogen sulfide, is hydrosulfuric acid.

2. If the anion name ends in "ite," change the termination to "ous."

Examples: HClO, hydrogen hypochlorite, is hypochlorous acid; HNO₂, hydrogen nitrite, is nitrous acid.

3. If the anion name ends in "ate," change the termination to "ic." Examples: H₂CO₃, hydrogen carbonate, is carbonic acid; H₂SO₄, hydrogen sulfate, is sulfuric acid; HClO₄, hydrogen perchlorate, is perchloric acid.

Water (H_2O) and ammonia (NH_3) are always called by their common names.

Chemical Formulas

The chemical formula is the chemist's shorthand method of designating a compound. From the examples referred to above, it can be seen that the formula consists of the symbols of the elements found in the compound. Numerical subscripts are used to designate the relative number of atoms of each element in the compound. (The subscript 1 is always omitted.) A subscript refers only to whatever is immediately to its left. In K_2CO_3 there are two atoms of potassium, one atom of carbon, and three atoms of oxygen. In $Ca(OH)_2$ the parenthesis precedes the subscript; therefore there are two atoms of hydrogen, two atoms of oxygen, and one atom of calcium. Whenever an ion is shown, the numerical magnitude of its charge is designated by a superscript to its right. The algebraic sign ($+$ or $-$) precedes the superscript to indicate the nature of the charge; thus the sulfate ion is SO_4^{-2} (also written $SO_4^=$ or SO_4^{--}), and the ferric ion is Fe^{+3} (or Fe^{+++}).

The order in which the symbols are written is the same as the order in which the elements are mentioned in naming the compound according to the rules given in this chapter. When oxygen is not specifically mentioned in the name of the substance but is merely implied by the suffix, it is written last in the formula. Go back over this chapter and compare all the names and formulas that have been given as examples. You should be able to write the formula of any compound you can name.

Salts, although composed of at least two different kinds of ions, also have formulas. The formula of a salt is made by putting together the proper numbers of ion formulas to yield electrical neutrality. Subscript numbers are used in the same way as previously described, except that if the ion contains more than one atom its symbol is enclosed in a parenthesis before the subscript is written. The charge signs of the ions are generally omitted when we consider the salt in the solid state. Examples: Sodium chloride, NaCl; sodium sulfate, Na_2SO_4; calcium nitrate, $Ca(NO_3)_2$; diammonium monohydrogen phosphate, $(NH_4)_2HPO_4$.

A formula which is not a description of a single whole molecule is called an *empirical* formula. The formulas of salts described in the preceding paragraph are empirical formulas. The empirical formula for a salt is used when the salt is in the solid state; but when it is in solution, with the ions independently movable, the actual molecular formulas of the individual ions are ordinarily used. Thus, in the solid state the substance sodium chloride we describe as NaCl, but in solutions we write $Na^+ + Cl^-$.

NAMES AND FORMULAS OF COMPOUNDS

The molecular weight of any molecule or ion can be calculated by adding together the atomic weights of the atoms in the molecular formula, each taken as many times as called for by the formula. This quantity in grams is called the *formula weight* of the substance. It is identical with a *mol* of the substance. If the formula is empirical, the formula weight is actually one or more mols of the ions concerned. Thus the formula weight of aluminum chloride, $AlCl_3$, is one mol of aluminum ion plus three mols of chloride ion; the formula weight of magnesium ammonium phosphate, $MgNH_4PO_4$, is one mol of each of the three ions. Nevertheless, a formula weight of a salt is regularly referred to as a "mol" of the salt. This is a relic of the days when the ions of a salt were thought to be bonded together into a single molecule, but it causes no confusion when once understood.

Determination of the Formula of a Compound

All chemical formulas were determined originally by means of laboratory experiments. All that is needed is a careful chemical analysis of the compound and its molecular weight. From the chemical analysis we calculate the number of *grams* of each element present in a gram-molecular weight (mol) of the compound. The next step is to find how many *gram atoms* of each element there are in that weight of it. This is done by dividing each calculated weight by the appropriate gram-atomic weight. The symbol of an element in a formula designates an atom in a molecule of the compound and at the same time a gram atom of the element in a *mol* of it. Therefore the numbers of gram atoms of the elements in a mol of the compound, as determined by analysis, are the subscript numbers of the symbols in the formula.

Suppose we have the following experimental data: Alcohol has a molecular weight of about 45. It contains 52.1 per cent by weight of carbon, (at. wt. = 12.01), 13.1 per cent by weight of hydrogen (at. wt. = 1.008), and the remainder, 34.8 per cent by weight, is oxygen (at. wt. = 16.000). We proceed. 52.1% of 45 g. is $45 \times .521 = 23.4$ g. of carbon in 1 mol of alcohol; but a gram atom of carbon is 12.01 g., so this is $23.4 \div 12.01 = 1.95$ gram atoms of carbon. Similarly, 13.1% of 45 g. is 5.9 g. of hydrogen; so we have $5.9 \div 1.008 = 5.85$ gram atoms of hydrogen in each mol of alcohol. Finally, 0.348×45 g. = 15.7 g. of oxygen, which is $15.7 \div 16.0 = 0.98$ gram atom of oxygen per mol of alcohol. The formula is then $C_{1.95}H_{5.85}O_{0.98}$, which obviously must be C_2H_6O, for there are no fractions of atoms in a molecule.

The empirical formula is the simplest possible formula for a substance; hence it can be obtained from analytical data alone. This is fortunate, for any molecular weight measurement of a salt gives only the *average* of the molecular weights of its ions. To obtain the formula of a salt, *any* corresponding weights of the elements concerned are taken and the numbers of gram-atomic weights are obtained by dividing by the respective atomic weights. Thus, if 1.00 g. of copper (at. wt. = 63.6) is found to combine with 1.11 g. of chlorine (at. wt. = 35.5), we have $1.00 \div 63.6 = 0.0157$ gram atom of copper, to $1.11 \div 35.5 = 0.0313$ gram atom of chlorine, or $Cu_{0.0157} Cl_{0.0313}$. But fractions of atoms are impossible, so the simplest possible formula is obtained by dividing both subscripts by the smaller. This gives $Cu_{1.00} Cl_{1.995}$, which is $CuCl_2$. If the analytical data are given in the form of percentages and these are the only data given, divide each percentile value by the appropriate gram-atomic weight and proceed as in the $CuCl_2$ example above. An empirical formula may also be calculated for a molecular compound when it is inconvenient or impossible to determine the molecular weight. In that case the molecular formula may later prove to be a multiple of the empirical formula.

Percentage Composition from Formulas

Since the formula of a compound is obtained from its percentage composition, its percentage composition can be obtained from the formula. What is the percentage of oxygen in sulfuric acid, H_2SO_4? Calculate the molecular weight first.

$$\begin{aligned}
\text{Hydrogen} & \quad 2 \times 1 = 2 \\
\text{Sulfur} & \quad 1 \times 32 = 32 \\
\text{Oxygen} & \quad 4 \times 16 = \underline{64} \\
& \quad \quad \quad \quad \quad 98, \text{ the molecular weight}
\end{aligned}$$

It is clear that 64 parts of the molecular weight are oxygen. The problem now is exactly the same as those worked in grade school—64 students in a class of 98 are boys; what percentage of the class is boys? Obviously $\frac{64}{98} \times 100 = 65.3$ per cent boys. The same reasoning shows that the percentage of oxygen $= \frac{64}{98} \times 100 = 65.3$, the percentage of hydrogen $= \frac{2}{98} \times 100 = 2.04$, and the percentage of sulfur $= \frac{32}{98} \times 100 = 32.66$.

QUESTIONS AND PROBLEMS

1. When 1.201 g. of pure carbon was burned and the resulting gas was absorbed in soda lime, the latter increased 4.401 g. in weight. What weight of oxygen combined with the 1.201 g. of carbon? The density of the gas was found to be 1.96 g. per l. What is the molecular weight? Now calculate the formula of the gas.
2. How many gram atoms of hydrogen are there in a mol of it?
3. What percentage of $Fe_2(SO_4)_3$ is sulfur?
4. Sodium sulfide, sodium sulfite, and sodium sulfate are weighed out into three different bottles so that each bottle contains 10 g. of sulfur. How many grams of each salt are necessary?
5. Iron forms three compounds with oxygen. Calculate the simplest formula for each from the following data. Name each compound.

NAMES AND FORMULAS OF COMPOUNDS

I	II	III
Fe 77.73%	Fe 72.35%	Fe 69.94%
O 22.26%	O 27.63%	O 30.05%

Derive the simplest formulas of the substances from the following percentage compositions:

A	B	C
Fe 27.93	Fe 36.76	Al 75.1
S 24.05	S 21.11	C 24.9
O 48.02	O 42.13	

6. Fill in the following table and have it checked by your instructor. Then learn the valences. On page 100 are additional negative valences you should know. Make a larger table of your own. (Not all the compounds corresponding to these formulas actually exist; sometimes the ions react with each other. This is not important for the present purpose.)

TEXTBOOK OF CHEMISTRY

	Oxide O^{--}	Chloride Cl^{-}	Nitrate NO_3^{-}	Sulfate SO_4^{--}	Carbonate CO_3^{--}	Phosphate PO_4^{---}
Ammonium NH_4^+						
Potassium K^+						
Silver Ag^+						
Sodium Na^+						
Lithium Li^+						
Cupric Cu^{++}						
Mercurous Hg_2^{++}						
Mercuric Hg^{++}						
Barium Ba^{++}						
Calcium Ca^{++}						
Lead Pb^{++}						
Magnesium Mg^{++}						
Nickel Ni^{++}						
Strontium Sr^{++}						
Zinc Zn^{++}						
Cadmium Cd^{++}						
Chromic Cr^{+3}						
Cobaltous Co^{++}						
Manganous Mn^{++}						
Ferrous Fe^{++}						
Ferric Fe^{+3}						
Stannous Sn^{++}						
Stannic Sn^{+4}						
Aluminum Al^{+3}						
Bismuth Bi^{+3}						
Antimonous Sb^{+3}						
Arsenious As^{+3}						
Cerous Ce^{+3}						
Ceric Ce^{+4}						

NAMES AND FORMULAS OF COMPOUNDS

	Chlorate ClO$_3^-$	Hydroxide OH$^-$	Permanganate MnO$_4^-$	Sulfide S^{--}	Chromate CrO$_4^{--}$	Dichromate Cr$_2$O$_7^{--}$	Borate BO$_3^{---}$
NH$_4^+$							
K$^+$							
Ag$^+$							
Na$^+$							
Li$^+$							
Cu^{++}							
Hg$_2^{++}$							
Hg^{++}							
Ba^{++}							
Ca^{++}							
Pb^{++}							
Mg^{++}							
Ni^{++}							
Sr^{++}							
Zn^{++}							
Cd^{++}							
Cr^{+++}							
Co^{++}							
Mn^{++}							
Fe^{++}							
Fe^{+++}							
Sn^{++}							
Sn^{+4}							
Al^{+++}							
Bi^{+++}							
Sb^{+++}							
As^{+++}							
Ce^{+++}							
Ce^{+4}							

Additional Anions

Monovalent	Divalent	Trivalent
$C_2H_3O_2^-$ acetate	$C_2O_4^{--}$ oxalate	AsO_4^{---} arsenate
Br^- bromide	SO_3^{--} sulfite	$Fe(CN)_6^{---}$ ferricyanide
F^- fluoride	SiO_3^{--} silicate	AsO_3^{---} arsenite
I^- iodide	SiF_6^{--} fluosilicate	SbS_4^{---} thioantimonate
NO_2^- nitrite	$C_4H_4O_6^{--}$ tartrate	
ClO^- hypochlorite	$S_2O_3^{--}$ thiosulfate	

» 9 «

TYPES OF CHEMICAL REACTIONS[1]

Chemical changes are quantitative in nature. According to the *Law of Conservation of Mass*, the total mass of the resultants equals that of the reactants in any chemical change. By "reactants" we mean the original substances; by "resultants" we mean the new substances produced by the reaction. Thus when carbon burns in oxygen, carbon and oxygen are the reactants; carbon dioxide is the product.

$$C + O_2 \longrightarrow CO_2$$
reactants yield products

This is a very simple chemical reaction, but others are much more complicated. Imagine trying to do this problem: "Write equations for all the chemical reactions involved from the time a grain of wheat is planted in the ground until the plant is grown and the stalk bearing the wheat is ready for harvest." Whole books would be needed to describe these changes. Furthermore, they cannot be completely described, for at present we do not know enough regarding plant growth. We are equally ignorant regarding the growth of animals. Probably hundreds of different chemical reactions take place in our bodies every day. Although spinach is supposed to build muscle, no one has been able to write all the chemical reactions involved in this transformation. We know that some transformations occur in steps. Starch to sugar to alcohol to carbon dioxide and water is one of many examples. Nitrogen in air to nitrogen in clover to nitrogen in beefsteak to nitrogen in the muscle of your arm is another transformation which certainly has many intermediate steps or reactions. It is well, therefore, to start with the very simple

[1] Chapters 3 through 7 dealt with the structure of substances; they described molecules and atoms and the fundamental facts about their behavior. Review these chapters before reading further. Make a list of the points which are not clear and discuss them with your instructor. *Do not skip over this fundamental material, for upon it a clear understanding of chemistry is built.*

chemical reactions and work gradually toward understanding the more difficult ones.

Among the simplest chemical reactions are many in which *elements* are either reactants or products. These may be conveniently divided into three classifications:

1. Direct union: $A + B \longrightarrow AB$
2. Decomposition: $AB \longrightarrow A + B$
3. Displacement: $AB + C \longrightarrow CB + A$

Whenever an element goes into combination it gains, loses, or shares electrons. When it is set free the reverse occurs.

Another simple but important type of chemical reaction, called *metathesis*, usually involves ions rather than free elements. Metathetical reactions may in turn be divided into classes. The simplest of these consists in the uniting of ions in a solution to form insoluble crystals which settle to the bottom of the container. This is called precipitation. Probably the most important type of metathetical reaction is the neutralization of acids by bases. The term acid is familiar; everyone knows that an acid fruit is a sour one. Chemists know much more about acids than the mere fact that they taste sour; for one example, they change the colors of certain dyes. The properties of acids will be discussed in greater detail at a later point. For the present the only additional fact that needs to be stated is that a molecule of an acid contains a covalently bound proton (hydrogen ion) which can be transferred from the electron pair it shares to an electron pair in another molecule. The molecule which takes the proton from the acid is called a base. Thus we can add to our list of reaction types:

4. Metathesis
    a. Precipitation: $A^+ + X^- + B^+ + Y^- \longrightarrow A^+ + Y^- + \underline{BX}$
    b. Neutralization: $HX + A^+ + Y^- \longrightarrow A^+ + X^- + HY$

Direct Union Reactions

A lecture demonstration frequently given, but *with great caution*, is that of placing about 3 ml. of liquid bromine in a tall cylinder and then adding very small pieces of potassium. A loud crackling noise is heard, flashes of light are seen, and a white solid remains in the cylinder. In other words, a brown liquid reacts with a silver-white metal to produce a white solid; heat is also liberated. A glance at the periodic table will show that potassium is a metal of the lithium family, and that bromine has the same outer electronic structure as the typical non-metal, fluorine. This reaction, therefore, is similar to that between lithium and fluorine which was described in detail in Chapter 6. Each potassium atom loses its single valence electron to a bromine atom which, by gaining it, completes its valence layer. Since bromine, like fluorine, is diatomic, it must be written Br$_2$; hence the equation for the reaction is

$$2\text{ K} + \text{Br}_2 \longrightarrow 2\text{ KBr}$$

The potassium bromide crystals contain potassium ions, K$^+$, and bromide ions, Br$^-$, but since they are not independently movable in the solid state, the empirical formula is used.

Direct Union as Oxidation and Reduction. Non-metals regularly enter into direct union reactions with metals in the same way that fluorine and bromine do with lithium and potassium, namely, by taking electrons from them. Taking electrons from an atom *increases* its valence, algebraically speaking. That is, a change in valence from a negative value to a less negative, zero, or positive value is considered an increase, just as a change in temperature from $-10°$ to $-5°$, $0°$, or $+5°$ is considered a rise (increase). Oxygen, the most abundant and important of the non-metals, was recognized as the typical valence increaser long before electrons were heard of. Its name was therefore given to the process. Any increase in valence or oxidation number is called *oxidation*. Reduction in valence or oxidation number is called *reduction*. This is illustrated by the following diagram.

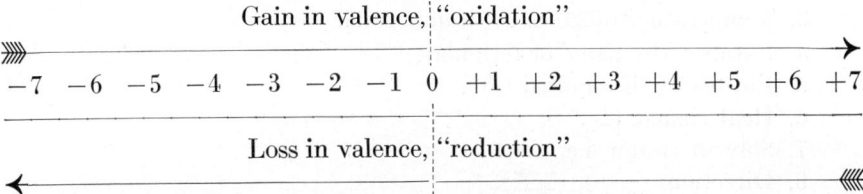

Note the way these words are used in the following sentences and practice making similar sentences about other reactions involving electron transfer as you encounter them.

Potassium loses electrons and is therefore oxidized.
Potassium gains in valence. It changes from neutral (zero) to plus 1.
Potassium is the reducing agent.
Bromine gains electrons and is therefore reduced.
Bromine loses in valence. It changes from neutral (zero) to minus 1.
Bromine is the oxidizing agent.

In addition to the essential facts about the numbers and formulas of the molecules involved, shorthand indications of many additional pieces of information may be included in a chemical equation. The symbol delta, Δ, is used to indicate a heat change. If it is to the right of the arrow, heat is liberated; if to the left, heat is absorbed. Sometimes in writing equations it is convenient to show the state (solid, liquid, or gas) of the substances. A line under the formula—thus, H$_2$O—means that the substance is a solid. H$_2$O means water in the gaseous state. S(l) means sulfur in the liquid state.

The symbol ⚡ is used to signify that an electric current was used. An arrow pointing in one direction is used if the reaction goes to completion. Two arrows, one pointing in each direction, ⇌, indicate that the reaction does not go to completion; instead, an equilibrium exists between the substances on the left and right of the arrows. If other than normal temperatures are used, this is indicated by writing the temperature above the arrow. For example, $\xrightarrow{1000°}$ means that the reaction was carried out at one thousand degrees centigrade. Sometimes a promoter (catalyst) of some kind is needed to change the rate of reaction; in this case, it is written below the arrow. An arrow with MnO_2 (manganese dioxide) under it, $\xrightarrow[MnO_2]{}$, indicates that MnO_2 was the catalyst but was not used up in the reaction. Some reactions will take place only in certain solvents and it is often necessary to indicate these solvents. KOH(alc.) means potassium hydroxide dissolved in alcohol ("alcoholic KOH"). Since water is the only *common* solvent that permits the free, independent movement of ions, its presence is implied by the use of ionic formulas and need not be specified.

To summarize, a complete, balanced equation should indicate:

1. Reactants and resultants (formulas).
2. States: solid, liquid (l), or gas, if important or unusual.
3. Temperature (degrees C.) if abnormal.
4. Catalyst (by name or formula).
5. Electricity, if required (⚡).
6. Heat change (Δ).
7. Solvent (water, i.e., (aq)).
8. Direction: (⟶), (⇌).

Frequently it is taken for granted that some of these points are understood in a particular reaction, and hence they are omitted; but the student in the laboratory will find it helpful to record all of them to make the story of the reaction more complete.

If the equation for the reaction between potassium and bromine had been written in the following way:

$$K + Br_2 \longrightarrow KBr$$

it would be considered incomplete by the chemist, for there are not the same number of atoms of each element on each side of the arrow. Two atoms of bromine are on the left, but only one on the right. To make the right side balance, a 2 must be placed before the K and *not* below the Br, for potassium bromide contains only one atom of bromine per atom of potassium.

$$K + Br_2 \longrightarrow 2\ KBr$$

The equation is still unbalanced. The bromine atoms check, but not the potassium. The number 2 must be placed before the K to the left of the arrow.

$$2\ K + Br_2 \longrightarrow 2\ KBr$$

The equation is balanced. If we wished to indicate states, etc., for this reaction the balanced equation could be altered:

$$2\,\overline{K} + \overline{Br_2} \longrightarrow \underline{2\,KBr + \Delta}$$

(The temperature produced by the heat of the reaction vaporizes both potassium and bromine. The white smoke observed is solid potassium bromide.)

Decomposition

If one chemical compound breaks down into two or more substances, it has been decomposed, and the reaction is called decomposition. This term implies that at a previous time the compound was produced by some other chemical reaction. If red oxide of mercury, mercuric oxide, HgO, is heated in a test tube as shown in Fig. 9.1 liquid mercury condenses on the upper inner wall of the tube. A glowing splint held in the test tube bursts into flame, showing the presence of oxygen. The red oxide disappears so the reaction must go to completion. At some previous time the mercury must have united with oxygen, thus giving up two electrons per atom to each oxygen atom.

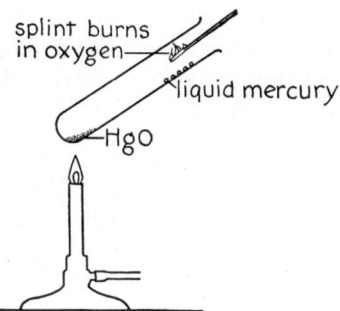

FIG. 9.1. Splint burns in oxygen obtained by heating mercuric oxide.

$$2\,Hg + O_2 \longrightarrow 2\,HgO$$

This is the change which must have preceded the decomposition of the HgO. It may have been prepared indirectly, but at least these electron changes have taken place. The following equation tells the story of the decomposition of HgO:

$$2\,\underline{HgO} + \Delta \longrightarrow 2\,\overline{Hg} + \vec{O_2}$$

Mercury in the gaseous state soon condenses on the walls of the test tube as droplets of liquid mercury. *In this reaction, the mercury ion gains electrons, loses in valence ($+2$ to 0), is reduced, and is the oxidizing agent; oxygen loses electrons, gains in valence (-2 to 0), is oxidized, and is the reducing agent.* Each of these statements would be reversed if oxygen reacted with mercury to form mercuric oxide.

Both direct union reactions and decomposition reactions exist which involve only compounds. These are frequently more complex than those that have just been described, and do not necessarily involve any valence changes. If the number of electrons which other elements share *with oxygen* remains unchanged, it is generally considered that no oxidation or reduction has taken place.[2] Frequently two molecules which will unite at a moderate

[2] This will be further explained in connection with *oxidation numbers* in Chapter 10.

temperature form a compound which will decompose into the original components at a higher temperature. Such a reaction is said to be *reversible*, and can be written with a double arrow to indicate the fact.

Ammonia, NH_3, and hydrogen chloride, HCl, unite at room temperature to form ammonium chloride, NH_4Cl. No oxidation or reduction is involved. The reaction is reversible. If the white, solid, salt-like NH_4Cl is heated, it breaks up into NH_3 and HCl and disappears. As soon as they get away from the heat, the two invisible gases unite again to form a white smoke of NH_4Cl crystals.

$$\Delta + \underline{NH_4Cl} \rightleftarrows \overline{NH_3} + \overline{HCl}$$

In the decomposition of limestone (calcium carbonate), $CaCO_3$, the electron-sharing process is rearranged. No element actually changes in valence. Sometimes the picture is clearer if the electronic arrangement is illustrated. Several compounds break down in a manner similar to calcium carbonate, and similar electronic structures can be drawn for them.

$$Ca^{++} \begin{bmatrix} :\ddot{O}: \\ \ddot{C}::\ddot{O} \\ :\ddot{O}: \end{bmatrix}^{--} \longrightarrow Ca^{++} \left[:\ddot{O}: \right]^{--} + \ddot{O}::C::\ddot{O}$$

$$\underline{CaCO_3} \xrightarrow{\Delta} \underline{CaO} + \overline{CO_2}$$

Displacement

The reaction of a free element, either metal or non-metal, with a compound may result in setting free another element. Such a reaction is called displacement. Displacements always involve the transfer of electrons, and therefore oxidation and reduction. When one metal displaces another the electrons go from the neutral atom of the free metal to the positive ion of the compound, which thus becomes a neutral atom of free metal. This can easily be seen by dipping a piece of thin iron wire into a solution of copper sulfate.

$$\underline{Fe} + Cu^{++} + SO_4^{--} \longrightarrow \underline{Cu} + Fe^{++} + SO_4^{--}$$

Some of the solid iron disappears, but the ferrous ion, Fe^{++}, can be detected in the solution by appropriate tests. On the iron wire that remains is found an adherent layer of reddish metallic copper. Iron is the reducing agent, is oxidized, loses electrons to Cu^{++}, and gains in valence. The copper ion is the oxidizing agent, is reduced, gains electrons from iron, and loses in valence.

Note that the sulfate ion, SO_4^{--}, is present before and after the reaction. Any time an ion or molecule occurs on both sides of an equation it can be omitted from both sides of the arrow, and chemically the equation is just as informative. Thus by writing:

$$Cu^{++} + Fe \longrightarrow Fe^{++} + Cu$$

TYPES OF CHEMICAL REACTIONS

we imply that the copper ion, in solution, reacts with iron, acquiring two electrons from it to become the uncharged copper atom; the iron acquires a charge of $+2$ through the loss of two electrons. No matter what negative ion was originally present in solution with copper, this reaction would still occur. We shall include all the ions involved in reactions if only to familiarize you with typical compounds that can be used.

Displacement reactions depend upon differences in the tendencies of atoms to gain or lose electrons. This can be shown by putting into test tubes water solutions of sodium chloride, NaCl, sodium bromide, NaBr, and sodium iodide, NaI, respectively, and then adding chlorine, Cl_2, to some of each salt solution. The experiment is repeated with bromine and again with iodine.

Chlorine causes no change in the NaCl solution; free bromine is liberated from the NaBr solution, and free iodine from the NaI solution.

$$Cl_2 + Na^+ + Cl^- \longrightarrow \text{no reaction}^3$$
$$Cl_2 + 2\ Na^+ + 2\ Br^- \longrightarrow 2\ Na^+ + 2\ Cl^- + Br_2$$
$$Cl_2 + 2\ Na^+ + 2\ I^- \longrightarrow 2\ Na^+ + 2\ Cl^- + I_2$$

Bromine water causes no change with either the NaCl or the NaBr solutions, but free iodine is liberated from the NaI solution.

$$Br_2 + 2\ Na^+ + 2\ I^- \longrightarrow 2\ Na^+ + 2\ Br^- + I_2$$

Iodine has no effect on any of the salts.

Chlorine will replace bromine and also iodine from their compounds. Bromine will replace iodine but not chlorine. Iodine will not replace either chlorine or bromine. Therefore, chlorine has a greater affinity for electrons than bromine, and bromine has a greater affinity than iodine. The activity of chlorine is greater than that of bromine, and the latter is greater than that of iodine. If other non-metals were included, a longer series of relative activities or probable order of substitution could be obtained. In the reaction

$$Cl_2 + 2\ Na^+ + 2\ Br^- \longrightarrow 2\ Na^+ + 2\ Cl^- + Br_2$$

chlorine is the oxidizing agent and the bromide ion, Br^-, is oxidized to free bromine. In the reaction

$$Br_2 + 2\ Na^+ + 2\ I^- \longrightarrow 2\ Na^+ + 2\ Br^- + I_2$$

bromine is the oxidizing agent and the iodide ion, I^-, is oxidized to free iodine. Fluorine is more active than chlorine, and sulfur is less active than iodine. The enlarged list would be F, O, Cl, Br, I, and S. A more complete list is given in Table 9.1.

A similar list could be made for the relative activities of the metals. One metal would be at the bottom of the list and would not substitute for any

[3] In this and the following equations in this section note the use of ionic formulas for the salts. This is done because they are in solution. The ions are separate from each other and are able to move and react independently.

TABLE 9.1. ELECTROCHEMICAL SERIES (NON-METALS)

For various reasons it is impossible to arrange the non-metals in a series which represents their relative activity with the same accuracy as can be done in the case of the metals.

Name	Symbol	Melting point	Some Oxides and Their Names
Fluorine	F	−223	
Oxygen	O	−218.4	
Chlorine	Cl	−102	Cl_2O, chlorine monoxide
			ClO_2, chlorine dioxide
			Cl_2O_7, chlorine heptoxide
Bromine	Br	−7.3	
Iodine	I	114	IO_2, iodine dioxide
			I_2O_5, iodine pentoxide
Sulfur	S	112.8 (Rhombic)	SO_2, sulfur dioxide
			SO_3, sulfur trioxide
Nitrogen	N	−209.8	N_2O, nitrous oxide
			NO, nitric oxide
			NO_2, nitrogen dioxide
			N_2O_3, nitrogen trioxide
			N_2O_5, nitrogen pentoxide
Phosphorus	P	44.1 (Yellow)	P_2O_3, phosphorus trioxide
			P_2O_5, phosphorus pentoxide
Carbon	C	3537 (Sublimes)	CO, carbon monoxide
			CO_2, carbon dioxide
Boron	B	2300	B_2O_3, boric oxide
Silicon	Si	1420	SiO_2, silicon dioxide
Titanium	Ti	1800	TiO_2, titanium dioxide

other metallic ion in a compound. The metal which would substitute for metallic ions of all the other metals would head the list. All other metals would be ranked between the top and bottom metals. Such a list, known as the electrochemical series of the metals, appears on page 143. The alkali metals in Group I in the periodic table are at the top of the list, and the noble metals—silver, platinum, and gold—are at the bottom.

Notice that hydrogen is placed in this second list. It displaces metal ions and is displaced by metals according to the rules just given, exactly as though it were a metal.

Metathesis

Reactions which can be described by the general equation

$$AB + CD \longrightarrow AD + BC$$

are called metathesis reactions. Earlier names were "double decomposition" and "double displacement." Since all formulas used to be written empirically, with no distinction between salts composed of independent ions, and electrically neutral, covalently bound molecules such as acetic acid, it seemed as though these reactions involved the decomposition of two molecules and the formation of two new ones. The actual facts are much simpler.

TYPES OF CHEMICAL REACTIONS

When written with empirical formulas all metathesis reactions look alike, but when written with formulas which show the actual molecules or ions involved, it can be seen that they fall into two classes: precipitation reactions and neutralization reactions.

Precipitation Reactions

$$Ag^+ + NO_3^- + Na^+ + Cl^- \longrightarrow \underline{AgCl} + Na^+ + NO_3^-$$

The fact that silver nitrate and sodium chloride are shown as ions in the left member of the equation implies that water solutions of the two salts were mixed. When this was done the sodium ions, which had been moving freely and independently, colliding with neighbors and bouncing apart, did not change their behavior. Neither did the nitrate ions; they too behaved just the same in the mixture as in the original pure salt solution. But the silver and chloride ions, while still as indifferent as ever to the sodium and nitrate ions, are not indifferent to each other. Whenever they collide they stick together. Alternating in a regular manner, they form orderly crystals of silver chloride which precipitate from the solution. In the crystals each ion retains its individuality; no valence changes have taken place. Precipitation reactions take place whenever two oppositely charged ions are brought together in solution in such concentrations that the rate of formation of crystals of the corresponding salt is greater than its rate of solution. These reactions are very important in chemical analysis and in industry, for they offer a convenient means of separating a pure compound from a mixture.

Neutralization Reactions

$$HF + Na^+ + OH^- \longrightarrow Na^+ + F^- + H_2O$$

hydrofluoric acid has uncharged molecules held together by covalent bonds, H:F̈:. At the moment of collision with a hydroxide ion, :Ö:H⁻, the state of affairs may be represented as $\left[:\ddot{F}:H:\overset{H}{\underset{..}{\ddot{O}}}: \right]^-$. A fraction of a second later this "collision complex" breaks up again, but when it does the hydrogen nucleus, a single positive charge, nearly always goes with the hydroxide ion. This makes the latter an uncharged molecule of water, H:Ö:, and leaves behind a negatively charged fluoride ion, :F̈:⁻.

$$\left[:\ddot{F}:H:\overset{H}{\underset{..}{\ddot{O}}}: \right]^- \longrightarrow :\ddot{F}:^- + H:\overset{H}{\underset{..}{\ddot{O}}}:$$

The fluoride ion was formed from the uncharged hydrofluoric acid molecule by taking from it the *nucleus* of a hydrogen atom, i.e., a proton, with its charge of +1. This explains its negative charge. The sodium ion takes no part whatever in the reaction.

The word *neutralization* used to describe this type of reaction does not refer to electrical neutralization but rather to the more or less complete disappearance of the acid and alkaline properties, respectively, which characterized the two original solutions. The change in properties occurs for the same reason that the reaction occurs, namely, because the proton is held more tightly in its new position than in its old one. Special attention is called to the fact that *reactions of this type involve merely the transfer of a proton from one electron pair to another and are frequently called "proton transfer" reactions.*

Completion of Metathetical Reactions

For every metathetical reaction it is possible to write an equation showing the reverse reaction. The elementary student is frequently at a loss to know why the reaction goes one way rather than the other. The simplest rule is that such reactions proceed in the direction which removes ions from the solution. The commonest cases have just been given. In precipitations the formation of a solid removes ions from the solution; if the material redissolved, it would increase the number of ions in solution. In neutralizations consideration must be given to the fact that all acids yield protons to water to a greater or less extent, producing ions. The base that takes the protons from the acid must hold them tighter than the original acid did or it would not have succeeded in taking them from it. Therefore the number of ions in the solution is reduced.

If a reaction produces a gas which escapes entirely from the solution, no reverse reaction whatever can take place. It is common for neutralization reactions to produce gases. Consider adding $Ca(H_2PO_4)_2$ to water and then adding some KCN.

$$Ca^{++} + 2\,H_2PO_4^- + 2\,K^+ + 2\,CN^- \longrightarrow Ca^{++} + 2\,K^+ + 2\,HPO_4^{--} + 2\,\overline{HCN}$$

Similarly

$$Ca^{++} + 2\,H_2PO_4^- + 2\,Na^+ + 2\,HCO_3^- \longrightarrow Ca^{++} + 2Na^+ + 2\,HPO_4^{--} + H_2CO_3$$
$$H_2CO_3 \longrightarrow H_2O + \overline{CO_2}$$

Chemical Calculations

When it is possible to write a chemical equation for a reaction, many useful facts can be learned from it. The equation for the direct union of potassium with bromine, like any other equation, remains true if both members are multiplied by the same number. This equation, in its simplest interpretation, says: "Two potassium atoms react with a molecule of bromine to produce two potassium ions and two bromide ions (in the form of crystalline potassium bromide)." But every term on both sides may be multiplied by N, Avogadro's number, and the new statement will be as true as the original one. It will then

TYPES OF CHEMICAL REACTIONS

say: "Two gram atoms of potassium plus one mol of bromine gives two mols of potassium bromide." The second meaning is the more important because we work in the laboratory with mols of substances (or appreciable fractions thereof), not with individual molecules. This meaning is implied in every equation.

The quantitative story told by a balanced equation is very important. The balanced equation is used as a starting point for all calculations of the weight relationship of reactants and resultants. Two simple problems will be worked to illustrate these weight relationships.

How many grams of potassium are needed to react with 10 grams of bromine? How many grams of potassium bromide will be produced?

$$2\,K + Br_2 \longrightarrow 2\,KBr$$

or

2 atoms of potassium + 1 molecule of bromine (2 atoms) $\longrightarrow$ 2 "molecules" of potassium bromide (2 potassium ions and 2 bromide ions)

or

2 gram atoms of potassium + a mol of bromine $\longrightarrow$ 2 mols of potassium bromide

or

2(39.1) g. of potassium + (79.9 + 79.9) g. of bromine $\longrightarrow$ 2(39.1 + 79.9) g. of potassium bromide

78.2 g. + 159.8 g. of reactants $\longrightarrow$ 238 g. of resultants

To solve the problem, the following method is used:

Write the chemical equation and put the x in the problem above its formula and the given quantity above its formula. Below each of these formulas write the appropriate piece of information from what is implied by the equation.

$$\begin{array}{ccc} x \text{ g.} & 10 \text{ g.} & \\ 2\,K & + \quad Br_2 & \longrightarrow 2\,KBr \\ 78.2 \text{ g.} & 159.8 \text{ g.} & \end{array}$$

Inspection of the balanced equation shows that 1 mol of bromine reacts with 2 gram atoms of potassium. Only 10 g. of bromine is used in the problem, that is, $\frac{10}{159.8}$ mol. Let us "round off" the ratio and call it $\frac{1}{16}$ mol. Obviously $\frac{1}{16}$ mol of bromine will react with only $\frac{1}{16}$ of 2 gram atoms of potassium; if you use only $\frac{1}{16}$ as much of one reactant as the equation calls for, you will need only $\frac{1}{16}$ as much of the other. Omitting the reasoning, we can sum up the procedure briefly. Because you want your answer to be in grams of potassium, start with grams of potassium, thus

$$x = 78.2 \text{ g. of potassium} \times \ldots$$

and multiply it by the ratio between the amount of bromine used in the problem and that used in the equation.

$$x = 78.2 \text{ g. of potassium} \times \frac{10 \text{ g. of bromine}}{159.8 \text{ g. of bromine}}$$

$$x = 4.89 \text{ g. of potassium}$$

The solution of the second problem is as follows:

$$2 \text{ K} + \text{Br}_2 \longrightarrow 2 \text{ KBr}$$
$$\phantom{2 \text{ K} + {}} 159.8 \text{ g.} \phantom{\longrightarrow {}} 238 \text{ g.}$$

$$x = 238 \text{ g. KBr} \times \frac{10 \text{ g. Br}_2}{159.8 \text{ g. Br}_2} = 14.8 \text{ g. KBr}$$

That is, $\frac{1}{16}$ of the equation's amount of bromine not only will require $\frac{1}{16}$ of the equation's amount of potassium but will produce $\frac{1}{16}$ of the equation's amount of potassium bromide.

One more problem to illustrate the same idea. How many grams of potassium are required to form 10 mols of potassium bromide?

$$\begin{array}{ccc} x \text{ g.} & & 10 \text{ mols} \\ 2 \text{ K} & + \text{ Br}_2 \longrightarrow & 2 \text{ KBr} \\ 78.2 \text{ g.} & & 2 \text{ mols} \end{array}$$

$$x = 78.2 \text{ g. K} \times \frac{10 \text{ mols KBr}}{2 \text{ mols KBr}} = 391 \text{ g. K}$$

It is wise to label your quantities, as has been done above, in order to make sure that the units used in the ratio cancel out, leaving it a pure number, and that the label on the answer is the same as that on the quantity with which you started.

In the case of *gases only*, volumes may be used as given quantities or obtained as the answer just as conveniently as grams or mols. It is only necessary to remember that one mol of *any gas* occupies 22.4 l at S.T.P.

QUESTIONS AND PROBLEMS

1. How many grams of red oxide of mercury (mercuric oxide) must be decomposed to yield 5 mols of oxygen? How many gram atoms of mercury will result?
2. How many grams of mercuric oxide must you put into a test tube in order to prepare 18 g. of oxygen, if you heat it only long enough to decompose 60 per cent of the oxide?

$$\begin{array}{cc} x \text{ g.} & 18 \text{ g.} \\ 2 \text{ HgO} \longrightarrow & 2 \text{ Hg} + \text{O}_2 \\ 2(200.6 + 16) & 32 \text{ g.} \end{array}$$

TYPES OF CHEMICAL REACTIONS

The amount of HgO which must decompose can be found as follows:

$$x = 2 \times 216.6 \text{ g. HgO} \times \frac{18 \text{ g. O}_2}{32 \text{ g. O}_2}$$

However, this is only 60 per cent of the HgO in the tube. If this amount is $\frac{60}{100}$ of the whole, then the whole is $\frac{100}{60}$ of this[4] and this additional ratio can be inserted directly in the statement above:

$$X = \left(2 \times 216.6 \times \frac{18}{32} \times \frac{100}{60}\right) \text{ g. HgO}$$

3. A sample of natural limestone containing 15 per cent iron oxide, 2 per cent aluminum oxide, and 5 per cent other non-volatile impurities is brought into the laboratory. One kg. of this is heated until decomposition is complete. What weight of CO_2 results?

4. Sixty ml. of bromine water containing 0.04 gram of bromine per ml. are added to 100 ml. of water in which are dissolved 3 g. of NaI. How many grams of iodine are liberated? How many milligrams of NaI or of bromine are left in solution?

$$\begin{array}{ccccc}
60 \times 0.04 \text{ g.} & & 3 \text{ g.} & & x \text{ g.} \\
\text{Br}_2 & + & 2 \text{ NaI} & \longrightarrow & 2 \text{ NaBr} + \text{I}_2 \\
2 \times 80 \text{ g.} & & 2 \times 150 \text{ g.} & & 2 \times 127 \text{ g.}
\end{array}$$

Here we know the amounts of both reactants. Unless by coincidence they are present in exactly equivalent amounts, a portion of one will remain after the reaction. Obviously the reaction will stop when either the bromine or the sodium iodide is used up. To determine which is present in excess:

$$\frac{60 \times 0.04}{2 \times 80} = 0.015 \quad \text{and} \quad \frac{3}{2 \times 150} = 0.01$$

The amount of bromine in the problem is 0.015 of that called for by the equation, and the amount of sodium iodide is only 0.01 of the amount of sodium iodide in the equation. Therefore bromine is present in excess and the sodium iodide determines the amount of iodine. The NaI ratio must be used in the calculation.

$$x = 2 \times 127 \text{ g. I}_2 \times \frac{3 \text{ g. NaI}}{2 \times 150 \text{ g. NaI}}$$

Find the weight of bromine left in solution.

5. Fifty ml. of water containing 0.015 g. of dissolved chlorine per ml. are added to 50 ml. of water in which are dissolved 4.0 g. of NaBr. How many grams of bromine will be liberated? Which reactant is present in excess?

6. How many grams of silver nitrate and how many of sodium chloride are needed to precipitate 3 mols of silver chloride?

7. If solutions containing respectively 0.5 mol of silver nitrate and 0.6 mol of sodium chloride are mixed, how many mols of silver chloride will precipitate?

---

[4] If you are not acquainted with this simple way of handling percentages try your own way and convince yourself that this short cut gives the same results.

8. Ten g. each of bromine and sodium chloride are separately dissolved in water and the solutions mixed. How many grams of sodium bromide will be formed?
9. Balance the following equations and point out for each reaction: the type of reaction, which element gains electrons, which element loses electrons, the oxidizing agent, the reducing agent, which element is oxidized, and which is reduced.

$$Fe_2O_3 + \underline{H_2} \xrightarrow{\Delta} \overline{H_2O} + \underline{Fe}$$

$$Pb^{++} + NO_3^- + \underline{Fe} \longrightarrow Fe^{++} + NO_3^- + \underline{Pb}$$

$$Ba^{++} + Cl^- + Na^+ + SO_4^{--} \longrightarrow \underline{BaSO_4} + Na^+ + Cl^-$$

$$\underline{Au_2O_3} + \Delta \longrightarrow \underline{Au} + \overline{O_2}$$

$$\overline{H_2} + \overline{O_2} \longrightarrow H_2O + \Delta$$

10. Suggest a procedure for checking the validity of the Law of Conservation of Mass if the title of the experiment is "Burning a Candle," "Reaction Between AgNO₃ and NaCl," "A Growing plant."

10

OXYGEN

The substance oxygen has been mentioned frequently in the preceding chapters without any special introduction or description, on the assumption that everyone has at least heard of it. Oxygen plays a fundamental role in chemistry. In later chapters you will find that it is the type element for the whole class of non-metals and that for nearly every element its compounds are among the most important ones studied. Naturally enough it is the first element prepared in every beginning laboratory course. Oxygen is the most abundant element known. Possibly you did not realize that your own body is 65 per cent oxygen. Carbon, the next most abundant element of which you are made, is present to the extent of 20 per cent. Some of the other more important elements in the body and the percentage by weight of each are given for comparison.

Hydrogen	10	Potassium	.01
Nitrogen	2.5	Sodium	.01
Calcium	2.5	Magnesium	0.07
Phosphorus	1.14	Iron	0.01
Sulfur	0.14		

Iodine, fluorine, silicon, copper..........traces

Water is $\frac{8}{9}$ oxygen; the earth's crust contains many oxides and complex compounds rich in this element. Many salts and most acids and bases, and thousands of organic compounds contain oxygen. We require oxygen in the form of water, in organic compounds which we eat, and in the air we breathe. Death follows in a few minutes if oxygen is eliminated from the air we breathe, in a few days if we have no water to drink, and in a few weeks if we eat no food. Oxygen is essential for combustion. Our present civilization could not be maintained without fire, for it would be difficult to get along without airplanes, automobiles, stoves, steam engines, and steamships.

History of the Discovery of Oxygen

Joseph Priestley, who is usually credited with the discovery of oxygen, was born near Leeds, England, in 1733. Although he studied for the ministry, he was none too successful; instead, his name goes down in history for his experiments in his avocation, science. His sympathy for the American Revolutionists resulted in the destruction of his church, home, and equipment. He escaped from England and came to America. In 1794 he settled in Northumberland, Pennsylvania, where he continued to preach and to study the properties of gases. He was a great friend of Benjamin Franklin. Through the efforts of Pennsylvania State College, his old home and his scientific apparatus have been preserved.

Fig. 10.1. Joseph Priestley. (Courtesy, *Journal of Chemical Education*.)

In 1774 Priestley conducted some experiments on the decomposition of substances placed in an inverted tube above mercury. Heat was obtained by converging the sun's rays on the top of the tube by means of a lens, or burning glass, as it was called. He found that mercuric oxide liberated a gas in which substances burned brilliantly. Mice placed in the gas became livelier, and he himself felt exhilarated when he breathed it. He did not recognize the gas as a new element, but considered it only another kind of "air."

Priestley was not the first man to discover this gas, but because

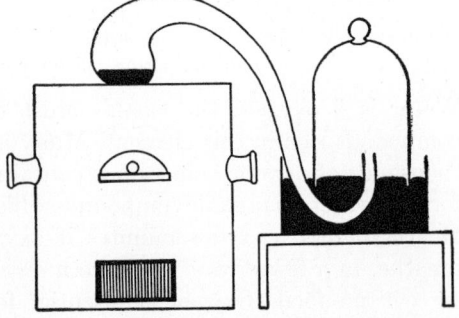

Fig. 10.2. Equipment used by Lavoisier to prepare oxygen.

his results were *published first* he is credited with its discovery. In 1771 a Swedish drug clerk, Scheele, heated potassium nitrate, silver carbonate, mercuric carbonate, and other salts, and obtained a gas which he described as having the same properties as the gas which Priestley later obtained from mercuric oxide. Both men recognized that this gas was present in air. Early claims to the recognition of at least two different substances in the air date back to 8th-century Chinese records. The Chinese called the active constituent in air "Yin"; we call it oxygen.

FIG. 10.3. Diorama of Lavoisier in his laboratory. (Courtesy, *Journal of Chemical Education*.)

Antoine Laurent Lavoisier, son of wealthy French parents, was a keen student of physics, mathematics, and chemistry. After Priestley had visited him in Paris and told of preparing an "air" from mercuric oxide, Lavoisier repeated the experiment in the apparatus shown in Fig. 10.2. He placed 4 oz. of mercury in a retort with a bent neck and inserted the end of the neck in a bell jar resting in mercury. He heated the retort continuously for twelve days. Red particles appeared on the surface of the mercury in the retort. Four-fifths of the original air was left; this gas would not support combustion. He separated the red powder from the mercury and heated it, obtaining a gas and mercury. This gas supported combustion, as did the one described by Priestley. The volume of the gas obtained was equal to the loss in volume of the air in the bell jar. Lavoisier named the gas "oxygen" or "acid former," for he thought that it was a constituent of all acids. Although this is not true, his other conclusion, that oxygen is present in the air, was correct. Furthermore, he showed that a diamond would not burn in the absence of oxygen. He is sometimes called the "father of modern chemistry," for his textbook,

Traité Elémentaire de Chimie published in 1789, was the first book written in the language chemists use today. He coined the word "oxide," explained combustion, and served the Royalist party as comptroller of munitions and tax collector. Although in sympathy with the poor, his loyalty to the Royalists brought him to the guillotine.

Preparation of Oxygen

By Heating Compounds. Oxygen can be obtained by heating any peroxide, some oxides, and some salts. Lavoisier's experiment proved that the reaction between mercury and oxygen is reversible.

$$2 \text{ Hg} + O_2 \longrightarrow 2 \text{ HgO}$$

and

$$2 \text{ HgO} \xrightarrow{\Delta} 2 \text{ Hg} + O_2$$

All elements except the inert gases will combine either directly or indirectly with oxygen to form oxides. Some elements combine with oxygen to form several oxides because of the variable valence of the element. If an element forms more than one oxide, it is often easier to decompose the one containing the larger amount of oxygen and obtain oxygen than to decompose the other. This is shown in Table 10.1.

TABLE 10.1. MELTING POINT OF OXIDES IN ° C.

(Dec. = decomposes)

Substance	Melting Point	Substance	Melting Point
FeO	1420	MnO	1650
Fe_2O_3	1560 Dec.	MnO_2	Dec.
PbO	888	MnO_3	Dec.
Pb_2O_3	360 Dec.	Mn_2O_7	Explodes
PbO_2	290 Dec.	I_2O_5	300 Dec.
Cu_2O	1235	Oxides of chlorine	Explode
CuO	1026 Dec.		

Some higher oxides can be decomposed and the lower oxides produced. The equation for the decomposition of MnO_2 is:

$$3 \text{ MnO}_2 \xrightarrow{535° \text{ C.}} \text{Mn}_3\text{O}_4 + \overline{\text{O}_2}$$

Peroxides are oxygen compounds in which pairs of oxygen atoms are covalently bound together. Some metals will combine directly with oxygen to form peroxides. Thus if air is passed over sodium which is warmed, the reaction is:

$$2 \text{ Na} + O_2 \longrightarrow Na_2O_2$$

All peroxides are quite unstable. They readily decompose upon heating.

$$2 \text{ Na}_2\text{O}_2 \longrightarrow 2 \text{ Na}_2\text{O} + \overline{\text{O}_2}$$
$$2 \text{ BaO}_2 \longrightarrow 2 \text{ BaO} + \overline{\text{O}_2}$$

Some peroxides will liberate oxygen even on the addition of water. The other product is a hydroxide. The equation for the reaction between Na_2O_2 and water is:

$$2\ Na_2O_2 + 2\ H_2O \longrightarrow 4\ Na^+ + 4\ OH^- + O_2$$

A convenient method for producing oxygen in the laboratory is by decomposing certain salts[1] which contain it. However, not all salts which contain oxygen will liberate oxygen on being heated. One which does may liberate either part or all of its oxygen. This behavior is like that of oxides.

If potassium nitrate, KNO_3, is placed in a test tube and heated to 400° C., oxygen is liberated and potassium nitrite, KNO_2, is formed. The equation for the reaction is:

$$2\ KNO_3 \xrightarrow{400°\ C.} 2\ KNO_2 + O_2$$

The test tube should not be clamped vertically, or the burner will set the rubber stopper on fire. On the other hand, the tube must not be horizontal, because molten salts which give up oxygen will readily oxidize rubber if they come in contact with it. If the stopper catches on fire, an explosion may occur.

The salt, potassium chlorate, $KClO_3$, loses all its oxygen on being heated.

$$2\ KClO_3 \xrightarrow{400°\ C.} 2\ KCl + 3\ O_2$$

The reaction temperature required for the decomposition of $KClO_3$ can be lowered by the addition of a catalyst (page 104). Students working in the laboratory often add a little manganese dioxide, MnO_2, or ferric oxide, Fe_2O_3, to one portion of $KClO_3$ and compare the rate of evolution of oxygen with that in a control sample containing no catalyst. Oxygen is liberated much more rapidly even at 200° C. with MnO_2 than it is at 400° without the catalyst. Care must be taken to introduce no combustible matter, for mixtures of chlorates and such materials are used as explosives: NEVER UNDER ANY CONDITION grind a chlorate and sulfur together in a mortar, for they will detonate violently.

By Using an Electric Current. If the two terminals of a direct current are dipped in water containing a little sulfuric acid so that the solution will conduct the current, oxygen gas is liberated at one terminal and hydrogen at the other. The gases can be kept separate. Other substances such as sodium hydroxide may be used instead of sulfuric acid. Although the process is expensive, it is used if very pure oxygen is desired. The equation for the reaction is:

$$2\ H_2O \xrightarrow{\triangle} 2\ H_2 + O_2$$

Since hydrogen is required in large volume by industries, the process is used

[1] An explanation of the reason for classifying certain chemicals as "salts" is given in Chapter 16. For present purposes it is sufficient to say that most salts are compounds of a metal with a non-metal or with two non-metals. In the second case one of the non-metals is usually oxygen.

commercially. The chemistry of electrolysis will be taken up in Chapter 18 on electrochemistry.

By Using Liquid Air. An unlimited supply of oxygen is available in the atmosphere and is obtained on a commercial scale by liquefying air and then allowing it to evaporate. Nitrogen boils off first since its boiling point is $-195°$. At atmospheric pressure oxygen boils at $-183°$; therefore it remains as a pale blue liquid. Oxygen can be obtained as a pale blue solid at $-218.4°$. It is stored commercially not as the liquid or solid but as the gas; steel cylinders capable of withstanding 100 atmospheres pressure are used. Although the gas is not absolutely pure oxygen, it is satisfactory for commercial use. The energy required to obtain oxygen by the liquefaction of air is less than that required by the electrolysis of water or by any process involving the formation and decomposition of chemicals.

Physical Properties of Oxygen

The weight of a liter of oxygen is 1.429 grams at S.T.P. This value need not be remembered. You can always obtain it in a moment by dividing the weight of a mol by 22.4. A liter of dry air at S.T.P. weighs 1.293 grams. This is less than the weight of a liter of oxygen because nitrogen, the chief constituent of air, has a lower molecular weight (28) than that of oxygen. At 0° C., 4.89 ml. of oxygen will dissolve in 100 ml. of water. This solubility is greater than that of nitrogen (2.35 ml. at the same temperature).

The Oxygen Molecule

Monatomic molecules composed of a single oxygen atom do not exist under ordinary conditions. If we say of a compound, "It contains oxygen," we mean that there may be one or more oxygen atoms in each of its molecules. Ordinary atmospheric oxygen is diatomic; its formula is O_2. This is what is meant when one says "oxygen" without qualification. The triatomic molecule O_3 is formed from oxygen by the action of ultraviolet light or an electrical discharge. This is ozone. It is an entirely different substance from oxygen. It is 50 per cent denser, has a characteristic strong smell, and is much more reactive. At its boiling point, $-183°$ C., oxygen is *polymerized* to some extent into still another different substance, O_4. A molecule which is a multiple of another is said to be a polymer of the latter. O_4 is pale blue and non-magnetic. It readily breaks down again into O_2, which is colorless and slightly magnetic.

$$2\ O_2 \rightleftarrows O_4$$

Chemical Properties of Oxygen

At normal temperatures oxygen is considered only moderately active. Increases in temperature change this characteristic. A piece of coal will remain exposed to the air for centuries with little change. A diamond will also remain as such indefinitely. Heat either of them in the air and they burn. A striking chemical property of oxygen is its ability to unite directly with other elements to form oxides. The inert gases, the halogens, and the inactive metals platinum, silver, and gold are the exceptions. All of these except the inert gases can be united with oxygen by indirect methods to form at least one oxide.

Rates of reactions of elements with oxygen depend upon the element as well as its environment and physical state. To determine the ease of oxidation of metals we might place a sample of each metal on a watch glass exposed to moist air, in a bottle containing dry air, and in a bottle containing no oxygen, and at definite intervals observe what has happened. Such an experiment would show that all metals are stable in the absence of oxygen, some metals react slowly with oxygen, others not at all, and still others very rapidly. The reaction of an element with oxygen is more rapid if traces of water are present, for this catalyzes the reaction. Of the elements in the following list, all but the last four react with oxygen and form oxides: K, Na, Ba, Sr, Ca, Mg, Al, Mn, Zn, Cr, Cd, Fe, Co, Ni, Sn, Pb, H, Cu, As, Bi, Sb, Hg, Ag, Pd, Pt, and Au. These four—Ag, Pd, Pt, and Au—do not form oxides by direct union with oxygen, but oxides can be obtained by indirect methods.

Some elements form more than one oxide; therefore we must know how to determine *which oxide is formed.* If picture wire containing many thin strands of iron is warmed and plunged into a bottle of oxygen, it bursts into flame. A little sulfur is usually placed on the tip so that the reaction will be quicker, for the burning sulfur liberates heat which starts the reaction between iron and oxygen. Is the oxide formed FeO, Fe_2O_3, or Fe_3O_4? In this case it is easy to identify it, for the product formed is magnetic and Fe_3O_4 is the only magnetic oxide of iron.

$$3\ Fe + 2\ O_2 \longrightarrow Fe_3O_4 + \Delta$$

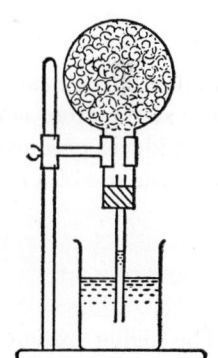

Fig. 10.4. Rusting of iron.

Iron products are not useful unless they are kept polished and bright. If iron is kept *dry*, it does not react rapidly with oxygen. In the presence of moisture and oxygen, the metal *rusts* or *corrodes* or *oxidizes*, forming the oxide Fe_2O_3, which is red in color. High concentrations of oxygen usually yield higher metal oxides. Some metals react with oxygen quite rapidly and yet corrode slowly. Aluminum quickly tarnishes or forms an oxide, but corrodes more slowly than iron. At first sight this statement seems impossible; however, it is true, for aluminum oxide forms an adherent film on the surface of the metal and actually protects it, whereas Fe_2O_3 flakes off and the process continues as long as iron and oxygen meet (Fig. 10.4).

If the metals K, Na, Ba, Sr, and Ca are exposed to air, they react very quickly with oxygen. Potassium reacts at such a rate that it is melted by the liberated heat; this speeds up the reaction, and soon the metal bursts into flame. None of these five metals forms protective coatings of oxides. The silvery bright appearance of each one disappears almost as soon as the metal comes in contact with oxygen.

$$4\,Na + O_2 \longrightarrow 2\,Na_2O + \Delta$$
$$\text{Sodium oxide}$$

$$2\,Ca + O_2 \longrightarrow 2\,CaO + \Delta$$
$$\text{Calcium oxide}$$

The action of magnesium with oxygen is similar to that of aluminum. It tarnishes quickly, but the protective film will for a long time prevent further oxidation. A strip of magnesium can be just ignited at the temperature of a lighted match, and it burns readily in air, whereas in oxygen the flash of light is so brilliant as to be almost blinding.

$$2\,Mg + O_2 \longrightarrow 2\,MgO + \Delta$$

Some non-metals combine readily with oxygen, while others must be heated to high temperatures before the reaction starts. In each case the union of the element with oxygen results in the liberation of heat. If carbon is heated in an insufficient supply of oxygen, the lower oxide, carbon monoxide, is formed.

$$2\,C + O_2 \longrightarrow 2\,CO + \Delta$$

With a greater concentration of oxygen, complete oxidation results and carbon dioxide is formed.

$$C + O_2 \longrightarrow CO_2 + \Delta$$

Sulfur burns readily in air and brilliantly in a bottle of oxygen. Although the sulfur atom is capable of combining with three atoms of oxygen, little trioxide is produced in ordinary burning. Careful control of temperature and the use of a catalyst are necessary to obtain sulfur trioxide.

$$S + O_2 \longrightarrow SO_2 + \Delta$$
$$2\,SO_2 + O_2 \xrightarrow{\text{catalyst}} 2\,SO_3 + \Delta$$

The higher oxide of phosphorus is produced when phosphorus burns in air or oxygen. Red phosphorus can be ignited with a hot wire. If burning phosphorus is lowered into a bottle of oxygen, the reaction is vigorous and dense white smoke is formed. The smoke is solid phosphorus pentoxide.

$$4\,P + 5\,O_2 \longrightarrow 2\,P_2O_5 + \Delta$$

Students in the laboratory test for the presence of oxygen by lowering a glowing splint into a bottle of the gas. If the concentration is high, the splint bursts into flame.

Properties of Oxides in the Presence of Water

All oxides can be divided into two groups: metal oxides and non-metal oxides. The chemical properties of oxides in these two classes are strikingly different. This is best shown by allowing them to react with water; in the case of a metal oxide the product is a base, and in the case of a non-metal oxide it is an acid. The reason for this difference is that the metal oxides contain a free oxide ion, whereas the non-metal atom is covalently bound to the oxygen in the non-metal. The oxide ion itself is an extremely strong base, taking protons from practically any acid; but when the oxygen is forced to share electrons with other non-metal atoms, it becomes less willing to share them with protons in addition and is therefore a much weaker base. When a weak base does acquire a proton, the resulting molecule is relatively willing to lose it again and is therefore an acid of appreciable strength. The weaker a base is, the stronger is the corresponding acid which is formed by the union of the base with protons.

Many metal oxides are not soluble enough to react with water to any great extent. Those that are sufficiently soluble react with water because the oxide ion is a base and water is an acid, although an exceedingly weak one. When the oxide ion takes a proton from water, the result is two hydroxide ions.

$$:\ddot{\underset{..}{O}}:^{--} + :\underset{\underset{H}{|}}{\ddot{O}}:H \longrightarrow :\ddot{\underset{..}{O}}:H^- + :\ddot{\underset{..}{O}}:H^-$$

The oxides of the metals Na, K, Ca, and Ba are soluble in water and so are the resulting hydroxides (that of calcium is only moderately so). Typical equations are:

$$Na_2O + H_2O \longrightarrow 2\ Na^+ + 2\ OH^- \quad \text{(sodium hydroxide)}$$
$$CaO + H_2O \longrightarrow Ca^{++} + 2\ OH^- \quad \text{(calcium hydroxide)}$$

The hydroxide ion is still a very strong base, although not as strong as the oxide ion. Therefore solutions of these hydroxides are strongly basic and will injure the skin or clothing. If spilled, they should be rinsed away with plenty of water and the remaining solution neutralized with dilute acetic acid.

If a non-metal oxide reacts with water—and most of those that are sufficiently soluble do—it is for a quite different reason. Since the oxygen atom has only six valence electrons, any non-metal oxide will contain at least one oxygen atom which is sharing two electron pairs. Test this out, remembering that each non-metal atom, including oxygen, must be surrounded by a complete octet of valence electrons. Oxygen, one of the most electrophilic (electron-loving) of all elements, does not like to have to share electrons with other non-metal atoms which are also electrophilic. It wants to have the whole valence octet to itself, or at least shared only with hydrogen, which is only slightly electrophilic. The oxygen atom which has a covalence of two in a non-metal oxide can remedy this situation if the oxide combines with a molecule of water. Thus chlorine monoxide, Cl_2O, reacts with water according to the equation:

$$:\overset{..}{\underset{..}{Cl}}:\overset{..}{\underset{..}{O}}: + :\overset{..}{\underset{..}{O}}:H \longrightarrow 2 :\overset{..}{\underset{..}{Cl}}:\overset{..}{\underset{..}{O}}: \quad \text{(hypochlorous acid)}$$
$$:\overset{..}{\underset{..}{Cl}}: \qquad\quad H \qquad\qquad\quad H$$

In sulfur dioxide (SO_2) the di-covalent oxygen atom is sharing both electron pairs with the *same* sulfur atom. Here again, reaction with water produces a substance in which no oxygen atom has to share two pairs of electrons with a strongly electrophilic atom.

$$:\overset{..}{\underset{..}{O}}:\overset{..}{\underset{H}{S}}::\overset{..}{\underset{..}{O}}: + :\overset{..}{\underset{..}{O}}:H \longrightarrow H:\overset{..}{\underset{..}{O}}:\overset{..}{\underset{:\overset{..}{\underset{..}{O}}:}{S}}:\overset{..}{\underset{..}{O}}:H \quad \text{(sulfurous acid)}$$

The conventional equations for these reactions are:

$$Cl_2O + H_2O \longrightarrow 2\ HClO$$
$$SO_2 + H_2O \longrightarrow H_2SO_3$$

Several reactions of this type are of commercial importance. Among them are:

$$SO_3 + H_2O \longrightarrow H_2SO_4 \text{ (sulfuric acid)}$$
$$CO_2 + H_2O \longrightarrow H_2CO_3 \text{ (carbonic acid)}$$
$$P_2O_5 + 3\ H_2O \longrightarrow 2\ H_3PO_4 \text{ (phosphoric acid)}$$

The contrast between the basic nature of metal oxides and the acid-forming properties of non-metal oxides is so great and so important that metals are frequently referred to as "basic elements" and non-metals as "acidic elements." It will be seen, however, that oxygen is the key element in both cases. Neither metals nor metal ions are themselves bases; the metals simply turn oxygen into the strong base, the oxide ion, by their willingness to give up electrons completely to the oxygen. Non-metals, by insisting on sharing electrons with oxygen, lower its basic strength to a level that permits the easy escape of protons if they are present. In other words, the plain oxide ion is a stronger base than any ion containing oxygen and another non-metallic element.

Oxidizing and Reducing Agents

Although non-metals do not give up electrons completely to oxygen as metals do, the electrons which they share with oxygen are really largely lost, for their average position is much nearer the strongly electrophilic oxygen atoms. The action of oxygen on both classes of elements is therefore similar, a taking away of electrons from them. Oxygen is the earliest known and most important of the electron-takers, but the effect upon the electron-loser is the same when the electron-taker is chlorine or any other electrophilic molecule. The process of de-electronation was named *oxidation* when it was studied with oxygen as the de-electronating agent, and that name is now used for it regardless of the identity of the *oxidizing agent*. Thus chlorine is properly described as a strong oxidizing agent.

The case of chlorine shows that it is not necessary for an oxidizing agent to contain oxygen; neither is it necessary for it to be an element. All that is necessary is that two strongly electrophilic atoms be covalently bound together. Thus all chlorine-oxygen compounds are oxidizing agents. But oxygen compounds with slightly electrophilic non-metals are not oxidizing agents. Silicon dioxide is 56 per cent oxygen, but those who recognize it as the main constituent of common sand will know that it is not an oxidizing agent!

Whenever an oxidizing agent gains electrons it is said to have been *reduced*, and the substance which was oxidized is called the *reducing agent*. From what has been said, it should be possible to deduce that the active metals and the less electrophilic non-metals are reducing agents. Very important among them are hydrogen, carbon, and their compounds.

Combustion

Electron transfer reactions usually involve relatively large amounts of energy. At room temperature or even somewhat above it, however, they are usually slow enough so that the energy which is evolved escapes as fast as it is produced and the temperature does not rise. All chemical reactions increase in speed as the temperature is raised, and usually quite rapidly. A temperature is presently reached in many cases at which the heat evolved by the reaction can no longer be dissipated; the reaction accordingly speeds up, the temperature shoots up of its own accord, and the mixture glows or bursts into flame. The temperature at which this occurs is called the kindling point. Any chemical reaction which takes place with the emission of both light and heat is called combustion. If one of the reactants is a gas into which the other reactant is introduced in any form but in relatively small quantities, the gas is said to support the combustion of the other substance. In the case of two gases, which one is said to support the combustion of the other obviously involves an arbitrary choice of experimental conditions. Combustion in air is the most familiar example of this phenomenon. If a substance is said to be combustible, without particularization, the implication is that it will burn in *oxygen*. Similarly, if a gas is said to support combustion, without specifying what, it is taken for granted that it supports the combustion of the familiar list of ordinary combustibles. The word combustion is synonymous with one meaning of "burning" but is preferred in scientific discussions because it has only one meaning. By way of contrast, we speak of "burning love," the "burning taste" of tabasco sauce, or "burning the toast" when actually no combustion occurs.

Explosive Combustion

Ordinarily fuels burn at a moderate speed, governed by the rate at which atmospheric oxygen can reach the combustible substance. If the air supply at the base of your Bunsen burner is shut, some of the gas may have time to rise 10 to 20 cm. above the top of the tube before air reaches it, so the flame is long. When some air is admitted at the base it does not take as long for the remainder of the needed oxygen to reach the burning gas, and the flame is correspondingly short. (Since the same amount of heat is produced in both cases, the *temperature* of the more concentrated flame is higher.) If *all* the needed oxygen is mixed with the gas before ignition, the mixture burns in a small fraction of a second, i.e., it *explodes*. Some combustible gases form explosive mixtures with air even when the proportions are considerably different from those required for perfect combustion. Acetylene, C_2H_2, is notoriously dangerous in this way.

Science Service

FIG. 10.5. Scene of a dust explosion in a starch factory where 43 men lost their lives and $3,000,000 damage was done.

The combustion of solid fuel can be speeded up by blowing air into the fuel bed. Dividing the fuel more finely so as to offer more surface of contact with the air is also effective. Excelsior burns faster than logs, given a sufficient air supply. It is also much easier to ignite, since it is easier to raise a small piece of material to the kindling point. The extreme case in subdividing a solid is reached with *dust*.

Because of the rapid rate at which small particles (with a relatively great

OXYGEN

proportion of their mass exposed as surface) can be oxidized, combustible dusts are a serious industrial hazard. If you have ever been through a large flour mill you know that precautions are taken to keep dust at a minimum because a spark in dusty air may mean an explosion (Fig. 10.5). As many coal mine explosions have been caused by dust as by gas. If there is coal dust on the floors of a mine a small gas explosion at a working face can raise a cloud of it. This, ignited by the first explosion, produces a larger one which can in turn be similarly propagated throughout the mine. Powdered coal is blown into the fireboxes in many great central power stations and burned just like gas. Powdered sugar and grain elevator dust have caused great explosions.

A small-scale explosion simulating that of a flour mill may be carried out with the apparatus shown in Fig. 10.6. A can with a loose-fitting top is used. A hole is punched in the bottom of the can and a funnel forced through the opening. A candle is sealed in the can and lighted, the funnel is then filled with lampblack, and the top is placed on the can. Air is immediately forced through the funnel, thus creating a dust which is ignited by the candle flame. An explosion results and the top of the can is blown into the air.

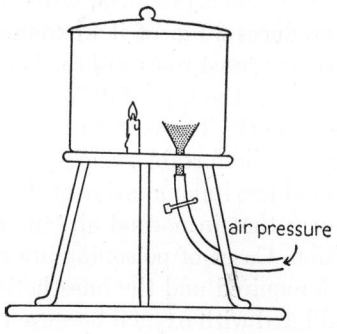

FIG. 10.6. Dust explosion.

Uses of Oxygen

Human beings have always breathed oxygen in the air, drunk oxygen in the form of water, and eaten oxygen in the form of plant and animal tissue. Energy is required when we walk or exert ourselves in any way. Our bodies would soon cool to the surrounding temperature were it not for oxidation reactions which produce energy. The evaporation of water from our bodies in hot weather is nature's provision for combating excess heat. Waste body tissues are oxidized to soluble compounds and thus eliminated. Entire courses in chemistry, known as physiological chemistry, are devoted to the study of reactions in the body.

Far more complicated than most of us realize is the process by which molecular oxygen dissolves in moisture in lung tissue, diffuses into the blood stream, reacts with hemoglobin to produce red oxy-hemoglobin (the coloring material in the blood), is released from this compound and from the oxidation of products resulting from the food we eat, forms carbon dioxide, and diffuses back through the lung tissue and thence into exhaled breath. Failure of one step in this series of complicated reactions means that we cannot survive. If fats, proteins, or carbohydrates are to be burned in a crucible, they must be heated to high temperatures. These same materials, or compounds produced from them, burn in the body at its temperature of about

37° C. Catalysts play an important role in making such oxidation possible. It is thought that the energy which is necessary for physical exertion comes from the oxidation of an organic compound, glycogen, $C_6H_{10}O_5$. This is oxidized to lactic acid, the acid in sour milk. The body immediately tries to convert lactic acid to glycogen. The energy required for this change is supplied by further oxidation of some molecules of lactic acid to carbon dioxide. Hence carbon dioxide is finally exhaled in the breath. The rate at which lactic acid is produced is frequently expressed in the statement that a sprinter produces 30 g. of it in running the hundred-yard dash. After the race the runner must rest until the body can convert the excess lactic acid to glycogen, because the rate of diffusion of oxygen is too slow for long-continued strenuous work. The oxygen tent is used to make patients who have pneumonia more comfortable. Such patients do not breathe pure oxygen, for that soon produces inflammation of the lungs. The concentration of oxygen is increased over that in normal air, the ratio being determined by the patient's condition. Cases of poisoning are also treated in oxygen tents. Where anesthesia is required and the anesthetic is nitrous oxide, N_2O, or ethylene, C_2H_4, it is diluted with oxygen because the patient must have oxygen even though he is unconscious.

Of the many chemical industries which require oxygen, the most important one is the metal industry. If the cheap reducing agent, carbon, is heated with naturally occurring metal oxides, the metal and oxides of carbon are formed:

Fig. 10.7. Oxy-acetylene flame used in welding piping. (Courtesy, Air Reduction Sales Co.)

some metal ores $+$ C $\longrightarrow$ metal $+$ oxides of carbon

Exact equations for these reactions are given in the chapters dealing with the metals. The temperature necessary for the reduction of the ore is obtained by burning some carbon compound or coal with a blast of air. When air is used, the nitrogen in it is raised to the same temperature as the burning fuel and this involves a great waste of heat. It was thought that improvements in liquefying air might result in the commercial development of oxygen furnaces. These could be used successfully at high altitudes where difficulty is now encountered with air. The furnace gases have some fuel value because of carbon monoxide being present, but such a fuel would be more valuable if it were not diluted with nitrogen. The improvements in question were made in Germany during

OXYGEN

World War II and are only now being made available in the United States; they promise to reduce the cost of reasonably pure oxygen from its former level of $300 per ton to $5 per ton, or even less in large installations.

The steel worker depends upon oxygen for welding and cutting steel. Both oxy-acetylene (Fig. 10.7) and oxy-hydrogen torches are used; however the electric arc is replacing the oxy-acetylene torch for welding. Steel framework can be wrecked quickly by cutting it apart with a flame which is hot enough to melt the alloy. As soon as the metal is melted more oxygen is turned on and the metal oxidizes rapidly. Steel-cutting is not confined to work in the air; special equipment has been developed so that it can be done under water. Absorbent carbon soaked in liquid oxygen has been used instead of dynamite in coal mines and in making tunnels. Today one can buy oxygen in cylinders at pressures of over 100 atmospheres, and liquid oxygen in Dewar flasks so well constructed that they will stand handling in shipment.

QUESTIONS AND PROBLEMS

1. Calculate the percentage of oxygen in water, sulfur dioxide, carbon dioxide, deuterium oxide, and hydrogen peroxide.
2. Calculate the weight of 25 ml. of oxygen at S.T.P.
3. What volume of air at S.T.P. must be used in order to supply enough oxygen to burn 128 g. of sulfur?
4. What volume of gases measured over water at 23° when the barometer reads 755 mm. is produced by the electrolysis of 90 g. of water?
5. What weights of mercuric oxide, barium peroxide, potassium chlorate, and sodium chlorate must be decomposed to furnish one liter of oxygen at S.T.P.?
6. A mixture consisting of 5 g. of the catalyst MnO_2 and 10.6 g. of $NaClO_3$ is heated until the liberation of oxygen is complete. What is the weight of the residue? What volume does the oxygen occupy if collected over water at 20° C. and at one atmosphere pressure?
7. Twenty g. of carbon are burned in 100 l. of air. How many grams of carbon monoxide can be produced, assuming that the carbon burns wholly to the monoxide? (All gases at S.T.P.)
8. It is desired to prepare exactly 0.9145 g. of oxygen. The gas is to be collected over water at 25° and at a pressure of 740 mm. What volume will the oxygen occupy under these conditions?
9. What types of compounds liberate oxygen when heated?
10. What weight of phosphorus should be lowered into a 600-ml. bottle containing oxygen at 25° and 740 mm. if the phosphorus is to combine with all the oxygen in the bottle?
11. How do we account for the presence of such a large quantity of the active element oxygen in the atmosphere?
12. If one cubic mile of petroleum has been burned to date above the ground,

calculate the percentage increase in the concentration of carbon dioxide in the air if all the carbon dioxide thus produced is in the air above your state and it is evenly distributed within 5 miles from the earth. (Assume petroleum to be C_8H_{18}.)

REFERENCES
Articles

"Dust Explosions."   Price, D. J.   *J. Chem. Ed.* **3**, 1008–1017 (1926).
"Priestley's Life." Browne, C. A.   *J. Chem. Ed.* **14**, 503–515 (1937). An excellent article.

» 11 «

OZONE AND THE PEROXIDES

OZONE

In addition to ordinary oxygen, O_2, oxygen atoms can form the molecule O_3. When two different substances are both composed of one single kind of atom they are said to be *allotropic* modifications of the element. If two allotropic forms of an element have identical molecules, merely arranged in different patterns in their crystals, they may not differ very much from each other. If the molecules are different, the two forms may resemble each other only in giving the same products after a chemical reaction has taken place. This is the case with O_2 and O_3, so it is natural that the latter has been given a name of its own, ozone. It comes from the Greek word meaning "to smell." The strong, peculiar smell of ozone is familiar to all who have been in the vicinity of big electrical machinery or strong ultraviolet lights. A trace of ozone as small as one part in 10,000,000 can be detected in air by this odor. Ozone is noticeably blue (the liquid is dark blue), 1.5 times as dense as oxygen, and has a boiling point 71° higher.

Chemically, ozone not only is much more active than molecular oxygen; it is one of the most powerful oxidizing agents known. Such metals as silver and mercury, although not tarnished by O_2, are quickly covered with a coating of oxide in the presence of O_3. A spectacular demonstration consists in tying a weight to a rubber band and hanging the band in front of the outlet of an ozone machine. It is only a matter of seconds until the band breaks. The probable lasting quality of rubber goods exposed to the sunlight and air can thus be predicted in a few minutes with such a test, for ozone accomplishes in a few seconds or minutes changes which would require much longer under ordinary conditions. A piece of paper moistened with a solution of potassium iodide is unaffected by molecular oxygen. Ozone liberates iodine quickly. A little starch applied to the paper is turned blue by the free iodine.

Ozone is formed by the addition of an oxygen atom to an oxygen molecule, the added atom sharing one of the previously unshared electron pairs in the O_2 molecule. This appears to be permitted by the O_2 only with some reluctance, for the third oxygen atom is rather easily broken off again. This accounts for the greater reactivity of ozone as compared with oxygen. It also accounts for the fact that a large amount of energy is used up in the formation of ozone from oxygen. Much more energy is used up in breaking the multiple bonds of an O_2 molecule than is given out when the resulting atoms combine with other O_2 molecules.

Formation of Ozone

Oxygen atoms are momentarily produced in some chemical reactions, but ozone results only rarely and never in more than traces. It is not practicable to prepare it by high temperature, for thermal collisions break O_3 molecules apart far faster than they do the more stable O_2 molecules. Oxygen molecules absorb ultraviolet light, with resulting dissociation and ozone formation. This process, taking place on a large scale in the outer reaches of the earth's atmosphere, removes from the incoming sunlight all but the very near ultraviolet and is probably responsible for the fact that our eyes are not sensitive to ultraviolet light. No appreciable amounts of the ozone produced either in this way or by lightning persist for any length of time; the ozone decomposes spontaneously into ordinary oxygen, or reacts with oxidizable impurities in the air.

The only practical method of making ozone is by passing cold, dry oxygen through a *silent discharge*. The apparatus consists essentially of a condenser, between whose charged plates the oxygen can be passed. Large numbers of gaseous ions are always present in any gas from which they have not been intentionally removed; they are continually being produced by passage of cosmic rays, etc. These ions are driven back and forth through the oxygen by an alternating potential of several thousand volts applied to the condenser plates. They dissociate molecules which they strike, or at least "excite" them to a reactive state. The yield of ozone may be better than 10 per cent at room temperature and is almost 100 per cent when the apparatus is cooled with liquid air. The liquid ozone which is produced in the latter case is dangerously explosive because its decomposition is exothermic.

Uses of Ozone

The industrial use of ozone is still in the experimental stage. In a recent trial in Philadelphia[1] the addition of 20 lbs. of ozone per million gallons of city water completely destroyed all foreign tastes in the water, reduced the color and odor to half the original values or less, reduced the chlorine demand (for sterilization) 75 per cent, made clarification possible with one-third to one-half the usual amount of alum, and removed the undesirable manganous

---

[1] This and an experiment in sterilizing a swimming pool by means of ozone are summarized in *Chem. Abstr.* **38**, 1825 (1944).

ion, Mn^{++}, by oxidizing it to insoluble MnO_2. Ozone is used to some extent to bleach certain foods. However, the difficulty is to lower its cost to a level comparable with the cost of other means of accomplishing these ends. The use of ozone to sterilize and deodorize air in living spaces has been proposed, but the present consensus is that a concentration sufficient to be effective will be dangerous to health.

PEROXIDES

The metals near the top of the electrochemical series can give electrons to an oxygen molecule without breaking it up. The result is the peroxide ion, O_2^{--}. The electronic formula is $:\overset{..}{O}:\overset{..}{O}:^{--}$. With only a single covalent bond to hold the two atoms together, this ion is much more reactive than the O_2 molecule.

Many metal peroxides are prepared for various commercial uses; the commonest in the laboratory are those of sodium and barium. All peroxides react with water or stronger acids to produce hydrogen peroxide, a very weak acid. In the case of sodium peroxide, which is easily soluble, the reaction is very rapid and produces a dangerous amount of heat. Thus moisture in the air can easily cause sodium peroxide to set fire to paper in contact with it. For this reason the material should not be poured from the bottle onto pieces of paper nor should any that is left over be thrown into waste jars. The equation for the reaction with water is

$$Na_2O_2 + 2\ H_2O \longrightarrow 2\ Na^+ + 2\ OH^- + H_2O_2$$

If barium peroxide is treated with sulfuric or phosphoric acid the product other than hydrogen peroxide is insoluble and can be removed by filtration.

$$BaO_2 + H^+ + HSO_4^- \longrightarrow BaSO_4 + H_2O_2$$
$$3\ BaO_2 + 2\ H_3PO_4 \longrightarrow Ba_3(PO_4)_2 + 3\ H_2O_2$$

This was until recently the commercial method for the preparation of H_2O_2. The product is a 3 per cent solution and is usually sold in drugstores under the designation "ten-volume." This means that the solution will yield ten times its volume of oxygen when the hydrogen peroxide in it decomposes. Attempts to concentrate this solution by the evaporation of water result only in decomposing the H_2O_2 unless it is very pure and the conditions are carefully controlled.

In addition to the metallic peroxides, which contain the peroxide ion, it is possible to prepare a long list of compounds in which one or both of the peroxide oxygens share an electron pair with some other non-metallic atom. A simple example is peroxymonosulfuric acid, $H:\overset{..}{\underset{..}{O}}:\overset{\overset{..}{O}:}{\underset{:\overset{..}{O}:}{S}}:\overset{..}{O}:\overset{..}{O}:H$. All of them react with water or acids to give hydrogen peroxide, but more slowly than do the metallic peroxides, because a covalent bond has to be broken. Each has individual properties which are responsible for many special uses.

Commercial Preparation of H_2O_2

The most important of all peroxides is peroxydisulfuric acid. When moderately concentrated sulfuric acid or ammonium bisulfate is electrolyzed (details of electrolytic reactions are given in Chapter 18), the anode removes an electron from one of the oxygen atoms, thus:

$$H^+ \text{ (or } NH_4^+) + \begin{bmatrix} \ddots \ddots \\ :O: \\ H:O: S :O: \\ :O: \end{bmatrix}^- \longrightarrow H^+ \text{ (or } NH_4^+) + \begin{bmatrix} :O: \\ H:O: S :O\cdot \\ :O: \end{bmatrix}^0 + \ominus$$

The electron immediately discharges a proton at the cathode. Two of the uncharged bisulfate fragments then join to form a molecule of peroxydisulfuric acid in the same way and for the same reason as two chlorine atoms combine to form Cl_2. The formula of the product

$$\begin{array}{cc} :O: & :O: \\ H:O: S :O:O: S :O:H \\ :O: & :O: \end{array}$$

plainly shows the peroxide linkage in the middle. The ammonium salt of this acid is a valuable, strong oxidizing agent. The name is commonly shortened to ammonium persulfate. When steam is passed through a solution containing either $(NH_4)_2S_2O_8$ or $H_2S_2O_8$, H_2O_2 is formed and distills over, and the original bisulfate ions are regenerated.

$$2\ NH_4^+ + S_2O_8^{--} + 2\ H_2O \longrightarrow 2\ NH_4^+ + 2\ HSO_4^- + H_2O_2$$

This is the present commercial method for the preparation of H_2O_2. The distillate is both purer and much more concentrated than the filtrate from the BaO_2 method. This new product has opened a wide new field for itself; where the old 3 per cent solution was mainly a bottled item sold in drugstores, 30 per cent H_2O_2 is now shipped in tank cars. It is used to bleach paper pulp and cotton cloth, to develop vat dyes (an oxidative process) and as a powerful oxidizing agent in chemical industries. A particular point in favor of hydrogen peroxide as an oxidizing agent is that it leaves no residue, and any excess can be decomposed catalytically into oxygen and water. Although the dilute solution is used as a throat gargle, bacteriological tests show that it is not an efficient antiseptic.

Concentrated Hydrogen Peroxide

The greater purity of the modern product led to the discovery that pure hydrogen peroxide could be concentrated by evaporation (the boiling point of H_2O_2 is 52° higher than that of water) without serious decomposition. In 1944 it was found that the Germans had been using the reaction between 80 per cent H_2O_2 and a concentrated sodium permanganate solution to generate a mixture of steam and oxygen to drive the fuel pump of the V-2 rocket.

$$2\ Na^+ + 2\ MnO_4^- + 3\ H_2O_2 \longrightarrow 3\ \overline{O_2} + 2\ \underline{MnO_2} + 2\ Na^+ + 2\ OH^- + 2\ H_2O$$

When the U.S. War Department asked for H_2O_2 of this concentration for experimental purposes it was only a short time before an American manufacturer, taking extra pains about the purity, was able to produce 95 per cent H_2O_2. This very pure material is quite stable and withstands the shock of a bullet or even a detonator, whereas the presence of a slight trace of organic impurity makes it behave more like nitroglycerine. The Buffalo Electro-Chemical Co. has recently completed a new plant for the manufacture of highly concentrated hydrogen peroxide and is now shipping it in 250-pound drums and even in tank cars. Their product contains 90 per cent H_2O_2, 10 per cent water and virtually nothing else. When stored below 30° C. it decomposes at the rate of less than 1 per cent a year, but it can ignite dirty clothing or wooden floors if spilled. This 90 per cent H_2O_2 is more useful than the common 30 per cent solution, not merely because it is three times as concentrated, but also because it is soluble in organic liquids. The relative absence of water increases its efficiency in many processes.

The 30 per cent solution of H_2O_2 regularly sold as concentrated hydrogen peroxide is not as pure and therefore not as stable as the special material mentioned in the preceding paragraph. It is not sensitive to shock but it may gradually decompose. Chemists emphasize repeatedly that one should *read the labels on bottles before opening them.* The label on a bottle of hydrogen peroxide should say to *point the bottle away from the face when opening it.* The bottles are usually closed with a cork which has a screw cap over it, or with a glass screw cap with a washer under it. If any peroxide has decomposed, the oxygen which has been released will exert a pressure on the cap. A bottle of concentrated peroxide has been known to blow the bottle top through an inch-thick wooden shelf above it. Bases, yeast, organic matter, manganese dioxide, and finely divided platinum illustrate the variety of substances which will cause hydrogen peroxide to decompose. Acids and some organic compounds such as acetanilide act as negative catalysts and are used as preservatives.

Dilute hydrogen peroxide is used in the laboratory as a mild oxidizing agent. For example, it oxidizes black lead sulfide to white lead sulfate; hence old paintings containing lead pigments can be brightened with H_2O_2.

$$\underline{PbS} + 4\ H_2O_2 \longrightarrow \underline{PbSO_4} + 4\ H_2O$$

White manganous hydroxide is oxidized to black manganese dioxide.

$$\underline{Mn(OH)_2} + H_2O_2 \longrightarrow \underline{MnO_2} + 2\ H_2O$$

Free iodine is liberated from solutions of iodides.

$$2\,H^+ + 2\,I^- + H_2O_2 \longrightarrow I_2 + 2\,H_2O$$

Hydrogen peroxide will react with bases to form peroxides and water. This is similar to the action of acid+base $\longrightarrow$ salt+water. Since two hydrogen atoms are replaced, H_2O_2 is considered a dibasic acid.

$$H_2O_2 + Ba^{++} + 2\,OH^- \rightleftarrows BaO_2 + 2\,H_2O$$

It is not always possible to tell from the formula of a compound whether or not it is a peroxide. Knowing that barium, manganese, and lead all form divalent cations, one might jump to the conclusion that BaO_2, MnO_2, and PbO_2 are all peroxides. That this is false in the case of the last two can be proved by a simple experiment in *qualitative analysis*. Any peroxide will yield H_2O_2 if treated with dilute sulfuric acid.

$$Na_2O_2 + H_2SO_4 \longrightarrow 2\,Na^+ + SO_4^= + H_2O_2$$

After the salt in question has been so treated, the acid solution can be tested for the presence of H_2O_2 by adding a little very dilute potassium dichromate, $K_2Cr_2O_7$, and then ether, which will float on top of the solution. When the test tube is shaken and the ether allowed to float back to the top it will be colored a fine blue by the perchromic acid it has extracted from the solution if any H_2O_2 was present in the first place. The formula of the unstable perchromic acid has not been determined. The failure of this test with MnO_2 and PbO_2 shows that these compounds are dioxides rather than peroxides. That is, the metals have the oxidation number of $+4$, whereas the oxygen has the normal oxidation number of -2. The unusual valence for the metals is confirmed by the fact that lead dioxide will dissolve in cold acetic acid to form lead tetra-acetate, and manganese dioxide in cold hydrochloric acid to form $MnCl_4$.

QUESTIONS AND PROBLEMS

1. a. How many grams of BaO_2 are needed to prepare 5 l. of a 3 per cent solution of H_2O_2, s.g. 1.01?
   1 liter of water weighs 1000 g.
   s.g. of the H_2O_2 solution = 1.01.
   $\therefore$ 5 l. of the solution weigh $1000 \times 1.01 \times 5 = 5050$ g.
   But of this weight only 3 per cent is H_2O_2.
   Hence the H_2O_2 required is $5050 \times .03$ g.

$$\underset{169.4}{\underset{BaO_2}{x\text{ g.}}} + \underset{98\text{ g.}}{\underset{H_2SO_4}{y\text{ g.}}} \longrightarrow \underline{BaSO_4} + \underset{34}{\underset{H_2O_2}{5050 \times .03\text{ g.}}}$$

$$x = \frac{5050 \times .03 \times 169.4}{34} \text{ g. of BaO}_2$$

b. What volume of sulfuric acid is needed, s.g. 1.30, 40 per cent H$_2$SO$_4$ by weight?

Solve for y:

$$y = \frac{5050 \times .03 \times 98}{34} \text{ g. of pure H}_2\text{SO}_4 \text{ needed.}$$

To find the volume of acid needed:
s.g. of the acid = 1.30.
∴ 1 ml. of the acid weighs 1.30 g.
This acid is 40 per cent H$_2$SO$_4$ by weight, the other 60 per cent is water.
∴ 1 ml. contains 1.30 × 0.4 g. of pure H$_2$SO$_4$.

REFERENCES

"Highly Concentrated Hydrogen Peroxide." Shanley, E. S. and Greenspan, F. P. *Ind. and Eng. Chem.* **39**, 1536–1543 (1946).

» 12 «

HYDROGEN

Discovery of Hydrogen

Records are incomplete prior to 1650, when Turquet de Mayerne reported that an inflammable gas could be obtained from iron and sulfuric acid. In 1766, Sir Henry Cavendish (1731–1810), an English scientist, proved that the gas obtained from the reaction of a metal with an acid was an individual substance; he called it "inflammable air." He found that it would react with oxygen to produce water. His one mistake regarding this gas was the fact that he thought it came from the metal and not the acid. Lavoisier gave this gas its present name, hydrogen, meaning "water former."

Occurrence of Hydrogen

Hydrogen is found in unimportant quantities in some gaseous emanations from the earth such as the *solfataras* of Iceland, the petroleum fields of Pennsylvania and Ohio, some volcanoes, jets of steam in Tuscany, and salt beds in Strassfurt. It is also occluded in certain meteorites, minerals, and clays. Some metals absorb large volumes of hydrogen, and wherever these metals are found free in nature hydrogen may be found associated with them. The most important of these metals are iron, cobalt, nickel, platinum, and palladium. Hydrogen is a normal product of anaerobic decomposition and is found in the intestinal gases of many animals, in the gases escaping from septic tanks, and in sewage sludge gas. Its concentration in the atmosphere, never above 0.02 of 1 per cent, may have been produced by the anaerobic decomposition of organic matter. Spectroscopic observations show that hydrogen completely surrounds the sun. Photographs of the sun's chromosphere show flames of incandescent hydrogen 300,000 miles high and over 100,000 miles wide.

In the combined state hydrogen is abundantly distributed throughout nature. It forms $\frac{1}{9}$ the weight of water and $\frac{1}{4}$ the weight of marsh gas, and

HYDROGEN

is an essential constituent of cellulose, sugar, starch, fats, proteins, oils, petroleum, and all hydrocarbons. In fact, *nearly all organic compounds contain hydrogen.* It is a constituent of acids and bases. In smaller quantities it occurs in combination with phosphorus, sulfur, boron, and nitrogen (as ammonia). In some mineral springs it is liberated as the gas hydrogen sulfide, H_2S. Water is the cheapest source of hydrogen.

Preparation of Hydrogen

When any new substance is discovered, it remains a laboratory curiosity until some use for it is found. The uses to which hydrogen could be put were a long time in coming, but they are increasing steadily. Old expensive methods of preparing hydrogen have given way to cheaper commercial processes, and several procedures are now available.

Hydrogen from Water. The cheapness of the raw material makes water the most important source of commercial hydrogen. The gas is prepared in three ways: by the reaction of *metals with water, non-metals with water,* and the *electrolysis of water.*

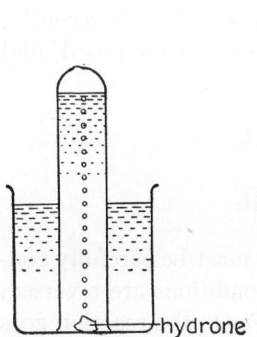

FIG. 12.1. Hydrogen gas collected by displacement of water.

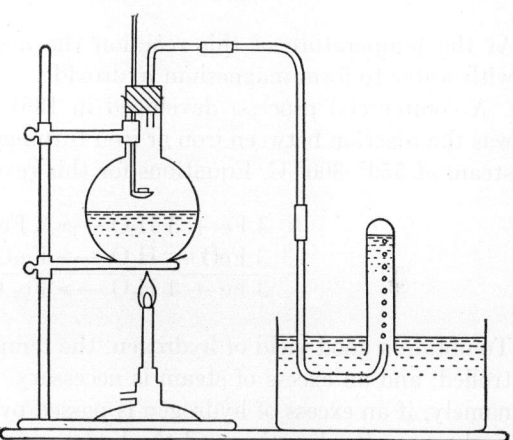

FIG. 12.2. Preparation of hydrogen by the reaction between magnesium and steam.

The metals can be divided into three groups according to the ease with which they react with water and liberate hydrogen. Some react at room temperature with no application of external heat, others must be heated, and still others will not react at all. The alkali metals react vigorously, even violently. *Never under any conditions drop more than a very small piece of sodium or potassium into water.* (Several serious accidents have been caused in this way. One teacher lost his eyesight because of just such carelessness on the part of a student.) Potassium dropped on water catches fire and burns. A small piece of sodium skims around over the surface with a sizzling noise. The reaction between sodium and water is:

$$2\ \underline{Na} + 2\ H_2O \longrightarrow 2\ Na^+ + 2\ OH^- + \overline{H_2} + \Delta$$

To decrease the speed of this reaction and thus the hazard, some laboratories use an alloy of lead and sodium (65 per cent Pb, 35 per cent Na) called "hydrone." It is heavy enough to sink readily. Hydrogen is collected in an inverted tube as shown in Fig. 12.1. If samples of all the metals are added to water, only the alkali metals and the heavier alkaline earth metals, starting with calcium, are found to liberate hydrogen at room temperature.

A strip of magnesium placed in water produces no visible evolution of hydrogen, but it liberates hydrogen from steam. A suitable apparatus is shown in Fig. 12.2. Water is first heated to boiling to drive the air from the flask; then a spoon with magnesium ribbon wrapped around it is held in a flame until the magnesium ribbon ignites, and the connection is quickly fitted in place. Hydrogen is caught in the inverted tube.

$$Mg + \overline{H_2O} \longrightarrow MgO + \overline{H_2} + \Delta$$

At the temperature of this reaction the magnesium oxide does not react with water to form magnesium hydroxide.

A commercial process, developed in 1861 and important until recently, was the reaction between iron or iron turnings (greater surface exposed) and steam at 550°–800° C. Equations for this reaction are:

$$\begin{array}{l} 3\ Fe + 3\ H_2O \longrightarrow 3\ FeO + 3\ H_2 \\ \underline{3\ FeO + H_2O \longrightarrow Fe_3O_4 + H_2} \\ 3\ Fe + 4\ H_2O \longrightarrow Fe_3O_4 + 4\ H_2 \end{array}$$

To obtain a good yield of hydrogen, the temperature must be carefully controlled, and an excess of steam is necessary. If the conditions are reversed, namely, if an excess of hydrogen is passed over hot Fe_3O_4, the reaction goes in the opposite direction and the hydrogen reduces the iron of the oxide to metallic iron. This reaction is not extraordinary, for there are many which do not go to completion. Arrows pointing in each direction indicate that the reaction is reversible.

$$3\ \underline{Fe} + \overline{4\ H_2O} \rightleftarrows \underline{Fe_3O_4} + \overline{4\ H_2}$$

In an equilibrium reaction the quantity of resultants which are produced depends upon the nature of reactants and also upon relative concentrations of reactants and resultants. To illustrate further the principle of chemical equilibrium, suppose that some iron filings and water are sealed in a strong tube and it is heated. At first, the reaction will progress rapidly from left to right, as indicated in the above equation. As soon as an appreciable amount

HYDROGEN

of H_2 and Fe_3O_4 is formed, these molecules collide, and some react to form water and iron. The rate at which the reaction goes from left to right soon equals the rate from right to left, and an equilibrium has been reached.

It is important to remember that an equilibrium reaction represents not a condition of no reaction but a condition of *equal rates of reaction*. Because something about the term equilibrium is frequently associated with equal, you may be inclined to think of equal molar quantities of reactants and resultants as being at equilibrium. This is wrong, for rarely does equilibrium represent equal concentrations of materials. A good illustration is a seesaw, with yourself on one end at a certain distance from the center, and someone weighing either more or less than you at a point on the other side so that you just balance. The board is at equilibrium, but your quantities (weights) are not the same. Just as a fat man and a small child might be at equilibrium on the seesaw, so also can chemical reactions be at equilibrium when there is a large excess of one substance. Chemists discovered long ago that the equilibrium point of equilibrium reactions could be changed by altering the conditions.

Cheap electricity has made it possible for electrochemical reactions to compete with high temperature reactions such as the one between iron and steam. If a direct current flows through water containing an electrolyte such as sulfuric acid, sodium hydroxide, or sodium sulfate, oxygen is liberated at one electrode and hydrogen at the other. A simple apparatus which can be used is shown in Fig. 12.3. As mentioned before,

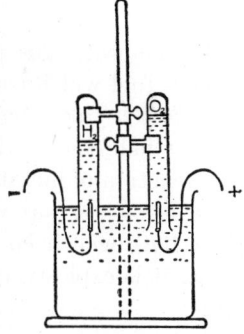

FIG. 12.3. Electrolysis of water.

we need not understand electricity in order to use it; the chemistry of these reactions will be discussed in Chapter 18. These substances, called electrolytes, are added to make the solution a better conductor of electricity.

$$2\ H_2O \xrightarrow{\text{\AE}} 2\ \overline{H_2} + \overline{O_2}$$

The equation shows that two volumes of hydrogen are liberated per volume of oxygen. The most modern commercial electrical units use alkaline electrolytes.

One reaction of commercial importance is the "water gas" process, which consists in passing steam over the non-metal, carbon (coke at 1000° C.). The resultant mixture of carbon monoxide and hydrogen can be burned as a fuel.

$$\underline{C} + \overline{H_2O} \xrightarrow{1000°\ C.} \overline{CO} + \overline{H_2}$$

A blast of air is forced through coke until it is white-hot; the air is then shut off and steam is forced through the coke. The temperature soon drops; the steam is shut off and the remaining coke is again heated to 1000°. If the only end product desired is hydrogen, the mixture of H_2 and CO is passed with additional steam at a more moderate temperature over catalysts of thorium, chromium, and iron oxides until the CO is converted into CO_2.

$$CO + H_2O \xrightarrow{500°C} CO_2 + H_2$$

The carbon dioxide can be efficiently removed by passing the mixture of gases, at high pressure, through cold water. The solubility of hydrogen is very low.

A mixture of CO and H_2 containing a much larger percentage of the latter than does water gas is produced by the reaction of steam with natural gas. Natural gas is mainly methane, CH_4. The equation for its reaction with steam is:

$$CH_4 + H_2O \longrightarrow CO + 3\ H_2$$

By the water-gas process coal could be converted at the mines into a gaseous fuel which could be piped throughout the country.

Hydrogen from Acids. Metals are frequently divided into two groups: those which react with acids and liberate hydrogen, and those which do not. The reaction of metals with water, which has been mentioned, falls into this class, for water has weak acid properties. Sodium and potassium will displace hydrogen from stronger acids too, of course. (Do not try the experiment. It is explosively violent.) The equations, for purposes of comparison, are:

$$\underline{Na} + 2\ H^+ + 2\ Cl^- \longrightarrow 2\ Na^+ + 2\ Cl^- + \overline{H_2}$$

$$\underline{K} + 2\ H^+ + 2\ Cl^- \longrightarrow 2\ K^+ + 2\ Cl^- + \overline{H_2}$$

Less active metals, such as iron and zinc, which do not liberate hydrogen from water at room temperature with appreciable speed, will do so at a reasonable rate from ordinary acids. Such a process is of no commercial importance because the acids are expensive; but it is excellent in the laboratory, for the reaction will take place at room temperature and the rate of the evolution of gas can be easily controlled by regulating the temperature and concentration of the acid. A salt is always the other product of the reaction between an acid and a metal. The following equations illustrate reactions between metals and acids:

$$\underline{Mg} + 2\ HC_2H_3O_2 \longrightarrow \underset{\text{magnesium acetate}}{Mg^{++} + 2\ C_2H_3O_2^-} + \overline{H_2}$$
$$\text{acetic acid}$$

$$2\ \underline{Al} + 3\ H^+ + 3\ HSO_4^- \longrightarrow 2\ Al^{+++} + 3\ SO_4^{--} + 3\ \overline{H_2}$$

If you add samples of several metals to hydrochloric acid, you will find quite a difference in the rate of liberation of hydrogen. This is because of the difference in the ease with which they give up electrons, for the reaction with acids is essentially the electronation of protons. The *activity series* or *elec-*

HYDROGEN

trochemical series of the metals, which is shown in Table 12.1, is essentially similar to that for the non-metals which was given on page 108. Just as in the case of non-metals, the series gives the order in which the metals will replace each other from compounds. Notice, however, that the metals and hydrogen are set free by reduction (electronation), whereas the reverse is true of the non-metals. In general, *any element in the series will replace any element below it from its compounds*. Thus all the elements above hydrogen will replace it from acids; those below will not. From this series we should expect iron to replace copper ions from solution. This can be shown to be the case, for an iron nail placed in a solution of copper sulfate is quickly coated with copper. Magnesium will replace lead and lead will replace mercury. The closer any two elements are to each other in the electrochemical series (frequently abbreviated to E.C.S.), the less probable it is that the higher metal will, under all conditions, replace the lower one from compounds. The E.C.S. is more accurate, the farther apart the metals are.

TABLE 12.1. ELECTROCHEMICAL SERIES (METALS AND HYDROGEN)

Name	Symbol	Notes
1. Potassium	K	1. Elements 1–5 liberate hydrogen from cold water.
2. Barium	Ba	$2\ Na + 2\ HOH \longrightarrow 2\ NaOH + \overline{H_2}$
3. Strontium	Sr	
4. Calcium	Ca	2. Elements 1–12 liberate hydrogen from steam.
5. Sodium	Na	$Mg + H_2O \longrightarrow MgO + \overline{H_2}$
6. Magnesium	Mg	3. Elements 1–16 liberate hydrogen from acids.
7. Aluminum	Al	$Zn + 2\ HCl \longrightarrow ZnCl_2 + \overline{H_2}$
8. Manganese	Mn	4. Elements 1–22 will react with oxygen and form oxides.
9. Zinc	Zn	$4\ Al + 3\ O_2 \longrightarrow 2\ Al_2O_3$
10. Chromium	Cr	5. Elements 23–25 form oxides by indirect methods.
11. Iron	Fe	$AuCl_3 + 3\ KOH \longrightarrow Au(OH)_3 + 3\ KCl$
12. Cadmium	Cd	$2\ Au(OH)_3 \longrightarrow \overline{Au_2O_3} + 3\ H_2O$
13. Cobalt	Co	
14. Nickel	Ni	6. If heated, the oxides of elements 21–25 decompose to form metals and oxygen.
15. Tin	Sn	$2\ HgO \xrightarrow{\Delta} 2\ Hg + \overline{O_2}$
16. Lead	Pb	
17. Hydrogen	H	7. Compounds of elements 1–11 are not reduced by hydrogen to produce metals.
18. Copper	Cu	$MgO + H_2 \longrightarrow$ no reaction
19. Arsenic	As	8. Oxides of elements 12–25 can be reduced by hydrogen.
20. Bismuth	Bi	$Fe_3O_4 + 4\ H_2 \longrightarrow 3\ Fe + 4\ H_2O$
21. Antimony	Sb	9. Oxides of metals below hydrogen are *easily* reduced.
22. Mercury	Hg	$CuO + H_2 \longrightarrow Cu + H_2O$
23. Silver	Ag	
24. Platinum	Pt	
25. Gold	Au	

The E.C.S. table should be consulted in regard to every metal which is studied in the laboratory. Learn the element's relative position in the table and determine from the accompanying notes which ones apply to it.

Hydrogen from Solutions of Hydroxides. Several elements liberate hydrogen vigorously from water if the water contains enough sodium or potassium hydroxide to react with the product other than hydrogen. Among these are the metals zinc and aluminum and the non-metal silicon. When zinc starts to react with plain water, the hydroxide is produced, as in the case of sodium, but zinc hydroxide is insoluble. It coats over the surface of the metal and stops the reaction.

$$\underline{Zn} + 2\ H_2O \longrightarrow \underline{Zn(OH)_2} + \overline{H_2}$$

Zinc, however, is one of a considerable class of metals which show some characteristics of non-metals; for example, $Zn(OH)_2$ is a weak acid as well as a base. To call attention to this, the formula may be rewritten H_2ZnO_2. If a sufficient amount of a soluble hydroxide is present it will dissolve the zinc hydroxide as fast as it is formed, according to the equation:

$$\underline{H_2ZnO_2} + 2\ Na^+ + 2\ OH^- \longrightarrow 2\ Na^+ + ZnO_2^{--} + 2\ H_2O$$

This permits the evolution of hydrogen to continue rapidly. The two equations may be added together, and the zinc hydroxide and water canceled out.

$$\underline{Zn} + 2\ Na^+ + 2\ OH^- \longrightarrow 2\ Na^+ + ZnO_2^{--} + \overline{H_2}$$

The ion ZnO_2^{--} is called the zincate ion; here also the zinc shows a behavior characteristic of a non-metal, for it is part of a negative ion.

Aluminum is ordinarily prevented from reacting with water by a coating of Al_2O_3, but this substance behaves not merely as a metallic oxide would behave, but also as though it were a non-metallic oxide. It reacts with sodium hydroxide to form the soluble salt, sodium aluminate, thus:

$$\underline{Al_2O_3} + 2\ Na^+ + 2\ OH^- \longrightarrow 2\ Na^+ + 2\ AlO_2^- + H_2O$$

In a sodium hydroxide solution, then, the surface of aluminum is immediately cleaned so that the active metal can liberate hydrogen from water according to the expected equation:

$$2\ \underline{Al} + 6\ H_2O \longrightarrow 2\ \underline{Al(OH)_3} + 3\ \overline{H_2}$$

Aluminum hydroxide is not actually precipitated, however, because it reacts even more readily with the hydroxide ion than does the corresponding oxide. Again rewriting the formula of the hydroxide to emphasize its acidic behavior, we have:

$$2\ \underline{HAlO_2 \cdot H_2O} + 2\ Na^+ + 2\ OH^- \longrightarrow 2\ Na^+ + 2\ AlO_2^- + 4\ H_2O$$

This equation combined with the preceding one gives:

$$2\ \underline{Al} + 2\ H_2O + 2\ Na^+ + 2\ OH^- \longrightarrow 2\ Na^+ + 2\ AlO_2^- + 3\ \overline{H_2}$$

HYDROGEN

The ability of some elements to form compounds in which they act as metals and others in which they act as non-metals is so important that it will be discussed in detail under amphoteric substances.

The non-metal silicon reacts with sodium hydroxide solutions in a similar manner, yielding sodium silicate and hydrogen:

$$\underline{Si} + 2\,Na^+ + 2\,OH^- + H_2O \longrightarrow 2\,Na^+ + SiO_3^{--} + 2\,\overline{H_2}$$

Here too we may imagine an acidic hydroxide as an intermediate step. Since it does not behave like a base, it is called silicic acid and written H_4SiO_4 or, after losing water, H_2SiO_3. A hydrogen-generating kit used during World War II contained silicon (in the form of an alloy with iron called ferrosilicon) and dry sodium hydroxide. The addition of water quickly caused the production of enough H_2 to inflate a small balloon which carried aloft a radio aerial for emergency broadcasting.

Hydrogen by Other Methods. Hydrogen is produced during the "cracking" of petroleum hydrocarbons in producing gasoline and other products. Some of it is recombined with particular products for special purposes; more of it is burned as fuel.

Ammonia is also cracked.

$$2\,NH_3 \xrightarrow[\text{Catalyst}]{600°\ C.} N_2 + 3\,H_2$$

The gas mixture produced is 25 per cent nitrogen by volume, but this rather inert gas is as effective as hydrogen in such uses as excluding oxygen from metals in annealing ovens. To those who know that ammonia is prepared from hydrogen and nitrogen in the first place, it may seem uneconomic to reverse the process. The explanation lies in the fact that ammonia is easily liquefiable. Enough of it to produce 3000 cu. ft. of hydrogen can be shipped in a single light-walled cylinder.

Other substances than those mentioned can react with water to produce hydrogen. Among them are barium sulfide, BaS, ferrosilicon (an alloy of iron and silicon), and the hydrides of the metals 1–5 in the E.C.S., such as sodium hydride, NaH. These substances are too expensive for ordinary commercial use.

Laboratory Preparation of Hydrogen

A simple apparatus used in preparing small amounts of hydrogen is shown in Fig. 12.4. The acid is poured through the thistle tube and quickly comes in contact with the metal. Two precautions are necessary. The reaction is exothermic; therefore add the acid gradually, for otherwise the hydrogen will be liberated so rapidly that it may force the acid out of the thistle tube because of the back pressure produced. Keep all flames away from the gas escaping from the bottle until you are certain that no oxygen is mixed with the hydrogen; for such a mixture, if ignited, may explode with sufficient force to blow the bottle to bits. The best test of the purity of hydrogen is to collect the gas by displacement of water and then bring a test tube full of it near a flame. Quiet burning indicates pure hydrogen, but a "pop" shows that oxygen is mixed with the hydrogen. (Why should the test tube be kept inverted while it is being brought near the flame?) Mossy zinc and hydrochloric acid are frequently used in a hydrogen generator such as this.

It is often desirable to have a continuous supply of hydrogen available as needed. The Kipp generator shown in Fig. 12.5 is excellent for this purpose. The metal is placed in the upper bulb of the lower section; and the upper section, which has a long tube extending down to the bottom of the lower

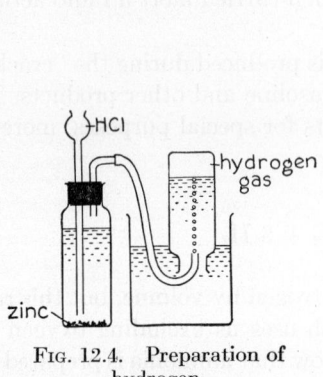

Fig. 12.4. Preparation of hydrogen.

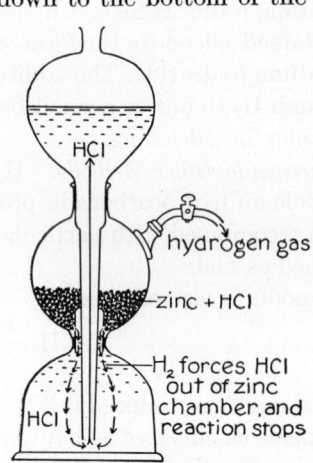

Fig. 12.5. A Kipp generator.

section, is fitted in place. Acid poured in at the top goes to the bottom and fills the lowest compartment and finally comes in contact with the metal. If the stopcock is open, hydrogen escapes; if it is closed, the gas soon fills the middle compartment, and the pressure created by the gas forces the acid back *down* and *up* through the tube and into the upper compartment. The reaction stops as soon as the acid is no longer in contact with the metal. Never leave the stopcock wide open for more than a few seconds, or the reaction between metal and acid may be so rapid that the hydrogen cannot escape through the tube fast enough, and the back pressure produced will force the acid out of the opening into which it was originally poured. The Kipp generator is used for other gases such as carbon dioxide and hydrogen sulfide.

$$\underline{Zn} + 2\,H^+ + 2\,Cl^- \longrightarrow Zn^{++} + 2\,Cl^- + \overline{H_2}$$

$$\underline{CaCO_3} + 2\,H^+ + 2\,Cl^- \longrightarrow Ca^{++} + 2\,Cl^- + H_2O + \overline{CO_2}$$

$$\underline{FeS} + 2\,H^+ + 2\,Cl^- \longrightarrow Fe^{++} + 2\,Cl^- + \overline{H_2S}$$

Limestone and ferrous sulfide are used instead of zinc to obtain carbon dioxide and hydrogen sulfide.

Physical Properties of Hydrogen

Pure hydrogen gas is colorless, odorless, and tasteless. Any odor detected as it is prepared in the laboratory comes from impurities in the gas. It is the lightest of all gases, one liter weighing $\left(\frac{2.016}{22.4}\right)$ or 0.08987 g. at S.T.P. The solubilities of hydrogen, nitrogen, and oxygen in ml. per 100 ml. of water at 0° C. are 2.1, 2.35, and 4.89 respectively. Hence hydrogen is the least soluble of these three gases. The thermal conductivity of hydrogen gas is seven times that of air. The gas can be liquefied under a pressure of 180 atmospheres. Expansion of the gas under these conditions causes some of it to liquefy because the gas absorbs heat from its surroundings. Liquid hydrogen is clear and colorless; it boils at $-252.5°$ C., and has the greatest specific heat (6.4) of any liquid known. In the liquid state hydrogen is a non-conductor of electricity. If liquid hydrogen is cooled by rapid evaporation under reduced pressure, some of it solidifies to a transparent solid which melts at $-259°$ C.

The absorption of hydrogen by some metals, particularly if in a finely divided state, is frequently called occlusion. One ml. of palladium will absorb over 900 ml. of hydrogen gas. One important property of hydrogen when absorbed by palladium is its great chemical activity. Oxygen and hydrogen do not react at room temperature, but this reaction occurs when the hydrogen is absorbed by palladium. The hydrogen occluded in palladium is thought to be in the monatomic state and hence more active.

$$H_2 \longrightarrow 2\ H$$

Some reactions involving the use of hydrogen commercially take place at a rapid rate only if certain metals are present. These metals may be responsible for converting some molecular hydrogen into the monatomic form.

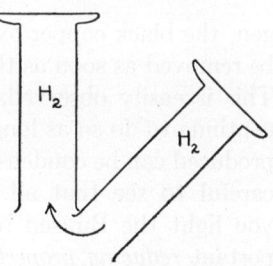

Fig. 12.6. Hydrogen is poured upward.

Hydrogen, the lightest of all gases, diffuses the most rapidly. This constitutes a real problem in its use for balloon ascensions. Great improvements have been made during recent years in coating fabrics so that they are both flexible and reasonably resistant to the diffusion of hydrogen. Bottles filled with the gas should be kept inverted until ready for use. Hydrogen is "poured upward" from one cylinder to another, as shown in Fig. 12.6. The rapid rate of diffusion can be demonstrated by lowering a beaker filled with hydrogen over a porous cup fastened into a bottle partially filled with water. Hydrogen diffuses through the porous cup more rapidly than the oxygen and nitrogen in the air diffuse out. A greater pressure is created inside than without, thus forcing water from the delivery tube of the bottle. To those unacquainted with the properties of gases, this seems almost like "magic." If you wish your voice to sound peculiar, breathe some hydrogen and then talk—the frequency of vibration of the vocal cords of the larynx varies inversely with the density of the gas which surrounds them. A person with a low-pitched voice will suddenly burst forth with high squeaky sounds. Wind instruments show the same characteristic. Keep flames and lighted cigarettes away when you breathe hydrogen.

Chemical Properties of Hydrogen

In the electrochemical series hydrogen was placed with the metals. It is not a metal, but it does show some characteristics of metals. In substitution reactions it will displace metals, and some metals will displace it from compounds.

$$\underline{Zn} + 2\ H^+ + 2\ Cl^- \longrightarrow Zn^{++} + 2\ Cl^- + \overline{H_2} + \Delta$$

$$\overline{H_2} + \underline{CuO} \longrightarrow \underline{Cu} + \overline{H_2O} + \Delta$$

The apparatus shown in Fig. 12.7 can be used to illustrate both reactions. Zinc is placed in the bottle, the bottle is filled about three-fourths with water, and hydrochloric acid is added through the thistle tube. Any water in the hydrogen escaping from the generator is removed by means of a tube filled with calcium chloride which has a great affinity for water but none for hydrogen. After the small amount of air has been swept out of the generator by the stream of hydrogen, the black copper oxide in the test tube is heated gently. The flame can be removed as soon as the reaction starts because the reaction is exothermic. This is easily observed, for the material suddenly begins to glow and will continue to do so as long as the reaction is in progress. The water which is produced can be condensed in another test tube immersed in an ice bath. Be careful to see that all the oxygen is removed from the apparatus before you light the Bunsen burner. Why? This reaction illustrates the very important *reducing property* of hydrogen. The high cost of hydrogen is the only reason for its not being used commercially to an even greater extent as a reducing agent for obtaining metals from their oxides.

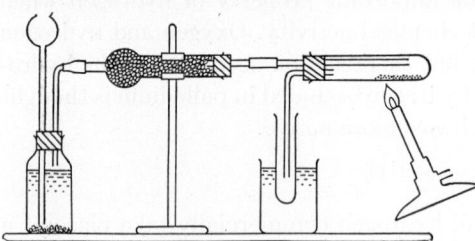

Fig. 12.7. Preparation of hydrogen and reduction of copper oxide.

Hydrogen will burn in the presence of oxygen over a wide range of concentrations of the two gases. They combine very slowly at temperatures below 400° C. Above 600° C. the reaction is rapid, and it is explosive if there is between 5 and 70 per cent of hydrogen in the mixture. Violent explosions occur when two parts of hydrogen are mixed with one part of oxygen. Soap bubbles filled with this mixture rise rapidly; if, as the bubble rises in the air, it is ignited with a long taper, the results are spectacular and sometimes almost deafening. Hydrogen burns with a colorless flame. Any color observed when it is burning is due to impurities in the air or to some substance vaporizing from the tip from which the gas is escaping. Hydrogen burning from a glass tip always has the characteristic yellow color of a sodium flame because of the sodium compounds in glass.

Hydrogen reacts with many other non-metals besides oxygen. The Haber process for producing ammonia on a commercial scale consists in passing nitrogen and hydrogen at high pressure and temperature over a suitable catalyst. Chlorine combines with hydrogen *explosively* in the presence of sunlight to form hydrogen chloride, HCl. The water solution of this gas is called hydrochloric acid. Less electrophilic non-metals may require indirect methods for forming hydrogen compounds. Among such compounds are hydrogen sulfide, H_2S, which has the characteristic odor of rotten eggs; phosphine, PH_3, which burns spontaneously in air; highly poisonous arsine, AsH_3; and the similar but less stable gas stibine, SbH_3.

Hydrogen is unique in being the first and at the same time the last (active) element in its period. We have already said that it may thus be considered to be the first element in Group I A in the periodic system, and at the same time the first element in Group VII A. The resemblance to the metals in Group I is largely formal. Hydrogen loses electrons; but the proton, which is all there is left when a hydrogen atom loses an electron, is too small to exist as an independent cation like Li^+. Instead, it promptly shares an electron pair belonging to the octet of some non-metallic atom in the vicinity. For example, in the reduction of copper oxide described on page 148 the hydrogen atoms lose electrons to the Cu^{++} ion, changing it to metallic copper and themselves to protons. The protons then attach themselves to the oxide ion, converting it into H_2O. Thus, although the hydrogen has acquired a valence of $+1$, it is an oxidation number, not an electrovalence.

The resemblance of hydrogen to the elements in Group VII is much stronger than its resemblance to those in Group I. In all its compounds with the non-metals hydrogen completes its valence layer, acquiring the structure of the following inert gas, by forming one covalent bond, just as do F, Cl, Br and I. Hydrogen can also attain the helium structure by outright capture of an electron from a sufficiently active metal (Nos. 1–5 in the E.C.S.), forming the monovalent anion, H^-, called the hydride ion.

$$2 \underline{Na} + \overline{H_2} \longrightarrow 2 \underline{NaH}$$

Sodium hydride is a salt, but reacts with water, liberating H_2.

$$\underline{NaH} + H_2O \longrightarrow Na^+ + OH^- + \overline{H_2}$$

It is an excellent reducing agent, less violent than sodium, and has recently become available for commercial use. The compounds of hydrogen and carbon constitute one large group of hydrogen compounds. These substances, called hydrocarbons, are important and will be discussed in detail later.

Some organic compounds such as liquid fats will combine with hydrogen and form solids. This process is called *hydrogenation*. These compounds which are capable of adding hydrogen are said to be "unsaturated."

"Atomic" Hydrogen

When Irving Langmuir (General Electric Co.) discovered that hydrogen at reduced pressure in an incandescent lamp conducted heat away from the filament faster than he had expected, he attributed this to the fact that some of it was in the form of monatomic molecules. Believing that the hot tungsten of the filament had produced the reaction

$$H_2 + \Delta \longrightarrow 2H$$

he proved this by blowing a stream of H_2 through an arc between tungsten electrodes. Although the H atoms which were produced rapidly recombined with each other, their presence could be detected at a considerable distance from the arc by their ability to react at room temperature with many substances which react with H_2 only at high temperatures. H cannot be preserved; the reaction

$$2H \longrightarrow H_2 + \Delta$$

takes place almost immediately. The amount of heat liberated is enormous, 90,000 calories per mol of H_2. It was found that the recombination reaction could be accelerated by playing the blast of gas upon a metallic surface. The practical application of this was obvious. If the blast is played upon metals which are to be welded, the heat from the formation of H_2 can be used for the welding. The commercial apparatus, the general plan of which is shown in Fig. 12.8, is known as the atomic hydrogen torch; temperatures of 4000° to 5000° C. may be attained with it. The inner cone of the flame is due to the recombination of hydrogen atoms to form molecules, and the outer cone is due to hydrogen molecules burning in the oxygen of the air. The heat of formation of H_2 from 2 H is about 1.5 times that of H_2O from H_2; therefore the inner zone is the hotter.

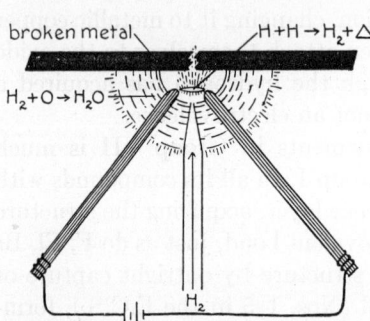

Fig. 12.8. High temperatures are produced with the atomic hydrogen torch.

Determination of the Valence of a Metal by Displacement of Hydrogen from an Acid

A convenient way of determining experimentally the valence of any active metal is to see how many gram atoms of hydrogen one gram atom of the metal can displace from an acid. It is much easier to measure the volumes of gases than to weigh them, so we remind ourselves that, since the formula of hydrogen is H_2, one mol of it is two gram atoms. One gram atom of H_2 is therefore half a mol and will occupy half the molar volume, namely, 11.2 l. at S.T.P.

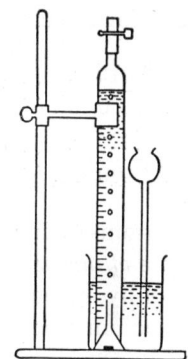

Fig. 12.9. Determination of the hydrogen equivalent of magnesium.

For simultaneous comparisons, three sets of the laboratory apparatus shown in Fig. 12.9 can be used to determine the combining capacity of active elements. Each burette is filled with water and inverted in a beaker of water. Definite weights of sodium, magnesium, and aluminum respectively are placed under the three funnels. What weight of each metal will be used? If a gram-atomic weight is used, the volume of hydrogen liberated will more than fill each burette; therefore some ratio of these weights is preferable. Except for experimental difficulties we might select any ratio:

    1 at. wt. of Na : 1 at. wt. of Mg : 1 at. wt. of Al
    23 g. of Na   : 24.32 g. of Mg   : 27 g. of Al
    23 lb. of Na   : 24.32 lb. of Mg : 27 lb. of Al

Much better for this experiment is:

    23 mg. of Na : 24.32 mg. of Mg : 27 mg. of Al

The relative number of atoms in each case will be 1:1:1. If 23 mg. of Na, 24.32 mg. of Mg, and 27 mg. of Al are placed under the funnels and some hydrochloric acid is poured through the thistle tube so that it comes in contact with each metal, hydrogen is liberated. (The acid is not needed for the sodium experiment.) When the evolution of H_2 stops it will be obvious that the amounts of hydrogen are to each other as 1:2:3. It will be interesting to calculate the volume of hydrogen liberated in each burette to standard conditions of 0° C. and 760 mm. over mercury. If no mistake has been made, the volumes of hydrogen obtained will be as follows:

    1 milligram-atomic weight of sodium (23 mg.) ⟶ 11 ml. of hydrogen
1 milligram-atomic weight of magnesium (24.32 mg.) ⟶ 22 ml. of hydrogen
    1 milligram-atomic weight of aluminum (27 mg.) ⟶ 33 ml. of hydrogen

The weight of the hydrogen liberated from the sodium would be:

$$\frac{2.016 \text{ g.}}{22,400 \text{ ml.}} \times 11 \text{ ml.} = 1 \text{ mg. (approx.)}$$

(A gram-molecular weight of any gas at S.T.P. occupies 22.4 liters.)

Since 23 mg. of sodium release 1 mg. of hydrogen, 23 g. of sodium or *1 gram-atomic weight* will release 1 g. of hydrogen. Therefore one atom of sodium releases one atom of hydrogen. This is why the valence of sodium is said to be 1; moreover, *it is based on laboratory experimentation*.

Similar calculations for the magnesium and aluminum experiments are:

$$\frac{2.016 \text{ g.}}{22,400 \text{ ml.}} \times 22 \text{ ml.} = 2 \text{ mg. of hydrogen from } 24.32 \text{ mg. of magnesium}$$

$$\frac{2.016 \text{ g.}}{22,400 \text{ ml.}} \times 33 \text{ ml.} = 3 \text{ mg. of hydrogen from } 27 \text{ mg. of aluminum}$$

One gram-atomic weight of magnesium will release 2 g. of hydrogen. *The valence of magnesium is 2*. One gram-atomic weight of aluminum will release 3 g. of hydrogen. *The valence of aluminum is 3*. Expressed in terms of atoms, one sodium atom liberates one hydrogen atom, one magnesium atom liberates two hydrogen atoms, and one aluminum atom displaces three hydrogen atoms. The simplest equations to show these facts are:

$$\text{Na} + \text{HCl} \longrightarrow \text{NaCl} + \text{H}$$
$$\text{Mg} + 2 \text{ HCl} \longrightarrow \text{MgCl}_2 + 2 \text{ H}$$
$$\text{Al} + 3 \text{ HCl} \longrightarrow \text{AlCl}_3 + 3 \text{ H}$$

More properly, to show the actual molecular species involved:

$$2 \underline{\text{Na}} + 2 \text{ H}^+ + 2 \text{ Cl}^- \longrightarrow 2 \text{ Na}^+ + 2 \text{ Cl}^- + \overline{\text{H}_2}$$
$$\underline{\text{Mg}} + 2 \text{ H}^+ + 2 \text{ Cl}^- \longrightarrow \text{Mg}^{++} + 2 \text{ Cl}^- + \overline{\text{H}_2}$$
$$2 \underline{\text{Al}} + 6 \text{ H}^+ + 6 \text{ Cl}^- \longrightarrow 2 \text{ Al}^{+++} + 6 \text{ Cl}^- + 3 \overline{\text{H}_2}$$

The formulas of the salts show that one sodium atom combines with one chlorine atom, the magnesium atom with two chlorine atoms, and the aluminum with three.

The equivalent weight of an element is defined as the number of grams of the element which will react with, replace, or be otherwise equivalent to 1.008 grams of hydrogen. The valence of an element equals its atomic weight divided by its equivalent weight. For example, 12.16 g. of magnesium will liberate 1 g. of hydrogen.

$$\frac{\text{atomic weight}}{\text{equivalent weight}} = \text{valence.} \qquad \frac{24.32}{12.16} = 2 = \text{valence of magnesium.}$$

Nine g. of aluminum will liberate 1 g. of hydrogen. $\frac{27}{9} = 3 =$ valence of aluminum.

From the compound, H_2O, or water, it is observed that one atom of oxygen combines with two atoms of hydrogen; thus we say that oxygen has a valence of 2. In the compound, P_2O_5, the valence of phosphorus is 5 because the valence of oxygen is 2.

When, as in some cases, it is impossible to determine the valence of an atom or radical on the basis of the volume of hydrogen which it displaces or the weight of chlorine with which it combines, an indirect method can be used. If the metal would not replace hydrogen but would form a compound with oxygen, its valence could be determined by analyzing the oxide and calculating the ratio of atoms of metal to oxygen atoms. Suppose that the analysis gave 2 atoms of metal to 7 atoms of oxygen; the formula would then be M_2O_7 ("M" standing for the metal). The valence of "M" would equal $\dfrac{7 \text{ oxygen atoms} \times \text{its valence of 2}}{2 \text{ atoms of "M"}}$, or 7. In other words, the valence of each atom of "M" in the compound M_2O_7 is equivalent to what it would be if each atom replaced 7 atoms of hydrogen.

Exact Atomic Weights from Equivalent Weights

The preceding section showed how to find the valence of an element by using its atomic weight and the experimentally determined equivalent weight. It has only recently been possible to make accurate direct determinations of atomic weights by means of the mass spectrograph. Earlier atomic weight determinations were indirect but nonetheless extremely accurate. They depended experimentally upon carefully determined equivalent weights and theoretically upon the principle that the valence of an element has to be a *whole number*. If any rough approximation of the atomic weight can be obtained, this can be used with the equivalent weight, as just described, to calculate the valence. Because of the inaccuracy of the atomic weight the valence will not be a whole number, but the true value has to be integral; so it can be rounded off to a whole number with complete confidence. Then, in the equation

$$\frac{\text{atomic weight}}{\text{equivalent weight}} = \text{valence}$$

the inaccurate value for the atomic weight can be replaced by x and solved for, using the accurate equivalent weight and the rounded-off valence.

Approximate Atomic Weights. As soon as Avogadro's Law became known and accepted, it was easy to decide upon reasonably accurate atomic weights for any gaseous element. It was only necessary to find what weight of the element was present in a mol of it, and divide that by the number of atoms in the molecule. (The number of atoms in each molecule of a gaseous element can always be determined by applying Avogadro's Law to reactions in which it is produced or used up.) This gives a result as accurate as the experimental data from which it came. A mol of the element contains N molecules, and n×N atoms of the element in question, where n is the number of atoms of it in each molecule. So if the total weight of the element in one mol (weight of n×N atoms) is divided by n, the result is the weight of N atoms. But the weight of N atoms, in grams, is numerically equal to the weight of one atom in atomic-weight units.[1] The argument is the same as in the case of molecules. For this reason we have the definition, N atoms = 1 gram-atomic weight, or *gram atom*, for short.

It is also possible to determine the approximate atomic weight of an element by finding the smallest weight of it which is present in a mol of any of its gaseous compounds, even though the number of atoms in each molecule is not known. Since there must be one or two or three or four atoms of an element in each molecule of any of its compounds, there must be one or two or three or four gram-atomic weights of it in a gram-molecular weight of the compound. If several compounds are analyzed, one must surely contain only a single atom of the element to the molecule and thus only a single gram atom to a mol, for the simplest molecules are the easiest to prepare. The experimental difficulties in making accurate measurements of gases, coupled with uncertainties in the necessary gas law corrections, prevent any high degree of accuracy in atomic weight determinations made by this method. It has, however, been of great value in ascertaining the approximate value of the atomic weight.

The Law of Dulong and Petit

Many elements, particularly metals, do not form any stable gaseous compounds. Fortunately, as early as 1819, Dulong and Petit discovered that, with very few exceptions, one gram atom (N atoms, you will remember) of any *solid* element has approximately the same heat capacity as one gram atom of any other solid element. This means that it takes the same amount of energy to raise the temperature of that many atoms the same amount. (This is definitely not true in the case of gases, for differing amounts of the energy, depending on the shape of the molecules, impart rotational and vibrational energy to them as well as kinetic energy.) If the temperature rise is 1° C., the amount of heat energy needed is usually between $5\frac{3}{4}$ and $6\frac{3}{4}$ calories;[2] this is called the *atomic heat* (short for "gram-atomic heat capacity"). Its average value is taken as 6.4 cal. per degree; and evidently, within the degree of variation noted, the approximate atomic weight of an element is the number of grams of it which can be raised 1° C. in temperature by 6.4 cal. of heat energy.

As an example of the application of the law of Dulong and Petit, consider iron. It is found by experiment that the specific heat[3] of iron is 0.112 cal. per

[1]
$$\begin{array}{llll}
16\ 2\frac{1}{2}\text{-oz. eggs} & =\ 16 \times 2\frac{1}{2} \text{ oz.} & =\ 48 \text{ oz.} & =\ 2\frac{1}{2} \text{ lbs.} \\
2000\ 24\text{-lb. sacks} & =\ 2000 \times 24 \text{ lb.} & =\ 48{,}000 \text{ lbs.} & =\ 24 \text{ tons.} \\
\text{N 35-unit atoms} = & \text{N} \times 35 \text{ units} = & 35\text{N units} = 35 \text{ g.}
\end{array}$$

[2] A calorie is the amount of energy needed to raise the temperature of 1 g. of water 1° C.

[3] The specific heat of a substance is its heat capacity per gram.

HYDROGEN

degree. If the temperature of 1 g. of iron can be raised 1° by 0.112 cal., 6.4 cal. will be able to raise the temperature of $6.4 \div 0.112 = 57$ g. The atomic weight is thus shown to be in the vicinity of 57, but it may be several units more or less, on account of the approximate nature of the law. Analysis shows that pure ferric oxide contains 69.95 per cent of iron. If 69.95 g. of iron combines with 30.05 g. of oxygen, the equivalent weight of which is exactly 8, the equivalent weight of iron is

$$69.95 \text{ g. iron} \times \frac{8.000 \text{ g. oxygen}}{30.05 \text{ g. oxygen}} = 18.62 \text{ g. iron}$$

from which the valence is:

$$\frac{\text{Approximate atomic weight}}{\text{Equivalent weight}} = \frac{57}{18.62} = \text{approximate valence} = 3.06$$

Pictures, Inc.

FIG. 12.10. The German Zeppelin *Hindenburg* in flames.

Obviously the true valence of iron in this compound is 3. Continuing, then

$$\text{Eq. wt.} \times \text{valence} = 18.62 \times 3 = 55.86 = \text{at. wt. of iron}$$

These methods were invaluable in fixing the atomic weights used by Mendeléeff in setting up the periodic table. Once that had been done, the atomic weights of the remaining undiscovered elements could be estimated from those of their neighbors with sufficient approximation to serve as a starting point for calculating the exact atomic weight. It was necessary only to place the element in the table by means of its properties. The discovery of the X-ray method for determining atomic numbers eliminated any possibility of error in placement.

Uses of Hydrogen

Hydrogen was once the only gas used to fill balloons and dirigibles. It has been replaced by helium in the United States, the only country in which helium occurs in quantity. The use of hydrogen offers some saving in lifting power, but this is more than offset by the enormous fire hazard. The many disasters which have been caused by hydrogen catching on fire can be prevented only if an inert gas is used; helium is the only other possibility.

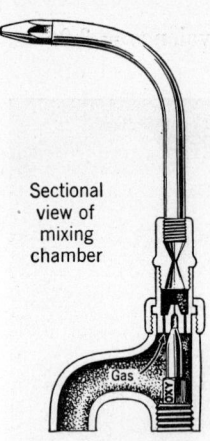

FIG. 12.11. Sectional view of oxy-hydrogen blowpipe. (Courtesy, Hoke, Inc.)

The *reducing power of hydrogen* makes it valuable in converting some metal oxides into metals. In the manufacture of tungsten filament lamps a regular supply of hydrogen is required to prepare the reducing atmosphere in which the filaments are heated during the final drawing of the wire. In general, hydrogen can be used whenever a non-oxidizing or reducing atmosphere is necessary in preparing and annealing alloys. If oxygen does come in contact with a metal at high temperatures and an oxide is formed, hydrogen reduces the metal to its metallic state and steam escapes from the furnace.

The *limelight* of the old theater, also called a Drummond[4] light, was made by directing the flame of an oxy-hydrogen torch (see Fig. 12.11) against a cylinder of lime. As the hydrogen burns, the heat liberated raises the temperature of the CaO to "whiteness." The light produced is equal to that of the electric arc.

The *oxy-hydrogen blowpipe* does not give as high a temperature as the atomic-hydrogen blowpipe, but it is more economical to operate. It is used for the autogenous welding of metals (uniting pieces of metal by fusing them without solder), in the working of platinum metals, and in both constructing and wrecking steel structures. The design of an oxygen-hydrogen blowpipe is shown in Fig. 12.11. Note that oxygen is forced into the center of the gas cone so that the burning will involve pure oxygen and hydrogen as much as possible. The same type of equipment is used in the oxygen-acetylene blowpipe, a competitor of the oxygen-hydrogen unit. Acetylene, which can be obtained from calcium carbide, will be discussed in the chapters on organic compounds.

Hydrogen is an important raw material in the *production of many important*

[4] Thomas Drummond, 1797–1840, British engineer.

chemicals now synthesized in the laboratory. Until 1925 *wood alcohol* (methanol), CH_3OH, was prepared by destructive distillation of wood, and in some plants this was the chief product of the ovens. These distillers must now compete (but they cannot) with the makers of a synthetic product. In the synthetic process, carbon monoxide and hydrogen are passed over catalysts such as finely divided copper and zinc oxide.

$$CO + 2\ H_2 \longrightarrow CH_3OH$$

Formaldehyde, HCHO, another substance obtained from wood, is synthesized by the same type of process.

$$CO + H_2 \longrightarrow HCHO$$

FIG. 12.12. Commercial hydrogenation units. (Courtesy, Wurster & Sanger, Inc., Chicago.)

The synthesis of ammonia is discussed on page 416. The *synthesis of gasoline* by the "liquefaction" of coal, which is based on the reaction of coal with hydrogen, is a process which provided much badly needed gasoline for Germany during World War II. It is known as the Bergius process.

Hardening of liquid fats with hydrogen is another important achievement of chemistry. Cottonseed, cocoanut, and other oils are heated under pressure at about 175° in the presence of catalyst such as finely divided nickel. Hydrogen adds on and the product solidifies at room temperature. Some hydrogenation tanks will hold 15 tons of oil at one charge. In the wet process a nickel salt (such as nickel formate) is added; hydrogen reduces this salt, producing metallic nickel which serves as the catalyst. During hydrogenation some hydrogen is allowed to escape so that any carbon monoxide or carbon dioxide which has been produced can be removed. The process requires a pressure of about 60 pounds per square inch and several hours for the reaction. Filter presses are used to separate the catalyst from the finished product, and the catalyst can be used again. As the temperature drops, the hydrogenated product solidifies. Fig. 12.12 shows a hydrogenation unit.

QUESTIONS AND PROBLEMS

1. Two g. each of sodium, zinc, chromium, and aluminum are treated with excess sulfuric acid. What volume of hydrogen at S.T.P. is liberated by each metal?
2. Calculate the percentage of hydrogen in CH_4, $C_{12}H_{22}O_{11}$, H_2SO_4, and $Ca(H_2PO_4)_2$.
3. How many grams of CuO can be reduced by the H_2 obtained from the electrolysis of 5.4 g. of water?
4. What is the heaviest piece of magnesium which could be used in the experiment described on page 151 using a 50-ml. burette and collecting the gas over water at 2° and 745 mm. pressure?
5. 387.6 ml. of hydrogen were collected in the laboratory over water at 23° and 735 mm. pressure. How many grams of zinc must react with H_2SO_4 to prepare this much hydrogen?
6. Compare the volumes of hydrogen obtained from the reaction of 2.92-g. portions of zinc with HCl, H_2SO_4, H_3PO_4, and NaOH.
7. To a flask are added 6.08 g. of magnesium and 30.0 ml. of HCl, s.g. 1.15, 30.0 per cent HCl by weight. What volume of hydrogen at S.T.P. is liberated?
8. Compare the rates of diffusion of hydrogen and helium; of hydrogen and oxygen.
9. When the *Hindenburg* burned over Lakehurst in May, 1937, she was carrying 6,700,000 cu. ft. of hydrogen. (1 cu. ft = 28.32 l.).
    a. How many tons of water were formed by this combustion?
    b. What volume of air was necessary to burn the hydrogen?
    c. Assuming S.T.P., how many liters of water would have to be electrolyzed to produce this much hydrogen?
    d. What was the gross lifting power of the *Hindenburg* in tons?
10. How many grams of water are necessary to produce 11.2 l. of hydrogen at S.T.P. by electrolysis; by the reaction with sodium; by the reaction with hot carbon; by the reaction with iron?
11. A mixture of 33.6 l. of hydrogen and 28 l. of oxygen at S.T.P. is exploded. Find the weight of each substance present after the explosion.
12. How many gram-molecular volumes of hydrogen could be liberated from an acid by gram-atomic weights of potassium, calcium, aluminum, and cadmium?

HYDROGEN

13. Hydrogen is passed over hot CuO. The water formed is collected and found to weigh 12 g. What weight of hydrogen reacted with the CuO? What is the loss in weight of the CuO?
14. Which of the following metals will replace tin from a solution of $SnCl_2$: Zn, Cu, Mg, Fe, Cd, Pb, As, Au? Write the equations.
15. Show the electron changes involved in three methods for the preparation of hydrogen.
16. Write the formula for five hydrogen compounds.
17. List the important uses of hydrogen. Are any of these of significance as far as you personally are concerned?
18. A gas is known to be one of the following: Hydrogen, oxygen, nitrogen, carbon dioxide, helium. How can it be identified?
19. Can water serve as an oxidizing agent?
20. Assume that the paper in this book is 90 per cent $(C_6H_{10}O_5)_n$. Calculate the weight of hydrogen in the book.
21. When 1.201 g. of pure carbon was burned and the resulting gas absorbed in soda lime, the latter increased 4.401 g. in weight. What weight of oxygen combined with the 1.201 g. of carbon? What is the equivalent weight of carbon?
22. Complete the following table by calculation or by data already given or calculated in this chapter.

Substance	Density at S.T.P.	Wt. of 1 Mol.	% of C	g. C in 1 Mol
Gas from problem 21	1.96 g. l.			
Methane	0.71 " "		75	
Acetylene	1.16 " "		92	
Cyclopropane	1.88 " "		86	
Butane	2.59 " "		83	
Benzene	3.22 " "		92	

From column 5 of the above table, what is the probable atomic weight of carbon? How many figures can be trusted to be accurate?

23. From the data in problems 21 and 22, what is the formula of the oxide of carbon produced in problem 21? What is the valence of carbon in it? Can any valence be other than an integer? Use the valence and the equivalent weight to calculate the exact atomic weight of carbon. How many figures are reliable?
24. Assuming that substances 2–6 in problem 22 contain only carbon and hydrogen, calculate their formulas.
25. How many gram atoms of hydrogen are there in a mol of it? How many equivalents of hydrogen are there in a gram atom of it? In a mol of it? What is the volume at S.T.P. of one equivalent of hydrogen?
26. When 1.000 g. of aluminum is dissolved in acid, 1259 ml. of hydrogen (calculated to S.T.P.) are liberated. What is the equivalent weight of aluminum?
27. The specific heat of aluminum was found by Tilden in 1902 to average 0.236 cal. per degree between 15° C. and 435° C. In 1910 Schimpff found an average value of 0.217 cal. per degree between 17° C. and 100° C. To

what two values for the atomic weight of aluminum do these specific heats lead? Use each of the atomic weights you have just calculated, together with the equivalent weight from problem 26, to derive the valence of aluminum, and then calculate the precise atomic weight.

REFERENCES

Articles

"Preparation of Pure Hydrogen." Kanolt, C. W., and Cook, J. W.   *Ind. and Eng. Chem.* **17,** 183–187 (1925).

"Laboratory Preparation of Hydrogen." Alexander, L. T., and Byers, H. G.   *J. Chem. Ed.* **9,** 916–920 (1932).

"Hydrogen from Natural Gas." Karzhavin, W. A.   *Ind. and Eng. Chem.* **28,** 1042–1044 (1936).

"Hydrogen from Oil." Weaver, E. R.   *Chem. and Met. Eng.* **28,** 764–768, 939–945, 1072–1075 (1923).

"Production of Hydrogen." Taylor, H. S.   *Chem. and Met. Eng.* **27,** 1263 (1922).

"Hydrogenation of Coal and Oil." Pier, M.   *Ind. and Eng. Chem.* **29,** 140–145 (1937).

"Hydrogen from Water Gas." Claude, G.   *Ind. and Eng. Chem.* **14,** 1118–1119 (1922).

"Hydrides." Durrant, A., *et al.*   *J. Chem. Soc.* 730–743 (1934).

"Heavy Hydrogen." Lewis, G. N., and MacDonald, R. T.   *J. Chem. Physics* **1,** 341–345 (1933).

"Significance of Hydrogen Isotopes." Urey, H. C.   *Ind. and Eng. Chem.* **26,** 803–806 (1934).

"Atomic Weight of Hydrogen." Brescia, F., and Rosenthal, R.   *J. Chem. Ed.* **16,** 494–495 (1939).

"Bulk Production of Hydrogen." Brownlie, D.   *Ind. and Eng. Chem.* **30,** 1139 (1938).

» 13 «

PROPERTIES OF LIQUIDS AND SOLIDS

To emphasize the similarities of some properties of liquids and solids, these two will be discussed in one chapter. The forces of attraction between molecules in the liquid state are of considerable magnitude. This is one great difference between gases and liquids. In the solid state these forces are still greater. Have you ever looked at an automobile spring? Quite small, isn't it? The attractive forces between the atoms which go to make up this valuable piece of metal are extremely large. Even in a liquid the molecules are so close together that there are practically no free paths. (When a mol of water, 18 ml., is converted into the gaseous state it expands to 22,400 ml. The difference is empty space.) Molecules lying at the surface of the liquid are not subjected to attractive forces in all directions as are the molecules within the liquid. This is shown in Fig. 13.1. These unbalanced forces at the surface give rise to a resultant force called the *surface tension*. As a result of this tension the surface of a liquid is in a state of stress, or continuous pull. This causes the liquid to tend to take on a spherical shape; a raindrop is a familiar example. When the volume of liquid is small, the attractive forces are sufficient to have the smallest possible surface of the liquid exposed.

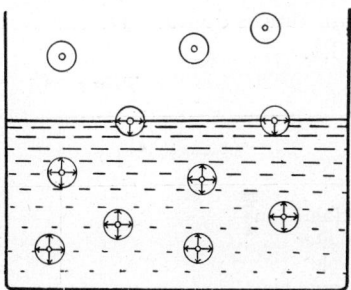

Fig. 13.1. Unbalanced forces at the surface of a liquid give rise to surface tension.

An increase in the temperature of a liquid produces an increase in the kinetic energy of molecules and therefore increases the probability of the molecules moving so far apart that the attractive forces can no longer hold them together. As the surface tension decreases, the surface exposed tends to increase. If the temperature is raised to the critical temperature, the molecules move so far apart at the surface that molecular attraction is overcome. At this temperature there is no surface tension.

Evaporation

Molecules in the liquid state are like molecules in the gaseous state in that they do not all have the same kinetic energy. If a molecule of the liquid has sufficient kinetic energy, when it approaches the surface it will overcome the attractive forces between molecules and escape or *evaporate*. This does not mean that the gas is hotter than the liquid which it leaves behind; these "hot" molecules expend most of their energy in overcoming the attraction of their neighbors as they escape. Each time a molecule of high kinetic energy escapes from the liquid, the mean kinetic energy of the liquid is lowered and the liquid becomes cooler. If the temperature is to remain constant, heat must be added. If you have ever poured some ether on your hand you probably noticed the cooling effect as it evaporated. In driving a car through the desert it is a common practice to moisten a towel with water and hang it in the car window. As the water evaporates, heat is absorbed from the surrounding air which is thus cooled. The heat of vaporization of one gram of water is approximately 540 calories. The cooling effect which could be obtained by vaporizing one bucket of water, provided it could be done efficiently, is greater than that of six buckets of ice which absorb heat by just melting. All substances do not have the same heats of vaporization, as is shown in Table 13.1.

TABLE 13.1. HEAT OF VAPORIZATION, H_v

Substance	Temperature in ° C. at Which H_v Was Determined	H_v in Calories per Gram
Aluminum	1800	1994
Water	100	539.55
Gold	2600	445.7
Ammonia	0	301.6
Alcohol	78.3	204
Acetic acid	18.3	96.8
Sulfur dioxide	0	91.3
Benzene	100	90.6
Carbon disulfide	46.2	84.1
Ether	34.6	83.9
Mercury	357	70.8
Turpentine	156	68.6
Chloroform	61.5	59.0
Carbon dioxide	0	55.0
Carbon tetrachloride	76.7	46.4
Bromine	58.8	44.8

Liquefaction

Liquefaction can be induced either by changing a gas into a liquid—this is the opposite of vaporization—or by changing a solid into a liquid. Molecules in the solid state are believed to be so close together that movement is restricted to oscillations about fixed points of equilibrium. That molecules of a solid do have some freedom of movement can be shown by placing a piece of lead on some gold and leaving the two in contact for some time. If this lead is then sectioned into thin slices and analyzed, it will be found to contain gold. Some diffusion or movement of atoms must have taken place.

When a solid is heated, the kinetic energy imparted to the molecules increases the amplitude of oscillations. Continued heating results in motion sufficient to separate the molecules to such an extent that the solid liquefies. The temperature at which this occurs is the point of fusion. The calories of heat required to change one gram of a substance from the solid to the liquid state at its melting point is the *heat of fusion*. The heat of fusion of ice is approximately 80 calories per gram. This means that 80 calories are required to change one gram of ice at 0° to water at 0°. As you might suspect, solids vary as to heats of fusion. The heats of fusion of several solids are given in Table 13.2.

Table 13.2. Heat of Fusion, H_f

Substance	Temperature in ° C. at Which H_f Was Determined	H_f in Calories per Gram
Mercury	−38.9	2.77
Carbon monoxide	−207	8.0
Methyl alcohol	−98	16.4
Ethyl alcohol	−112	24.9
Benzene	5.5	30.1
Copper	1083	43.2
Iron	1525	48.0
Aluminum	660	70.8
Nickel	1452	73.9
Water	0	79.67
Ammonia	−77.7	83.9
Sodium chloride	804.3	123.5
Sodium fluoride	992.2	186

Specific Heat

The *specific heat* of a substance is the number of calories required to raise the temperature of one gram of it 1° C. under certain specified conditions. The specific heat of liquid water is one calorie. The specific heat of ice is only 0.5 calorie. We have already mentioned the interesting observation made in 1819 by Dulong and Petit that the product obtained by multiplying the specific heat of a solid element by its atomic weight is usually about 6.3. Table 13.3 gives the specific heats of some elements. In a table containing the specific heat data for over two hundred liquid inorganic and organic compounds, the only liquid with a specific heat greater than water was liquid ammonia. At 0° C. its specific heat is 1.098.

TEXTBOOK OF CHEMISTRY

TABLE 13.3. SPECIFIC HEATS OF ELEMENTS, S_h

Element	Temperature in ° C. at Which Determination Was Made	S_h in Calories per Gram
Lead	20	.0306
Gold	18	.0312
Platinum	20	.0324
Mercury	20	.0332
Silver	20	.0558
Copper	20	.0921
Zinc	20	.0925
Iron	20	.107
Carbon	20	.12
Silicon	13.9	.168
Aluminum	20	.214
Hydrogen	−252	.233
Boron	100	.25
Sodium	20	.295
Oxygen	−200	.394
Nitrogen	−200	.474

Vapor Pressure

After molecules leave the surface of a liquid, they are free to move in any direction just as do any other molecules in the gaseous state. Two cases in particular should be considered, namely, those of liquids in open and in closed vessels.

If a liquid is allowed to evaporate from a beaker in the laboratory, the molecules of the vapor[1] leave the immediate vicinity from which they came, and eventually become scattered throughout the atmosphere. In the atmosphere, according to Dalton's Law of Partial Pressures, these molecules exert their own pressure, depending on the number present. As in the case of any other gas, this is the *partial pressure* of the vapor. The partial pressure is not a fixed quantity; it varies from zero to the saturation value at any one temperature, and it varies with temperature as well.

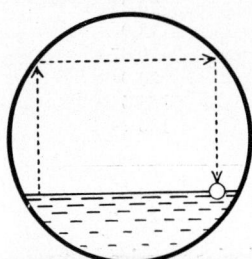

FIG. 13.2. A molecule which escapes from the surface of a liquid travels in straight lines.

If the liquid evaporates into a closed container, Fig. 13.2, the vapor molecules cannot leave the vicinity of the liquid. The attractive forces which hold the liquid molecules in close association may cause the return to the liquid of some of the molecules which originally broke away. This tendency is counterbalanced by the tendency of other molecules to escape. Eventually, a dynamic equilibrium is reached, where just as many molecules are return-

[1] The word "vapor" is synonymous with "gas" but is used when one is thinking of the corresponding liquid or solid at the same time.

PROPERTIES OF LIQUIDS AND SOLIDS

ing to the liquid from the vapor as are leaving the liquid to go into the gaseous state. At this saturation pressure the vapor and liquid will remain indefinitely at equilibrium; hence the pressure of the vapor over a liquid at equilibrium is called the *vapor pressure*.[2] (Likewise the pressure exerted by a vapor when an equilibrium is reached between a solid and its vapor is referred to as the vapor pressure of the solid. The vapor pressure of a solution is defined in like manner.)

As the temperature increases, the molecules in both the liquid and the gaseous states move faster. Eventually, if the temperature is high enough, the vapor pressure will increase until it equals one atmosphere, and this temperature is the boiling point of the liquid. The actual temperature at which a liquid boils depends upon the barometric pressure.

Water boils at a fairly low temperature; ether at a still lower temperature; mercury at a fairly high temperature; therefore, the vapor pressure varies from one liquid to another. The vapor pressures of water, carbon disulfide, and ether at 20° are 17.36, 297.5, and 432.8 mm. respectively, as shown in Fig. 13.3.

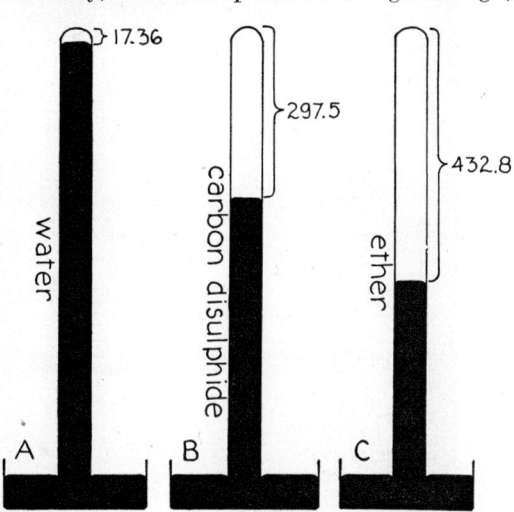

FIG. 13.3. The vapor pressure of water, carbon disulfide, and ether.

The steam engine is based on the principle that molecules in the gaseous state create a pressure which can be used to operate a piston. Other liquids have been used in boilers, and great interest has been developed in the mercury boiler.

The heat of vaporization varies among liquids. Since one gram of water absorbs 540 calories, water is an excellent substance for transferring heat from one place to another and is used in steam heating systems. To condense the gram of water, 540 calories must be liberated. There is one objection to the use of water in heating systems. If the steam is to be carried far and there is much heat loss in transit, some steam will condense where it is undesirable. To overcome this the steam is superheated; but this results in the development of high pressures, a characteristic desirable in the steam boiler but not in a heating unit. A mixture of two organic substances, diphenyl and diphenyl oxide, is non-corrosive and stable at boiler temperatures and is largely used for heat transfer at temperatures from 250° to 350° C.

[2] It is also, curiously, sometimes called the vapor tension or, in the special case of water, the aqueous tension.

Fig. 13.4. Boiler using Dowtherm. (Courtesy, Eclipse Fuel Engineering Co.)

The family kitchen provides other practical illustrations of vapor pressure and evaporation. Have you ever tried to evaporate the water from milk by boiling it until a dry residue remains? If so, you know that you cannot add water to the residue, stir it up, and have a white liquid which tastes like milk. It is unpalatable. Yet you have undoubtedly used evaporated milk. If milk is placed in a flask with a 1-hole stopper and the flask is connected to a vacuum pump, the equilibrium which would normally be set up by the water molecules in the flask is disturbed (Fig. 13.5). Water molecules escape and cannot return. All the water could be evaporated at room temperature

PROPERTIES OF LIQUIDS AND SOLIDS   167

in a short time; but since milk can be heated to about 60° without a change in flavor, both heat and decreased pressure are used commercially. This process is called vacuum evaporation. Less familiar in this country than evaporated milk is milk which has been dried completely (see Fig. 13.6). The need to conserve shipping space during World War II gave a tremendous impetus to the development of vacuum evaporation. Powdered milk, eggs,

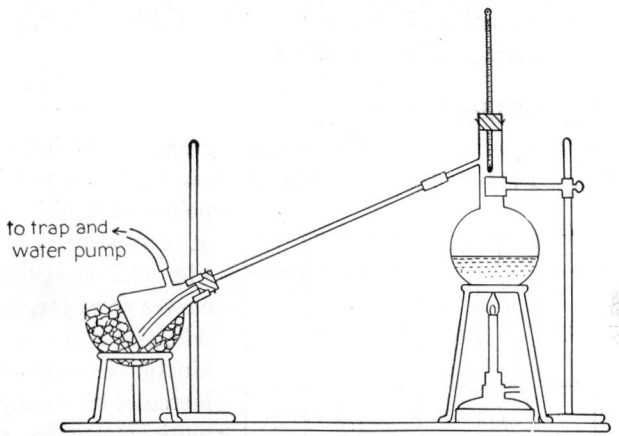

FIG. 13.5.   Vacuum distillation.

FIG. 13.6.   Experimental roller dryer in operation. Note film of dried milk. (Courtesy, Borden Research Laboratory, Syracuse, N. Y.)

and orange juice were almost the only form of these foods available in England. The armies used great quantities of desiccated foods of many kinds. Neither penicillin nor blood plasma could have been shipped overseas in quantity without vacuum evaporation.

At a given temperature the average kinetic energies of molecules of water, ether, carbon disulfide, etc., in the liquid state[3] are *all the same.* Yet their vapor pressures are *different.* This difference must be due to differences in the strength of attraction between molecules. Ether molecules apparently are not strongly attracted to each other.

Boiling Points of Liquids

The boiling point of any liquid is the temperature at which the vapor pressure of the liquid is equal to atmospheric pressure. When possible, boiling points of liquids are measured at atmospheric pressure. In Fig. 13.7 the vapor pressure curves of water, carbon disulfide, and ether are shown. The kinetic energy of molecules increases with temperature and more molecules escape from the surface film of the liquid. If the temperature is raised sufficiently, the vapor pressure increases until it equals atmospheric pressure. Further application of heat causes not an increase in temperature but only a more rapid exit of molecules from the liquid. *Superheating* occurs if sufficient surface is not exposed so that the molecules can escape rapidly. Usually during superheating, large gas bubbles form in the body of the liquid and force the liquid up with them. Mild superheating causes the liquid to "bump"; more drastic superheating results in the liquid being forced from the container. Careless students frequently superheat liquids.

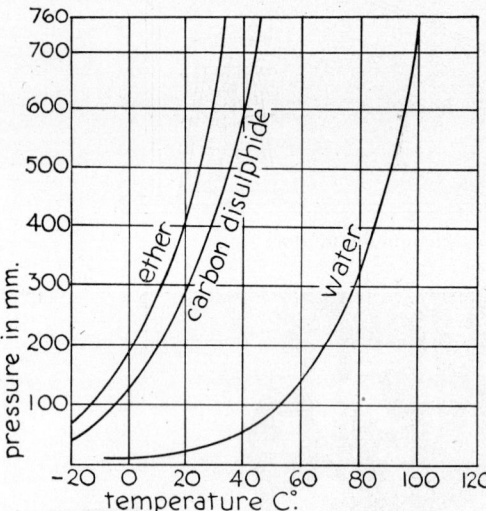

FIG. 13.7. Vapor pressure curves of water, carbon disulfide, and ether.

The boiling point of a liquid depends upon the atmospheric pressure. You have probably heard that at high altitudes potatoes cannot be cooked by boiling. The low atmospheric pressure prevailing at such altitudes causes the water to boil away before the temperature reaches 100° C., and the potatoes remain hard. It is difficult to cook some foods such as tough meat and poultry even at lower altitudes. To shorten the cooking time, steam

[3] This has been shown to be true for molecules of all gases. Review pages 40–41.

pressure cookers are sometimes used. Because the steam cannot escape from this cooker, it increases the pressure downward on the surface of the liquid. In this way more heat can be applied without the water boiling away and thus a higher temperature can be maintained. Besides being used for cooking, steam autoclaves are indispensable in hospitals, public health laboratories, and any other place where sterilization of equipment is required (Fig. 13.8). The higher the temperature, the more easily bacteria are killed.

Vapor Pressure of Solids

The odor of moth balls, crystalline camphor, and iodine, and the disappearance of snow at temperatures below 0° C. prove that molecules of some solids escape; in other words, these substances have appreciable vapor pressures. As with liquids, an increase in temperature increases the vapor pressure. This change is due to the decreased attractive forces between the mol-

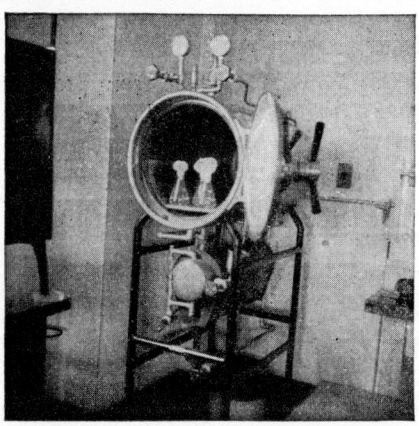

Fig. 13.8. Autoclave used for sterilization.

ecules in the solid state. However, a glass beaker can be heated from 0° to 500° C. and it does not disappear. There are dozens of similar examples of solids which have very low vapor pressures. Sufficient increase in temperature causes a solid substance to either melt or decompose. *The temperature at which the vapor pressure of the solid equals that of the liquid is the melting point*, and at this temperature the orderly arrangement of atoms and molecules in the crystal disappears. At the melting point solid and liquid can remain at equilibrium indefinitely. The melting point of a solid is also the freezing point of the liquid.

Just as it is possible to superheat a liquid it is also possible to supercool one. Unless nuclei for crystal formations are present, crystals will not form. Liquids which have been supercooled can often be crystallized by dropping even invisible specks of dirt into them, but a crystal of the same substance is preferred. As crystallization takes place, the heat of fusion which is *liberated* raises the temperature to the true freezing point of the substance.

Substances Without Definite Melting Points

Glass is an excellent example of a supercooled liquid. It can be cooled several hundred degrees below the liquefaction temperature and still remain an amorphous solid (without form). Materials such as glass which appear to be solid but are non-crystalline as proved by X-ray analysis are called vitreous solids. Another example of a supercooled liquid is tar, which will shatter almost like glass on a cold day, whereas on a hot day it can be poured like a syrup. The best-known method for identifying substances as either vitreous or crystalline solids is by X-rays. Some substances such as sulfur can be obtained in the solid form, either crystalline or amorphous; other similar examples will be mentioned later.

Sublimation

It might be assumed from preceding statements that all solids capable of being obtained also in the gaseous state pass through the liquid state.

$$\text{Solid} \underset{\text{solidify}}{\overset{\text{melt}}{\rightleftarrows}} \text{Liquid} \underset{\text{liquefy}}{\overset{\text{vaporize}}{\rightleftarrows}} \text{Gas}$$

This is not the case. Some solids will vaporize under ordinary pressure without fusing. This process is called *sublimation*. (The interpretation frequently given to the term sublimation is Solid $\longrightarrow$ Gas $\longrightarrow$ Solid.)

If solid iodine is heated in a test tube, it disappears at the bottom and condenses at the top of the tube. No liquid iodine is observed. Iodine can be melted at 114° C. provided it is heated very carefully. Ammonium chloride reacts in a different way, in that the compound decomposes and then recombines.

$$\underline{NH_4Cl} \overset{\Delta}{\longrightarrow} \overline{NH_3} + \overline{HCl} \longrightarrow \underline{NH_4Cl}$$

Solid carbon dioxide ("dry ice") is another substance which sublimes. It melts at $-56.6°$ C. at a pressure of 5.2 atmospheres, and at atmospheric pressure it sublimes at $-78.5°$ C.

QUESTIONS AND PROBLEMS

1. By the Law of Dulong and Petit and the specific heats given in Table 13.3, calculate the atomic weights of all the elements mentioned there. Turn back to the periodic table on page 82 and check the elements for which the result was useless or very poor. Predict an additional similar case, look up the data, and test your prediction.
2. How many calories of heat are required to change 100 g. of ice at $-20°$ to steam at 100°?
3. The home of Professor Smith is 40 ft. $\times$ 30 ft. $\times$ 20 ft. He burns 10 tons of coal each winter. One gram of coal liberates 8000 calories. If his house is filled with ice at 0° C., could the ice be melted with the coal (assuming there is 100 per cent efficiency)?
    If he had a hot-water heating system which held 500 l. of water and the

PROPERTIES OF LIQUIDS AND SOLIDS

water entered the heater at 40° C. and left at 80° C., how many times would the water recirculate during the winter? (Assume that there is 100 per cent efficiency.)

4. In working with liquids, less frequently with solids, we use the idea of specific gravity (which will be abbreviated s.g.). By definition,

$$\text{s.g.} = \frac{\text{weight of any volume of a substance}}{\text{weight of an equal volume of water at the same temperature}}.$$

Specific gravity is a number without units; it is a ratio which tells how many times as heavy as water any given substance is. Thus, since the s.g. of mercury is 13.54, any volume of mercury will weigh 13.54 times as much as the same volume of water. With the metric system it is useful to remember that, for all except the most exact calculations, 1 cc. or 1 ml. of water weighs 1 g. Specific gravity and density thus are practically equal numerically. (This is not the case with the English system of weights and measures, which is usually used by engineers.) One ml. of mercury then weighs 13.54 g. What is the weight of 10 ml. of concentrated sulfuric acid, s.g. 1.82?

5. Find the weight of 400 ml. of pure water; of sea water, s.g. 1.026; of sulfuric acid, s.g. 1.82; of alcohol, s.g. 0.79; of glycerine, s.g. 1.26.

6. Find the volume of 20 g. of nitric acid, s.g. 1.20; of 30 g. of sulfuric acid; of 16 g. of alcohol.

7. Calculate the weight of cubes of the following metals measuring 3 cm. on a side: Aluminum, s.g. 2.7; iron, s.g. 7.86; copper, s.g. 8.92; silver, s.g. 10.5; gold, s.g. 19.3; platinum, s.g. 21.45.

8. Suppose that your chemistry professor offered you free a sphere of solid gold, 8 in. in diameter, on condition that you carry it to your dormitory. Could you do it? One cu. ft. of water weighs 62.4 lb. What would similar spheres of silver and platinum weigh?

» 14 «

SOLUTIONS

A solution is a homogeneous mixture of two or more substances. The components are referred to as the *solvent* and the *solute*. Theoretically, there are nine kinds of solutions:

1. Solids in liquids
2. Solids in solids
3. Solids in gases
4. Liquids in liquids
5. Liquids in solids
6. Liquids in gases
7. Gases in liquids
8. Gases in solids
9. Gases in gases

You may have thought of a solution as being necessarily a liquid. The chemist finds it to his advantage to use the term solution in a broader sense, to distinguish between substances which have reacted with each other on mixing, and those which have merely mixed perfectly. Air, for example, is a solution; it contains not only oxygen and nitrogen, but many other substances in varying amounts. Any substance that has a smell has dissolved in air to some extent. The fundamental criteria prove that air is a solution, not a compound. First, its composition is variable. Second, the components show their own individual properties, diluted, but the same qualitatively as in the pure state.

Solutions in the gaseous state are of no particular interest as such, because each gas behaves just as though it were the only gas present in the space. Solid solutions are of great interest but involve such complexities that their study is usually reserved for advanced courses. The remainder of this chapter therefore will deal only with liquid solutions.

Liquid Solvents

Any substance in the liquid state can be considered as a solvent. It is only within recent years that the properties of liquid solvents other than water have been studied in any detail, and these investigations are still in their infancy. How many *pure substances* can you list that you have seen in the liquid state? No doubt you will begin the list with water; but you have certainly seen many others. It would take many pages to list all the substances which can be liquefied, and all of these would be included: water; fused salts; molten metals; liquefied gases such as oxygen, nitrogen, helium, ammonia (NH_3), etc.; organic compounds such as alcohol, carbon disulfide, benzene, ether, acetone, and thousands of others. Chemists used to refer to water as the universal solvent because it would dissolve more compounds than any other solvent. An organic compound acetamide, CH_3CONH_2, which melts at about 80° C. has been found to be an excellent solvent, for it will dissolve many more substances than water. Imagine having dozens of tubes of melted acetamide and adding to them some of every chemical on the side shelf and finding that only about one out of every hundred is insoluble. Laboratory work soon proves that water is a poor solvent for sulfur, fats, and petroleum. Carbon disulfide will dissolve sulfur. Melted salts are usually good solvents for other salts.

Polar and Non-polar Solvents

Water and benzene are both liquids, but the latter does not dissolve salt. At first this was explained on the basis of the mutual attraction of two similar substances, but this is really no explanation. The explanation must involve the characteristics of the molecules of the solvent. An electrovalent compound such as solid NaCl consists of charged particles of Na^+ and Cl^- arranged in definite fixed positions in the crystal lattice. The attractive forces between these ions must be responsible for the crystal holding its shape. If these forces did not exist, the crystal would be expected to crumble to dust, and it does so when it is put in water. Therefore water must be capable of altering these forces, whereas the liquid benzene is not.

The reason why water can dissolve ionic crystals can be discovered from a study of its structure. In complete confirmation of theoretical predictions, it has been proved experimentally that the lines joining the oxygen nucleus with the protons make practically a right angle with each other. The water molecule is therefore not spherically symmetrical. At any considerable distance it is of course electrically neutral, but at close range the left side, as shown here, is found to consist of a cloud of electrons. On the right side

$$\left[- \ddot{\underset{..}{O}} \begin{matrix} H \\ H \end{matrix} + \right]$$

are the two positively charged protons. The electrons which they share with the oxygen are chiefly the property of the latter, and spend only a small part of their time in the region to the right in the diagram. A molecule one end of which is positive and one end negative is called an electrical dipole, or is said to be *polar*. A substance made up of polar molecules is called a polar substance. The electrical attractive forces between these molecules are much stronger than simple van der Waals forces. (Salts, whose molecules are two kinds of oppositely charged ions, are also considered polar substances.)

Two oppositely charged objects (e.g., the plates of a condenser or a cation and an anion) attract each other with a force proportional to the product of their charges divided by the square of the distance between them. This attractive force is at the maximum value when the space between the charged objects is a vacuum. Any substance whatever that is placed between the objects lessens the force because the molecules are distorted; the electron clouds shift toward the positive charge and the atomic nuclei toward the negative one, neutralizing both to some extent. The *dielectric constant* of a substance is defined as the ratio of the attractive force *in vacuo* to that when the given substance is interposed between the charged objects. Thus the statement that the dielectric constant of benzene is 2.28 means that the force between two charged objects is 2.28 times as great *in vacuo* as it is when they are separated by benzene. This is a typical value for the dielectric constant of an ordinary liquid, but polar liquids give far higher values. Polar liquids cut down the attractive force between charged objects much more effectively than ordinary liquids because, instead of merely distorting slightly, the whole molecule turns its positive end toward the negative charge and its negative end toward the positive charge. Water is an extreme case; its dielectric constant is 81, far higher than that of any other *common* liquid.

When water comes in contact with a salt its molecules are pulled in between the surface ions of the latter, the positive ion pulling on the negative end and the negative ion on the positive end of the water molecule. The water between them lessens the attraction of the ions for each other in accordance with the principle described in the preceding paragraph, and this allows more water to work its way in. Presently the ions are surrounded as shown in Fig. 14.1, and drift away into the solution. If either the liquid or the solid were non-polar no solution would take place. If *both* were non-polar, molecules of the solid would be held together by no strong forces and would offer no strong resistance to molecules of the liquid to prevent their working their way into it and vice versa; solution would again be possible.

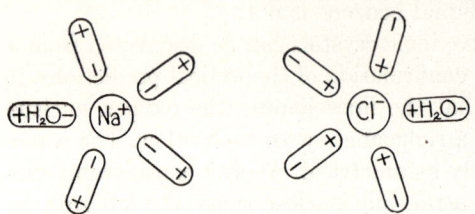

FIG. 14.1. Water dipoles separate sodium and chloride ions. The positive sodium ion attracts the negative end of the dipolar H₂O molecule. The chloride ion is surrounded by the positive end of the dipolar H₂O molecule.

Saturated Solutions

The process of solution is similar to evaporation in that it involves the separation of the substance into its individual molecules or ions. A further point of similarity is the fact that it is reversible. Ions already dissolved may

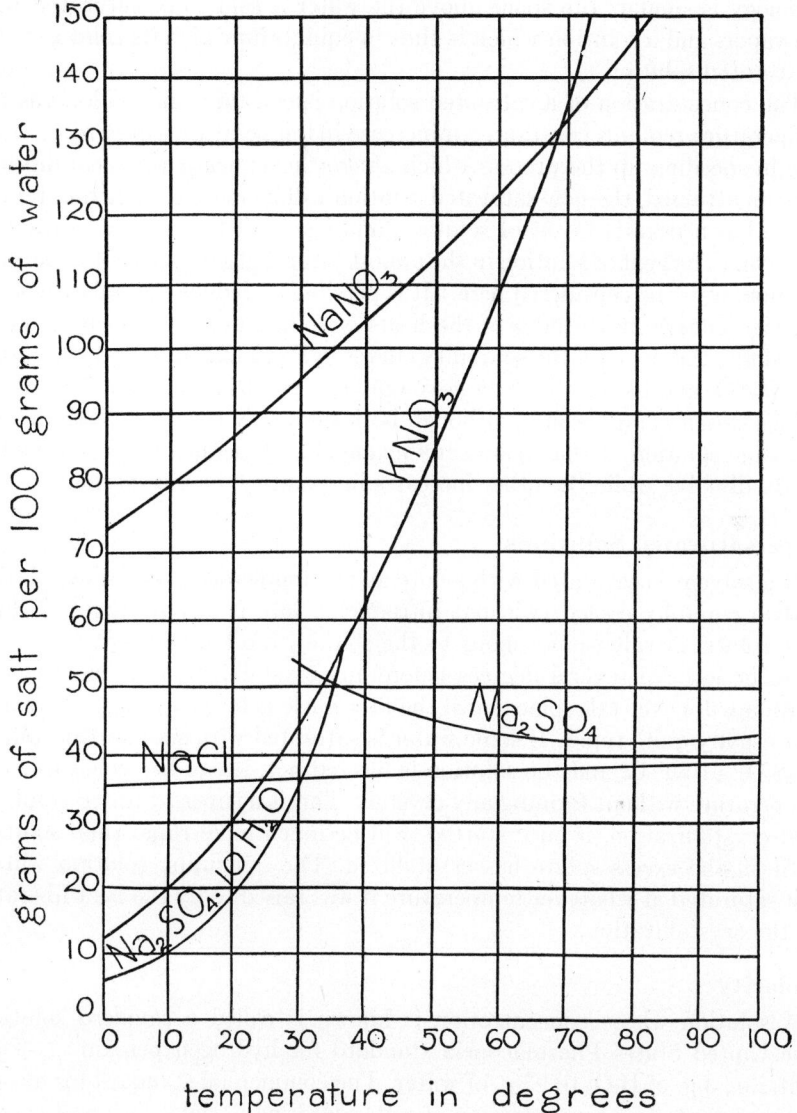

Fig. 14.2. Solubility curves.

strike the crystal and again become a part of it. They will do so at an increasing rate as the concentration of the solution increases. The concentration must eventually rise to such a value that the rate of crystallization equals the rate of solution. Thereafter it will remain constant, although both processes continue at full speed. The situation is like that in a closed container in which water has evaporated until its vapor pressure has been attained. Even the terminology is similar; the space above the water is said to be saturated with the vapor, and a solution which is thus in equilibrium with its solid is called a saturated solution.

The concentration of a saturated solution is constant only as long as the temperature remains constant. An increase in temperature will be more effective in speeding up the process which *absorbs* heat; hence when equilibrium is again attained, the new saturated solution will be more concentrated if the solute has a negative heat of solution, and less so if the heat of solution is positive. (The heat of solution in the almost saturated solution, not in a dilute solution, must be considered here.) It is possible to deduce not only the signs but the relative magnitudes of the heats of solution of the various salts by examining the slopes of the solubility curves in Fig. 14.2. Note that the curves for Na_2SO_4 and its decahydrate have only one point in common. It is called the *transition point* because, although both salts may be in equilibrium with the same solution at that point, any change in temperature will cause all of one to dissolve while the other increases in quantity, or vice versa.

Supersaturated Solutions

If a solvent is saturated with solute at one temperature and the solution is then carefully cooled (without introducing into it any particles of dust, dirt, solute, or salt isomorphous to the solute), the temperature can sometimes be lowered several degrees before any crystallization occurs. Crystallization will never take place until the first nucleus for it appears; thereafter it is usually quite rapid. If some water is saturated with sodium thiosulfate, $Na_2S_2O_3$, at 50° C. and the solution is filtered hot, it can be cooled to room temperature without forming any crystals. This is a supersaturated solution; in it crystallization, if once started, will be much more rapid than solution until all the excess solute has crystallized. The remaining solution will be just saturated at whatever temperature it was raised to by the heat liberated by the crystallization.

Molarity

A solution whose concentration is known is called a *standard* solution. The United States Pharmacopeia standard for hydrogen peroxide is 3 per cent, i.e., 3 g. of H_2O_2 to 97 g. of water. The commercial standard for alcohol is 95 per cent. The concentration of a standard industrial solution of caustic soda is 6.364 lb. per gallon. A pound of salt in a barrel of water would also be a standard solution. All these concentrations are expressed in units appropriate to the purpose for which they are designed; none of them are appropriate for expressing the amount of chemical reaction of which a given amount of the solution is capable, or comparing solutions of two different chemicals in this respect.

Chemical reactions do not take place gram for gram. The weight of magnesium which will react with a given quantity of hydrochloric acid is entirely different from the weight of zinc which will react with the same quantity of acid. Chemical reactions occur a *molecule* at a time; so the mol, not the gram, is the appropriate unit of quantity to use in stating the amount of a chemical.

In expressing concentrations the word "per" is always used. "Per" can be translated into mathematical terms by means of the division sign, ÷, so it is natural to find that the mathematical definition of concentration indicates that a division is performed:

$$\text{Concentration} = \frac{\text{Quantity}}{\text{Volume}}$$

If the quantity of material is expressed in mols and the volume of the solution in liters, the concentration is given the special name *molarity*. A solution containing 6 mols of solute per liter is said to be 6 molar, abbreviated as 6 M in writing.

The molarity of a solution of sodium chloride containing 100 g. of salt per 400 ml. of solution can be obtained as follows: Transform the given quantities to the units specified in the definition of molarity. To turn grams into mols, divide by the molecular weight (or formula weight):

$$100 \text{ g. NaCl} \div 58.5 \text{ g./mol} = 1.71 \text{ mols}$$

To turn milliliters into liters, point off three places to the left: 400 ml. = 0.400 l. Then substitute in the mathematical definition:

$$\text{Molarity} = \frac{1.71 \text{ mols}}{0.400 \text{ l.}} = 4.27$$

the solution is 4.27 M.

Chemists buy many solutions whose composition is specified in terms of specific gravity rather than concentration. This is because it is much easier to test the specific gravity with a hydrometer (this is what a filling station attendant does when he checks a battery) than to make a chemical analysis. When the only materials present are water and the desired chemical, it may do just as well. All handbooks of chemistry and physics contain tables giving the correspondence between specific gravity and concentration. Let us see how such a value can be determined in a specific case.

Suppose that a sample of a pure sulfuric acid solution has a specific gravity at 60° F. of 1.813. When analyzed chemically, it is found to contain 88.7 per cent H_2SO_4. One l. of this solution weighs 1813 g. and contains 1813 × 0.887 = 1609 g. of H_2SO_4, which is 1609 ÷ 98.08 = 16.4 mols. The solution is 16.4 M.

What volume of this concentrated sulfuric acid will be needed to make 2.5 l. of 3 M solution? Solving the definition of molarity for mols, we get

$$\text{mols} = \text{liters} \times \text{M}$$

which shows that for a given number of mols of solute, the molarity and the volume of the solution are inversely proportional to each other. When a solution is diluted, the number of mols of solute is unchanged, so we can find the volume at one concentration from that at the other by multiplying the latter by the inverse ratio of the concentrations.

$$\text{Vol. of conc. acid} = 2.5 \text{ l.} \times \frac{3 \text{ M}}{16.4 \text{ M}} = 0.458 \text{ l.}$$

It is easier and there is less chance of error to decide which way to write the ratio by common sense rather than by considering whether the ratio is direct or inverse. Obviously the volume of the concentrated acid will be less than that of the solution formed by diluting it; therefore the fraction must be written with the smaller number on top.

Normality

Another distinctively chemical unit of quantity is the equivalent (see page 152). In chemical reactions molar ratios may have any small whole-number value, but the ratio between equivalents is always 1:1. Hence it is sometimes convenient to express concentrations in terms of equivalents per liter. In this case the concentration is given the special name *normality*. It is defined mathematically by:

$$\text{Normality} = \frac{\text{No. of equivalents}}{\text{No. of liters}}$$

At the same time the definition of equivalent must be extended for that on page 152 applied only to elements. In the case of ions, the extension is easy. For elements,

$$\text{Equivalent weight} = \frac{\text{Atomic weight}}{\text{Valence}}$$

so for ions,

$$\text{Equivalent weight} = \frac{\text{Molecular weight}}{\text{Valence}}$$

For neutral molecules which have no valence, we divide by the number of protons which a molecule of the substance can lose to a base or remove from an acid. A mol of H_2SO_4 is thus two equivalents of it. If a sulfuric acid solution has a concentration of 0.75 M, it is also 1.5 N.

If the molar or normal concentration of a solution is 1, no numeral is written in front of the M or N unless the intention is to indicate the degree of accuracy of the standardization by the number of zeros. Thus M HCl means that the acid is 1 molar to an unspecified degree of approximation, whereas 1.000 M HCl means that the true concentration is probably nearer that value than to 0.999 M or 1.001 M.

SOLUTIONS

The expression of concentrations in terms of normality is largely restricted to solutions of strong acids and bases; this subject will be discussed further at a later point. Concentration can also be expressed in terms of *molality* (see page 186).

SOLUTIONS OF GASES IN LIQUIDS

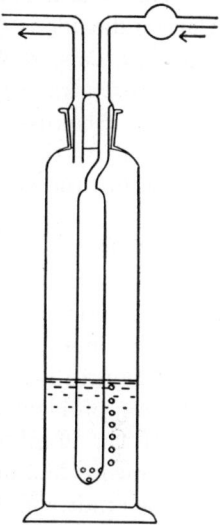

FIG. 14.3. Gas-washing bottle.

If a gas is bubbled through a liquid as shown in Fig. 14.3, some of the gas may dissolve in the liquid and form a solution of gas in liquid, the liquid being considered the solvent and the gas the solute. Suppose that we have ten sets of apparatus similar to that in Fig. 14.3, and that different gases are bubbled through water at 0° C., until the water in each container is saturated with the particular gas. If a known volume of the water from each container is then heated until all the gas is liberated, and a suitable apparatus is available for catching the gas, the volume of gas dissolved can be measured. The experiment can be repeated at different temperatures and the volume of gas soluble per liter of water determined at each temperature. A study of several gases will show that some are only slightly soluble in water, others moderately soluble, and still others very soluble. The solubility of ten common gases is given in Table 14.1.

TABLE 14.1. SOLUBILITY OF GASES IN WATER
(Volume of gas dissolved in 1 l. of water at 20° C.)

A Few Hundredths of a Liter	A Few Liters	Tens or Hundreds of Liters
Carbon monoxide, CO Hydrogen, H_2 Oxygen, O_2 Nitrogen, N_2	Hydrogen sulfide, H_2S Chlorine, Cl_2 Carbon dioxide, CO_2	Hydrogen chloride, HCl Ammonia, NH_3 Sulfur dioxide, SO_2

The solubility of any gas decreases as the temperature rises and it becomes zero at the boiling point.

Henry's Law

You may have noticed that in Table 14.1 the pressure of the gas was not specified. For the gases in the first two columns the pressure makes no difference as long as the solubility is expressed in terms of the *volume* of gas dissolved. This experimental fact is the foundation of Henry's Law, which states that *the weight of a gas dissolved is proportional to the pressure*. The relation between these two statements is given by the gas law statement that the weight of gas present in a given volume of it is proportional to the pressure. Henry's Law does not apply to the very soluble gases.

Henry's Law is applied practically in the carbonated beverage industry. Carbon dioxide is dissolved under a pressure of about 5 atm. and the bottle is tightly capped. When the cap is removed the pressure above the liquid drops to 1 atm. and the CO_2 begins to escape from the now supersaturated solution. Shaking speeds up this process. The froth on ice cream sodas is produced by the CO_2 which escapes as the stream of carbonated water is driven into the beverage under high pressure.

Solubility of Mixed Gases

Dalton's Law of Partial Pressures states that each gas in a mixture exerts the same pressure that it would exert if the others were not there. It follows from this and from Henry's Law that each gas will dissolve in a mixture in proportion to its partial pressure and its own characteristic solubility. The following problem will illustrate these principles:

At 0° C., 49 ml. of oxygen will dissolve in 1 l. of water, and at the same temperature 23.5 ml. of nitrogen will dissolve in this amount of water. What volume of air will dissolve in 1 l. of water at 0° C.? The pressure due to the oxygen in air is 0.2 atm. (air is about 20 per cent O_2) and the pressure due to the nitrogen is 0.8 atm.

$$0.2 \times 49 \text{ ml. oxygen} = 9.8 \text{ ml. of oxygen}$$
$$0.8 \times 23.5 \text{ ml. nitrogen} = 18.8 \text{ ml. of nitrogen}$$
$$\text{Total ml. of } O_2 + N_2 \text{ per liter} = 28.6 \text{ ml. of air}$$

If 1 l. of water saturated with air is boiled and the gases which escape are cooled and measured, the volume will be 28.6 ml., of which $\frac{9.8}{28.6}$ or 34 per cent by volume will be oxygen. The gaseous atmosphere in which we live is one part oxygen to four parts nitrogen, whereas the air in water in which fish live contains one part of oxygen to two parts of nitrogen. Human blood is saturated with nitrogen, and when the pressure is suddenly decreased (as when a diver ascends to the surface too rapidly or a pilot climbs to high altitudes at the maximum rate) bubbles of it are released in the bloodstream, causing cramps ("the bends"), paralysis, and sometimes death. This can be avoided by means of an artificial atmosphere in which the inert diluent gas is less soluble than nitrogen. Helium, the least soluble of all the gases, is used with great success for this purpose.

Very Soluble Gases

For water to dissolve more than a few per cent of its own volume of a gas is an indication that chemical reaction has taken place. In the case of the very soluble gases the large evolution of heat makes this obvious. Proof that some chemical reaction has taken place even with the moderately soluble gases will be given in the chapter on acids and also under the respective gases. To the extent that water is removed by chemical reaction and altered by becoming a solution of the reaction product, it is unreasonable to expect Henry's Law to be obeyed. With ammonia, for example, by the time the solution is saturated, approximately half the original water has reacted and the remainder is a concentrated solution of ammonium hydroxide, NH_4OH.

$$NH_3 + H_2O \rightleftarrows NH_4OH$$

All these reactions are reversible; all the reaction products will decompose as the original gas is driven off by heat.

Solutions of Liquids in Liquids

The chemist is familiar with hundreds of pure liquids. You could probably make quite an impressive list from your own experience. Water, alcohol, glycerin, carbon disulfide, benzene, carbon tetrachloride, chloroform, and liquid elements such as mercury and bromine would surely be included. Gasoline and kerosene are liquids, but they are not pure compounds. Sulfuric, acetic, phosphoric, and nitric acids can be obtained in the pure state without extra water and under these conditions can be considered as pure liquid compounds. When absolutely pure, these acids have the following specific gravities: H_2SO_4, 1.8305; $HC_2H_3O_2$, 1.0498; HNO_3, 1.5129; H_3PO_4, 1.870. H_2SO_4, $HC_2H_3O_2$, and H_3PO_4 at the specific gravities just listed are all solids at 10° C. These four common acids and alcohol and glycerine are among the pure liquids which are *miscible* with water. The solution might be 0.01 of 1 per cent H_2O and 99.99 per cent H_2SO_4, or 99.99 per cent H_2O and 0.01 of 1 per cent H_2SO_4, or any other combination desired. It would be impossible to get such ratios of solute and solvent with water and mercury, gasoline, or carbon disulfide, because mercury, gasoline, and carbon disulfide are for practical purposes insoluble in water; they are said to be *immiscible* with it.

In between miscible and immiscible pairs of liquids there are all degrees of partial solubility. Examples of liquids having appreciable but limited solubility in water are ether, phenol (carbolic acid), and bromine. The greater the degree of similarity (chemical structure, boiling point, dielectric constant, etc.) between two liquids the greater their mutual solubility may be expected to be. Although this subject is very complex, it may be useful to remember two simple constitutional rules for comparing other liquids to water: (1) The grouping $H:\overset{..}{O}:-$ in any molecule is a strong point of resemblance to water. (2) Carbon atoms not attached to oxygen make a molecule dissimilar to water.

Many liquid-liquid solutions occur in nature (e.g., petroleum) or are produced in fermentations or synthetic chemical operations; they must be separated into their constituents in order to be properly utilized. This is usually effected by *fractional distillation*, a process which takes advantage of the different rates of evaporation and condensation. Fig. 14.4 shows a laboratory distillation setup, and Fig. 14.5 an elaborate commercial one. Great industries are built about distillation processes and whole books have been written about them. The principles are discussed in courses on physical chemistry.

Solutions of Solids in Liquids

Solutions of solids in liquids is so broad a subject that only a portion of it can be considered here. This discussion will be largely limited to solutions of salts in water, which are of particular importance in inorganic chemistry.

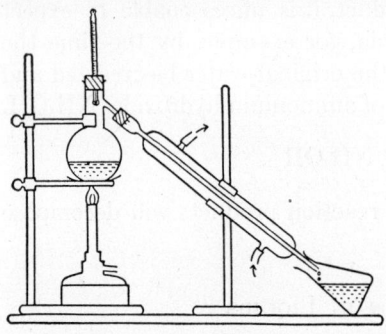

Fig. 14.4. Distillation.

When a salt dissolves in water two things occur: Ions of the salt *leave* the crystal and they *join* the water. As stated on page 174, the separation of the ions from the crystal is essentially the same process as evaporation and therefore uses up energy. The required energy may be obtained from the kinetic energy of neighboring molecules; in this case the temperature will fall, just as it does when a liquid evaporates from your skin. But solution does not necessarily proceed with the absorption of heat, for the second process *produces* energy. The absorption of ions by the water produces energy because of the attraction that exists between any ion and the oppositely charged end of each water molecule. The amount of energy so produced may be less than, equal to, or more than that needed to separate the ions from the crystal. Correspondingly, when a salt dissolves in water the temperature may fall, remain the same, or rise; the salt is said to have a negative, zero, or positive *heat of solution*, respectively.

The *hydration* of ions, to which reference was made in the preceding paragraph, is a phenomenon which may range from the mere turning of water molecules so as to point the proper pole toward an adjacent ion, to a state in which certain water molecules are more or less permanently combined with each ion. In the latter case, which occurs when the ion has a high enough electrical or magnetic field strength on its surface, actual covalent bonds may be formed. Hydration may thus be either a physical or a chemical phenomenon, and it includes border-line cases which may be considered either way. An interesting experiment on the hydration of ions may be performed by dropping common salt into a carbonated beverage. As the ions hydrate themselves they reduce the amount of water available to hold the carbon dioxide in solution, and consequently there is an immediate evolution of bubbles of CO_2.

When crystallization takes place from a solution containing strongly hydrated ions, the ions may take their water of hydration with them into the crystal. The resulting crystalline hydrate is definitely a different substance from the anhydrous salt and may have a negative heat of solution whereas that of the other is positive. Water may also enter the crystal independently. Thus in "green vitriol," ferrous sulfate hexahydrate, all six water

FIG. 14.5. Distillation equipment for the production of ethyl alcohol in the plant at Peoria, Illinois. (Courtesy, Commercial Solvents Corporation.)

molecules are attached to the ferrous ion, but in "blue vitriol," copper sulfate pentahydrate, only four of the water molecules are attached to the copper ion. For many hydrated crystals detailed information is not available, so chemical formulas are usually noncommittal. Thus the formula of the iron salt is written $FeSO_4 \cdot 6H_2O$, and that of the copper salt $CuSO_4 \cdot 5H_2O$; the dot merely states that the water is part of the crystal.

Effect of Solutes upon the Vapor Pressure of Solvents

Evaporation from a liquid takes place when one of the molecules on its surface acquires an upward velocity sufficiently great to enable it to escape.

184 TEXTBOOK OF CHEMISTRY

If a mol of any solute is dissolved in 99 mols of water, 99 out of every hundred molecules will be water molecules and 1 will not. If any given molecule on the surface of the solution receives an upward blow that will enable a water molecule to evaporate, 99 times out of a hundred the molecule will *be* a water molecule and will evaporate; but the hundredth time it will not be a water molecule and whether it *evaporates* or not will have nothing to do with the vapor pressure of *water*. In such a solution the rate of evaporation of water is 99 per cent of that of pure water. Accordingly the vapor pressure of the water will be 99 per cent of the vapor pressure of pure water. Since evaporation is entirely a matter of energy, the weight of the dissolved molecule is of no importance. It can even be an ion; the result will be the same.

Raoult's Law

In 1881 Raoult proved experimentally that many properties of solutions depend upon the number of mols of solute added to a solvent. Raoult's Law may be stated: *Any property of a substance in a solution is shown to an extent proportional to the mol fraction of that substance in the solution.* The fraction of the molecules which are of a given kind is called the *mol fraction* of the corresponding substance. In the example just given, the mol fraction of water in the solution is 0.99, that of the solute 0.01. Applying Raoult's Law to the solute, we can predict that the *lowering* of the vapor pressure of the solution will be twice as great in a solution containing 2 mols of solute to 98 of water as it is in this case.

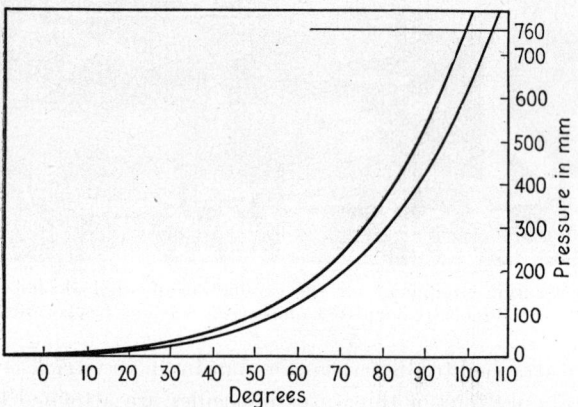

Fig. 14.6. Vapor pressure curves of water and a solution.

Freezing and Boiling Points and Vapor Pressure

The boiling and freezing points of a liquid have already been defined in terms of vapor pressure. The freezing point is the temperature at which the solid and the liquid have the same vapor pressure. The standard boiling point is the temperature at which the vapor pressure is 760 mm. Since the

SOLUTIONS

vapor pressure of a solution is lower than that of pure water (and since it is pure ice that freezes out of a solution), the boiling and freezing points of solutions differ from those of pure water.

The boiling point of the solution will be higher than that of pure water. The reason for this can be seen in Fig. 14.6. The upper curve gives the vapor pressure of pure water, the lower that of a solution in which the mol fraction of the water is 0.80. At 100° C. the vapor pressure of the solution is only 0.80 × 760 mm. = 608 mm.; the temperature must be raised 6° higher to bring the vapor pressure up to 760 mm. so that the solution can boil.

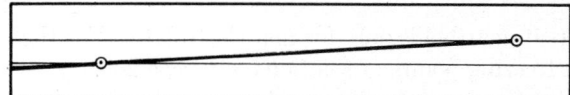

FIG. 14.7. Vapor pressures of ice, water, and solution.

The situation in regard to the freezing point cannot be shown in Fig. 14.6 because the scale is so small that the lines for water and the solution are indistinguishable from each other below about 20° C. A highly magnified section of the diagram is shown in Fig. 14.7. The upper and lower lines, nearly parallel over this 2-degree range of temperature, are again the vapor pressure curves for pure water and a solution. The solution in this case contains 1 mol of solute to 1000 g. (= 1000 ÷ 18.02 = 55.5 mols) of water; the mol fraction of water is 55.5 ÷ 56.5, or 0.982. The diagonal line in the figure shows the vapor pressure of ice, which drops more rapidly than does that of supercooled water as the temperature is lowered. The encircled point at the right is the freezing point of pure water; it has the coordinates 4.57 mm. and 0° C. The encircled point at the left is the freezing point of the solution, at −1.86° C. At this temperature ice and the solution have a vapor pressure of 3.94 mm., and that of supercooled water is 4.01 mm.

Molecular Weight Determination

The measurement of freezing-point depressions (and, less conveniently, of boiling-point elevations) gives us a way of determining molecular weights which is very important because it can be used with substances which cannot be turned into a gas. The fact that the upper and lower curves in Fig. 14.7 are so nearly parallel and that all three are so nearly straight makes Raoult's Law apply practically as accurately to freezing-point depressions as it does to vapor pressure lowerings, in dilute solution. In applying this law it is necessary to know the amounts of both the solute and the solvent, but the amount of water in a solution of a given molarity can be calculated only if the density of the solution is known. Therefore, in molecular weight determinations we weigh both the solute and the water and express the concentrations in terms of *molality* instead of molarity. A 1-molal solution is one containing 1 mol of solute per thousand grams of water. Mathematically,

$$\text{Molality} = \frac{\text{Grams of solute per 1000 g. of water}}{\text{Gram-mol. wt. of solute}}$$

Experiments have shown that the freezing point of a 1-molal solution is $-1.86°$ C. This lowering of the freezing point is called the molal freezing-point depression. The freezing-point depressions in more dilute solutions are proportionally smaller. In a 0.1-molal solution the freezing point is $-0.186°$ C.; therefore, mathematically

$$\text{Freezing point of solution} = (\text{molality})(-1.86° \text{ C.})$$

This simple treatment holds only for non-electrolytes. For the effect of electrolytes upon freezing points of solutions, see page 208.

Let us try a sample molecular weight determination. A compound[1] has been shown by analysis to have the empirical formula CH_3ON. In order to determine whether its true molecular formula is this or some multiple of it, we need to know the molecular weight. When 1.15 g. of the substance is added to 20 g. of water and dissolved, the new freezing point is found to be 1.19° lower than that of pure water.

From the above discussion,

$$\text{Molality} = \frac{\text{grams of solute in 1000 g. of water}}{\text{gram-mol. wt. of solute}} = \frac{\text{freezing point of solution}}{-1.86° \text{ C.}}$$

therefore,

$$\text{Gram-molecular weight of solute} = \frac{(\text{Grams of solute in 1000 g. of water})(-1.86° \text{ C.})}{\text{Freezing point of solution}}$$

Since there are 1.15 g. of solute in 20 g. of water, there are $\left(\frac{1.15}{20}\right) 1000 =$ 57.5 g. of solute in 1000 g. of water. By substitution in the above we get:

$$\text{Gram-mol. wt.} = \frac{(57.5)(-1.86)}{-1.19} = 89.9 \text{ g.}$$

Since the sum of the gram-atomic weights for CH_3ON is $12+3+16+14 = 45$, it is obvious that the formula should be $C_2H_6O_2N_2$, the sum of whose gram-atomic weights is 90 which agrees with the experimental value calculated above.

The molecular weights of non-volatile solutes can be equally well determined by means of the boiling-point elevation. The molal boiling-point elevation for water is 0.52° C. We are not limited to water-soluble substances, for the principles that have been discussed here apply to all solutions. The molal freezing- and boiling-point constants are naturally different for each solvent. They depend upon the heats of fusion and of vaporization.

[1] Methylolurea.

SOLUTIONS

Osmosis

Cell walls and other membranes frequently permit the passage of water at a rate proportional to its mol fraction in a solution, but do not permit the passage of molecules of the solute. They are therefore said to be semi-per-

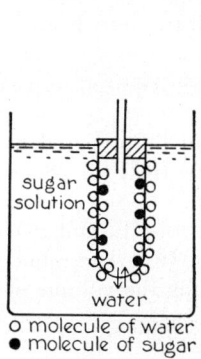

o molecule of water
● molecule of sugar

FIG. 14.8. Uneven rates of diffusion through a membrane.

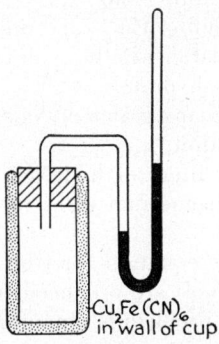

FIG. 14.9. Porous cup impregnated with $Cu_2Fe(CN)_6$ is used to measure osmotic pressure.

meable. *The net flow due to unequal rates of diffusion of a liquid through a semi-permeable membrane is called osmosis* (Fig. 14.8). Osmosis proceeds in such a direction as to dilute the more concentrated solution; and if this is in a closed container, it may produce high pressure (Fig. 14.9). Osmosis is of great physiological importance.

QUESTIONS AND PROBLEMS

1. At 0° C., water dissolves 2.15 per cent of its own volume of hydrogen. How many grams of hydrogen will dissolve in 10 l. of water at that temperature when the pressure is 2 atm.?
2. What volume of hydrogen at S.T.P. is liberated by the reaction between excess zinc and 100 ml. of concentrated HCl solution, s.g. 1.18? This is the standard commercial concentration; the solution is 36 per cent HCl.
3. Calculate the molarity of the following solutions from the data given: phosphoric acid, s.g. 1.526, 70 per cent H_3PO_4; sodium hydroxide, s.g. 1.525, 50 per cent NaOH; magnesium chloride, s.g. 1.154, 37 per cent $MgCl_2 \cdot 6 H_2O$; "battery acid," s.g. 1.250, $\frac{1}{3} H_2SO_4$.
4. A solution of table salt which is saturated at 20° C. contains 26 per cent NaCl and is 5.326 M. What is its specific gravity?
5. What is the molality of a solution made by dissolving 1.00 g. of urea, $CO(NH_2)_2$, in 23.0 g. of water? What is its freezing point?

6. What is the molarity of a nitric acid solution which contains 12.6 g. of solute in 50 ml. of solution? Of a sodium hydroxide solution containing 2 g. of NaOH in 20 ml. of solution?
7. a. How many grams of copper sulfate are needed to prepare 1 liter of 1 M $CuSO_4$? Two bottles of the solid are available; one contains white $CuSO_4$, the other blue $CuSO_4 \cdot 5\ H_2O$. One formula weight of either contains one mol of Cu^{++} and one of SO_4^{--}; hence the same solution is produced no matter whether you take 159.6 g. of the anhydrous salt or 249.7 g. of the pentahydrate.

   b. How many grams of $Na_2SO_4 \cdot 10\ H_2O$ are required to make 250 ml. of a M/2 solution?
8. How many liters of hydrogen at S.T.P. can be prepared by reacting an excess of magnesium with: (a) 50 ml. of 3 M HCl; (b) 28.6 ml. of 0.25 M HCl?

   From the equation (or from the formulas of HCl and H_2) we note that 22.4 l. (1 mol) are produced from 2 mols of HCl. The number of mols of HCl in the problem is obtained by multiplying the volume of the solution by its molarity, so we have:

$$\text{Volume of } H_2 = 22.4 \text{ l. } H_2 \times \frac{(0.050 \text{ l.}) \times (3 \text{ mols HCl per liter})}{2 \text{ mols HCl}}$$

9. How many ml. of 5 M HCl are required to dissolve 5.6 g. of iron? Ferrous ion, Fe^{++}, is formed.
10. Find the molarity of a sulfuric acid solution, 75 ml. of which dissolves 6.52 g. of zinc.
11. Calculate the normality of an acid solution if 24 ml. of it is required to neutralize 10 ml. of 0.2 N base.
12. Eighteen g. of sugar, $C_{12}H_{22}O_{11}$, are dissolved in 110 g. of water. At what temperature does the solution freeze?
13. How many pounds of glycerin, $C_3H_8(OH)_3$, must be added to 5 gal. (= 40 lb.) of water in a radiator to lower the freezing point to $-10°$ C.? (Do not convert English to metric units, or vice versa. Solve the problem first in grams of glycerin per 1000 g. of water, convert that to grams per 40 g., and call the result pounds per 5 gal.)
14. A non-electrolyte is 42 per cent carbon, 6.4 per cent hydrogen, and 51.5 per cent oxygen; 10.3 g. of the substance dissolved in 30 g. of water gives a solution which boils at 100.52° C. A student claimed that the substance is sugar. Do you think he was correct?
15. The three chief types of automobile radiator anti-freeze preparations consist almost entirely of glycerin, methanol, CH_3OH, and ethyleneglycol, $C_2H_4(OH)_2$, respectively. What weights of each of the other two would it take to replace 1 lb. of the most efficient one?
16. Must radiator anti-freezes be polar or non-polar liquids?
17. Define solution. Give examples of four types of solution.
18. Is milk a true solution?
19. A liquid is known to be either pure water or a solution containing 10 per cent of alcohol. How could you identify it by physical tests?

20. A white powder is known to be cornstarch or powdered sugar. How could you identify it without tasting or destroying any of it?
21. A solution is known to contain 1.5 g. of solute per 25 ml. of water. The solute is either sugar or urea. How could you tell which, by physical tests?

REFERENCES

Articles

"Solutions of Electrolytes." Davidson, A. W. *J. Chem. Ed.* **12**, 24 (1935).

» 15 «

WATER, ACIDS, AND BASES

Water is such a common and familiar substance that it is a little difficult to realize that it is a very peculiar one. If water is compared with other substances which are liquids at room temperature it is found to have the highest specific heat, heat of fusion, heat of vaporization, and dielectric constant. Water is the only substance, liquid at room temperature, which expands on freezing. It is strange, in fact, that it *is* a liquid, for other substances of similar molecular weight have boiling points two to three hundred degrees lower than that of water. These peculiarities of water are of extreme practical importance. The high specific heat accounts for the moderating influence that the oceans have upon climate. The high heat of fusion (80 cal. per gram) makes ice the most efficient refrigerating agent, pound for pound. The high heat of vaporization (540 cal. per gram) makes water the best cooling agent within its temperature range. The high dielectric constant is responsible for the solvent properties of water upon salts and for the possibility of the electronic heating of water-containing substances, as in diathermy (artificial fever) and the seemingly magical transformation of a package from a deep-freezer into a steaming hot meal in a matter of seconds. The expansion which takes place, as water in minute crevices freezes into ice, tears down cliffs and splits rocks into sand, altering the face of the earth. But for the fact that ice floats on water, our rivers and seas would be like the Siberian tundras, solid ice except for a few feet that melt in summer. Curiously enough, skating would be impossible. The slipperiness of ice depends upon the fact that it melts a trifle under pressure, which tends to reduce its volume to that corresponding to liquid water.

The high dielectric constant of water has already been explained (page 174) in terms of the structure of the molecule, and been shown to account for the ability of water to dissolve salts. Of course water molecules attract each other as well as ions of a salt. The positive pole of one water molecule tends to be pulled toward the negative end of another. This effect is in addition to that of the van der Waals forces, and is much stronger. At high temperatures thermal agitation keeps the molecules from adhering to each other with any degree of permanence. At lower temperatures this is not the case; furthermore, an interesting and until recently unsuspected valence phenomenon takes place which, in conjunction with the attractive force just mentioned, explains the other peculiarities of water which have been cited.

Hydrogen Bonding

Most ions are much larger than water molecules; hence toward them, as has been said (page 173), the water molecules behave like simple dipoles. Actually, however, the water molecule is a quadripole. The protons (hydrogen nuclei) are the two positive poles and the extremities of the orbits that contain the unshared valence electrons are the two negative poles. Therefore, when two water molecules adhere, a hydrogen of one is drawn to one of these negative poles, thus:

$$\ddot{\text{H}:\ddot{\text{O}}:\text{H}:\ddot{\text{O}}:}$$
$$\quad\text{H}\quad\;\text{H}$$

It is held there by the attractive force between the two opposite charges. This force is less than one-tenth of the force that holds the proton to its own oxygen atom, but far greater than the ordinary van der Waals forces between non-polar molecules. Accordingly there is an *association* of the two water molecules into a single molecule of double the size. Linus Pauling (California Institute of Technology) and W. H. Rodebush (University of Illinois), who have developed this idea and proved it in many interesting ways, call a hydrogen atom a *hydrogen bond* when it is thus holding two other atoms together. Only the atoms which do not give hydrogen a fair share of the electrons in a covalent bond can be held together in this fashion.

Expansion on Freezing

The thermal motions of molecules tend to keep a certain amount of empty space between them, even in the case of liquids and solids. The quantity of empty space diminishes as the temperature falls; therefore substances regularly contract as they cool. Water does so at first, but at a continually increasing rate there are formed molecules not merely of H:Ö:H:Ö:, but also of H:Ö:H:Ö: and even of H:Ö:H:Ö: (sometimes called dihydrol, trihydrol, and tetrahydrol, to distinguish them from simple H_2O, or hydrol, molecules). Although these formulas do not accurately represent the shapes of these molecules, they do suggest that it is impossible to pack them as closely as individual H_2O units could be packed, and experiments with scale models show this to be the case. By the time the temperature has fallen to 4° C., the increase in volume due to the formation of these larger molecules equals the decrease in volume due to lessening thermal motions, and below that temperature exceeds the decrease in volume. Water therefore expands slightly as it is cooled, down to its freezing point, 0° C. In the process of freezing, molecules of a liquid ordinarily fall into the positions corresponding to the closest possible packing (the remaining thermal motion being converted into vibration about those positions), but in the case of water, hydrogen bonding prevents this. The process illustrated in the formulas for the polyhydrols goes to completion. Every hydrogen atom forms a hydrogen bond and the entire crystal becomes a gigantic molecule occupying nearly 10 per cent more volume than the water from which it forms. When ice melts, the hydrogen bonds are broken, which takes much energy; hence ice has a higher heat of fusion than does any substance held together only by van der Waals forces. More such bonds are broken as water warms up and evaporates; so the specific heat and the heat of vaporization are also abnormally high.

Ionization of Water

When a dihydrol molecule is broken apart by a thermal collision it may break at either end of the hydrogen bond. In the one case it will yield the two original water molecules:

$$\overset{..}{\text{H:O}}:\overset{..}{\text{H:O}}: \longrightarrow \overset{..}{\text{H:O}}: + \overset{..}{\text{H:O}}:$$
$$\ \ \text{H}\ \ \ \ \ \text{H}\ \ \ \ \ \ \ \ \ \text{H}\ \ \ \ \ \ \text{H}$$

or, with ordinary formulas,

$$(H_2O)_2 \longrightarrow 2\ H_2O$$

In the other case the double molecule will yield a pair of ions:

$$\overset{..}{\text{H:O}}:\overset{..}{\text{H:O}}: \longrightarrow \overset{..}{\text{H:O}}:\text{H}^+ + :\overset{..}{\underset{..}{\text{O}}}:^-$$
$$\ \ \text{H}\ \ \ \ \ \text{H}\ \ \ \ \ \ \ \ \ \text{H}\ \ \ \ \ \ \ \ \text{H}$$

or, again,

$$(H_2O)_2 \longrightarrow H_3O^+ + OH^-$$

Experiment shows that both these methods of rupture actually take place, and the first occurs to an enormously greater extent than the second; for the purest water is a conductor of electricity, but only to an extremely slight degree. The actual amount of each ion present in a liter of pure water at room temperature is 10^{-7} mols (one ten-millionth of a mol). The ion with the extra proton, H_3O^+, has been given the name *hydronium ion*; the negative one, OH^-, is called the *hydroxide ion*.

Acids and Bases

Hydrogen is the only element with which a covalent bond can be broken without at the same time breaking up an octet. This is because the entire valence layer of the hydrogen atom in a compound consists of the electron pair which it is sharing. At the moment of collision the nucleus of a hydrogen atom can thus leave an electron pair of an octet in one molecule and join an electron pair in another molecule, without any great disturbance in either octet. This property of proton transfer is the most important property of combined hydrogen. Compounds which show it (not all hydrogen compounds do) are called acids (pages 109–110 and 123–124). Table 15.1 lists some of the most important acids. The names and formulas should be committed to memory.

TABLE 15.1. SOME IMPORTANT ACIDS

Name	Formula	Ions [a]	Strength [b]
Hydrochloric acid	HCl	H^+ and Cl^-	Strong
Nitric acid	HNO_3	H^+ and NO_3^-	Strong
Sulfuric acid	H_2SO_4	H^+ and HSO_4^-	Strong
Bisulfate ion	HSO_4^-	H^+ and SO_4^{--}	Moderate
Phosphoric acid	H_3PO_4	H^+ and $H_2PO_4^-$	Moderate
Acetic acid	$HC_2H_3O_2$	H^+ and $C_2H_3O_2^-$	Weak
Dihydrogen phosphate ion	$H_2PO_4^-$	H^+ and HPO_4^{--}	Weak

[a] For the use of H^+ in place of H_3O^+, see page 195.
[b] For the definition of "strong" in this sense, see page 194.

A substance whose molecule readily takes a proton from an acid is called a base. Table 15.2 lists some of the most important bases, which should also be learned.

TABLE 15.2. SOME IMPORTANT BASES

Name of Compound	Formula	Electronic Structure of Base
Calcium oxide	CaO	$:\!\ddot{\underset{..}{O}}\!:^{--}$
Sodium hydroxide	$NaOH$	$:\!\ddot{\underset{..}{O}}\!:\!H^-$
Potassium hydroxide	KOH	$:\!\ddot{\underset{..}{O}}\!:\!H^-$
Calcium hydroxide	$Ca(OH)_2$	$:\!\ddot{\underset{..}{O}}\!:\!H^-$
Sodium carbonate	Na_2CO_3	$:\!\dot{\underset{..}{O}}\!:\!\!C\!::\!\ddot{\underset{..}{O}}\!:^{--}$ with $:\!\dot{\underset{..}{O}}\!:$ below
Ammonia	NH_3	$H\!:\!\ddot{N}\!:\!H$ H
Ammonium hydroxide	NH_4OH	$H\!:\!\ddot{N}\!:\!H$ and $:\!\ddot{\underset{..}{O}}\!:\!H^-$ H

Strictly speaking, according to modern theories in regard to acids and bases, the anions listed in the third column are the bases. However, it is common practice to call compounds bases if they contain anions which are *strong* bases. For example, sodium carbonate is usually called a base because when dissolved in water its solution contains the carbonate ion which is a strong base and is actually responsible for the basic properties of the solution. But sodium sulfate is not called a base even though its water solution contains much sulfate ion; the latter is a weak base.

Strength of Acids and Bases

A substance which will yield a proton, but only with great difficulty, is said to be a very *weak* acid; frequently it is not actually *called* an acid, chemists merely remembering that it acts as an acid toward excellent bases. Water is such a substance. In the ionization of water, one molecule acts as an acid and the other as a base.

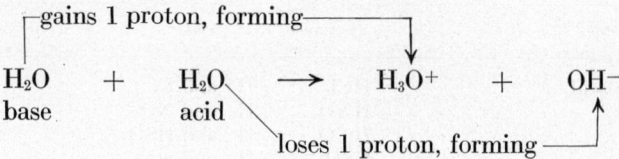

It is obviously possible for the same molecule to act as either an acid or a base if it has both a proton which can be lost and an unshared electron pair which can accept a proton.

Protons which can be lost ⟨ H:O:H ⟩ Electron pairs which can be shared

But it cannot be both a *strong* acid and a *strong* base at the same time, for a strong acid is one which is willing to lose a proton and a strong base is one which is anxious to gain one. A molecule cannot at the same time hold one proton loosely and pull strongly on another one.

Water is so weakly basic that it is not able to take protons to any large extent except from the really strong acids; so it is not ordinarily called a base. The fact that water is an extremely weak acid means that the hydroxide ion is a very strong base; if a water molecule gives up a proton with difficulty (is a weak acid) it is because the remainder of the molecule, which is the hydroxide ion, is holding onto the proton tightly (is a strong base). Similarly, since water is a weak base, the hydronium ion must be a strong acid; if a water molecule has only a slight tendency to take up a proton (is a weak base), then when it has done so the resulting molecule, the hydronium ion, readily loses the proton again (is a strong acid).

The "Hydrogen Ion"

When any acid is dissolved in water it reacts with the water to an extent depending upon its strength and produces hydronium ions. If the reaction goes to completion in a reasonably concentrated solution (say 3 M) the acid is called a *strong acid*. This is the case with the three acids described as "strong" in Table 15.1. The equation for the reaction of hydrochloric acid with water is:

$$HCl + H_2O \longrightarrow H_3O^+ + Cl^-$$

The other equations are similar. It will be seen that in any solution of a strong acid, the actual acid present is the hydronium ion. This explains the fact that the *acid* properties of all strong acids are identical. When Arrhenius explained this identity in 1881 in terms of ions, it did not occur to him that water actually entered into the reaction. He thought that the proton merely separated from the rest of the acid. He therefore said that hydrogen chloride *ionizes* into the hydrogen ion and the chloride ion when it dissolves in water, and he wrote the equation:

$$HCl \longrightarrow H^+ + Cl^-$$

We now know more about what happens, but we still use the terminology of Arrhenius most of the time. Even though we know that free hydrogen ions (i.e., protons) actually exist only momentarily, in flames and discharge tubes, we say that "hydrogen ions" are present in acid solutions. No one is confused because everyone knows that only *hydrated* hydrogen ions—namely, hydronium ions—can exist in solution. Similarly, it is usually perfectly satisfactory to use the formula H^+ in place of H_3O^+. The omission of the water of hydration attached to ions is, in fact, almost universal, even in cases where a definitely known number of water molecules are actually covalently bound to an ion.

Neutralization

Whenever an acid loses a proton to a base it turns the latter into a new but weaker acid. Whenever a base takes a proton from an acid it turns the latter into a new but weaker base. This is illustrated by the equations:

Acid	+	Base	→	Weaker Acid	+	Weaker Base
HCl	+	H_2O	→	H_3O^+	+	Cl^-
$HC_2H_3O_2$	+	$Na^+ + OH^-$	→	H_2O	+	$Na^+ + C_2H_3O_2^-$
$H_3O^+ + Cl^-$	+	NH_3	→	NH_4^+	+ $Cl^- +$	H_2O
$NH_4^+ + Cl^-$	+ $Na^+ + OH^-$	→	H_2O	+ $Na^+ +$	$Cl^- + NH_3$
$Na^+ + HSO_4^-$	+	$Na^+ + C_2H_3O_2^-$	→	$HC_2H_3O_2$	+	$2 Na^+ + SO_4^{--}$
H_3O^+	+ $Cl^- + Na^+ + OH^-$	→	H_2O	+ $Na^+ +$	$Cl^- + H_2O$

You may wonder why, in the last equation, Cl^- is not shown as acting as a base. This is because, although it is a base, it is a far weaker base than OH^-. (It is an even weaker base than H_2O.) In a mixture of bases it is the stronger one which gets the protons. We know that this is true because we know that H_2O (formed from H^+ and OH^-) is not appreciably ionized, whereas HCl (which would be formed if Cl^- successfully acted as a base) is completely ionized. This is emphasized in the first equation, where even H₂O removes protons from HCl, showing that the Cl⁻ ion cannot have much affinity for the proton.

Since the acid and base produced in a neutralization are always weaker than the ones from which they came, the characteristic properties of acids that were observable in the acid solution, and of bases that were observable in the base solution, have more or less disappeared from the mixed solution. It is for this reason that an acid is said to *neutralize* a base, and vice versa. (Electrical neutrality is not in question here; all solutions are electrically neutral.)

Neutralization is not necessarily complete. If a strong acid is added to an equivalent quantity of a weak base, the resulting solution will show no basic properties, but will still be appreciably acid. This is the case, for example, when the extremely strong acid hydrogen chloride is added to the extremely weak base water. The acid properties of the resulting solution of hydronium chloride are still so outstanding that it is regularly called hydrochloric acid. The stronger the base that is added, the more complete is the disappearance of the acid properties of the solution to which it is added. The reverse is also true. When the word *neutral* is used, it means that neutralization has been complete for both acid and base, so that the H⁺ and OH⁻ concentrations in the resulting solution are the same as those in pure water.

Titration

An important branch of analytical chemistry is called *volumetric analysis*, because the amount of reagent used is determined by measuring the volume of a standard solution. The process of determining just how much of the standard solution is required to react with the sample being analyzed is called *titration*. Acidimetry and alkalimetry (the analysis of acids and of bases respectively) are regularly performed by means of titrations. In a titration the solutions are usually measured by means of burettes (see Fig. 15.1). The point at which the desired reaction is complete is called the *end point*. Some indicator must be used to determine the end point of a titration. Many indicators are available because fortunately there are numbers of dyes which are acids and which, on losing a proton, rearrange their bonding and change color. For example, litmus, a very weak acid extracted from a certain lichen, is pink; but when it is neutralized, i.e., loses its proton, it becomes a weak base which is blue.

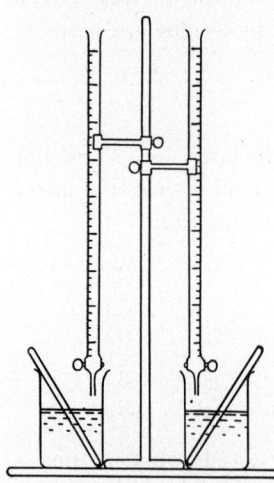

Fig. 15.1. Burettes for titration.

Indicator acids differ in strength. Some ionize considerably even in a somewhat acid solution; others are such weak acids that the solution must be fairly basic before they lose protons and change color. When a strong acid is titrated with a soluble hydroxide the weaker acid and the weaker base that are produced are both water; hence the end point of the titration is the neutral point. A few indicators change color quite near the neutral point, but these are not the only ones that can be used in this case. A single drop of a 1-molar solution of hydrochloric acid added to 50 ml. of water or neutral salt solution will increase the acidity 10,000-fold; a drop of a 1-molar solution of sodium hydroxide will decrease the acidity to the same extent. Many indicators change color within this range, and any of them can be used without causing an error greater than one drop. If a weak acid is used, the base which it leaves will be correspondingly strong and the solution will be basic at the end point. Therefore an indicator must be chosen which changes color at about the same degree of alkalinity. Similarly, for a weak base which becomes an acid of appreciable strength, an indicator must be selected which changes color in a solution of the proper acidity. Further discussion of this part of the subject will be presented in the chapter on chemical equilibrium, when it will be possible to describe a method for exactly specifying the degree of acidity or alkalinity of a solution.

Use of Normalities in Titrations

A 1-molar solution of hydrochloric acid will neutralize an equal volume of a 1-molar solution of sodium hydroxide. If the solutions have different molarities, the amounts required will be inversely proportional to them. But a liter of 1-molar sulfuric acid will neutralize *two* liters of 1-molar sodium hydroxide, and a liter of 1-molar hydrochloric acid will neutralize only half a liter of 1-molar barium hydroxide, $Ba(OH)_2$. To avoid having to keep in mind the factor of 2 in such cases, we can express the concentration more conveniently in terms of normality, the definition of which we repeat here (see page 178):

$$\text{Normality} = \frac{\text{Number of equivalents}}{\text{Number of liters}}$$

where an *equivalent* of an acid or base is that quantity of it which will yield or neutralize one mol of hydrogen ion. A 1-molar solution of HCl is thus also 1-normal; but a 1-molar solution of H_2SO_4 is 2-normal, written 2 N. If the concentrations are expressed in normalities it is always true that:

$$(\text{ml. of acid}) \times (\text{N of acid}) = (\text{ml. of base}) \times (\text{N of base})$$

regardless of what particular acid or base is used. Thus:

10 ml. of 6 N HCl neutralize 20 ml. of 3 N NaOH; $10 \times 6 = 20 \times 3$
10 ml. of 6 N H_2SO_4 neutralize 20 ml. of 3 N KOH; $10 \times 6 = 20 \times 3$
10 ml. of 6 N HNO_3 neutralize 20 ml. of 3 N $Ba(OH)_2$; $10 \times 6 = 20 \times 3$

In analytical chemistry particularly, it is sometimes convenient to speak of equivalents of salts. An equivalent of a salt can be defined as consisting of one equivalent of the negative ion plus one equivalent of the positive ion. An equivalent of an ion has already been defined (page 178) as equal to the ionic weight divided by the valence. Thus an alternative definition for the equivalent weight of a salt is:

$$1 \text{ equivalent} = \frac{\text{Formula weight}}{\text{Total valence of either cations } or \text{ anions}}$$

The definition of equivalent weight for acids and bases is merely a special case of the above.

Calculations

If any two substances will react, one equivalent of one will react with one equivalent of the other and form one equivalent of each product. This statement is of fundamental importance, for it explains why this concept is so useful. It is possible to save a great deal of time in many calculations, particularly analytical ones, by using it. The following example will make this clear:

A sample of barium nitrate, $Ba(NO_3)_2$, was titrated with sulfuric acid. 22.34 ml. of 1.036 N acid was required to precipitate all the Ba^{++} as $BaSO_4$. (This titration requires a different type of indicator from that used in acidimetry, but is nevertheless practicable.) What weight of $Ba(NO_3)_2$ was present in the sample?

There are several ways of doing this problem; most students do it the longest way in an examination. Carry out the arithmetic for each of the two following methods and time yourself to see which takes longer.

Method 1. (a) Write the balanced equation. (b) Calculate the grams of acid in the volume of solution used. (c) Set up the proportion, formula weight of H_2SO_4: formula weight of $Ba(NO_3)_2$::g. of acid in 22.34 ml.:g. of $Ba(NO_3)_2$. (d) Solve the proportion.

Method 2. (a) Find the number of equivalents of acid used by multiplying the normality by the volume in ml.: 1.036×0.02234 eq. This is the number of equivalents of every other substance in the equation, including $Ba(NO_3)_2$. (b) One equivalent of $Ba(NO_3)_2$ weighs $\frac{Ba(NO_3)_2}{2}$ g. (c) Multiply (a) by (b) for the answer.

Heats of Neutralization

When an equivalent of any strong acid neutralizes an equivalent of any strong base, exactly the same reaction takes place. This is easily seen in the equations:

$$H^+ + Cl^- + Na^+ + OH^- \longrightarrow Na^+ + Cl^- + H_2O$$
$$H^+ + NO_3^- + K^+ + OH^- \longrightarrow K^+ + NO_3^- + H_2O$$

One mol of hydrogen ion neutralizes one mol of hydroxide ion to form a mol of water. None of the other ions present take any part in the reaction, so it makes no difference what they are. It is for this reason that the *heat of neutralization* of all strong acids and bases is the same. For every mol of water that is formed, 13,700 cal. of heat are produced. If a neutralization involves any additional reaction, the heat of that reaction (positive or negative) is added to the heat of neutralization. Two neutralizations of sulfuric acid will show this:

$$2\ Na^+ + 2\ OH^- + H^+ + HSO_4^- \longrightarrow 2\ Na^+ + SO_4^{--} + 2\ H_2O + 29{,}400 \text{ cal.}$$
$$Ba^{++} + 2\ OH^- + H^+ + HSO_4^- \longrightarrow \underline{BaSO_4} + 2\ H_2O + 34{,}400 \text{ cal.}$$

In each of these equations two mols of water are formed, but by two different reactions; in one case the hydroxide ion takes a proton from the hydrogen ion:

$$OH^- + H_3O^+ \longrightarrow H_2O + H_2O$$

and in the other case from the bisulfate ion:

$$OH^- + HSO_4^- \longrightarrow SO_4^{--} + H_2O$$

The first of these two reactions is the one which, as has been said, liberates 13,700 cal. of heat. The second is a different reaction and must be expected to liberate a different amount of heat. The actual heat of the total reaction is 29,400 cal., which shows that the heat of neutralization of the bisulfate ion is 15,700 cal. When sulfuric acid is neutralized by barium hydroxide a salt is precipitated instead of being left as ions in the solution. This is a third reaction and has its own heat effect (5000 cal.). All these differences from the first simple case are clearly predicted by the equations as written, but would not even be suggested if empirical formulas were used.

QUESTIONS AND PROBLEMS

1. How many calories of heat are required to change 20 g. of ice at $-10°$ C. to steam at $100°$ C.? The specific heat of ice is 0.5 cal. per degree. What three other quantities are required?
2. The home of Professor Smith is 28 ft. $\times$ 34 ft. $\times$ 19 ft. He burns 10 long tons of coal each winter. One g. of coal liberates 8000 cal. If his house is filled with ice at $0°$ C., could the ice be melted with the coal (assuming 100 per cent efficiency)? Assume that 1 cu. ft. of water is 1000 oz. and that a long ton is equal to a metric ton.

    If he had a hot-water heating system which held 100 gal. of water that entered the heater at $45°$ C. and left it at $70°$ C., how many times would the water recirculate during the winter? (Assume perfect efficiency.)
3. What is a hydrogen bond?

4. What is a polyhydrol?
5. At what temperature is water at its maximum density?
6. How many mols of water are there in a liter of water?
7. What is an electrolyte?
8. Is the ionization of water an acid-base reaction? Is that of HCl?
9. Can an acid be strong and dilute at the same time?
10. Is the negative ion of a strong acid a stronger or a weaker base than water? How do you know?
11. How many calories of heat are produced by mixing 800 ml. of nitric acid of s.g. 1.096 and 17.0 per cent HNO_3 by weight with 800 ml. of potassium hydroxide of s.g. 1.149 and 16.0 per cent KOH by weight?
12. How many grams are there in one equivalent of calcium hydroxide, $Ca(OH)_2$? Of calcium carbonate, $CaCO_3$? of perchloric acid, $HClO_4$? Of ammonium sulfate, $(NH_4)_2SO_4$?
13. How many grams of calcium carbonate can be dissolved by 2 l. of 6 N HCl? How many grams of $CaCl_2$ will be formed? How many grams of $CaCl_2 \cdot 6 H_2O$ can be crystallized from the solution?
14. What volume of 0.1 N H_2SO_4 will neutralize 25 ml. of 0.5 N NaOH? What volume of 0.1 N HCl?
15. What is the normality of a solution of acid 10 ml. of which will dissolve 1.003 g. of $CaCO_3$?

» 16 «

PROPERTIES OF IONS. SALTS

IONS

Theories of Ionization

Had we been studying chemistry for the first time prior to 1884, we might easily have joined the scoffers who doubted Svante Arrhenius when he proposed *a theory of electrolytic dissociation*. His theory differed from that of Davy and Faraday in that he believed *dissociation was produced by the water and not by the electric current*. He thought that as a substance dissolved in water the impact of water molecules against this substance caused it to dissociate into ions. No explanation was available at that time to account for the positive and negative charges, for the electron concept came later. In the case of salt, Arrhenius believed that as salt dissolved, some of the molecules were dissociated into positive Na^+ ions and negative Cl^- ions. Two reactions were taking place simultaneously: molecules of salt were dissociating and ions were colliding to form molecules of salt. A certain degree of order was bound to result from these two reactions; hence the ratio of molecules to ions would be constant under any set of standard conditions. According to Arrhenius, the probability of ions of opposite charges colliding would be much greater in concentrated solutions than in dilute solutions, because in the latter the ions might wander at random for some time without once colliding with an ion of opposite sign. It followed from this that the degree of ionization depended upon dilution. In an infinitely dilute solution ionization should approach 100 per cent. An increase in temperature should increase the speed of the water molecules and hence their bombarding effect, and this should produce greater dissociation. *At any moment there would be a dynamic equilibrium between the molar concentration of molecules of salt and the molar concentration of sodium and chloride ions in the solution.* The following equation expresses this statement in chemical terms; any symbol in brackets refers to its *molar concentration:*

$$[NaCl] \rightleftarrows [Na^+] + [Cl^-]$$

Each of the concentrations in the above equation remains constant under a given set of conditions; the double arrow means that Na^+ and Cl^- ions are coming together as frequently as other Na^+ and Cl^- are breaking apart.

Arrhenius knew that a solution of salt:
1. Plus a solution of silver nitrate yields a white precipitate of AgCl.
2. Is a conductor of electricity.
3. Has an abnormally high boiling point.
4. Has an abnormally high osmotic pressure.
5. Has an abnormally low freezing point.

On the basis of these facts, he concluded that acids, bases, and salts in water solution dissociate into positive and negative ions and also that the solution is electrically neutral:
1. Salt plus water yielded ions of the salt.
2. Electricity did not produce the ions.
3. The solution was electrically neutral.
4. Ions did not have the same chemical properties as metals.
5. Molecules and ions were in equilibrium.

Arrhenius was certain that the ions in solution differed from the elements. For example, metallic sodium added to water reacts vigorously with it. Chlorine is a greenish-yellow gas, a powerful oxidizing agent, and very poisonous; but when salt is added to water, no chlorine gas can be smelled. He could answer his critics only by saying that the difference between ions and atoms would be discovered. He believed that such molecules as copper sulfate, $CuSO_4$, dissociated into two ions, Cu^{++} and (SO_4^{--}), and that the (SO_4^{--}) group remained intact and acted as a unit in solution.

One question often put to him concerned positive and negative ions in one solution at the same time. He granted that opposite charges should and did attract each other, but he assumed that some molecules were dissociating so that one factor balanced the other.

As with most theories, Arrhenius' theory has been modified as more data were obtained. It failed in particular to explain the fact that very concentrated solutions of substances were poorer conductors than solutions of the same substance diluted 1 to 100. If conductivity depended upon the number of ions present, as Arrhenius thought, then something remained to be explained. X-ray analysis of crystals of such compounds as sodium chloride indicates that even in the solid state we cannot say that a particular Na^+ ion is definitely paired with a particular Cl^- ion. The positive sodium ions alternate with negative chloride ions to form a network or pattern called the crystal lattice. In the salt crystal each sodium ion is surrounded by six chloride ions, and each chloride ion by six sodium ions. The distances between the atoms being constant, it is improbable that a particular positive ion belongs to one chloride ion any more than to any of the other five chloride ions. Since there are no molecules in crystal salt, it would seem foolish to assume that molecules were present in a salt solution. Modifications of the old theory had accounted for concentrated solutions being poorer conductors of electricity by assuming that more of the substance was present in the molecular state in such a solution. But does this explanation hold if the substance is 100 per cent ionized?

In 1924 Debye and Hückel offered a plausible theory to account for the fact that concentrated solutions of electrolytes may be poor conductors of electricity. Their theory assumes that strong electrolytes are 100 per cent ionized in all concentrations of solute in solvent. In a concentrated solution each positive ion is completely surrounded with negative ions, and vice versa, and hence has little freedom of movement (see Fig. 16.1). The attrac-

```
         Cl⁻        Cl⁻
                    Na⁺
     Cl⁻            Cl⁻        Na⁺
 Cl⁻ Na⁺ Cl⁻
     Cl⁻            Na⁺
                Na⁺ Cl⁻ Na⁺
          Na⁺ Cl⁻   Na⁺        Na⁺
```

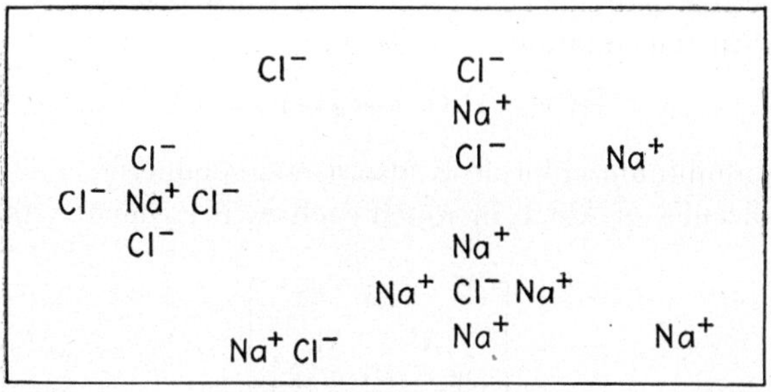

Fig. 16.1. Some possible ionic distributions in a solution of sodium chloride.

tive forces around each ion impede its freedom of movement and therefore decrease the conductivity of the solution. The Arrhenius theory considers a definite percentage of molecules ionized, and the remainder undissociated. The Debye-Hückel theory assumes 100 per cent ionization, but holds that, because of the restricted movement of the ions, the measured effect is the same as though some of the ions did not exist as such.

Modern investigations prove that the restriction of movement of the ions extends to the formation of ion pairs, ion triples, and larger ion clusters; these are, in effect, little fragments of the original crystal (Fig. 16.1), but are continually breaking up or adding new ions. It can be seen that this picture reconciles the ideas of Arrhenius quite well with our present knowledge of the structure of matter as far as salts are concerned. The definite molecules such as NaCl which he imagined are replaced by ion clusters differing from each other in size and charge. Substances which are composed entirely of ions, either free or clumped together in ion clusters or crystals, are called *strong electrolytes*.

Another class of substances exists which yield conducting solutions in water but which in the pure state, either solid or liquid, contain no ions. They are composed entirely of neutral molecules, the atoms of which are held together by covalent bonds. For them the Arrhenius theory needs but one modification: The ions found in their solutions are produced not by the thermal impact of water molecules upon those of the solute, but by chemical reaction with water. A review of the material on acids in the preceding chapter will show that acids belong to this class; in fact, they form the most important part of it. Some substances which from their formulas appear to be salts also belong to it, actually being covalently bound substances in the pure state. In some cases the reaction with water to form ions is so much more rapid than the reverse reaction that solutions of only moderate dilution contain practically none of the original molecules; in reality they are strong electrolytes. An acid of this type is HCl. The covalent nature of its bonding is indicated by the fact that it is a gas and that the pure anhydrous liquid is non-conducting, but this acid reacts practically completely with water in accordance with the equation:

$$HCl + H_2O \longrightarrow H_3O^+ + Cl^-$$

Pure molten aluminum chloride is also a non-conductor, and easily evaporates into molecules of Al_2Cl_6 in which each Al is covalently bonded to four Cl atoms:

$$\begin{bmatrix} Cl & & Cl & & Cl \\ & Al & & Al & \\ Cl & & Cl & & Cl \end{bmatrix}$$

Aluminum chloride reacts completely with water according to the equation:

$$Al_2Cl_6 + 12\ H_2O \longrightarrow 2\ Al(H_2O)_6^{+++} + 6\ Cl^-$$

In other cases the reaction with water to produce ions goes slowly and the reverse reaction is fast enough so that only a few ions are present in the solution at any one time. Examples include both acids, such as acetic acid:

$$HC_2H_3O_2 + H_2O \rightleftarrows H_3O^+ + C_2H_3O_2^-$$

and salts, such as cupric chloride:

$$\begin{bmatrix} H_2O & ++ & Cl^- \\ & Cu & \\ Cl^- & & OH_2 \end{bmatrix} + H_2O \rightleftarrows \begin{bmatrix} H_2O & ++ & Cl^- \\ & Cu & \\ H_2O & & OH_2 \end{bmatrix}^+ + Cl$$

and

$$\begin{bmatrix} H_2O & ++ & Cl^- \\ & Cu & \\ H_2O & & OH_2 \end{bmatrix}^+ + H_2O \rightleftarrows \begin{bmatrix} H_2O & ++ & OH_2 \\ & Cu & \\ H_2O & & OH_2 \end{bmatrix}^{++} + Cl^-$$

Substances in this second class are called *weak electrolytes*.

In only one familiar weak electrolyte—ammonium hydroxide—are the molecules actually shaken apart into ions by the impact of other molecules. In its molecule, NH_4OH, the NH_4^+ and OH^- ions are held together only by a hydrogen bond which is much weaker than most covalent bonds. Furthermore, the hydrogen bond can break without disrupting any valence octet.

Measurement of the Strength of Acids and Bases

If you were asked whether you would prefer to drink a tablespoonful of concentrated carbonic acid or sulfuric acid, you would probably choose the carbonic acid. But why do you prefer one acid to the other? Like almost everyone, you will probably say that sulfuric acid is a *strong acid* and carbonic acid is a *weak acid*. But when it comes to defining a strong acid, a weak acid, a strong base, and a weak base, the usual answer is that vinegar, boric acid, and carbonated water are all weak acids; muriatic (HCl) acid and sulfuric acid are strong acids; lye is a strong base, and ammonia is a weak base. "Strong" is associated with burning or caustic properties, for such substances destroy tissue. These descriptive terms still do not explain why one acid is strong and another is weak. Two acids may each be of the same normality; that is, it may take the same volume of a base to neutralize a given quantity of each acid; yet one will burn the skin and the other will not.

Several observations dealing with freezing-point lowering, boiling-point rise, and osmotic pressure (discussed on pages 206-208) can be made in the laboratory which will throw some light on the subject. If the freezing points of a 1-normal solution of a strong acid and a weak acid are determined, we find that the strong acid must be cooled to a lower temperature before it freezes. Likewise, a 1-normal solution of a strong base freezes at a lower temperature than a 1-normal solution of a weak base. The conclusion is that the apparent ionization is greater in strong acids and bases than in weak ones. The fraction of the substance in the form of free ions can be calculated from the freezing point of the solution (page 209. See page 203 on the Debye-Hückel theory of complete ionization of strong electrolytes.)

A laboratory experiment which further illustrates the difference between strong acids and strong bases may be carried out with the apparatus shown in Fig. 16.2. Two terminals of the apparatus are connected to a source of electric current; the other two, extending below and to the left of the apparatus, are dipped into a solution whose conductivity is to be measured. Electrons flow through the light bulb when the circuit is complete. If the solution is a good conductor of electricity and thus offers little resistance to the current, the light bulb will glow brightly. A poor conductor offers great resistance; hence the glow will be slight. If the electrodes are placed in contact with dry salt, a sugar solution, or distilled water, the bulb will not glow at all. If several sets of apparatus are available so that tests can be

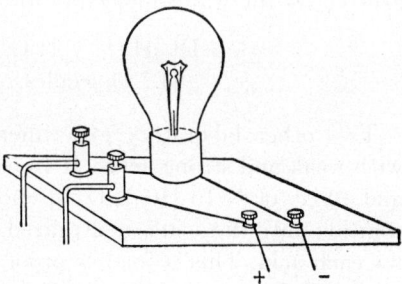

FIG. 16.2. Conductivity of solutions.

made on N/10 solutions of different acids and bases at the same time, the bulbs will glow with varying degrees of intensity, and the acids and bases which are called strong will produce the brightest glow. The greater the glow, the greater the number of free ions.

Such experiments lead to the conclusion that since strong and weak acids have only the proton in common, the difference is due to the relative ability of acids to release the proton to water. A strong acid contains a high concentration of hydronium ions; a weak acid, a low concentration. We must assume that there is an equilibrium in the solution due to the competition between water molecules and negative ions for the proton. If the water molecules win, the acid is strong. In the case of hydrogen chloride in water, both the Cl^- ion and the water molecules have an affinity for the proton, but the water molecules must have the greater affinity because the solution is a good conductor of electricity. Calculations with freezing-point data indicate that approximately 90 per cent of the HCl is in the form of free ions. No appreciable amount of it can still be in the form of covalently bound hydrogen chloride molecules, for the dilute solution shows no trace of the strong, sharp smell of that substance. The deficiency in the number of ions is due to the clustering of hydronium and chloride ions. A N/10 solution of HCl always shows this same percentage of free ions, but again it must be emphasized that this equilibrium does not represent a static condition. Rearrangements are probably taking place rapidly, and the concentration of ions represents the number in that state at any one moment. (A motion-picture theater with a capacity audience is analogous. Some people leave the theater, but others enter. The number of individuals in the audience remains constant, but its personnel does not.)

From the freezing point of a N/10 solution of acetic acid, it appears that among every 100 molecules only 1.3 dissociate into ions; in other words, an average of 1.3 per cent of the molecules dissociate. The tendency for the acetate radical to keep the proton must be greater than the attractive force exerted by the water molecules for the proton.

$$HC_2H_3O_2 + H_2O \rightleftharpoons H_3O^+ + C_2H_3O_2^-$$
98.7 molecules   1.3 ions   1.3 ions

Two other laboratory experiments should be mentioned in connection with weak and strong acids. If 10 cc. of N/10 HCl are placed in one beaker and 10 cc. of N/10 $HC_2H_3O_2$ in another, and N/10 NaOH is added to each solution until the acid is neutralized, 10 cc. of NaOH are found to be required for each acid. This is further proof that the above can be correctly written as equilibria reactions. The (OH^-) ions of the NaOH use up the hydronium ions to form water.

$$H_3O^+ + OH^- \longrightarrow 2\ H_2O$$

As H_3O^+ ions are used up, more acid molecules (in the case of acetic acid)

PROPERTIES OF IONS. SALTS

or ion clusters (in the case of hydrochloric acid) dissociate until all the acid has been neutralized. Remembering what was said on page 195, we cancel water out of both sides of the above equation and write:

$$H^+ + Cl^- + Na^+ + OH^- \longrightarrow Na^+ + Cl^- + H_2O$$

Another experiment which will illustrate the difference between a strong and a weak acid may be conducted as shown in Fig. 16.3. If 100 ml. of N/10 HCl are added to one tube, and 100 ml. of N/10 $HC_2H_3O_2$ to the other, the acids will react with zinc to liberate hydrogen. The same volume of hydrogen is liberated in each case; but the weak acid reacts with the zinc much more slowly, for in the time 1 ml. of hydrogen is being liberated from the acetic acid, 70 ml. will be liberated from the hydrochloric acid. Eventually 112 ml. of hydrogen will be liberated from each reaction ($11,200 \times 0.1 \times \frac{100}{1000} = 112$ ml.). (One l. of 1 N acid contains 1 g. or 11,200 ml. of replaceable hydrogen.) The reaction is exothermic; care is necessary in adding the strong acid to the zinc because the heat liberated raises the temperature of the solution, and the hotter the solution the more rapid the reaction.

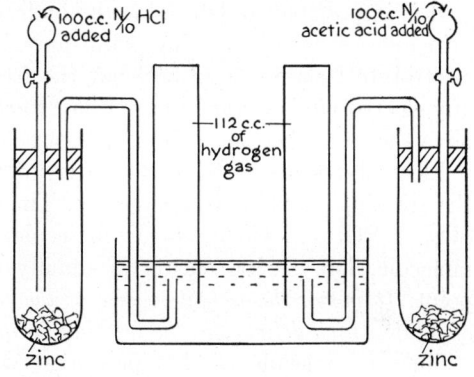

FIG. 16.3. Equal volumes of hydrogen are liberated by reacting zinc with either 100 ml. of N/10 HCl or 100 ml. of N/10 acetic acid.

Table 16.1 contains a list of some of the more important weak acids,

TABLE 16.1. PERCENTAGE OF FREE IONS IN DILUTE SOLUTIONS OF SOME WEAK ACIDS

Name	Formula	Concentration	Molecules and Ions	Per Cent of Free Ions	
Sodium bisulfate	$NaHSO_4$	N/10	$HSO_4^- \rightleftarrows H^+ + SO_4^{--}$	60	
Oxalic acid	$H_2C_2O_4$	N/10	$H_2C_2O_4 \rightleftarrows H^+ + HC_2O_4^-$	40	moderately strong
Phosphoric acid	H_3PO_4	M/10	$H_3PO_4 \rightleftarrows H^+ + H_2PO_4^-$	27	
Uni-bivalent salt	M_2X	M/10	Ion clusters $\rightleftarrows 2M^+ + X^{--}$	75	
Bi-bivalent salt	MX	M/10	Ion clusters $\rightleftarrows M^{++} + X^{--}$	40	
Acetic acid	$HC_2H_3O_2$	N/10	$HC_2H_3O_2 \rightleftarrows H^+ + C_2H_3O_2^-$	1.3	
Oxalic acid	$H_2C_2O_4$	N/10	$HC_2O_4^- \rightleftarrows H^+ + C_2O_4^{--}$	1.0	
Carbonic acid	H_2CO_3	M/10	$H_2CO_3 \rightleftarrows H^+ + HCO_3^-$	0.17	
Hydrosulfuric acid	H_2S	M/10	$H_2S \rightleftarrows H^+ + HS^-$	0.07	weak
Monosodium phosphate	NaH_2PO_4	M/10	$H_2PO_4^- \rightleftarrows H^+ + HPO_4^{--}$	0.1	
Ammonium hydroxide	NH_4OH	N/10	$NH_4OH \rightleftarrows NH_4^+ + OH^-$	1.3	
Mercuric chloride	$(HgCl_2)x$	N/10	$HgCl_2 \rightleftarrows Hg^{++} + 2Cl^-$ (An exception)	1.0	
Hydrocyanic acid	HCN	N/10	$HCN \rightleftarrows H^+ + CN^-$	0.01	
Boric acid	H_3BO_3	N/10	$H_3BO_3 \rightleftarrows H^+ + H_2BO_3^-$	0.01	
Sodium bisulfide	NaHS	M/10	$HS^- \rightleftarrows H^+ + S^{--}$	0.0001	very weak
Disodium phosphate	Na_2HPO_4	M/10	$HPO_4^{--} \rightleftarrows H^+ + PO_4^{---}$	0.005	
Water	H_2O		$H_2O \rightleftarrows H^+ + OH^-$ (Considered as both acid and base)	0.000001	

together with other substances for comparison. The column headed "Per cent of free ions" is calculated on the assumption that all ion clusters present correspond to M^+X^-, $M^{++}X^{--}$, $X^-M^{++}X^-$, or $M^+X^{--}M^+$, as the case may be. This is not precisely accurate.

Effect of Electrolytes on Freezing and Boiling Points of Solutions

It is impossible to determine the molecular weights of electrolytes by the principle of molal freezing-point lowering. A molal solution of a nonelectrolyte freezes at $-1.86°$, but the freezing point of a molal solution of any electrolyte is lower than $-1.86°$. Furthermore, if any two salt solutions have the same freezing points, it is purely accidental.

Electrolytes produce ions in water, and an ion is as effective in lowering the freezing point as is a molecule. Thus one H^+, Na^+, Cl^-, OH^-, NO_3^-, SO_4^{--}, PO_4^{---}, Ca^{++}, sugar molecule, alcohol molecule, or any other molecule, ion, or ion cluster is equally effective in lowering the freezing point. *It is not the weight or size of the particle but the number of particles of solute which determines the freezing point of the solution.*

Since a molecule of HCl produces two ions we should expect a molal solution of HCl to contain twice as many particles as a molal solution of sugar. If this were true, the freezing point would be lowered 2×1.86, or $3.72°$. Likewise, since a molecule of $CaCl_2$ produces three ions, 1 Ca^{++} and 2 Cl^-, a molal solution of this salt should freeze at $-5.58°$. Actually the lowering of the freezing point is not this great in either case. Although strong electrolytes are 100 per cent ions, at any given instant some of the ions are so close to each other that they can be said to be paired as molecules. In this state they produce the same effect on the freezing point as though they were undissociated. It is the *active* or *free ions* which are responsible for the abnormal lowering.

To illustrate further the effect of electrolytes upon the freezing point of solutions, the following example is given: A mol of a certain compound, MX, is added to 1000 g. of water and the solution freezes at $-2.232°$. What fraction of the mol is present as active or free ions? In the equation below, MX may be a covalently bound molecule or an ion cluster.

$$\begin{array}{ccc} MX & \rightleftarrows \; M^+ \; + & X^- \\ 1-x & x & x \end{array}$$

Let x be the fraction of a mol which is present as free ions; then $(1-x)$ equals the mols of MX present in the molecular state, and x equals the mols of M^+ ions and also the mols of X^- ions. For each M^+ ion, an X^- ion also exists. The total number of units in the solution which can lower the freezing point is *the sum* of the mols of molecules or ion clusters, plus the mols of free ions, or $(1-x)+x+x$, or $1+x$.

PROPERTIES OF IONS. SALTS

Thus $(1 + x) 1.86 = 2.232$
or $1.86 + 1.86 x = 2.232$
or $1.86 x = 0.372$; so $x = 0.2$

Twenty per cent of the compound appears to be dissociated, i.e., present in the form of free ions.

The molal freezing-point lowerings for several electrolytes are given in Table 16.2. The freezing-point depression of each of these compounds is

TABLE 16.2. MOLAL FREEZING-POINT LOWERING

Name	Formula	Molal Freezing-Point Lowering in ° C.
Silver nitrate	$AgNO_3$	2.62
Calcium chloride	$CaCl_2$	5.2
Phosphoric acid	H_3PO_4	2.14
Sulfuric acid	H_2SO_4	4.04
Sodium chloride	NaCl	3.37
Magnesium sulfate	$MgSO_4$	2.02

abnormal, which indicates some association of the ions into clusters. The molal freezing-point lowering is not the same for all solvents. Thus for water it is 1.86°; benzene, 4.9°; phenol, 7.4°; ethylene dibromide, 11.8°; and triphenyl methane, 12.4°. A mol of a solute dissolved in 1000 g. of triphenyl methane will form a solution which freezes at 12.4° below the melting point of triphenyl methane (93.4°).

The following statement is a general equation by which such problems may be solved:

$$\frac{\text{grams of solute}}{\text{gram-molecular wt. of solute}} \times \frac{1000}{\text{grams of solvent}} \times K_f[1 + (n - 1)\alpha] = \text{freezing-point lowering which is always a positive number}$$

n = number of particles the solute dissociates into
α = fraction of free ions
K_f = molal freezing-point lowering; for water it is 1.86. (If boiling-point rise is desired, substitute its value. See the next paragraph.)

All the statements applying to freezing-point lowering apply also to boiling-point rise. Two mols per 1000 g. of water boil at 101.04°. Electrolytes produce abnormally high boiling-point elevations. All solvents do not have the same boiling-point elevation per mol of solute added; for water it is 0.52°; phenol, 3.04°; benzene, 2.67°; and nitrobenzene, 5.02°.

Acid-Base Properties of Anions

A negative ion whose formula begins with H is nearly always an acid. No anion is a strong acid; the strongest ones, such as HSO_4^-, are about half dissociated in 0.1 M solutions of their sodium salts. This is another way of saying that the reaction

$$Na^+ + HSO_4^- + H_2O \rightleftarrows Na^+ + H_3O^+ + SO_4^{--}$$

for example, is in equilibrium when the amounts of HSO_4^-, H_3O^+, and SO_4^{--} are about equal. In the case of a strong acid, it will be remembered (page 195), the corresponding reaction goes to completion (or practically so).

Some moderately weak anion acids are nevertheless useful for their mild, controlled acidity. $H_2PO_4^-$ gives an acid taste to beverages and jellies and is the acid in phosphate-type baking powders. $HC_4H_4O_6^-$ is the acid in tartrate baking powders and "cream of tartar." HSO_3^- is the acid in photographers' acid fixing bath. These acids are comparable in strength to acetic acid, familiar in vinegar. Many other anion acids are too weak ordinarily to be thought of as acids. They are, in fact, stronger bases than they are acids. An example is HCO_3^-, in baking soda.

Nomenclature. Any anion containing acid hydrogen may be named by prefixing "hydrogen," preceded by a numerical prefix if necessary, to the name of the completely neutralized anion. Thus $H_2PO_4^-$ is dihydrogen phosphate and $HC_4H_4O_6^-$ is monohydrogen tartrate. If the parent anion is *divalent*, the corresponding anion acid is regularly named by prefixing "bi-" to its name. Thus HSO_4^- is bisulfate, HSO_3^- is bisulfite, $HC_4H_4O_6^-$ is bitartrate, and HCO_3^- is bicarbonate.

All anions are bases; a number of them are commercially very important as such. Some of these are listed in Table 16.3. This list contains a large

TABLE 16.3. ANIONS IMPORTANT AS BASES

Name	Formula	Basic Strength
Amide ion	NH_2^-	Extreme
Oxide ion	O^{--}	"
Hydroxide ion	OH^-	Highest available in water solutions
Sulfide ion	S^{--}	High
Silicate ion	SiO_3^{--}	"
Phosphate ion	PO_4^{---}	"
Carbonate ion	CO_3^{--}	Good
Tetraborate ion	$B_4O_7^{--}$	Mild
Hydrogen phosphate ion	HPO_4^{--}	"
Bicarbonate ion	HCO_3^-	"
Acetate ion	$C_2H_3O_2^-$	Very mild

proportion of the most important bases, because nearly all inorganic bases are anions. There are no important cation bases and the only important neutral molecule inorganic base is ammonia, NH_3.

In spite of the emphasis given the basic character of anions, it is important to remember that *the basic properties of the anions of all strong acids are too* weak to be demonstrated except under very special circumstances. They are all weaker bases than water and therefore do not impart any alkalinity to solutions containing them. Noteworthy among these are Br$^-$, I$^-$, Cl$^-$, NO$_3^-$, HSO$_4^-$, MnO$_4^-$, ClO$_3^-$, IO$_3^-$, BrO$_3^-$, ClO$_4^-$, and IO$_4^-$. SO$_4^{--}$, although not the anion of a really strong acid, is so weakly basic that it may as well be considered in the same class. The above-mentioned ions are never *called* bases; neither are the anion acids which are strong enough to produce sour solutions. In fact, *it is rare to hear the anion of any acid stronger than acetic acid referred to as a base.*

Acid-Base Properties of Cations

We have just said that no cation is an important base. The repulsion between the ionic charge and a proton is sufficient to account for this. Review the explanation on page 123 of why the metals (particularly sodium and potassium) are commonly referred to as "basic elements" and be sure that you understand that no contradiction is involved.

The hydronium ion, H$_3$O$^+$, commonly called the hydrogen ion and written H$^+$, is the most important of all acids and the strongest acid which can exist in water solution. The ammonium ion, NH$_4^+$, is the only other cation you are likely to encounter which has H in its formula. It is an acid, as would be expected, but a very weak one. This does not mean that no other cations than these two are acids. Water of hydration is regularly omitted from the formulas of ions (page 195); in many ions the degree of hydration amounts to chemical combination and the nature of the water is so altered as to make it definitely acidic.

Hydration of Ions

The nature of the hydration of ions was discussed on page 204. At this point we wish to consider what it is about a particular cation that leads (or does not lead) to the formation of covalent bonds between it and oxygen atoms in the surrounding water molecules. As might be expected, the formation of bonds depends upon the strength of the electric and magnetic fields at the surface of the ion in question.

Rare Gas-Type Ions. Elements in the A families of the periodic system form ions identical in structure with the nearest inert gas. These ions naturally have little if any magnetic field. They have electric fields which depend upon their charges and radii. A given charge produces a more intense field if concentrated in a small space. The size of an ion having a given rare-gas structure decreases as the atomic number increases; the increased nuclear charge pulls all the electrons closer. Compare the radii[1] of the ions listed below, all of which have the neon structure:

Ion:	N^{---}	O^{--}	F$^-$	Na$^+$	Mg^{++}	Al^{+++}	Si^{++++}
Radius:	1.71	1.40	1.36	0.95	0.65	0.50	0.41

[1] Expressed in angstrom units. 1 A = 10^{-8} cm.

The first four ions have weak electric fields which attract the oppositely charged ends of adjacent water molecules, but not strongly enough to cause any formation of covalent bonds or any considerable alteration of the chemical nature of the water. The magnesium ion is a border-line case. No water molecule is permanently bound to a magnesium ion, but during the moment that it *is* bound to the cation the nature of the water is somewhat altered; it is a perceptibly stronger acid. No cation above Mg in the E.C.S. is strongly enough hydrated to be an acid. Al^{+++}, however, has a strong enough electric field at its surface to cause the formation of a definite chemical compound, $Al(H_2O)_6^{+++}$. The oxygen atoms of the water actually share electrons with the aluminum to a considerable extent, just as though it were a non-metal. This weakens the ability of the oxygens to hold their protons. Hydrated aluminum ion is therefore an acid; solutions containing it are sour and react with active metals to yield H_2. What has been said about aluminum is equally true about any other ion whose radius is small compared with its charge.

Non-Rare Gas-Type Ions. Ions of the transition elements have 9 to 18 electrons in their outside layer. As a result they have magnetic fields which aid them in the formation of dative bonds with any molecule or ion which is willing to share an electron pair with them. These ions do not need as much electric field as do rare gas-type ions, in order to turn their water of hydration into an acid. Even those of medium size and moderate charge do this. Thus all the hydrated ions of the transition metals in the first long period are acids. It is possible to recognize by glancing at a salt that it is a compound of a transition metal, because practically all the ions of these elements are colored. Color in an ion seems to be connected with the presence of electrons in an incomplete shell. For example, Ti^{++++}, which has 8 M electrons, is colorless; but Ti^{+++}, which has 9 in the M layer, is blue. Cu^{++}, with 17 M electrons, is blue (at least the hydrated ion is), whereas Cu^+, with the M layer full, is colorless.

SALTS[2]

Preparation of Salts

A salt is any substance which in solution yields ions other than H^+ or (OH^-). It may also yield one or the other of these ions at the same time. Acid salts contain some replaceable H^+ ions, and basic salts some replaceable (OH^-) ions. $KHSO_4$ is an acid salt and $Ca(OH)Cl$ is a basic salt. The terms monobasic, dibasic, and tribasic acids, although somewhat confusing, must be used because they are part of our system of nomenclature. A monobasic acid yields one H^+ ion per molecule, dibasic acids yield two H^+ ions per molecule, and tribasic acids yield three H^+ ions. Using the Brönsted system,

---

[2] The nomenclature for salts was given on page 99.

we would designate these as monoprotic, diprotic, and triprotic respectively. Examples:

Monobasic or monoprotic acids—HCl, HBr, HI, HCN, HNO$_3$, H(C$_2$H$_3$O$_2$).
Dibasic or diprotic acids—H$_2$SO$_4$, H$_2$SO$_3$, H$_2$S, H$_2$CO$_3$, H$_2$(C$_2$O$_4$)
Tribasic or triprotic acids—H$_3$PO$_4$, H$_3$BO$_3$, H$_3$AsO$_4$, H$_3$AlO$_3$

Likewise bases with only one replaceable (OH$^-$) ion are called monoacid bases, those with two are diacid bases, and those with three are triacid bases.

Monoacid bases—KOH, NaOH, NH$_4$OH, LiOH
Diacid bases—Ca(OH)$_2$, Ba(OH)$_2$, Sr(OH)$_2$, Mg(OH)$_2$
Triacid bases—Al(OH)$_3$, As(OH)$_3$

(Aluminum hydroxide is listed as both an acid and a base. The reason for this is discussed on page 447 under amphoteric substances.)

Most of the processes for the formation of salts involve reactions between ions. The fundamental materials are the elements. These in turn may be combined with oxygen to form metallic and non-metallic oxides. The water solutions of oxides are either basic or acidic, and the neutralization of acids and bases produces salts. Methods other than the neutralization of acids and bases can be used to prepare salts. These methods are summarized in the accompanying chart.

Types of Substances Used in Forming Salts

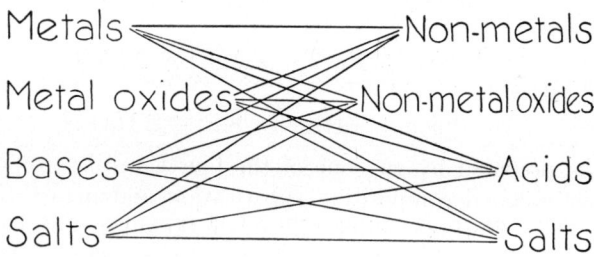

Various combinations of these substances produce salts. Several examples are given to show the numerous procedures.

1. Metal + non-metal
$$2\,Na + Cl_2 \longrightarrow 2\,NaCl$$
2. Metal + non-metal oxide
$$Mg + 2\,NO_2 \longrightarrow Mg(NO_2)_2$$
3. Metal + acid
$$Zn + 2\,HCl \longrightarrow ZnCl_2 + \overline{H_2}$$
4. Metal + salt
$$Fe + CuSO_4 \longrightarrow FeSO_4 + Cu$$
5. Metal + base
$$2\,Al + 2\,NaOH + 2\,H_2O \longrightarrow 2\,NaAlO_2 + \overline{3\,H_2}$$

6. Metal oxide + non-metal
$$2 F_2 + 2 Na_2O \longrightarrow 4 NaF + O_2 \text{ (?)}$$
7. Metal oxide + non-metal oxide
$$CaO + CO_2 \longrightarrow CaCO_3$$
8. Metal oxide + acid
$$CaO + H_2SO_4 \longrightarrow CaSO_4 + H_2O$$
9. Metal oxide + salt
$$CaO + (NH_4)_2SO_4 \longrightarrow CaSO_4 + \overline{2 NH_3} + H_2O$$
10. Metal oxide + base
$$Al_2O_3 + 6 NaOH \xrightarrow{\Delta} 2 Na_3AlO_3 + 3 H_2O$$
11. Base + non-metal
$$H_2O + 2 NaOH + Si \longrightarrow Na_2SiO_3 + \overline{2 H_2}$$
12. Base + non-metal oxide
$$Ca(OH)_2 + CO_2 \longrightarrow CaCO_3 + H_2O$$
13. Base + acid
$$2 NaOH + H_2SO_4 \longrightarrow Na_2SO_4 + 2 H_2O$$
14. Base + salt
$$Ba(OH)_2 + K_2SO_4 \longrightarrow \underline{BaSO_4} + 2 KOH$$
15. Salt + non-metal
$$2 NaI + Cl_2 \longrightarrow NaCl + I_2$$
16. Salt + non-metal oxide
$$Na_2CO_3 + SiO_2 \xrightarrow{\Delta} Na_2SiO_3 + CO_2$$
17. Salt + acid
$$AgNO_3 + HCl \longrightarrow \underline{AgCl} + HNO_3$$
18. Salt + salt
$$AgNO_3 + NaCl \longrightarrow \underline{AgCl} + NaNO_3$$
19. Non-metal oxide + acid
$$SiO_2 + 4 HF \longrightarrow SiF_4 + 2 H_2O$$

Salts can be prepared by any one of the four general types of chemical reaction: direct union, decomposition, substitution, and metathesis or double substitution. The following examples illustrate these types of reactions.

Preparation of salts by direct union:

1. Metal + non-metal $\quad\quad 2 Na + Cl_2 \longrightarrow 2 NaCl$
2. Metal oxide + non-metal oxide $\quad CaO + CO_2 \longrightarrow CaCO_3$
3. Salt + salt to form double and complex salts
   a. Double salt:
   $$K_2SO_4 + Al_2(SO_4)_3 + 24 H_2O \longrightarrow K_2SO_4 \cdot Al_2(SO_4)_3 \cdot 24 H_2O$$
   b. Complex salt:
   $$Fe(CN)_2 + 4 KCN \longrightarrow K_4^+[Fe(CN)_6^{----}]$$
4. Salt + solvent $CuSO_4 + 5 H_2O \longrightarrow CuSO_4 \cdot 5 H_2O$ (copper sulfate pentahydrate)
5. Hydride + hydride
$$HCl + NH_3 \longrightarrow NH_4Cl$$

PROPERTIES OF IONS. SALTS

Preparation of salts by decomposition:

    Salt + Δ ⟶ salt + "X"   2 NaClO₃ ⟶ 2 NaCl + $\overline{3\ O_2}$

Preparation of salts by substitution:
1. Salt + metal   Fe + CuSO₄ ⟶ FeSO₄ + Cu
2. Acid + metal   H₂SO₄ + Zn ⟶ ZnSO₄ + $\overline{H_2}$
3. Base + metal   2 NaOH + Zn ⟶ Na₂ZnO₂ + $\overline{H_2}$
4. Salt + non-metal   2 NaI + Br₂ ⟶ 2 NaBr + I₂

Preparation of salts by metathesis:
1. Acid + base   KOH + HNO₃ ⟶ KNO₃ + H₂O
2. Acid + salt   H₂SO₄ + Ba(NO₃)₂ ⟶ BaSO₄ + 2 HNO₃
3. Base + salt   3 NaOH + FeCl₃ ⟶ $\overline{Fe(OH)_3}$ + 3 NaCl
4. Salt + salt   AgNO₃ + NaCl ⟶ $\underline{AgCl}$ + NaNO₃

Techniques Used in Obtaining Pure Salts

The equations just given show that a wide variety of procedures are available for preparing a salt in the laboratory. Which method is to be selected? Why is one preferable to another? These two questions must be answered every time a compound is to be prepared in the laboratory.

The procedures involving ionic reactions are usually grouped under four headings:

    1. Formation of a precipitate
    2. Formation of a gas
    3. Formation of more solvent
    4. Fractional crystallization

If you were to prepare some *pure* BaSO₄ by means of one of the following four reactions, which one would you choose?

$$Ba(OH)_2 + H_2SO_4 \longrightarrow \underline{BaSO_4} + 2\ H_2O$$
(neutralize and evaporate to dryness or filter)

$$BaCl_2 + H_2SO_4 \longrightarrow \underline{BaSO_4} + 2\ HCl$$
(add equivalent amounts and filter)

$$BaCl_2 + H_2SO_4 \xrightarrow{\Delta} \underline{BaSO_4} + \overline{2\ HCl}$$
(add equivalent amounts and boil to dryness)

$$BaS + ZnSO_4 \rightleftarrows BaSO_4 + ZnS$$
(fractional crystallization)

You certainly would not choose fractional crystallization because it is very time-consuming; it is selected only as a last resort. However, it is sometimes resorted to in obtaining crystals of sodium compounds because they are nearly all water-soluble; radium salts are obtained commercially by this process. Since the production of heat costs money, you would exclude processes requiring great quantities of heat if possible. The ideal method of forming a salt from its ions is to neutralize an acid with a base, for there is no opportunity for the salt to be contaminated with anything other than the solvent.

Solubility of Salts

The degree to which any substance dissolves in water is apparently inexplicable. All attempts to formulate broad rules of solubility are at best only general statements. Hence we must take it as a matter of fact that there are great differences in solubility. No beginning chemistry student can know whether or not a particular salt is soluble in water; only after he has actually worked in the laboratory is he able to make general statements like the following regarding the salts *most frequently used in laboratory experiments*:

1. Nitrates, chlorates, and acetates are soluble.
2. Chlorides, except those of Ag^+, Pb^{++}, and Hg^+, are soluble. Bromides and iodides are similar to chlorides in their solubility.
3. Sulfates, except those of Ba^{++}, Sr^{++}, and Pb^{++}, are soluble. $CaSO_4$ and Ag_2SO_4 are slightly soluble.
4. All sulfides are insoluble except those of K^+, Na^+, and NH_4^+. The sulfides of Mg^{++}, Ca^{++}, Ba^{++}, Sr^{++}, Al^{+++}, and Cr^{+++} cannot be precipitated because they hydrolyze.
5. All carbonates, phosphates, and silicates are insoluble except those of Na^+, K^+, and NH_4^+.
6. Soluble salts are in general highly ionized, with the exceptions of $HgCl_2$, $Hg(CN)_2$, and $Pb(C_2H_3O_2)_2$.
7. Salts of amphoteric elements are likely to hydrolyze and may form insoluble hydroxides.
8. With but a few exceptions, the valuable sources of elements in nature are their insoluble compounds.

Hydrolysis of Salts

The term *hydrolysis*, which means water-splitting, is applied to reactions of the type

$$PCl_3 + 3\ H_2O \longrightarrow H_3PO_3 + 3\ \overline{HCl}$$

in which the water splits the covalent bonds between the two non-metals in the phosphorus trichloride molecule. In the process the water molecule itself is split. The name is also applied to reactions between salts and water; even though the ions of salts are already separate from each other, the water molecules actually are split in these cases too, so the name is still considered appropriate.

Hydrolysis of Salts of Weak Acids. Anions which are bases impart basic properties to solutions containing them. They make them feel slippery between the fingers, change the colors of sufficiently acidic indicators, and neutralize acids. Water is an acid, so these anions react with water, producing the OH⁻ ion to an extent depending upon their basicity. For example:

$$2\,Na^+ + CO_3^{--} + H_2O \rightleftarrows 2\,Na^+ + HCO_3^- + OH^-$$

Since OH⁻ is a stronger base than CO_3^{--} and HCO_3^- is a stronger acid than water, the reverse reaction proceeds even more readily. In N/10 solution the reaction reaches equilibrium when the CO_3^{--} ions are 24 times as numerous as the HCO_3^- ions. This is commonly expressed, "The sodium carbonate is 4 per cent hydrolyzed," although the sodium ion has nothing to do with the reaction. Salts whose anions are stronger bases than the carbonate ion are correspondingly more hydrolyzed. We do not speak of the hydrolysis of sodium hydroxide, however, because the equation would be meaningless, the products being the same as the reactants. Salts whose anions are stronger bases than the hydroxide ion—such as sodium amide, $NaNH_2$; calcium oxide, CaO; magnesium nitride, Mg_3N_2; sodium hydride, NaH; and calcium phosphide, Ca_3P_2—are 100 per cent hydrolyzed.

Hydrolysis of Salts of Weak Bases. Salts with acidic or potentially acidic cations (e.g., $Al_2(SO_4)_3 \cdot 6\,H_2O$ or $AlCl_3$) impart acidic properties to solutions containing them. The solutions taste sour, change the colors of appropriate indicators, neutralize bases, and react with metals, liberating hydrogen. Water is a base, so they react with it, producing the hydrogen ion to an extent depending upon their acidity. For example:

$$\begin{bmatrix} H_2O & _{+++} & OH_2 \\ H_2O & Al & OH_2 \\ H_2O & & OH_2 \end{bmatrix}^{+++} + 3\,Cl^- + H_2O \rightleftarrows \begin{bmatrix} H_2O & _{+++} & OH^- \\ H_2O & Al & OH_2 \\ H_2O & & OH_2 \end{bmatrix}^{++} + H_3O^+ + 3\,Cl^-$$

Here again the products of the reaction are a stronger base and a stronger acid than the original ones; thus equilibrium is reached while the H⁺ concentration is only moderate. The chloride ions have nothing to do with the reaction.

The decrease in the charge of the aluminum ion resulting from the loss of the proton makes it a weaker acid. The loss of a second proton takes place only to a slight extent as long as no stronger base than water is present. The somewhat better base, the acetate ion, if present in an equivalent concentration, can readily remove a second and to some extent[3] even a third proton. Omitting, for convenience, the ions not reacting, we have

$$\begin{bmatrix} H_2O & _{+++} & OH^- \\ H_2O & Al & OH_2 \\ H_2O & & OH_2 \end{bmatrix}^{++} + C_2H_3O_2^- \rightleftarrows \begin{bmatrix} H_2O & _{+++} & OH^- \\ H_2O & Al & OH^- \\ H_2O & & OH_2 \end{bmatrix}^+ + HC_2H_3O_2$$

[3] But the neutral product, aluminum hydroxide, must not form to any appreciable extent, even in this practically neutral solution, or a precipitate will appear, for the substance is very insoluble. This may be because of the absence of any charge that causes the molecules to repel each other.

and $\begin{bmatrix} H_2O & _{+++} & OH^- \\ H_2O & Al & OH^- \\ H_2O & & OH_2 \end{bmatrix}^+ + C_2H_3O_2^- \rightleftarrows \begin{bmatrix} H_2O & _{+++} & OH^- \\ H_2O & Al & OH^- \\ H_2O & & OH^- \end{bmatrix}^\circ + HC_2H_3O_2$

Even a fourth proton can be lost to a strong base like OH$^-$, leaving the aluminum in a negative ion, called the aluminate ion. Each successive step of this hydrolysis takes place to a less extent in any given solution.

Although the water molecules shown in the formulas of the hydrated aluminum ion and its dissociation products are definitely part of the larger molecule in each case, they are not bound strongly and are easily lost on drying. For this reason it was a long time before they were known to be part of the structure. The water of hydration was neglected in writing the formulas, and still is except for purposes of instruction. The old way of describing the first reaction in this section was as follows:

$$Al^{+++} + 3Cl^- + H_2O \rightleftarrows Al(OH)^{++} + H^+ + 3Cl^-$$

Only the water molecule which splits up was shown, and this was not shown *attached* to the Al^{+++}, as it actually is. The other five water molecules which are part of the aluminum ion in solution were completely neglected, and so was the free one which captures the proton from the first. It can readily be seen why this reaction is considered another case of hydrolysis; a water molecule is split. This is true, regardless of the fact that the molecule was part of a larger structure, nor does it depend upon what becomes of the proton it loses. However, it is not customary to speak of hydrolysis when the base which reacts with the hydrated ion is any other than water or the anion of the salt itself.

To sum up, a salt will be hydrolyzed if:

1. its anion is a moderate or good base, or
2. its cation is an acid, or
3. if both the above conditions hold true at the same time.

In (1) the solution will of course be basic; in (2) it will be acidic; but in (3) it will be nearly neutral, because the acid cation and the basic anion react with each other. For this reason the hydrolysis goes much further than in (1) or (2). A larger proportion of the cations lose protons because they are being neutralized by the anion, which is a stronger base than water (water is the only base in the second case); likewise a larger proportion of the anions gain protons because they are being neutralized by the cation, which is a stronger acid than water (water is the only acid in the first case).

It is not hard to tell with reasonable certainty whether or not an anion is a base. If it is not familiar to you, it is almost certain to be a base; the only anions which are not basic enough to produce hydrolysis are those found in formulas of strong acids, and you should know the relatively few strong acids. It is equally easy to tell which cations are acids. If a cation has a charge *greater* than 2, or if it is in a B family of the periodic system and has a charge of 2, the ion will be hydrated in solution and is an acid.

Complex Ions

Many substances besides water may form dative bonds with transition metal ions. The central ion thus acquires a new valence layer, composed of the electron pairs which the surrounding molecules or ions share with it. Examples include copper-ammonia ion, $Cu(NH_3)_4^{++}$; ferrocyanide ion, $Fe(CN)_6^{----}$; cobaltinitrite ion, $Co(NO_2)_6^{---}$; nitroprusside ion, $Fe(CN)_5NO^{--}$; chlorozincate ion, $ZnCl_4^{--}$; and iodomercurate ion, HgI_4^{--}. Many of these are of commercial or analytical importance. It will be noticed that covalences of 6 are frequent among them. This would be impossible for atoms in the first row (period) of the periodic system, but most of the transition metal ions have unfilled orbits in the layer beneath the valence layer, with energies nearly the same as those of the valence layer. Orbits of both layers may be used for the shared electrons, making possible covalences as high as 8. Occasionally, particularly in larger atoms, more than four orbits in the valence layer are used, although never until all the lower-lying orbits are filled, for their energy is considerably higher than that of the orbits of the regular valence octet.

Compounds in which a cation has thus built up a valence layer are called *complexes*. If only O^{--}, OH^-, and H_2O constitute the surrounding group of molecules or ions, the name is not usually applied, but this is a matter of history, not logic. The fact that such water molecules are actually chemically combined was not realized until a late date. In the meantime the term "complex" had come to be used for more easily recognizable cases.

QUESTIONS AND PROBLEMS

1. Can an ion be electrically neutral? Are there any ions in a crystal of rock salt?
2. What is an electrolyte? Are concentrated solutions of electrolytes good conductors of electricity? Explain.
3. Define acids and bases in any system.
4. Define normal and molar solutions.
5. How many grams of sulfur are needed to form 500 ml. of H_2SO_4, s.g. 1.72 and 80 per cent H_2SO_4 by weight? What is the normality of the solution?
6. How many ml. of NaOH of s.g. 1.52 and 50 per cent NaOH will be needed to neutralize the H_2SO_4 in question 5?
7. How many grams of Na_2SO_4 will be formed in question 6?
8. How many grams of sodium acetate could be formed from 1 gal. of vinegar of s.g. 1.006 and 5 per cent $HC_2H_3O_2$ by weight?
9. How many calories of heat are produced by mixing 1,125 ml. of HNO_3 of

s.g. 1.0256 and 5 per cent HNO_3 by weight with 500 ml. of potassium hydroxide of s.g. 1.0452 and 5 per cent KOH by weight?
10. Write equations for the hydrolysis of $FeCl_3$, NaCl, $NH_4C_2H_3O_2$, and Na_2SiO_3.
11. Why has it been necessary to consider the formation of the hydronium ions?
12. How many grams of calcium carbonate can be dissolved with 10 l. of 12-molar HCl? How many grams of calcium chloride will be formed?
13. How could you separate a mixture of $BaSO_4$, NaCl, and $NaNO_3$ and obtain the pure salts? Do you believe that you could do it in an hour? Why?
14. What general methods of preparing salts are the most suitable? Which one is least desirable? What is meant by fractional crystallization?

REFERENCES

Books

Salts, Acids and Bases. Walden, P. McGraw-Hill Book Company, Inc.

Articles

"Simplified Nomenclature for Proton Transfer." Alyea, H. N. *J. Chem. Ed.* **16,** 535-538 (1939).
"Ionization." Hazelhurst, T. H. *J. Chem. Ed.* **14,** 316-320 (1937).

» 17 «

CHEMICAL EQUILIBRIA

The term equilibrium has been used frequently in the preceding chapters in connection with both physical and chemical changes. Let us recall some of these examples. In the saturated solution an equilibrium exists between the undissolved substance and the solute dissolved in the solvent. The rate at which molecules leave the solvent and attach themselves to the crystals of the solid just equals the rate at which molecules are separating from the crystal in the process of dissolving. The freezing point of a liquid is the temperature at which the liquid and its solid are in equilibrium. Freezing and melting are taking place at the same rate. The vapor pressure of a liquid is the pressure of its own gas which is in equilibrium with it. Molecules are evaporating from the liquid and condensing into it at the same rate. These are examples of physical equilibria. If two chemical reactions are directly opposed (so that the reactants of one are the products of the other, and vice versa) a chemical equilibrium is obtained when the changes in the two directions are taking place at the same rate. Chemical equilibrium differs from physical equilibrium in that the changes produce new compounds.

Reversible Reactions and Equilibria

Most chemical reactions between moderately simple molecules are reversible; that is, the opposite reaction also takes place. (This is true of all metathetical reactions.) E.g.

$$A + B \rightleftarrows C + D$$

In words, this reversible reaction means that A reacts with B to produce C and D, which in turn are reacting with each other to produce A and B. Equilibrium exists when the speed of the reaction between C and D is as fast as that between A and B. In such cases, no matter which set of reactants you begin with, the other set will be produced by the reaction and the reverse reaction will start. An equilibrium is the automatic result, for if one reaction proceeds more rapidly than the other it will slow down because it is using up the substances which cause it, faster than they are being produced by the opposed reaction. At the same time the other reaction must increase its rate because its reactants are being produced faster than it is using them up; hence the two rates must eventually become equal. When equilibrium has been reached, there will be no further changes in the relative quantities of the substances involved, even though both reactions continue at full speed. If there then remains, say, 15 per cent of one reactant, we say that the reaction which uses it up has gone 85 per cent to completion. The completeness of reactions can vary all the way from zero to 100 per cent. In some chemical reactions the desired substances are produced in such small quantities at equilibrium that the process is worthless. Sometimes, however, it is possible to remove them as fast as they are formed, and equilibrium is never attained. For instance, in the preceding illustration, if D is removed by some means as fast as it forms, the reaction between C and D to form A and B cannot occur since no D is available for reaction. Equilibria and the knowledge of how to control them are extremely important in chemical industries.

Factors Which Affect the Speed of a Chemical Reaction

The characteristic feature of a chemical equilibrium is the fact that two opposing reactions are proceeding at the same speed. Hence if we are to understand equilibria, we must know what factors govern reaction speed. Let us consider the nature of chemical reactions from the kinetic molecular point of view. When one substance reacts with another the reaction occurs only as the molecules of the one collide with the molecules of the other. There is no reaction between molecules at a distance; they must collide, i.e., come in contact with each other. Not all collisions necessarily result in reaction; if the molecules do not hit each other hard enough to disarrange their structures sufficiently, they may rebound unchanged. The rate at which the reaction proceeds depends upon the rate at which successful collisions take place; and this, other factors remaining constant, is obviously proportional to the total number of collisions per second between the proper molecules.

The Concentration Law

Let us consider first the simple case in which one molecule of one kind reacts with one of another kind:

$$H_2 + I_2 \longrightarrow 2\,HI$$

and see how the rate of such collisions is affected by increasing the concentration of hydrogen or iodine, or both. An individual H_2 molecule may collide with any I_2 molecule in the reaction vessel. Obviously the closer these

CHEMICAL EQUILIBRIA

are together the more frequently will a given H_2 molecule run into one of them. Since every H_2 molecule is colliding with I_2 molecules as frequently as is the one we chose to consider, the rate at which H_2—I_2 collisions take place is proportional to the concentration of hydrogen as well as to that of iodine. Expressed mathematically:

$$\text{Collision rate} = k \cdot [H_2] \cdot [I_2]$$

The quantities within the brackets are the concentrations of the substances indicated by the formulas, expressed numerically in any convenient units. (Mols per liter, pounds per cubic foot, and for gases any pressure unit, are common.) Of course the number of collisions per second is not *equal* to the product of the concentrations; it merely varies with them. To transform the variation into an equation we introduce a proportionality constant, k. Its numerical value is determined by the choice of units for the concentrations, the size of the vessel, and so on. The concentrations are multiplied because if a quantity is proportional to each of two others it is proportional to their product. For example: If in a given small unit of volume we have one molecule each of hydrogen and iodine, there is but one possible collision; see container I in Fig. 17.1. If we treble the number of H_2 molecules we have

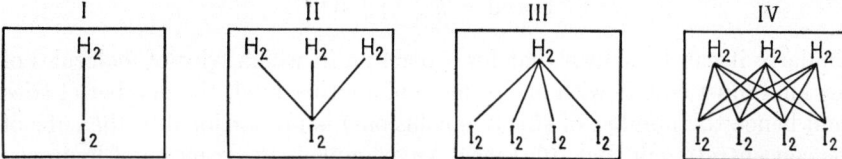

FIG. 17.1. Collision rate is proportional to the product of the concentrations of the reactants.

trebled the number of possible collisions; see container II. If, instead, we quadruple the number of I_2 molecules, we quadruple the number of possible collisions; see container III. But if we treble the one and quadruple the other, the number of possible collisions is 3×4, or 12 times as great; see container IV.

The speed of reaction is not *equal* to the collision rate; usually only a very small fraction of the collisions are effective. Therefore when we write

$$\text{Speed} = k \cdot [H_2] \cdot [I_2]$$

the k has a different numerical value from that used in the preceding equation. The reason that we call it a "constant" is that its value is not changed by any possible alteration in any other quantity *which is mentioned in the mathematical equation.*

The reaction between nitric oxide and oxygen to form the brown gas nitrogen dioxide (a step in the manufacture of nitric acid from ammonia) offers an example of a more complicated case.

$$O_2 + 2\,NO \longrightarrow 2\,NO_2$$

Here it is necessary that the O_2 molecule meet *two* NO molecules in order that a reaction have a chance to take place. The rate of reaction is proportional to the concentration of oxygen, of course, but it must be proportional to the number of *pairs* of NO molecules per unit volume. If an O_2 molecule takes the place of an H_2 molecule in the preceding reaction, the place of the I_2 molecule is taken by a pair of NO molecules.

The number of potential pairs of molecules present in a given volume is not directly proportional to the concentration; the number of pairs increases faster than the number of molecules. With two molecules only one pair is possible; a third molecule could form a pair with either of those already present (making three pairs); a fourth molecule would add three more pairs; a fifth would add four more, and so on. The law of proportionality is not easy to understand, nor is it simple. But when the numbers are as large as those in even an extremely dilute solution or a gas at very low pressure, the number of pairs is proportional to the square of the concentration to within an infinitesimal error.

Since the speed of reaction is always proportional to the rate at which potentially effective collisions occur, we can now write for this case

$$\text{Speed} = k \cdot [O_2] \cdot [NO]^2$$

Similarly it can be shown that for a reaction in which trios of molecules of one kind must collide with one or more of another kind, the number of trios (and hence the number of effective collisions) is proportional to the cube of the concentration of that substance. An example is the reaction of hydrogen with nitrogen to form ammonia.

$$3\,H_2 + N_2 \longrightarrow 2\,NH_3$$

where
$$\text{Speed} = k \cdot [H_2]^3 \cdot [N_2]$$

We shall now state explicitly the generalization suggested by the foregoing discussion:

The speed of a chemical reaction is proportional to the concentrations of the reacting substances, each taken to the power given by the number of molecules of the substance in the chemical equation for the reaction.

This statement is known as the Concentration Law. It was formulated in 1867 by Guldberg and Waage, who called it the Law of Mass Action. It has been thoroughly verified by experiment.

Homogeneous and Heterogeneous Reactions

When a reaction takes place in a clear solution or in a mixture of gases it is called homogeneous. When a solid is acted upon by a liquid or gas the reaction is said to be heterogeneous. In the first case—the one which we have been discussing—there is no difficulty in defining the concentrations. When a solid is involved it is impossible to use its concentration because it is not homogeneously distributed. The specific reaction rate of a solid is not subject to variations due to changes in concentration; whatever value should be used for it is a *constant* value. If, therefore, it is omitted from the speed equation the result will be a different but still constant value for the proportionality constant. When this is determined experimentally the effect of the solid is automatically included. Thus for the reaction of steam on red hot iron:

$$3\ \underline{Fe} + 4\ \overline{\underline{H_2O}} \longrightarrow \underline{Fe_3O_4} + 4\ \overline{\underline{H_2}}$$

we write:

$$\text{Speed} = k \cdot [H_2O]^4$$

In the constant we lump together all the constant factors, such as the surface area of the amount of iron used, the specific reactivity of iron at the temperature chosen, the fraction of collisions which are effective, and the conversion factors made necessary by our choice of units for the speed of reaction and the concentration of steam. We are left with the Concentration Law's simple statement about what will happen to the speed of the reaction if we vary the only variable concentration, that of steam, while keeping everything else constant.

The Effect of Temperature

In order to react, two molecules must collide with a certain minimum violence. This energy which must be present at the collision is called the *energy of activation*.[1] It is different for each reaction. If a reaction proceeds slowly at a given temperature it is because most of the collisions are unsuccessful because they lack the energy of activation. If all molecules had exactly the same kinetic energy at a given temperature, there would be no reaction if the temperature were such that the energy per molecule was less than the energy of activation; but when the temperature rose to such a point that the kinetic energy of the molecules equaled the activation energy, suddenly every collision would result in reaction. The speed of reaction would be too fast to measure. Obviously this is not the case.

There is no contradiction here with the kinetic theory. It is only in collisions between *two* molecules that there is equal distribution of energy. In a triple collision one molecule may bounce away with much more than its share of the energy, or be heavily slowed down. Mathematical investigation shows that most of the molecules will have the average energy or a little more or less, but that a few will have a great deal more or less energy than the average. A precise equation is obtained from which the curves in Fig. 17.2 were plotted. The average energy, b, corresponding to the higher

---

[1] The name comes from the fact that it is possible to "activate" a molecule by increasing its *internal* (as opposed to its kinetic) energy to such a point that the slightest collision will result in reaction. This may be done by raising an electron to an orbit of higher than normal energy by means of irradiation or electron bombardment. Sometimes a step in a chemical reaction has one or more activated molecules as its immediate resultants.

temperature, T_2, is only a little greater than the average energy, a, at the lower temperature, T_1. If the energy of activation for a reaction is c, the shaded region under the curve and to the right of c represents the number of molecules with energy enough to react on collision. The total area under the curve represents the whole number of molecules. It can be seen that the speed of reaction is much higher at T_2 than at T_1. A reaction having a considerably higher heat of activation, d, will go extremely slowly at T_1 and many times as rapidly at T_2. In general, an increase in temperature of 10° C. will double or treble the speed of a reaction which is already proceeding at a moderate rate. *The higher the energy of activation, the greater will be the effect of raising the temperature.*

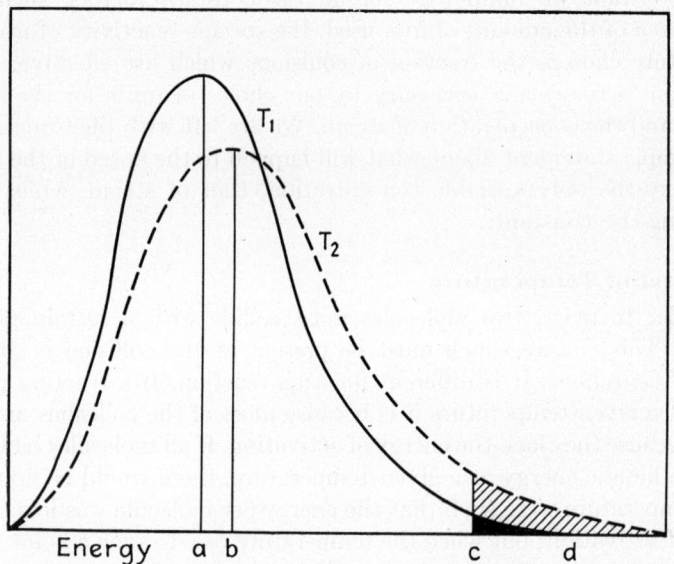

FIG. 17.2. Distribution of energy among molecules at two temperatures. Energy is plotted to the right, number of molecules upward.

The Effect of Catalysts

A catalyst is a substance which alters the speed of a reaction without itself being permanently changed. If the over-all result is to *speed up* the reaction, the process is spoken of as *positive catalysis*. If, however, the effect of the catalyst is to *slow down* the reaction, it is called *negative* catalysis. In the ordinary course of events the catalyst appears to combine with one of the reactants in the catalyzed reaction, and this intermediate catalytic compound then reacts with the other reactant. In this second reaction the final product is formed and the catalyst is set free again. This is a good illustration of the old saying, "the longest way round is sometimes the shortest way home." If the series of reactions which include the catalyst have lower

CHEMICAL EQUILIBRIA

energies of activation than the reaction which would take place in its absence, they will proceed faster than it does. It is quite possible that a large fraction of the molecules colliding with the catalyst may have energy enough to react with it, even at a temperature so low that few or practically none of the molecules of the main reactants would have sufficient energy to react on colliding with each other. The reaction that releases the catalyst must also be relatively rapid if positive catalysis is to result. If an uncatalyzed reaction is reversible, the same reaction catalyzed will also be reversible. Furthermore—and this is extremely important—*catalysis always speeds up the direct and the reverse reactions in the same proportion.*

The Equilibrium Constant

When two molecules of hydrogen iodide collide with sufficient violence, their atoms may change partners and leave the collision as molecules of hydrogen and iodine.

$$2\ HI \longrightarrow H_2 + I_2$$

This equation is the reverse of that on page 222. The two equations, then, describe a reversible reaction; and an equilibrium will result when hydrogen iodide is confined in a reaction vessel under the proper conditions. Likewise, a mixture of hydrogen and iodine will come to equilibrium when a certain amount of hydrogen iodide has been produced. A single equation with a double arrow is regularly used to describe this:

$$H_2 + I_2 \rightleftarrows 2\ HI$$

Such an equation is usually written with the starting materials on the left if that is convenient, but an experiment might well begin with all the substances present. Written in either direction, a double-arrow equation means exactly the same thing, that a specified equilibrium exists.

From such an equation two speed-of-reaction statements can be written:

$$S_r = k_r \cdot [H_2] \cdot [I_2]$$

and

$$S_l = k_l \cdot [HI]^2$$

where the subscript r refers to the direct reaction (the one progressing to the right), and the subscript l to the reaction progressing to the left. But when equilibrium has been obtained, the speeds of these two reactions will be equal; hence, since things equal to equal things are equal to each other.

$$S_r = S_l$$

therefore

$$k_r \cdot [H_2] \cdot [I_2] = k_l \cdot [HI]^2$$

Dividing both members of this equation by $k_l \cdot [H_2] \cdot [I_2]$, we get

$$\frac{k_r}{k_l} = \frac{[HI]^2}{[H_2] \cdot [I_2]}$$

But the quotient of two constants is a constant, so this may be written

$$\frac{[HI]^2}{[H_2] \cdot [I_2]} = K_E$$

This new constant, K_E, is called the *equilibrium constant*. It is important to realize to just what extent it *is* a constant. By the standard conventions of mathematics, the equation just written means that K_E has a numerical value characteristic of this particular chemical reaction, which will not be changed by any changes that may be made in any of the quantities *mentioned in the mathematical equation*, namely, the concentrations. But no claim is made that changes in other conditions will have no effect on the equilibrium constant. Its value changes in a definite way as the temperature changes, for example, but at any fixed temperature it remains constant despite all concentration changes.

The following examples show how chemists derive the numerical value of an equilibrium constant. *The value for K_E cannot be obtained unless the substances in the system can be subjected to quantitative analysis.*

Example 1. Reactions of gases.

$$N_2 + 3 H_2 \rightleftarrows 2 NH_3$$

At a temperature at which hydrogen and nitrogen can combine, these gases are enclosed in a container. Some ammonia soon forms and presently equilibrium is reached. On analysis we find that 20 per cent by volume of the gas is N_2, 70 per cent is H_2, and 10 per cent is NH_3.

It is a consequence of Dalton's Law of Partial Pressures that the individual pressure of each gas in a mixture of gases is given by multiplying the total pressure in the container by the per cent by volume of each gas in it. Thus if the pressure is 10 atm., the respective partial pressures are 2, 7, and 1 atm.

$$K_E = \frac{[NH_3]^2}{[N_2] \cdot [H_2]^3}$$

The numerical value for K_E is

$$K_E = \frac{(1)^2}{(2) \cdot (7)^3} = \frac{1}{686} = 0.00146$$

Example 2. One substance a solid.

$$\overline{C} + \overline{H_2O} \rightleftarrows \overline{CO} + \overline{H_2}$$

Any solid which takes part in a reaction is considered a constant.

$$\frac{[CO][H_2]}{[H_2O]} = K_E$$

CHEMICAL EQUILIBRIA

If the percentage composition of each gas is known, K_E can be calculated as in Example 1.

Many reversible reactions are of great commercial importance. Among these are:

$3 \overline{H_2} + \overline{N_2} \rightleftarrows 2 \overline{NH_3}$ (p. 416, fertilizer, explosives, dyes)

$H_2O + \overline{CO_2} \rightleftarrows H_2CO_3$ (p. 665, beverages, water treatment)

$H_2SO_4 + \underline{NaCl} \rightleftarrows \underline{NaHSO_4} + \overline{HCl}$ (p. 339, textiles, tin cans, glue, chemicals)

$\underline{CaCO_3} \rightleftarrows \underline{CaO} + \overline{CO_2}$ (pp. 353, 522, agriculture, building, paper, sodium hydroxide)

$2 \underline{NaHCO_3} \rightleftarrows \underline{Na_2CO_3} + \overline{H_2O} + \overline{CO_2}$ (pp. 353, 467, soda, soap, glass)

$NH_4^+ + HCO_3^- + Na^+ + Cl^- \rightleftarrows \underline{NaHCO_3} + NH_4^+ + Cl^-$ (p. 353, soda)

$\underline{Ca_3(PO_4)_2} + 2 H_3PO_4 \rightleftarrows 2 \underline{CaHPO_4} + \underline{Ca(H_2PO_4)_2}$ (p. 434, fertilizer)

$Na^+ + AlO_2^- + 2 H_2O \rightleftarrows \underline{Al(OH)_3} + Na^+ + OH^-$ (p. 509, aluminum)

$\underline{Fe_2O_3} + 3 \overline{CO} \rightleftarrows 2 \underline{Fe} + 3 \overline{CO_2}$ (p. 602, iron and steel)

$\underline{Pb} + \underline{PbO_2} + 2H^+ + 2HSO_4^- \rightleftarrows 2 \underline{PbSO_4} + 2 H_2O$ (p. 256, batteries)

The equilibrium constants for these reactions, once they have been determined experimentally by research workers, enable the chemical engineer to work out practical processes for obtaining the desired products.

Ways of Disturbing the Equilibrium of a Chemical Reaction

One of the most far-reaching generalizations in chemistry sums up the effect of changes in the factors (such as concentration, temperature, and pressure) governing an equilibrium. Called the *Principle of Le Chatelier*, it states that *any reaction at equilibrium will adjust itself to reduce the effect of any change in conditions.*[2]

Three important factors which will disturb the equilibrium of a chemical reaction are *change in concentration, temperature*, and *pressure*.

An erroneous conception of a catalyst is very frequent. *If a reaction will not occur without a catalyst, it cannot be induced with a catalyst.* No catalyst will ever be found to speed up a reaction that, thermodynamically, cannot even be started. (The calculations involved here are beyond the scope of this book.) *The value of a catalyst rests in the fact that it can hasten the attainment of equilibrium.* It never changes the numerical value of K_E by one iota.

Changing the concentration of one of the reactants or resultants will affect the equilibrium. The reaction between iron and steam, previously cited, illus-

---

[2] The word "stress" is frequently used to mean change in conditions in stating this principle.

trates this principle. If water vapor is passed over iron, hydrogen is liberated; and if hydrogen is passed over magnetic oxide of iron, water and steam are produced. If the four are at equilibrium in a closed system and hydrogen is forced into the container, more water is formed. If, after the new equilibrium is reached, some water vapor is forced into the container, the equilibrium again shifts, and more hydrogen is produced.

Another example is the reaction between chlorine and water.

$$Cl_2 + H_2O \rightleftarrows H^+ + Cl^- + HClO$$

If, after equilibrium has been reached, the solution is placed in the sunlight, the concentration of chlorine decreases until all of it disappears, the reason being that hypochlorous acid decomposes in the sunlight to form hydrochloric acid and oxygen.

$$2\ HClO \longrightarrow \overline{O_2} + 2\ H^+ + 2\ Cl^-$$

As HClO disappears, more chlorine reacts with water and forms more HClO. The HClO in turn decomposes. The equilibrium can also be shifted from left to right[3] by the addition of sodium hydroxide, which reacts with both acids to form salts. More acid will form until the supply of chlorine is exhausted. The reaction is then said to have gone to completion to the right. Either reaction which enters into an equilibrium may be sent to completion by removing *any one* of its products. For example, the reaction may be sent to completion to the left by exposing the mixture in an open dish so that the chlorine can evaporate. As it evaporates, it will at first be replenished by the reaction of the two acids; but when the chlorine is gone from the solution the reaction to the right ceases, so no more acids are formed and the amounts originally present are used up.

Since either reaction can thus be made to go to completion, an equilibrium mixture can be regarded equally well as being entirely composed of either set of reactants, as far as its use is concerned. Regardless of what percentage of the chlorine atoms in the mixture are in the form of Cl_2 molecules, chlorine water may be considered as simply a solution of chlorine in water, from the point of view of using it for any purpose requiring chlorine. It can equally well be considered as simply a mixture of hydrochloric and hypochlorous acids when it is desired to use it as a source of the hydrogen ion, the chloride ion, or hypochlorous acid.

If neither of the reactions of an equilibrium is sent to actual completion by complete removal of one of the substances which enter into it, a new equilibrium will result from changing any of the concentrations. If the original value for K_E is known, it can be used to calculate all the new concentrations, for no change in concentration can possibly alter the value of K_E. Numerical calculations of this sort will be discussed in a later section.

[3] Note this phrase. It is a shorter way of saying that the new equilibrium mixture contains a smaller amount of the substances on the left side of the equation than the original equilibrium did.

It is thus evident that the Concentration Law is a quantitative statement of *part* of what the Principle of Le Chatelier describes in a qualitative way.

Within certain limits, the effect of a change in temperature is extremely important in influencing chemical equilibria. A glance at page 225 will show the reason why: An increase in temperature increases the speed of reaction to an extent that depends upon the energies of activation, not upon the concentrations. Since the energy of activation for one reaction of an equilibrium pair is always different from that of the opposite reaction, the speed of the two reactions will be affected differently by a temperature change, and *the value of* K_E *will change*. The direction of the change in K_E is described by Van't Hoff's Law, which is therefore another special application of Le Chatelier's Principle. Van't Hoff's Law is as follows: *If heat is applied to a system which is in equilibrium, the equilibrium is shifted in the direction of the reaction which will absorb heat.* The reaction which absorbs heat is the endothermic reaction; i.e., in the equilibrium below, the reaction to the left is the endothermic reaction. The reaction to the right gives up heat and is called the exothermic reaction of the equilibrium. It is clear, according to Van't Hoff's Law, that the reaction

$$2\,SO_2 + O_2 \rightleftarrows 2\,SO_3 + \Delta$$

should not be carried out at any higher temperature than necessary. The rate of this reaction at room temperature is very slow, but as the temperature is raised, the velocity increases. Simultaneously the equilibrium shifts to the left. The solution to the dilemma, described on page 229, is to use a catalyst so that equilibrium will be obtained rapidly at the lowest possible temperature.

We said above that the energy of activation for the direct reaction always differs from that for the reverse reaction in an equilibrium. This is because the activated state is the same for both reactions in an equilibrium.

$$2\,SO_2 + O_2 \rightleftarrows \binom{\text{collision}}{\text{complex}} \rightleftarrows 2\,SO_3 + \Delta$$

The energy relationships can be made clearer by writing the different parts of the equation on different levels. The SO_3 will be on the lowest level, because in changing into SO_3 the SO_2-O_2 mixture *lost* energy, namely, the heat of reaction. The collision complex must be on the highest level because it is formed from the original mixture by the addition of a lot of kinetic energy.

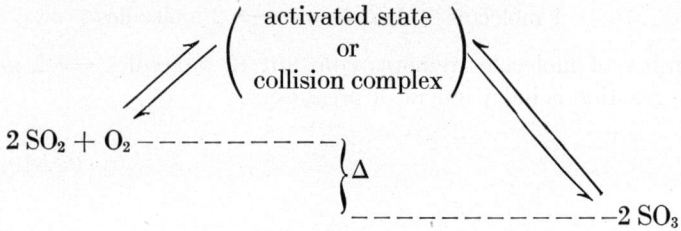

The kinetic energy which colliding molecules must have in order to reach the activated state is the energy of activation. The energy of activation for SO_3 is greater than that for the SO_2-O_2 mixture because the SO_3 had less internal energy to start with. The difference, Δ, between the activation energies is precisely the energy given out by the exothermic reaction or absorbed by the endothermic reaction, i.e., the heat of reaction. This is the explanation of Van't Hoff's Law. When a system in equilibrium is raised to a higher temperature both the direct and the reverse reactions are speeded up, but the endothermic reaction is speeded up more because it has the higher energy of activation.

The effect of pressure upon a chemical equilibrium depends upon the compressibilities of the reactants. It is negligible except for gases. The concentration of a gas, of course, varies directly with the pressure, so that whenever a gas is one of the reactants, its pressure rather than its molar concentration is used in the Concentration Law. In numerical calculations the use of this law and the K_E for the particular reaction is indispensable. When we wish only to know the direction of the equilibrium shift produced by raising the pressure (while keeping the composition of the feed mixture the same) there is an easy way to apply the Principle of Le Chatelier. Simply look at the chemical equation for the reaction and see whether either reaction, if it took place in a closed container, would reduce the number of molecules present. If so, this reaction would be favored by the increase in pressure, for a reduction in the number of molecules would reduce the pressure, thus reducing the "stress" which the increase in pressure imposes. Consider the reaction

$$N_2 \;+\; 3\,H_2 \;\rightleftarrows\; 2\,NH_3$$
$$1 \text{ molecule} + 3 \text{ molecules} \longrightarrow 2 \text{ molecules}$$
$$4 \text{ molecules} \longrightarrow 2 \text{ molecules}$$

Doubling the pressure suddenly would momentarily increase the speed of the direct reaction sixteen-fold and that of the reverse reaction four-fold. When equilibrium was again obtained, the percentage of ammonia in the mixture would be higher than before. In this reaction the greatest yield of ammonia is obtained at high pressure. If the system is at equilibrium at a given temperature and the pressure is then increased, more NH_3 is formed. This reaction is carried out on a commercial scale at as much as 1000 atm. pressure. In the reaction,

$$H_2 \;+\; Cl_2 \;\rightleftarrows\; 2\,HCl$$
$$1 \text{ molecule} + 1 \text{ molecule} \longrightarrow 2 \text{ molecules}$$

the number of molecules remains constant (2 molecules $\longrightarrow$ 2 molecules) and the reaction is independent of pressure.

EQUILIBRIUM OF A SUBSTANCE WITH ITS IONS

Ionization of Weak Acids

The dissociation of a compound into ions can be considered as a special case of chemical equilibrium. Water is regularly one of the reacting substances but is not mentioned in the chemical equation or the Concentration Law expression for K_E. Let us see how this can be. Consider the reaction which takes place (to an extent to be determined) when 0.1 mol of acetic acid, $HC_2H_3O_2$, is diluted with water to a volume of 1 l.

$$HC_2H_3O_2 + H_2O \rightleftarrows H_3O^+ + C_2H_3O_2^-$$

If this reaction were to go to completion to the right, the amount of water would diminish from 994 g. (55.2 mols) to 992.2 g. (55.1 mols). This is a change of less than 0.2 of 1 per cent, which is negligible. Therefore, in the expression

$$\frac{[H_3O^+] \cdot [C_2H_3O^-]}{[HC_2H_3O_2] \cdot [H_2O]} = K_E$$

we may regard $[H_2O]$ as a constant and assimilate it into the equilibrium constant by multiplying both sides of the above equation by it. The new constant is written K_I to distinguish it from the ordinary equilibrium constant, and is called the ionization constant. We have already explained (page 195) why we omit the water from the chemical equation and write it as follows:

$$HC_2H_3O_2 \rightleftarrows H^+ + C_2H_3O_2^-$$

Thus the expression for the ionization constant is simplified to:

$$\frac{[H^+] \cdot [C_2H_3O_2^-]}{[HC_2H_3O_2]} = K_I$$

Since this procedure is simpler but still perfectly satisfactory, everyone follows it.

Calculation of an Ionization Constant. The extent to which the reaction with water takes place before coming to equilibrium depends upon how strong the acid is. K_I is therefore an ideal measure of the strength of an acid, and its numerical value must be determined for each weak acid. Let us assume that chemists can determine the actual concentration of H^+ ions in a solution. (The procedure is discussed on page 238.) They have found that at 18° for every 100 molecules in an M/10 acetic acid solution, *on an average* 98.67 molecules are undissociated and 1.33 molecules are dissociated into H^+ ions and $(C_2H_3O_2^-)$ ions. It is customary in calculating the numerical value for K_I to express the solute and its ions in molar concentrations. We may now substitute numerical values in the equation for K_I.

$$\frac{[0.1 \times 0.0133][0.1 \times 0.0133]}{[0.1 - 0.1 \times 0.0133]} = K_I$$

or
$$\frac{(0.00133)(0.00133)}{(0.09867)} = 0.000018 = 1.8 \times 10^{-5}$$

In discussing equilibrium constants it was shown that the *numerical value for K_E is constant. Likewise the numerical value for K_I is constant.* Suppose that nine volumes of water are now added to the M/10 solution of acetic acid. The solution is 0.01 molar. If we assume that the degree of ionization is the same in the M/100 solution as in the M/10 acetic acid (which is *not true*), the value for K_I is:

$$\frac{(0.01 \times 0.013)(0.01 \times 0.013)}{(0.01 - 0.01 \times 0.013)} = 1.8 \times 10^{-8}$$

On the basis of this assumption, the value for K_I has changed from 1.8×10^{-5} to 1.8×10^{-8}. But K_I *must remain constant*; hence more acetic acid will ionize. (All substances which ionize approach 100 per cent ionization at infinite dilution.) Ionization required in the M/100 solution for K_I to equal 1.8×10^{-5} would be as follows:

Let x = the degree of ionization or dissociation in the M/100 solution; then:

$$\frac{(0.01\,x)(0.01\,x)}{(0.01 - 0.01\,x)} = 1.8 \times 10^{-5}$$

This can be solved by using the general quadratic equation

$$x = \frac{-b \pm \sqrt{b^2 - 4ac}}{2a}$$

$$x = 0.0417$$

In an M/100 solution of acetic acid the degree of ionization as calculated is 4.17 per cent. Experiments in the laboratory agree with this, for the measured H^+ ion concentration in a solution of this concentration is $4 \cdot 10^{-4}$, which is 0.01×0.04.

Ionization of Water

Pure water is, as we already know, a very weak acid; it ionizes according to the equation

$$2\,H_2O \rightleftarrows H_3O^+ + OH^-$$

Usually written

$$H_2O \rightleftarrows H^+ + OH^-$$

The water molecule which was omitted in the second form of the equation is the one which acted as a base by taking the proton from the other. It is the same one that is omitted from the equation for the ionization of any other acid and is assimilated into the ionization constant. Here, however, the acid itself is water, so the expression for K_I,

$$\frac{[H^+] \cdot [OH^-]}{[H_2O]} = K_I$$

still contains the concentration of water. Once more we multiply both members of the equation by $[H_2O]$; the new constant, equal to $K_I \cdot [H_2O]$, is designated K_W. We have, then, the interesting result that *in any solution the product of the concentrations of hydrogen and hydroxide ions is constant.*

$$[H^+] \cdot [OH^-] = K_W$$

The actual concentration of H^+ ions in pure water has been determined by means of the hydrogen electrode (page 263). It is only 0.0000001 mol per liter, more conveniently expressed as 10^{-7} M. Referring to the chemical equation, we see that 1 OH^- ion is formed for each H^+ ion; hence the molar concentration of OH^- ions in pure water is also 10^{-7}. Substituting these values in the expression for K_W, we find that the numerical value of this constant is

$$[10^{-7}] \cdot [10^{-7}] = 10^{-14} = K_W$$

It follows that in any solution in which the (H^+) increases, the (OH^-) must decrease, and vice versa; for the product of the two is always 1×10^{-14} at 25° C. A few examples will illustrate this statement.

Example 1. What is the concentration of hydroxyl ions in a 0.1 M solution of HNO_3 if the nitric acid is 100 per cent ionized and each ion is active?

$$[H^+][OH^-] = 1 \times 10^{-14}$$

The concentration of hydrogen ions equals 0.1 mol or 1×10^{-1} mol.

$$(1 \times 10^{-1}) \times [OH^-] = 1 \times 10^{-14}$$
$$[OH^-] = \frac{1 \times 10^{-14}}{1 \times 10^{-1}} = 1 \times 10^{-13} \text{ mols}$$

of hydroxyl ions per liter.

Example 2. What is the concentration of hydrogen ions in a 0.001 M solution of NaOH if the sodium hydroxide is 100 per cent ionized and each ion is active?

$$[H^+] \times (1 \times 10^{-3}) = 1 \times 10^{-14}$$
$$[H^+] = 1 \times 10^{-11}$$

Example 3. What is the concentration of hydroxyl ions in a 0.1 M solution of $HC_2H_3O_2$ if the acetic acid is 1 per cent ionized?

The concentration of H^+ ions is $(0.1) \times (0.01)$, or 0.001 mol per liter.

$$(1 \times 10^{-3}) \times [OH^-] = 1 \times 10^{-14}$$
$$[OH^-] = 1 \times 10^{-11} \text{ mols per liter}$$

If you were to count all the (OH⁻) ions in one drop ($\frac{1}{20}$ ml.) of this solution at the rate of 5 per second, how long would it take? There are 6×10^{23} atoms in 1 gram atom of hydrogen.

$$\frac{6 \times 10^{23} \times 1 \times 10^{-11}}{1000 \times 20 \times 5} = \text{answer in seconds}$$

At the same rate of counting, how long would it take to count all the hydrogen ions in one drop of pure water?

The Degree of Acidity of a Solution. pH. The amount of acid in a solution is a different thing from the acidity of the solution. A solution one liter of which contains a mol of hydrochloric or nitric acid is much more strongly acidic than it would be if it contained a mol of acetic acid. In the first solution there is a mol of hydrogen ions, because the reaction of a strong acid with water is complete.

i.e., $\qquad\qquad HCl + H_2O \longrightarrow H_3O^+ + Cl^-$
or briefly, $\qquad\qquad HCl \longrightarrow H^+ + Cl^-$
$\qquad\qquad\qquad\qquad$ (0) mol $\quad$ 1 mol $\quad$ 1 mol

In the second solution there is nearly a mol of $HC_2H_3O_2$ molecules and only a small fraction of a mol of H^+.

$$HC_2H_3O_2 \rightleftarrows H^+ + C_2H_3O_2^-$$
$\qquad$ 0.9957 mol $\qquad$ 0.0043 mol $\quad$ 0.0043 mol

It would take just 1 mol of sodium hydroxide to neutralize either solution, but all the properties of acids are shown a thousand times as intensely in the HCl solution as in the $HC_2H_3O_2$ solution. It has been found that the concentration of H^+ ions in a solution is a perfect measure of its degree of acidity, as contrasted with its content of (weak or strong) acid.

There are innumerable practical applications of a knowledge of hydrogen ion concentration. These have made it imperative that some simple method be devised for expressing it numerically; it is folly to expect the layman to talk in terms of 1×10 to the -7, -11, etc. The term now most commonly used to express the acidity (or alkalinity) of a solution is pH, devised by Sörensen. The p represents potential, because the actual concentration of hydrogen ions in a solution was originally determined by measuring the voltage of a cell in which one electrode was covered with hydrogen. The mathematical expression for pH is:

$$pH = \log \frac{1}{[H^+]}$$

pH equals the logarithm of the reciprocal of the molar hydrogen ion concentration. Numerically it is equal to the logarithm of the number of liters of the solution which contains 1 mol of H^+ ion.

CHEMICAL EQUILIBRIA

TABLE 17.1. pH VALUES OF VARIOUS ACIDS AND BASES (0.1 N)

Acids	pH Value	Bases	pH Value
Hydrochloric acid	1.0	Sodium bicarbonate	8.4
Sulfuric acid	1.2	Borax	9.2
Phosphoric acid	1.5	Ammonia	11.1
Sulfurous acid	1.5	Sodium carbonate	11.6
Acetic acid	2.9	Trisodium phosphate	12.0
Alum	3.2	Sodium silicate	12.2
Carbonic acid	3.8	Lime (saturated)	12.3
Boric acid	5.2	Sodium hydroxide	13.0

TABLE 17.2. APPROXIMATE pH OF SOME COMMON SUBSTANCES

Apples	3	Milk of magnesia	10.5
Asparagus	5.5	Sauerkraut	3.5
Beer	4–5	Salmon	6.2
Cabbage	5.3	Shrimp	7
Carrots	5	Tomatoes	4.2
Ginger ale	2–4	Sea water	8.2
Lemons	2.3	Human spinal fluid	7.4
Cows' milk	6.6	Human urine	4.8–8.4

The mathematical definition of pH looks rather formidable, but it is not necessary to use it unless very accurate work (i.e., work involving fractions of a pH unit) is being done. Instead, we can make use of the fact that when [H$^+$] is expressed as M/10, M/1000, etc., pH is numerically equal to the number of zeros in the denominator. Of course if [H$^+$] is expressed expo-

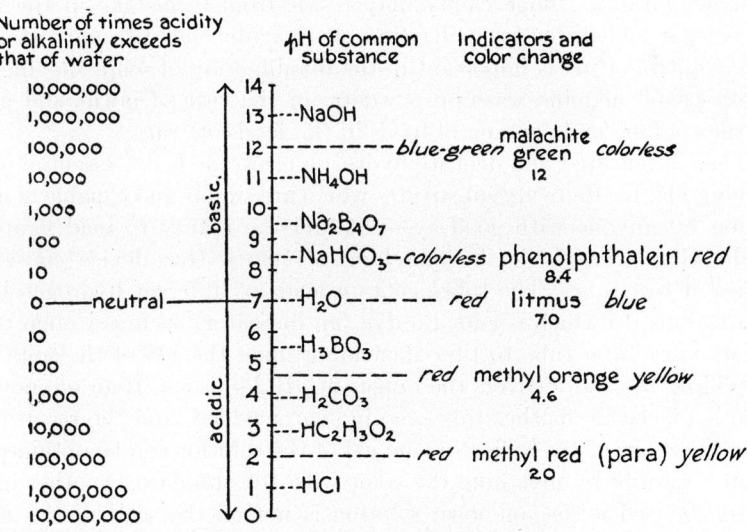

FIG. 17.3. pH scale. $pH = \log \frac{1}{[H^+]}$.

nentially, as 10^{-7} or 10^{-4} for example, the corresponding pH's are 7 and 4 respectively.

It should be noted that a solution with a pH of 6 has 10 times as many hydrogen ions as a solution with a pH of 7, one with a pH of 5 has 100 times as many as one of 7, one with a pH of 4 has 1000 times as many as one of 7, etc. The pH scale is shown graphically in Fig. 17.3.

The information in this figure aids us to understand many of the following chemical facts. Strong acids have low pH values. Strong bases have high pH values. Boric acid can be used as an eyewash because it is a very weak acid. Water used for drinking purposes usually has a pH between 7.0 and 7.8; if the pH value were low, the water would corrode or dissolve iron pipes. The human body has the property of maintaining a pH constancy in the blood stream of nearly 7.2. The pH rises slightly after a meal because some hydrochloric acid is needed for the digestion of food in the stomach. Any marked change in it results in immediate death.

Impurities are removed from water most rapidly when coagulants are added at a definite pH; this value must be determined for each water supply. Corrosion control is often a problem of controlling pH. The bleaching of paper and other fabrics is done most efficiently at some particular pH. Farmers add lime to the soil to neutralize acidity and thus control pH. The brewing and fermentation industries depend to no small extent upon control of pH for maximum production. Many old industries which depended upon "rule of thumb," "luck," or "a sign of the moon" really depended upon control of pH. Cream is churned to butter most quickly at a certain pH. The large baking establishments now carefully control the pH of the dough. "Grainy" fudge candy may result from a mistake in the amount of vinegar added, for crystallization of sugar depends to some extent upon pH. Control of pH is important in the manufacture of soap, shaving cream, tooth paste, alkaline washing powders; in the care of lawns and gardens; in the cooking and canning of food; in the foods we eat.

The complicated and delicate hydrogen electrode is not essential in determining pH, for there are substitutes which are simple and capable of manipulation by anyone with good eyesight and the ability to read figures. The underlying principle is the matching of colors. One device consists of a series of test tubes. The tubes contain acids of different hydrogen ion concentrations, to which is added a dye (an indicator) such as Congo red. The colors vary from tube to tube depending upon the pH of the solution and providing the series covers the ranges of pH 2.0 to 5.2. If an unknown solution is placed in another tube, the indicator added, and the resulting color is in the range of the indicator, the pH of the solution can be obtained in less than a minute by matching the color with the standard. Another indicator must be used if the unknown solution is not on the scale of the standard indicator. Dozens of organic dyes show gradual color changes with change in pH. Colors corresponding to the solutions may be painted on paper and used instead of the solutions. Colored glass disks are also used. (A commercial device on the market determines the pH by means of glass electrodes. The electrodes are dipped in the solution whose pH is desired, several knobs are turned, a button is pushed, and the pH is read on a dial. Anyone can push the button and read the dial.)

Controlling pH

If the pH of a solution is too high for a given purpose it can be lowered to the desired point by adding an acid; if it is too low, a base is added to raise it. It might seem natural to use a strong acid or base, but this is not always convenient. A single drop of N HCl added to 50 ml. of pure water will lower the pH from 7 to 3; a single drop of N NaOH will raise the pH of the water to 11. You might as well try to plant tulips with a steam shovel as use NaOH and HCl to make an accurate adjustment to an intermediate pH. Obviously weaker acids and bases are called for here.

The Common Ion Effect. It is not necessary to have an array of successively weaker acids to produce successively higher pH's, because any weak acid can be weakened still further, to any desired extent, by adding an appropriate base. To avoid chemical complications and to facilitate the computation of quantities it is customary to add the conjugate base (negative ion) of the acid itself, in the form of the sodium salt of that acid. The result can be calculated from the Concentration Law.

What change in pH will be produced if 0.1 mol of $NaC_2H_3O_2$ is dissolved in 1 l. of M/10 $HC_2H_3O_2$ solution? On page 233 we said that in M/10 acetic acid solution $[H^+] = 0.00133$. The pH of this solution is then log $\frac{1}{0.00133} = 2.88$. On the same page we showed that K_I for $HC_2H_3O_2$ was 1.8×10^{-5}. Then, according to the Mass Law,

$$\frac{[H^+] \cdot [C_2H_3O_2^-]}{[HC_2H_3O_2]} = 1.8 \times 10^{-5}$$

Now if 0.1 mol of $NaC_2H_3O_2$ is added, the concentration of acetate ions is momentarily $0.1+0.00133$. The equilibrium is destroyed, for the probability of collisions between $C_2H_3O_2^-$ ions and H^+ ions is greater than it was before the addition of the $NaC_2H_3O_2$, and therefore *more acetic acid molecules must form* before equilibrium is again established. Let x equal the number of mols of H^+ and also of $C_2H_3O_2^-$ which must recombine so that K_I will remain constant.

The original hydrogen ion concentration will be diminished by x since each mol of acetic acid formed uses up 1 mol of H^+. Similarly the $C_2H_3O_2^-$ concentration will be diminished by an amount x and the unionized acetic acid concentration will be increased by an amount x.

Substituting these facts in the expression for the Concentration Law, we have

$$\frac{(0.00133 - x)(0.10133 - x)}{(0.09867 + x)} = 1.8 \cdot 10^{-5}$$

$$x = 0.001312$$

The new concentration of hydrogen ions is $0.00133 - 0.001312$, or 0.000018 mols per liter. Accordingly the pH of the solution is given by $\log \frac{1}{0.000018} = 4.74$. The addition of a salt which contains an ion $(C_2H_3O_2)^-$ in common with the acetic acid has thus raised its pH nearly two units.

In order for the addition of a salt to lower the acidity (raise the pH), the essential point is that the anion of the salt must be a base.

This ion may be common to the acid as in the above case, but it is not necessary that it be related to the acid. For instance, HCl on ionizing gives the very weak base Cl$^-$. Addition of sodium chloride to this solution would not effectively raise the pH since the Cl$^-$ ion has little tendency to combine with the proton in solution. For similar reasons NaNO$_3$ would not be used because NO$_3^-$ is too weak as a base. None of the negative ions (conjugate bases) of the strong acids—HCl, H$_2$SO$_4$, HNO$_3$—when introduced to an acid solution will raise the pH. But such ions as CO$_3^=$, C$_2$H$_3$O$_2^-$ and PO$_4^\equiv$ are strong bases and will consequently react with protons in strong acid solutions and thus raise the pH of the solution. These and other suitable ions may be introduced in the form of any convenient soluble metallic salt. They are generally introduced as sodium and potassium salts since the Na$^+$ and K$^+$ ions have no tendency to form insoluble compounds with the negative ion of the acid.

Buffer Salts

How would you prepare a solution to which either acid or base could be added without the solution changing in pH? Can it be done? If this were impossible, you would not be alive. The pH of the blood must remain constant at a pH of about 7.2. When we eat, hydrochloric acid must be generated so that the gastric juice can act effectively upon the food in the stomach. If hydrogen ions were withdrawn from the blood and there were no mechanism to counteract this effect, the blood would become more alkaline. The oxidation of food products in the body results in the formation of carbon dioxide which tends to produce an acid reaction in the blood. Yet the blood does not become excessively alkaline during the digestion of food, or excessively acid when we are working (when substances are being rapidly burned in the body).

In order that the addition of an acid to a solution shall not make it acid, a base must be present to react with it; similarly, if the addition of a base is not to make the solution basic, an acid must be present to react with the added base. How can both acid and base be present at the same time without their reacting with each other? There are two ways. In the first place, a single substance can be both an acid and a base. In this case either it must be very weak in both ways, like water, or it must be much weaker in one way than in the other, like $H_2PO_4^-$. In the first case it is ineffective and in the second it is unequally effective; both are unsatisfactory. In the second place, an acid and a base can be present together in a solution if their reaction with each other produces the same acid and base. This occurs when the base is the conjugate base of the acid, namely, its own anion. For example, if an acetate ion takes a proton from an acetic acid molecule, the products are an acetic acid molecule and an acetate ion. A solution of low hydrogen ion concentration which contains relatively large amounts of both a weak acid and its anion can react with considerable amounts of added H^+ ion or OH^- with very little change in pH. The reason for this can be seen by examining the numerical situation in the Mass Law expression for the equilibrium constant of acetic acid mixed with sodium acetate. Substituting the numerical value for x in the equation at the end of the preceding section, we have

$$\frac{(0.000018)(0.10002)}{(0.09998)} = 1.8 \cdot 10^{-5}$$

Both acetate ion and acetic acid are practically 0.1 M, but the H^+ concentration, 0.000018 M, is much smaller; as a matter of fact, it is only $\frac{0.000018}{0.1}$, or 0.00018 (less than 2 ten-thousandths) as large. The addition of 0.001 mol of NaOH per liter would be more than 50 times as much as would be needed to use up all the free H^+ in the solution, but it would neutralize only 1 per cent of the acetic acid (0.001 is 1 per cent of 0.1) and increase the amount of acetate ion by that same fraction. This increase of 1 per cent in the numerator and the decrease of 1 per cent in the denominator of the fraction would increase its value 2 per cent, but equilibrium could be restored by a 2 per cent decrease in the concentration of H^+. So we see that this amount of base, instead of making the solution strongly basic, has a negligible effect on the acidity of an acetic acid–acetate mixture.

A solution which thus resists change in pH is said to be *buffered*. If buffered strongly enough, it may be added to other solutions, bacterial cultures, etc., to buffer them, in which case it is called a *buffer solution*. In buffer mixtures the acid may be an anion as well as the base. E.g., $H_2PO_4^-$ is an acid because it can give up protons:

$$\underset{\text{acid}}{H_2PO_4^-} + \underset{\text{base}}{OH^-} \longrightarrow HPO_4^{--} + H_2O$$

Or it can act as a base:

$$H_2PO_4^- + H^+ \longrightarrow H_3PO_4$$

Thus mixtures of the three sodium phosphates are frequently used as *buffer salts*. Trisodium phosphate gives a strongly basic solution (*p*H of 12.0), disodium phosphate solution has a *p*H of 8.4, and monosodium phosphate has a *p*H of 4.6. If Na_3PO_4 and Na_2HPO_4 are mixed, the *p*H of the solution is between 8.4 and 12.0, depending upon the ratio of salts present. Such a mixture will react with either acid or base.

$$\begin{cases} Na_3PO_4 \\ Na_2HPO_4 \end{cases} + NaOH \longrightarrow \text{more trisodium phosphate}$$

$$\begin{cases} Na_3PO_4 \\ Na_2HPO_4 \end{cases} + H_3PO_4 \longrightarrow \text{more disodium phosphate}$$

Likewise a mixture of disodium phosphate and monosodium phosphate will react with either an acid or a base.

$$\begin{cases} Na_2HPO_4 \\ NaH_2PO_4 \end{cases} + NaOH \longrightarrow \text{more disodium phosphate}$$

$$\begin{cases} Na_2HPO_4 \\ NaH_2PO_4 \end{cases} + H_3PO_4 \longrightarrow \text{more monosodium phosphate}$$

Of course there is a limit to the amount of acid or base which can be added.

Saturated Solutions. Solubility Product

As has been said, the concentration of solute in a saturated solution is constant at a given temperature. When hydrogen sulfide is bubbled into a solution of lead acetate, black lead sulfide precipitates. As shown in Fig. 17.4, an equilibrium exists between solid lead sulfide and Pb^{++} and S^{--} ions in solution.

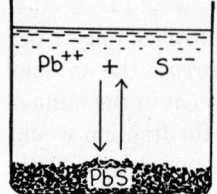

FIG. 17.4. A precipitate of PbS is in equilibrium with Pb^{++} and S^{--} ions.

$$PbS \rightleftarrows Pb^{++} + S^{--}$$

At equilibrium, the rate at which solid lead sulfide dissolves just equals the rate at which lead and sulfide ions recombine. We can therefore write

$$\frac{[Pb^{++}][S^{--}]}{[PbS]} = K_E$$

Since the amount of solid lead sulfide is immaterial, the factor [PbS] may be considered as a constant. (For example, the amount of sugar which dissolves in 100 ml. of water does not vary with a change in the amount of solid sugar in the solution. The only effect of more or less of the solid phase is to alter the time required to reach saturation equilibrium.) Multiplying both sides of the equation by [PbS], we get

$$[Pb^{++}] \cdot [S^{--}] = K_E \cdot [PbS] = K_{sp}$$

CHEMICAL EQUILIBRIA

When the concentration of the solid is thus assimilated into the equilibrium constant for a saturated solution, the new constant is called the *solubility product*. The above equation means: *At a definite temperature the product of the molar concentrations of the ions of a solute, in a saturated solution of that solute, is a constant.* This statement is much more accurate for sparingly soluble solutes than for very soluble compounds. If the activity coefficient of a substance is approximately equal to unity, the solubility product law is very exact. Numerical values may be obtained for K_{sp}, providing it is possible to obtain accurate analyses of the ions in solution. By analysis, the molar concentration of lead ions in a saturated solution is 2×10^{-14}. The value for K_{sp} is:

$$(2 \times 10^{-14})(2 \times 10^{-14}) = 4 \times 10^{-28} = K_{sp}$$

It is assumed that there is one sulfide ion for each lead ion and that all the PbS in solution is dissociated.

Silver chloride and magnesium hydroxide are only slightly soluble in water. If the solubility products of these compounds are assumed to be K_{sp} for $AgCl = 1 \times 10^{-10}$ and for $Mg(OH)_2 = 0.32 \times 10^{-10}$, and we wish to know the molar concentration of ions in each solution, we can calculate them as follows:

$$[Ag^+][Cl^-] = K_{sp} = 1 \times 10^{-10}$$
$$\text{Let } x = [Ag^+] \text{ and also } [Cl^-]$$

then $x^2 = 1 \times 10^{-10}$, $x = 1 \times 10^{-5} = 0.00001 =$ molar concentration of Ag^+ and also Cl^-. The actual number of grams of silver ion in a liter of the solution is 0.00001 multiplied by the atomic weight of silver.

$$[Mg^{++}][OH^-][OH^-] = K_{sp} = 0.32 \times 10^{-10}$$
$$[Mg^{++}][OH^-]^2 = 0.32 \times 10^{-10}$$

Let $x = [Mg^{++}]$. The concentration of hydroxyl ions is twice as great as that of the magnesium ions since two hydroxyl ions are formed for each magnesium ion; therefore $[OH^-] = 2x$.

$$(x)(2x)^2 = 0.32 \times 10^{-10}$$
$$4x^3 = 0.32 \times 10^{-10}$$
$$x^3 = 0.08 \times 10^{-10} = 8 \times 10^{-12}$$
$$x = 2 \times 10^{-4} = 0.0002$$

The number of grams of magnesium ion in a liter of the solution is 0.0002 multiplied by the gram-atomic weight of magnesium. Table 17.3 gives the solubility product values for a few slightly soluble substances. It is assumed that solutions of these solutes are completely ionized; according to the Debye-Hückel theory they would be regarded as 100 per cent ionized. The temperature at which the K_{sp} values were obtained was approximately 20° C.

TABLE 17.3. SOLUBILITY PRODUCTS

Compound	Formula	Solubility Product
Aluminum hydroxide	$Al(OH)_3$	1.1×10^{-15}
Barium sulfate	$BaSO_4$	1×10^{-10}
Calcium carbonate	$CaCO_3$	0.9×10^{-8}
Calcium sulfate	$CaSO_4$	6.1×10^{-5}
Cupric sulfide	CuS	2×10^{-48}
Ferrous sulfide	FeS	3.7×10^{-19}
Lead sulfate	$PbSO_4$	1×10^{-8}
Lead sulfide	PbS	4×10^{-28}
Magnesium hydroxide	$Mg(OH)_2$	0.32×10^{-10}
Mercuric sulfide	HgS	4×10^{-50}
Silver chloride	$AgCl$	1×10^{-10}
Strontium carbonate	$SrCO_3$	1×10^{-9}
Zinc sulfide	ZnS	1×10^{-23}

Although solubility product data are not as accurate for very soluble substances as for those listed in Table 17.3, equilibria effects are just as apparent. In Fig. 17.5 the effect of a common ion on a saturated solution of NaCl is illustrated. If HCl is bubbled into a saturated solution of NaCl, crystals of NaCl will soon deposit. Since the product of the molar concentrations of the ions of a substance in a saturated solution of that substance is constant, the addition of the common Cl⁻ ion causes some NaCl to precipitate. If some saturated $(NH_4)_2SO_4$ is added to a saturated $CaSO_4$ solution, more calcium sulfate will precipitate. In this example the solubility of $(NH_4)_2SO_4$ is large compared to that of $CaSO_4$, so the concentration of sulfate ion times the concentration of calcium ion momentarily *after mixing* exceeds the K_{sp} for $CaSO_4$. Would you expect any KNO_3 to precipitate from 1 l. of 1-molar KNO_3 if 1 l. of 1-molar $NaNO_3$ were mixed with it? Why? There are many practical industrial applications of common ion effect; it is used in the chemical laboratory in the quantitative precipitation of substances.

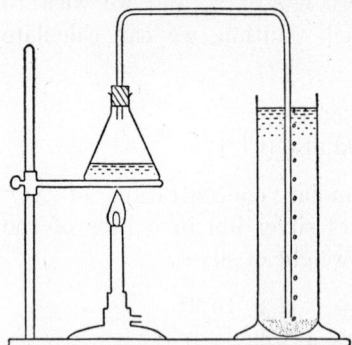

FIG. 17.5. Common-ion effect. HCl gas bubbled into a saturated solution of NaCl causes some of the salt to precipitate.

QUESTIONS AND PROBLEMS

1. K_I of formic acid, $HCHO_2$, is 2×10^{-4}. Compare the degree of dissociation in a 0.01 M solution with that in a 0.001 M solution.

CHEMICAL EQUILIBRIA

2. What is the molar concentration of H^+ in each of the solutions in Question 1?
3. Calculate the pH of each solution in question 1.
4. How many times as fast do nitrogen and hydrogen unite to form ammonia if the pressure of a given mixture is increased 100-fold? How is the rate of decomposition of ammonia in the same mixture affected by this change in pressure?
5. If a reaction produces 0.01 mol per second at 20° C., how much would it be likely to produce at 100° C.? How much faster should cooking take place in a pressure cooker under a gauge pressure of 15 lbs./sq. in. (=2 atm. total)? Estimate the temperature in the cooker from a table of the vapor pressure of water.
6. Ammonia, NH_3, reacts largely with water to form ammonium hydroxide, NH_4OH (the N and the O are joined by a hydrogen bond), which in turn dissociates slightly into NH_4^+ and OH^- ions. Explain why it is justifiable to call the solution "ammonia water" or simply "ammonia."
7. Could a mixture of Na_3PO_4 and NaH_2PO_4 be used as a buffer solution? Why? In an equimolar mixture of a weak acid and its sodium salt, how does the hydrogen ion concentration compare with the K_I of the acid?
8. What is the molar concentration of $[OH^-]$ in 0.1 M NH_4OH? If NH_4Cl is added to the solution, how will $[OH^-]$ change? Would NaCl have the same effect? NH_4NO_3? K_I of $NH_4OH = 1.8 \times 10^{-5}$.
9. Calculate the pH of a 0.1 M solution of NH_4OH. $K_I = 1.8 \times 10^{-5}$. If NH_4Cl is added until the total $[NH_4^+] = 1$, what will be the pH of the solution? What is such a solution called?
10. Without including acetic acid, name three acid buffer solutions.
11. Calculate the pH of 1 N acetic acid; $K_I = 1.8 \times 10^{-5}$. What is the pH of the solution after sodium acetate has been added so that the total $[C_2H_3O_2^-] = 1$?
12. In question 8, the $[OH^-]$ in 0.1 M NH_4OH has been found. Is the $[OH^-]$ sufficient to precipitate $Mg(OH)_2$ from a solution where $[Mg^{++}] = 0.1$? $Fe(OH)_3$ from a solution where $[Fe^{+++}] = 0.1$?

The K_{sp} of $Mg(OH)_2 = 3 \times 10^{-11}$
The K_{sp} of $Fe(OH)_3 = 1 \times 10^{-36}$

REFERENCES

Books

The A.B.C. of Hydrogen Ion Control. La Motte Chem. Co., Baltimore, Md.

Articles

"Hydrogen-Ion Concentration." Ashley, R. H. *J. Chem. Ed.* **5**, 1647–1663 (1928).

» 18 «

ELECTRICITY AS A TOOL OF THE CHEMIST

Students in the laboratory are always thrilled with what they can do with electricity, even though they may have difficulty in answering the question, "What is electricity?" Electric trains, refrigerators, sewing machines, radios, razors, heating pads, lights are only a few of the varied uses of electricity today.

In his laboratory the chemist needs a source of electricity for lighting the room, heating ovens, using X-ray tubes, preparing chemicals such as oxygen, hydrogen, and chlorine by electrolysis, analyzing copper by electrodeposition, determining the conductivity of solutions, oxidizing and reducing chemicals, and dozens of other purposes.

Types of Conductors of Electricity

The following five classes of substances conduct electricity. Examples are given of each one.

1. Solids—carbon, iron, silver, copper
2. Liquids—fused salts, mercury
3. Gases (particularly at low pressure)
4. Aqueous solutions—acids, bases, salts
5. Some non-aqueous solutions—lead acetate in pure hydrogen acetate (glacial acetic acid)

The flow of electricity through a solid such as iron or carbon consists of the passage of a stream of electrons through the space between atoms. Regardless of whether the electrons are merely shoved along from the outer electron orbit of one atom to the next and so on, or weave their way through the atom like a fullback running for a touchdown, they move in the conductor. Just as the football player meets various degrees of opposition or resistance to his movement with the ball, so electrons encounter different degrees of resistance to their movement through conductors. The greater the resistance the greater the heat produced as the electrons move through the wire. This principle is illustrated every time you turn on a light; the wire leading to the bulb does not get hot, but the tungsten filament in the light bulb reaches incandescence. Electrons can move in two ways in the wire; either they can go in one direction all the time, or they can go first in one direction and then in the other. An electron flow of the first type is called *direct current*; and of the latter, *alternating current*. In chemical reactions the direct current is used; but since an alternating current is cheaper to produce, whenever possible this current is used commercially for light, heat, and the operation of motors.

The fact that the conductivity of solid conductors usually decreases with an increase in temperature leads us to believe that electrons normally pass through the space lattice of the solid. As the temperature is increased, the vibration of atoms increases and some of them are thrown out of line, thus increasing the resistance to the passage of electrons through the metal.

Conduction through a liquid involves the migration of ions, as shown in Fig. 18.1. The flow of electrons in the two wires A and C is in the same direction; but in the liquid positive ions are moving in one direction and negative ions in the other. The liquid always remains neutral because there is an equal number of positive and negative charges in it be-

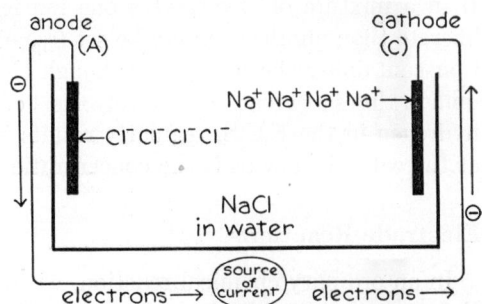

Fig. 18.1. Electrolysis of sodium chloride.

fore and after the current passes through it. Every time an electron is accepted from one terminal, one is yielded to the other. The total number of ions in the liquid may or may not become less as the electric current passes through it. Ions are always neutralized by the passage of the current, but in some cases an equal number are produced at the same time.

The two poles, or terminals, in a liquid are called electrodes. The one from which electrons are pulled by the dynamo is called the *anode*. Pulling electrons out of it makes it positive in charge; hence it attracts negative ions, which are for this reason called *anions*. The other pole is called the *cathode*. Electrons are forced into it, making it negative. It attracts positive ions, which are therefore called *cations*. In fused sodium chloride, to cite a simple case, Na^+ ions throughout the melt migrate in the direction of the cathode, and all the Cl^- ions travel in the opposite direction. At the cathode, electrons are forced onto the Na^+ ions which come into contact with it, turning them into neutral atoms of sodium metal. At the anode, electrons are torn from the Cl^- ions which touch it, leaving them neutral chlorine atoms which promptly pair off as Cl_2 molecules. This process is called *electrolysis*. The transmission of an electric current by ions always involves chemical decomposition. It is therefore referred to as electrolytic conduction, in contrast to metallic conduction which involves no chemical change. Since the cathode gives electrons, the cathode reaction is always a reduction. Correspondingly, the anode always takes electrons; so the anode reaction is always an oxidation. No chemical oxidizing agent can pull as hard for electrons as an anode; no chemical reducing agent can yield electrons as readily as a cathode. Oxidations and reductions can be performed electrolytically which are impossible in an ordinary chemical reaction.

The metals from the top of the E.C.S. down through aluminum are prepared by electrolysis of fused salts. Many more electrolyses are performed in water solutions. In all cases where more than one kind of ion of the same charge is present (i.e., in all solutions), the ease or difficulty with which each ion gains or loses electrons is much more important than its concentration, in determining in what relative proportions they react at the electrodes. If in a mixture of electrolytes one ion is inherently appreciably easier to liberate than another, it may be set free exclusively by electrolyzing a solution containing the ions, even though the concentration of the other is a million times as great. Thus electrolysis of solutions of salts of metals above hydrogen in the E.C.S. regularly results in the evolution of hydrogen only at the cathode, low as is the concentration of H^+ ions in the solution.

Electrode Reactions

In an ordinary chemical reaction, when electron transfer takes place, the electron goes directly from one molecule to the other and oxidation and reduction occur at the same place. Naturally only a single equation is written. In electrolysis the oxidation takes place at the anode and the reduction at the cathode, some distance away. It is possible and sometimes desirable to write separate equations for the two electrode reactions. The electrons which are transferred in an ordinary chemical reaction are not shown in the equation because they are never free. In electrode reactions the electrons are considered free during the time they are flowing through the wire from the anode to the cathode, and they *must* be shown. Otherwise the equation will not be balanced electrically. The symbol ⊖ is used to represent an electron. The equations for the anode reaction and the cathode reaction may be combined by addition to form the ordinary chemical equation for the reaction. In doing this we must first multiply each equation by a number such that the electrons will cancel out. The sign ⚠ is used to show that an electric current is necessary for the reaction to take place. *Remember that an electric current does not produce the ions in solution; they are already present.*

The electrode reactions for the electrolysis of fused NaCl are as follows:

(cathode) $\quad 2\,Na^+ + 2\ominus \xrightarrow{A} 2\,Na \quad$ (doubled to make the electrons balance)

(anode) $\quad \underline{\quad 2\,Cl^- \xrightarrow{A} \overline{Cl_2} + 2\ominus \quad}$

$$2\,Na^+ + 2\,Cl^+ \xrightarrow{A} 2\,Na + \overline{Cl_2}$$

If potassium fluoride is added to lower the melting point, the reaction is no different, because K^+ ion is harder to reduce than Na^+, and F^- is harder to oxidize than Cl^-. If a water solution of NaCl is used, the anode reaction remains the same but the cathode reaction is different; the reason is given on page 248.

(unchanged ions to balance) $\quad 2\,Na^+ \longrightarrow 2\,Na^+$

(cathode) $\quad 2\,H_2O + 2\ominus \xrightarrow{A} \overline{H_2} + 2\,OH^-$

(anode) $\quad \underline{\quad 2\,Cl^- \xrightarrow{A} \overline{Cl_2} + 2\ominus \quad}$

$$2\,Na^+ + 2\,Cl^- + 2\,H_2O \xrightarrow{A} \overline{H_2} + 2\,Na^+ + 2\,OH^- + \overline{Cl_2}$$

In writing the equation for the cathode reaction we use H_2O rather than H^+ because it is necessary to take into consideration the fact that an OH^- ion is produced every time an H^+ ion is reduced to the free state. It would not do to write $H^+ + OH^-$ because water is so slightly ionized. This is a case in which the total number of ions in the solution remains constant.

The electrolysis of a solution of sodium hydroxide results in the production of hydrogen and oxygen. Water is used up, and the number of Na^+ and OH^- ions in the solution remains constant.

(cathode) $\quad 4\,H_2O + 4\ominus \xrightarrow{A} 2\,\overline{H_2} + 4\,OH^-$

(anode) $\quad \underline{\quad 4\,OH^- \xrightarrow{A} \overline{O_2} + 2\,H_2O + 4\ominus \quad}$

$$2\,H_2O \xrightarrow{A} 2\,\overline{H_2} + \overline{O_2}$$

The rearrangement which takes place at the anode when OH^- ions lose electrons is thought to be due to two *neutral* OH molecules combining and liberating an atom of oxygen:

$$2\,OH \longrightarrow H_2O + O$$

Oxygen is also liberated at the anode when sulfate or nitrate ions are present in the solution. The oxygen apparently comes from the hydroxide ions from water. The NO_3^- or SO_4^{--} ions are unchanged.

Electrolytic Production of Metals

Metals only moderately more active than hydrogen (from zinc on down in the E.C.S.) can be made to plate out from solutions containing their ions by careful control of conditions. This is the basis of the electrolytic method of obtaining zinc from its ore. An electrolytic method was developed during World War II for manganese. The equations are similar.

(cathode) $\quad\quad\quad 2\,Zn^{++} + 4\,\ominus \xrightarrow{E} 2\,\underline{Zn}$

(anode) $\quad\quad\quad\quad\quad 2\,H_2O \xrightarrow{E} 4\,H^+ + \overline{O_2} + 4\,\ominus$

$\quad\quad\quad\quad\quad\quad\quad\quad 2\,SO_4^{--} \longrightarrow 2\,SO_4^{--}$

$$2\,Zn^{++} + 2\,SO_4^{--} + 2\,H_2O \xrightarrow{E} 2\,\underline{Zn} + 4\,H^+ + 2\,SO_4^{--} + \overline{O_2}$$

The solutions to be electrolyzed are obtained by leaching the ore with dilute acid. The advantage with zinc lies in the readiness with which the solution can be purified from contaminating metals before electrolysis. In the case of manganese, lower-grade ores can be treated in this way than was previously practical. The electrolysis of fused salts or mixtures of salts is the only practical method of obtaining the more active metals, such as sodium, magnesium, and aluminum. These important processes will be discussed in detail in connection with the metals involved.

Electrolytic Purification of Metals

Cheaper electricity has made possible many interesting new applications, noteworthy among which is its use in the purification of metals. Electrolytic separation has superseded older and more complicated time-consuming processes. Such advertisements as "Metal electrolytically refined" which are now frequent, imply—and it is nearly always true—that the metal has been highly purified. Copper probably is the best example of electrolytic refining (see page 575), because traces of certain impurities in this metal greatly decrease its conductivity and flexibility.

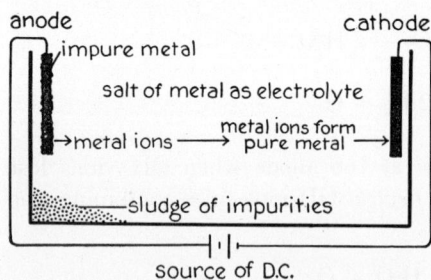

FIG. 18.2. Electrolytic refining of metals.

In the electrolyses described up to this point it has been implied that the electrodes are inert, and this is the case. In research work platinum is ordinarily used when inert electrodes are desired. In industrial processes carbon in the form of graphite provides electrodes that are almost inert. But in electrolytic refining the essence of the process is that the anode is a heavy casting of the metal to be refined. When the current is turned on and electrons are pulled out of it, the metal atoms give them up completely and go into the solution as ions. They do this before the charge on the anode as a whole becomes high enough to cause oxygen to be set free from the solution. Simultaneously ions of the metal already in solution plate out on the cathode, which is a thin strip or bar of previously refined metal. Of course the electrolyte (i.e., the solution) must contain anions to maintain electrical neutrality all the way from one electrode to the other, and these anions must be too stable to be discharged at the anode. Fig. 18.2 illustrates the general process of electrolytic refining.

(anode)   Metal $\longrightarrow$ M(ion) + electrons
(cathode)   M(ion) + electrons $\longrightarrow$ metal (pure)

Care is necessary if the process is to function satisfactorily. The voltage and temperature must be accurately controlled. Not all salts of the metal will serve equally well as electrolytes. If the impurities in the anode are sand, carbon, or inactive metals such as gold or silver, they will fall to the bottom as a sludge. If the impurities are more active metals than the one being refined, they will go into solution at the anode but fail to discharge at the cathode. If the voltage is just enough to dissolve the main metal at the anode it is more than enough to dissolve more active metals; but although this voltage is also just sufficient to discharge the ions of the main metal at the cathode, it is too low to discharge the ions of more active metals. Eventually so many soluble impurities accumulate in the electrolyte that it must be either purified or discarded.

Really pure iron was never seen in appreciable quantities until it was prepared electrolytically during World War II. Thousands of pounds of iron of 99.99+ per cent purity were prepared for special uses. This high purity is characteristic of the electrolytic process.

Electroplating

Cheap metals such as iron are coated with silver, chromium, cadmium, nickel, gold, and other metals to increase their durability and attractiveness. (Knives, forks, and spoons made of iron would have a red coating of rust every day.) Electroplated bearings which will withstand mechanical wear have been developed. However, not all metal platings are produced by electrolytic processes. (See page 549 for dipping, spraying, and other processes.)

Extreme care is necessary in electroplating. The object to be electroplated is cleaned thoroughly to remove grease, dirt, and oxide film, and is then used as the cathode. The metal to be deposited may be introduced by using one of its salts as the electrolyte, or the pure metal may be suspended as the anode in a suitable electrolyte. Such factors as temperature, amperage, concentration of electrolyte, and foreign substances in the electrolyte are all extremely important. For example, in analytical chemistry copper is frequently determined by electroplating it on platinum electrodes; but unless the amperage is carefully controlled, the copper will deposit in such a spongy form that it will fall off the electrode before it can be weighed. A method has been discovered for plating nickel in such a way that no buffing or polishing of the finished article is necessary. Chromium can be deposited either bright for decorative purposes or dull for military uses. Plating baths frequently contain several substances, some of them added on a purely empirical basis. It is often desirable to have the metal which is to be plated in the form of a complex ion with a low K_I. By this means the simple ion is maintained at a low concentration, but the equilibrium replenishes it from the complex as fast as it is plated out. The situation is analogous to that in a concentrated solution of a weak acid with respect to the hydrogen ion.

By suitably controlling the ion concentrations, voltage, current density, and acidity, and by using addition agents of various sorts, it has proved possible in some cases to cause two metals to plate out *together*. In other words, an *alloy* can be plated out.

Electroplating is used in making electrotypes. The cast or mold, as it is called, is coated with copper dust and suspended in a copper solution through which an electric current is passed until a suitable protective coating is deposited on the cast. This can be used for printing. Sometimes it is necessary to strengthen the copper by backing it with lead or type-metal. (Newspapers use a more rapid process. The impression of the type is stamped in papier-mâché; this is the mold upon which the metal used in printing is poured. This is not electroplating.) As a rule, athletic medals are made by coating a wax or plaster of Paris mold with graphite so that it will conduct a current, and electroplating copper or another metal on the mold. The back of the metal is usually filled in with a less expensive metal.

Methods of Producing an Electric Current

An electric current consists of a flow of electrons through a wire. Currents may be produced either mechanically or chemically. The machine used for causing electrons to flow through a wire is called a generator or a dynamo. (A magneto is a particular type of small generator.) A dynamo acts by moving wires through a magnetic field, or vice versa, the action of the field upon the loose electrons in the wire setting them into motion. The moving part of the dynamo is turned by a steam or water turbine, or some other source of mechanical power. The amount of power needed to turn it depends upon the amount of work the electrons have to do in moving through the line. The simplest type of dynamo moves the electrons in one direction for a fraction of a second, then stops them and moves them in the opposite direction, producing an *alternating current*. (An A.C. generator is sometimes called an alternator.) There are 60 such cycles per second in standard municipal supplies. By proper connections a dynamo may be made to produce *direct current*, or alternating current can be rectified into direct. In a direct current the electrons always move in the same direction. Direct current is regularly used in electrolyses.

Any redox reaction is a potential chemical source of an electric current (always a direct current). If the oxidizing and reducing agents are not allowed to come into contact with each other, the electrons can be made to flow through a wire on their way from the latter to the former. It is always necessary, however, for both chemicals to be in contact with a solution containing a plentiful supply of ions (i.e., an *electrolyte*) which can maintain electrical neutrality by their migration. Devices of this sort were first made by the Italian physicist Volta, and hence are called *voltaic cells* or, if the context is clear, cells. A group of cells connected together is called a *battery*. An automobile storage battery is properly thus called; it consists of three cells. But it is incorrect to refer to a single flashlight cell as a battery (see any dictionary).

The Zinc-Hydrogen Cell. If a piece of zinc is dipped into a solution of hydrochloric acid, hydrogen gas is liberated from the zinc surface, and zinc goes into solution as Zn^{++} ions. The energy of this reaction is liberated as heat energy and cannot be harnessed as it is in a voltaic cell. Close examination of the zinc during the reaction shows that most of its surface is insulated from the solution by an adhering layer of gas, and that most of the hydrogen bubbles are escaping from specks of impurities on its surface. If a piece of very pure zinc and dilute acid are used, there will be no appreciable production of hydrogen until the surface is touched with a conductor of electricity.

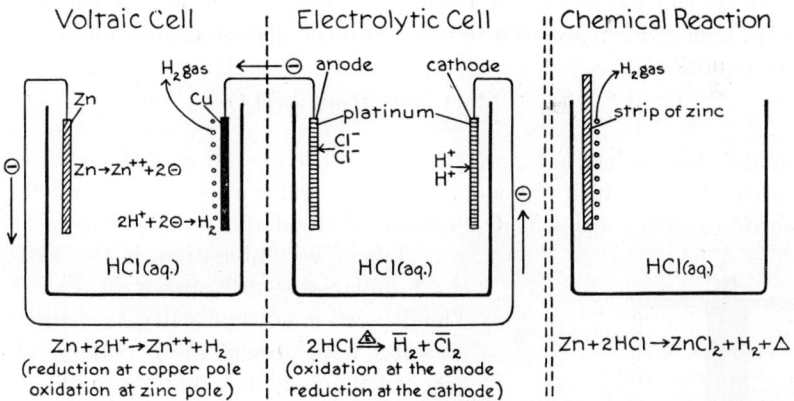

Fig. 18.3. Voltaic cell as a source of electricity and the electrolysis of hydrochloric acid. Chemical reaction between zinc and hydrochloric acid.

If, for example, a piece of copper wire is put down through the HCl solution until it touches the zinc, bubbles of hydrogen will immediately begin to evolve vigorously along the entire submerged surface of the wire. The copper is not attacked chemically, but the zinc goes into solution. The next step is to attach the copper wire to the zinc rod at its upper end, *above the solution*. The other end of the wire may then be put into the solution *anywhere*, and bubbles of H_2 will be given off from it. We now have, in fact, a voltaic cell, in which the separation of the oxidizing agent, H^+, from the reducing agent, Zn, is effected by the curious reluctance of H_2 bubbles to leave a zinc surface. The copper wire may be interrupted anywhere between the zinc rod and the place where the wire enters the solution, and a piece of electrical apparatus inserted, to be operated by the current of electrons flowing from the zinc to the hydrogen ions at the other end of the wire. In Fig. 18.3 an electrolytic cell has been thus introduced into the circuit. The reaction in this cell is one which absorbs energy and therefore will not proceed of its own accord; it can be forced to go by the application of a potential of 1.36 volts. The zinc-hydrogen voltaic cell produces a voltage of approximately 0.75; therefore two cells are joined in series (the Cu electrode of one to the Zn of the other) to effect the electrolysis of HCl. For simplicity only one cell of this battery is shown in Fig. 18.3. Davy discovered sodium and potassium in 1807 by melting and electrolyzing the corresponding hydroxides with a series of these cells.

The Dry Cell. Leclanché improved the zinc-hydrogen cell by substituting ammonium chloride for hydrochloric acid as the source of protons. The ammonium ion is a far weaker acid than the hydronium ion, so it is possible to have a high concentration of it in the solution without its directly attacking the zinc. Around the carbon rod he introduced powdered manganese dioxide as a *depolarizer*. Polarization is the accumulation around an electrode of products which tend to stop or reverse the reaction; in this case the product was H_2. Leclanché expected it to react with the manganese dioxide according to the equation

$$\overline{H_2} + \underline{MnO_2} \longrightarrow \underline{MnO} + H_2O$$

He found that he had not merely improved the operation of the cell, he had approximately doubled the voltage. It was really a new cell, in which the powerful oxidizing agent MnO_2 replaced the moderate oxidizing agent H^+.

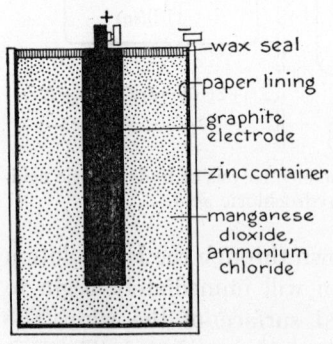

Fig. 18.4. The dry cell.

Leclanché's combination is the basis of the familiar dry cell shown in Fig. 18.4. The dry cell is not really dry, it is moist; if no water were present the necessary migration of ions could not take place. The container is made of zinc and is marked $(-$ pole$)$[1] because electrons are emitted from it. The graphite (carbon) rod is marked $(+$ pole$)$ because electrons flow into it.

[1] The attempt to apply the terms "anode" and "cathode" to voltaic cells leads to confusion and has been largely abandoned on this account.

The electrolyte, NH_4Cl solution, is mixed with some porous material (sawdust or charcoal) and manganese dioxide. A paper lining keeps the MnO_2 from coming into contact with the zinc, and a wax or pitch seal keeps the cell from leaking, drying out, or taking up moisture from the air. If the terminals are connected, electrons flow in the external circuit from zinc to carbon. The equation for the reaction at the zinc pole is simple:

$$\underline{Zn} \longrightarrow Zn^{++} + 2 \ominus$$

The Zn^{++} ions migrate toward the carbon pole. The reaction at the other pole (which really consists of the entire surface of the MnO_2, all of which is in electrical contact with the graphite electrode) is probably

$$2 \ominus + \underline{MnO_2} + 4 NH_4^+ + 4 Cl^- \longrightarrow Mn^{++} + 4 Cl^- + 2 H_2O + 4 NH_3$$

The Cl^- ions migrate toward the zinc pole. As fast as the new Zn^{++} ions meet the ammonia they react with it to form the complex zinc ammonia ion.

$$Zn(H_2O)_4^{++} + 4 NH_3 \longrightarrow Zn(NH_3)_4^{++} + 4 H_2O$$

This reaction lowers the concentration of zinc ion and thereby further increases the voltage of the cell. The total cell reaction is thus:

$$\underline{Zn} + \underline{MnO_2} + 4 NH_4^+ + 4 Cl^- \longrightarrow Zn(NH_3)_4^{++} + Mn^{++} + 4 Cl^- + 2 H_2O$$

Even though the production of hydrogen gas is prevented, polarization is still possible, because the zinc ions and the ammonia molecules have to move through the cell before they can react with each other. If a flashlight is used too long at one time the light becomes dim because Zn^{++} and NH_3 accumulate at their respective electrodes. If the light is given a rest, diffusion remedies this polarization and the light is brighter when next used.

The Daniell Cell. The Leclanché type of cell is excellent for intermittent work, but not really satisfactory for work which requires a continuous current drain. The invention of the telegraph made necessary a non-polarizable cell, for it operated with a circuit that was kept closed except when a message was actually being sent. This was furnished by the Daniell cell, which derives its energy from the reactions

and
$$\underline{Zn} \longrightarrow Zn^{++} + 2 \ominus$$
$$Cu^{++} + 2 \ominus \longrightarrow \underline{Cu}$$

An electrode potential of 1.1 volts can be obtained with this cell. Until the development of electronics made possible the easy rectification of the by then universally available alternating current, the telegraph companies used thousands of Daniell cells. They used the particular modification known as the *gravity cell* because of the ingenious use of the force of gravity to keep the necessary two solutions from mixing.

The construction of this cell is shown in Fig. 18.5. Sheets of copper are placed in the bottom of a large beaker and crystals of CuSO₄ and saturated copper sulfate solution are poured over the copper. A dilute solution of ZnSO₄ is poured carefully over the heavier CuSO₄ solution so that the two do not mix, and a heavy zinc electrode with a large surface exposed is hung in the ZnSO₄ solution. If the two metals are connected externally, electrons flow from zinc to copper. This cell is inherently non-polarizable. Any accumulation of Zn^{++} ions around the zinc electrode makes the solution denser; hence it drops down away from the electrode. The deposition of copper on the other electrode merely increases its size.

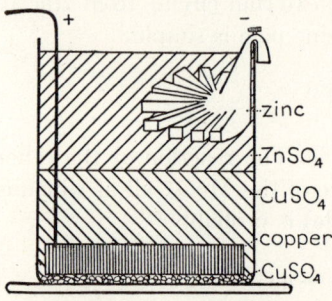

Fig. 18.5. A gravity cell.

The gravity cell must be kept on a closed circuit. As long as the current is flowing, all the cations are urged by electrical forces in the direction of the copper electrode. If the circuit is opened, copper ions will diffuse upward in spite of the lower density of the upper solution, and will eventually reach and react wastefully with the zinc electrode. If it is desired to operate a Daniell cell on an open circuit, the ZnSO₄ solution and the Zn electrode in it are separated from the CuSO₄ solution by a porous porcelain cup to impede diffusion.

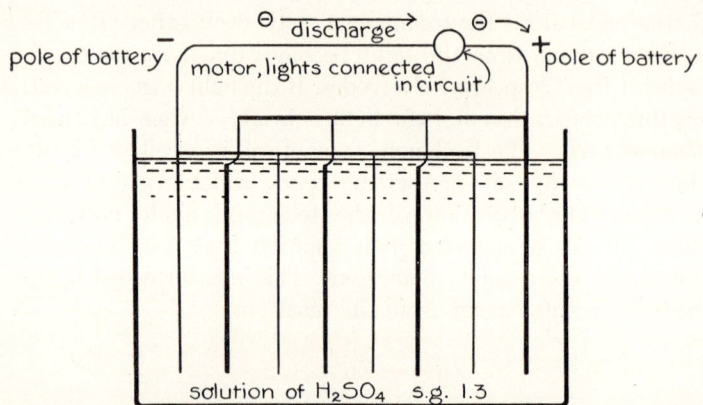

Fig. 18.6. Lead storage battery.

The Lead Storage Cell. A cell in which the original active materials can be regenerated by forcing a current through in the opposite direction to that in which it flows during discharge is called a *storage cell*. No electricity is actually stored; during both discharge and charge, as many electrons

ELECTRICITY AS A TOOL OF THE CHEMIST

come out one electrode as go into the other. What *is* stored is chemical energy produced in the cell from the electrical energy of the recharging current.

The lead storage cell is an extremely useful cell, for it is sturdy, capable of recharge, and relatively inexpensive. The principle is illustrated in Fig. 18.6. Although only a few plates are shown in this figure, the battery consists of many plates joined together in parallel, thus increasing the capacity of the cell. The plates, often called grids, are made of lead or an alloy of lead and antimony. One plate is coated with red-brown lead dioxide, PbO_2; this is the positive pole. The other is coated with spongy lead; this is the negative pole. These plates are dipped into sulfuric acid of s.g. about 1.3 and 40 per cent H_2SO_4 by weight. If the two terminals are connected, electrons flow in the external circuit from the lead plate to the plate coated with PbO_2; the cell develops about 2.2 volts. Three of these cells are connected in series to form a standard 6-volt automobile battery.

Reactions at the
lead plate $\quad\quad\quad\quad Pb + SO_4^{--} \longrightarrow PbSO_4 + 2\ominus$
Reactions at the
PbO_2 plate $\quad 2\ominus + PbO_2 + 4\,H^+ + SO_4^{--} \longrightarrow PbSO_4 + 2\,H_2O$
Total $\quad\quad\quad\quad Pb + PbO_2 + 2\,H_2SO_4 \longrightarrow 2\,PbSO_4 + 2\,H_2O$

During the discharge of a lead storage battery each plate is used up, the concentration of sulfuric acid in the cell decreases, and insoluble white lead sulfate forms at each pole. The cell is exhausted when any one of the reactants has been consumed. To *recharge* a "dead" battery electrons must be forced to flow in the opposite direction, thereby *reversing each* of the reactions which occurred during discharge. The concentration of sulfuric acid in a charged battery is much higher than in a discharged battery; hence the statement that a charged battery never freezes in cold weather—the sulfuric acid lowers the freezing point of the solution.

A speedy method for testing whether or not a battery is charged is to determine the specific gravity of the solution in the cell. This is done with a hydrometer (Fig. 18.7). The float in the hydrometer is calibrated to record accurately the specific gravity of solutions over a limited range. The usual limits are a specific gravity of 1.3 for a charged battery and 1.15 for a "dead" one. Some water is electrolyzed during the charging process, for the battery is functioning as an electrolytic cell. The more nearly charged it is, the greater the amount of hydrogen liberated. The storage battery attendant usually says that the battery is charged if it is "gassing well."

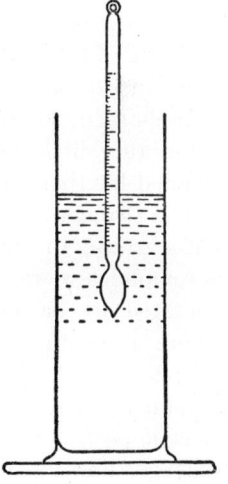

Fig. 18.7. A specific gravity spindle.

Batteries used in lighting plants last many years, whereas those in automobiles have a short life because of several factors: impure water used in refilling the battery, allowing it to stand for a long time without recharging, too rapid discharging, vibrations which break the insulation, and freezing. If a battery remains discharged for a long time, the $PbSO_4$ crystallizes and cannot be easily electrolyzed again. If a battery is short-circuited externally, it discharges so rapidly that some lead and lead dioxide fall off the plates to the bottom of the cell and thereby produce an internal short circuit which ruins the cell.

Another popular storage cell is the *Edison cell*. The positive plate of the charged cell consists of black nickelic hydroxide, $Ni(OH)_3$, and the negative plate has a deposit of finely divided iron on it. The electrolyte is a 20 per cent solution of potassium hydroxide which may also contain some lithium hydroxide, $LiOH$, to increase the capacity of the cell. When the cell delivers a current, the iron on the negative plate is oxidized to ferrous hydroxide, $Fe(OH)_2$, and the nickelic hydroxide is reduced to nickelous hydroxide, $Ni(OH)_2$. The chemical reactions for the Edison cell are as follows:

$$\text{Discharge of the Edison Cell}$$

$$\text{Positive pole} \quad 2\,Ni(OH)_3 + 2\,\ominus \longrightarrow 2\,Ni(OH)_2 + 2\,(OH^-)$$

$$\text{Negative pole} \begin{cases} Fe \longrightarrow Fe^{++} + 2\,\ominus \\ Fe^{++} + 2\,(OH^-) \longrightarrow Fe(OH)_2 \end{cases}$$

$$\overline{2\,Ni(OH)_3 + Fe \longrightarrow 2\,Ni(OH)_2 + Fe(OH)_2}$$

As with the lead storage battery, these reactions are reversed during the charging of the battery by inducing a flow of electrons in the opposite direction. An Edison cell develops about 1.5 volts, but it drops off as the battery is discharged. These cells have an advantage over the lead cells in that they deteriorate little even if left uncharged for a long time. A longer life is claimed for them; however, they are more expensive than the lead cells.

The storage battery industry has grown rapidly since automobiles adopted self-starters. In the early days of automobile manufacture some electric automobiles were built. Small trucks in express yards and mines are operated by batteries today. Batteries are invaluable as stand-by units where a constant source of electricity is required, as in hospitals and for telephone systems. Farm homes not within reach of power lines can use gasoline-driven electric generators and storage batteries as a source of electric power. Small windmill generators are used to charge a single storage battery. These generators furnish sufficient current for one or two lights and the radio, and have been sold by the thousand during the past few years.

The Quantitative Nature of Electrochemical Reactions

This chapter thus far has dealt with the sources of electrons, types of conductors of electricity, uses of electricity (electrolytic reactions), and

ELECTRICITY AS A TOOL OF THE CHEMIST

methods of producing an electric current. Many such observations were made before the quantitative nature of these reactions was known. We should also consider a possible explanation for the production of an electric current in the voltaic and similar cells.

The strength of a current is proportional to the potential difference between the ends of a conductor, and inversely proportional to the resistance of the conductor. The international unit of current strength, the *ampere*, is defined as *the current which, flowing uniformly for one second, deposits under specified conditions 0.001118 g. of silver from a solution of $AgNO_3$*. The unit of resistance, the *ohm*, is the resistance offered by a tube of mercury of uniform cross section, 106.3 cm. in length, containing 14.4521 g. of mercury at 0° C. The *volt* is the electromotive force necessary to drive a current of one ampere through a resistance of one ohm.

$$\text{Amperes} = \frac{\text{volts}}{\text{ohms}}$$

If one ampere flows for one second, a definite quantity of electricity (number of electrons) has passed; this quantity is called *one coulomb*.

$$\text{Amperes} \times \text{seconds} = \text{coulombs}$$

During the years 1832–33 Michael Faraday made two quantitative observations regarding the amounts of substances which are liberated in electrolytic cells. These are known as *Faraday's Laws*.

1. *Chemical action of electricity is proportional to the absolute quantity of electricity which passes through the conductor.*

2. *The weights of ions deposited by the passage of the same quantity of electricity are proportional to their chemical equivalents.*

Thus if one ampere flowing for one hour liberates y grams of a substance, two amperes flowing for one hour or one ampere flowing for two hours will liberate $2y$ grams.

The second law, although startling at the time of its discovery, is a logical conclusion of our present knowledge of the structure of atoms. Consider the simplest example, the hydrogen atom. To convert one hydrogen ion to one hydrogen atom requires that the hydrogen ion be combined with one electron.

$$H^+ + \ominus \longrightarrow H \text{ atom}$$

Changing any positive ion to the corresponding atom requires the addition of electrons equal to the valence of the ion. Divalent Cu^{++} requires two electrons and trivalent Al^{+++} three.

$$Cu^{++} + 2\ominus \longrightarrow Cu \text{ atom}$$
$$Al^{+++} + 3\ominus \longrightarrow Al \text{ atom}$$

Since the flow of electricity is a flow of electrons, if a current liberates y

atoms of hydrogen, it will also liberate y/2 copper atoms or y/3 aluminum atoms. If the number of electrons that pass through a system is N (Avogadro's number), N atoms of hydrogen, N/2 atoms of copper, N/3 atoms of aluminum are liberated. In other words, one gram atom of hydrogen, one-half a gram atom of copper, and one-third a gram atom of aluminum are set free. The quantities in grams are: 1 g. hydrogen, $\frac{63.57}{2} = 31.785$ g. copper, and $\frac{26.97}{3} = 8.99$ g. aluminum. This is shown graphically in Fig. 18.8. If

1 Faraday liberates	H	Cu	Al
gram atoms	1	½	⅓
grams	1	31.785	8.99

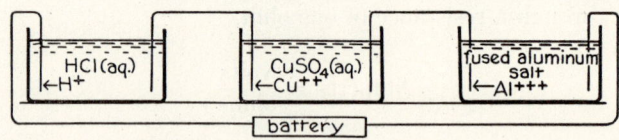

FIG. 18.8. Quantities of hydrogen, copper, and aluminum liberated by one Faraday.

an electric current is allowed to flow through the series of conductors in the beakers in this figure until 1.008 g. hydrogen or the equivalent weight of any of the other substances is liberated, it will be found that the *quantity of electricity required is 96,500 coulombs. This quantity, 96,500 coulombs, is known as 1 Faraday and is N electrons.*

If the voltage is kept constant at 110 and the resistance at 11 ohms, how many grams of copper can be deposited from a solution of copper sulfate in one day?

$$\frac{\text{volts}}{\text{ohms}} = \text{amperes}$$

$$\text{amperes} \times \text{seconds} = \text{coulombs} \qquad \frac{\text{coulombs}}{96{,}500} = \text{Faradays}$$

$$1 \text{ F deposits} \left(\frac{\text{gram-atomic weight of Cu}}{2}\right)$$

$$\frac{\frac{110}{11} \times 24 \times 60 \times 60 \times \frac{63.57}{2}}{96{,}500} = \text{answer in grams}$$

How many Faradays are required to liberate the copper in 140 g. $CuSO_4 \cdot 5\,H_2O$?

$$\frac{\frac{Cu}{CuSO_4 \cdot 5\,H_2O} \times 140}{\frac{63.57}{2}} = \text{answer in Faradays}$$

ELECTRICITY AS A TOOL OF THE CHEMIST

Any form of energy may be considered as the product of two factors: capacity and intensity. *In electricity the capacity factor is the charge and the intensity factor is the voltage.* Electrical energy is therefore equal to coulombs times volts. Electricity from a single dry cell would operate a little flashlight but would be entirely inadequate for a washing machine, electric toaster, electric iron, radio, electric refrigerator, and all the electric lights. We must pay the lighting company for both the coulombs used (capacity factor) and the maximum voltage required (intensity factor). We buy electricity by the watt-hour or 1000 watt-hours (kilowatt-hour). A volt-coulomb = one joule = one watt-second. One watt-second equals the electrical work done by a current of one ampere flowing under an electromotive force of one volt for one second.

Cell Potentials[2]

You will recall that active metals in solution tend to remain as ions in solution, and that the ions of the metals near the bottom of the E.C.S. readily take on electrons. A piece of zinc placed in a solution of copper sulfate is quickly coated with copper because the tendency of zinc to give up electrons is sufficient for it to go into solution and give up its electrons to the cupric ion, Cu^{++}.

$$\frac{\begin{array}{r}Zn \longrightarrow Zn^{++} + 2e^-\\ Cu^{++} + 2e^- \longrightarrow Cu\end{array}}{Zn + Cu^{++} \longrightarrow Zn^{++} + Cu}$$

You can quickly demonstrate the selective deposition of metals by placing an iron nail in a solution containing both zinc and copper ions. Iron is below zinc and above copper in the E.C.S., so it should replace Cu^{++} but not Zn^{++}. This is exactly what happens; the nail is quickly coated with copper, but no zinc is deposited. A change from metal to metallic ion involves the loss of one or more electrons, depending upon the valence of the ion. The measure of the driving force of these substitution reactions is called the electromotive force (E.M.F.) and its quantitative unit is the volt. Each reaction capable of producing a flow of electrons (electric current) creates a definite E.M.F. or voltage. If two metals close to each other in the E.C.S. are used in a voltaic cell, the voltage is low; if they are far apart, the voltage is greater.

Every metal placed in contact with water tends to go into solution (solution potential), thereby producing ions of the metal. This solution potential or solution tension depends upon the position of the metal in the E.C.S. If a metal such as zinc is placed in contact with a solution containing Zn^{++} ions, two opposing forces must be considered: one is the tendency of the metal to form ions, and the other the tendency of the ions in solution to form

[2] Review the discussion of the E.C.S. on pp. 142-143.

the metal. One force is greater than the other in all metals; with zinc the tendency to go into solution dominates, causing the plate to become negative because of the electrons stored on it. Atoms of zinc tend to form Zn^{++} ions. The solution containing an excess of Zn^{++} ions therefore becomes positive with respect to the plate, and an E.M.F. is set up. We can thus consider this as an equilibrium reaction.

$$\underline{Zn} \rightleftarrows Zn^{++} + 2\ominus$$

Removal of electrons causes the reaction to go from left to right, and addition of Zn^{++} ions to the solution or the application of an E.M.F. in the opposite direction causes Zn^{++} ions to deposit as metallic zinc.

The E.M.F. between a metal and its ions in solution cannot be measured directly, but it can be measured indirectly by comparison with a hydrogen electrode. To illustrate, suppose that a strip of platinum metal is dipped into a solution of 1-normal sulfuric acid (which contains hydrogen ions) in one container, and this solution is joined by a suitable conductor to a solution of 1-normal zinc sulfate in which there is a zinc rod. If hydrogen gas is bubbled into the solution so that the platinum electrode is surrounded by the gas, a measurable E.M.F. is recorded between the platinum and zinc electrodes. The positive pole of the cell is the strip of platinum (hydrogen electrode), and the negative pole is the zinc. The E.M.F. measured will be 0.76 volt. The reactions at the poles are:

$$\begin{array}{ll} \text{Positive pole} & 2\,H^+ + 2\ominus \longrightarrow \overline{H_2} \\ \text{Negative pole} & \underline{Zn} \longrightarrow Zn^{++} + 2\ominus \\ \hline & \underline{Zn} + 2\,H^+ \longrightarrow Zn^{++} + \overline{H_2} \end{array}$$

The apparatus used is shown in Fig. 13.9. Why it is impossible to measure the single potential difference between a metal in contact with a solution of its ions may not at first be clear, but it becomes clear when connecting the voltmeter is considered. One contact of the voltmeter can be connected to the metal; but if the other contact is made to the solution a second potential is immediately produced because of the contact of this substance with the solution. The voltmeter reading is thus the sum of the potential differences of the two electrodes in solution instead of the one potential difference desired. This difficulty can be overcome by assuming that the potential difference at one electrode is constant and giving it the value of zero. All other potential differences are then measured *relative* to this one and can be compared accurately. (Temperatures on both the Fahrenheit and centigrade scales are expressed relative to a particular temperature which is arbitrarily selected as the standard; hence the above idea is not new.)

For convenience, the hydrogen electrode is selected for reference. Hydrogen gas in contact with a platinum electrode has a tendency to ionize, giving electrons to the metal and thus making it negative. In fact, it behaves as

ELECTRICITY AS A TOOL OF THE CHEMIST

though equilibrium had been established between H₂ in solution and a monomolecular layer of H, plating (for monatomic hydrogen is metallic in nature) the platinum. This layer of H would establish equilibrium with its ions in the solution just as any other metal would. Because of the hydrogen ions already present in the solution, there is a tendency for these ions to produce an opposing force, and an equilibrium is reached between these two forces.

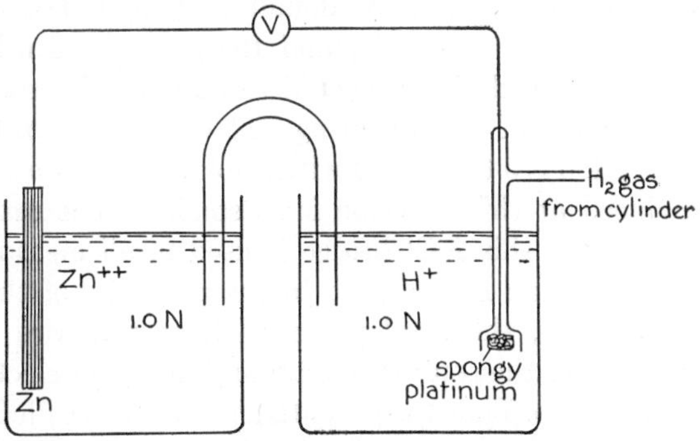

$$H_2 \rightleftarrows 2H \rightleftarrows 2H^+ + 2\ominus$$

FIG. 18.9. Measurement of electrode potentials with the hydrogen electrode.

The actual measurements for comparison are made under the controlled conditions of hydrogen gas at 1 atm. pressure bubbled on the surface of a platinum-black (platinum

FIG. 18.10. Typical equipment for the measurement of the concentration of hydrogen ions with the hydrogen gas electrode. (Courtesy, Leeds and Northrup Co.)

foil coated with spongy platinum) electrode dipped in a 1-normal solution of H$^+$ ions. A constant stream of hydrogen gas must be bubbled around the electrode so that the solution is at all times saturated with hydrogen gas. A definite, though not measurable, potential is set up in this electrode, and the potential can be accurately reproduced. If this electrode is connected to another electrode as shown in Fig. 18.10, the voltage of the resulting cell can be accurately measured. The usual connection is a tube filled with a solution of potassium chloride; the potential produced at this junction is so small that it can be disregarded. Furthermore, since this KCl bridge is used in all measurements it has a constant value and can be included in the potential of the hydrogen electrode. For convenience, the total potential from the wire attached to the platinum electrode to the solution containing the other electrode is given the arbitrary value of zero. Thus the potential measured is called that of the other electrode in contact with the solution in which it is immersed. The E.M.F. values thus obtained are not the real potentials, but the measured potentials from which the unknown potential of the hydrogen electrode is not deducted. Since they can be compared with each other, such values are of considerable importance. In the system

$$(Pt)\overline{H_2}|H^+\|Zn^{++}|Zn$$

an E.M.F. of 0.76 volt is obtained when 1-normal solutions are used. In the system

$$(Pt)\overline{H_2}|H^+\|Cu^{++}|Cu$$

the E.M.F. is 0.34 volt. Remember, in connection with these two systems, that in the case of Zn^{++}|Zn the tendency is for metallic zinc to go into solution and that in the second case the reverse is true, namely, Cu^{++} ions form metallic copper. The flow of electrons is opposite in the two cases. *Therefore if one electrode potential is to be called positive, the other must be negative.* Either choice might be made, but it is convenient to make the choice in such a way that a positive potential means that a metal has *a greater* tendency than hydrogen to give up electrons and form positive ions in solution. Thus the more active a metal is, the higher is its electrode potential and the higher its place in the E.C.S. Potassium has an electrode potential of +2.922 volts. Zinc, which is lower in the E.C.S. has a potential of +0.762 volt, and lead is lower with +0.126 volt. Hydrogen is given the arbitrary value of zero. Copper, which is below hydrogen, has an E.M.F. of −0.34 volt, and gold −1.4 volts. Even non-metals and negative radicals can be included in the electrode potential table, for in reality this table indicates the relative ease with which substances can be oxidized and reduced. Those near the top are easily oxidized, or they are good reducing agents; those at the bottom are easily reduced, or they are good oxidizing agents.

ELECTRICITY AS A TOOL OF THE CHEMIST

If a metal has a great tendency to give up electrons and form positive ions it must be correspondingly difficult to force its ions to accept electrons and form the metal. Accordingly, if the setup of a cell is such as to force one of the electrode reactions, as shown in Table 18.1, to go from right to

TABLE 18.1. ELECTRODE POTENTIALS

Hydrogen electrode equal to zero. Electrodes are in contact with 1-normal solutions. Temperature 25° C.

Element	Reaction at Electrode	Potential in Volts
K	K $\longrightarrow$ K$^+$ + $\ominus$	+2.922
Ba	Ba $\longrightarrow$ Ba^{++} + 2 $\ominus$	+2.90
Sr	Sr $\longrightarrow$ Sr^{++} + 2 $\ominus$	+2.89
Ca	Ca $\longrightarrow$ Ca^{++} + 2 $\ominus$	+2.87
Na	Na $\longrightarrow$ Na$^+$ + $\ominus$	+2.712
Mg	Mg $\longrightarrow$ Mg^{++} + 2 $\ominus$	+2.34
Al	Al $\longrightarrow$ Al^{+++} + 3 $\ominus$	+1.67
Mn	Mn $\longrightarrow$ Mn^{++} + 2 $\ominus$	+1.05
Zn	Zn $\longrightarrow$ Zn^{++} + 2 $\ominus$	+0.762
Fe	Fe $\longrightarrow$ Fe^{++} + 2 $\ominus$	+0.440
Cd	Cd $\longrightarrow$ Cd^{++} + 2 $\ominus$	+0.402
Co	Co $\longrightarrow$ Co^{++} + 2 $\ominus$	+0.277
Ni	Ni $\longrightarrow$ Ni^{++} + 2 $\ominus$	+0.250
Sn	Sn $\longrightarrow$ Sn^{++} + 2 $\ominus$	+0.136
Pb	Pb $\longrightarrow$ Pb^{++} + 2 $\ominus$	+0.126
H	H$_2$ $\longrightarrow$ 2 H$^+$ + 2 $\ominus$	0.00
Cu	Cu $\longrightarrow$ Cu^{++} + 2 $\ominus$	−0.3448
Hg	2 Hg $\longrightarrow$ Hg$_2^{++}$ + 2 $\ominus$	−0.7986
Ag	Ag $\longrightarrow$ Ag$^+$ + $\ominus$	−0.7995
Au	Au $\longrightarrow$ Au^{+++} + 3 $\ominus$	−1.42
Non-Metals		
S (at Pt)	S^{--} $\longrightarrow$ S + 2 $\ominus$	+0.51
I (at Pt)	2 I$^-$ $\longrightarrow$ I$_2$ + 2 $\ominus$	−0.54
Br (at Pt)	2 Br$^-$ $\longrightarrow$ Br$_2$ + 2 $\ominus$	−1.065
Cl (at Pt)	2 Cl$^-$ $\longrightarrow$ Cl$_2$ + 2 $\ominus$	−1.36

left instead of from left to right, the sign of the corresponding electrode potential must be reversed. The E.M.F. of any voltaic cell then equals the algebraic sum of the two simple electrode potentials. The E.M.F. of the cell Fe|Fe^{++}‖Pb^{++}|Pb is +0.440 + (−0.126) = +0.314. Note that the electrode potential of Pb is written with reversed sign, because the electrode reaction is reversed in the cell. Electrons come from the Fe and go through the external circuit into the Pb; hence the Fe is the negative pole and the Pb the positive pole. The convention in writing electrode reactions like the above is that the electrode which gives electrons to the external circuit is put on the left.

Whenever a cell is arranged so that a given metal electrode is the *negative* pole of the cell, electrons are flowing out of it into the external circuit. This is not in conflict with the fact that such an electrode has a more positive electrode potential than the other electrode of the cell; on the contrary, it is a necessary consequence of that fact. The term "electropositive" or simply "positive" has been applied to elements which have a strong tendency to form positive ions. But students, on encountering this term, tend to think that a "positive" element is thus called because it tends to form the positive pole of a cell. Similarly, the use of "electronegative" to describe elements which tend to form negative ions suggests the false conclusion that a "negative" element should form the negative pole of a cell in which it is used. The tendency of modern writers is to avoid this confusion by calling an element which readily gives up electrons and forms positive ions "electrodotic" (electron-giving), and one which prefers to take up electrons and form negative ions "electrophilic" (electron-loving).

If the E.M.F. of any cell, calculated as above, is positive, the cell is a voltaic cell, running of its own accord in the direction indicated. If the E.M.F. is negative, the cell is an electrolytic cell, and will run in the indicated direction only if an external E.M.F. is applied.

We are now in a position to understand more clearly the deposition of metals. The deposition potential of any substance is the E.M.F. which will just produce continuous electrolysis. In the commercial deposition of a metal, the potential difference required has been found to depend upon polarization at the poles, temperature, concentration, and type of electrolyte. The greater the difference in deposition potentials, the easier it is to make a quantitative electrolytic separation. Sometimes, by varying the electrolyte, two or more metals can be plated simultaneously as an alloy.

Uses of Electrode Potentials

The E.M.F. of a cell depends upon the concentrations of the ions which are in equilibrium with the electrodes. If one of the electrodes is a hydrogen electrode and the concentration of the ions in equilibrium with the other electrode can be kept constant, the voltage of the cell will be a measure of the concentration (or more accurately, the activity) of H_3O^+ ions in that part of it which is in contact with the hydrogen electrode. For use in industry (where innumerable acidity measurements have to be made) the hydrogen electrode has grave disadvantages, among which are its dependence upon atmospheric pressure and its complexity.[3] Fortunately systems exist which although more complex theoretically are much simpler to use. One of the most popular is called the *glass electrode*. It appears that H_3O^+ ions can move through a thin glass membrane, but in moving from a solution of high acidity to one of low acidity the H_3O^+ ions produce a potential difference corresponding to the difference in hydrogen ion concentration. The glass electrode is a glass tube with a thin glass membrane closing off its bottom.

[3] See Fig. 18.10. Not only is a heavy cylinder of compressed H_2 needed, but the commercial gas must be purified by being passed over heated copper to remove traces of oxygen.

Inside it there is a little 0.1000 N HCl solution into which a standard electrode dips. If this glass electrode is dipped into a solution of unknown acidity, together with an identical standard electrode, the two will form a cell in which the E.M.F.'s of the two standard electrodes cancel out, leaving only that due to the passage of hydrogen ions through the glass membrane. Commercial instruments for measuring such potentials (see Fig. 18.11) can

FIG. 18.11. Portable universal indicator of the concentration of hydrogen ions. Can be used with glass electrodes, or for measuring oxidation or reduction potentials. (Courtesy, Leeds and Northrup Co.)

even be calibrated to read directly in pH. The solution to be tested is put into a small beaker and brought up under the two electrodes shown at the front corner of the instrument, a button is pushed, a dial is read, and the determination is complete. A needle-like glass electrode has been constructed which can be inserted in the blood stream or other parts of the body and the concentration of hydrogen ions of the solution surrounding the electrode obtained. In water purification the hydrogen ion concentration must be carefully controlled if the maximum purification is to be obtained. Measurements of hydrogen ion concentration are made in control laboratories in the baking, food-canning, and fermentation industries and in health laboratories.

Electrometric Titrations. No expensive electrical apparatus is needed for an ordinary acid-base titration in a college laboratory; an indicator serves perfectly to show the end point. In industrial laboratories many solutions are too opaque or too strongly colored to make the use of indicators possible, and yet they must be titrated. Here such apparatus as has just been described is invaluable; it is necessary only to insert the electrodes and add acid or base until the correct pH has been reached. Many other titrations can also be followed electrometrically. If either of the reacting substances is an acid, a base, or an oxidizing or reducing agent, a cell can be designed which will show a sharp change in potential when the last of the substance is used up. Thousands of such measurements are made every day in industrial laboratories.

QUESTIONS AND PROBLEMS

1. By writing complete equations, show that electrolysis of aqueous solutions of KOH, K_2SO_4, and H_2SO_4 gives the same result as the electrolysis of pure water. Is this true if a solution of KBr is used?
2. Write complete equations for the electrolysis of water solutions of $CuSO_4$, $FeCl_3$, and LiOH. In each case point out where oxidation and reduction take place.
3. How many grams of copper will be deposited by a current of 1.2 amperes flowing for 50 minutes through a solution of cupric chloride? Would half as much or twice as much copper be deposited under these conditions if the solution were cuprous chloride?
4. How many liters of gases can be obtained by the electrolysis of Na_2SO_4(aq) for one hour, voltage = 120 V. and resistance = 40 ohms?
5.   *a.* How many grams of $CuSO_4 \cdot 5 H_2O$ are required to make 2 l. of solution?
   b. How many Faradays are needed to deposit the copper electrolytically?
   c. If the voltage is 120 and the resistance 10 ohms, how many hours must the current flow to deposit the copper?
6. What must be the total resistance of a circuit in order to deposit 26.97 g. of silver in 804 minutes and 10 seconds when the voltage is 100?
7.   *a.* How many copper atoms will be deposited by the electrolysis of a 2-molar $CuSO_4$ solution in one hour if the voltage is kept constant at 30 and the resistance is 450 ohms?
   b. If the gas evolved at the other electrode were collected, what would be its volume at S.T.P.? How many molecules of gas would be obtained?
8. What weight of bromine can be obtained by passing an electric current through 3.6 l. of 1.1 M NaBr if the voltage is held at 110 and the resistance at 11 ohms for 25.46 days?
9. How many Faradays are required to deposit 24.5 g. of platinum from a solution of $PtCl_4$; 35.91 g. of silver from a solution of $AgNO_3$; 14.4 g. of chromium from a solution of $CrCl_3$; 5.6 l. of chlorine from a solution of NaCl?
10. If a current of electricity flows through a series of beakers containing respectively solutions of $CoCl_2$, $K_2Cu(CN)_3$, $Pb(NO_3)_2$, and $SnCl_4$, what

weight of metal will have deposited in each case by the time the cathode in the first beaker shows an increase in weight of 14 g.?

11. The following is a schematic representation of three voltaic cells:
Zn | Zn^{++} ‖ Pb^{++} | Pb;   Fe | Fe^{++} ‖ Cu^{++} | Cu;   Cd | Cd^{++} ‖ Ag^+ | Ag.
The solutions in each cell are 1-normal.

   (a) What is the E.M.F. of each cell?
   (b) Show by equations the reaction in each cell.
   (c) At which pole does oxidation take place?
   (d) If the first cell is allowed to deliver a current until the strip of metallic zinc shows a loss in weight of 0.65., what will be the change in weight of the lead pole?

12. List five types of conductors of electricity. Distinguish between direct and alternating currents.
13. List several common electroplated articles around the home.
14. Could the lead storage battery be removed from a car and used as a source of current in the home to operate electric lights, radio, etc.? Explain.
15. You can earn thousands of dollars by developing a more economical method of storing electrical energy. For example, in many states the wind blows several hours nearly every day. If it could be used to operate electrical generators in the summer and the electrical energy could be either stored or converted into chemical energy for use in the winter, the heating problem would be solved. Some have suggested that water be electrolyzed and the hydrogen stored. How can this be done economically?

REFERENCES

Books

Electrochemistry.   Dole, J. M.   McGraw-Hill Book Company, Inc.

Articles

"Storage Batteries."   Reinhardt, W. L.   *Ind. and Eng. Chem.* **19,** 1124-1126 (1927).

"*Electrochemistry of Rare Metals.*"   Fink, Colin G.   *J. Chem. Ed.* **16,** 108-112 (1939).

» 19 «

THE ATMOSPHERE

The gaseous envelope surrounding the earth is called the atmosphere, and the gas is called air. In 1772, Rutherford, an Edinburgh physician and botanist, proved that it contained at least two constituents by burning in it such substances as carbon and phosphorus. The residue would not support combustion. He observed that this same residue was obtained after animals had utilized the oxygen in air, and the carbon dioxide produced by the animals had been removed by passing the residual gas through an alkali. The residue, which always amounted to about 78 per cent of the original gas, was studied in detail by Lavoisier, who concluded that it was an element. The same gas was later obtained from niter (KNO_3); hence the name, nitrogen, for this gas. It was many years later that nitrogen thus obtained from the air was shown to be a mixture of gases. Scheele and Cavendish should be credited with independently discovering nitrogen. The next most abundant constituent in the atmosphere is oxygen, which is present to the extent of about 21 per cent.

Other substances present in the air in variable amounts are oxides of nitrogen, hydrogen sulfide and oxides of sulfur, ozone, particles of solids usually referred to as dust, and water vapor. Needless to say, the chemist considers *air to be a mixture and not a compound*. Within recent years many studies have been made of the composition of the stratosphere. Although man has been able to go only about 14 miles above the earth, it is probable that rocket flights will soon make possible the actual sampling of the upper reaches of the atmosphere to any desired height, so that estimates can be replaced by accurate knowledge. The various constituents and the percentage of each in the atmosphere are listed in Table 19.1.

Table 19.1 shows that both the composition and the density of the air vary with distance from the earth. Aviators flying at great heights have not only intense cold but also low pressure to combat; elaborate superchargers are

THE ATMOSPHERE

TABLE 19.1. COMPOSITION OF THE ATMOSPHERE

Substance	Percentage by Volume		
	Sea Level	30 Miles from Earth (Estimated)	60 Miles (Estimated)
Nitrogen	78.03	79.2	2.9
Oxygen	20.99	7.0	0.1
Argon	0.93	0.03	—
Carbon dioxide	0.03	—	—
Hydrogen	0.01	13.6	95
Neon	18×10^{-4}	—	—
Helium	5×10^{-4}	0.126	1.3
Krypton	1.1×10^{-4}	—	—
Xenon	8×10^{-6}	—	—
Pressure	760 mm.	0.4 mm.	0.006 mm.

necessary to supply the motors with air. The weight of 22.4 l. of air at sea level is about 29 g., whereas the same volume of air four miles from the earth weighs only about 12 g. At sea level the pressure due to air is 14.7 lb. per square inch.

Water Vapor

Although water vapor usually makes up only a small part of the atmosphere, it is the most talked-about constituent of air. The actual partial pressure of gaseous water in the air may vary from a fraction of a millimeter on a cold, dry day to perhaps 55 mm. on a hot day (40° C., or 104° F.) immediately over water. (Thus $\frac{55}{733}$ or $7\frac{1}{2}$ per cent of the molecules present, might be water, but such a temperature is rarely reached over a large body of water.) The amount of water present in the air is of importance when it comes to calculating how much rain could be precipitated from a given air mass, or how much water would have to be removed by an air conditioner. Much more interesting from the human point of view is the relationship of the partial pressure of water vapor in the air to the vapor pressure of water at that temperature. This is the *relative humidity*, or, more commonly, the humidity.

When the partial pressure of the water vapor in the air is equal to the vapor pressure of water at that temperature, we say that the humidity is 100 per cent. Under these conditions water would condense onto any surface as fast as it would evaporate from it, and a damp object would never dry. For this reason air having a humidity of 100 per cent is called *saturated*. At lower humidities evaporation takes place more rapidly than condensation and things tend to dry up. If a given solution has a vapor pressure 75 per cent of that of water, it will remain unchanged in concentration and amount when the humidity is 75 per cent. At higher humidities the solution will gain water from the air, diluting itself until its vapor pressure has risen to the equilibrium point. At lower humidities such a solution will lose water to the air until it dries up completely, or until increasing concentration has lowered its vapor pressure to a value equal to the partial pressure of the water vapor in the air. Wood contains in its fibers substances which dissolve water; hence it swells or shrinks according to the relative humidity of the atmosphere. Cotton similarly becomes softer or harsher; consequently many textile processes can be carried out only within certain humidity limits. In work with tobacco, paper, and many other substances this is equally true. Originally such industries went in search of a climate where the weather was suitable at least for a considerable portion of the time. Now they locate wherever it is most convenient and manufacture their own climate.

Air Conditioning

Adjusting the composition and temperature of air so that it is best adapted to a particular situation is called air conditioning. At one time it was generally believed that "stuffy" air was caused by the oxygen content becoming too low; but now we know that too high a humidity, too high a temperature, or poor circulation of air is responsible. Air can be recirculated several times before the oxygen content is lowered sufficiently to be undesirable. If air is merely recirculated, the humidity is continuously increased by the respiration of people in the room, and as the humidity approaches saturation the rate at which moisture can evaporate from the body decreases. The result is the usual discomfort felt in "stuffy" rooms. Ventilation engineers claim that the relative humidity in buildings should be 35 to 50 per cent in winter and 20 to 30 per cent in summer. These figures are ideal rather than practical. During the winter months the cold air which is brought into homes is at a very low humidity; as it becomes warm, more water should be vaporized to increase the humidity. The average home in the North is not equipped to evaporate 20 to 30 gallons of water each day, but fully this much is required for a suitable relative humidity in extremely cold weather. An additional difficulty is that at humidities above 30 per cent moisture "sweats out" on windows. Humidities as low as those suggested for summer would make cooling unnecessary in most of the United States much of the time. Even at 50 per cent humidity, air at a temperature of 80° F. feels pleasantly cool.

Many different kinds of apparatus are used in air conditioning. In some units the air is cleansed by being bubbled through water; this removes dust and soluble substances and at the same time increases the humidity. The temperature and humidity are adjusted before the air in factories, theaters, etc., is recirculated. Air conditioning greatly increases the pleasure of riding on trains and of shopping, the number of summer theatergoers, and the efficiency of workmen. Working conditions in mines have been greatly improved by the installation of air-conditioning units. The temperature in mines increases with depth. There are instances in which gold ores were

THE ATMOSPHERE

available but at a depth so great that the high temperatures prohibited operation. Many recent industrial developments in the South have been made possible by air conditioning. This is particularly important in textile mills, for efficient spinning depends on the maintenance of a fairly exact humidity.

In some industrial processes and frequently in research investigations, *exact* humidities must be maintained within closed systems. This can be accomplished by bubbling air through saturated salt solutions containing an excess of the solid phase. This air can be recirculated at 20°, thus maintaining the following constant relative humidities: $KC_2H_3O_2$, 20 per cent; $Zn(NO_3)_2 \cdot 6 H_2O$, 42 per cent; $NaNO_2$, 66 per cent; $KHSO_4$, 86 per cent; and $Pb(NO_3)_2$, 98 per cent. Many other salts may be used to maintain constant humidities.

Fig. 19.1. Humidity in the air is carefully controlled in the paper-testing laboratory. (Courtesy, N. Y. State College of Forestry, Syracuse.)

Refrigeration units are used in dual roles in localities where temperature changes are not extreme. During hot weather the cooling unit is used as usual. In *cold weather the system is reversed*; the compressor compartment is kept in the space which is to be heated and the expansion chamber is placed outdoors. Where temperature changes are not large, this method of heating is recognized by engineers as the most efficient process known. When a refrigeration unit is thus used to bring heat energy inside from outdoors, it is called a "heat pump."

Removal of Water from Gases

The drying of gases is extremely important in many industrial operations and numerous research investigations. Several factors must be considered in choosing the proper drying agent. It would be foolish to attempt to dry moist hydrogen chloride gas by bubbling it through a concentrated solution of sodium hydroxide, for the gas would combine chemically with the sorbent, forming salt and water. The drying agent selected must not react chemically with the substance to be dried. The degree of drying can be controlled by the temperature, the rate of flow of gas over the drying agent, and the type of drying agent. That all agents are not equally effective can be shown by measuring the amount of water remaining in the gas. The United States Bureau of standards has published data on the relative efficiency of the most common drying agents. For gases in which only traces of water are present, phosphorus pentoxide is most efficient. In order following it are BaO, $Mg(ClO_4)_2$, CaO, $CaSO_4$, Al_2O_3, KOH, silica gel, $CaCl_2$, NaOH, and $Ba(ClO_4)_2$. Alumina, silica and the two perchlorates are modern developments. In some cases, the drying agents act by forming compounds; for example, $Mg(ClO_4)_2$ removes water by forming hydrates; P_2O_5, by forming phosphoric acid; and CaO, by forming $Ca(OH)_2$. Solutions of KOH, $CaCl_2$ and H_2SO_4 remove water by forming solutions of low vapor tension. "Silica gel," SiO_2, and "Hydralo," Al_2O_3, remove water by forming surface compounds with it. Heating to 300° C. drives the water off, regenerating the drying agent. These agents are well suited for drying large amounts of air needed in certain processes. Silica gel was used to dehydrate the air inside the airtight coverings of airplane motors and other machinery which were shipped overseas during the recent war. It was mixed with a little blue $CoCl_2$, which remained unchanged as long as the silica gel was not "saturated." If the drying capacity of the silica gel became exhausted (perhaps on account of the covering being torn), as soon as the humidity rose to ordinary levels the $CoCl_2$ would give warning by turning into *pink* $CoCl_2 \cdot 6\ H_2O$.

Dust in the Atmosphere

It is only within recent years that we have become "dust-conscious." In the past, industry was permitted to pollute the atmosphere irrespective of damage and inconvenience to others; but public opinion has been gradually aroused as thousands of acres of plant life were destroyed, whole cities blackened, and the lives of hundreds of people ended prematurely by lung infections caused by dust particles in the atmosphere. Now we know that most dust and smoke nuisances can be successfully controlled. Dust particles are beneficial to mankind, for they serve as nuclei upon which molecules of water condense to form raindrops. Beautiful sunsets are produced by dust particles in the atmosphere. Volcanic eruptions have produced large quantities of dust which have been carried halfway around the globe, and the great dust storms in the "dust bowl" of the United States have deposited dust in various parts of the country. But for the continuous production of dust, day after day, city factories are unexcelled. Some such dusts are unburned carbon in the form of black smoke, finely divided ashes which are blown up the chimney, products of grinding wheels, leather dust, wood dust, cement dusts, and sand dusts. (Toxic gases are frequently produced along with solid dust particles. The hydrolysis of fluorides which resulted in the formation of HF has caused the death of several people in Europe. Sulfur dioxide and sulfur trioxide from combustion of coal produce sufficient acid to destroy much plant life in cities. Poisonous arsenic and selenium compounds which are easily volatilized have in the past caused considerable damage. The

Fig. 19.2. A Cottrell precipitator on (at left) and off (at right). The pictures were taken two minutes apart. (Courtesy, Western Precipitation Co.)

annual damage due to carbon monoxide, which is produced by the incomplete combustion of automobile fuels, is undoubtedly great, although difficult to estimate.)

An apparatus now available makes it possible to determine the number of dust particles per cc. of air. There may be over 100,000 particles per cc.; it is not uncommon for the dust count in some cities to vary between 5000 and 10,000. The greatest single achievement for decreasing the dust in the atmosphere is the Cottrell precipitator (Fig. 19.2). A discussion of the precipitation of dust is given in the chapter on colloids.

State laws usually require employers to furnish suitable protection to workmen who are exposed to dust; but too often gas masks and other similar equipment are not provided. Workmen may be exposed to some dusts such as silica for many years before any ill effects appear. The symptoms are similar to those of tuberculosis; hence the disease is called silicosis. There is no cure for silicosis; only preventive measures are possible.[1] Dusts in the lungs are of two types: those which can be absorbed and carried into the blood stream and thus eliminated by the body, and those which either cannot be absorbed or if absorbed cannot be eliminated. The latter are more dangerous. We still have much to learn regarding the role of air in the so-called "air-borne diseases"; but in many of them the germs are associated with dust particles and droplets of moisture.

The Carbon and Nitrogen Cycles

Although the percentages of nitrogen, oxygen, and carbon dioxide in the air are in the order of 78, 21, and 0.03, the importance of the 0.03 of 1 per cent carbon dioxide cannot be underestimated. Several important compensating factors keep the carbon dioxide content of the air constant. During animal metabolism, air is taken into the lungs; the oxygen taken from this air is replaced by the carbon dioxide formed in the body as the result of the oxidation of organic compounds. The oxygen content of exhaled air is about 15.9 per cent, and the CO_2 content is 3.7 per cent. An adult inhales about 0.5 l. of air per breath, or between 16 and 18 cu. ft. of air per hour.

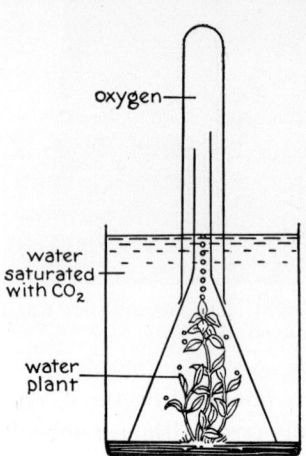

Fig. 19.3. Green leaves of water plants placed in water saturated with carbon dioxide and exposed to sunlight liberate oxygen.

The amount of carbon dioxide produced by animals is small compared with that resulting from the combustion of fuels in homes and factories; this amounts to over 5,000,000,000 tons per year. Forest fires are also producers of large volumes of carbon dioxide. The automobile is responsible for increasing the carbon dioxide content in congested sections of cities.

We need have no fear that this great volume of carbon dioxide will accumulate and finally make the earth uninhabitable, because other factors in the carbon cycle balance its production. The first of these is plant life. Botany students demonstrate the absorption of CO_2 and the liberation of O_2 by placing in the sunlight green leaves of water plants in water saturated with CO_2. The apparatus is shown in Fig. 19.3. A complex organic compound, chlorophyll, which is the green coloring compound in plant tissue, will in the presence of sunlight catalyze the reaction between carbon dioxide and the water whereby cell tissue and other complicated organic compounds are produced; at the same time, oxygen is liberated. This marvelous transformation, absolutely essential to plant and therefore to animal life, is

[1] An aerosol (page 303) of aluminum dust, when breathed at intervals, seems to prevent silicosis. See *Sat. Eve. Post*, June 15, 1946, p. 74.

still not understood. In the future, perhaps, chemists will be able to write equations for all the reactions in this part of the carbon cycle, and to duplicate nature's processes in synthesizing starches, sugars, and cellulose. Experiments in greenhouses have shown that plants grow more rapidly in high concentrations of carbon dioxide. Hence, should the CO_2 content of the atmosphere increase, plant growth would probably increase until the carbon dioxide content was again lowered. The great deposits of plant growth converted into coal and petroleum in the past are today being transformed into carbon dioxide again.

Two other factors in maintaining the carbon balance are the solubility of CO_2 in water and the reactions between carbonic acid and insoluble substances such as feldspars. The calcium carbonate formed is only slightly soluble in water; but as CO_2 dissolves in water to form H_2CO_3, there is a reaction between H_2CO_3 and $CaCO_3$, and soluble $Ca(HCO_3)_2$ is formed. An equilibrium exists between all the compounds, and any of the reactions may be reversed.

$$CO_2 + H_2O \rightleftarrows H_2CO_3$$
$$H_2CO_3 \rightleftarrows H^+ + HCO_3^-$$
$$H_2CO_3 + \underline{CaCO_3} \rightleftarrows Ca^{++} + 2\ HCO_3^-$$

Green algae sometimes grow so rapidly in water and utilize CO_2 in such quantities that the reactions go from right to left and $CaCO_3$ actually precipitates. If the CO_2 content of the air above the water is high, the equilibrium shifts from left to right and more CO_2 dissolves which in turn dissolves more $CaCO_3$. Shell fish deposit and store up calcium carbonate in their shells. Some ground waters, such as those at Saratoga Springs, New York, are supersaturated solutions of CO_2 and many salts. In the far distant past, CO_2 must have been stored up in the ground in such a form that it was easily released.

Chemists have established many steps in the *nitrogen cycle*, a cycle of great significance in our own welfare. Although the atmosphere is 78 per cent nitrogen, animals cannot use any of it in this form. We are completely dependent upon plants for its conversion into plant proteins which we can assimilate.

The synthesis of nitrogen compounds, such as $NaNO_3$, KNO_3, NH_4NO_3, $(NH_4)_3PO_4$, and $(NH_4)_2SO_4$, is discussed later; here our interest is focused upon the nitrogen cycle in nature. These compounds are utilized by plants in the production of proteins, the complex organic compounds which contain nitrogen along with carbon, hydrogen, and oxygen. (Some proteins also contain other elements.) Bacteria in the nodules on the roots of leguminous plants "fix" nitrogen; in other words, they convert molecular nitrogen into ammonia and other simple compounds such as nitrites and nitrates; hence these bacteria are called nitrifying bacteria. The nitrites and nitrates are then utilized by plants in the production of plant proteins. Certain leguminous plants—for example, clover and alfalfa—fix more nitrogen than is required for their own growth, and can therefore be used to enrich the nitrogen content of the soil. The decomposition of plant and animal tissue is also important in the nitrogen cycle because of the variety of products resulting; some of these are shown in Fig. 19.4. Some nitrogen is fixed during electrical storms because lightning produces conditions suitable for nitrogen and oxygen to unite and form oxides of nitrogen. These in turn dissolve and react with water; the nitrous and nitric acids thus formed react with basic constituents of the soil and produce salts. Thus nitrogen becomes available

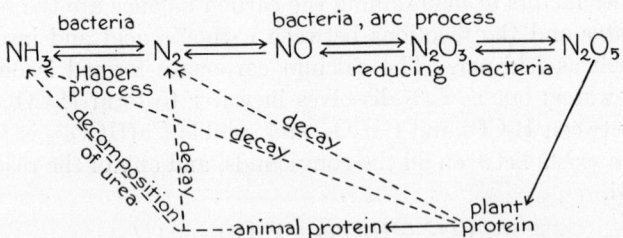

FIG. 19.4. A few steps in the complicated nitrogen cycle.

for all types of plants. However, without the synthesis of usable nitrogen compounds in the laboratory, the population of the world could not have expanded to its present level, for a world-wide food shortage would have developed years ago.

Inert Gases in the Atmosphere

The entire group of inert gases remained undiscovered until comparatively recently. Previously there had been no reason to suspect even the presence of such a group; but the discovery of one led quickly to the discovery of all the others. The inert gases are called the zero group because they are so inactive.

The world is indebted to the great English astronomer, Sir Joseph Lockyer, for the discovery of the first element in Group 0. With a spectroscope, Lockyer found a substance in the chromosphere of the sun which was unknown on the earth, and which he named "helium," from "helios," the Greek word for "sun." Any substance which can be obtained in the luminous state can be studied with the spectroscope. Bright lines appear; the color, intensity, and the distances between them depend upon the element under examination. A scale inside the instrument makes it possible to assign positions to each line produced by each element. Lockyer announced the discovery of helium after he was convinced that a line he observed in the spectroscope did not correspond with that for any known element.

Working on the principle that gases at low pressure become luminous when an electric current flows through them, the American mineralogical chemist, Hillebrand, observed that a gas was evolved when he treated the mineral uraninite with acid. Although he thought that this gas was nitrogen, Sir William Ramsay disagreed. The latter repeated the experiment, using another mineral, cleveite, and found this gas to be a mixture of gases. When he studied the luminous spectrum with the spectroscope, he found that one bright line corresponded with the line which Lockyer had observed in the chromosphere. Helium was thus isolated on the earth by Ramsay in 1895.

Helium was not the first of the inert gases to be discovered on the earth, for the presence of argon, "the lazy one," was announced in 1894 by Sir William Ramsay and Lord Rayleigh. Some years prior, Lord Rayleigh, while making careful measurements of the densities of gases, had observed that the density of the nitrogen obtained from its compounds was always less than the density of that obtained from the air after the removal of oxygen, carbon dioxide, moisture, dust, and all other known substances except nitrogen. Why should nitrogen from the air be heavier than nitrogen from compounds? Ramsay passed the nitrogen from the air back and forth over hot magnesium, which was known to react with nitrogen to form magnesium nitride, Mg_3N_2. All the nitrogen did not react with the magnesium. The remaining gas was $\frac{15}{14}$ as heavy as the original gas. What was it? Was it a different form of nitrogen? A study of the spectrum of this gas showed some nitrogen lines; *but there were also other lines never before observed in connection with any known element.* Ramsay and Rayleigh concluded that this residual gas must be a new element, and since it would not combine with any other element they called it argon.

With the discovery of the first of the inert gases, the quest for others began, for it did not appear logical that there could be only one element in this new group in the periodic table. The discovery of the others—krypton, neon, and xenon—would have been extremely difficult without another research tool, namely, liquid air. Since the nitrogen residue would not react with any other substances, a separation by means of chemical reactions was obviously impossible. Dr. Morris Travers, working with Ramsay, allowed liquid air to evaporate until only a small portion remained. When this was vaporized, new lines appeared in the spectrum and a new inert element, krypton, was discovered. Neon was discovered by liquefying impure argon and collecting the fraction of the gas which boiled off first. The crimson light in the luminous tube was sufficient indication of another new element. By repeated fractionation of the krypton fraction, another inert gas was discovered; this gas, called xenon, "the stranger," produces a beautiful blue glow in vacuum tubes.

One product of radium disintegration was discovered by Dorn in 1900 and named radon. Ramsay and Gray isolated it in 1908 and called it niton. Both names are still used.

The critical temperature, critical pressure, and the boiling points of the inert gases are shown in Table 19.2. All these gases have been solidified. Helium is the most difficult to freeze, for a temperature of less than $-272.2°$

TABLE 19.2. CRITICAL TEMPERATURE, CRITICAL PRESSURE, AND BOILING POINTS OF THE INERT GASES

	Helium	Neon	Argon	Krypton	Xenon	Radon
Critical temperature, °C.	−268	−220	−117	−63	−15	104.5
Critical pressure, atmospheres	2.75	29	52	54.3	54	62.5
Boiling point, °C.	−268.75	−233	−186	−152	−109	−62

(absolute zero is −273°) is required. The inert gases are monatomic in the gaseous state. Thus 22.4 l. or a G.M.V. of argon weighs 39.94 g. (the atomic weight of argon is 39.94). One l. of argon weighs $\frac{39.94}{22.4}$, or 1.78 g. One l. of helium at S.T.P. weighs $\frac{4.003}{22.4}$, or 0.179 g.

Until recently it was assumed that the inert gases formed no compounds. However, certain compounds of boron trifluoride, BF_3, have been shown to exist at low temperature. The possibility of the formation of such compounds is due to the fact that boron is an extremely small atom, with only three valence electrons. Accordingly BF_3 has the structure

$$:\ddot{F}:B\begin{matrix}:\ddot{F}:\\:\ddot{F}:\end{matrix}$$

in which the boron has only *six* electrons in its valence layer. It is stable, but has a very strong tendency to draw into its valence layer an *electron pair* from any atom which has one to share. The compounds of BF_3 with argon are unstable and dissociate above their melting points. The most stable of them is $A \cdot 2\ BF_3$.

Uses for the Inert Gases

No use has as yet been found for *xenon* and *krypton*. If a demand materializes, they could be obtained from liquid air columns. Although they would increase the efficiency of electric lights, their cost prohibits this. Radon is used in radiotherapy.

Argon. It is estimated that over one million cubic feet of argon are used annually to fill incandescent electric lamps. The smaller the lamp, the purer the argon used; for example, the 50- to 100-watt bulbs have about 86 per cent argon to 14 per cent nitrogen. Since argon is inert, it does not combine with the tungsten filament at any temperature. Argon is put in the lamp at about $\frac{1}{3}$ atmospheric pressure; a greater pressure would break the glass when the filament is hot. Using argon instead of nitrogen to fill bulbs saves consumers over 100 million dollars per year. Small amounts of argon are used in luminous tubes which produce a purple light at low pressure.

Neon. The orange-red glow of neon signs is so familiar that the principal use of this gas is obvious. It is also used in sodium vapor lamps, trouble finders for detecting faulty spark plugs in engines, glow lamps, and stroboscopic lamps. The electrical conductivity of neon is 75 times as great as that of air. The fact that neon signs operate at high voltage and low amperage—usually 15,000 volts and 25 milliamperes—makes the cost of operation extremely low. If there were no waste in filling the tubes, one cubic foot of neon would be sufficient to fill four miles of tubing; however, there is great waste. If a little mercury is put into the neon tube a blue light is produced. Other gases are also used in "neon" signs; thus helium gives yellow, carbon dioxide white, and argon a different blue from that just mentioned. By making use of mixtures and special glasses, all colors of the rainbow can be produced. For example, red glass filters out the orange from ordinary neon light, transmitting only the deep red; uranium glass, by fluorescing under the ultraviolet present in the mercury-containing tubes, produces a bright green glow.

Helium. The fact that helium is lighter than air and will not burn indicates the greatest use for this inert gas. During World War I Sir William Ramsay suggested that it be used in airships in place of hydrogen which, although cheap and light, is inflammable; but no supply was available for immediate use at that time. In 1905 a gas well in Cowley County, Kansas, produced gas that would not burn; careful analysis by Cady and McFarland of the University of Kansas showed that it contained 1.84 per cent helium. Analyses of gases from other wells in the oil belt of the Southwest led to the discovery that helium occurred in several places. The government has reserved the 50,000-acre Cliffside field near Amarillo, Texas, which contains a large supply of natural gas rich in helium, and it controls another large source of helium near Shiprock, N. M. The Bureau of Mines operated five extraction plants during World War II, three of them working on privately owned gas. (The gas was not wasted. After removal of its helium, the remainder was sent on to the regular industrial markets.) They produced 370 million cu. ft. of helium during the war at a cost of less than a cent per cubic foot. Most of this went to the Navy for inflating the blimps used in anti-submarine duty. It was transported in special tank cars holding 200,000 cu. ft. of gas. A 90-mile special pipe line brought the gas from one of the plants to the railroad. The helium replacement in an airship in one year's operation is about 1.5 times the volume of the ship, as compared with 8 to 10 times the volume if hydrogen is used. Other gases diffuse into the helium chambers; when the airship is no longer buoyant, these gases are cooled with liquid air and passed over special "activated" charcoal which at this low temperature removes the impurities. The helium is compressed in cylinders and ready for use again. The lifting power of helium is only slightly less than that of H_2. The relative densities of hydrogen, helium, and air are 2, 4, and 29 respectively. Thus 22.4 l. of hydrogen will lift $29-2$ or 27 g., and 22.4 l. of helium will lift 29−4 or 25 g. Hydrogen's efficiency over helium is thus only 2 g. per 22.4 l.

Peacetime Uses of Helium[2]

Where it is necessary for divers, caisson workers, or other persons to work under pressure, helium sometimes is used as a diluent with oxygen to provide a breathing atmosphere. If air is used, nitrogen is dissolved in the tissues of the body under pressure. When pressure is relieved, the nitrogen forms bubbles resulting in the painful illness commonly called "the bends." As helium is relatively insoluble, this illness does not occur when it is used. Helium also is used in artificial-breathing atmospheres whenever breathing by a patient is laborious. The lightness and rapid diffusion rate of helium reduce the effort required to breathe. Helium is used as a diluent in some types of anesthetics to reduce the hazards of inflammability and explosion. A new and growing use for helium is to provide an inert and at the same time excellent thermal and electrical conducting atmosphere for arc-welding light metals. Experiments have proved that helium is the best gas for this purpose. The gas-shielded arc-welding method was developed originally to be used in welding magnesium metal, which ignites in the presence of oxygen at welding temperatures. The method has been expanded to facilitate the welding of aluminum and stainless steel, normally without the use of flux. If a light-metal era occurs in the future, as many prominent industrialists predict, gas-shielded arc welding may prove to be the greatest post-war use for helium. Approximately 600,000 cu. ft. of helium was shipped to non-government users in April, 1946. This is nearly as much as was used in the entire year of 1938.

Liquid helium has made possible cryogenic or low-temperature research. Some metals such as mercury, lead, tin, and titanium become superconductors or perfect conductors of electricity at the temperature of liquid helium—an interesting phenomenon which as yet cannot be explained.

There is no appreciable supply of helium outside the United States as far as is now known, but our own reserves are ample. At the peak, our production capacity was over three-quarters of a million cubic feet daily, more than twice the maximum rate of use. With the close of the war, the excess supply of helium in storage was pumped back into the ground.

QUESTIONS AND PROBLEMS

1. If you are standing in a room 40 ft. square and 10 ft. high, and the air in the room is saturated with water vapor at 20° C., do you weigh more or less

[2] This paragraph is reprinted from Bureau of Mines *Information Circular 7344*.

than the water vapor in the room? Calculate the weight of the air in the room.
2. What weight of oxygen does a cylinder of 5 cu. ft. capacity contain if the oxygen is at 110 atm. pressure and the temperature is 27° C.?
3. Plot a curve of the relative humidity in the chemical laboratory for one month.
4. Make a sketch of the carbon and nitrogen cycles.
5. Why do we not recover helium from the atmosphere?
6. Compare the rates of diffusion of the inert gases.
7. How do we account for the lack of chemical activity of the inert gases?
8. If possible, visit a weather bureau and list the recording apparatus used there.
9. What weight of P_2O_5 would be required to dry 1000 l. of air saturated with water vapor at 25° C.? Assume that H_3PO_4 is formed.
10. What commercial methods are used to adjust the humidity of air in large buildings?

REFERENCES

Books

Inert Gases. Chemistry of the Rarer Elements. Hopkins, B. S. D. C. Heath & Company.

Articles

"Helium and Natural Gas." Seibel, C. W. *J. Chem. Ed.* **3,** 45–49 (1926).
"Stratosphere Flights." Piccard, Jean and Jeanette. *Ind. and Eng. Chem.* **27,** 122–27 (1935).
"Traces from Tons." Metzger, F. J. *Ind. and Eng. Chem.* **27,** 112–116 (1935).
"Argon in Light Bulbs." Bartlett, G. *J. Chem. Ed.* **4,** 1376–1385 (1927).
"Some Uses for Atmospheric Gases." Bartlett, G. *J. Chem. Ed.* **5,** 1327–1332 (1928).
"Beginnings of the Helium Industry." Cady, H. P. *Ind. and Eng. Chem.* **30,** 845 (1938).
"Production of Helium at Amarillo." Seibel, C. W. *Ind. and Eng. Chem.* **30,** 848 (1938).
"Air Conditioning Equipment." Ingels, Margaret. *Ind. and Eng. Chem.* **30,** 980 (1938).
"Argon-boron Trifluoride." Booth, H. S., and Willson, K. S. *J.A.C.S.* **57,** 2273–2284 (1935).
"The Properties and Uses of Helium." Wheeler, H. P., Jr. U. S. Bureau of Mines *Information Circular 7344.*

» 20 «

WATER—ITS PURIFICATION AND USES

The discussions pertaining to water in the preceding chapters have referred to the pure compound, H_2O. When you drink a glass of water, you do not drink pure H_2O; the water will almost surely contain dissolved salts and gases, and it may be slightly colored, have a distinct taste, and contain some bacteria and other organic matter. This is only to be expected because of the many sources of water supplies.

Fig. 20.1. Erosion of soil by water. Grand Canyon.

In some localities the only available water is the rain which is carried from the roofs of buildings and stored in cisterns. Such water has a very low inorganic residue but is frequently colored because of its contact with wood and other building materials. Almost without exception, the large cities of the world must rely upon rainfall for their water supply. Several cities in the United States have surface supplies of water. New York City's water comes from several watersheds or drainage areas and is impounded in large reservoirs or artificial lakes. Cleveland's supply comes from Lake Erie. Lake Michigan furnishes an abundant supply for Chicago, and Lake Pontchartrain plays a similar role for New Orleans. On the other hand, Los Angeles and San Francisco must go many miles inland to obtain sufficient water. No great population center can ever develop without a suitable water supply.

In many regions it is possible to tap ground-water supplies which will be adequate. Ground water is sometimes under such pressure that the water either rises to levels above that of the supply or even comes to the surface as at Saratoga Spa, New York, Fort Stockton, Texas, and numerous places in the Northwest. The mineral content of ground waters varies within large limits. Water from some shallow wells contains less residue on evaporation than do certain surface supplies. The water in the salt wells near Syracuse, New York, is in a sense a saturated salt solution. The Hathorn well at Saratoga Spa contains about 15 g. of residue per liter of water, and the Great Salt Lake in Utah contains about 20 per cent dissolved solids.

Purification and Uses

Water is said to be satisfactory for drinking purposes when the color, odor, and taste are not objectionable; injurious inorganic constituents are below allowable limits; and it is free of pathogenic (disease-producing) organisms. (It is extremely difficult to detect the presence of pathogenic organisms in water; another group of organisms, the coli-aerogenes group, is used as an indicator of pollution. Their presence shows that the water is at least under suspicion.) The inorganic constituents which usually cause trouble are Pb^{++}, Zn^{++}, and Cu^{++} ions which come from contact with pipes, and the fluoride ion which is present as fluorides in some waters. The three metallic ions are toxic; fluorides cause mottled teeth. Color in water is frequently due to its contact with organic matter such as dead leaves. Green algae in lakes are not harmful, but they give the water a greenish color and may produce disagreeable tastes and odors when they die. Some industrial wastes, even though present in extremely small amounts, may impart a very disagreeable taste. Phenol, C_6H_5OH (often called carbolic acid), is detectable if present to the extent of 1 mg. per l. (One mg. per l. = 1 part per million [1 p.p.m.].) Chlorinating water which contains phenol accentuates its presence so that it can be detected in one part per billion. Tastes and odors are best removed by aeration and filtration through materials such as activated carbon which have a specific sorptive property for these substances.

The process chosen for the purification of a water supply naturally depends upon the use to which the water is to be put. The Colorado River is extremely muddy, which means that the water is not suitable for use in irrigation. The water is purified by plain sedimentation in Lake Mead, which was created by the construction of Hoover Dam. Today it is almost impossible to obtain a surface water supply which is absolutely free from human pollution because of the sewage which is dumped into streams and drains into lakes. When this surface water is the only available supply, it must be purified.

Simple sedimentation does not usually yield water sufficiently free from color and turbidity to be satisfactory for domestic use, so it is commonly *coagulated* before sedimentation. Coagulation consists in the formation of a gelatinous precipitate of hydrous aluminum or ferric hydroxide throughout the water. The filaments of this sticky material entangle in their meshes particles of clay which are too small to settle, and carry them down. Even bacteria are caught; up to 90 per cent of the microorganisms present in a water supply may be removed by coagulation followed by filtration. (See

FIG. 20.2. Water purification plant.   FIG. 20.3. Filtration galleries, water purification plant.

Figs. 20.2 and 20.3.) If the water itself is not acid, the hydrolysis of the hydrated trivalent metal ion will produce the desired precipitate; otherwise lime may be added to remove the protons from it. In the following equation the coagulant is "chlorinated copperas" ($FeSO_4Cl$), and "milk of lime" ($Ca(OH)_2$) is added as the base to coagulate it.

$$2\,Fe^{+++} + 2\,SO_4^{--} + 2\,Cl^- + 3\,Ca^{++} + 6\,OH^- \longrightarrow$$
$$2\,\underline{Fe(OH)_3} + 3\,Ca^{++} + 2\,SO_4^{--} + 2\,Cl^-$$

After the water has been clarified it is sterilized, usually by the addition of from 0.5 to 1.5 lb. of chlorine to each million pounds of water. This practice has revolutionized public health standards. Typhoid fever, for example, used to be one of the major causes of death; 135 out of every 100,000 people in the United States died of it in 1904. Chlorination was introduced in 1909, and never thereafter has the typhoid death rate reached 25 per 100,000. In the past twenty-five years it has ranged from 1 to 4 per 100,000, and practically none of these cases have originated from city water supplies. For the sterilization of relatively small quantities of drinking water, as for soldiers, any hypochlorite serves exactly the same purpose as chlorine, though more expensive. The actual germ killer in all cases is hypochlorous acid, produced by hydrolysis from either chlorine (page 343) or the ClO$^-$ ion (page 345). Ozone is beginning to be used in place of chlorine to a slight extent (page 132).

Although a water may be satisfactory for drinking purposes as far as taste, odor, and absence of pollution are concerned, it may contain inorganic constituents in varying quantities. Which ones should be present and in what amount in an ideal drinking water is a matter of opinion. Apparently, acclimation is an important factor, for there are few who do not boast of the fine drinking water in their community. Thus the waters of Saratoga Spa are praised for their iron content which is often of value in treating anemia, their high magnesium content which acts as a purgative, and their high bicarbonate content which neutralizes mineral acids and hence overcomes hyperacidity. Some waters are claimed to be beneficial because of the radioactive material they contain, in spite of the fact that fatal cases of radium poisoning have occurred from drinking strongly radioactive water. Sulfur waters which contain so much H_2S that one needs to hold his nose while drinking them are also listed among the "health-giving" waters. Low-residue waters and waters which contain lithium salts receive their share of praise. About the only claim which is 100 per cent substantiated clinically is the fact that goiter incidence is lower in communities where iodides are present in the water. However, large-scale experiments are in progress to determine whether or not, as has been suggested, it is true that an amount of the fluoride ion too small to cause mottling of the teeth may be able to increase their resistance to decay. The effect of inorganic constituents in water on our systems needs scientific investigation. If by drinking the correct water everyone could avoid rheumatism, neuritis, arthritis, diabetes, dyspepsia, hyperacidity, anemia, and cancer, we ought to drink synthetic water solutions to which has been added the correct amount of each specific constituent.

In many of the industrial uses for water—in steam boilers, cooking, brewing, and laundries—the presence of inorganic salts is detrimental. The chief offenders are Fe^{++}, Mn^{++}, Ca^{++}, and Mg^{++} ions. Ferrous iron is oxidized to ferric iron which precipitates as red ferric oxide and stains clothes red. Divalent manganese compounds are oxidized to insoluble colored tetravalent manganese compounds. Calcium and magnesium ions form insoluble compounds or scales in boilers, thereby decreasing the efficiency of heat exchange; they also form insoluble compounds with soaps.

Detergents. A chemical which assists water to wash dirt away is called a detergent. Soap is the commonest detergent. The formula of a typical soap, sodium palmitate, is given in detail to show the two features of molecular structure which are responsible for its ability to wash away grease.

$$\left[\begin{array}{c} \text{H H H H H H H H H H H H H H H} \quad \ddot{\text{O}}\!:\! \\ \text{H}\!:\!\text{C}\!:\!\text{C}\!:\!\text{C}\!:\!\text{C}\!:\!\text{C}\!:\!\text{C}\!:\!\text{C}\!:\!\text{C}\!:\!\text{C}\!:\!\text{C}\!:\!\text{C}\!:\!\text{C}\!:\!\text{C}\!:\!\text{C}\!:\!\text{C} \\ \text{H H H H H H H H H H H H H H H} \quad \ddot{\text{O}}\!:\! \end{array} \right]^{-} + \text{Na}^{+}$$

The palmitate ion, $C_{16}H_{31}O_2^-$, is the actual detergent. It owes its effectiveness to the fact that one end of the molecule (the hydrocarbon end) is soluble in oils and greases, and the other end (the ionic end) is soluble in water. As the grease is emulsified (page 302), each particle becomes coated with a complete layer of palmitate ions, all oriented so that their hydrocarbon "tails" are in the grease and their ionic "heads" are in the water. The sodium ions remain in the water. The emulsified particles cannot join together again, because a water layer is always held between them. There are many soaps, but all are salts of long-chain acids of this type.

Synthetic detergents other than soap ("soapless soaps") are becoming common, now that we know what features a molecule must have in order to be a good detergent. The oil-soluble end is always a chain of eight or more carbon atoms. For the water-soluble end of a "soapless soap" there are several choices: (1) the hydrocarbon chain may be attached to a sulfur-oxygen instead of to a carbon-oxygen combination. Thus we have sulfates

$$\text{R}\!:\!\ddot{\text{O}}\!:\!\overset{:\ddot{\text{O}}:}{\underset{:\ddot{\text{O}}:}{\text{S}}}\!:\!\ddot{\text{O}}\!:\!{}^{-}, \text{ and sulfonates, } \text{R}\!:\!\overset{:\ddot{\text{O}}:}{\underset{:\ddot{\text{O}}:}{\text{S}}}\!:\!\ddot{\text{O}}\!:\!{}^{-}.$$

(R stands for the hydrocarbon chain, or *radical*.) (2) The ion may be *positively* charged. In this case it consists of an ammonium ion, NH_4^+, in which all the hydrogens have been replaced by hydrocarbon radicals, at least one of which is long. (3) The water-soluble end may owe its polar nature to several $-\!:\!\ddot{\text{O}}\!:\!\text{H}$ groups on adjacent carbon atoms of the chain.

These synthetic detergents have two important advantages over soap. First, they are not appreciably basic; therefore they produce neutral solutions and do not react with acids. Second, their calcium and magnesium salts are soluble even in salt water; hence they can be used successfully in sea water and hard water for they have the distinct advantage of not forming soap "curds."

Water Softening. When an ordinary sodium soap is used in water containing Ca^{++} or Mg^{++} ions it reacts with them, forming insoluble soaps, thus:

$$Ca^{++} + SO_4^{--} + 2\ Na^+ + 2\ C_{16}H_{31}O_2^- \longrightarrow \underline{Ca(C_{16}H_{31}O_2)_2} + 2\ Na^+ + SO_4^{--}$$
$$Mg^{++} + 2\ Cl^- + 2\ Na^+ + 2\ C_{18}H_{35}O_2^- \longrightarrow \underline{Mg(C_{18}H_{35}O_2)_2} + 2\ Na^+ + 2\ Cl^-$$

The calcium and magnesium soaps are the sticky, dirt-catching material of which bathtub rings and "tattle-tale gray" are composed. All the Ca^{++} and Mg^{++} ions must be used up before any soap can be left free in solution to form a lather or serve as an emulsifying agent.

Water containing Ca^{++} or Mg^{++} ions is called *hard water*. The process of removing these ions from water is called softening. Of the many processes available for this purpose, only the following five will be discussed:
1. Distillation.
2. Change of temperature.
3. Addition of chemicals which produce insoluble calcium and magnesium compounds.
4. Base exchange or zeolite reactions.
5. Addition of chemicals which form soluble complex ions.

The distillation of water produces a distillate which is free from inorganic residue, but the process is costly. Chemical laboratories must resort to this process to produce the pure water required for many chemical reactions. Until recently, distilled water was essential for storage batteries and for certain chemical processes, but now water which has been "de-ionized" by exchange reactions frequently serves just as well.

For most purposes it makes no difference what negative ions are present in hard water; but if bicarbonate ions, HCO_3^-, are present, some of the hardness can be removed by merely heating the water. Bicarbonate ions are in equilibrium with carbonate ions and carbonic acid, and the latter with carbon dioxide and water (page 665). When the water is boiled, CO_2 is driven off, destroying the equilibrium. The reactions go to completion in the direction of CO_2 and CO_3^{--}, and the latter precipitates $CaCO_3$ from the solution until it is no longer supersaturated with respect to that salt.

$$Ca^{++} + 2\,HCO_3^- \longrightarrow \underline{CaCO_3} + H_2O + \overline{CO_2}$$

Some $MgCO_3$ might precipitate in the same way, although it is nearly twice as soluble as $CaCO_3$. The fraction of the hardness which can be removed in this way is called "temporary hardness." Temporary hardness is responsible for much teakettle scale, and may completely stop up pipes in hot-water heaters. Its removal by heating is not practical because of the expense and because the water may still be hard after heating. Hardness is expressed in terms of so many "grains per gallon"; one grain per gallon equals 17 parts per million (p.p.m.). One p.p.m. is 1 mg. per liter. Hence, a water might be softened as much as possible by boiling and still have a hardness of about 10 grains per gallon because of the solubility of $CaCO_3$ and $MgCO_3$. The solubility of $CaCO_3$ is about 0.060 g./l.; of $MgCO_3$, 0.100 g./l.

The addition of chemicals which produce insoluble compounds with calcium and magnesium ions and the subsequent removal of the precipitate by decantation or filtration is another common procedure used in water softening. It is frequently called the "lime and soda ash process," for the chemicals added are lime, CaO, and soda ash or sodium carbonate, Na_2CO_3. Lime, which is necessary in order to remove hardness due to Mg^{++}, forms $Ca(OH)_2$ in the presence of water.

$$CaO + H_2O \longrightarrow Ca^{++} + 2\,OH^-$$

The hydroxide ions first neutralize any bicarbonate ions that may be present, forming enough carbonate ion to precipitate not only the added calcium ion but an equal amount of the calcium ion from that which was already present in the solution.

$$Ca^{++} + 2\,OH^- + Ca^{++} + 2\,HCO_3^- \longrightarrow 2\,CaCO_3 + 2\,H_2O$$

Further addition of lime results in the precipitation of nearly all the magnesium ion as the hydroxide, which is less than one-tenth as soluble as the carbonate. An equivalent amount of calcium ion is left in the solution in its place.

$$Ca^{++} + 2\,OH^- + Mg^{++} + SO_4^{--} \longrightarrow Ca^{++} + SO_4^{--} + Mg(OH)_2$$

Finally, sufficient soda ash is added to precipitate as much of the calcium ion, original and added, as is practicable.

$$2\,Na^+ + CO_3^{--} + Ca^{++} + SO_4^{--} \longrightarrow 2\,Na^+ + SO_4^{--} + CaCO_3$$

According to the solubility product principle (page 244), the addition of excess reagent would lower the amount of Mg^{++} and Ca^{++} remaining in solution, but the amount of excess that can be added is limited both by cost and by the increase in pH caused by the basic reagents. The total hardness remaining after softening by the lime-soda ash process is not likely to be less than 50 p.p.m. In determining the hardness analytically, standard soap solution is added to a known volume of the water until shaking results in a permanent lather. In Fig. 20.4 several milliliters of soap solution have been added to the left-hand sample of hard water, but this was not enough to soften it. One drop of soap solution was all that was needed to produce permanent suds in the perfectly soft water at the right. The soap solution makes no distinction between Ca^{++} and Mg^{++} ions, being precipitated by both alike. In calculating the results it is assumed that all the hardness was due to $CaCO_3$ in solution; and the number of parts of $CaCO_3$ per million of water, so calculated, is given as the hardness. Each "p.p.m.," therefore, corresponds to a molarity of 10^{-5} of Ca^{++} and Mg^{++} taken together.

If water of zero hardness is required, the zeolite cation-exchange process is used. The zeolites, both natural and artificial, are aluminosilicate minerals which are insoluble but which establish an equilibrium between their cations and those of any solution with which they are in contact. One of them, which is well known commercially, is called "Permutit"; hence the name, "Permutit water softener." "Permutit" contains sodium ions which trade places with calcium or magnesium ions in hard water. The equilibrium lies far to the right in the following reversible reactions.

$$Na_2Ze + Ca^{++} + SO_4^{--} \rightleftarrows CaZe + 2 Na^+ + SO_4^{--}$$

$$Na_2Ze + Mg^{++} + 2 Cl^- \rightleftarrows MgZe + 2 Na^- + 2 Cl^-$$

For the sake of brevity, Ze is used here instead of the actual formula of the complicated anion of the zeolite (see page 463). Common salt, NaCl, is used to reverse the reaction. A saturated solution of it

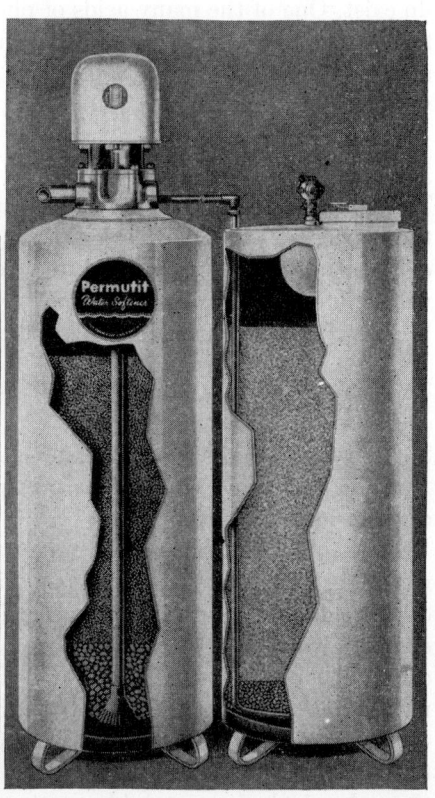

Fig. 20.4. Note the absence of soapsuds in hard water (left), and their presence in the Permutit-softened water (right). (Courtesy, The Permutit Co.)

Fig. 20.5. Permutit automatic zeolite water softener. The tank at the right contains coarse salt. (Courtesy, The Permutit Co.)

has a molar concentration of Na^+ ions 100,000 times as great as that of Ca^{++} ions in even very hard water. When the zeolite sand in the softener has exhausted its *base*[1] *exchange capacity*, that is, softened all the water it can, water saturated with NaCl is placed in contact with it. The softening reaction is reversed, the liberated Ca^{++} and Mg^{++} ions and the

[1] This word is used here in the old sense that a metal is the "base" of a salt. It does not refer to alkalinity.

excess brine are washed away to the sewer, and the regenerated sand is ready to use again for softening. Fig. 20.5 shows a typical home installation.

An interesting and useful development in water softening has taken place during the past few years. Although it was believed until recently that calcium did not form soluble complex ions, such as are common to many other metallic ions, the Hall Laboratories of Pittsburgh, on the basis of more thorough studies of the properties of phosphates, have proved that they do exist. One of the many acids of phosphorus, metaphosphoric acid, HPO_3, forms several polymers, one of which is $(HPO_3)_6$. The sodium salt of this acid, sodium hexametaphosphate, $Na_6P_6O_{18}$, is water-soluble and will react with calcium ions to form stable complexes.

$$2\,Ca^{++} + 4\,HCO_3^- + 6\,Na^+ + P_6O_{18}^{6-} \longrightarrow 6\,Na^+ + 4\,HCO_3^- + (Ca_2P_6O_{18})^{--}$$

The complex calcium-containing ion is so stable that it will form even at the expense of dissolving calcium soaps that have been precipitated. Thus clothes that have been washed in hard water and rinsed free of excess soap will produce a good suds if they are sloshed about in water containing "Calgon" (a trade name for this sodium metaphosphate).

$$2\,\underline{Ca(C_{16}H_{31}O_2)_2} + 6\,Na^+ + P_6O_{18}^{6-} \longrightarrow 6\,Na^+ + 4\,C_{16}H_{31}O_2^- + Ca_2P_6O_{18}^{--}$$

Sodium metaphosphate will dissolve about its own weight of calcium soap. In water softening, 15 g. of the metaphosphate are added for each gram of calcium ion.

The zeolite process does not reduce the number of ions in the water which it softens; it merely replaces one kind of ion with another. A recently developed two-stage process makes it possible to de-ionize water almost completely. The water is first passed through an ion exchanger operating on an H^+ instead of a Na^+ cycle. The exchange material, of an organic nature, takes all the metal ions from the solution, yielding H^+ ions in return. (It is regenerated by treatment with sulfuric acid.) The water now contains the acids corresponding to the salts originally present. It is next passed through a bed of an insoluble synthetic resin of a strongly basic nature (an organic derivative of ammonia) which takes the protons from all the hydronium ions present and holds them by covalent bonds to nitrogen atoms exposed on the surface of its pores. This gives this surface a positive charge which prevents the corresponding anions from passing on with the water. They are adsorbed, and the water flows on, ion-free. This second material is regenerated by treating it with a sodium hydroxide solution which takes the protons away from the surface and thereby releases the bound anions into the solution, to be washed away with it into the drain. De-ionized water is much cheaper than distilled water and is practically as pure, and hence has replaced it successfully for most purposes.

Sewage Disposal

The problem of disposing of human and industrial wastes is far from easy, and it is acute in large centers of population. The most common practices for disposal of wastes in the United States are the following:

1. *Dumping.* The easiest, but by far the most dangerous, disposal method is to dump wastes into a nearby lake or stream.

2. *Sedimentation.* If sewage is allowed to remain quiescent for about an hour, an appreciable amount of organic matter will settle. This heavy material, called "sewage sludge," can be dried and either burned or used as fill. Sometimes it is stored in large vats and allowed to ferment or decompose; the gases thus produced are usually rich in methane, CH_4, and can be used as fuel. The fermented sludge is then dried.

3. *Sedimentation plus Aerobic Filtration Through Filter Beds Filled with Coarse Gravel or Stone.* Biological reactions and the sorption of finely suspended material by the plant and animal growth on the gravel or stone bring about further purification. The sludge is treated as in (2).

Fig. 20.6. Settling tank for sewage purification.

4. *Activated Sludge Process.* The sewage is mixed with previously settled sludge, the mixture is aerated, and organic matter is allowed to settle. The sludge, called "activated sludge," contains a great amount of small forms of plant and animal life which concentrate the organic matter in the incoming sewage by using it as food material and also by sorbing it. The sludge remaining after further settling is either fermented or dried and sold as a fertilizer. The dried sludge from the Milwaukee sewage treatment plant is sold under the trade name of "Milorganite."

5. *Chemical Treatment plus Sedimentation.* Much of the organic matter in sewage is in the colloidal state (p. 299) and can therefore be precipitated by control of pH and neutralization of the electrically charged particles. One common procedure is to bubble chlorine into copperas, $FeSO_4$, to oxidize it to a ferric compound, and to add this (with or without lime) to the sewage. The organic matter then settles rapidly and the remaining liquid is usually nearly as clear as drinking water. The sludge is generally dried in an incinerator.

There are several places in the United States where one city dumps its sewage into a river and another city farther downstream uses this river for its water supply. That such polluted water can be rendered tasteless, odorless, colorless, and free from harmful bacteria is a tribute to bacteriologists, chemists, and engineers the world over.

Hydroponics

The study of the water culture of plants, called hydroponics by Dr. W. F. Gericke of the California Agricultural Experiment Station at Berkeley, is not new, but only rather recently has it led to any practical application. In 1699 an Englishman, John Woodward, studied the growth of spearmint and potatoes in river and spring water without any soil. In 1859 a German, Knop, improved on Woodward's idea by adding chemical nutrients to the water. For the past 75 years the growing of plants without soil has been rather commonplace as an experimental technique. The new emphasis arose from the creation of the name hydroponics, the popular appeal of a new hobby, and, of most importance, the possibility of cultivating food plants in places where regular truck gardens are impossible.

Although composed largely of water, plants will not grow in pure water; they must in addition have a continuous supply of nutrients for the development of tissues. The roots of crop plants grow in water solutions just as truly as water cress or a floating seaweed. The water solution in the soil is in a very thin film which furnishes the plant with the elements essential for its growth. The continuous cropping of the soil results in the depletion of these essential chemicals; hence the development of the fertilizer industry.

ADVANTAGES OF HYDROPONICS	DISADVANTAGES OF HYDROPONICS
Faster growth	Anchorage of plants
Greater yields	Aeration of roots
Smaller space	Difficulty in adjusting concentrations of chemicals
No weeds	
Reduced labor costs	Difficulty in keeping the supply of iron in solution
Freedom from soil-borne diseases	
	Continuous attention required

The three most important methods of culture in which nutrient solutions are employed are sand culture, water culture, and subirrigation. Irrespective of the method selected, great care must be used in controlling the concentration of chemical nutrients. Plants require potassium, calcium, magnesium, nitrogen, phosphorus, and sulfur in relatively large quantities, as well as traces of iron, boron, manganese, copper, and zinc. The pH range maintained for most plants is slightly acid, pH 4.0 to 6.0.

Formulas for culture solutions have been published by many investigators. Typical of these is the "TC" solution developed at the University of California.

Fig. 20.7. Hydroponics. Mrs. Gericke holds a cluster of 26 ripe tomatoes. A basin 10 ft.×2 ft.×1.5 ft. containing 20 plants produced 352 lbs. of tomatoes. (Courtesy, W. F. Gericke.)

"TC" SOLUTION

Salts	Ounces per 100 Gallons of Water
$Ca(NO_3)_2$	9
KNO_3	9
$(NH_4)_2HPO_4$	2
$MgSO_4$	3

Iron is added in the form of 0.5 per cent iron tartrate solution at the rate of 5 cc. per gallon about twice weekly. Manganese is added as hydrated manganese chloride to give a concentration of 0.5 part per million (5 p.p.m. may be toxic). Boron is added as boric acid to give 0.5 p.p.m. (2.5 to 5.0 p.p.m. are toxic), and zinc as zinc sulfate to give 0.05 p.p.m.

(Can the four salts listed above be obtained as anhydrous salts? If not, calculate the weights of the hydrates required, and express the results as grams per liter. What would be the molarity of each solution?)

Considerable manipulation of the concentration of nutrients is required, depending upon the temperature, light, and age of the plant. When the nutrients are controlled properly, yields have been enormous. Tobacco plants 20 feet high have been grown. The 217 tons of tomatoes per acre claimed to have been grown by hydroponics as compared with 5 tons per acre in the field is indicative of the possibilities for increasing the food supply. During World War II the entire fresh vegetable supply for the important air station on soilless Ascension Island, a fueling stop between Brazil and Africa, was grown by hydroponics. Similar installations were made on some of the barren Pacific islands. Some chemists predict that hydroponics will solve the world's food problem, for it enables nations with dense populations and little agricultural land to grow their own foodstuffs.

Mining the Ocean

No discussion of water would be complete without mention of the oceans. The total amount of water which they contain is estimated at 324 million cubic miles, enough to cover the earth with water to a depth of two miles if the land had first been leveled off smoothly. This volume of water is some 30 times as great as the volume of all land masses above sea level, and weighs about 1.5 quintillion ($1.5 \cdot 10^{18}$) tons. A single cubic mile of sea water weighs more than 4.5 billion tons and contains a veritable treasure house of dissolved material. The common salt in it is worth a billion dollars, but although it overshadows the other materials in weight (65 million tons) it is not the most valuable. The magnesium metal which could be made from a cubic mile of sea water would weigh nearly a tenth as much as the salt and be worth at least a third more. The same water contains half a billion pounds of bromine, worth $125,000,000. Nearly every other useful element is present in quantities enormous in the aggregate, but only the three substances mentioned above are in sufficient concentrations to be extracted commercially at the present time. Gold from sea water is still a dream; the metal is there, but the cost of extracting it is greater than the value of the gold obtained.

QUESTIONS AND PROBLEMS

1. Analysis of the city water of Syracuse gives the following figures in parts per million for the following ions:

Ca^{++}	33
Mg^{++}	6.1
HCO_3^-	113
SO_4^{--}	13
Cl^-	1.5

   a. How many grams of a sodium palmitate soap will be used to precipitate the Ca^{++} and Mg^{++} from 1 l. of water?
   b. A large cake of soap weighs 6 oz. and costs 16 cents. How much does it cost to soften a gallon of this water with soap, assuming it to be sodium palmitate?
   c. How many milligrams of ammonium oxalate are required to precipitate the Ca^{++} from a liter of this water? How many milligrams of $BaCl_2$ to precipitate the SO_4^{--}?
   d. Assuming that all the Ca^{++} and Mg^{++} are present as bicarbonates, how much lime will be needed per gallon to soften the water?
2. Look up the analysis of the water in your home community, and answer the above questions. Figures for several large cities are given in Lange's *Handbook of Chemistry*.
3. Visit a water purification plant and sketch the steps in the process.
4. What is sodium hexametaphosphate? For what is it used? Secure from a grocery store a list of commercial water softeners sold there for kitchen use.

REFERENCES

Books

The Chemistry of Water and Sewage Treatment. Buswell, A. M. A.C.S. Monograph No. 38.
Water Supply and Treatment. Hoover, C. P. National Lime Association, Washington, D. C.
Standard Methods of Water Analysis. American Public Health Association, New York.

Articles

"Greens Grow for GI's on Soilless Ascension." W. Robert Moore. *Nat. Geog. Mag.* 88, 219 (1945).

» 21 «

COLLOIDS

Probably no subject serves better to unite the interests of various scientific groups than colloid chemistry. Practically every intelligent individual finds this subject important, providing it is discussed from the angle in which he is interested. However, to treat the subject from the point of view of the forestry student interested in the colloidal nature of cellulose and wood, the home economics student who wishes to understand the colloidal nature of foods, the agricultural student who is interested in the colloidal property of soils, the medical student whose interest lies in colloidal properties of living tissues and pharmaceuticals, and the engineering student who is interested in the structural properties of concrete, artificial building materials, clays, enamels, ores, and alloys, would require not a chapter but a book.

What is colloid chemistry? The more you study it, the harder it is to define. Professor Bancroft of Cornell University defined it broadly as follows: "Colloid Chemistry is the chemistry of grains, drops, bubbles, filaments, and films"—the same as saying that colloid chemistry is a very broad subject. The student of colloid chemistry is interested in grains—small solid particles; drops—small liquid particles; bubbles—small gas particles; filaments —particles in which all dimensions but one are small; and films—which have at least one dimension that is small.

Colloid chemistry deals with particles of rather definite dimensions. If they are too small, they will be in true solution. Salt and sugar dissolve in water to form true solutions. (The properties of true solutions have been discussed in an earlier chapter.) Sand thoroughly agitated in water will momentarily represent particles quite evenly distributed throughout a liquid, but in a matter of seconds the sand settles. If each particle of sand is cut in two, they will settle more slowly. This process of subdivision could be continued until the particles settle extremely slowly. Obviously, if the particles are subdivided sufficiently they approach the dimensions of water

COLLOIDS

molecules; they may settle, but so slowly that the rate is very difficult to measure. Gold particles can be prepared which settle in water at the rate of about 1 cm. in eight years. Particles in the colloidal state are of such size that they are neither in true solution nor in suspension.

The unit of measure for colloidal particles is the mμ. One micron, μ, is one thousandth of a millimeter, and one millimicron, mμ, is one millionth of a millimeter. Substances in the colloidal state are usually from 5 mμ to 200 mμ in diameter. Table 21.1 gives the diameters and particle sizes of several substances.

TABLE 21.1. SIZE OF PARTICLES

1 millimicron, mμ = 10A (10 Angstrom units)

$$= \frac{1}{1,000,000} \text{ mm.}$$

Particles	Size
H$_2$ molecule (diameter)	0.067 mμ
H$_2$O molecule (diameter)	0.113 mμ
NaCl molecule (diameter)	0.26 mμ
CO$_2$ molecule (diameter)	0.285 mμ
Sugar molecule (diameter)	0.7 mμ
Chloroform molecule (diameter)	0.8 mμ
Colloidal gold (diameter)	2–40 mμ
Bacteriophage (diameter)	20–40 mμ
Visibility of microscope	0.13 μ
Fine dust	2.0 μ
Brownian movement	4.0 μ
Anthrax bacilli (length)	6 μ
Red blood corpuscles (diameter)	7.5 μ

Heretofore the words solute and solvent have been used when referring to solutions, but a new terminology is necessary for colloidal solutions. The term *sol* is used to refer to a colloidal solution. The medium surrounding the colloidal particles is called the *dispersion medium* or *external phase*, and the particles are referred to as the *dispersed medium* or *internal phase*.

Each of the three states of matter—solid, liquid, and gas—can be used as both external and internal phases. Examples of these are given in Table 21.2.

TABLE 21.2. SOME COMMON TYPES OF COLLOIDS

External Phase	Internal Phase	Example
Gas	Liquid	Fog ⎫ Aerosols
Gas	Solid	Smoke ⎭
Gas	Gas	(Nonexistent)
Liquid	Liquid	Emulsion (milk)
Liquid	Solid	Suspension (red gold sol)
Liquid	Gas	Foam
Solid	Liquid	Gels
Solid	Solid	Ruby glass
Solid	Gas	Gas entrapped in rare minerals

Sols may thus be divided into eight groups according to the external and internal phases which are combined. An equally interesting and useful classification could be based on Bancroft's definition of sols. If you have ever blown soap bubbles, you have prepared a sol, for the *film* was of the dimensions of colloids. Cellulose and many other fibrous materials contain some *filaments* of colloidal diameter. Many rocks contain small *bubbles* of gas; the foam on carbonated beverages also contains some very small *bubbles*. Oil-in-water emulsions—milk and mayonnaise, for example—are *drops* of liquid dispersed in a liquid; a fog consists of drops of liquid in a gas. Gold in ruby glass, a gold sol of gold in water, and smoke in air are examples of *grains* dispersed in solids, liquids, and gases.

How many atoms or molecules are contained in one colloid particle? The following simple calculaton will show that the number is quite large. How many atoms of gold are in a spherical colloidal gold particle which is 40 mμ in diameter? 1 cc. of gold weighs 19.3 g. At. wt. of gold = 197.2. 197.2 g. of gold contains 6×10^{23} atoms. Volume of a sphere $= \frac{4}{3} \pi r^3 = 4.189 r^3$.

$$\frac{4.189 \times (2 \times 10^{-6} \text{ cm.})^3 \times 19.3 \times 6 \times 10^{23}}{197.2} = \text{approx. 2,000,000 atoms of gold}$$

Although solid gold is yellow in color, it may be prepared in the colloidal state in very small particles which are ruby red, or in larger blue aggregates which tend to settle rapidly.

Theoretically at least, it is possible by selecting the proper external phase to prepare all substances in the colloidal state. The one outstanding property characteristic of all sols is the enormous surface area which they present. Calculate the surface area of 1 g. of gold in the colloidal state, assuming that each particle has a diameter of 40 mμ. If your interest lies in the field of biology, you know the approximate number of red blood corpuscles per cc. of blood. Assuming that they are spherical, calculate the total surface area of the red blood corpuscles in the body.

Preparation of Colloids

The preparation of a sol consists in obtaining a dispersed phase in the range of particle size between true solution and suspension; there are two ways of doing this.

True solution	COLLOIDAL STATE	Suspension
Condensation yields ⟶	or SOL FORMATION	⟵ Dispersion yields

Molecules in true solution may be converted into molecular aggregates by suitable chemical methods, and sols be produced by condensation. Large masses may be subdivided by suitable chemical or mechanical means into sols by dispersion.

COLLOIDS

Condensation. When H₂S gas is bubbled into a solution containing As₂O₃, a yellow precipitate of As₂S₃ should form (Fig. 21.1).

$$As_2O_3 + 3\ H_2S \longrightarrow As_2S_3 + 3\ H_2O$$

The only difficulty is in getting the precipitate to form. Instead, a sol forms which contains as the dispersed phase aggregates of As₂S₃ that are too small to settle. This sol has been prepared by condensation.

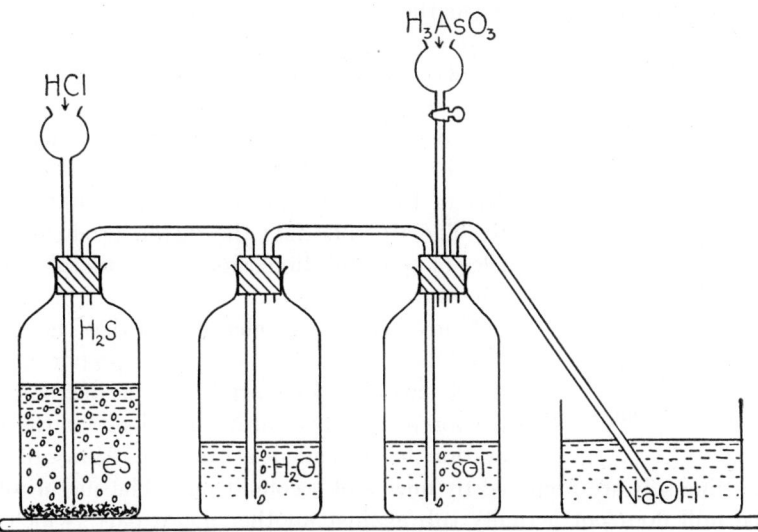

FIG. 21.1. Preparation of colloidal arsenic trisulfide.

Another sol easy to prepare by condensation is obtained by adding a ferric chloride solution, drop by drop, to boiling water. A few drops of concentrated ferric chloride added to 400 ml. of boiling water produce a deep red color, whereas the same quantity added to this volume of cold water produces only the faintest yellow color. In cold water the iron is present as ferric ions. Boiling speeds up the hydrolysis of FeCl₃, thereby producing Fe(OH)₃. The high temperature also results in varying amounts of intermolecular dehydration which aids in the condensation by increasing the molecular size. In this process two OH groups attached to different iron atoms react to liberate a molecule of water. The two iron atoms are then left attached to each other by the remaining oxygen atom. A single step can be shown as follows:

$$\begin{bmatrix} H_2O & OH \\ H_2O-Fe-OH \\ H_2O & OH \end{bmatrix} + \begin{bmatrix} HO & OH_2 \\ HO-Fe-OH_2 \\ HO & OH_2 \end{bmatrix} \longrightarrow \begin{bmatrix} H_2O & OH & HO & OH_2 \\ H_2O-Fe-O-Fe-OH_2 \\ H_2O & OH & HO & OH_2 \end{bmatrix} + H_2O$$

The composition of the colloidal particles is thus rather indefinite. Commonly, however, this is neglected and the hydrolysis is described by the simplified equation:

$$Fe^{+++} + 3\ Cl^- + 3\ H_2O \longrightarrow \underline{Fe(OH)_3} + 3\ H^+ + 3\ Cl^-$$

Colloidal gold which is of diagnostic value in medicine is prepared by reducing Au^{+++} ions to metallic gold. If conditions are controlled very carefully, a beautiful red gold sol may be prepared. Many other sols can be prepared by condensation methods.

Dispersion. If metal electrodes are held as shown in Fig. 21.2 and arced under N/1000 NaOH, metal sols may be obtained by dispersion. (Of course the external resistance must be such that the fuse does not melt.) This method, known as the Bredig Arc, is most frequently used to prepare sols of the chemically inert metals, like Au and Pt. The arc vaporizes the metal, producing particles of colloidal dimension which are taken up by the water.

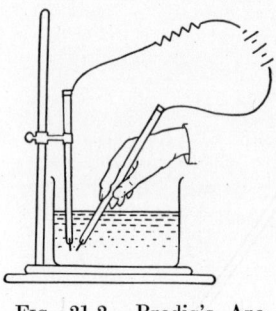

Fig. 21.2. Bredig's Arc sols.

Many types of mechanical devices have been developed in recent years for preparing very small particles. In most cases the degree of dispersion attained is hardly sufficient for the preparation to be called a true sol. Many of these border-line sols are prepared by means of a colloid mill. The metal rotator of the mill does not actually rub against another metal part (which may or may not be moving in the opposite direction), but it rotates at such great velocity that sufficient shearing forces are produced to disperse larger aggregates.

Hand-operated homogenizers which force liquids through a small opening at several hundred pounds pressure have the same general effect as colloid mills. Mayonnaise of the finest consistency is made by forcing olive oil, water (containing acetic acid), and an emulsifying agent (egg yolk which contains protein) through the homogenizer. Whole milk can be given the consistency of cream. Some cream cheeses are prepared by means of homogenizers.

Every time you wash your hands with soap and water you are using a colloid to aid in the dispersion of dirt, oil, and grease in water. Although two immiscible liquids may be mixed momentarily by sufficient agitation, the dispersion is unstable. It is difficult to remove dirt and grease from the hands with water alone. Gasoline and water can be shaken together to form a milky suspension, but in a few minutes the mixture "layers out" or separates. If soap is added to the water, the same amount of agitation will produce a much more stable dispersion of gasoline in water. Such oil-water-soap dispersions are called *emulsions*, for they are made by making two immiscible substances mix by using a third substance called an emulsifying agent. Soap is a good emulsifier because it tends to concentrate in the surface films which separate the small drops of oil from the water. This lowers the surface tension, and the oil droplets are, in a sense, not squeezed to the surface but remain dispersed throughout the water. A soap molecule is rather long; one end of it is believed to lie in the water film and the other in the oil. It is possible to prepare emulsions of 99 per cent oil and 1 per cent water, and vice versa. Emulsions of water in oil are prepared by substituting calcium and lead soaps for the common sodium and potassium soaps which are used to prepare oil in water emulsions.

FIG. 21.3. Portion of pilot milk plant with homogenizer in operation. (Courtesy, Borden Research Laboratory, Syracuse, N. Y.)

A dispersion of colloidal particles in the atmosphere is sometimes called an aerosol. This term has become familiar to the public in connection with the DDT bombs which protected our troops from insects in the Pacific islands. These devices are designed to spray into the air a mist of fine droplets of a dilute solution of insecticides (DDT and pyrethrum) in an extremely volatile non-toxic liquid ("freon," CCl_2F_2). The evaporation of each tiny droplet leaves a particle of insecticide which is of colloidal dimensions. The resulting *aerosol* remains in suspension indefinitely.

Another interesting method of preparing sols by dispersion is called *peptization*. There are two types of peptization. The first involves the fact that particles of some solids will take up enormous quantities of liquid and form a sol, with the liquid as the external phase. The second type involves the absorption of ions by particles which thus become charged. The repellent force produced by the like charges tends to disperse the particles throughout the liquid.

The housewife speaks of dissolving starch, glue, gelatin, and agar in hot water. Actually they have not dissolved, they have been *peptized*. They are not in true solution, as will be shown later. The changes which take place when such substances are heated with water are due to the fact that these substances *take up large quantities of water or swell*, thus forming sols which may, on cooling, be rigid, semi-rigid, gel, or jelly-like in structure. This process of solvation thus differs from hydrolysis (see page 216). Substances may be peptized in solvents other than water. Alcohols, ketones, and other organic compounds are used (in the varnish, shellac, and other industries) to peptize such common substances as gums, resins, shellac, pyroxylin, and cellulose.

Some inorganic substances which are not peptized by water are peptized by certain ions. Thus a student who is washing a precipitate of ZnS on a filter paper is disconcerted when the precipitate suddenly starts to go through the filter. Peptization is taking place. Usually the addition of a salt will prevent this, but it is difficult to find one which will not interfere with subsequent work.

Properties of Colloids

What type of experiments can be done with sols instead of solutions? Of course, the first idea which comes to mind is to try the same experiments as were conducted with true solutions—filtration; boiling-point, freezing-point, and osmotic pressure characteristics; conductivity; and chemical reactions in solution. But in addition, some experiments not possible with true solutions may be possible with sols. For example, a new study is suggested by the fact that the particles of the dispersed phase are large enough so that their properties can be studied. Are these particles in motion? Do they reflect light? Do they act like ions in the conduction of electricity? Can they be separated from the external phase by filtration? These are but a few of the many questions which may be raised in our search for further information regarding the properties of colloids.

Filtration. Substances in true solution pass through ordinary filter paper. A colloidal solution also passes through it. The many filter media available differ with respect to the ease with which particles penetrate them. Molecules of water will pass through eggshells, animal skins, parchment paper, and clay cups impregnated with solids; but Thomas Graham showed in 1861 that such substances as albumin, gelatin, and hydrous oxides did not penetrate or dialyze through membranes. If neither diffusion nor sedimentation takes place during dialysis, the substance is said to be in the colloidal state. Separation can be effected by means of an ultra-

FIG. 21.4. An ultra-filter.

filter like that shown in Fig. 21.4. The colloidal particles are retained on the membrane. Milk can be filtered through cellophane and a water-clear filtrate obtained.

Electrodialysis, another modification of dialysis, consists of passing an electric current through the dialysis cell. The electrolytes are rapidly washed away with distilled water which drips over the electrodes. This process is particularly valuable in the purification of biological sera.

The dispersed phase can be concentrated by hanging a dialysis sack in the air and blowing air against it. Water and other diffusible substances pass through the membrane, leaving a more concentrated colloid within it. This process is called pervaporation.

Boiling Point, Freezing Point, and Osmotic Pressure of Colloidal Solutions. It is impossible to make more than a few general statements regarding boiling and freezing points and osmotic pressure. One colloid may be prepared by the application of heat, whereas another may be destroyed. In general, freezing destroys the colloidal state and causes coagulation of the dispersed phase. No exact data pertaining to the molecular weight of colloids by boiling-point rise, freezing-point depression, or osmotic pressure determinations have been obtained because the effect of the colloid is too small to be measured. This is particularly true of the *suspensoid type* of sol such as the colloidal elements, hydroxides, and sulfides. Higher concentrations of the dispersed phase are obtained with the *emulsoid type* of colloid, such as soaps, gelatin, glue, and starch. There is one marked difference between suspensoid and emulsoid sols. When heated to dryness the emulsoid sols can be repeptized with water, but the suspensoid sols cannot. *Emulsoid sols* are called *reversible sols; suspensoid sols* are *irreversible sols.*

Tyndall Effect. The chemist is almost certain to see the Tyndall effect every day that the sun shines because the particles of ammonium chloride smoke in the laboratory serve as nuclei to reflect the beam of sunlight that comes in through the window. All theatergoers have observed the

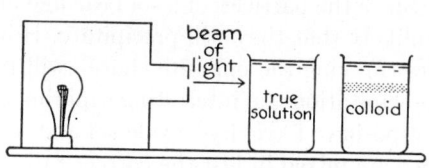

Fig. 21.5. Tyndall effect.

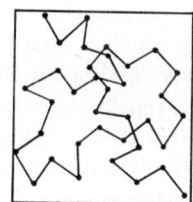

Fig. 21.6. Path of a colloidal particle.

Tyndall effect. If the air in the theater were absolutely dust-free, the beam of light from the projector would not show a Tyndall effect. If a strong pencil of light is passed through a true solution, we can hardly perceive that any light is passing through the liquid, provided that we view the light beam from the side. If the same pencil beam is passed through a colloidal solution, the colloidal particles reflect light and the distinct path of the beam can be seen. This phenomenon can be observed best in a dark room with an apparatus like that shown in Fig. 21.5.

Brownian Movement. Years ago, Robert Brown, a Scottish botanist, altered the apparatus used to show the Tyndall effect by arranging the solution so that the beam of light could be observed with a microscope, thus greatly magnifying the Tyndall effect. Today we can view sols with an instrument of this type known as the ultramicroscope, and we see tiny specks of light which indicate the presence of colloidal particles. These specks are in rapid motion, but we soon make a most amazing observation. The path of a colloidal particle consists of straight irregular zigzag lines, like those in Fig. 21.6. The motion is believed to be due to the uneven bombardment of the colloidal particles by molecules of the external phase. Since molecules are known to travel in straight lines, it is to be expected that the colloidal particles will also move in straight lines.

Electrical Properties of Colloids. Why don't the particles in the dispersed phase of a sol collide, agglomerate, and precipitate? There must be some reason why the particles of gold in a gold sol remain particles for many years. One of the early experiments conducted with colloidal solutions was that of passing an electric current through them. It was observed that under the influence of a direct current all the colloidal particles or dispersed phase migrated in one direction. This phenomenon was first called cataphoresis, but the more general term *electrophoresis* is now used. Colloidal particles are therefore electrically charged. The particles in the ferric hydroxide sol carry a positive charge, whereas colloidal elements, sulfides, paper, cotton, and silicates usually carry a negative charge.

It is possible to reverse the charge on colloidal particles, but it is much easier to do this with emulsoid sols such as gelatin than with suspensoid sols such as colloidal gold. The charge on a gelatin sol depends upon its method of preparation and the pH. Such substances as gelatin have a pH of minimum swelling which is frequently called the *isoelectric* point. Swelling is greater both above and below this point. Since the particles of a sol bear like charges and thus repel each other, it is unlikely that they will precipitate. However, it is logical that colloidal particles carrying the opposite charge will tend to neutralize each other and cause precipitation. An interesting experiment is to mix together various quantities of positive ferric hydroxide sol and negative arsenic trisulfide sol. When the two are mixed in just the correct ratios, complete coagulation occurs and the dispersed phases settle, leaving a colorless supernatant liquid. If the ratios are not correct, there is at least some neutralization of charges. Sols may also be coagulated by charged particles in true solution, that is, by ions.

The addition of salts to suspensoid sols usually results in rather effective coagulation. Positive ions are effective in coagulating negative sols, and negative ions are effective in coagulating positive sols. At first we should expect that a trivalent aluminum ion would be three times as effective, and a divalent barium ion twice as effective, as a monovalent sodium ion. Actually the coagulating powers of $Na^+ : Ba^{++} : Al^{+++}$ are as $1 : 40 : 1000$. The reason for this is not well understood at the present time.

The source of the electric charge is believed to be ions sorbed on the surface of the colloidal particles. Thus a colloidal gold particle might sorb Cl^- or OH^- ions from solution and thereby obtain a negative charge. Silver iodide sols have been prepared carrying a positive charge, Ag^+ ions sorbed, and also carrying a negative charge, I^- ions sorbed. When two such sols are mixed in the correct ratio so that the sorbed ions just neutralize each other, mutual coagulation occurs.

If a gold sol is mixed with a negative gelatin sol, the gold sol becomes more stable. Gelatin sol plus a gold sol is said to yield a protected gold sol. It is believed that gelatin surrounds the gold particles so that they take on the characteristics of an emulsoid sol. As such, they are not as easily coagulated by electrolytes. One important application of this protective action is made in the diagnosis of syphilis. Some protein material in normal spinal fluid has a protective action similar to that of gelatin. Thus a definite amount of a salt solution added to a gold sol will just coagulate the red gold particles, but the same amount of salt solution will not coagulate the same volume of the gold sol if some normal spinal fluid is added. The spinal fluid from a syphilitic patient has little protective action and may even enhance the coagulating effect of the salt solution. The same type of test is used in diagnosing other diseases.

Most particles of smoke and dust carry electrical charges. A charge can be induced on dust particles which do not ordinarily carry an appreciable one. This is the principle underlying the new devices which precipitate weed pollen from the atmosphere, thereby creating a more satisfactory environment for hay fever victims. Coal smoke and furnace dust are particularly obnoxious in cities. Some industrial plants emit from their smokestacks tons of solid particles which sooner or later lose their charge, coalesce, and settle in the vicinity. The charge of the particles in the smokestack may be utilized by means of a Cottrell precipitator, which draws the smoke particles between two plates of opposite sign and at a high electrical potential. The colloidal particles are drawn to them, lose their charges, and settle to the bottom of the precipitator. Fig. 19.2 shows the effectiveness with which the Cottrell precipitator removes smoke and dust particles from the atmosphere. A new and entirely mechanical apparatus depends upon centrifugal force for this separation.

Sorption. Chemists formerly used the two terms adsorption and absorption when referring to such phenomena as charcoal in gas masks adsorbing toxic gases and a solution of sodium hydroxide absorbing sulfur dioxide gas; but because of numerous border-line cases, the word *sorption* is now used to include both processes.

Colloids owe their large sorbing powers to the surface exposed. This can be illustrated by calculating the relative surfaces of a cube 1 m. on edge and an equal volume of material 10 mμ on edge. (What are the surfaces?) Much is yet to be understood regarding the exact action of these surface forces. That they are of great magnitude is obvious. Langmuir revolutionized the lighting industry when he found that tungsten wire sorbed sufficient oxygen to react later and cause the filament to break. Many more people would have been killed in the First World War were it not for the fact that charcoal sorbs toxic gases. Brown sugar syrup filtered through charcoal becomes as clear as water. A special activated carbon is now used in water purification to sorb tastes and odors. In some cases it is added to the water just before it goes through the sand filters.

Movement of industries to the South has given impetus to the air-conditioning industry. One method of removing water vapor from the air is to sorb it with silica gel or activated alumina. The large surfaces of these porous oxides are due to innumerable capillaries, many of which are only slightly larger in diameter than molecules. Such materials are also of great value as sorbents of organic vapors. Volatile solvents used in the paint, varnish, and lacquer industries are reclaimed by drawing the air containing these gases over suitable sorbents. Silica gel has been prepared in such a form that 1 g. of it will sorb 1.6 g. of benzene, C_6H_6, from an air stream saturated with this gas.

That you may appreciate the numerous applications of colloid chemistry, the following summary of practical applications is given. It could be expanded to include many hundreds of examples.

Carbon black industry—Each year over 400 million pounds of colloidal carbon compounded in rubber more than treble the life of the products. About 30 million pounds are used in printing inks each year.

Cellulose—The many products obtained from cellulose will be discussed in Chapter 39.

Ceramics—Many of the particles in clays are of colloidal size.

Chemical warfare—War gases, gas masks, smoke screens, and signal smokes are based on a knowledge of colloid chemistry.

Colloidal fuels—Coal is pulverized and mixed with oil to form a colloidal fuel.

Colloids in glass—Many of the colors produced in glass are due to colloids dispersed in it.

Dyeing—Many dyes are colloidal in nature. Leather, cloth, etc., have many properties of colloids—particularly the power of sorption.

Foam method for fighting fires—The foamite fire extinguisher uses CO_2 foam stabilized with the extract of licorice root, resins, etc.

Ore flotation—This process is discussed in Chapter 29.

Paper and printing industry—Printing is done with colloidal inks on cellulose which has many colloidal properties. The sizings used contain some particles of colloidal dimensions.

Pectin—This colloidal carbohydrate is necessary in the formation of fruit jellies; it can be purchased as a concentrated syrup.

Petroleum refining—Petroleum is filtered through sorbents to remove colored compounds as well as some sulfur-containing substances.
Photography—Photographic emulsions are colloids. See page 585.
Rubber—Rubber latex is colloidal.
Solid alcohol—This gel can be purchased on the market. It can be made by mixing 15 cc. of saturated calcium acetate with 85 cc. of 95 per cent alcohol.
Starch—Cornstarch pudding is made by pouring a water suspension of starch into boiling water.

QUESTIONS AND PROBLEMS

1. What role does colloid chemistry play in each of the following?
   - Ice cream
   - Jello desserts
   - Mayonnaise
   - Paint
   - Fingernail polish
   - Lipstick
2. How are emulsions prepared? How can they be broken?
3. What is ore flotation?
4. How does soap cleanse?
5. How would you prove whether a bottle of ink is a colloid?
6. Do colloidal particles carry an electrical charge? Explain.
7. How can pollen dust be removed from the air?
8. As a youngster you may have been told to fill a bottle with smoke. Before long the smoke disappears. Where does it go? Why does the smoking of tobacco produce a smoke? Does this indicate complete combustion? If the smoke is colloidal, is it produced by condensation or dispersion?
9. What is the "molecular weight" of a gold particle containing 2,000,000 atoms? What weight of gold, in the state of colloidal particles of this size, would be needed to depress the freezing point of 1000 g. of water 0.001°?

REFERENCES

Books

Colloid Chemistry. Hartman, R. J. Houghton Mifflin Company.
Colloid Chemistry. Weiser, H. B. John Wiley & Sons, Inc.
Colloidal Phenomena. Hauser, E. A. McGraw-Hill Book Company, Inc.
Colloid Chemistry. Thomas, A. W. McGraw-Hill Book Company, Inc.
Laboratory Manual of Colloid Chemistry. Holmes, H. N. John Wiley & Sons, Inc.

22

ALKALI METALS AND HALOGENS AND THEIR COMPOUNDS. PRODUCTS OF THE SALT INDUSTRY

This chapter will discuss two groups of elements in the periodic table—the alkali metals in Group I, and the non-metals in Group VII. The latter are called halogens, a term meaning "salt former." Hydrogen, although in Group VII, is not a halogen. (See the periodic table, page 82, for the subgroups in Groups I and VII.) Table 22.1 shows some of the general properties of these elements.

THE ALKALI METALS

Sources of the Alkali Metals

Lithium is well distributed throughout the world. One of the most unusual sources of lithium compounds is the springs at Conneautville, Pennsylvania, whose water contains 0.9 g. of LiCl per liter. A complex silicate, lepidolite, can be converted into a soluble compound by fusion with potassium sulfate.

Sodium is found in sodium chloride, which constitutes over two-thirds of the solid matter dissolved in sea water. Chile saltpeter, cryolite, Na_3AlF_6, and borax, $Na_2B_4O_7 \cdot 10 H_2O$, are other important naturally occurring sodium compounds.

Potassium, in the form of soluble potassium carbonate, or potash,[1] was first obtained by the early colonists in this country by leaching wood ashes, a process which is still used in some parts of the world. Potassium is abundant in the form of compounds, among them being orthoclase (one of the feldspars with the formula $KAlSi_3O_8$) and sylvite, KCl. Prior to the First World War, Germany had a monopoly of the world's potash supply, with her famous Stassfurt deposits of carnallite, $KCl \cdot MgCl_2 \cdot 6 H_2O$. At the present rate of consumption, this bed will not be exhausted for another thousand

[1] In industry the term "potash" is commonly used to mean any soluble potassium salt.

years. There are also similar deposits in Alsace-Lorraine, and Russia has recently discovered large potash deposits. The Dead Sea contains over a billion tons of salts rich in potassium compounds. There are deposits of potassium compounds in several places in southwestern United States; one is near the famous Carlsbad Caverns in New Mexico and another is in western Texas. The deposits of leucite, $KAlSi_2O_6$, in Wyoming are a potential source of potassium, but one which, because the process is expensive, will not be developed until other deposits are exhausted. Searles Lake, in the Mohave Desert near Trona, California, affords an unlimited supply. The bottom of this lake is a salt block some 60 feet high and over 12 square miles in area. The saturated brine which covers this salt block contains 4.75 per cent KCl, along with NaCl, Na_2SO_4, Na_2CO_3, $Na_2B_4O_7$, NaBr, LiCl, and NaI. This lake is the site of the American Potash and Chemical Corporation's plant, the first important development of the potash industry in this country. Over 400 tons of valuable product are removed from the lake daily and 1500 tons of worthless salts are dumped back into it because it has no outlet. At present this country requires over 1,000,000 tons of potash (calculated as K_2O) annually for fertilizers, and this amount will increase as the soluble potassium salts in the soil are depleted. The Carlsbad deposits were first worked in 1930, and this country became independent of foreign supplies of potash for the first time in 1934.

Rubidium and *cesium* are widely distributed in nature, usually associated in small quantities with other alkali metals. Both are associated with the lithium ore lepidolite. Traces of rubidium are also present in sea water, seaweed, tobacco, coffee, crude cream of tartar, and the ash of oak and beech trees. Cesium is present in some mineral waters.

Discovery of the Alkali Metals

Rubidium and *cesium* were discovered in 1860–1861 by Bunsen and Kirchhoff, working with a spectroscope. Cesium received its name from "caesius," meaning "sky blue," for its lines as observed with a spectroscope have this color. Rubidium owes its name to the fact that its spectrum lines are of the deepest red.

A young Swedish chemist, Arfvedson, treated the ore petalite, later known to be $LiAlSi_4O_{10}$, with barium carbonate and neutralized the soluble portion with acid. To his surprise, more acid was required for neutralization than should have been required even for NaOH. After many careful checks on his work, including a study of the salts, he reported the discovery of this new element, *lithium*.

As early as 1700 there were references to the natural and artificial alkalies, soda and potash. Yet scientists had to wait over one hundred years before the true characteristics of these substances were fully understood. Some thought that they contained nitrogen, and others believed that hydrogen was present. Sir Humphry Davy tried to electrolyze water solutions of soda

TABLE 22.1. PROPERTIES OF ALKALI METALS AND THE HALOGENS

Name	Lithium	Sodium	Potassium	Rubidium	Cesium	Fluorine	Chlorine	Bromine	Iodine
Symbol	Li	Na	K	Rb	Cs	F	Cl	Br	I
Atomic weight	6.94	22.997	39.096	85.44	132.91	19.00	35.457	79.916	126.92
Melting point	186	97.5	62.3	38.5	28.5	−223	−102	−7	113
Boiling point	1336	880	760	700	670	−187	−34.6	58.7	184.4
Color	silver white	silver	silver	silver white	silver	pale yellow	greenish yellow	red brown	violet
Solubility in water g./100 g. at 0°		React and form hydroxides.				Reacts and liberates oxygen.	1.46	4.2	0.03
Critical temperature	—	—	—	—	—	—	144	302	553
Critical pressure	—	—	—	—	—	—	76 atm.	—	—
Specific gravity	0.534	0.97	0.86	1.53	1.9	1.1 liquid	1.56 liquid	3.12 liquid	4.93
Color of ion		Excellent reducing agents.			All are colorless.		Excellent oxidizing agents.		
Chemical action									
Reaction with Oxygen		React at room temperature.					Do not form oxides by direct union.		
Reaction with hydrogen					All unite directly with hydrogen.				

and potash and thus obtain the metals, but all that he succeeded in doing was to decompose water. Finally he fused some potash and passed an electric current through the molten substance; this produced an intense light at the cathode. Being an excellent experimenter, he was soon able to carry out the electrolysis without the substance which was formed catching fire as soon as it came in contact with the oxygen of the air. Little metallic globules were obtained at the cathode. When dropped into water these particles skimmed about and burned with a lavender light. Since he prepared the metal from potash he called it *potassium*. A few days later, Davy succeeded in electrolyzing fused caustic soda which required a "greater intensity of action of the batteries" and thus he discovered a second element, *sodium*. The last member of the alkali metal family is the element with atomic number 87. It does not occur in nature in appreciable quantities, probably because none of its isotopes have stable nuclei. The isotopes which have been prepared artificially (in infinitesimal quantities) all have unstable nuclei which decompose radioactively within a short time. The name *francium* and symbol Fr have been proposed.

Preparation of the Alkali Metals. Their Properties and Uses

Commercial Preparation. The active alkali metals are never found free in nature, it is impossible to produce any of them commercially by heating their compounds, and a search for a still more active substance is futile because they head the activity list. Therefore the best method of inducing alkali metal ions to take on electrons is by using an electric current. This process is feasible only where cheap electricity is available; furthermore, the reaction must be carried out in the absence of oxygen and water.

Lithium is prepared by the electrolysis of a fusion mixture of LiCl and KCl; *potassium*, by the electrolysis of fused potassium hydroxide, KOH; and *cesium* and *rubidium*, by the electrolysis of the cyanides, CsCN and RbCN. Since the element sodium is much more important commercially than all the other alkali metals, the commercial procedure used in obtaining metallic sodium will be discussed in more detail.

The cheapest raw material for the preparation of *sodium* is sodium chloride. However, no sodium is produced by the electrolysis of a water solution of NaCl (page 249). The difficulties of handling molten NaCl (m.p. 804° C.) and its electrolysis products prevented its use until sodium became so important to industry that it had to be produced more cheaply. Instead, the more expensive NaOH was used because its melting point is nearly 500° lower than that of NaCl. The NaOH process was called the Castner process. It is now obsolete; for a number of years all the sodium made in the United States has been made from fused NaCl by the Downs process, as shown in Fig. 22.1. At the start of a run some potassium fluoride is added to lower the melting point; it is not decomposed. The chlorine which is simultaneously produced is an important by-product, for sodium, which less than a generation ago was hardly more than a laboratory curiosity, is now produced in great quantities. It is shipped to large users in special tank cars provided with steam coils by means of which it can be remelted at its destination.

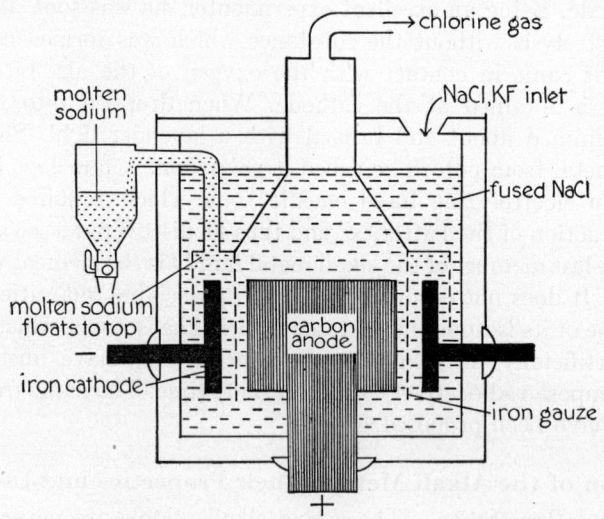

FIG. 22.1. Cross section of a circular cell for the production of metallic sodium. Cell devised by J. C. Downs.

Properties. All the alkali metals are silvery, soft, and of low density. They corrode or oxidize rapidly in the presence of oxygen to form oxides. The reactions are exothermic; the heat liberated raises the temperature of the reacting material, thereby increasing the rate of oxidation. *Always be careful with such reactions.* The metals react with water to form hydroxides.

$$2\ \underline{Li} + 2\ H_2O \longrightarrow 2\ Li^+ + 2\ OH^- + \overline{H_2} + \Delta$$

These active metals combine readily with most of the non-metals such as the halogens, oxygen, sulfur, and nitrogen. Lithium forms a fairly stable compound with silicon; the compound may be exposed to the air for a month without complete decomposition. They are good reducing agents and will liberate hydrogen not only from water but also from some organic compounds which are far weaker acids than water. Thus sodium ethylate is formed by the reaction of sodium with ethyl alcohol.

$$2\ \underline{Na} + 2\ C_2H_5OH \longrightarrow 2\ C_2H_5ONa + \overline{H_2}$$

Similarly molten sodium liberates hydrogen even from ammonia, forming sodium amide.

$$2\ Na(l.) + 2\ \overline{NH_3} \longrightarrow 2\ \underline{NaNH_2} + \overline{H_2}$$

Ammonia is a far weaker acid than water; the alkali metals dissolve in anhydrous liquid NH₃ without any reaction unless a catalyst is present. The beautiful deep-blue solutions which are formed show metallic-type conduction, and the metals can be recovered unchanged by evaporating the ammonia. The solutions are powerful reducing agents. Sodium ethylate and sodium amide are salts. The ethylate ion and the amide ion are far stronger bases than the hydroxide ion, corresponding to the fact that alcohol and ammonia are far weaker acids than water. Both are used as bases in the chemical industry, but only in non-aqueous solutions. In the presence of water both will be hydrolyzed completely. Sodium amide is also used in the manufacture of sodium cyanide, an important industrial chemical.

Hydrogen reacts with the alkali metals as though it were a halogen, forming salts whose negative ion is the hydride ion, H⁻.

$$2\ \underline{Na} + \overline{H_2} \longrightarrow 2\ \underline{NaH}$$

The hydride ion is an extremely strong reducing agent. Although, of necessity, not as strong in that respect as are the alkali metals, it reacts immediately with water, liberating hydrogen.

$$\underline{NaH} + H_2O \longrightarrow Na^+ + OH^- + \overline{H_2}$$

Sodium hydride, which has only recently become available commercially, can reduce mill scale, Fe₃O₄, to metallic iron.[2]

$$\underline{Fe_3O_4} + 4\ Na^+ + 4\ H^- \longrightarrow 3\ \underline{Fe} + 4\ Na^+ + 4\ OH^-$$

For this use it is dissolved in fused sodium hydroxide.

All the alkali metals except lithium can be stored conveniently under kerosene which keeps out the oxygen of the air. Lithium, however, is so light that it floats on oil; therefore it can best be stored in tubes which have been sealed in an inert atmosphere.

Remember the great danger to yourself and others when you work with these metals. Cesium is the most active; the others, in order, are rubidium, potassium, sodium, and lithium.

Uses. It has taken one hundred years for the alkali metals to cease being laboratory curiosities and come into practical use on a commercial basis. The danger in handling them and the high cost of production are two factors which have limited their use.

Because of their activity as electron donors, all the alkali metals are excellent reducing agents; but their initial cost makes this use expensive. *Rubidium* is still a laboratory curiosity. It can be used in photoelectric cells, but potassium is as effective and less costly. *Cesium* is alloyed with other metals and used as a "getter" in radio tubes to remove the last traces of oxygen. *Potassium* is used for some reactions in organic chemistry and in photoelectric cells.

[2] *Chem. and Eng. News* **24**, 1668 (1946).

Commercially, *sodium* is the most important of the alkali group. Prior to 1888 it was used as a reducing agent in the production of aluminum. It is used in the manufacture of tetraethyl lead (page 564), and serves as a reducing agent in many reactions in organic chemistry. Sodium is used for cooling exhaust valves in heavy-duty airplane, truck, and bus engines. Sodium lamps are used in lighting highways. Although their light is a rather weird yellow-orange, these lamps are efficient and produce no glare on the highway. Sodium lamps are now available for installation on automobiles, but further improvement is necessary, and attempts are being made in this direction. Sodium is an excellent conductor of electricity and is now cheaper *on a volume basis* than any other good conductor. Where a large enough conductor is needed so that the saving in the cost of metal is sufficient to pay for the necessary protective casing, sodium can actually replace copper to advantage. For example, the Dow Company, needing to transport a large amount of electricity at low voltage for its electrolytic operations, laid half a mile of 4-inch cast-iron pipe and filled it with sodium.

Lithium is used as a degasifier, deoxidizer, and desulfurizer for such metals as iron, nickel, and copper; and also as a refining agent for some of the lighter metals such as magnesium, calcium, and zinc. When lithium is present in cast iron, the molten metal can be poured at a lower temperature than is possible if there is none; furthermore, the cast iron shows an increase of about 0.3 in specific gravity, which indicates a sounder and denser metal. Experiments are being made on the effect of lithium added to carbon steels.

THE HALOGENS

Sources of the Halogens

None of the halogens is found free in nature because they are too active. *Chlorine*, the most important of the group, is found as NaCl in sea water and rock salt in Galicia, Tirol, Spain, and England. Other important chlorine compounds found in nature are KCl, $MgCl_2$, horn silver (AgCl), calomel (Hg_2Cl_2), and $CaCl_2$ in some brines. NaCl and KCl are present in most animal secretions, and HCl is a constituent of the gastric juice of animals.

Iodine is second in importance to most of us, for there is usually a bottle of tincture of (alcoholic solution of) iodine in our home. Iodine is widely distributed in nature, but it is rarely found in high concentrations in any one place. It is present in sea water to the extent of 1 in 280,000,000 parts. It occurs in combination in minerals with silver, mercury, and lead ores. The Saxon dolomite and the Swedish limestone contain traces of iodides. Some plants and animals have the interesting power of concentrating iodine; for example, the dried thyroid gland of sheep is 0.34 of 1 per cent iodine. One of the oldest sources of iodine is the ashes of certain seaweeds. The most important source of iodine until recently was Chile, with her deposits of iodine in the form of sodium iodate, NaIO$_3$. She produces about 300 tons yearly and could easily increase this tenfold. Her monopoly made iodine very expensive. Now, however, iodine is recovered from the salt brines associated with certain oil wells in California and Louisiana, and this has cut the Chilean monopoly price of $4.00 per pound to about half.

Bromine, third in importance, was until 1934 obtained almost entirely from the salt brines of Stassfurt, Germany, and from Michigan, Ohio, and West Virginia. With the development of anti-knock gasoline, new sources were required. The most abundant source in the world is sea water, which contains about 70 parts per million. The ingenious process for tapping this enormous supply will be described later in the chapter.

The chief sources of *fluorine* are cryolite, Na$_3$AlF$_6$, apatite, Ca$_5$(PO$_4$)$_3$F, and fluorite, CaF$_2$. It is present in traces in the human body, and is concentrated in larger amounts in the enamel of teeth.

Discovery of the Halogens

The halogens were discovered during the period 1811–1886, and were identified as elements in the following order: chlorine, iodine, bromine, and fluorine. *Chlorine* was prepared by Scheele in 1774 by the reaction between manganese dioxide and hydrochloric acid. He described its characteristics correctly, but believed that it was an oxide of some type. Sir Humphry Davy proved that it was an element, for all his efforts to decompose it failed. It is interesting to note that chlorine, bromine, and iodine were all discovered accidentally, whereas the isolation of fluorine was the result of arduous and dangerous work.

The discoverer of *iodine* was a French saltmaker, Barnard Courtois, who made a living by extracting salts from brown algae and seaweed. He was particularly interested in the recovery of potassium salts and used sulfuric acid to "destroy" certain sulfur compounds present in the mother liquor. As the story goes, one day in 1811 he must have added more sulfuric acid than usual, for beautiful clouds of violet vapor escaped from the container. The vapor, which had an odor similar to that of chlorine, condensed readily on cold objects and formed dark crystals almost metallic in character. After making a few observations, he turned this work over to two of his friends, Desormes and Clément, for more thorough study. Two years later Clément described the properties of iodine in great detail.

The French chemist, Balard, discovered *bromine* in 1826 when, while treating Montpellier salt brine (which contained bromides) with chlorine gas, he distilled a dark red liquid which boiled at 47° C. He named this substance bromine because of its "bad odor."

With the discovery of bromine, iodine, and chlorine, it was clear to the chemists that there was an undiscovered element above chlorine in the periodic table. The fluorides and hydrogen fluoride were known for many years before anyone was able to obtain the element fluorine in the free state. Davy,

Gay-Lussac, Thenard, George Knox and his brother Thomas all nearly lost their lives from breathing the fumes of hydrogen fluoride, and Louyet and Nicklès died. Moissan, the famous Frenchman who synthesized the first diamond, finally, in 1886, built an apparatus which would work. Two platinum-iridium electrodes were sealed into a platinum U-tube and an electric current was passed through a solution of dry potassium acid fluoride in anhydrous HF. (Pure hydrogen fluoride, HF, is a non-conductor.) Fluorine was obtained at the anode and burned brightly when brought in contact with silicon.

Preparation of the Halogens. Their Properties and Uses

Preparation. Chlorine, bromine, and iodine are produced in the United States. Although we import *iodine* to the extent of one to nearly three million pounds per year, there is no lack of raw material, for it is estimated that 3,000,000 pounds could be produced each year from the kelp along the Pacific coast. Plants were built and operated for a few years during the First World War, but were abandoned after the discovery of iodide ion in certain oil-well brines in California. The iodine is liberated from these brines by the action of chlorine.

$$2\ Na^+ + 2\ I^- + \overline{Cl_2} \longrightarrow 2\ Na^+ + 2\ Cl^- + \underline{I_2}$$

The discovery of this source of iodine cut Chile's former monopoly price in half. Our production was 300,000 pounds in 1937, and is much greater now. The crude Chilean $NaNO_3$ contains about 0.2 of 1 per cent sodium iodate; this is separated from the sodium nitrate by fractional crystallization. The $NaNO_3$ crystallizes first and the mother liquor gradually accumulates the iodine salts. The mother liquor is then treated with a reducing agent, usually sodium bisulfite, and the iodine is precipitated from solution. The iodine is pressed into cakes, sublimed, packed in wooden kegs, and covered with fresh cowhides to prevent loss by volatilization. (Iodine has an appreciable vapor pressure at room temperature.) The reaction for the reduction of iodate is as follows:

$$5\ Na^+ + 5\ HSO_3^- + 2\ H^+ + 2\ IO_3^- \longrightarrow 5\ Na^+ + 5\ HSO_4^- + \underline{I_2} + H_2O$$

The production of *bromine* from bromides depends upon the oxidation of the bromide ion to free bromine. When the bromide ion concentration is fairly high, as it is in the mother liquors from which other salts have already been crystallized as the main product, this is accomplished by means of electricity. The electrolytic process can be used because the bromide ion is more easily oxidized to free bromine than the chloride ion is to free chlorine. The bromine discharges at a lower potential than chlorine; therefore if the voltage is carefully controlled, only bromine is liberated.

The introduction of Ethyl anti-knock gasoline (in whose preparation bromine is used) in 1925 so increased the demand for bromine that it was obvious that a new source would have to be developed. A process was therefore devised for extracting it from sea water on a commercial scale. The Ethyl-Dow Corporation constructed a large plant for this purpose at the mouth of the Cape Fear River in North Carolina. The demand for bromine increased from 1,700,000 pounds in 1925 to about 17 million pounds in 1937. The tremendous demand for aviation gasoline in the Second World War required the construction of still another such plant.

Water from the ocean is pumped into the plant, most of the bromine is removed, and the water then flows back into the ocean many miles downstream. The steps in the recovery of bromine from sea water are as follows:

1. The pH of the water is changed from 7.2 to 3.2 by the addition of about 0.27 lb. of H_2SO_4 per ton of water. If this change was not made, the bromine would react with water as fast as it was liberated.

2. Chlorine is added; this oxidizes the bromide ion to bromine.

$$Cl_2 + 2\ Br^- \longrightarrow Br_2 + 2\ Cl^-$$

3. Air blown through the water picks up the bromine gas.

4. Air containing the bromine is passed through sorption towers filled with sodium carbonate solution. In pure water the following equilibrium[3] would be established:

$$3\ Br_2 + 3\ H_2O \rightleftharpoons 6\ H^+ + 5\ Br^- + BrO_3^-$$

but the presence of the base, CO_3^{--}, sends the reaction to completion to the right by removing the H^+ ions as fast as they are produced. The complete reaction, then, is:

$$6\ Na^+ + 3\ CO_3^{--} + 3\ Br_2 \longrightarrow 6\ Na^+ + 5\ Br^- + BrO_3^- + 3\ \overline{CO_2}$$

5. After a concentrated solution of sodium bromide and sodium bromate has been obtained, the disproportionation reaction is reversed by adding concentrated sulfuric acid. The solution is heated to drive out the bromine which then condenses as liquid bromine. In 1944 this country produced 102,000,000 lbs. of bromine.

Chlorine, a more active element than either bromine or iodine, requires powerful oxidizing agents for its production. Any one of the following reactions is used for the laboratory production of chlorine:

1. $\underline{MnO_2} + 4\ H^+ + 4\ Cl^- \longrightarrow Mn^{++} + 2\ Cl^- + 2\ H_2O + \overline{Cl_2}$

2. $\underline{MnO_2} + 2\ Na^+ + 2\ Cl^- + 4\ H_2SO_4 \longrightarrow$
$\qquad\qquad\qquad Mn^{++} + 2\ Na^+ + 4\ HSO_4^- + 2\ H_2O + \overline{Cl_2}$

[3] From one point of view this reaction is a hydrolysis, like the somewhat simpler reaction of Cl_2 with water (page 343). From the point of view of electron transfers, it may also be called a *disproportionation*. This term is applied to reactions in which the same element is both oxidized and reduced.

3. $2\,K^+ + 2\,MnO_4^- + 16\,H^+ + 16\,Cl^- \longrightarrow$
$\qquad\qquad 2\,K^+ + 2\,Mn^{++} + 6\,Cl^- + 8\,H_2O + 5\,\overline{Cl_2}$

4. $2\,K^+ + Cr_2O_7^{--} + 14\,H^+ + 14\,Cl^- \longrightarrow$
$\qquad\qquad 2\,K^+ + 2\,Cr^{+++} + 8\,Cl^- + 7\,H_2O + 3\,\overline{Cl_2}$

The Writing of Redox Equations

The four equations above are examples of electron transfer reactions. They are not as simple as the examples in Chapter 9 because they are complicated by simultaneous proton transfer reactions. When a complicated equation was first encountered, you were told that it was unnecessary to commit the coefficients to memory because they could be worked out whenever they were needed.

The Usefulness of Oxidation Numbers. Your first step in learning to balance redox equations is to review carefully the discussion of oxidation numbers (page 103). Arbitrary as the concept of the oxidation number may seem, it is useful, in two ways. In the first place, compounds of an element can very well be classified according to the oxidation state of that element in them. Compounds in which it has the same oxidation number are similar in their chemical reactions. Compounds of an element in which it has different oxidation numbers might almost as well contain different elements for all the similarity between them. This is true regardless of the similarity or dissimilarity of the formula. For example, sulfur trioxide, SO_3, and sulfuric acid, H_2SO_4, both of which contain sulfur in the +6 state of oxidation, can be used interchangeably in most reactions, whereas the sulfite ion, SO_3^{--}, which contains +4 sulfur and has a formula which appears similar to that of sulfur trioxide, is utterly dissimilar chemically; it is a base and a reducing agent, while SO_3 is acidic (in the sense that it can neutralize a base) and an oxidizing agent.

The second valuable use of oxidation numbers is in balancing equations for electron transfer reactions. Suppose that the reactants are known and the main products of the reaction have been identified. There remains the chemico-arithmetical problem of deciding the proper relative numbers of the various molecules to write in the equation; this is called balancing the equation. An equation is balanced when each side has the same number of each kind of atom involved and the same number of electrical charges. It then expresses the fundamental truth that neither atoms nor electrons disappear or are created during the course of a chemical reaction. It is usually easy enough to balance by trial and error methods an equation for a reaction not involving electron transfer, but when electron transfer is involved, the case is different. Unless the numbers of molecules of the oxidizing and reducing agents are chosen so that the number of electrons gained by the former is equal to the number lost by the latter, it will never be possible to balance both atoms and charges at the same time. Oxidation numbers make it easy to determine the number of electrons gained or lost by any molecule and to

ALKALI METALS AND HALOGENS

balance them. Whatever increase in oxidation number an atom undergoes during a reaction is the number of electrons it loses. The decrease in oxidation number is the number of electrons it gains.

Let us suppose that a solution of potassium permanganate and hydrochloric acid react and produce manganous chloride, potassium chloride, chlorine, and water as the products. The *unbalanced* chemical equation for this reaction is:

$$K^+ + MnO_4^- + H^+ + Cl^- \longrightarrow K^+ + Cl^- + Mn^{++} + \overline{Cl_2} + H_2O$$

Several things are apparent in this equation.
1. The manganese in the permanganate ion has changed in oxidation number from $+7$ to $+2$ to form the manganous ion.
2. *Some* of the chloride ion becomes uncharged chlorine, and thus changes in oxidation number from -1 to 0.
3. Study of the equation shows that these are the only elements whose oxidation numbers have changed.

Thus the fundamental reaction, which involves changes in the oxidation numbers, is:

$$\overset{+7}{Mn}O_4^- + H^+ + 2\ Cl^- \longrightarrow \overset{+2}{Mn}^{++} + \overset{0}{\overline{Cl_2}} + H_2O$$

The hydrogen ion is included to combine with the oxide ion of MnO_4^-. Two chloride ions are shown because at least that many are required to give the diatomic molecule of chlorine as a product.

In order for manganese to change in oxidation number from $+7$ to $+2$, five electrons must be gained by it to neutralize five of its positive charges. This is, of course, reduction. Similarly, for two chloride ions to become two uncharged chlorine atoms two electrons must be lost. This is oxidation. To summarize:

$$Mn^{+7} + 5e \longrightarrow Mn^{+2} \quad \text{(reduction)}$$
$$2\ Cl^{-1} - 2e \longrightarrow Cl_2^0 \quad \text{(oxidation)}$$

Manganese takes on the electrons which chlorine gives up. Electrons are not given up freely to space during a chemical reaction. Something must take them on; therefore, the *total* loss of electrons by chloride ions must equal the *total* gain of electrons by manganese.

The total loss and gain of electrons is equalized conveniently by multiplying each equation by the smallest numbers which give the least common multiple. Since in this case 10 is the least common multiple, multiply the reduction equation by 2 and the oxidation equation by 5; they become:

$$2\ Mn^{+7} + 10e \longrightarrow 2\ Mn^{+2}$$
$$10\ Cl^{-1} - 10e \longrightarrow 5\ Cl_2^0$$

Now the loss and gain of electrons is equal and the complex equation is *fundamentally* balanced except for adjusting the coefficients of the other ions, by inspection, to comply with the coefficients derived above. Thus we have:

$$2\ MnO_4^- + H^+ + 10\ Cl^- \longrightarrow 2\ Mn^{++} + 5\ \overline{Cl_2} + H_2O$$

Since 2 MnO_4^- have a total of 8 oxygens, 8 mols of water must be formed. This requires 16 H^+, or:

$$2\ MnO_4^- + 16\ H^+ + 10\ Cl^- \longrightarrow 2\ Mn^{++} + 5\ \overline{Cl_2} + 8\ H_2O$$

Actually we need not go any further than this, for this equation, as written, gives all the pertinent redox facts. Anything else present in the reaction vessel (as shown in the original equation) remains in the same condition after the reaction as before it. For instance, the K^+ ions do not undergo any change. However, a beginning student is frequently confused by seeing equations written only to this extent. The Mn^{++} ions on the right side of the equation with no negative ions to go with them might justifiably seem ridiculous to him. We shall show *all* the ions present on both sides of the arrow in all such equations throughout the book; but note that frequently some of these ions can be canceled, thus shortening the equation.

Since each MnO_4^- ion carries with it a K^+ ion, we can show two potassium ions on each side in the balanced equation:

$$2\ K^+ + 2\ MnO_4^- + 16\ H^+ + 10\ Cl^- \longrightarrow 2\ K^+ + 2\ Mn^{++} + 5\ Cl_2 + 8\ H_2O$$

The H^+ ions came from the HCl; therefore 16 H^+ came from 16 HCl. Obviously six more Cl^- ions are required on the left side. But these additional chloride ions do not lose electrons, for this has already been taken care of; therefore, these chloride ions will remain as chloride ions on the right side of the arrow. Furthermore, these six Cl^- ions are just what is needed to balance the rest of the + charges on the right side of the equation. Thus the final *completely* balanced equation becomes:

$$2\ K^+ + 2\ MnO_4^- + 16\ H^+ + 16\ Cl^- \longrightarrow 2\ K^+ + 2\ Mn^{++} + 6\ Cl^- + 5\ Cl_2 + 8H_2O$$

This may seem lengthy to you, but notice that each step is simple and actually represents the consecutive reasoning processes which a chemist follows from beginning to end in order completely to balance an equation. You need write the equation only once; you should then follow mentally this schematic reasoning procedure for deriving the coefficients in front of the ions and compounds. Following is a summary of the procedure:

1. Write the *complete* equation.
2. Determine by inspection which ions are changing in oxidation numbers.
3. Multiply these ions by appropriate coefficients to make the loss and gain of electrons equal.
4. Multiply all the other ions by appropriate coefficients to comply with those derived in step 3.

Commercial Preparation of Chlorine

For reasons of economy, common salt has been used as the raw material in the commercial preparation of chlorine for over 50 years. Therefore either metallic sodium or a sodium compound is always produced in an equivalent quantity. Sometimes the chlorine is the main product and sometimes it is the by-product, depending upon shifting industrial demands. Chlorine was first prepared commercially by means of the Deacon process, which consisted of burning hydrogen chloride in the presence of a catalyst at about 400° C. The catalyst was a copper salt deposited on a refractory material. An 80 per cent yield was considered very good.

$$4\ HCl + O_2 \rightleftarrows 2\ H_2O + Cl_2$$

The HCl used for this was part of the surplus which was produced (and at first mostly thrown away) during the operation of the Leblanc soda process (page 352). The abandonment of the Leblanc process withdrew this source of chlorine at about the time that Castner was developing the electrolysis of NaCl solutions (1892). Since then, chlorine has at times been burned with hydrogen to make HCl!

All chlorine is now manufactured electrolytically. The electrolysis of fused NaCl, discussed on page 314, is used to the extent that metallic sodium is needed. However, 90 per cent of all the chlorine is manufactured by the electrolysis of salt *solutions*, simultaneously with sodium hydroxide. The United States uses close to two million tons of chlorine a year. The mechanical details of the electrolysis cells are continually being improved in an attempt to lower the price and thus increase the use of the product. (In 1947 chlorine sold for as low as $35 per ton.) But the modern cell shown in Fig. 22.2 is the same in principle as its predecessors. The complete equation for the reaction is:

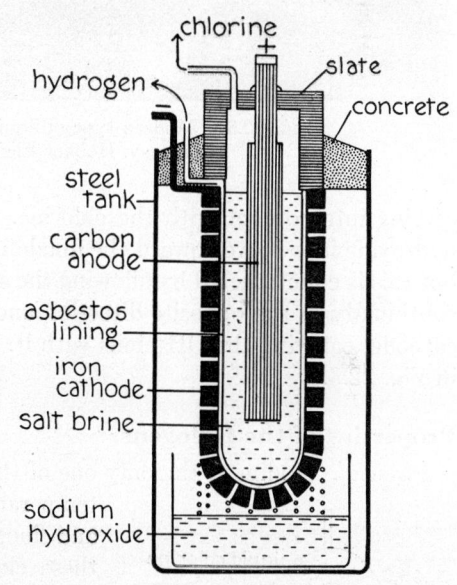

Fig. 22.2. Cross section of a Nelson electrolytic cell.

$$2\ Na^+ + 2\ Cl^- + 2\ H_2O \xrightarrow{\triangle} 2\ Na^+ + 2\ OH^- + \overline{H_2} + \overline{Cl_2}$$

Chlorine is liberated at the carbon anode, and hydrogen at the iron cathode.

The essential feature of any chlorine cell is the separate anode and cathode compartments. Above the surface of the liquid the separation is complete, to prevent the hydrogen and chlorine from mixing with each other. Below the liquid surface a porous asbestos diaphragm prevents the hydroxide ions, which are formed at the cathode simultaneously with the hydrogen, from

FIG. 22.3. Modern type of liquid chlorine cell equipment.
(Courtesy, Hooker Electrochemical Co.)

coming into contact with the chlorine, with which they would react. The hydroxide ions move toward the anode under the influence of their charges, but this is counteracted by allowing the solution to seep through the asbestos continually in the opposite direction and drain off through the holes in the cathode, carrying the OH$^-$ ions with it. A battery of chlorine cells is shown in Fig. 22.3.

Properties of the Halogens

Physical. Iodine is the only one of the halogens which is a solid at room temperature; bromine is a liquid, and chlorine and fluorine are both gases. The density of these elements is also in the same order, iodine being nearly five times as heavy as water; bromine has a density of 3.12, chlorine when liquefied has a density of 1.56, and liquid fluorine is slightly heavier than water. Although as elements the halogens are all colored (the depth of color increasing with increase in atomic weight), the ions are colorless. Thus silver-white sodium plus violet iodine yields white sodium iodide.

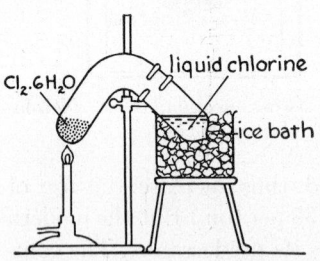

FIG. 22.4. Preparation of liquid chlorine from chlorine hexahydrate.

Iodine is handled commercially as a solid, the only prerequisite being that it be kept in a closed container; for otherwise, because of its high vapor pressure, it escapes. Bromine, being a liquid, can be easily handled in drums and glass containers. Years ago, when chlorine was to be moved from one place to another in the laboratory, it was converted into the solid hydrate, now considered to be $Cl_2 \cdot 6\ H_2O$. This hydrate is obtained when chlorine gas is bubbled into water which is cooled with a salt-ice mixture. Faraday heated a sealed tube of the hydrate (see Fig. 22.4) and cooled the other end of the tube, thus obtaining liquid chlorine.

Chemical. The halogens are the exact opposites of the alkali metals in chemical properties as well as position in the periodic table. Whereas the alkali metals, with only one valence electron, lose that electron with the greatest readiness, the halogens, with seven, are strongly electrophilic. Fluorine, since it is the smallest of the halogens, is the most vigorous electron taker of all (page 73). The other members of the halogen family follow in the order of their atomic numbers (and weights), $F > Cl > Br > I > At$. Although there is a big step down in activity from fluorine to chlorine, chlorine is still a very electrophilic element, comparable to oxygen. Even bromine is a good oxidizing agent, but iodine is only moderately good. The element with atomic number 85 does not exist in nature in appreciable quantities, but sufficient amounts of radioactive isotopes of it have been prepared artificially to show that it is a very weak oxidizing agent and is even willing to lose electrons, like a metal. The name *astatine* and symbol At have been proposed for it.

Fluorine is such a powerful oxidizing agent that it liberates oxygen from water at room temperature with explosive violence.

$$2\ \overline{F_2} + 2\ H_2O \longrightarrow \overline{O_2} + 4\ \overline{HF}$$

Each of the other three halogens reacts with water to a much less extent, but oxygen is not liberated except as the hypohalous acid first formed is decomposed by light. Cold water dissolves about three times its volume of chlorine (almost 1 per cent by weight at 1 atm. pressure). The equilibrium which is set up was discussed on page 230. Bromine forms a 4 per cent solution in cold water. It reacts with water in the same way that chlorine does.

$$Br_2 + H_2O \rightleftharpoons H^+ + Br^- + HBrO$$

The decomposition of the hypobromous acid is rapid in bright sunlight, and oxygen is liberated. Both HClO and HBrO have lower energies of activation than the halogen molecules from which they were formed and are therefore more active as well as more powerful oxidizing agents. Thus when chlorine is used in the sterilization of drinking water, it is actually the hypochlorous acid which reacts. Iodine is too insoluble in water to produce a solution of appreciable acidity or oxidizing power, but the same equilibrium may be shown to exist by adding a base. This sends the reaction to completion to the right, using up the trace of dissolved iodine. If there was previously an excess of undissolved iodine crystals, they promptly dissolve.

All the halogens react directly with metals to form halides, the rate of the reaction depending upon the relative activity of both the metals and the non-metals. Traces of water catalyze the reactions. Some of these reactions liberate so much heat that they are extremely dangerous—no chemist would ever drop a large piece of potassium into a flask of liquid bromine. Metal dusts sprinkled into chlorine or bromine gases react with a visible evolution of light. Even the noble metals react with the halogens. The valence of the metal in the metal halide depends upon the ratio of metal to halogen in the reaction mixture. Absolutely dry chlorine does not react with iron, but the reaction is vigorous if there is any moisture. In the installation of chlorine equipment, great care must be taken to assure that there will be no contact between moist chlorine and metals, for corrosion will occur rapidly. Chlorine gas which escapes from apparatus because of faulty connections may soon produce a lethal concentration. A concentration of 0.02 mg. per liter of air is very irritating; higher concentrations are fatal. (Data obtained during the First World War indicated a lower incidence of influenza and common colds, as well as a lower mortality, among workmen exposed to low concentrations of chlorine.) Chlorine and bromine gases are heavier than air; therefore in case of an accident, "start climbing" to get out of the danger zone. If liquid mercury and solid iodine are ground together in a mortar, either yellow mercurous iodide, HgI, or red mercuric iodide, HgI_2, will be formed, depending upon the ratio of mercury to iodine.

The halogens combine directly with several non-metals. Although they do not combine with oxygen and carbon, both oxygen and carbon halides can be prepared by indirect methods. Phosphorus and sulfur burn in chlorine, producing compounds similar to those formed by the direct union of these elements with oxygen.

$$2 P + 3 Cl_2 \longrightarrow 2 PCl_3 + \Delta$$
$$2 P + 5 Cl_2 \longrightarrow 2 PCl_5 + \Delta$$

The trichloride is a liquid and the pentachloride is a yellow solid at room temperature. Both fume in the presence of water and must be handled with great care.

$$2 S + Cl_2 \longrightarrow S_2Cl_2 + \Delta$$

The liquid S_2Cl_2, sulfur monochloride, is used in the vulcanization of rubber. It is also used in the manufacture of mustard gas.

The halogens will even combine with each other. Among the compounds formed, none of which are used commercially at present, are the following:

Formula	Name	Melting Point
IF_5	Iodine pentafluoride	$-8°$
ICl_3	Iodine trichloride	$33°$
ICl	Iodine monochloride	$27°$
BrF_3	Bromine fluoride	$5°$
BrI	Bromine iodide	$42°$

The halogens combine directly with hydrogen to form the corresponding hydrohalogen compounds whose properties will be discussed on page 335. The reactions between hydrogen and fluorine and hydrogen and chlorine, although slow if carried out in the dark, are rapid in the sunlight, and explosive in the presence of sunlight and a trace of moisture. The reaction between hydrogen and chlorine in the light is often demonstrated by bringing a burning magnesium ribbon near the glass reaction flask containing these gases. (*Never do this in the laboratory unless you have taken full precautions against flying glass.*)

Chain Reactions

The light does not produce its effect by heating the gases, but is directly utilized in splitting the diatomic molecule. The light energy so taken up dissociates some chlorine.

$$Cl_2 \xrightarrow{light} 2\ Cl$$

The energy of activation of monatomic chlorine is zero. In other words, a monatomic chlorine molecule will react with the next hydrogen molecule it touches, no matter how gentle the collision.

$$Cl + H_2 \longrightarrow HCl + H$$

The same is true of the monatomic hydrogen produced. It will react with diatomic chlorine.

$$H + Cl_2 \longrightarrow HCl + Cl$$

This is an example of a *chain reaction*. In explosions, chain reactions usually take place. Of course, in this case, many chains are ended by the combination of H and H, Cl and Cl, or H and Cl; but before this happens, the temperature has risen to the point where Cl_2 is being dissociated by thermal collisions, multiplying the number of chains rapidly.

Substitution Reactions

The halogens take part in a large number of substitution reactions, particularly with organic compounds. The reactions between the halogens and water have been mentioned. The activity list of the non-metals—$F > Cl > Br > I > S$—shows that all four of the halogens will replace the sulfur in sulfides.

$$I_2 + H_2S \longrightarrow \underline{S} + 2\ H^+ + 2\ I^-$$

This reaction is the basis of an iodimetric method for the quantitative determination of hydrogen sulfide in water. A measured amount of a standard solution of iodine (which is soluble in KI solution owing to the formation of the complex triiodide ion, I_3^-) is added and the unreacted excess is determined by titrating it with sodium thiosulfate solution.

$$I_2 + 4\ Na^+ + 2\ S_2O_3^{--} \longrightarrow 4\ Na^+ + S_4O_6^{--} + 2I^-$$

This titration is called *iodimetry*. The disappearance of the brownish yellow color of iodine is a fairly satisfactory end point, but the end point can be intensified to an extraordinary extent by adding 1 ml. of a 1 per cent starch sol as soon as the yellow color becomes pale. The solution immediately assumes the appearance of blue ink. The blue color fades as the iodine is used up, but is still clearly visible before the addition of the last drop of even 0.01 M $Na_2S_2O_3$. The strongly colored starch-iodine complex is not a chemical compound, but a curious sorption phenomenon. The starch molecule is an indefinitely long chain of $-C_6H_{10}O_5-$ units, which is coiled into a helical tube, like a screen-door spring. Iodine molecules fit conveniently into the hole down the center and are attracted to this position because the interior surface is entirely hydrocarbon in nature. Iodine is much more soluble in hydrocarbons than in water. Bromine will replace iodine from iodides as well as sulfur from sulfides.

$$2\ Na^+ + 2\ I^- + Br_2 \longrightarrow I_2 + 2\ Na^+ + 2\ Br^-$$

Chlorine will replace bromine, iodine, and sulfur from their compounds.

$$2\ K^+ + 2\ Br^- + Cl_2 \longrightarrow Br_2 + 2\ K^+ + 2\ Cl^-$$

Fluorine will replace chlorine, bromine, iodine, and sulfur. Two other reactions which are frequently used to illustrate the oxidizing property of chlorine are the replacement of nitrogen in ammonia and of carbon in turpentine.

$$2\ NH_3 + 3\ Cl_2 \longrightarrow N_2 + 6\ HCl$$
$$C_{10}H_{16} + 8\ Cl_2 \longrightarrow 10\ \underline{C} + 16\ HCl$$

The reaction between warm turpentine, $C_{10}H_{16}$, and chlorine is spectacular. If a piece of filter paper is dipped into warm turpentine and then lowered into a bottle of chlorine, there is a flash of light and a dense black smoke of finely divided carbon. The halogens oxidize many organic compounds, including rubber.

The halogens unite directly with many other compounds. Chlorine forms the hydrate, $Cl_2 \cdot 6\ H_2O$, and bromine forms the decahydrate, $Br_2 \cdot 10\ H_2O$. The poisonous gas phosgene, $COCl_2$, which can be easily liquefied (B.P. 8.3° C.), is produced by the direct union of carbon monoxide and chlorine. This compound, first used for military purposes in World War I, had been known by chemists for many years.

In some cases the lower halide is oxidized to one of higher valence by the addition of more of the halogen. Ferrous chloride, $FeCl_2$, is oxidized to ferric chloride, $FeCl_3$, by the addition of more chlorine.

$$2\ \underline{FeCl_2} + \overline{Cl_2} \longrightarrow 2\ \underline{FeCl_3}$$

In water and sewage purification, the iron in cheap copperas, $FeSO_4$, is oxidized to Fe^{+++} with chlorine, and the mixture containing the ferric ion is added to water as a coagulant. The action of the halogens with organic compounds will be discussed in Chapter 39.

The nitrogen halides are very dangerous compounds. Nitrogen triiodide is formed by the reaction between ammonium hydroxide and iodine. The brown precipitate of NI_3 can be filtered. If dry, this compound explodes upon being touched. *As a beginning student of chemistry, never work with these compounds.*

Uses of the Halogens

Fluorine, the most active of all elements, is so difficult and dangerous to handle that it is rarely seen in the laboratory. Until recently it had no commercial uses. When the Manhattan Project was begun during World War II, one of its tasks was to separate the isotopes of uranium by means of a gigantic mass spectrograph (called the Calutron by the University of California scientists who designed it). Uranium hexafluoride, UF_6, a volatile solid which sublimes without melting (its vapor pressure reaches 1 atm. at 56° C.), furnished the only practical method material for getting uranium into the needed gaseous form. The successful development of large-scale methods for handling fluorine for the preparation of this compound was one of the great triumphs of the Manhattan Project chemists. Fluorine is now available in small steel cylinders for those who desire to experiment with it.

Bromine as an element had practically no uses until World War I, when it became extremely important in the preparation of tear gas. Its use in the preparation of Ethyl fluid for anti-knock gasoline was mentioned earlier in this chapter. The availability of bromine at lower prices has brought about its increasing use in the manufacture of dyes and drugs.

Iodine is used in the manufacture of many organic dyes, in the synthesis of many drugs, and in the preparation of certain compounds required in photography. The alcoholic solution of potassium iodide and iodine, called tincture of iodine, still ranks as one of the best disinfectants. Iodine is of value as a mild oxidizing agent in determining the degree of unsaturation of some organic compounds. Thus the "iodine number" of fats is determined by adding iodine until the reaction ceases. Approximately 1,500,000 pounds of iodine were used in this country per year before the war; possibly twice as much is used now.

Chlorine is a powerful oxidizing agent and as such is used in the sterilization of drinking water, swimming pools, and pipe lines, and in the bleaching of pulp.[4] It is used as the oxidizing agent to liberate bromine and iodine from their compounds. Hundreds of organic chemicals[5] require chlorine either in an intermediate step or in the final compound. It is used to recover

[4] Pulp bleaching required 200,000 tons of Cl_2 in 1943.
[5] Chlorinated hydrocarbons, used as solvents, are expected to require 250,000 tons of chlorine a year in the near future. For one single compound of this class used as a degreaser, 100,000 tons of Cl_2 were used in 1943.

gold from gold ores and tin from tin cans; it reacts with the tin to form liquid SnCl₄.

$$Sn + 2\ Cl_2 \longrightarrow SnCl_4$$

This is then separated by distillation and used in the weighting of silk. Chlorine is shipped in the liquid form in steel cylinders and tank cars (Fig. 22.5).

Fig. 22.5. A 30-ton liquid chlorine tank car. (Courtesy, Hooker Electrochemical Co.)

THE ALKALI METAL HALIDES

A total of twenty simple halides can be formed from combinations of the five alkali metals and the four halogens. The metals have a valence of one in these compounds. All these salts are white and are solids at room temperature. Table 22.2 gives their formulas, melting points, boiling points, solubility in water, and some of their uses. Potassium also forms the compound KI_3 or $KI \cdot I_2$. Rubidium forms such compounds as $RbBr_3$ and RbI_3. Cesium forms three iodides: CsI, CsI_3, and CsI_5.

The deliquescent property of LiCl makes this salt of value in air conditioning. Bromides are of such importance in photography that they will be discussed in detail under that topic. For many years potassium bromide has been used medicinally as a sedative. The importance of sodium iodide in the prevention of goiter has been proved beyond a doubt.

The complicated organic hormone, thyroxine ($C_{15}H_{11}O_4NI_4$), regulates the function of the thyroid gland. A deficiency of this hormone causes goiter; if the deficiency is extreme, cretinism results. People who live inland usually have to drink water which is low in iodides and they eat but little sea food. Fish and other sea foods are richer in iodine compounds than most foods available inland. In regions where the soil contains iodides, iodine is available in plants, turnips being particularly efficient in storing it. In other

TABLE 22.2. ALKALI HALIDES—THEIR FORMULAS, MELTING POINTS, BOILING POINTS, SOLUBILITY IN WATER, AND USES

Formula	Melting Point, °C.	Boiling Point, °C.	Solubility in g./100/g. of Cold H₂O	Uses
LiF	870	1676	0.25	
LiCl	614	1353	45	Medicine. Air conditioning
LiBr	547	1265	143 LiBr·3 H₂O	Medicine
LiI	446	1190	151	
NaF	992	1700	4	Wood preservative. Insecticide. With AlF₃ in bath for ⚠ of aluminum
NaCl	801	1413	35	Too numerous to list
NaBr	755	1390	80	Source of bromine
NaI	651	1300	158	1 : 100,000 in iodized salt
KF	880	1500	92	
KCl	776	1500 sub.	35	Source of potassium
KBr	730	1380	53	In medicine as a sedative
KI	723	1330	127	To form AgI, which is used in photography
RbF	760	1410	130 18°	
RbCl	715	1390	77	
RbBr	682	1340	98	
RbI	642	1300	152 17°	
CsF	684	1250	very soluble	
CsCl	646	1290 sub.		
CsBr	636	1300	161 124 25°	
CsI	621	1280	44	

inland localities, however, a source of iodine must be created. Wholesale experiments have been carried on with school children on the prevention and treatment of goiter by adding NaI to the drinking water; and it appears that one part of NaI per million parts of water is effective. A more economical source of iodides is the iodized salt which is now so familiar. Cows fed this salt produce milk which is richer in iodine compounds than ordinary milk. What is the iodine content of the drinking water in your community? Is iodized salt used on the food you eat? If goiter is prevalent in your community, consult a physician before launching an iodide crusade of your own.

Some localities have a real problem in finding a water supply which is free from fluorides. Others are now considering *adding* fluoride ion to their drinking water. Fluorides are definitely poisonous to both animals and insects. But although a few parts of F⁻ ion per million of drinking water produce an unattractive mottling of the enamel of the teeth (and more serious symptoms in larger quantities), the use of water containing about 1 p.p.m. of it seems sharply to reduce liability to dental decay. The body apparently demands approximately the concentration of each element that it is used to. If it gets much less, deficiency symptoms result; a little more than the normal amount is toxic. The customary concentration of the fluoride ion is low owing to the insolubility of CaF_2; hence a smaller amount of a fluoride is poisonous. Iodine is a rather rare element, so iodides are next in toxicity. Bromides are commoner and less toxic. Chlorides are not considered toxic, but a few drinks of a 3 per cent salt solution (sea water) are fatal.

Sodium chloride is absolutely essential for normal growth. We take it into our bodies as one of the constituents of the foods we eat, in our drinking water, and as a seasoning on food. Livestock must be fed a sufficient amount of salt; and it is an integral part of the equipment of hunters, trappers, and explorers.

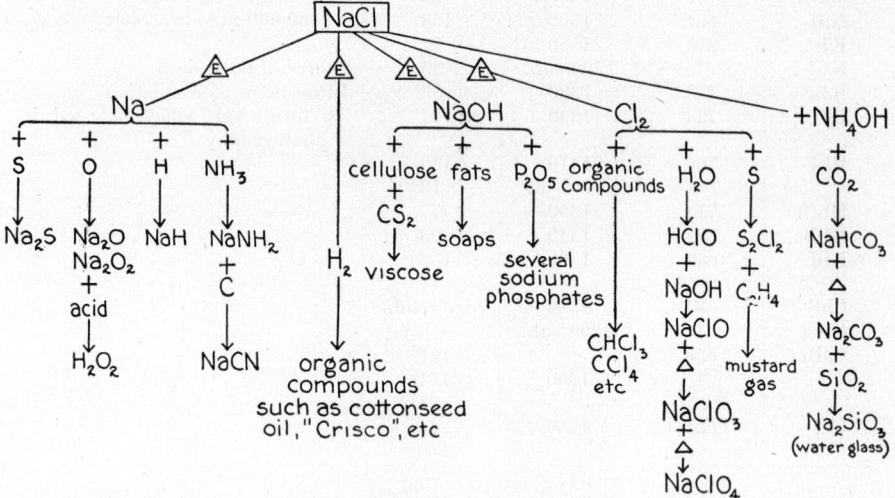

FIG. 22.6. A few products obtained from sodium chloride.

There are large salt deposits in New York State—the city of Syracuse is often called the "Salt City." Michigan, Kansas, and Louisiana also have large deposits. About 100,000 tons are produced annually by solar evaporation at Salt Lake City. About 0.25 lb. is secured per gallon of sea water on the Pacific coast. High freight rates, however, make it unprofitable to develop our western supplies fully. Fairly pure deposits of rock salt are mined in some parts of the world. The average annual production of salt in the United States during 1935–1939 was 8,667,000 tons, but during 1944 it was 15,700,000 tons.

Crude NaCl is a mixture of salts which in most cases can be separated into portions by fractional crystallization. If such a mixture is dissolved in the minimum amount of water and the solution is evaporated, the least soluble salt will crystallize first. Several salts can be separated by properly controlling the evaporation. Extensive refining processes are used in the preparation of table salt.

Sodium chloride is the starting point in the manufacture of a great many compounds, some of which are shown in Fig. 22.6.

THE HYDROGEN HALIDES

The four hydrogen halides are HF, HCl, HBr, and HI. Some of their properties are listed in Table 22.3. Although all four of these halides can be prepared by the direct union of the elements, this process is used only for the commercial preparation of hydrogen chloride. During the electrolysis of a salt solution, NaOH, Cl_2, and H_2 are produced. If the demand for NaOH and HCl

TABLE 22.3. SOME PROPERTIES OF THE HYDROGEN HALIDES

	$(HF)_x$	HCl	HBr	HI
Melting point, °C.	−83	−111	−86	−50.8
Boiling point, °C.	19.4	−85	−67	−35.5 at 4 atm.
Solubility in grams per 100 g. H_2O	∞ at 0°	82.3 at 0°	221 at 0°	425 ml./ml. at 10° C.
Concentration in per cent of constant boiling mixture	35	20	48	57
Boiling point of constant boiling solution	120	110	126	127
Chemicals used for preparation of the halide	$CaF_2 + H_2SO_4$	$NaCl + H_2SO_4$	$H_3PO_4 + NaBr$ or $PBr_3 + H_2O$	$PI_3 + H_2O$
Strength of water solution	weak acid	strong acid	strong acid	strong acid
Heat of formation in calories	38,000	22,000	8600	−6400

were good and the demand for chlorine poor, the chlorine and hydrogen gases could be united to form hydrogen chloride. However, because chlorine has usually been in greater demand than hydrogen chloride, the latter is not often prepared by electrolysis.

Preparation

We might at first think that all four compounds could be prepared by the reaction between a metal halide and the cheap acid, H_2SO_4. This method is satisfactory for the preparation of hydrogen fluoride and hydrogen chloride.

$$CaF_2 + H_2SO_4 \xrightarrow{\Delta} CaSO_4 + 2\,\overline{HF}$$
$$NaCl + H_2SO_4 \xrightarrow{\Delta} NaHSO_4 + \overline{HCl}$$

Br or I can be substituted for Cl in the second equation, but the HBr and HI which are produced are never pure; they are contaminated with their own oxidation products and the reduction products of the sulfuric acid. Hot concentrated H_2SO_4 is a strong oxidizing agent. It has no effect on HF or HCl, but oxidizes HBr to some extent and HI very largely. This is because the reducing powers of the hydrogen halides are just the reverse of the oxidizing powers of the corresponding halogens. HI is actually a good reducing agent. The reaction of hydrogen bromide with sulfuric acid is:

$$2\ HBr + H_2SO_4 \longrightarrow 2\ SO_2 + Br_2 + 2\ H_2O$$

Hydrogen iodide may reduce the sulfur several steps further; so several products may be obtained, depending upon the temperature and relative concentrations of the reactants, as shown by the following equations:

$$2\ \overline{HI} + H_2SO_4 \longrightarrow \overline{SO_2} + I_2 + 2\ H_2O$$
$$6\ \overline{HI} + H_2SO_4 \longrightarrow \underline{S} + 3\ I_2 + 4\ H_2O$$
$$8\ \overline{HI} + H_2SO_4 \longrightarrow \overline{H_2S} + 4\ I_2 + 4\ H_2O$$

These are excellent reactions with which to practice balancing equations by the redox equation rules given earlier in this chapter.

With extreme care, some HBr can be prepared by distilling HBr from a *dilute solution of H_2SO_4* which has been saturated with NaBr or KBr. However, the use of reactions in which oxidation is improbable is preferred. Hydrogen bromide can also be prepared by a reaction between bromine and the organic compound benzene, C_6H_6. The HBr is distilled from the mixture.

$$Br_2 + C_6H_6 \longrightarrow C_6H_5Br + \overline{HBr}$$

This method would be impractical unless there were a demand for the brombenzene. Phosphoric acid, H_3PO_4, is a high-boiling, non-oxidizing acid which can be used instead of sulfuric acid; however, the element phosphorus itself is more commonly used. If red phosphorus is placed in water and liquid bromine is added, the first reaction occurs between the phosphorus and the bromine, forming phosphorus tribromide, a liquid which fumes strongly in the air.

$$2\ \underline{P} + 3\ Br_2 \longrightarrow 2\ PBr_3$$

As soon as PBr_3 is formed, a reaction immediately takes place between it and the water, producing hydrogen bromide and phosphorous acid. This is another example of *hydrolysis*.

$$PBr_3 + 3\ H_2O \longrightarrow \overline{3\ HBr} + P(OH)_3\ \text{or}\ H_3PO_3$$

The HBr can be distilled and is usually collected in water to form a concentrated solution of hydrobromic acid. *Note that anhydrous HBr is called hydrogen bromide, whereas the water solution is called hydrobromic acid.*

ALKALI METALS AND HALOGENS

Hydrogen iodide is prepared by the same general method. Solid red phosphorus and solid iodine are usually melted together in the correct proportion to form solid phosphorus triiodide. Water is then added to the PI$_3$, and HI is distilled off.

$$PI_3 + 3\ H_2O \xrightarrow{\Delta} \overline{3\ HI} + H_3PO_3$$

If hydrogen sufide, H$_2$S, is bubbled into a water solution of KI·I$_2$, hydrogen iodide and sulfur are formed. The sulfur first forms in the colloidal state but can be coagulated by heat and filtered from the solution of HI.

$$H_2S + I_2 \longrightarrow \underline{S} + 2\ HI$$

Physical Properties

All the hydrogen halides are colorless gases with very penetrating pungent odors. They fume in moist air. If the anhydrous gases are breathed into the lungs, they quickly dissolve in the moisture, ionize, and destroy lung tissue. They can be liquefied quite readily because of their low critical pressures and high critical temperatures. Their solubility in water was given in Table 22.3.

The hydrogen halides all form *constant-boiling solutions*. Thus if a very concentrated solution is heated, the hydrogen halide will escape more rapidly than the water until a solution of some definite composition is reached. Any further heating results in the evaporation of a mixture of the hydrogen halide and water, the composition of which is exactly the same as that of the material being distilled. If a dilute solution of the hydrogen halide is heated, the escaping mixture will be rich in water and poor in halide until a mixture of the same definite composition as above is obtained. Further heating produces this constant-boiling mixture. It is impossible to separate HCl completely from water by simple distillation. The concentration and boiling points of these constant boiling mixtures were given in Table 22.3.

Chemical Properties of the Hydrogen Halides

The stability of the hydrogen halides varies in a manner that is parallel to their resistance to oxidation. (When the word "stability" is used without qualification, it means stability against thermal decomposition.) Hydrogen fluoride cannot be decomposed by heat. Hydrogen chloride is considered quite stable, for it can be heated to 1000° C. without decomposition. Hydrogen bromide decomposes at 800° C. Hydrogen iodide is unstable; it decomposes at 180° C.

Although the liquid or molten salts such as sodium chloride are good conductors of electricity, the liquid hydrogen halides are poor conductors; in other words, they are not ionized. This is used as evidence that such compounds as liquid HCl are covalent in nature. If HCl gas is dissolved in a non-basic solvent such as toluene, this solution is also a non-conductor; no ions have been formed. Because neither liquid HCl nor a non-conducting solution of HCl liberates H_2 from magnesium or CO_2 from $CaCO_3$, it was believed that acid properties were exhibited only by free hydrogen ions. This is not true. Hydrogen chloride must be a *stronger* acid than aqueous hydrochloric acid (hydronium chloride solution) or it would not react with water to *form* hydrochloric acid. The failure to show the expected acid reactions mentioned above is due to the instantaneous formation of an insoluble film of magnesium or calcium chloride. If magnesium is heated in dry HCl gas enough to break the $MgCl_2$ film, it burns, liberating hydrogen. The HCl solution in toluene will neutralize bases that are soluble in toluene; the neutralization can be followed with indicators.

The water solutions of the hydrogen halides have all the general properties of acids. These will be reviewed and slightly elaborated, with the more familiar hydrochloric acid as an example. Special characteristics of the other acids will be mentioned at the end of this section.

Hydrochloric acid is the example par excellence of a simple strong acid, because it is not an oxidizing agent and is a very poor reducing agent. Any of the metals above hydrogen in the E.C.S. reacts with it, liberating hydrogen. If the metal has more than one valence, the ion formed usually has the lower valence. Thus tin forms stannous chloride, $SnCl_2$, not stannic chloride, $SnCl_4$; and iron forms ferrous chloride, $FeCl_2$, not ferric chloride, $FeCl_3$.

$$\underline{Sn} + 2\ H^+ + 2\ Cl^- \longrightarrow Sn^{++} + 2\ Cl^- + \overline{H_2}$$
$$\underline{Fe} + 2\ H^+ + 2\ Cl^- \longrightarrow Fe^{++} + 2\ Cl^- + \overline{H_2}$$

Hydrochloric acid neutralizes bases. If the base is an oxide or hydroxide, the products are a salt and water.

$$MgO + 2\ H^+ + 2\ Cl^- \longrightarrow Mg^{++} + 2\ Cl^- + H_2O$$
$$K^+ + OH^- + H^+ + Cl^- \longrightarrow K^+ + Cl^- + H_2O$$

If the base is the anion of a weak acid, an equilibrium will result, the amount of H^+ left free depending upon the strength of the second acid.

$$3\ Na^+ + PO_4^{---} + 3\ H^+ + 3\ Cl^- \rightleftarrows 3\ Na^+ + 3\ Cl^- + H_3PO_4$$

This equilibrium may be disturbed by boiling off the second acid if it is more volatile (has a lower boiling point) than hydrochloric acid.

$$Na^+ + CN^- + H^+ + Cl^- \longrightarrow Na^+ + Cl^- + \overline{HCN}$$

The reaction then goes to completion to the right. Many acids are not volatile as such, but readily break down into the corresponding non-metallic oxide, or *acid anhydride*, and water. If the acid anhydride is boiled off as a gas, the reaction with hydrochloric acid goes to completion as before. In

ALKALI METALS AND HALOGENS

the case of sulfites (liberating sulfur dioxide) and carbonates (liberating carbon dioxide), most of the reaction takes place without heating.

$$2\ H^+ + 2\ Cl^- + 2\ Na^+ + SO_3^{--} \longrightarrow 2\ Na^+ + 2\ Cl^- + H_2O + \overline{SO_2}$$
$$2\ H^+ + 2\ Cl^- + \underline{CaCO_3} \longrightarrow Ca^{++} + 2\ Cl^- + H_2O + \overline{CO_2}$$

Special Properties. Hydriodic acid is used in the manufacture of some chemicals, but is rarely seen in the laboratory because it is expensive and will not keep. It is a sufficiently good reducing agent to be oxidized by atmospheric oxygen. Hydrobromic acid is only a mediocre reducing agent but is no commoner than hydriodic acid; it is more expensive than hydrochloric acid and does practically nothing that the cheaper acid cannot do. Hydrochloric acid is such a poor reducing agent that only the strongest oxidizing agents will oxidize the chloride ion to free chlorine. Equations for three of these reactions were given on page 319 in connection with the preparation of chlorine. A fourth oxidizing agent that can oxidize hydrochloric acid is nitric acid. The reaction between concentrated HCl and HNO_3 is as follows:

$$3\ H^+ + 3\ Cl^- + H^+ + NO_3^- \longrightarrow \overline{NOCl} + \overline{Cl_2} + 2\ H_2O$$

NOCl is called nitrosyl chloride; it promptly decomposes into nitric oxide, NO, and chlorine.

A mixture of three parts of concentrated hydrochloric acid and one of concentrated nitric acid is called *aqua regia*, because it can dissolve the noble metals, gold and platinum. Nitric acid alone cannot do this. In the reaction

$$\underline{Au} + 6\ H^+ + 6\ NO_3^- \rightleftarrows Au^{+++} + 3\ NO_3^- + 3\ \overline{NO_2} + 3\ H_2O$$

equilibrium lies far to the left. But if chloride ions are present, they send the reaction to completion in the other direction by turning the auric ions, Au^{+++}, into chloraurate ions, $AuCl_4^-$. For the same reason even chlorine water, which is a weaker oxidizing agent than nitric acid, can attack gold. In the case of platinum the chloroplatinate ion is formed, $PtCl_6^{--}$. The complete equation is:

$$\underline{Pt} + 4\ H^+ + 4\ NO_3^- + 6\ H^+ + 6\ Cl^- \longrightarrow$$
$$2\ H^+ + PtCl_6^{--} + 4\ H_2O + 4\ \overline{NO_2}$$

A striking difference between hydrofluoric acid and the other hydrohalogen acids is that it is weak. The order of strength of these acids is $HI > HBr > HCl > HF$, but the last step is very abrupt. The reason that the fluoride ion is appreciably basic whereas iodide, bromide, and chloride ions are not, is that the fluoride ion is so much smaller than the others. All halide ions have the same amount of negative charge to help them attract a proton; in the fluoride ion this charge is concentrated on a much smaller surface and is therefore far more effective. This is closely connected with the ability of fluoride ions to form hydrogen bonds (see page 191). Hydrogen fluoride polymerizes by means of hydrogen bonding in the same way that water does. However, a ring-shaped hexamer (sixfold polymer) seems to have exceptional stability.

$$6 \text{ HF} \rightleftarrows H_6F_6$$

As a result of this polymerization, hydrogen fluoride has about double the density that simple HF has. At one time it was believed to exist largely in the form H_2F_2, but this has been shown not to exist. In a solution of a soluble fluoride the addition of acid results in the formation of a bifluoride ion, $:\ddot{F}:H:\ddot{F}:^-$, for each hydrogen ion which is added. This ion is stable enough to permit the crystallization of salts like potassium bifluoride, KHF_2. In aqueous hydrofluoric acid, in addition to the monomer-hexamer equilibrium just given, the following ionization equilibrium exists:

$$2 \text{ HF} \rightleftarrows H^+ + HF_2^-$$

One other effect of the small size of the fluoride ion is to make it possible for fluoride ions to be drawn into a completed octet, increasing the covalence from four to six, even in the case of a third-period atom like silicon.

$$2 \text{ HF} + SiF_4 \rightleftarrows 2 H^+ + SiF_6^{--}$$

The corresponding reaction with the chloride ion will take place with a larger atom in the silicon family, tin, but not with silicon.

Uses of the Hydrogen Halides

Hydrogen fluoride has one use which makes it unique among these four compounds. It attacks silicon dioxide, whereas HCl, HBr, and HI have no effect on SiO_2 and glass. The reaction between HF and silicon dioxide is as follows:

$$SiO_2 + 4 \text{ HF} \longrightarrow \overline{SiF_4} + 2 H_2O$$

Silicon tetrafluoride is a gas. Thus if pure SiO_2 is treated with pure HF, nothing remains of the solid SiO_2. Both simple and complex silicates are attacked by HF. The reaction between calcium silicate and HF produces insoluble calcium fluoride, volatile SiF_4, and H_2O.

$$CaSiO_3 + 6 \text{ HF} \longrightarrow \underline{CaF_2} + \overline{SiF_4} + 3 H_2O$$

This peculiar property of HF makes its storage a difficult problem. It cannot be kept in a glass or porcelain container; wax, Bakelite, hard rubber, lead, or platinum must be used. Containers of HF must be kept sealed when not in use. The markings on household and laboratory thermometers, burettes, graduated cylinders, flasks, pipettes, beakers, etc., are etched with

HF. The glass surface is coated with paraffin and scratched where a mark is desired. The article is then exposed to the fumes of HF. The inside frosting of electric light bulbs is accomplished by means of a mixture of NH_4F and HF. During World War II, HF was found to be an excellent catalyst for the rearrangements of hydrocarbon molecules which convert ordinary gasoline into high octane aviation gasoline. Anhydrous liquid HF is now shipped in tank cars for that purpose. Owing to its polymerization, HF is much easier to liquefy than the other hydrogen halides. (It boils at 19° C.; the others, far below zero.) Hydrogen fluoride is used, as indicated previously, in the manufacture of fluosilicic acid, H_2SiF_6, from which many metal salts are prepared for industrial uses. The sodium salt, usually called sodium silico-fluoride in the trade, is used in Larvex to render wool clothing inedible by moth larvae. It is also used as a "laundry sour" to furnish the hydrogen ions needed for the removal of "bleach." Although not an acid itself, it is in equilibrium with a trace of hydrofluoric acid, in accordance with the hydrolysis reaction

$$2\ Na^+ + SiF_6^{--} + 3\ H_2O \rightleftarrows 2\ Na^+ + 2\ HF_2^- + 2\ HF + H_2SiO_3$$

This can be sent to completion by a stronger base than water. "Bleach" is a solution containing the hypochlorite ion, ClO^-, which is added in small quantities after the soap has been rinsed out to bleach the slight yellow color that cotton tends to develop. If any of it were left in the fabric it would weaken the threads; hence the "sour" is added to convert it into weak, volatile hypochlorous acid, HClO, which is driven off in drying and ironing. Hydrofluoric acid is a valuable reagent in the analytical laboratory, for the amount of silica in a sample can be determined by treating it with HF and determining the resulting loss in weight. All apparatus with which it comes in contact must be resistant to it. HF is an extremely dangerous chemical because it attacks the flesh and the wound heals very slowly. An HF burn should be washed at least four hours in running water, and bandaged with a suspension of MgO in glycerol. Some physicians recommend soaking the injured tissue in dilute ammonium hydroxide for four hours.

The cheapest of all acids is sulfuric and next to it is hydrochloric; therefore whenever a strong acid is required, one or the other is used. Hydrochloric acid is used to clean iron before it is coated with zinc or tin, a process which is called "pickling." The conversion of starch into sugars is carried out in an HCl solution. This is a hydrolysis reaction similar to that of digestion. The product may be a syrup of the Karo-brand type, or pure crystalline dextrose may be prepared. The cellulose in wood is related to starch and can also be hydrolyzed under the catalytic influence of HCl. The sugar which this process yields was used in Germany as food for stock to avoid the expense of purifying it. Hydrochloric acid has a multitude of other uses. Its consumption in the United States approaches 100,000 tons a year. Ammonium chloride, NH_4Cl, which is prepared by the direct union of NH_3 with HCl, is used for a great variety of uses ranging from dry cells to cough medicine and smoke screens.

Hydrogen bromide and hydrogen iodide have no important commercial uses. However, many of their salts are valuable; this will be discussed in connection with the metallic ions of these salts.

Tests for the Alkali Halides

If you were given a white substance which might contain any or all of the five alkali metallic ions and the four halide ions, how could you determine which ones were present? It may appear very difficult, in view of the fact that the preceding pages have stressed the uniformity in physical and chem-

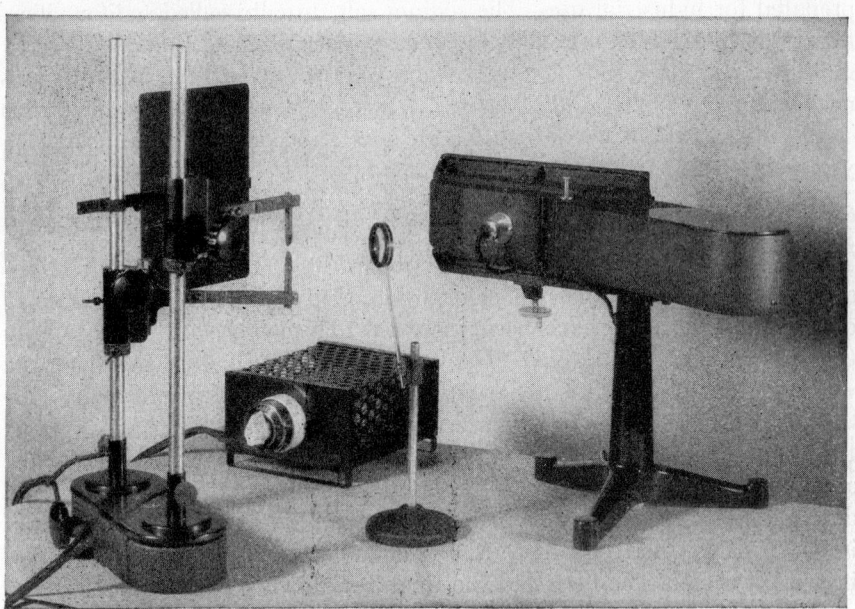

FIG. 22.7. Small Littrow spectrograph complete with accessory equipment set up for its use. On the left is the arc and spark stand with rheostat in the background. In the center is the condenser which focuses the image of the light source upon the slit in the spectrograph. (Courtesy, Bausch & Lomb Optical Co.)

ical characteristics within each group. The student in general chemistry seldom has an opportunity to work with Li^+, Cs^+, and Rb^+ ions, but compounds of the other six are among the usual laboratory reagents. The identification of the alkali metals will be discussed briefly; the halogens will be considered in more detail.

The Alkali Ions. The phosphate and carbonate of lithium are nearly insoluble in water. Lithium imparts a brilliant carmine color to the Bunsen burner flame. A complex acid known as chloroplatinic acid, H_2PtCl_6, reacts with rubidium and cesium to form insoluble yellow crystalline salts, Rb_2PtCl_6 and Cs_2PtCl_6. Potassium also forms a similar salt, K_2PtCl_6; this is usually precipitated from a mixture of alcohol and water in which it is less soluble. Other insoluble potassium salts are potassium perchlorate, $KClO_4$, and potassium cobaltinitrite, $K_3Co(NO_2)_6$. Perchloric acid is replacing chloroplatinic acid as a reagent for the precipitation of potassium because it is cheaper. A flame test is also used for identification. In making such a test, a clean platinum wire is dipped into a concentrated solution of the salt and then held in the oxidizing portion of the Bunsen flame. If a potassium salt is held in the flame and there is a piece of blue cobalt glass between the flame and the observer, the violet light produced by the potassium will pass through the glass, whereas the light from other metals does not. Two of the very few insoluble salts formed by sodium are sodium pyroantimonate, $Na_2H_2Sb_2O_7$, and sodium magnesium uranyl acetate,

$$NaC_2H_3O_2 \cdot Mg(C_2H_3O_2)_2 \cdot 3\ UO_2(C_2H_3O_2)_2 \cdot 6\ H_2O$$

Thanks to the spectrograph developed by the physicists, a new, more accurate, and more rapid method is available for detecting qualitatively the presence of the alkali elements. In fact, the refinements in technique have been so rapid that the procedure has been made semiquantitative. This instrument, which is shown in Fig. 22.7, is invaluable in identifying the alkali metals; other procedures are difficult, for these metals form so few insoluble compounds that it is hard to separate them. When atoms are heated sufficiently they emit light of definite wave lengths which can be measured very accurately with the spectrograph. Since each element produces several lines, some lines can be identified even though there is some overlapping. The spectrograph is used in chemical manufacturing plants for routine tests of the purity of products. Hospitals use it to follow changes in the concentration of alkali ions in the blood. It is also used in testing for traces of substances in water supplies, in poison cases, in crime detection, and in the search for new sources of rare elements in certain ores.

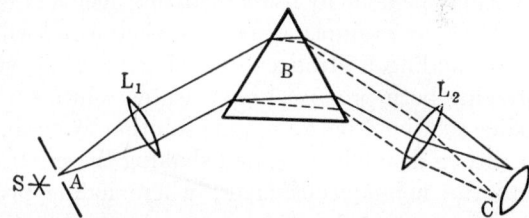

FIG. 22.8. Schematic diagram of a spectrograph. The two lenses serve to form images of the illuminated slit, and deviation by the prism produces separate images for each wave length in the original light. Light from S shines through slit A and is deviated by prism B. Colored images of the slit form at C. (From John S. Allen and others, *Atoms, Rocks and Galaxies*, Harper & Brothers.)

The Halogen Ions. Chemical procedures are still preferred for the detection of the halogens. The fluoride ion is identified by acidifying the sample with concentrated sulfuric acid and noting whether the gas which is liberated will etch glass. The bromide, iodide, and chloride ions are identified by (1) the formation of characteristic insoluble compounds; (2) the characteristic color of the halogen liberated by oxidation; (3) the combination of the liberated halogen with some other substance which will form a new compound that can be identified by its characteristic appearance.

If silver nitrate is added to a sample which may contain Cl⁻, Br⁻, and I⁻ ions, a white precipitate forms if only Cl⁻ ions are present, a yellow-white if only Br⁻ ions, and a deep yellow if only I⁻ ions are present. Silver chloride and silver bromide differ from silver iodide, AgI, in that they are soluble in ammonium hydroxide. Complex silver ions are formed. Silver ammonia chloride and silver ammonia bromide are soluble in water.

$$\underline{AgCl} + 2\ NH_4OH \longrightarrow Ag(NH_3)_2{}^+ + Cl^- + 2\ H_2O$$

If all three halides are present in one sample, the procedure is complicated because it is impossible to identify one in the presence of the other.

Because of differences in ease of oxidation it is possible to oxidize the halogens preferentially, oxidizing the iodide ion first, then the bromide ion. This may be done by using oxidizing agents of intermediate strength (Fe⁺⁺⁺ or HNO₂, for example, will liberate iodine but will not attack the bromide ion) or by adding a stronger oxidizing agent in small quantities. Iodine and bromine both produce brown water solutions; it is easy to distinguish an iodine solution from a bromine solution by adding carbon tetrachloride, CCl₄, or carbon disulfide, CS₂, and shaking the mixture. Most of the halogen goes into the non-aqueous layer, where iodine produces a deep violet color. Bromine in CCl₄ is still brown.

OXYGEN HALOGEN COMPOUNDS

One characteristic of the halogens, namely, their variable valence, accounts for the large number of compounds which they form. Many of these compounds are extremely useful; in the absence of any one of them several commodities which we have today would not be available.

Oxides of the Halogens

Although none of the halogens will combine directly with oxygen, oxides of all the halogens are known. This means that indirect methods must be used in preparing these compounds. The names and formulas of the oxides and their corresponding acids and salts are given in Table 22.4.

Of all the halogen oxides listed in Table 22.4, only two, ClO₂ and I₂O₅, are ever seen in the laboratory; and of these, only the first is of commercial importance. Chlorine dioxide belongs to the very small class of *odd molecules* (molecules with an odd number of electrons), whose existence violates all the familiar rules of valence. It is a strongly yellow gas which (startlingly perhaps, but not surprisingly, considering the odd electron) explodes violently upon the slightest provocation. However, it is not spontaneously explosive

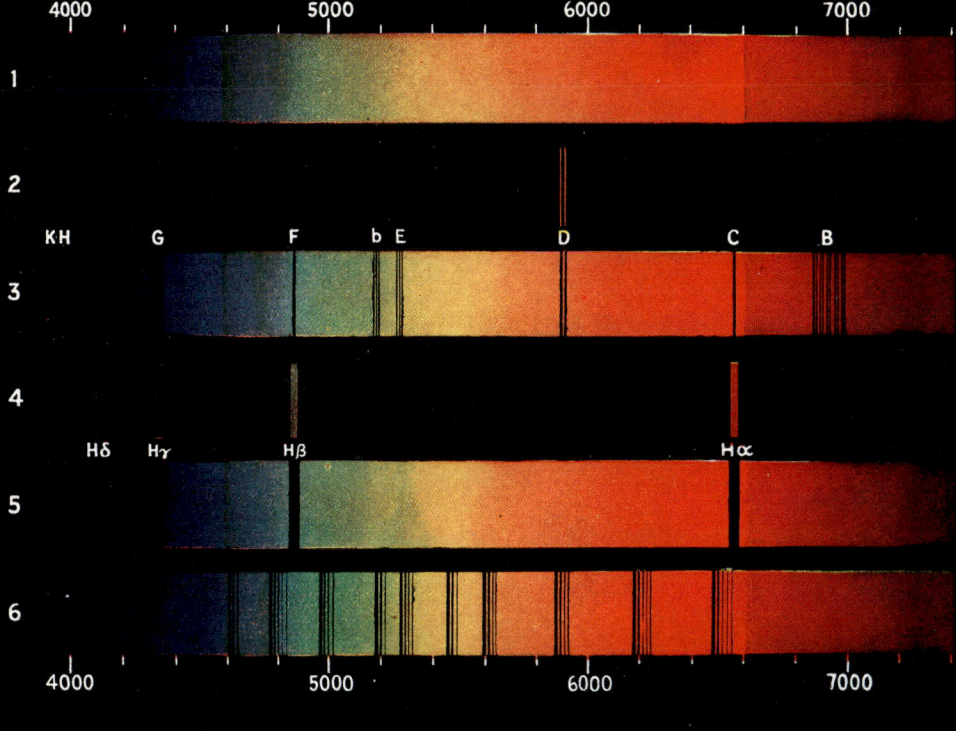

Fig. 22.9. (1) A continuous spectrum from an incandescent solid. (2) Flame spectrum of sodium (at the temperature of an arc a number of other emission lines are shown). (3) Solar spectrum, showing dark lines where relatively cool atoms in the outer atmosphere have *absorbed* light of that wave length coming from the interior. The dark (or Fraunhofer) lines marked D prove the presence of sodium in the sun. (4) Emission spectrum of hydrogen. Note that the C, F, and G Fraunhofer lines show that there is hydrogen in the sun. (5) Spectrum of Sirius, showing the absorption spectrum of hydrogen. (6) Spectrum of Betelgeuse, a cooler star. The absorption *bands* are those of molecules, not atoms. (From John C. Duncan, *Astronomy*, Harper & Brothers.)

ALKALI METALS AND HALOGENS

Table 22.4. Oxygen Halogen Compounds

Names and Formulas of Oxides, Oxy-acids, and Oxy-salts of the Halogens

Formula of Oxide	Name of Oxide	Boiling Point, °C.	Formula of Corresponding Acid	Name of Acid	Name of Sodium Salt. Sodium ....
F_2O	Fluorine	-167	......	....	....
Cl_2O	Chlorine monoxide	3.8	$H\overset{+1}{Cl}O$	hypochlorous	hypochlorite
$ClO_2{}^a$	Chlorine dioxide	9.9^b	$H\overset{+3}{Cl}O_2$	chlorous	chlorite
......	....	....	$H\overset{+5}{Cl}O_3$	chloric	chlorate
Cl_2O_7	Chlorine heptoxide	82^b	$H\overset{+7}{Cl}O_4$	perchloric	perchlorate
......	....	....	$H\overset{+1}{Br}O$	hypobromous	hypobromite
$Br_3O_8{}^c$	....	....	......	....	....
......	....	....	$H\overset{+5}{Br}O_3$	bromic	bromate
......	....	....	$H\overset{+1}{I}O$	hypoiodous	hypoiodite
IO_2	Iodine dioxide	97	......	....	....
I_2O_5	Iodine pentoxide	dec. at 130	$H\overset{+5}{I}O_3$	iodic	iodate
......	....	....	$H\overset{+7}{I}O_4$	periodic	periodate

[a] $2\ ClO_2 + H_2O \longrightarrow HClO_2 + HClO_3$. ClO_2 is a mixed anhydride.
[b] Explodes.
[c] Br_3O_8 is stable below $-80°$. Explodes at higher temperatures.

if its partial pressure is below 150 mm. If this pressure is kept down to 25 mm., the gas is safe against light, moderate heat, and even electric sparks; hence it is beginning to be used commercially to bleach flour and to prepare sodium chlorite, $NaClO_2$.

$$2\ ClO_2 + 2\ Na^+ + 2\ OH^- \longrightarrow 2\ Na^+ + ClO_2^- + ClO_3^- + H_2O$$

The ClO_2 used to prepare $NaClO_2$ is prepared from sodium chlorate, the inherent dangers being countered by the care and knowledge of the chemical manufacturing company concerned. Millers obtain it with convenience and perfect safety by passing air with some chlorine through a vessel containing solid $NaClO_2$.

$$\overline{Cl_2} + 2\ \underline{NaClO_2} \longrightarrow 2\ \underline{NaCl} + 2\ \overline{ClO_2}$$

Preparation, Properties, and Uses of Hypochlorous Acid and Its Salts

Free chlorine is required for the manufacture of all the oxy-chlorine acids and salts. When chlorine is dissolved in water, a small fraction of the portion dissolved reacts with water and the following equilibrium is produced:

$$Cl_2 + H_2O \rightleftarrows H^+ + Cl^- + HClO$$

Blue litmus paper put in the solution at first turns red, but in a few minutes this color disappears and the paper becomes white. Where did the red color go? HClO has oxidized or bleached the colored dye, litmus, into a colorless compound. Making the solution alkaline will not bring back the blue color because the litmus has been altered by oxidation with chlorine water.

Since the reaction between chlorine and water gives a mixture of two acids, how can pure HClO be made? If $CaCO_3$ is slowly added to chlorine water, the hydrochloric acid, being more highly ionized, reacts with calcium carbonate and the HClO remains unchanged. This mixture is then distilled and a more concentrated solution of hypochlorous acid is thus obtained. The equation for this reaction is:

$$CaCO_3 + 2\ H^+ + 2\ Cl^- + (2\ HClO) \longrightarrow (2\ HClO) + Ca^{++} + 2\ Cl^- + \overline{CO_2} + H_2O$$

Hypochlorous acid decomposes into Cl_2O and water on further attempts to concentrate it. It also decomposes, in a different way, on standing, particularly if it is warm or exposed to light. It is sometimes easier to balance the equation for a reaction of this type by writing the formula of the substance twice, as though the oxidizing and reducing agents were different substances.

$$\overset{+1}{HClO} + 2\ \overset{+1}{HClO} \longrightarrow 2\ \overset{-1}{Cl^-} + \overset{+5}{ClO_3^-} + 3\ H^+$$

(loses 1⊖ ; gains 2⊖)

The simplified equation is:

$$3\ HClO \longrightarrow 2\ HCl + HClO_3$$

Hypochlorous acid must be kept cold, or this reaction will take place and no HClO will remain.

Since the reaction,

$$Cl_2 + H_2O \rightleftarrows H^+ + Cl^- + HClO$$

is an equilibrium reaction, according to the Law of Mass Action it should be possible to shift the equilibrium from right to left by adding an excess of HCl. This procedure is used when it is desired to liberate free chlorine from a solution containing hypochlorites or hypochlorous acid.

$$HClO + H^+ + Cl^- \longrightarrow Cl_2 + H_2O$$

If chlorine is bubbled into cold sodium hydroxide, the HCl and HClO which form first are immediately neutralized by NaOH to form NaCl and NaClO. The final equation is:

$$Cl_2 + 2\ Na^+ + 2\ OH^- \longrightarrow 2\ Na^+ + Cl^- + ClO^- + H_2O$$

The same result can be achieved by electrolyzing a solution of NaCl and allowing the products to mix. Electrolysis can then be continued until all the Cl⁻ has been changed into ClO⁻.

The value of this solution as a disinfectant has been known for many years. It can be purchased in almost any grocery store under one of hundreds of local trade names; all can be identified by the statement on the label, "Active ingredient: sodium hypochlorite 5.25%." The characteristic odor, although usually called "chlorine smell," is actually that of hypochlorous acid produced by hydrolysis.

$$\text{Na}^+ + \text{ClO}^- + \text{H}_2\text{O} \rightleftharpoons \text{Na}^+ + \text{OH}^- + \text{HClO}$$

The same smell can sometimes be detected in swimming pools that have been chlorinated; the concentration of chlorine is so low that its reaction with water has gone practically to completion. The odor of chlorine itself, while similar, is distinguishable; check this statement in the laboratory. Still a third "chlorine smell" is the odor of chlorophenols sometimes present in city water (page 285). Neither chlorine nor hypochlorous acid can be present in water that has traveled any considerable distance through iron pipe.

Hypochlorous acid is a very weak acid but, like chlorine itself, it is a strong oxidizing agent. It has an important advantage over chlorine in that its energy of activation is much lower. This results in a higher speed of reaction at ordinary temperatures. In fact, many reactions of chlorine will not take place at all at room temperature.[6] When water is present, hypochlorous acid is formed immediately and reacts promptly. When hypochlorous acid reacts, the products are the same as those that would have been produced had chlorine itself been used, plus water. Water can be said to serve as a catalyst here. The easy formation of HClO from chlorine and water, and the high reactivity of HClO are more than a convenience, for in many cases a temperature high enough to cause chlorine to react will decompose the other reactant or the desired product. This is such an important factor that all but a small percentage of the tons of chlorine which are used commercially are used in water solution, HClO or ClO⁻ being the actual molecular species which reacts with the reducing agent.

Salts of Hypochlorous Acid. The hypochlorite ion appears to be a rather weak oxidizing agent. The fundamental reaction is:

$$2\,\text{H}^+ + :\!\ddot{\text{Cl}}\!:\!\ddot{\text{O}}\!:^- + 2\ominus \longrightarrow :\!\ddot{\text{Cl}}\!:^- + :\!\overset{\text{H}}{\underset{}{\ddot{\text{O}}}}\!:\!\text{H}$$

If the strong base, the oxide ion, is not removed by combining with protons to form water, the reaction tends to reverse. Protons are an essential reactant. If the solution is sufficiently basic so that the weak acid, HClO, has actually lost its protons to the base, leaving only ClO⁻, all the protons are so strongly held that few are available for the reaction. The addition of any acid (even

[6] *Chem. and Eng. News* **21**, 1317 (1943).

carbonic acid, H_2CO_3, from CO_2) increases the availability of protons and raises the oxidizing potential of the solution. This offers a convenient method of governing the strength of hypochlorite solutions as oxidizing agents.

Sodium and calcium hypochlorites are very important. The former has been used for years in the refining of kerosene and gasoline. It reacts with and oxidizes the sulfur compounds in petroleum which not only emit a disagreeable odor but are also responsible for corrosion. The sulfur compounds are oxidized to SO_3 during combustion; the SO_3 reacts with water to form sulfuric acid which in turn goes into the lubricating oil and thence into contact with the bearings. Cotton fabrics which are to be bleached are first treated with hot $Ca(OH)_2$ or Na_2CO_3 to remove grease, and then bleached with hypochlorite solution. As soon as the bleaching process is complete, the fabric is dipped into sodium thiosulfate solution which serves as an antichlor, neutralizing the excess chlorine. This process is a little too drastic for wool and silk because it destroys these fibers. LiClO, the only solid, stable alkali hypochlorite, is an excellent oxidizing and bleaching agent.

A recent hypochlorite bleaching agent is calcium hypochlorite, $Ca(ClO)_2$, known commercially as "H.T.H.," or "high-test hypochlorite." It is made by passing chlorine into milk of lime (a suspension of calcium hydroxide in its saturated solution).

$$Ca^{++} + 2\ OH^- + Cl_2 \longrightarrow Ca^{++} + ClO^- + Cl^- + H_2O$$

From this solution calcium hypochlorite crystallizes out as the tetrahydrate, $Ca(ClO)_2 \cdot 4\ H_2O$. It is quite stable and fairly soluble. The designation "high test" was given to it by way of contrast to the older and less satisfactory but still much used substance known as *bleaching powder* or, erroneously, "chloride of lime."

Bleaching powder is prepared by allowing chlorine to be absorbed by slaked lime, $Ca(OH)_2$, which is nearly dry. The reaction of the chlorine is the production of Cl^- and ClO^- ions, as before, but it stops when little more than half the hydroxide ions have been used up. The product was thought until recently to be a mixture of calcium chloride hypochlorite, $Ca^{++}\!\!\begin{smallmatrix}\diagup Cl^-\\ \diagdown ClO^-\end{smallmatrix}$, and unchanged calcium hydroxide. The latter being disregarded as an inert impurity, the formula was given as $Ca^{++}\!\!\begin{smallmatrix}\diagup Cl^-\\ \diagdown ClO^-\end{smallmatrix}$, $CaCl_2O$, $CaOCl_2$, or as CaCl(ClO). All these formulas were intended to indicate that the substance was one whose cations were all Ca^{++} and whose anions were alternately Cl^- and ClO^-. In 1935 X-ray photographs showed that little unchanged $Ca(OH)_2$ remained and that the new crystals were of two kinds, $Ca^{++}\!\!\begin{smallmatrix}\diagup Cl^-\\ \diagdown OH^-\end{smallmatrix}$ and

$\text{Ca}^{++}\!\!\begin{array}{c}\nearrow\text{OCl}^-\\ \searrow\text{OH}^-\end{array}$. Salts of this kind, having OH^- as one of two anions present, are commonly called "basic salts." They are all relatively insoluble.

The oxidizing power of bleaching materials is determined in the laboratory by measuring the amount of iodine liberated by a known amount of the "bleach." From this the analyst calculates the amount of Cl_2 that would be needed to liberate the same amount of iodine, and calls it the "available chlorine." Each ClO^- ion in the material corresponds to one molecule of "available chlorine." Therefore the available chlorine in bleaching powder would theoretically be $\dfrac{Cl_2}{Ca(OH)Cl + Ca(OH)ClO} \text{'} \dfrac{71}{40 + 17 + 35\frac{1}{2} + 40 + 17 + 51\frac{1}{2}}$, or 35 per cent. The commercial product runs very close to this value. The available chlorine of pure H.T.H. is $\dfrac{2\,Cl_2}{Ca(ClO)_2 \cdot 4H_2O}$, or $\dfrac{142}{40 + 103 + 72}$, or 66 per cent; but the commercial product is diluted with $Ca(OH)_2$ to a standard strength of 60 per cent.

Many pulp and paper mills now buy liquid chlorine in tank-car lots and make up their own bleaching solution instead of buying either bleaching powder or calcium hypochlorite. Where bleaching powder is still used industrially, it is usually treated first with sodium carbonate solution. This brings all the ClO^- ion into solution by precipitating the Ca^{++} as $CaCO_3$ as fast as the bleaching powder dissolves. The filtered solution contains the sodium ion and the three anions, Cl^-, ClO^-, and OH^-. It was used domestically under the name "Javelle water" until displaced by the more stable and pure sodium hypochlorite solutions prepared electrolytically. Both bleaching powder and Javelle water liberate chlorine as fast as their alkalinity is neutralized by atmospheric CO_2, owing to the presence of the chloride ion.

Chlorous acid is more stable than hypochlorous acid; it is a stronger acid and a stronger but less reactive oxidizing agent. It is never prepared as such. Sodium chlorite, $NaClO_2$, until recently a rare chemical curiosity, is now being produced on a commercial scale from chlorine dioxide. It is used to prepare chlorine dioxide (page 342) and is finding favor for the bleaching of paper pulp and cotton cloth. As compared with hypochlorite, it can be used to obtain a higher degree of whiteness without weakening the cellulose fibers themselves. The greater stability of chlorous as compared with hypochlorous acid permits the use of chlorite in moderately acid solution, which is sometimes a practical convenience. New uses are being developed.[7]

Preparation, Properties, and Uses of Chloric Acid and Its Salts

Since the preparation of chloric acid depends upon the production of a chlorate, the common procedures used in making chlorates will first be discussed.

[7] *Ibid.* 21, 1176 (1943).

One of the older methods consists of bubbling chlorine gas into concentrated potassium hydroxide. The chlorine first reacts with water to form HClO; this is neutralized to form KClO, which disproportionates into KCl and KClO$_3$. The total reaction is:

$$3\ Cl_2 + 6\ K^+ + 6\ OH^- \longrightarrow 6\ K^+ + 5\ Cl^- + ClO_3^- + 3\ H_2O$$

Potassium chlorate is soluble in cold water to the extent of 3.3 g./100 g. of H$_2$O, and potassium chloride is much more soluble (27.6 g./100 g. of H$_2$O). KClO$_3$ crystallizes when a saturated solution of the salts is cooled, and is further purified by recrystallization. The objection to this process is the fact that for every molecule of KClO$_3$, five molecules of KCl are formed; in other words, most of the KOH and Cl$_2$ are consumed in making a product for which there is little demand.

Potassium chlorate is now prepared by electrolyzing a hot (90° C.) saturated solution of KCl which contains a small amount of a catalyst, potassium chromate, K$_2$CrO$_4$. The electrodes are kept close enough together so that the electrolytic products mix; the temperature is maintained by a high rate of electrolysis. The direct products of electrolysis are, of course, those given as *reactants* in the equation in the preceding paragraph, and the reaction in that equation proceeds at the temperature which is maintained. A small amount of the electrolyte is continually withdrawn and cooled. KClO$_3$ crystallizes out and the KCl solution is returned to the cell. This process is much more economical than the old one because there is no by-product.

Chloric acid may be prepared by treating barium chlorate with sulfuric acid and filtering off the precipitated BaSO$_4$.

$$Ba^{++} + 2\ ClO_3^- + H^+ + HSO_4^- \longrightarrow \underline{BaSO_4} + 2\ H^+ + 2\ ClO_3^-$$

The dilute solution can be concentrated by evaporation up to a concentration of about 40 per cent, above which it begins to change to perchloric acid. The evaporation must take place below 40° C.; the acid may detonate violently if heated.[8] HClO$_3$ is a strong acid and a powerful oxidizing agent.

Some 5000 tons of KClO$_3$ are consumed each year in the United States. It is used in tablet form as a throat gargle; its use in tooth pastes was given considerable publicity after the First World War. It is also used in the process by which the dye, aniline black, is made. The oxidizing agent in matches is frequently KClO$_3$. KClO$_3$ is an excellent source of oxygen, and is used for this purpose by chemists in combustion experiments. If a mixture of sulfur and KClO$_3$ is put on an iron bar and struck with a hammer, there is a loud explosion. Although it is a good explosive, it is extremely dangerous if it is

---

[8] Too much emphasis cannot be given to the need for care in using chlorates in the laboratory. One student who read that a wooden splinter dropped into a test tube one-third full of molten KClO$_3$ would burn brightly repeated this experiment with some powdered charcoal. Result—a terrific explosion, in which he nearly lost his eyesight.

used in such a way that the free acid is formed. *Be careful not to use potassium chlorate when potassium chloride is called for; the result will be disastrous.*

The less expensive sodium, calcium, and magnesium chlorates are used as weed killers, but there is great danger of fire, for the dry powder, dry weeds, and a little friction are all that are needed to start one.

Phosphorus can be ignited under water by adding solid chlorates and some concentrated sulfuric acid. The chlorates furnish sufficient oxygen for the phosphorus to burn.

Preparation, Properties, and Uses of Perchloric Acid and Its Salts

In preparing perchloric acid, the salt of the acid is formed first and the free acid is then obtained from the salt. The perchlorate, $KClO_4$, is made by modifying the electrolytic process used in preparing $KClO_3$. Other perchlorates are made by electrolysis of the corresponding metallic salts. A laboratory procedure which has been used for many years consists in heating $KClO_3$ to approximately 500° C., or just above its melting point. If it is heated much above this temperature, KCl and O_2 are liberated.

$$2\ KClO_3 \xrightarrow{600°\ C.} 2\ KCl + 3\ O_2$$

$$4\ KClO_3 \longrightarrow 3\ KClO_4 + KCl$$

The perchlorates are less soluble than the chlorides, and can be separated by fractional crystallization. $NaClO_4$ can be made by a similar process. NH_4ClO_4 is obtained by the fractional crystallization of a solution of NH_4Cl and $NaClO_4$. As a group, the metal perchlorates are almost without exception soluble in water as well as in many non-aqueous solvents; the alkali perchlorates are the least soluble. The use of perchloric acid in the quantitative determination of potassium has already been mentioned.

The stability of oxy-halogen compounds increases as the oxygen content increases. Therefore the metallic perchlorates are more stable than the corresponding chlorates. They are also stronger oxidizing agents. There is no contradiction in this; high stability depends on high energy of activation, and high oxidizing power depends upon the total amount of energy that can be obtained from the reaction.

$KClO_4$ is used in blasting mixtures and, mixed with strontium compounds and organic matter, in railway signals. The total world production of $KClO_4$ is rather small, being approximately 250 tons annually, of which about 150 tons per year are consumed in the United States. Perchlorates are used as a weed killer. Great interest has been shown in the deliquescent property of anhydrous barium and magnesium perchlorate; they are next to P_2O_5 in removing water from the atmosphere. Both $Ba(ClO_4)_2$ and $Mg(ClO_4)_2$ can be purchased on the market. The perchlorates form several hydrates.

Perchloric acid may be prepared by electrical processes, and by the reaction of $Ba(ClO_4)_2$ with sulfuric acid; the $HClO_4$ is then distilled under high vacuum. The acid is stable below 90°. Anhydrous perchloric acid, pure $HClO_4$, is *extremely dangerous* to handle, for it explodes on contact with organic matter. A 60 or 70 per cent solution is used in the laboratory when a powerful oxidizing agent is required. (*Never work with perchloric acid in the laboratory without first familiarizing yourself with all the hazards.*) Perchloric acid is the strongest acid that has been measured so far. One proof of this is that fact that its monohydrate, $HClO_4 \cdot H_2O$, is stable at and above room temperature. This "hydrate" is actually the salt hydronium[9] perchlorate. Other strong acids form hydronium salts which can be crystallized from solution at low temperatures, but they decompose on being warmed a few degrees. The decomposition consists of the anion, acting as a base, taking a proton from the H_3O^+. Evidently ClO_4^- is the weakest anion base, which means that $HClO_4$ is the strongest acid.

Other Oxy-halogen Acids

Hypobromous acid is prepared by a process similar to that used in the preparation of hypochlorous acid.

$$Br_2 + H_2O \rightleftarrows H^+ + Br^- + HBrO$$

The neutralization of these acids with Na_2CO_3 and the recovery of the free bromine by treatment with concentrated sulfuric acid was discussed on page 319. Bromic acid is a good oxidizing agent and will oxidize free iodine to iodic acid.

$$2\ H^+ + 2\ BrO_3^- + I_2 \longrightarrow 2\ H^+ + 2\ IO_3^- + Br_2$$

Bromates are used in the chemical laboratory as powerful oxidizing agents, but are of no commercial importance except in the recovery of bromine from sea water.

The odor of hypoiodous acid can be detected in a solution of cold dilute KOH and I_2. The first reaction is believed to be:

$$I_2 + 2\ K^+ + 2\ OH^- \rightleftarrows 2\ K^+ + I^- + IO^- + H_2O$$

which is similar to the reaction of chlorine with KOH. The odor of HIO is due to the hydrolysis of potassium hypoiodite. HIO is a very weak acid.

$$K^+ + IO^- + H_2O \rightleftarrows K^+ + OH^- + HIO$$

If iodine is added to hot concentrated potassium hydroxide and the solution is then cooled, the KIO_3 precipitates.

$$3\ I_2 + 6\ K^+ + 6\ OH^- \longrightarrow 5\ K^+ + 5\ I^- + \underline{KIO_3} + 3\ H_2O$$

When chlorine is bubbled through a suspension of iodine in water, HIO_3 is obtained.

[9] This ion has also been called "oxonium."

$$5\ Cl_2 + I_2 + 6\ H_2O \longrightarrow 12\ H^+ + 2\ IO_3^- + 10\ Cl^-$$

The most important oxy-iodine compound is iodic acid, HIO_3, from which the white solid, I_2O_5, is prepared. Nitric acid is a sufficiently powerful oxidizing agent to oxidize iodine to iodic acid.

$$3\ I_2 + 10\ H^+ + 10\ NO_3^- \longrightarrow 6\ H^+ + 6\ IO_3^- + 10\ \overline{NO} + 2\ H_2O$$

The reaction between iodine and nitric acid is a good method of preparing iodine pentoxide. When a solution of HIO_3 is warmed carefully in a current of dry air, water is removed and the white solid anhydride remains.

$$2\ HIO_3 \xrightarrow{\Delta} I_2O_5 + H_2O$$

I_2O_5 starts to decompose at 300° C. so the temperature of dehydration must be kept below this point. One important use of I_2O_5 is in the determination and removal of carbon monoxide. Even traces of CO will reduce the iodine to the free state; the iodine is then volatilized and bubbled into a reducing agent such as sodium thiosulfate, and the excess thiosulfate in the solution is determined.

$$5\ CO + I_2O_5 \longrightarrow 5\ CO_2 + I_2$$

(Sometimes the carbon dioxide is measured instead of the free iodine.) Iodates are used in the chemical laboratory as oxidizing agents, and to some extent in medicine.

Electrolysis of iodic acid results in the formation of periodic acid, HIO_4. Because of its stability and powerful oxidizing properties, this acid is used as an oxidizing agent. It is obtained from the sodium salt, $NaIO_4$, in Chile saltpeter.

The valence electrons of iodine are in the fifth layer, which has room for many more electrons. This explains the ability of periodic acid to combine with two molecules of water, forming para-periodic acid, H_5IO_6, in which the iodine has a covalence of 6.

OTHER SALTS OF THE ALKALI METALS

The alkali metal halides are the initial materials from which other salts of commercial importance are prepared. Several of these compounds will be discussed here; other important ones, such as the sodium phosphates, will be left for later chapters.

Two manufactured sodium salts are found on almost every kitchen shelf. One is *sodium carbonate*, Na_2CO_3, known popularly as washing soda, but usually called soda ash in the commercial world. The other is *sodium bicarbonate*, $NaHCO_3$, or baking soda. The importance of Na_2CO_3 is indicated by the fact that 4,700,000 tons were produced in the United States in 1944, making the alkali industry one of our great industries. Sodium carbonate is used in the pulping process by which paper is made, in the manufacture of glass window panes, enamelware, and soaps. It is a constituent of many washing compounds; it is a water softener, and is used in petroleum refining and in countless other industries. Baking soda can be made by bubbling carbon dioxide into washing soda; it is used in cooking.

Soda Ash

Who first discovered that leaching the ashes of seaweeds gives a solution from which a fairly pure sodium carbonate can be obtained will never be known, for this compound has been used for many centuries. However, this source was expensive, and one which inland countries could not use. Sodium carbonate may even have been important in the discovery of glass, for it has been postulated that the Phoenician sailors rested their cooking utensils on lumps of natron, Na_2CO_3, and that as they cooked on the sand the Na_2CO_3 and SiO_2 reacted under the influence of the heat and formed glass.

The first important advancement in the soda ash industry was made during the French Revolution. Prior to 1787, France and other European countries obtained all their sodium carbonate from Spanish seaweed ash, called *barilla*, and from deposits of Na_2CO_3 controlled by the Arabs in Asia Minor. When England blocked the French water routes, the French Academy of Science was authorized to offer a prize of $20,000 (in our money) to anyone who could develop a suitable process for making soda ash from salt. In 1787, Nicholas Leblanc, physician to the Duc d'Orléans, invented a process which was soon undertaken on a commercial scale, thus greatly decreasing the cost of soda ash. (Leblanc never received the award. His patents were confiscated and the duke was guillotined, even though his money had been used in developing the process. Poverty-stricken, Leblanc committed suicide in 1806.)

The Leblanc process for manufacturing sodium carbonate consisted in first making sodium sulfate, or salt cake.

$$2\ \underline{NaCl} + H_2SO_4 \xrightarrow{\Delta} \underline{Na_2SO_4} + 2\ \overline{HCl}$$

The salt cake was heated with carbon as the reducing agent to form sodium sulfide.

$$\underline{Na_2SO_4} + 2\ \underline{C} \xrightarrow{\Delta} 2\ \overline{CO_2} + \underline{Na_2S}$$

The Na_2S, which was called "black ash" because it always contained some carbon, was then treated with limestone, $CaCO_3$, and sodium carbonate was separated from the mixture by leaching.

$$2\ Na^+ + S^{--} + \underline{CaCO_3} \longrightarrow \underline{CaS} + 2\ Na^+ + CO_3^{--}$$

Although at that time there was little demand for the by-product, HCl, and

H_2SO_4 was expensive, this process was the most economical one until the development of the Solvay process in 1863.

The British call the Solvay process *the ammonia-soda process*, for they claim that the process was fully developed in England prior to 1863. Ernest Solvay (1838–1922) as a boy of eighteen was employed in a gas works owned by his uncle, Semet Solvay. In an attempt to utilize the waste NH_3 which is a by-product of the coke industry, the boy mixed $NaCl$, NH_3, and CO_2, and obtained a white precipitate which was identified as $NaHCO_3$. Innumerable failures, the use of nearly all of the family funds, and five years of hard work preceded the development of suitable apparatus for the reactions; but by 1867 the process was in operation, the price of soda ash had dropped 75 per cent, and sales soon increased fifteenfold.

The large soda ash plant at Syracuse, New York, utilizes the Solvay process. This plant pipes and purifies the salt brine from deposits some twenty miles distant from Syracuse. The purified saturated salt solution is first treated with ammonia gas and then saturated with carbon dioxide; this results in the formation of crystals of the less soluble $NaHCO_3$ which are filtered from the solution of NH_4Cl.

1. $$NH_3 + H_2O \rightleftharpoons NH_4OH$$
2. $$CO_2 + H_2O \rightleftharpoons H_2CO_3$$
3. $$NH_4OH + H_2CO_3 \longrightarrow NH_4^+ + HCO_3^- + H_2O$$
4. $$NH_4^+ + HCO_3^- + Na^+ + Cl^- \longrightarrow NH_4^+ + Cl^- + \underline{NaHCO_3}$$

The $NaHCO_3$ crystals are dried and heated to form sodium carbonate.

5. $$2\ NaHCO_3 \xrightarrow{\Delta} Na_2CO_3 + \overline{CO_2} + H_2O$$

This carbon dioxide is returned to the absorption towers and used to prepare more $NaHCO_3$. The NH_3 is recovered by treating the NH_4Cl with lime water and steam. (Some NH_4Cl is purified and sold.)

6. $$2\ NH_4^+ + 2\ Cl^- + Ca^{++} + 2\ OH^- \xrightarrow{\Delta} 2\ \overline{NH_3} + Ca^{++} + 2\ Cl^- + 2\ H_2O$$

Carbon dioxide is prepared at the Syracuse plant by heating calcium carbonate.

7. $$CaCO_3 \xrightarrow{\Delta} CaO + \overline{CO_2}$$

Heat is required in the Solvay process to "burn" the limestone, convert the bicarbonate to carbonate, and generate the steam needed in the recovery of the ammonia. For the process to operate efficiently, great skill was required in designing suitable absorption towers. Tall towers called columns, which operate on the counter-current principle, provide the necessary surface for rapid absorption. Every effort is made to prevent the loss of the costly ammonia.

Calcium chloride, formerly considered a by-product, has gradually assumed the importance of a co-product, although still less than half the potential tonnage is evaporated for sale. It is used extensively as a soil binder in secondary roads, as well as to lay the dust on lesser roads, drives, tennis courts, and playgrounds. In freezing weather it thaws ice and prevents skidding on slippery highways. It is mixed with coal to hold the dust, and with coal as well as iron ore to prevent freezing in winter. It speeds up the curing of concrete, absorbs moisture in drying operations, and serves as the non-freezing medium in refrigeration brines.

Electrolytic Soda Ash. With the development of cheaper electric power and an increased demand for chlorine, it was only logical that sodium carbonate should be made from the sodium hydroxide which is obtained as a by-product in the electrolysis of salt. If carbon dioxide is bubbled into a solution of NaOH, sodium carbonate is formed.

$$2\,Na^+ + 2\,OH^- + \overline{CO_2} \longrightarrow 2\,Na^+ + CO_3^{--} + H_2O$$

(The CO_2 can be written H_2CO_3.) The sodium carbonate solution is concentrated by evaporation until the Na_2CO_3 crystallizes. If the end product

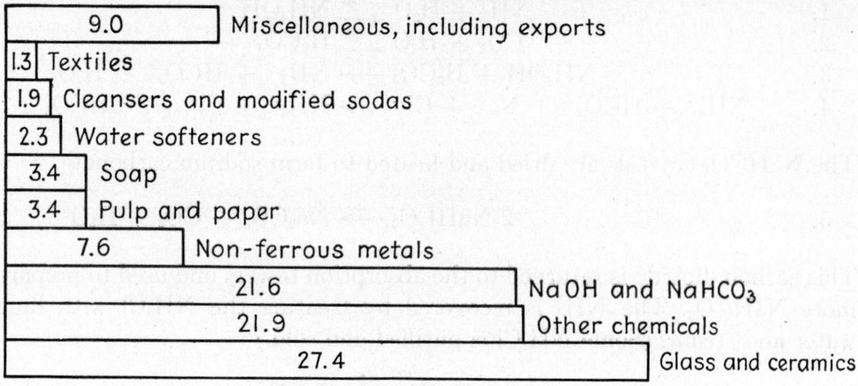

9.0	Miscellaneous, including exports
1.3	Textiles
1.9	Cleansers and modified sodas
2.3	Water softeners
3.4	Soap
3.4	Pulp and paper
7.6	Non-ferrous metals
21.6	NaOH and NaHCO₃
21.9	Other chemicals
27.4	Glass and ceramics

FIG. 22.10. Percentage distribution of sodium carbonate in industry.

desired is sodium bicarbonate, more carbon dioxide is bubbled into the saturated solution of sodium carbonate.

$$2\,Na^+ + CO_3^{--} + H_2CO_3 \longrightarrow 2\,Na^+ + 2\,HCO_3^-$$

However, most of the soda ash is still made by the Solvay process.

Products from salt fully illustrate what every chemist is schooled to remember, namely, that today's by-product may be tomorrow's chief product. Increased demands for chlorine have kept this industry on its toes for the past thirty years.

Properties and Uses of Sodium Carbonates. There are three hydrates of sodium carbonate, $Na_2CO_3 \cdot H_2O$, $Na_2CO_3 \cdot 7\,H_2O$, and $Na_2CO_3 \cdot 10\,H_2O$.

ALKALI METALS AND HALOGENS

"Trona," a natural product found in arid and desert regions, is called the sesquicarbonate. It consists of the double salt $Na_2CO_3 \cdot NaHCO_3 \cdot 2\,H_2O$ (often written $Na_3H(CO_3)_2 \cdot 2\,H_2O$). This compound is prepared by the Solvay process, and is becoming an important chemical. Although not important as a source of sodium carbonate, it is now used as a source of potassium chloride, borax, and boric acid, for these impurities can be recovered from the crude salt. Fig. 22.10 shows the present consumption of Na_2CO_3 in industry. The amount of NaOH produced from Na_2CO_3 in 1944 was limited by the available supply of the latter.

The bicarbonate ion is a mild base, the carbonate ion a moderately strong one. The pH values of 0.1 N solutions are respectively 8.4 and 11.6. (Compare values for other bases in Table 17.1, page 237.) Many of the uses of the sodium carbonates depend upon these facts. Sodium bicarbonate is used medicinally to neutralize hyperacidity in the body, in food to neutralize acidity in sour milk or molasses, and industrially to moderate the alkalinity of sodium carbonate. (A "modified soda" is Na_2CO_3, which has been made *less* basic by mixing it with $NaHCO_3$ or *more* basic by mixing NaOH with it, as the use requires.) In the manufacture of glass, sodium carbonate neutralizes the acid anhydride, silicon dioxide (sand). In soap-making it neutralizes the acids (pages 703–704) set free from the fats by hydrolysis. In the manufacture of chemicals it neutralizes various acids to form the desired salts. In cleaning and degreasing operations it establishes the degree of alkalinity which has been found to make soap most efficient.

The carbonate and bicarbonate ions have uses which do not depend upon their basicity. In water softening, the preparation of Javelle water, and the lime-soda process for making sodium hydroxide (to be discussed presently), sodium carbonate furnishes the carbonate ion to precipitate calcium carbonate. In baking powders and fire extinguishers sodium bicarbonate is the source of carbon dioxide, CO_2. All baking powders contain $NaHCO_3$ and some acid, which reacts with it according to the equation:

$$Na^+ + HCO_3^- + HX \longrightarrow Na^+ + X^- + H_2O + \overline{CO_2}$$

The bubbles of CO_2 *leaven* (lighten) the bread or cake. The acid, represented by HX in the above equation, is commonly one of three—the bitartrate ion, $HC_4H_4O_6^-$, the dihydrogen phosphate ion, $H_2PO_4^-$, or the aluminum ion, $Al(H_2O)_6^{+++}$. The bitartrate ion is used in the form of the potassium salt, $KHC_4H_4O_6$, commonly called cream of tartar. Calcium acid phosphate, $Ca(H_2PO_4)_2$, furnishes the dihydrogen phosphate ion. The hydrated aluminum ion is not put into the baking powder as such; instead, anhydrous sodium aluminum sulfate is used, which hydrates itself as soon as the water is added. This latter substance is obtained by drying sodium alum, $NaAl(SO_4)_2 \cdot 12\,H_2O$. For this reason baking powders that contain it are sometimes referred to as "alum baking powders," but in the trade $NaAl(SO_4)_2$ is called

"S.A.S." The chemical reaction in the case of this acid is not well represented by the type of reaction given above. It is:

$$Al(H_2O)_6^{+++} + 3\ HCO_3^- \longrightarrow \underline{Al(H_2O)_3(OH)_3} + 3\ H_2O + 3\ \overline{CO_2}$$

or, in conventional form:

$$2\ Al^{+++} + 3\ SO_4^{--} + 6\ Na^+ + 6\ HCO_3^- \xrightarrow{H_2O}$$
$$2\ \underline{Al(OH)_3} + 6\ Na^+ + 3\ SO_4^{--} + 6\ \overline{CO_2}$$

All baking powders are diluted to a standard strength with starch. They differ from each other in the rate at which CO_2 is liberated at different temperatures. Some, called "double-action" baking powders, contain two different acids, one of which reacts at a lower temperature than the other. The choice of baking powder depends entirely on which one gives best results; all leave only harmless products in foods.

Fire extinguishers of the type that has to be inverted in order to be used are filled with concentrated $NaHCO_3$ solution, above which is a small, open bottle of concentrated sulfuric acid. The reaction is:

$$2\ Na^+ + 2\ HCO_3^- + H_2SO_4 \longrightarrow 2\ Na^+ + SO_4^{--} + 2\ H_2O + 2\ \overline{CO_2}$$

The CO_2 supplies pressure to eject a stream of solution through the hose. The amount of acid is not sufficient to use up more than part of the $NaHCO_3$. The remainder can decompose in the heat of the fire, liberating CO_2 (equation 5, page 353), which helps extinguish the flame. Some extinguisher solutions also contain salts which exert a negative catalytic effect on combustion, or a foaming agent so that a froth is ejected which can float on oil or cling to a motor.

Sodium Hydroxide

When a strong base is required in water solution, the hydroxide ion is used. The cheapest hydroxide is that of calcium, $Ca(OH)_2$, called *lime*, but its limited solubility makes it impossible to raise the *p*H above 12.3. When a higher *p*H is required, sodium hydroxide is used. This material, known commercially as *soda lye* or *caustic soda*, was first prepared by the *causticization* of lime. Crude soda ash (85 per cent Na_2CO_3 and 15 per cent $NaHCO_3$) is treated with a suspension of calcium hydroxide in water at the boiling point.

$$2\ Na^+ + CO_3^{--} + \underline{Ca(OH)_2} \longrightarrow 2\ Na^+ + 2\ OH^- + \underline{CaCO_3}$$

The calcium carbonate is filtered off and the solution is concentrated by evaporation until it is 50 per cent or more NaOH. The 50 and 73 per cent solutions are shipped in tank cars; for the latter solution the car must be equipped with steam pipes, because the liquid solidifies on cooling. Sodium hydroxide is also sold as the pure solid in flakes, pellets, or sticks.

Sodium hydroxide is also produced electrolytically (pages 323–324). In 1921 only 100,000 tons were produced that way, three-eighths of that year's production of NaOH. In 1945 electrolytic NaOH accounted for some 60 per cent of the nearly $2\frac{1}{2}$ million tons of caustic which were manufactured. The increase in the relative importance of the electrolytic process was not gradual, but sudden. It was caused by the tremendous increase in the demand for chlorine in World War II, and by the development of the liquid ammonia process for purifying diaphragm cell NaOH from the accompanying NaCl. (NaCl is insoluble in liquid NH_3.) Previously, electrolytic NaOH had not been pure enough for many important uses, including the manufacture of rayon and cellophane.[10]

Potassium Salts

Of the several important potassium salts, only the carbonates will be considered here. Potassium is one of the elements essential for plant growth, and is found combined with several organic substances in plant tissue. The crystals in the bottom of a bottle of home-made grape juice are $KHC_4H_4O_6$, potassium acid tartrate. The sour taste of rhubarb is due to potassium acid oxalate which crystallizes out with the formation of both oxalic acid and water ($KHC_2O_4 \cdot H_2C_2O_4 \cdot 2\ H_2O$, sometimes called potassium tetraoxalate.) If these compounds are burned, K_2CO_3 is obtained. If wood is burned, the normal carbonate can be leached from the ashes; this was the early method of obtaining K_2CO_3. During the First World War some effort was made to recover K_2CO_3 from the waste or spent syrup from the sugar-beet industry; but now that KCl can be recovered from deposits of trona, several processes are available for making K_2CO_3.

Potassium carbonate is a white deliquescent salt which forms two common hydrates, $K_2CO_3 \cdot 2\ H_2O$ and $K_2CO_3 \cdot 3\ H_2O$. Its solutions are *much more* alkaline than those of sodium carbonate. K_2CO_3 is used in making soft and liquid soaps and hard glass. If carbon dioxide is bubbled into a solution of K_2CO_3, the acid salt, $KHCO_3$, is formed. This is found in many kitchens under the name of saleratus. It can, of course, be used instead of $NaHCO_3$ in baking, but the latter is now preferred.

QUESTIONS AND PROBLEMS

1. What is the commercial method of preparing each of the alkali metals?
2. If a large deposit of compounds of element 87 were found, what would be some properties of the element? Of element 85?

[10] *Chem. Trade J.*, Oct. 20, 1944.

3. Why did so many years elapse before the discovery of the common alkali metals?
4. Can all the alkali metals be stored *under* oil? Are they good conductors of electricity? List their most important uses.
5. What is a photoelectric cell?
6. What precautions should you take in working with the alkali metals?
7. What is sodium amide? Do the alkali metals form nitrides?
8. If the alkali metals cost the same per pound, which one would be the cheapest source of hydrogen?
9. Which were discovered first, the halogens or the alkali metals?
10. Which halogen is the most difficult to prepare? Which is the easiest?
11. List the halogens in the order of density, activity, ease of preparation, and value as oxidizing agents.
12. Outline the process for the recovery of bromine from sea water.
13. How many cubic feet of ocean water must be used to recover one ton of bromine? Assume that 60 mg. of bromine are recovered per liter of water.
14. How many tons of salt are required to liberate one ton of chlorine by the Deacon process if it is 70 per cent efficient?
15. If 0.02 mg. of chlorine per liter of air is very irritating, what weight of chlorine would be necessary to produce irritation over 10 sq. mi.? Assume that 20 per cent of the space is occupied by buildings whose average height is 400 ft. If each plane carries one ton of chlorine, how many planes will be required to carry the chlorine for a gas attack?
16. Complete these equations to show the oxidizing property of chlorine:

$$Na + Cl_2 \longrightarrow \qquad FeCl_2 + Cl_2 \longrightarrow$$
$$C_{10}H_{16} + Cl_2 \longrightarrow \qquad KI + Cl_2 \longrightarrow$$

17. Which halogen is present in thyroxine?
18. Compare the stabilities of the hydrohalogen acids.
19. List a suitable method for preparing each of the hydrohalogen acids.
20. Would you recommend $NaI + H_2SO_4 \xrightarrow{\Delta}$ as a suitable method for the preparation of HI? Why?
21. Show by equations the hydrolysis of phosphorus halides.
22. Compare the reducing properties of the hydrohalogen acids.
23. What is NOCl?
24. How is glass etched?
25. The following are white salts: NaI, KBr, LiCl, NaF, or NaCl. How would you identify them?
26. Ask your instructor to demonstrate the use of a spectroscope. Could you use it to answer question 25?
27. A solid is HgO, NaClO$_3$, AgCl, or AgI; how would you identify it?
28. How may the halide ions in a mixture of halides be preferentially oxidized?
29. Start with NaCl and write balanced equations for the preparation of each of the oxy-halogen sodium salts.
30. What precaution is necessary in using oxy-halogen compounds?
31. What is bleaching powder? How is it prepared?
32. Balance and show the electron changes in the reactions:

ALKALI METALS AND HALOGENS

$$I_2 + HNO_3 \longrightarrow NO + HIO_3 + H_2O$$
$$CO + I_2O_5 \longrightarrow CO_2 + I_2$$

33. Assuming 75 per cent efficiency, how many tons of NaCl are required to produce one ton of Na_2CO_3 by the Leblanc process?
34. Outline the steps in the Solvay soda process.
35. A white solid is NaOH, Na_2CO_3, or $NaHCO_3$; how would you identify it? If 1 mol of each of these is mixed with water and the solution is evaporated to dryness, what will be present in the residue?
36. If some NaOH were spilled on you, would you pour HCl on the base? Why? What would you do?
37. What is "modified soda"?
38. Weigh a box of baking soda. What volume of CO_2 at S.T.P. could be obtained from it?
39. What are leavening agents? Do you know a biological leavening agent?
40. List the water solutions of the following in order of increasing pH: NaCl, NaOH, Na_2CO_3, $NaHCO_3$, $FeCl_3$, and PCl_3.
41. Calculate the weight of one liter of each of the following gases at S.T.P.: SiF_4, H_2F_2, HBr, and Cl_2.
42. The average water consumption in a city of 250,000 population is 425 l. per capita per day. Chlorine is added to the water supply at the rate of 0.75 mg. per liter; it costs one and three-quarters cents per pound. Calculate the city's chlorine bill per year.
43. What volumes of H_2 and Cl_2 must be burned to produce 50 l. of 12-normal HCl?
44. What weight of $KMnO_4$ is required to liberate 60 l. of chlorine gas at 21° C. and 747 mm. pressure?
45. Write electronic formulas for ten different molecules (including ions) containing oxygen and a halogen.

REFERENCES

Books

Perchloric and Periodic Acids, etc.   Pamphlet by G. F. Smith Chemical Co., 867 McKinley Ave., Columbus, Ohio.
Manufacture of Soda.   Hou, T. P.   Reinhold Publishing Corporation.
Inorganic Chemical Technology.   Badger, W. L., and Baker, E. M.   McGraw-Hill Book Company, Inc.
Industrial Chemistry.   Riegel, E. R.   Chemical Catalogue Co.
Minerals Year Book.   Published yearly by the Department of Interior.
   An excellent source of information.

Articles

"Chlorine."   *Chem. and Met.* **51**, 115–122 (Aug., 1944).
"Bromine from Sea Water."   Stine, C. M. A.   *Ind. and Eng. Chem.*, **21**, 434–442 (1929).

"Bromine from Sea Water." Stewart, L. C. *Ind. and Eng. Chem.*, **26**, 361–369 (1934).

"Alkali Industry. Nelson Cell." Carrier, C. F. *Trans. Electrochem. Soc.* **35**, 239–249 (1919).

"Potash in the U. S." Mansfield, G. R. *J. Chem. Ed.* **7**, 737–761 (1930).

"Chemistry of Bleaching Powder." Ochi, S. *Trans. Electrochem. Soc.* **49**, 75 (1926).

"Baking Powder." Ziegler, P. F. *J. Chem. Ed.* **3**, 492–499 (1926).

"Potassium Chloride from the Brine of Searles Lake." Mumford, R. W. *Ind. and Eng. Chem.* **30**, 872 (1938).

"Potash in the Fertilizer Industry." Lodge, F. S. *Ind. and Eng. Chem.* **30**, 878 (1938).

"Potash in the Glass Industry." Fenn, A. N. *Ind. and Eng. Chem.* **30**, 891 (1938).

"The Sodium Industry." Gilbert, H. N. (Schoellkopf Medal Address.) *Chem. and Eng. News* **24**, 1668–1670 (1946).

"Fluorine Chemistry." A staff report. *Chemical Ind.* **59**, 1006 (1946).

» 23 «

SULFUR, SELENIUM, AND TELLURIUM

The preceding chapter dealt with the halogens (the right-hand subgroup of Group VII in the periodic table). Oxygen, sulfur, selenium, tellurium, and polonium constitute the corresponding subgroup of Group VI. Although these elements resemble one another in many ways, these resemblances are by no means as well marked as was true of the halogens. The most striking similarities in this group are shown by the compounds of sulfur, selenium, and tellurium. The non-metallic characteristic is most evident in oxygen, and this characteristic decreases in the order O–S–Se–Te–Po. Oxygen has been discussed in earlier chapters, and polonium will be considered with the radioactive elements; selenium and tellurium will be discussed with sulfur in this chapter.

SULFUR

Sulfur must be included in any list of essential elements, for it is required in the building of both plant and animal protein. Modern civilization has created many additional uses for sulfur and its compounds which were not essential to human existence centuries ago. As a matter of fact, sulfur is now so important a factor that its price is often considered an accurate barometer of business.

The history of sulfur is as old as mankind's. Sulfur is the famous brimstone of the Bible. It has been used in ointments for centuries. Linen was bleached with it 2000 years ago, and Egyptian paintings of about 1600 B.C. contain colors which required the use of its compounds. Romans used sulfur in incendiary war materials and in casting bronze statues. Homer referred to its use as a disinfectant, and Pliny mentioned different kinds of sulfur (probably differences in purity).

At one time all combustible material was thought to contain sulfur; and even Davy, in 1808, believed that oxygen was present in sulfur. From the time that Gay-Lussac and Thenard proved that sulfur was an element, developments in this industry have been very rapid.

Occurrence

Any element which is essential for plant and animal growth would be expected to be widely distributed in nature; for otherwise, plant and animal life could not survive. However, it does not follow that such an element constitutes a high percentage of the earth's crust. Sulfur is present in the small amount of only 0.05 of 1 per cent; like oxygen, it is found in nature both free and combined.

Combined sulfur is usually found in two forms, metal sulfides and metal sulfates. Almost all the natural metal sufides are insoluble in water, as are most of the important supplies of sulfates. However, the ocean contains approximately 1×10^{12} tons of sulfur as sulfate. The importance of sulfides and sulfates as sources of sulfur and sulfur compounds varies from time to time. Some petroleum refineries are now constructing units for the recovery of sulfur from petroleum, and this may be important in future sulfur production. Some coke plants recover sulfur. Formerly, in the production of a valuable metal by the reduction of metal sulfides, the sulfur was considered a useless by-product and allowed to escape as sulfur dioxide; but now many metallurgical plants recover this gas. Table 23.1 lists some of the more important compounds from which sulfur is obtained. Pyrites, FeS_2, is an important source of sulfur but not of iron, for it is quite expensive to remove all the sulfur from the iron. About a million tons are burned annually in the United States, replacing about 360,000 tons of sulfur. Before World War I we imported nearly half of this from Spain, but in 1943 we produced 800,000 tons.

TABLE 23.1. IMPORTANT COMPOUNDS OF SULFUR FOUND IN NATURE

Name	Formula	Name	Formula
Chalcocite	CuS	Anhydrite	$CaSO_4$
Chalcopyrite	$CuFeS_2$	Barite	$BaSO_4$
Galena	PbS	Celestite	$SrSO_4$
Iron pyrites (fool's gold)	FeS_2	Epsom salt	$MgSO_4 \cdot 7 H_2O$
Zinc blende	ZnS	Gypsum	$CaSO_4 \cdot 2 H_2O$

Free sulfur is frequently found near volcanoes, both active and extinct. Large deposits are also found mixed with limestone and gypsum. Among the theories advanced to explain this are reactions between sulfur dioxide, SO_2, and hydrogen sulfide, H_2S; oxidation of H_2S; weathering of metallic sulfides; and reduction of sulfates by bacteria.

The three major types of free sulfur deposits are *solfataras*, *fumarole*, and *gypsum*. The deposits found near the volcanoes of Japan and Chile are

SULFUR, SELENIUM, AND TELLURIUM

solfataric; fumarole deposits incrust some of the hot springs in Yellowstone Park; and the large deposits of our Gulf Coast and of Sicily are gypsum.

Sulfur Mining in the United States

Herman Frasch deserves the credit for the development of the sulfur industry in the United States. Frasch had attained great success as an inventor in other fields before he attempted to remove sulfur from the ground. His wide interests are indicated by patents on the refining of paraffin wax, separation of volatile constituents of oils, manufacture of wax paper, preparation of white lead from galena ore, improvements in the Solvay process, thermal electric generators, electric light carbons, apparatus for the removal of sulfur from petroleum, etc. In 1890 he applied for a patent on an improvement in the sulfur industry which was to make him still more famous. Native sulfur was known to be present in Calcasieu Parish, Louisiana, 1000 feet below the surface; and several concerns had tried to mine it but had failed because of quicksand 500 feet above the sulfur. Frasch decided that the only way to mine the sulfur was to melt it in the ground and then pump it to the surface as a liquid. He realized the widespread skepticism accorded his project; as he put it, "A fair illustration of public opinion is the remark of the mail boy who drove me to the railroad the morning after our first pumping. He said: 'Well, you pumped sulfur sure, but nobody believed it but the old carpenter, and they say he's half crazy.' " Fig. 23.1 shows graphically the principle underlying the Frasch process. The Louisiana and Texas deposits soon furnished sufficient sulfur to supply the world's demands; Texas is now the leading sulfur producing state in this country.

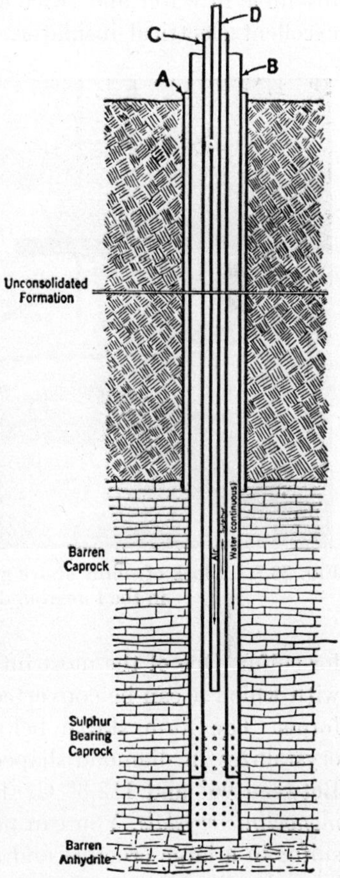

FIG. 23.1. Principle of the Frasch process. A, pipe; B, steam; C, sulfur line; D, air. (Courtesy, Freeport Sulphur Co.)

Prewar production of sulfur in the United States averaged a little over 2 million tons a year. About a quarter of this was exported; our exports about equal the total production of all the rest of the world.[1] At the war peak,

[1] Prior to 1900 Sicily and Italy held a monopoly on the production of sulfur. The story of the breaking of this monopoly is very exciting; chemistry students should read original articles concerning it.

attained in 1942, our sulfur production reached 3.5 million tons. Since this proved to be more than could be used, the production rate was reduced. The reserves of free sulfur in the Gulf coast region should meet our needs for at least the next fifty years.

Properties of Sulfur

Sulfur is a tasteless and nearly odorless yellow solid at room temperature, insoluble in water and twice as dense; it is a poor conductor of heat and an excellent electrical insulator. Carbon disulfide, CS_2, is an excellent solvent

FIG. 23.2. Block of sulfur above ground. Note the molten sulfur running on to the bed in the foreground. (Courtesy, Freeport Sulphur Co.)

for sulfur. One of the most interesting properties of the element is the ease with which it can be converted from one to the other of its three allotropic forms. The form stable below 96° C. is called *rhombic sulfur* because it crystallizes in diamond-shaped crystals belonging to the rhombic system. Between 96° and 112.8° C. (its melting point) the stable form consists of *monoclinic crystals*. You can produce this form in the laboratory by melting sulfur in a large crucible and allowing it to cool until the surface solidifies. Then break the surface crust and pour out the molten sulfur in the center, and you will see monoclinic needles of sulfur protruding from the wall. These needles melt at 119° C. If left undisturbed, the monoclinic crystals will revert to the rhombic form in a few days. Both these kinds of crystals are composed of identical molecules, differently arranged. A striking difference from oxygen is the fact that these molecules consist of 8-membered rings. The O_2 molecule is possible only because the small size of the oxygen atom makes multiple bonding possible. The sulfur atom has six valence electrons just as the oxygen atom does, but is too large to form a triple bond.

When two sulfur atoms combine, one of them still has an incomplete octet, :S̈:S̈, and the addition of more atoms always leaves the last one incomplete until the chain is long enough for the last atom to form a bond with the first. Sulfur solutions and melted sulfur (at the melting point) also contain S_8 molecules.

Fig. 23.3. Central collecting basin for sulfur from the sulfur well. (Courtesy Freeport Sulphur Co.)

If melted sulfur is heated to a higher temperature, the clear, straw-colored, thin liquid darkens and becomes thick. At 230° C. it is dark reddish-brown (black except in thin layers) and so viscous that it will not run out of an inverted test tube. With further heating the viscosity decreases; at 440° C., the boiling point, the liquid is nearly black and fairly fluid. If the boiling sulfur is cooled slowly, all these changes reverse themselves in order; but if it is cooled suddenly by being poured into cold water, an elastic product known as *amorphous sulfur* (or sometimes $S\mu$) is obtained. It is clear and, if the original sulfur was perfectly pure, of the same color as just-melted sulfur ($S\lambda$), but it is not soluble in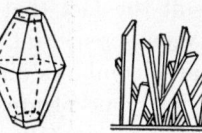

Fig. 23.4. Crystals of rhombic and monoclinic sulfur.

CS_2. If amorphous sulfur is left standing, the rubber-like properties disappear; it becomes opaque and brittle because of its transformation into microcrystals of rhombic sulfur. The rubber-like nature of $S\mu$ suggests that it has rubber-like molecules, i.e., enormously long, kinky chains. This has recently been confirmed. They are formed as the result of breakages in the S_8 rings, followed by attachment of the incomplete end of one chain to a complete octet in a *different* chain. The chain length reaches several thousand atoms, and explains the viscosity, insolubility, and failure to crystallize. When the liquid boils the chains are broken up. The density of the vapor corresponds to an average molecular weight of about 250 (S_8). Further dissociation takes place as the temperature rises, but sulfur must be heated to about 2000° C. before it becomes monatomic. *Flowers of sulfur* may be obtained by distilling sulfur and condensing the gas on a cold surface. Because the gas condenses without going through the liquid state, this sulfur is often called sublimed sulfur. All these sulfur changes are shown in the accompanying diagram.

$$\text{roll sulfur} \xrightarrow[\text{melts}]{112.8°} S_{\lambda\text{(fluid)}} \xrightarrow{230°} S_{\mu\text{(viscous)}} \xrightarrow[\text{boils}]{440°} S_8 \xrightarrow{\text{cool}} \text{"flowers of sulfur"}$$

with branches:
- $S_{\lambda\text{(fluid)}} \xrightarrow[\text{quickly}]{\text{cool}} S\text{(monoclinic)}$
- $S_{\mu\text{(viscous)}} \xrightarrow[\text{quickly}]{\text{cool}} S_\mu\text{(rubber-like)} \xrightarrow[\text{standing}]{\text{on long}} S\text{(rhombic)}$
- $S_{\mu\text{(viscous)}} \xrightarrow[\text{slowly}]{\text{cool}} \text{goes through all changes to } S\text{(rhombic)}$

The chemical properties of sulfur are those of oxygen, modified by the larger size of the sulfur atom. Sulfur may be expected to combine with the same large array of other elements as does oxygen. Its larger valence layer makes the sulfur atom less electrophilic than the smaller oxygen atom. This means that sulfur has less tendency to gain electrons than does oxygen. It also means that sulfur is much more willing to share electrons with the strongly electrophilic elements, namely, the halogens, oxygen, and nitrogen. In bonds between sulfur and such elements, the other elements, being more electrophilic than sulfur, are considered to be the owners of the shared electrons. Sulfur therefore can have *positive* oxidation numbers, although oxygen cannot. The greater willingness of sulfur to share electrons has as a further result the fact that sulfur can easily display a covalence of four, whereas oxygen is reluctant to have a covalence of three. Sulfur resembles oxygen in that it combines directly with most of the elements. It is oxidized rapidly by hot, concentrated nitric and sulfuric acids. With alkalies it disproportionates (see page 319), but the reaction is slower than is the case with chlorine, and the products, S^{--} and SO_3^{--}, react further with each other in complicated ways.

Uses of Sulfur

Sulfur is one of the essential elements of the chemical industry. Its uses, which are almost innumerable, may be divided into two groups: those in which the element itself is used, and those in which some compound of the element is used. Although the latter are more numerous, this statement must not be taken to imply that the free element is of no importance.

Elementary sulfur is used in the rubber industry, 100 pounds being required to manufacture 250 pounds of hard rubber, and one pound of sulfur being contained in every 50 pounds of soft rubber. The use of elementary sulfur in the vulcanization of rubber is discussed in the chapter dealing with organic compounds. Without sulfur and lime-sulfur sprays, insects and other plant pests would have a gala day. Although other sprays are available, hundreds of tons of sulfur are used each year in our combat with these pests. For example, 12 to 20 pounds of finely powdered sulfur per acre are required to destroy the cotton insect pests; airplanes are now extensively used for distributing the sulfur dust. Sulfur assists in the weathering of rock; hence some phosphate fertilizers contain it. Sulfur is a good insulator. Artificial slate can be made from melted sulfur mixed with asbestos, and excellent acid-resisting vessels are made from powdered coke and sulfur. Black gunpowder contains sulfur, charcoal, and potassium nitrate. Sulfur serves as a bonding agent for coal, sand, pumice, bitumens, and fibrous materials. An excellent cement for cast-iron water mains, etc., contains 40 per cent by weight of sulfur and 60 per cent sand. Organic sulfides can be used to vary the plasticity of the cements; these sulfides can be used in the mortar joints of tile floors or even as the bonding material between paving bricks.

Sulfur compounds are used at some stage in the manufacture or preparation of aniline dyes, bleaching agents, celluloid, explosives, fireworks, insecticides, matches, moving-picture films, plastics, steel pickling baths, and tanning. (One chemical company's advertisement lists over fifty different uses for sulfur compounds, among which are the following: aluminum sulfate in paper; sulfuric acid in the manufacture of aluminum; sulfuric acid, sodium sulfide, and sodium sulfate in the making of rayon; filter alum in water purification; basic chrome sulfate in leather upholstery, and sulfuric acid in making dyes for cloth.)

SULFIDES

Hydrogen Sulfide

Hydrogen sulfide, H_2S, is present in the gases escaping from many oil wells, volcanoes, and sulfur spring water. Protein contains sulfur and its anaerobic decomposition results in the formation of H_2S; it is this gas that gives rotten eggs their characteristic foul odor. H_2S is also produced by the destructive distillation of soft coal. H_2S is a toxic gas; continued exposure to as little as one part in 1000 parts of air is fatal.

Preparation. Hydrogen sulfide can be prepared by the direct union of the elements, the action of acids on sulfides, and the reduction of compounds of sulfur such as the sulfites and sulfates. If hydrogen gas is passed through a tube containing some hot sulfur, the two combine to form H₂S. On being heated, it easily decomposes into hydrogen and sulfur. Therefore the equation should indicate a reversible reaction.

$$H_2 + S \rightleftarrows H_2S$$

However, this reaction is of no commercial importance.

The most convenient means of preparing H₂S in the laboratory is to use a Kipp generator containing ferrous sulfide, FeS, and a dilute acid such as HCl.

$$\underline{FeS} + 2\ H^+ + 2\ Cl^- \longrightarrow Fe^{++} + 2\ Cl^- + \overline{H_2S}$$

Other sulfides may be substituted for FeS; however, iron pyrites, FeS₂, although cheaper than FeS, is unsatisfactory because this sulfide does not react with dilute acids.

Metal sulfates and sulfites can be reduced with carbon to form carbon dioxide and metal sulfides, the latter then being treated with dilute acids to produce H₂S.

H₂S can also be prepared by the reaction between paraffin and sulfur. If shavings of paraffin, powdered sulfur, and some shreds of asbestos (to give more surface) are heated together, H₂S is liberated. This procedure has one advantage in that the reaction stops as soon as the source of heat is removed.

Physical Properties. Hydrogen sulfide (mol. wt. 34) is slightly heavier than air. It is a colorless gas and can be readily condensed to a colorless liquid. It melts at −82.9° C. and boils at −59.6° C. At 0° C. 4.37 ml. will dissolve in 1 ml. of water. The gas is obtainable on the market in steel cylinders.

Chemical Properties. The fact that water from sulfur springs soon becomes milky when exposed to the oxygen of the air demonstrates that H₂S is easily oxidized.

$$2\ H_2S + O_2 \longrightarrow 2\ H_2O + 2\ S$$

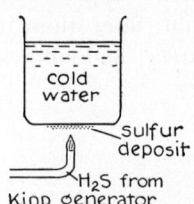

FIG. 23.5. Burning of hydrogen sulfide.

If hydrogen sulfide gas is allowed to escape from a Kipp generator and is heated with a Bunsen flame, free sulfur will collect on the bottom of a beaker which is cooled with water (Fig. 23.5). The inner cone of the flame is hot enough to decompose H₂S into hydrogen and sulfur, and the two elements burn at the surface of the flame.

$$\underline{S} + \overline{O_2} \longrightarrow \overline{SO_2}$$
$$2\ \underline{H_2} + \overline{O_2} \longrightarrow 2\ \overline{H_2O}$$

If there is an excess of oxygen, the flame will be the same blue as that obtained when sulfur is burned.

$$2\ \overline{H_2S} + 3\ \overline{O_2} \longrightarrow 2\ \overline{H_2O} + 2\ \overline{SO_2}$$

Hydrogen sulfide is both a reducing agent and an acid. It is such a powerful reducing agent that even a mild oxidizing agent will oxidize it. The product of oxidation depends upon the strength of the oxidizing agent, the temperature, and the concentrations of the reactants. The first step in the oxidation of the S^{--} ion results in the liberation of free sulfur, further oxidation changes the sulfur to SO_2, and complete oxidation yields SO_3. At room temperature, molecular oxygen, potassium dichromate, potassium permanganate, nitric acid, and even iodine and ferric chloride liberate free sulfur from H_2S. You should be able to write the equations for these reactions yourself. (In the case of HNO_3, assume that NO is formed.) Sulfur dioxide and hydrogen sulfide react to form sulfur and water. If one cylinder is filled with SO_2 and inverted over another filled with H_2S, yellow "sulfur smoke" is formed.

$$\overline{SO_2} + 2\ \overline{H_2S} \longrightarrow 3\ \underline{S} + 2\ \overline{H_2O}$$

It is much easier to oxidize H_2S to free sulfur than it is to oxidize the sulfur thus produced.

Hydrogen sulfide, although a stronger acid than water, is still a very weak acid. Its water solution may be called hydrosulfuric acid. The saturated solution is about 0.1 M and has a pH of about 4.5, between that of H_3BO_3 and H_2CO_3. This acidity is due almost entirely to the dissociation

$$H_2S \rightleftarrows H^+ + HS^-$$

The second dissociation

$$HS^- \rightleftarrows H^+ + S^{--}$$

is appreciable, but the hydrosulfide ion is only a trifle stronger an acid than water. For every S^{--} ion in a solution of H_2S, there are 10^{10} HS$^-$ ions. If HS$^-$ is almost as weak an acid as water, S^{--} must correspondingly be almost as strong a base as OH$^-$. This is the case. Na_2S is about 50 per cent hydrolyzed in water solution.

$$2\ Na^+ + S^{--} + H_2O \rightleftarrows 2\ Na^+ + HS^- + OH^-$$

Metal Sulfides

The fact that many insoluble sulfides are found in nature suggests a use for H_2S in the laboratory. If sulfides can be precipitated in an insoluble state in nature, it should be possible to do this in the laboratory. If all metal sulfides were insoluble in water, H_2S would be of no value in the separation of metallic ions; but fortunately the sulfides differ so greatly in solubility that this forms the usual means of classifying them into three groups: (1) those insoluble even in a 0.3 molar acid; (2) those soluble in dilute acid but insoluble in an alkaline solution, or hydrolyzing and forming insoluble hydroxides; and (3) those soluble in both acid and basic solutions. Table 23.2 lists some of the common metallic ions which are classified in these groups.

TABLE 23.2. SOLUBILITY OF SULFIDES

Sulfides Insoluble in a 0.3 M HCl Solution	Sulfides Insoluble or Hydrolyzed in Basic Solutions	Soluble Sulfides
Ag^+, Pb^{++}, Hg^{++}, Cd^{++}, Cu^{++}, Bi^{+++}, As^{+++}, Sb^{+++}, and Sn^{++}	Co^{++}, Ni^{++}, Mn^{++}, Zn^{++}, Fe^{+++}, Al^{+++}, and Cr^{+++}	Ba^{++}, Sr^{++}, Ca^{++}, Mg^{++}, K^+, Na^+, and NH_4^+

Some sulfides such as Al_2S_3 can be kept as such only in the absence of water because they hydrolyze easily. Al_2S_3 can be prepared by the direct union of sulfur and aluminum. If H_2S is added to an alkaline solution containing the Al^{+++} ion, the precipitate which forms is not the sulfide but the hydroxide.

$$Na^+ + Al(H_2O)_2(OH)_4^- + H_2S \longrightarrow Na^+ + HS^- + \underline{Al(H_2O)_3(OH)_3}$$

Many procedures are used by analytical chemists to separate elements into groups; each one has both advantages and disadvantages. Table 23.3 shows the steps in one popular method of separating the common metallic ions, in which H_2S is used as one of the precipitating agents. After the group separation, further tests are required for the identification of the elements in each group.

TABLE 23.3. SEPARATION OF SEVERAL COMMON METALS INTO GROUPS

(All the substances are assumed to be present in the form of soluble compounds.)

	Add 6 normal HCl to the solution in slight excess.				
Precipitate AgCl PbCl$_2$ Hg$_2$Cl$_2$	Filtrate: Add H$_2$S.				
	Precipitate CdS, CuS, Bi$_2$S$_3$, PbS, HgS, As$_2$S$_3$ Sb$_2$S$_3$, SnS	Filtrate: Add NH$_4$OH + NH$_4$Cl after boiling off H$_2$S.			
		Precipitate Fe(OH)$_3$ Al(OH)$_3$ Cr(OH)$_3$	Filtrate: Add (NH$_4$)$_2$S.		
			Precipitate CoS, NiS, MnS, ZnS	Filtrate: Add NH$_4$Cl and (NH$_4$)$_2$CO$_3$.	
				Precipitate BaCO$_3$ SrCO$_3$ CaCO$_3$ MgCO$_3$· (NH$_4$)$_2$CO$_3$	Filtrate K$^+$, Na$^+$, NH$_4^+$
Group I	II	III	IV	V	VI

SULFUR, SELENIUM, AND TELLURIUM

Valuable information regarding the presence or absence of an element can sometimes be obtained by observing the color of the sulfide which is formed. HgS, PbS, CuS, NiS, and CoS are black; ZnS is white; Bi_2S_3, Ag_2S, and SnS are brown; CdS, As_2S_3, and SnS_2 are yellow; and Sb_2S_3 is orange. The listing of the groups in Table 23.3 does not correspond to their listing in the periodic table.

Polysulfides

The fact that hydrogen and oxygen form two oxides, H_2O and H_2O_2, should familiarize us with the idea of polysulfides. Like hydrogen peroxide, the higher sulfides of hydrogen such as H_2S_2 and H_2S_3 are unstable. The metal peroxides are analogous to the polysulfides, although the latter are more complicated in that they are more numerous.

Ammonia forms several different sulfides: $(NH_4)_2S$, $(NH_4)_2S_2$, $(NH_4)_2S_3$, $(NH_4)_2S_4$, and $(NH_4)_2S_5$. All of these may be present in one solution. Instead of using the formula for each one, chemists use $(NH_4)_2S_x$ to represent all of them; the yellow compound is called ammonium polysulfide. Sodium forms the polysulfides Na_2S_4 and Na_2S_5. If slaked lime and sulfur are boiled together, a mixture of calcium polysulfides, CaS_4 and CaS_5, is formed. The red solution, known as lime-sulfur spray, is used against many enemies of plant life. This solution also contains some calcium thiosulfate, CaS_2O_3. No single equation can be written for these reactions; they take place to different extents, depending on the conditions.

Again like hydrogen peroxide, the polysulfides are also mild oxidizing agents. An interesting example of the oxidizing power of $(NH_4)_2S_x$ is its oxidation of arsenious sulfide to the soluble ammonium thioarsenate. Note that the valence of the arsenic changes from As^{+3} to As^{+5}.

$$\underline{As_2S_3} + 8\ NH_4^+ + 4\ S_2^{--} \longrightarrow 8\ NH_4^+ + 2\ AsS_4^{---} + S_3^{--}$$

(With a higher polysulfide the equation is more complicated.) A solution of *pure* $(NH_4)_2S$ is colorless, whereas the polysulfides are colored.

Non-Metal Sulfides

Sulfur forms sulfides with the non-metals that are analogous to the non-metal oxides. They are covalently bound, non-salt-like compounds. Thus there are boron, carbon, nitrogen, and phosphorus sulfides. (The compounds with oxygen and the halogens are not called sulfides, because the sulfur is the positive element in them. The halides and oxides of sulfur will be discussed in later paragraphs.) Boron and nitrogen sulfides are not of interest at present.

Carbon disulfide, CS_2, is a colorless liquid which melts at $-108.6°$ and boils at the very low temperature of $46.3°$. Its specific gravity is 1.26. The liquid has a high vapor pressure even at room temperature, and its kindling temperature is so low that a warm glass rod will ignite it and you can hold your hand (at least for a while) in the burning liquid. CS_2 vapor is very toxic. From the fact that carbon burns and forms carbon dioxide, the same reaction might be expected between carbon and sulfur.

$$C + 2\,S \longrightarrow CS_2$$

Of course this reaction can occur only in the absence of oxygen. Since the two combine only at high temperatures, it is a common practice to heat powdered coke and sulfur in an electric furnace, the CS_2 gas produced being cooled and liquefied.

The liquid has many uses because of its value as a solvent. Being immiscible with water, CS_2 is a good solvent for some substances that are insoluble or only slightly soluble in water, such as rubber, resins, fats, oils, iodine, phosphorus, and sulfur. Carbon disulfide is also used in the manufacture of rayon (page 708).

White phosphorus and sulfur combine explosively. Red phosphorus and sulfur combine readily if heated gently. Of the several sulfides, *tetraphosphorus trisulfide*, P_4S_3, is the most important inasmuch as it is used in the manufacture of the "strike anywhere" type of match.

Sulfur Halides

Although oxygen does not combine directly with the halogens, sulfur does. It forms a hexafluoride, mono-, di-, and tetra-chlorides, etc. Of all of these, only the monochloride is of commercial importance at present. Its molecular formula is S_2Cl_2, twice the empirical formula which gave the substance its name. S_2Cl_2 is a red-yellow liquid, s.g. 1.687, M.P. $-80°$ C., and B.P. $138°$ C. It is a most disagreeable chemical to handle, for it has a pungent odor and it fumes in moist air. It is prepared by passing dry chlorine over fused sulfur and then condensing the S_2Cl_2 which is produced. Several substances are produced when it hydrolyzes, as shown by the following equations:

$$S_2Cl_2 + 2\,H_2O \longrightarrow 2\,HCl + H_2S + SO_2$$
$$2\,H_2S + SO_2 \longrightarrow 2\,H_2O + 3\,S$$

Another procedure for preparing S_2Cl_2 is to pass dry chlorine into carbon disulfide which contains a little free iodine.

$$CS_2 + 3\,Cl_2 \longrightarrow S_2Cl_2 + CCl_4$$

The two liquids are separated by distillation.

Mustard gas, $(C_2H_4Cl)_2S$, the persistent "blister gas" which was the most effective chemical harassing agent of World War I, is prepared by the reaction between sulfur monochloride and ethylene. This substance is a liquid at ordinary temperatures, and its vapor pressure is sufficiently low to make it volatilize only slowly.

Not all the uses of S_2Cl_2 are destructive; it is an excellent solvent for sulfur.

Solutions of sulfur in sulfur monochloride are used in the vulcanization of rubber (page 688).

OXYGEN COMPOUNDS OF SULFUR

To give an idea of the variety of oxygen compounds of sulfur which exist, a few of the simplest will be listed. COS, carbonyl sulfide; $SOCl_2$, thionyl chloride; SO_2Cl_2, sulfuryl chloride; SO, sulfur monoxide; SO_2, sulfur dioxide; SO_3, sulfur trioxide; SO_4, sulfur tetroxide; S_2O_3, sulfur suboxide; and S_2O_7, sulfur heptoxide. Of these, only two—SO_2 and SO_3—are important.

Sulfur Dioxide

Preparation. Sulfur dioxide is sometimes found in mineral spring waters and it is usually a constituent of the gases escaping from volcanoes. Because it is heavier than air, it is extremely destructive to all forms of life near an erupting volcano.

There are numerous satisfactory methods for preparing this gas in the laboratory, such as burning sulfur, roasting sulfides, reducing the sulfate ion, and liberating the gas from sulfites.

Burning sulfur:

$$S + \overline{O_2} \longrightarrow \overline{SO_2} + \Delta$$

Roasting iron pyrites:

$$4\,\underline{FeS_2} + 11\,\overline{O_2} \longrightarrow 2\,\underline{Fe_2O_3} + 8\,\overline{SO_2}$$

Roasting copper sulfide ore (important source of copper):

$$2\,\underline{CuS} + 3\,\overline{O_2} \longrightarrow 2\,\underline{CuO} + 2\,\overline{SO_2}$$

Reducing the sulfate ion:

$$\underline{Cu} + 2\,H_2SO_4 \longrightarrow CuSO_4 + 2\,\overline{H_2O} + \overline{SO_2}$$

$$\underline{C} + 2\,H_2SO_4 \longrightarrow \overline{CO_2} + 2\,\overline{SO_2} + 2\,\overline{H_2O}$$

Metal sulfates can be reduced with carbon, but the reduction usually goes further than SO_2, and sulfides are formed. Thus, Na_2SO_4, in the form of salt cake, is reduced with carbon to form Na_2S, which is used in making Kraft paper from southern pine.

$$Na_2SO_4 + 4\,\underline{C} \longrightarrow \underline{Na_2S} + 4\,\overline{CO}$$

Liberating SO_2 from sulfites:

Metal sulfites and metal acid sulfites + an acid

$$Na^+ + HSO_3^- + H^+ + HSO_4^- \longrightarrow Na^+ + HSO_4^- + H_2SO_3$$
$$\longrightarrow H_2O + \overline{SO_2}$$

Physical Properties. Sulfur dioxide melts at $-72.7°$ and boils at $-10°$ C.; hence at room temperature it is a gas. Since it has such a high boiling point, the gas can be readily liquefied in the laboratory by passing it through a glass tube immersed in a salt-ice mixture, as shown in Fig. 23.6. The liquid has such a low vapor pressure at room temperature that it can be shipped in strong tin cans. The gas has a penetrating, choking odor. 0.228 g. of SO_2 dissolves in 1 cc. of water at 0° C.

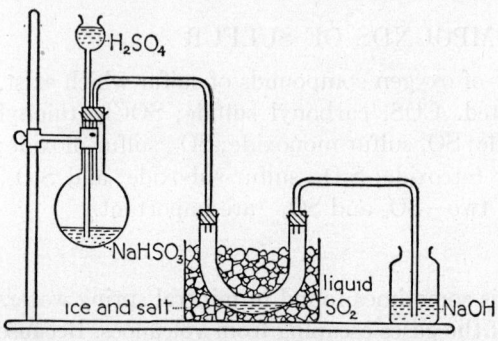

Fig. 23.6. The preparation of sulfur dioxide.

Chemical Properties. That sulfur can have several valences is indicated by the compounds H_2S, SO_2, and SO_3. Sulfur dioxide can therefore act as either an *oxidizing agent* or a *reducing agent*. A water solution of SO_2 has *acid properties*. The oxidizing power of SO_2 was illustrated in the preparation of flowers of sulfur ("sulfur smoke," page 369).

$$\underset{\text{loses }2\ominus}{\overset{\text{gains }4\ominus}{2\ H_2S + SO_2 \longrightarrow 3\ S + 2\ H_2O}}$$

In reactions with powerful oxidizing agents such as ozone, potassium permanganate, hydrogen peroxide, iodine solution, potassium iodate, or potassium dichromate, sulfur dioxide acts as a reducing agent. Molecular oxygen in the presence of suitable catalysts will also oxidize SO_2. Can you complete these equations which illustrate the reducing property of sulfur dioxide? No other oxidation or reduction products than those shown exist; balance the equations according to the rules (page 322), supplying inert ions where they are implied, acid where indicated (if needed), and water as required.

$$SO_2 + O_2 \xrightarrow{\text{Catalyst}} SO_3$$
$$SO_2 + O_3 \longrightarrow SO_3 + O_2$$
$$SO_2 + H_2O_2 \longrightarrow SO_4^{--}$$
$$I_2 + SO_2 \longrightarrow I^- + SO_4^{--}$$
$$IO_3^- + SO_2 \longrightarrow I_2 + HSO_4^-$$
$$MnO_4^- + SO_2 \longrightarrow Mn^{++} + SO_4^{--}$$
$$Cr_2O_7^{--} + SO_2 \xrightarrow{\text{acid}} Cr^{+++} + SO_4^{--}$$

Sulfur dioxide dissolves in water and reacts with it to form sulfurous acid,

H$_2$SO$_3$. Sulfur dioxide is the anhydride of H$_2$SO$_3$. The following equilibria exist in a water solution of sulfur dioxide:

$$\overline{SO_2} + H_2O \rightleftarrows H_2SO_3 \rightleftarrows H^+ + HSO_3^- \rightleftarrows 2H^+ + SO_3^{--}$$

Sulfurous acid is a weak dibasic[2] acid which forms both the normal and the acid salts. The above equilibria may be shifted from left to right by the addition of a strong base, and in the opposite direction by heat or the addition of a highly ionized acid.

The most important salt of sulfurous acid is calcium acid sulfite, Ca(HSO$_3$)$_2$, which is used in the sulfite process for manufacturing paper. The sulfite is made by bubbling sulfur dioxide into the solution of the metallic hydroxide. Logs are cut into small chips, covered with the sulfite solution (known as sulfite liquor to the paper trade), and digested or heated under 100 pounds pressure for several hours. This process disintegrates and separates the lignin, or bonding material of wood, from the cellulose fibers. The paper industry buys dry lime and liquid SO$_2$ in cylinders and makes its own "sulfite liquor."

Any bottle labeled "sulfite" will nearly always give a test for the SO$_4^{--}$ radical because sulfites are reducing agents and are easily oxidized to sulfates by molecular oxygen.

Uses of Sulfur Dioxide, Sulfurous Acid, and Sulfites. Sulfur dioxide and its water solutions have been used for centuries as antiseptics and preservatives. Sulfur is often burned in the holds of ships to sterilize the ship, kill fungus growths, rats, etc. SO$_2$ prevents bacterial fermentations; for example, in the manufacture of cornstarch it is used in the bath in which the kernels of corn are soaked; without it, various types of bacterial fermentations would occur.

Dry sulfur dioxide gas is used in many refrigeration units. (If the gas is moist, the metal parts will corrode.) It is especially well adapted for this purpose because the change from the liquid to the gaseous state can be carried out within the temperature range desired, and at low pressure. Sulfur dioxide is inexpensive; it is toxic, but its odor warns of its presence. Its heat of vaporization, 94.9 cal./g., compares favorably with that of other refrigerants. Sulfur dioxide is also used in the liquid state as a preferential solvent for certain objectionable substances naturally present in lubricating oils. The most important use of SO$_2$, by a large margin, is in the manufacture of sulfuric acid.

Sulfurous acid is not of any particular use as an acid, because any attempt to concentrate it decomposes it into its anhydride (SO$_2$) and water. But when SO$_2$ is used as a reducing agent, it is usually used in the presence of water, and therefore in the form of H$_2$SO$_3$. When SO$_2$ is in equilibrium with its solution in water, H$_2$SO$_3$, there is some seven times as great a concentration of it in

[2] The term *diprotic* is also used synonymously with "dibasic" to mean that an acid has two replaceable protons.

the water as there is above the water. Sulfur dioxide is used to bleach substances too delicate to withstand the harsh action of chlorine, such as wool, hat straw, dried fruits, and white wines. The bleaching action here is one of reduction, not oxidation, and this produces an interesting after-effect. When chlorine takes electrons away from a molecule of a colored impurity in cotton cloth or elsewhere, the molecule usually breaks up into a number of much smaller and simpler ones, and is thus gone forever. But when such a molecule is decolorized by adding electrons, it usually retains its structure. After a while atmospheric oxygen may take the added electrons away again, and the straw or silk will return to its original yellowish color.

The use of SO_2 in foods, to bleach them (or to prevent oxidational darkening on exposure to air) and prevent fermentation and mold growth, was once vigorously opposed by pure-food enthusiasts, but no one has ever offered evidence of any harmful physiological effect in the quantities in which it is used. On the other hand, there is an interesting and entirely accidental advantage. It happens that ascorbic acid, vitamin C, in fruits is largely destroyed by atmospheric oxidation during the drying process, but this does not occur if the fruit is first "sulfured," because the resulting slight increase in acidity lowers the oxidizability of vitamin C. Bleached dried fruit is therefore more healthful than the old-fashioned dark-colored kind.

The *sulfite ion*, regularly occurring as sodium sulfite, Na_2SO_3, is important in photography. Photographic developers are reducing agents which reduce silver ions in AgCl or AgBr crystals in exposed portions of the sensitive material to the black metallic silver of which the image is composed. In doing so they are themselves oxidized to products which have two objectionable qualities. They are colored and hence stain the film or print, and they catalyze the oxidation of the unused developer by the atmosphere. The SO_3^{--} ion combines with these oxidation products, reducing them to colorless compounds without catalytic activity.

Sulfur Trioxide

Preparation. When sulfur burns and forms sulfur dioxide, a little sulfur trioxide is also formed.

$$2\ SO_2 + O_2 \rightleftarrows 2\ SO_3 + \Delta$$

The yield from this method is always very small. Since SO_3 is the anhydride of the extremely useful sulfuric acid, it was to be expected that attempts would be made to increase the efficiency of the reaction. Several catalysts have been found which function satisfactorily in converting SO_2 to SO_3; they will be discussed in the next section.

Physical Properties. Sulfur trioxide melts at 16.8° and boils at 44.8° C. Solid SO_3 is white; liquid SO_3 is colorless. It readily crystallizes to a solid which contains some of the polymer $(SO_3)_2$. Sulfur trioxide fumes strongly in moist air, forming small droplets of H_2SO_4. This makes it impossible to absorb SO_3 from an air stream by bubbling it through water, although concentrated sulfuric acid can be used successfully as the absorbent. SO_3 molecules move at a velocity[3] of about 137 meters per second; so it takes only a short time for all of them to strike the wall of the bubble and be absorbed. But if the bubble is surrounded by water instead of concentrated H_2SO_4, evaporating water molecules (moving at about 400 meters per second) convert nearly all the SO_3 into mist droplets of H_2SO_4 solution before the SO_3 can reach the water surface. These droplets, of visible size, have no more kinetic energy than a water or SO_3 molecule;[4] hence their velocity is negligible and they do not reach the bubble wall in any practicable length of time.

Chemical Properties. Sulfur trioxide is an acid anhydride; it reacts chemically with water to form sulfuric acid which in turn forms several hydrates. Because of its *exothermic* reaction with water, great care is necessary in handling it. Sulfur trioxide is a good oxidizing agent, and serious burns result if it is spilled on the skin.

Sulfuric Acid

Processes for the Commercial Manufacture of Sulfuric Acid. The alchemists' process for making H_2SO_4 could not possibly be used today on a commercial scale. They used sulfates which could be broken down to liberate SO_3 and dissolved the gas in water. Typical of these reactions is the decomposition of ferric sulfate.

$$Fe_2(SO_4)_3 \xrightarrow{\Delta} Fe_2O_3 + 3\ SO_3$$

$$3\ SO_3 + 3\ H_2O \longrightarrow 3\ H_2SO_4$$

Sulfuric acid is now usually prepared by either the lead chamber or the contact process.

The Lead Chamber Process. The lead chamber process, which has been in use for over a century, derives its name from the fact that the chemical reactions take place in large lead towers and chambers. Although, like most metals, lead is attacked by sulfuric acid, a coating of insoluble lead sulfate forms on the surface of the lead containers and thus protects the metal from further oxidation. The following steps are necessary in the production of sulfuric acid by this process: (1) preparation of SO_2; (2) purification of SO_2, if necessary; (3) oxidation of SO_2 with oxides of nitrogen; (4) sorption of SO_3; (5) recovery of lower oxides of nitrogen; and (6) oxidation of the lower oxides of nitrogen. In brief, the process depends upon the fact that although molecular oxygen is a poor oxidizing agent for SO_2, it will oxidize the lower oxides of nitrogen to the higher oxides and these in turn will oxidize SO_2 to SO_3.

[3] Graham's Law, page 38.
[4] Brownian movement, page 40.

$$\overline{SO_2} + \overline{O_2} \longrightarrow SO_3 \text{ (very slow)}$$
$$\overline{SO_2} + \text{higher oxides of nitrogen} \longrightarrow \overline{SO_3} + \text{lower oxides of nitrogen}$$
$$\text{(very rapid)}$$
$$\text{Lower oxides of nitrogen} + \overline{O_2} \longrightarrow \text{higher oxides of nitrogen}$$
$$\text{(very rapid)}$$

Note that oxides of nitrogen are necessary to start the reaction and that if the process is to be *economically sound* the oxides of nitrogen must be recovered and used repeatedly. The catalyst is more valuable than sulfuric acid; hence it would be poor economy to use this process if the catalyst could be used only once. It was no easy task to design apparatus which would make the process

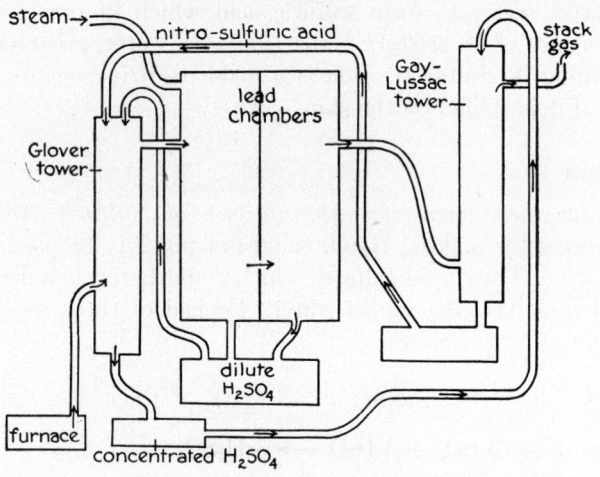

FIG. 23.7. The lead chamber process for the manufacture of sulfuric acid.

continuous and the recovery of the oxides of nitrogen nearly complete. The development of the first commercial plant for manufacturing sulfuric acid by the lead chamber process was a great feat of chemical engineering in its day. The fundamental parts of the lead chamber plant are shown in Fig. 23.7. The process will be considered in its various steps.

About 78 per cent of the sulfur dioxide used in making H_2SO_4 in the United States is obtained by burning sulfur. The sulfur contained in pyrites sells for about half the price of native sulfur, but it can be used only on the Atlantic coast or near our own mines, for rail freight rates on the iron and the useless impurities it contains would soon eat up the difference. Less than an eighth of our H_2SO_4 is made from SO_2 produced by burning pyrites. The remaining tenth is produced at smelters from SO_2 which is a by-product of the roasting of sulfide ores of copper, lead, and especially zinc. SO_2 not prepared from brimstone must usually be freed from dust by means of a Cottrell precipitator (page 275). The hot gases (generally containing about

SULFUR, SELENIUM, AND TELLURIUM

8 per cent SO$_2$) are led into the base of the reaction chamber known as the Glover tower. Glover towers are rectangular boxes made of sheet lead and filled with broken quartz. The burner gases pass upward through this tower while dilute acid from the lead chambers and the acid from the Gay-Lussac tower trickle downward. In order to understand what happens in this tower, we must look first at the Gay-Lussac tower, where the catalyst is recovered from the air leaving the lead chambers. This gas passes upward through the tower, in a countercurrent to concentrated H$_2$SO$_4$ which trickles down through it. The reaction may be expressed as follows:

$$\overline{NO} + \overline{NO_2} + 2\ H_2SO_4 \longrightarrow 2\ H(NO)SO_4 + H_2O$$

The unfamiliar formula is that of nitrosylsulfuric acid, which remains dissolved in the excess H$_2$SO$_4$ and is pumped to the top of the Glover tower.

The electronic structure of nitrosylsulfuric acid is:

$$\begin{array}{c} \ddot{\text{:O:}} \\ \text{H:}\ddot{\text{O}}\text{:}\ddot{\text{S}}\text{:}\ddot{\text{O}}\text{:}\ddot{\text{N}}\text{::}\ddot{\text{O}} \\ \ddot{\text{:O:}} \end{array}$$

White crystals of the pure substance sometimes form on the walls of a lead chamber which is not operating properly; hence they are sometimes called "chamber crystals."

The reaction for the formation of nitrosylsulfuric acid is reversible. In the Glover tower it is driven to the left by the water in the more dilute chamber acid, and the oxides of nitrogen thus released are boiled off by the hot gases from the sulfur burner and carried on with them into the lead chambers. An excess of chamber acid is used to take advantage of the heat in the burner gases, which evaporates a considerable amount of water from the dilute acid. The acid that leaves the Glover tower has been stripped of oxides of nitrogen and concentrated to 78 per cent. This is concentrated enough for use in the Gay-Lussac tower and the necessary amount is pumped up and sprayed into the top of the tower. The remainder is sold.

The gases from the Glover tower, NO, NO$_2$, SO$_2$ and air, enter a series of lead chambers (only two are shown in the figure). Steam is also injected, and myriad repetitions of the cycle of reactions described on page 377 produce sulfuric acid. The product has a concentration of about 62 per cent. The part of it which is not used in the immediate vicinity for the manufacture of soluble phosphate fertilizers must be concentrated before being shipped, in order to avoid payment of freight on water. In concentrating the chamber acid the lead pans used as evaporators are placed above the burners—a clever use of the excess heat developed during the production of SO$_2$. After H$_2$SO$_4$ has been concentrated to 77 per cent it dissolves the protective coating of PbSO$_4$ from the pans; hence duriron containers must be used for further concentration. This concentrated acid is known to the trade as "oil of vitriol." Sulfuric acid is now shipped in iron tank cars, for concentrated sulfuric acid does not attack iron beyond forming a protective coating of iron sulfate.

The steps in the manufacture of sulfuric acid by the lead chamber process can be summarized as follows:

1. Sulfur or sulfur compounds must be converted into SO_2.
2. It may be necessary to purify the SO_2.
3. The SO_2 is oxidized to SO_3 by the use of oxides of nitrogen in the Glover tower and the lead chambers.
4. The lower oxides of nitrogen are retained in the Gay-Lussac tower.
5. These oxides of nitrogen are returned, in the presence of sulfuric acid, to the Glover tower and the lead chambers where they are reoxidized and the cycle is repeated.
6. The dilute acid which collects in the lead chambers is usually further concentrated by the evaporation of water before it is shipped from the plant.

The earlier lead chamber plants contained the lower Glover tower and several lead chambers, all about 14 ft. high and varying in floor space from 70×25 ft. cross section for the first large one to 25×25 ft. for the last small one. The lead chambers were made of sheet lead; the seams were melted together with an air-hydrogen blowpipe. The Gay-Lussac tower was about 70 ft. high and about 13 ft. in diameter, circular, lined with lead, and filled with graduated quartz lumps, large at the bottom and smaller at the top. More recent plants have been constructed of acid-proof masonry. The Anaconda Copper Company plant is entirely composed of Glover towers. Another new development is the Mills-Packards design, in which the acid chambers are shaped like truncated cones. Both of these designs are much more efficient than the old lead chamber plants. It had been thought that they might lead to something of a "come-back" for this process, which at one time seemed destined to obsolescence because of the contact process. During World War II, however, the contact process still further increased its lead. Of 819,190 tons of sulfuric acid (calculated as 100 per cent H_2SO_4) produced in October, 1944, only 285,278 tons (35 per cent) were made by the lead chamber process.

The Contact Process. It was only logical that cheaper and more efficient catalysts would be sought for the reaction between sulfur dioxide and molecular oxygen. In 1901 a German chemist, Knietsch, patented a process which proved successful. He found that if a mixture of air and sulfur dioxide is passed through a series of iron tubes which contain metallic platinum deposited on a supporting material such as asbestos or magnesium sulfate so that a large surface is exposed, the sulfur dioxide is efficiently converted to sulfur trioxide. That platinum is a catalyst for this reaction was discovered in 1831. The two factors which must be carefully controlled if the process is to be successful are the purity of the gases and the reaction temperature.

The temperature-conversion curve in Fig. 23.8 shows that the process is inefficient at both low and high temperatures. The reason for the low-temperature inefficiency is obvious. Why should the process be inefficient at high temperatures? SO_3 is formed with the evolution of heat, but heat also decomposes SO_3 into SO_2. The equation should indicate this equilibrium.

$$2\ SO_2 + O_2 \rightleftarrows 2\ SO_3 + 45{,}000 \text{ cal.}$$

If the temperature is too high, the equilibrium shifts from right to left and the yield is small.

The poisoning of catalysts is a "bugbear" in all catalytic processes. For example, arsenic and several other substances often found with sulfur poison platinum. If this happens, the catalytic mass must be removed and the platinum dissolved, purified, and redeposited by reduction upon a fresh catalytic support. Silica gel is also used as a support for platinum. Obviously the loss of platinum is small, for otherwise its use as a catalyst would not be successful.

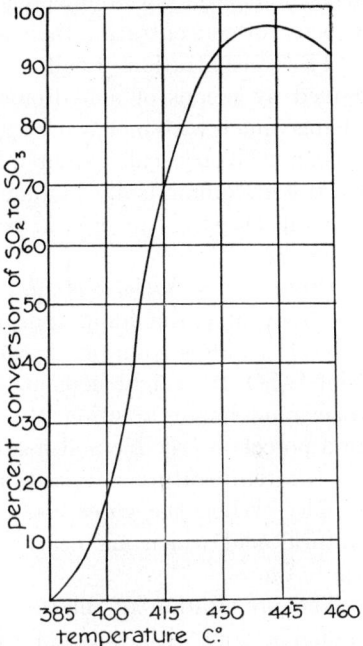

FIG. 23.8. Effect of change in temperature on percentage conversion of sulfur dioxide to sulfur trioxide, using Holmes chalky catalysts containing platinum.

Several other catalysts have been discovered which can be substituted for platinum. In the presence of Fe^{+++}, K^+, and Ca^{++} ions as promoters, vanadium pentoxide, V_2O_5, has been used successfully. Higher yields, less trouble with catalytic poisons, and lower cost are claimed for the vanadium catalysts. On the other hand, they have no salvage value and it is said that they cannot handle overloads as well. The relative merits of platinum and vanadium pentoxide catalysts have not yet been settled.

The SO_3 produced by the contact process, as has been mentioned, is absorbed in concentrated H_2SO_4. A chemical reaction results:

$$SO_3 + H_2SO_4 \rightleftarrows H_2S_2O_7$$

$H_2S_2O_7$ is called pyrosulfuric acid, but its solution in sulfuric acid is called "oleum," or "fuming sulfuric acid." The former name comes from its oily consistency, the latter from the fumes it produces when exposed to air. For some chemical purposes oleum containing 15 or 30 per cent SO_3 is used as such, but most of it is diluted to a strength of about 95 per cent H_2SO_4 (100 per cent H_2SO_4 still fumes slightly). Chamber acid or 77 per cent acid instead of plain water may be used for the dilution, thereby turning all the material into concentrated acid. Some lead chamber sulfuric acid plants have built adjacent contact plants for the express purpose of avoiding the expense of concentrating their product.

The concentration of sulfuric acid below 96 per cent can easily be determined by means of a hydrometer. (At 96 per cent the density ceases to change much with increasing concentration.) The hydrometer generally used has an arbitrary scale invented by Baumé, and specific gravities are usually expressed commercially in Baumé degrees (Bé.°). Thus chamber acid (62 per cent H_2SO_4) is 50° Bé., 77 per cent acid is 60° Bé., and concentrated acid is 66° Bé.

Properties of Sulfuric Acid. If a bottle of concentrated sulfuric acid is rotated gently, the liquid appears to be oily; hence the name "oil of vitriol" for the colorless solution. A solution of H_2SO_4 of s.g. 1.835 and 98.33 per cent H_2SO_4 by weight boils at 338° with little decomposition; thus it forms a constant-boiling solution. If a few drops of concentrated H_2SO_4 are placed in a porcelain crucible and heated, dense clouds of white mist soon appear. As the temperature is raised, H_2SO_4 decomposes into SO_3 and H_2O more rapidly. When the gases cool, they recombine, forming small droplets of sulfuric acid which are nearly colloidal in size, thus producing the dense white fumes.

The preparation of dilute from concentrated solutions of sulfuric acid should be done with *caution*, for heat is liberated when sulfuric acid is diluted with water. Water is lighter than the acid; hence when water is poured on the concentrated acid it floats on the surface and dilutes the boundary layer. So much heat may be liberated that the solution boils and the hot concentrated acid splatters in all directions. For this reason, *the concentrated acid should be poured carefully into the water.*

Sulfuric acid is a *strong acid*, an *oxidizing agent*, and a dehydrating agent. The acid forms several hydrates with the evolution of much heat. The monohydrate is hydronium bisulfate. The reaction goes to completion as fast as the necessary water is added.

$$H_2SO_4 + H_2O \longrightarrow H_3O^+ + HSO_4^-$$

or, commonly,
$$H_2SO_4 \longrightarrow H^+ + HSO_4^-$$

The second step in the dissociation of this dibasic acid depends upon the degree of dilution.

$$H^+ + HSO_4^- \rightleftharpoons 2\,H^+ + SO_4^{--}$$

In a 0.1 M solution of sulfuric acid the bisulfate ion is about 30 per cent dissociated, so the H^+ ion concentration is about 0.13 M. Both normal and acid salts such as Na_2SO_4 and $NaHSO_4$ are readily formed.

Sulfuric acid does not act upon poor reducing agents unless it is hot and concentrated. Then, however, it can dissolve copper and even silver. In such cases the sulfur is reduced only to the tetravalent state; SO_2 is produced.

$$\underline{Cu} + 2\ H_2SO_4 \longrightarrow \underline{CuSO_4} + \overline{SO_2} + 2\ H_2O$$

Sulfuric acid can be reduced to free sulfur and even H_2S providing it is in contact with a powerful reducing agent such as hydrogen iodide.

$$6\ HI + H_2SO_4 \longrightarrow 3\ I_2 + 4\ H_2O + \underline{S}$$

$$8\ HI + H_2SO_4 \longrightarrow 4\ I_2 + 4\ H_2O + \overline{H_2S}$$

The fact that sugar, wood, and other carbonaceous substances are quickly charred by sulfuric acid shows its dehydrating power. The effect of pouring some concentrated sulfuric acid on a 3-cm. layer of sugar in a beaker is shown in Fig. 23.9. Since concentrated sulfuric acid forms a constant-boiling solution, B.P. 338° C., we would not expect that water molecules would tend to escape rapidly from the surface of the solution at room temperature, but rather the reverse—that these molecules in the gaseous state above the solution would strike the surface and remain there because of the low vapor pressure of the solution. Concentrated H_2SO_4 is used as a drying agent, beakers of it being frequently placed inside analytical balance cases to maintain a dry atmosphere. Air bubbled through concentrated H_2SO_4 comes out nearly moisture-free. (The last traces of moisture in air can be removed by P_2O_5, which is an even better drying agent than H_2SO_4, or by means of liquid air traps to freeze out the water.)

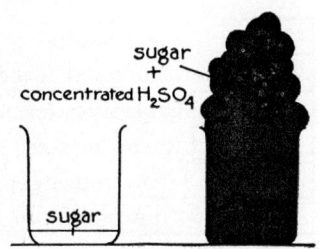

FIG. 23.9. Sulfuric acid dehydrates sugar.

Uses of Sulfuric Acid. Because of its high boiling point, H_2SO_4 is used to displace low-boiling acids from their salts. Tons of HCl are made by heating salt and sulfuric acid together.

$$NaCl + H_2SO_4 \xrightarrow{\Delta} NaHSO_4 + \overline{HCl}$$

Most of the lead chamber acid is used in rendering phosphate rock soluble and thus available as a fertilizer. In doing this it acts as an acid, adding protons to the PO_4^{---} ion of $Ca_3(PO_4)_2$; $Ca(H_2PO_4)_2$ is soluble. Another important use of H_2SO_4 as an acid is in the "pickling" of iron and steel. Before the metal can be coated with tin (for tin cans, etc.) or galvanized with zinc (for buckets, corrugated roofing, wire, etc.) the surface must be freed of the "scale" of iron oxide that forms while the white-hot billets are being rolled. Sulfuric acid does this cheaply, although unfortunately 2 or 3 per cent of the iron itself is also dissolved.

$$\underline{Fe} + \underline{Fe_3O_4} + 4\ H^+ + 4\ HSO_4^- \longrightarrow 4\ Fe^{++} + 4\ SO_4^{--} + 4\ H_2O$$

The petroleum industry uses a large amount of sulfuric acid as an oxidizing agent to remove certain undesirable compounds from petroleum (page 683). Organic chemical industries use H_2SO_4 as a dehydrating agent to combine with the water set free in a type of reaction called nitration (page 705), which is fundamental in the production of celluloid, dyes, drugs, and explosives. Nitration is a reversible reaction which would not otherwise go to completion. In the similar reactions of sulfonation and sulfation, used in making synthetic detergents (page 288), H_2SO_4 is used not only as one of the main reactants but as a dehydrating agent, as in nitrations, to combine with the water which is formed. After having been used for such a purpose, the spent acid can be reconcentrated and used again. Fig. 23.10 shows how sulfuric acid touches practically every phase of modern industrial civilization.

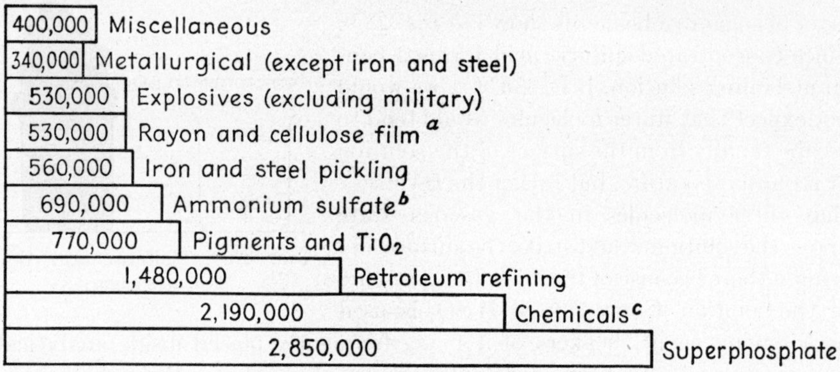

Amount	Use
400,000	Miscellaneous
340,000	Metallurgical (except iron and steel)
530,000	Explosives (excluding military)
530,000	Rayon and cellulose film [a]
560,000	Iron and steel pickling
690,000	Ammonium sulfate [b]
770,000	Pigments and TiO_2
1,480,000	Petroleum refining
2,190,000	Chemicals [c]
2,850,000	Superphosphate

Fig. 23.10. Sulfuric acid consumed in the United States (1944) in short tons of 100 per cent H_2SO_4. Total, 10,850,000 tons.

[a] The acid is used in the regenerating bath to neutralize bases used in dissolving the cellulose.
[b] See page 414.
[c] Including H_3PO_4, $Al_2(SO_4)_3$, HF, HNO_3, HCl, $CuSO_4$, alcohol, isopropyl alcohol, intermediates, and dyes.

Salts of Sulfuric Acid. Several of the sulfates are known by common names, such as:

Alum, $KAl(SO_4)_2 \cdot 12\ H_2O$
Barytes ⎫
Blanc-fixe ⎬ $BaSO_4$
Fixed white ⎭
Blue vitriol, $CuSO_4 \cdot 5\ H_2O$

Copperas ⎫ $FeSO_4 \cdot 7\ H_2O$
Green vitriol ⎭
Epsom salt, $MgSO_4 \cdot 7\ H_2O$
Glauber's salt, $Na_2SO_4 \cdot 10\ H_2O$
Gypsum, $CaSO_4 \cdot 2\ H_2O$
Plaster of Paris, $(CaSO_4)_2 \cdot H_2O$

Alums are important in the dyeing of cloth, and aluminum sulfate is used as a coagulant in water purification. $BaSO_4$ is used as a paint pigment. $CuSO_4$ is a mild disinfectant and a specific agent for the destruction of algae in lakes and reservoirs. $FeSO_4$ is chlorinated and used as a coagulant in water purification. Both Epsom salt and Glauber's salt are used medicinally, and the latter is also used in mordanting cloth. Natural gypsum, if carefully heated, loses three quarters of its water; it is then known as plaster of Paris and is widely used in the making of casts and molds and in the preparation of plaster and gypsum wallboard.

$$2 \; CaSO_4 \cdot 2 \; H_2O \longrightarrow (CaSO_4)_2 \cdot H_2O + 3 \; H_2O$$

Thiosulfuric acid is the sulfur acid next in importance to sulfuric acid. The sodium salt of this acid, $Na_2S_2O_3$, is called sodium thiosulfate and is also known as "photographers' hypo."[5] Two facts must be kept in mind if the structural formula of $Na_2S_2O_3$ is to be written correctly. Sodium sulfite is easily oxidized with oxygen to form sodium sulfate. Since sulfur is just below oxygen and in the same group in the periodic table, perhaps it can be substituted for oxygen in this reaction:

$$Na_2SO_3 + O \longrightarrow Na_2SO_4$$
$$Na_2SO_3 + S \longrightarrow Na_2S_2O_3$$

This compound forms when this substitution is made, and its formula is:

$$2 \; Na^+ + \;\; \ddot{:}\ddot{O}\ddot{:} \atop {:\ddot{O}:\ddot{S}:\ddot{S}: \atop :\ddot{O}:}$$

When an atom of sulfur has thus taken the place of an atom of oxygen, the name of the new compound is formed by adding the prefix *thio-* (from the Greek word for sulfur) to the name of the old one. $Na_2S_2O_3$ is prepared commercially by neutralizing a solution of sulfurous acid with sodium carbonate to produce sodium sulfite, and by boiling this sulfite with sulfur. When this concentrated solution is cooled, $Na_2S_2O_3 \cdot 5 \; H_2O$ separates in colorless monoclinic crystals.

$$H_2O + SO_2 \longrightarrow H_2SO_3$$
$$H_2SO_3 + 2 \; Na^+ + CO_3^{--} \longrightarrow 2 \; Na^+ + SO_3^{--} + \overline{CO_2} + H_2O$$
$$2 \; Na^+ + SO_3^{--} + \underline{S} \longrightarrow 2 \; Na^+ + S_2O_3^{--}$$

A water solution of hypo exposed to the air soon becomes milky because the carbon dioxide of the air dissolves in the solution and produces carbonic acid which is sufficiently strong to liberate thiosulfuric acid. This acid then decomposes, producing sulfurous acid and free sulfur (milk of sulfur). These reactions are indicated by the following equilibria:

$$2 \; Na^+ + S_2O_3^{--} + H_2CO_3 \rightleftarrows 2 \; Na^+ + CO_3^{--} + H_2S_2O_3$$
$$\rightleftarrows H_2SO_3 + S$$
$$\rightleftarrows H^+ + HSO_3$$

[5] When the art of photography was discovered over a century ago, sodium thiosulfate was thought to be sodium hyposulfite. (The sulfur content of half-dehydrated $Na_2S_2O_3 \cdot 5 \; H_2O$ is about that calculated for the expected hyposulfite, Na_2SO_2.) Photographers still call it that.

Photographers like to have alum in the "fixing bath" because $Al(H_2O)_6^{+++}$ hardens the gelatin; but that ion is also an acid. How, then, can the decomposition of the hypo be prevented? Will a high concentration of the HSO_3^- ion serve as a "preservative"? The earlier discussion of the common ion effect gives an affirmative answer. For the use of hypo in photography, see page 587.

Sodium thiosulfate is a good reducing agent and will convert the halogens into halide ions. The concentration of iodine in iodine solutions is frequently determined by titrating the solution with standard $Na_2S_2O_3$; the end point is reached when the brown color disappears. The colorless salt, $Na_2S_4O_6$, called sodium tetrathionate, is formed when $Na_2S_2O_3$ is oxidized with a halogen.

$$I_2 + 4\ Na^+ + 2\ S_2O_3^{--} \longrightarrow 4\ Na^+ + 2\ I^- + S_4O_6^{--}$$

The structural formula for the tetrathionate ion is:

$$\begin{array}{ccc} :\!\ddot{O}\!: & :\!\ddot{O}\!: & \\ :\!\ddot{O}\!:\!S\!:\!S\!:\!S\!:\!\ddot{O}\!: & & \\ :\!\ddot{O}\!: & :\!\ddot{O}\!: & \end{array}^{--}$$

The fact that chlorine is used as a bleaching agent indicates that hypo could be used as an "antichlor." In bleaching, it is often necessary to remove the excess bleaching agent quickly so that the fabric will not be weakened by oxidation with the halogen; dipping the fabric into a solution of hypo as soon as bleaching is completed averts this danger. At times water supplies must be overchlorinated, and here again hypo is used to remove the excess chlorine. Hypo has a limited use in dissolving insoluble silver halides from silver ores.

$$\underline{AgCl} + 2\ Na^+ + S_2O_3^{--} \longrightarrow 2\ Na^+ + Cl^- + AgS_2O_3^-$$

In calculating the strength of $Na_2S_2O_3$ when it is used as a reducing agent, it should be noted that a 1-normal solution of an oxidizing or reducing agent is capable of changing the equivalent of 1 gram-ion of hydrogen to hydrogen gas, or vice versa. Thus in the reaction between iodine and sodium thiosulfate a normal solution of iodine contains 1 atomic weight of iodine per liter, and a normal solution of $Na_2S_2O_3$ contains 1 molecular weight per liter.

$$I_2 \backsimeq 2\ Na_2S_2O_3 \backsimeq O \backsimeq 2\ H$$

A normal solution of $KMnO_4$ used as an oxidizing agent would be $\dfrac{KMnO_4}{5}$ g. per liter, if the manganese changes from Mn^{+7} to Mn^{++}. For $K_2Cr_2O_7$ solutions in which the $Cr^{+6} \longrightarrow Cr^{+3}$, the normality of the solution as an oxidizing agent is $\dfrac{K_2Cr_2O_7}{6}$ g. per liter. What weight of KIO_3 should be present per liter if 1-normal KIO_3 is to be used as an oxidizing agent and the iodine changes in valence from I^{+5} to $I°$?

Other Sulfur Acids

Although there are many other sulfur acids, most of them are of purely academic interest and therefore only the two most important—peroxydisulfuric acid and pyrosulfuric acid—will be mentioned briefly.

Peroxydisulfuric acid, $H_2S_2O_8$, and its salts are powerful oxidizing agents. The acid is formed during the electrolysis of concentrated sulfuric acid. The electrolysis cell must be kept cold and a diaphragm must be used to keep the hydrogen gas produced at the cathode from coming in contact with the peroxydisulfuric acid produced at the anode. The acid is a white solid at room temperature.

$$2 H^+ + 2\ominus \xrightarrow{\triangle} H_2 \text{ (cathode)}$$

$$2 HSO_4^- - 2\ominus \xrightarrow{\triangle} H_2S_2O_8 \text{ (anode)}$$

Electrolysis of $KHSO_4$ yields $K_2S_2O_8$, potassium peroxydisulfate; and electrolysis of cold $(NH_4)HSO_4$ yields $(NH_4)_2S_2O_8$, ammonium peroxydisulfate. Both of these are powerful oxidizing agents. An acid solution of the manganous ion to which they are added is oxidized to the permanganate ion, MnO_4^-.

$$10 K^+ + 5 S_2O_8^{--} + 2 Mn^{++} + 2 SO_4^{--} + 8 H_2O \longrightarrow$$
$$10 K^+ + 4 H^+ + 12 HSO_4^- + 2 MnO_4^-$$

The relation of peroxydisulfuric acid and the peroxydisulfates to hydrogen peroxide was discussed on pages 133–134. This discussion should be reviewed carefully at this point.

Pyrosulfuric acid, $H_2S_2O_7$, was mentioned in connection with the contact process for sulfuric acid. Its properties are mainly those of sulfuric acid, intensified. Its name derives from the early method of forming pyrosulfates by the thermal decomposition of bisulfates.

True hyposulfurous acid, H_2SO_2, is too unstable or too reactive to exist, although organic derivatives of it (in which the H is replaced by hydrocarbon radicals) are stable. However, a commercially important substance which is related to it, and is equally related to sulfurous acid, is produced by reducing sodium bisulfite with zinc.

$$H_2SO_3 + 2\,Na^+ + 2\,HSO_3^- + \underline{Zn} \longrightarrow \underline{ZnSO_3} + 2\,Na^+ + S_2O_4^{--} + 2\,H_2O$$

With equal inaccuracy, the product in solution is known as either "sodium hyposulfite" or "sodium hydrosulfite." The formula of the anion is:

$$\overset{..}{\underset{..}{:O:}}\quad \overset{..}{\underset{..}{:O:}}{}^{--}$$
$$:\!\overset{..}{\underset{..}{O}}\!:\!\overset{..}{\underset{..}{S}}\!:\!\overset{..}{\underset{..}{O}}\!:\!\overset{..}{\underset{..}{S}}\!:$$

In computing oxidation numbers it is assumed that oxygen owns all the electrons that it shares; thus it can be seen that the first sulfur atom, which is sharing all but two electrons of the octet with oxygen, has an oxidation number of +4. Only the second is true hyposulfite sulfur. The substance is a powerful reducing agent; it even liberates H_2 from water, although slowly. It is used in dyeing.

When the molecules of the very stable and insoluble *vat dyes* are electronated by means of hydrosulfite, they are converted into colorless, soluble substances with which cloth can easily be impregnated. The electrons are then taken back by means of some oxidizing agent (chlorous acid and hydrogen peroxide are two good ones for the purpose) and the original dye is reformed within the fibers of the cloth and cannot be washed away. The original vat dye, indigo, was first found in a plant of that name. It was reduced by bacterial fermentation in a vat containing a decoction of the plant, and the impregnated cloth was then hung in the air for a long time while the action of atmospheric oxygen gradually developed the blue color.

SELENIUM AND TELLURIUM

Selenium and tellurium are in the same subgroup of the periodic table as sulfur, selenium just below sulfur and tellurium below selenium. From this it should follow that many of their properties are similar to those of sulfur. That this is true is shown by the compounds listed in Table 23.4, for they show the same valence changes. However, tellurium is the most metallic of the three. Salts of the corresponding acids listed in this table are known.

TABLE 23.4. COMPOUNDS OF SULFUR, SELENIUM, AND TELLURIUM

H_2S, hydrogen sulfide	H_2Se, hydrogen selenide	H_2Te, hydrogen telluride
SO_2, sulfur dioxide	SeO_2, selenium dioxide	TeO_2, tellurium dioxide
H_2SO_3, sulfurous acid	H_2SeO_3, selenous acid	H_2TeO_3, tellurous acid
SO_3, sulfur trioxide	SeO_3, (unknown)	TeO_3, tellurium trioxide
H_2SO_4, sulfuric acid	H_2SeO_4, selenic acid	He_2TeO_4, telluric acid

Selenium and tellurium were almost laboratory curiosities thirty years ago, but have many uses today.

Selenium

In 1817 Berzelius discovered selenium in the flue dust of pyrites burners in a sulfuric acid plant. This element is widely distributed in the earth's crust and is more abundant than silver or platinum, but the amount in any one place is small. There are many natural metallic selenides, copper selenide, Cu_2Se, being typical. The most important sources of selenium in this country are as a by-product in the copper industry (the flue dust contains it) and in association with the uranium and radium ores of the high plateaus of Colorado and Utah; it is also present in the water of the Colorado River. Selenium compounds are extremely toxic; they weaken the heart and paralyze the central nervous system. In some parts of South Dakota and Wyoming, where the rainfall is apparently insufficient to leach out the selenium compounds, it occurs in the soil in sufficient quantity to be toxic to plant growth. Although all plants do not take up selenium to the same extent, the absorption of selenium compounds has necessitated the withdrawal of some 50,000 acres of land from grazing because of the loss of livestock which have fed on the plants in this soil.

Selenium is extracted from the anodic mud of electrolytic copper refineries. The selenium-bearing material is leached with hydrochloric acid and a strong oxidizing agent such as a chlorate, and is then precipitated as a red amorphous powder by means of the reducing agent, sulfur dioxide.

$$\underline{SeO_2} + H_2SO_3 \longrightarrow \underline{Se} + H^+ + HSO_4^-$$

(This equation shows that selenium dioxide can also be an oxidizing agent.) On drying, the red selenium changes to a black form which can be melted under a sodium nitrate flux and cast into sticks or cakes. It melts at 217° C. and boils at about 688° C.

Hydrogen selenide has many properties similar to those of hydrogen sulfide. It has the odor of rotten horse-radish.

Selenium and its compounds are widely used commercially. It gives glass a rose-red tint which neutralizes the green tint produced by ferrous iron. This use was discovered during the First World War, when our Brazilian supply of the manganese dioxide hitherto used for this purpose was cut off by the lack of ships. Scarlet-red signal glass, glazes, and enamels contain selenium, the color depending upon the degree of dispersion of the selenium. Insulated electric wires are made flame-proof by means of selenium. In the colloidal form, selenium is a germicide, fungicide, and insecticide; research in this field is still in progress. That selenium may act as a negative catalyst for oxidation reactions is shown by the patents granted on its use to prevent the oxidation of lubricating oil in the crankcases of automobiles. Selenium photoelectric cells are based on its interesting property of conducting electricity better when exposed to light. Its presence in rubber increases resistance to abrasion. Selenium is used in manufacturing one type of stainless steel, in making free-cutting brass, and for coating light magnesium alloys to make them resistant to the corrosive action of salt-water spray. In 1909 selenium sold for $3.00 a pound, and less than 10 tons were produced in this country. Over 100 tons were produced in 1938, and the price had dropped to about $1.75 per pound.

Tellurium

Tellurium is metallic in appearance but non-metallic in properties. It was discovered in a gold ore by an Austrian, Franz Müller, in 1782. Believing that the substance was a peculiar form of antimony, he had a chemist friend, Bergman, check his work; both men agreed that it was not antimony. Tellurium melts at 452° C. and boils at 1390° C. Tellurium is obtained as a by-product in the refining of nickel-copper ores, and from the Cottrell precipitator dust from superphosphate plants in Russia. The element is a poorer conductor of electricity than any other metal.

Of the many tellurides in nature, sylvanite, $(AuAg)Te_2$, is one of the most important. Tellurium dioxide is acidic. Tellurites hydrolyze readily with the precipitation of TeO_2. H_2Te is unstable and has a very repulsive odor. Tellurium compounds are less easily reduced than those of selenium; they are not reduced by sulfur dioxide with the liberation of tellurium. In its +6 oxidation state, tellurium, owing to the large size of its valence layer, displays a covalence of 6. Thus simple tellurate ions do not exist. Instead, each one draws an oxygen from each of two other tellurate ions into its valence layer, and these in turn do likewise until the ion is indefinitely large. As a result, sodium tellurate does not really dissolve in water; it forms only colloidal dispersions. The formula is really $(Na_2TeO_4)_x$.

Tellurium is used in rectifiers of electric current and in free-machining steels. Electroplated on silver, it gives a black finish. Blue, brown, and red colored glass are made with it. Lead-tellurium alloys (0.6 of 1 per cent Te) are both extremely resistant to corrosion and quite flexible. Many investigations have been made regarding the bactericidal properties of tellurium compounds. About 10 tons of the element are produced per year in the United States at a cost of $2.00 per pound. Sixty tons could be produced annually with the present equipment if new markets could be found.

QUESTIONS AND PROBLEMS

1. Write the formulas for compounds of sulfur to indicate the various valences of sulfur. Start with sulfur and show by equations how each of these can be formed.
2. Outline briefly sulfur mining in the United States.

SULFUR, SELENIUM, AND TELLURIUM 391

3. Trace the changes in sulfur with change in temperature.
4. Make a list of the uses of sulfur and sulfur compounds in the home.
5. Compare the value of H_2S, H_2SO_3, and H_2SO_4 as oxidizing, reducing, and dehydrating agents. Which is the strongest acid?
6. An unknown contains Cd^{++}, Zn^{++}, and Mg^{++}; how would you separate these three? If it contains Ag^+, Cu^{++}, Fe^{+++}, Zn^{++}, Ba^{++}, and Na^+, how would you separate them?
7. Show by two equations that polysulfides are oxidizing agents.
8. List some properties of CS_2, P_4S_3, and S_2Cl_2.
9. How many tons of 98 per cent pure sulfur are required to produce 30 tons of 50° Bé. H_2SO_4?
10. Compare the action of dilute and concentrated H_2SO_4 on copper.
11. What property of SO_2 makes it valuable as a refrigerant?
12. What is nitrosylsulfuric acid?
13. Outline two important processes for the manufacture of sulfuric acid.
14. List six sulfates and give a commercial use of each one.
15. How is sodium thiosulfate prepared? List some important uses of it.
16. Why is the manufacture of H_2SO_4 often referred to as a barometer of industry?
17. How are selenium and tellurium prepared commercially? List their uses. Compare their properties with those of sulfur.
18. What volume of N/10 H_2S can be produced from 1 g. of sulfur? What weight of CuS can be obtained by adding the above H_2S solution to 999 ml. of 2.04 N copper sulfate solution?
19. What volumes of air and of SO_2 would be required (S.T.P.) to produce 100 l. of 18 N H_2SO_4 by the contact process?
20. What weight of sulfur is required to prepare 1 lb. of $Na_2S_2O_3 \cdot 5\ H_2O$?
21. Apply Le Chatelier's Principle to the reactions:

$$SO_2 + O_2 \longrightarrow$$
and $$H_2S + SO_2 \longrightarrow$$

22. What weight of FeS should be placed in a Kipp generator if 72 students in the laboratory each use 311 ml. of H_2S (S.T.P.) in their experiments?
23. Compare the rates of diffusion of H_2S and SO_2.
24. Which of the following burn readily: P_4S_3, CS_2, H_2S, SO_2, and SO_3?
25. What volume of H_2S (S.T.P.) is required to reduce 5 mols of iodine?
26. If the only solution of H_2SO_4 in the laboratory was 0.1 normal, would you rather make a 0.01 normal or a 1.0 normal solution of H_2SO_4 from it? Why?
27. If an unknown is one of the following, how could you identify it? (Each is available as a clear solution.) HIO_3, $Na_2S_2O_3$, $Na_2S_4O_6$, Na_2S, $CaOCl_2$.
28. With sulfur as one raw material, show by equations how the following can be made: H_2S, H_2SO_3, H_2SO_4, Na_2SO_3, $H_2S_2O_8$, $Na_2S_2O_3$, $Na_2S_4O_6$, $CuSO_4$, $(C_2H_5Cl)_2S$, and S_2Cl_2.
29. If you were asked to identify a white salt known to be Na_2SO_4, Na_2SO_3, Na_2S, $Na_2S_2O_3$, or $Na_2S_4O_6$, what procedure would you use? What would you expect to happen if you add HCl? A solution of barium chloride?

REFERENCES

Books

Sulfuric acid, sulfur dioxide, raw materials, the chamber process, the contact process, and concentration of acid are covered in the four volumes by Lunge and Cumming, revised by Wyld, Parker, and Miles. These books were published by Gurney and Jackson, London, 1924–1925.

Articles

Sulfur

"Sulfur." Cunningham, W. A. *J. Chem. Ed.* **12**, 17–23, 83–87, 120–124 (1935).
"Sulfur Mining." Lundy, W. T. *Chem. and Met. Eng.* **41**, 116–120 (1934).
"Toxic Property of Sulfur." Williams, R. C., and Young, H. C. *Ind. and Eng. Chem.* **21**, 359–362 (1929).
"Perkin Medal Award to Herman Frasch." *Ind. and Eng. Chem.* **4**, 131–147 (1912).
"Poisonous Nature of Selenium in Soil." Franke, K. W., and Painter, E. P. *Ind. and Eng. Chem.* **29**, 591–598 (1937).
"Sulfur Industry." Mason, D. B. *Ind. and Eng. Chem.* **30**, 740 (1938).
"Sulfur Mining." Butterworth, C. F., and Schwab, J. W. *Ind. and Eng. Chem.* **30**, 746 (1938).
"Discovery of Tellurium and Selenium." Weeks, M. E. *J. Chem. Ed.* **9**, 474–485 (1932).
"Hydrogen Sulfide as a Poison." Yant, W. P., and Sayers, R. R. *J. Chem. Ed.* **4**, 613–619 (1927).
"Hydrogen Sulfide Precipitation." Edmonds, S. M., and Curtman, L. J. *J. Chem. Ed.* **11**, 305–307 (1934).
"Notes on Hydrogen Sulfide Poisoning." Allyn, L. B. *Ind. and Eng. Chem.* **23**, 234 (1931).

Sulfur Dioxide

"Sulfur Dioxide as a Refrigerant." Johnston, C. E. *Ind. and Eng. Chem.* **24**, 626–630 (1932).
"Anhydrous Liquid Sulfur Dioxide." Hitchcock, L. B., and Scribner, A. K. *Ind. and Eng. Chem.* **23**, 743-749 (1931).
"The Common Refrigerants." Beamensderfer, J. S. *Ind. and Eng. Chem.* **27**, 1027–1030 (1935).

Sulfuric Acid

"Sulfuric Acid, Pressure Synthesis of H_2SO_4 Manufacture." Berl, E. *Chem. and Met. Eng.* **41**, 571–575 (1934).
"New Contact Acid Plant." Dinsmoor, D. S. *Chem. and Met. Eng.* **38**, 330–333 (1931).
"Developments in H_2SO_4 Manufacture." Spangler, S. F. *Ind. and Eng. Chem.* **21**, 417–421 (1929).

"Contact Process of Sulfuric Acid Manufacture." Chase, M. F., and Pierce, F. E. *Ind. and Eng. Chem.* **14,** 498–503 (1922).

"New Catalyst for Sulfuric Acid." Scott, W. W., and Layfield, E. B. *Ind. and Eng. Chem.* **23,** 617–620 (1931).

"Vanadium Catalysts." Elder, A. L., and Holmes, H. N. *Ind. and Eng. Chem.* **22,** 471–473 (1930).

» 24 «

NITROGEN AND ITS COMPOUNDS[1]

Nitrogen is the first element in Group V. (The others will be discussed in succeeding chapters.) Although nitrogen has only five valence electrons, it is still, owing to its small size, a typical, strongly electrophilic non-metal. It is able to form double, triple, and hydrogen bonds. It is a key element both in the food which is essential to life and in the explosives which destroy life.

Preparation of Nitrogen

Fairly pure nitrogen can be easily prepared by passing dry air over hot copper, for the oxygen reacts with copper to form CuO and leaves nitrogen with only traces of impurities. Phosphorus burned in air combines with oxygen to form phosphorus pentoxide; since this is very soluble in water it can be separated from the residual gas. The fact that oxygen is used so widely commercially—in the liquid air industry, for example—makes nitrogen also available as a by-product. A demand for both these gases makes each one less expensive to the consumer.

If *pure* nitrogen is desired, neither copper nor phosphorus will be used. On being heated, ammonium nitrite, NH_4NO_2, decomposes into nitrogen and water. Since ammonium nitrite is extremely unstable, it is more common to use the more stable sodium nitrite and ammonium chloride. If these two salts are added to water and the solution is warmed gently, pure nitrogen gas is produced.

$$Na^+ + NO_2^- + NH_4^+ + Cl^- \longrightarrow Na^+ + Cl^- + 2\ H_2O + \overline{N_2}$$

Ammonia gas can be oxidized to nitrogen by being passed through a hot tube filled with copper oxide. The CuO must be regenerated as soon as all

[1] The discovery of nitrogen and its significance in the atmosphere were discussed in chap. 19.

of it has been reduced; hence this process is not continuous. The equation for this reaction is:

$$2\ \overline{NH_3} + 3\ \underline{CuO} \longrightarrow 3\ \underline{Cu} + 3\ \overline{H_2O} + \overline{N_2}$$

The advantage in using CuO as the oxidizing agent is that the oxidation stops with the formation of nitrogen gas.

If there is no objection to the presence of hydrogen as well, nitrogen may be obtained by the catalytic decomposition of ammonia at moderately high temperature.

$$2\ \overline{NH_3} \xrightarrow{\Delta} 3\ \overline{H_2} + \overline{N_2}$$

This method is cheaper for an industrial user than buying nitrogen in cylinders because of the cost of shipping the heavy steel cylinders needed for a gas at high pressure. Ammonia is easily liquefied; hence an ammonia cylinder has light walls and holds several times as much nitrogen per liter volume. Chlorine oxidizes ammonia to nitrogen and hydrogen chloride.

$$\overline{2\ NH_3} + \overline{3\ Cl_2} \longrightarrow \overline{6\ HCl} + \overline{N_2}$$

Phosphorus reduces nitric oxide to nitrogen.

$$10\ \overline{NO} + 4\ \underline{P} \longrightarrow 2\ \underline{P_2O_5} + 5\ \overline{N_2}$$

Properties of Nitrogen

Does nitrogen have any color, odor, or taste? Is it more or less soluble in water than oxygen? (See page 120.) It freezes to a white solid at $-210°$ C.

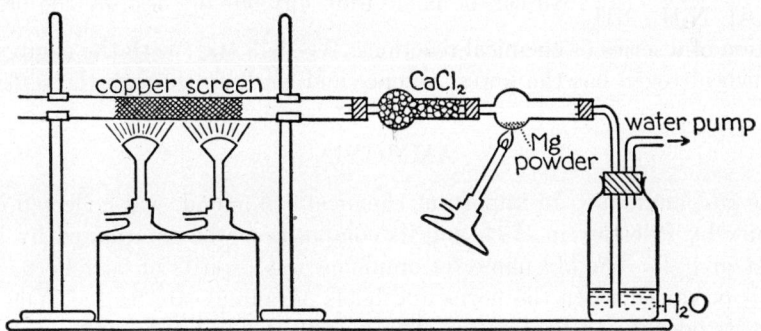

FIG. 24.1. Preparation of nitrogen and magnesium nitride.

and boils at $-196°$ C. Its presence in the atmosphere indicates that its most important chemical property is its inertness. As in the case of oxygen, this is due to the multiple bonding of the N_2 molecule. Its electronic structure is:

$$:N:::N:$$

This triple bond gives the nitrogen molecule unusual stability (i.e., a very high energy of activation). Chemists carried on innumerable experiments before they found satisfactory methods of making it combine with other elements. The commercial methods, which will be discussed under nitrogen fixation, include the direct union of nitrogen with hydrogen and with oxygen. If *heated sufficiently*, nitrogen combines readily with the non-metals, boron and silicon, and with all the metals near the top of the E.C.S. Many metals form nitrides. The nitride ion, N^{---}, is an extremely strong base and reacts with water to form ammonia and the hydroxide ion.

$$\underline{Mg_3N_2} + 6\ H_2O \longrightarrow 3\ \underline{Mg(OH)_2} + 2\ \overline{NH_3}$$

Calcium carbide, CaC_2, combines with nitrogen in the electric furnace to form calcium cyanamide (page 415).

Valences of Nitrogen and Its Compounds

As we saw earlier, the outer electron shell has a maximum of eight electrons, and any outer shell which is incomplete can either lose all its electrons or take on sufficient to make a total of eight; hence the maximum valence change of any element is eight. These changes were brought out in earlier chapters in connection with the halogens and sulfur $\left(\begin{smallmatrix}+7 & -1\\ HClO_4 & HCl\end{smallmatrix}\right)$, $\left(\begin{smallmatrix}+6 & -2\\ H_2SO_4 & H_2S\end{smallmatrix}\right)$. Nitrogen also shows this same valence change $\left(\begin{smallmatrix}-3 & +5\\ NH_3 & HNO_3\end{smallmatrix}\right)$. One of the most interesting properties of nitrogen is the fact that it has *so many different valences* $\begin{smallmatrix}+5 & +4 & +3 & +2 & +1 & 0\\ N_2O_5, & NO_2, & N_2O_3, & NO, & N_2O, & N_2,\\ -1 & -2 & -3 &&&\\ NH_2OH, & N_2H_4, & NH_3 &&&\end{smallmatrix}$. All can be made from any one of these by the proper selection of a series of chemical reactions. We shall start with the compound in which nitrogen has the lowest valence and work up through the series.

AMMONIA

The gas, ammonia, an important chemical compound, was collected over mercury by Priestley in 1774, and its composition was determined by Berthollet in 1785. The old name for ammonia was "spirits of hartshorn," for NH_3 is produced when the horns and hoofs of animals are heated. You can detect its odor if you heat pieces of fingernail in a test tube. NH_3 is widely distributed in nature, for nitrogen is a constituent of plant and animal life. The reduction of nitrogen compounds and the anaerobic decomposition of plant and animal tissue result in the formation of ammonia. Barnyard manure, rich in ammonia, is used as a fertilizer. Urea, a normal constituent of the urine, hydrolyzes to form ammonia.[2]

[2] In formulas, organic chemists represent a covalent bond by a line. Bonds to H are often omitted. Unshared electron pairs are not shown at all.

NITROGEN AND ITS COMPOUNDS

$$\begin{array}{c} NH_2 \\ | \\ C{=}O \\ | \\ NH_2 \end{array} + \begin{array}{c} H \\ | \\ O \\ | \\ H \end{array} \longrightarrow CO_2 + 2\,NH_3$$

If coal, which is partially stabilized organic matter, is further decomposed by heat, ammonia is one of the many compounds liberated. Ammonia, combined with carbonic acid in the form of ammonium bicarbonate, is found to some extent in nearly all water supplies.

$$\overline{NH_3} + \overline{CO_2} + H_2O \rightleftarrows NH_4^+ + HCO_3^-$$

Natural deposits of ammonium salts are rare, although there are deposits of ammonium nitrate, NH_4NO_3, in Tennessee; there are also several natural very complex insoluble ammonium salts. *Nearly all the simple ammonium salts are water-soluble.*

Ammonia is usually prepared in the laboratory either by the hydrolysis of nitrides or by the reaction between non-volatile bases and ammonium salts.

$$NH_4^+ + Cl^- + Na^+ + OH^-$$
$$\longrightarrow Na^+ + Cl^- + H_2O + \overline{NH_3}$$

The commercial methods of preparing NH_3 will be discussed in the section on nitrogen fixation.

Physical Properties of Ammonia

Ammonia gas is colorless and has a choking pungent odor. Since the molecular weight of the gas is only 17, it is about one-half as heavy as air and must be collected in inverted bottles. Ammonia gas is a satisfactory refrigerant because it can be liquefied at a relatively high temperature and low pressure. Its critical pressure is 112.3 atm. and its critical temperature is 132° C. Liquid ammonia

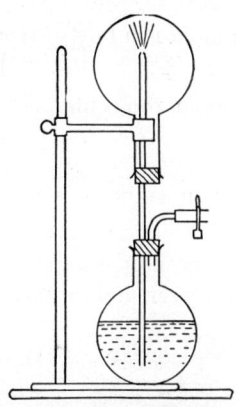

FIG. 24.2. Ammonia fountain.
Fill the upper flask with dry ammonia gas and quickly insert the 1-hole stopper. Add 5 drops of phenolphthalein to the water in the lower flask so that the solution which will form in the upper flask will be visible more easily. Blow into the side arm to force a little water into the upper flask. As the ammonia dissolves in water, more water rises into the upper flask. What other gases could be substituted for ammonia?

vaporizes with the sorption of 297 calories of heat per gram; in other words, changing a small volume of liquid to gas produces a great cooling effect. What is the H_v for water? At a temperature of 26° C., liquid ammonia exerts a pressure of only 10.2 atm.; thus the compressor unit does not operate at a high pressure. Ammonia is very soluble in water. At 0°,

1176 ml. of NH₃ dissolve in 1 cc. of H₂O; at 20°, 702 ml. dissolve per cc. of H₂O. (See page 179 for the solubility of gases in liquids.) An interesting demonstration of its solubility in water is the ammonia fountain shown in Fig. 24.2.

Chemical Properties of Ammonia

Ammonia gas warns us of its presence so quickly that we usually do not think of it as being poisonous. However, experiments show that for equal concentrations in the atmosphere it ranks *between carbon monoxide and benzene* in toxicity; it is only slightly less poisonous than carbon monoxide.

The following equilibria exist in a water solution containing ammonia:

$$NH_3 + H_2O \rightleftarrows NH_4OH \rightleftarrows NH_4^+ + OH^-$$

Ammonia is a fairly strong base. In other words, the lone electron pair on an ammonia molecule, H:N̈:, with H above and below, readily accepts a proton. But when the NH₃ molecule collides with a water molecule, H:N:H:Ö:, with H's below, the proton which that lone pair accepts refuses to relinquish the electron pair it was sharing with oxygen and forms a hydrogen bond (page 191). The resulting ammonium hydroxide molecule, with the electronic structure just shown, is not appreciably basic, but is in equilibrium with enough NH₃ molecules and OH⁻ ions so that the solution is moderately basic (page 237). The addition of an ammonium salt readily lowers the pH of this solution, through the common ion effect, to a point at which it will no longer turn phenolphthalein pink or precipitate Mg(OH)₂ from a solution of a magnesium salt.

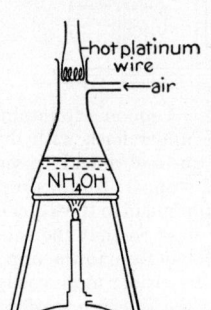

FIG. 24.3. Catalytic oxidation of ammonia.

That ammonia is a *reducing agent* was illustrated (page 395) in the reaction between CuO and NH₃. Some metals react with ammonia to form nitrides. The surface of steel can be hardened by heating it in the presence of NH₃; iron nitride, Fe₂N, is formed.

If concentrated HCl is placed on one watch glass and concentrated NH₄OH on another and air is blown across them, a dense white smoke of ammonium chloride forms. NH₄Cl is easily decomposed by heat into NH₃ and HCl. This salt, used as a smoke screen, is sometimes decomposed by the exhaust heat from airplane motors; as the NH₃ and HCl recombine, a white smoke is formed. Janitors in chemistry buildings always complain at having to wash the windows so frequently because of the deposit of NH$_4$Cl on the window panes. Ammonia burns readily in oxygen but not in air. There are many catalysts which speed up its burning in air. If a side-arm flask containing NH$_4$OH is warmed and air is blown in the side-arm as shown in Fig. 24.3, a hot platinum wire lowered into the neck of the flask becomes red hot and ammonia is rapidly oxidized to nitric oxide. (See page 417 for the commercial application.)

$$4\ \overline{NH_3} + 5\ \overline{O_2} \longrightarrow 4\ \overline{NO} + 6\ \overline{H_2O} + \Delta$$

The reaction of ammonia with the more active metals was described on page 314 in connection with sodium, and should be reviewed at this point.

Complex Ions of Ammonia

In the section on complex formation (page 219) we mentioned that the lone pair of electrons on an ammonia molecule could be coordinated by a metal ion. Complex formation with ammonia is a very common and in many cases important phenomenon. The formation of the silver ammonia ion explains the solubility of silver chloride in dilute ammonium hydroxide.

$$\underline{AgCl} + 2\ H\!:\!\overset{H}{\underset{H}{N}}\!:\!H\!:\!\overset{..}{O}\!: \rightleftarrows H\!:\!\overset{H}{\underset{H}{N}}\!:\!Ag\!:\!\overset{H}{\underset{H}{N}}\!:\!H\ + Cl^- + H_2O$$

This is an equilibrium reaction and can be reversed by adding acid. (Why?) It will go to completion to the right if the concentration of the silver ion in equilibrium with the complex (at the existing ammonia concentration) is less than that in equilibrium with the "insoluble" silver salt. Thus dilute ammonia will dissolve AgCl (K$_{sp}$ = 1.6·10^{-10}), but fairly concentrated ammonia is required for AgBr (K$_{sp}$ = 7.7·10^{-13}) and even concentrated (15 M) NH$_4$OH has no appreciable effect on AgI (K$_{sp}$ = 1.7·10^{-16}). If ammonium hydroxide is added very slowly to a solution of copper sulfate, a pale blue precipitate of copper hydroxide forms first. If more ammonium hydroxide is added, this precipitate dissolves and a deep blue solution appears.

$$2\ NH_4OH + Cu(H_2O)_4{}^{++} + SO_4{}^{--} \longrightarrow$$
$$\underline{Cu(H_2O)_2(OH)_2} + 2\ NH_4{}^+ + SO_4{}^{--} + 2\ H_2O$$

$$4\ NH_4OH + \underline{Cu(H_2O)_2(OH)_2} \longrightarrow Cu(NH_3)_4{}^{++} + 2\ OH^- + 6\ H_2O$$

The formation of this dark blue color on addition of ammonia is a good qualitative test for the copper ion. Its disappearance on the addition of a standardized NaCN solution (colorless Cu(CN)$_3{}^{--}$ is formed) is the basis of a rapid quantitative method of analysis. Gas masks containing CuSO$_4$ are very efficient for men who have to work in air containing ammonia.

Ammonia cannot usually be dried by passing it over salts which dry air by forming hydrates, because it combines with them just as water does. These compounds are called *ammoniates*, by analogy with hydrates, and we can speak of ammonia of crystallization just as we do of water of crystallization. They undoubtedly contain at least part of the ammonia in the form of a complex ion. Other ions whose formation of ammonia complexes is of chemical importance are Ni^{++}, Cr^{+++}, Co^{++}, Co^{+++}, Ca^{++}, and Pt^{++++}.

Uses of Ammonia

Ammonia is used in a multitude of ways. It is the starting point in the manufacture of most nitric acid. It is still used in most large commercial refrigerating installations. In solution it is familiar as "household ammonia" or "spirit of hartshorn," used for various cleaning purposes. By its catalytic decomposition ammonia can serve as a source of hydrogen as well as of nitrogen. It is the source of practically all the ammonium salts and is a valuable reagent in organic syntheses.

Tests for Ammonia or the Ammonium Ion

The properties of the NH_4^+ ion are extremely similar to those of another ion having the same charge and radius, namely, the K^+ ion. The ammonium ion will interfere with any test involving the precipitation of a potassium salt, and vice versa. Two striking points of difference are that the ammonium ion is a weak acid and a weak reducing agent, whereas the potassium ion is neither. Taking advantage of the first fact, we commonly test for NH_4^+ by treating the substance with NaOH and warming it gently (see the equation below). If NH_4^+ is present, the characteristic odor of NH_3 will be noticed, and the gas evolved will turn red litmus blue. Another test is to add "Nessler's Reagent," which contains KOH, HgO, and KI. A brown color shows the presence of ammonia.

Ammonium Salts

Ammonium salts are prepared by bubbling ammonia into various acids. Water solutions of the salts contain the reactive ammonium ion. Ammonia can be liberated from any of its salts by treating them with a non-volatile base.

$$NH_4Cl + NaOH \xrightarrow{\Delta} NaCl + \overline{NH_3} + \overline{H_2O}$$

All ammonium salts decompose upon being heated, some explosively. The following equations show some of the decomposition reactions:

$$NH_4Cl \xrightarrow{\Delta} \overline{NH_3} + \overline{HCl}$$

$$(NH_4)_2Cr_2O_7 \xrightarrow{\Delta} \overline{N_2} + 4\,\overline{H_2O} + Cr_2O_3$$

$$\text{NH}_4\text{HCO}_3 \xrightarrow{\Delta} \overline{\text{NH}_3} + \overline{\text{H}_2\text{O}} + \overline{\text{CO}_2}$$

$$\text{NH}_4\text{NO}_2 \xrightarrow{\Delta} \overline{\text{N}_2} + 2\text{ H}_2\text{O}$$

$$\text{NH}_4\text{NO}_3 \xrightarrow{\Delta} \overline{\text{N}_2\text{O}} + 2\text{ H}_2\text{O}$$

To prove for yourself that ammonium bicarbonate is not very stable, smell a bottle of the salt; you can detect the odor of ammonia *without difficulty*.

Ammonium salts make good fertilizers because the nitrogen is used by plants as food. NH_4HCO_3 is used in the manufacture of soda crackers.

FIG. 24.4. Fires set at Texas City by the explosion of ammonium nitrate fertilizer on a burning freighter. The fire at the extreme left is at the dock where the ship was berthed; the others were set when flying pieces of steel pierced oil tanks, stills, and gas lines. The Monsanto plant in the foreground produced one-eighth of the styrene (page 690) used in the production of synthetic rubber during World War II. (*Life* photograph by James Laughead. Copyright *Time*, Inc.)

NH_4Cl is used as a soldering flux. Both ions are active—the ammonium ion as an acid, the chloride ion as a complex-former—in dissolving the oxide film on the metal. In the case of galvanized iron the reaction is:

$$\text{ZnO} + 4\text{ NH}_4\text{Cl} \longrightarrow (\text{NH}_4)_2\text{ZnCl}_4 + 2\overline{\text{NH}_3} + \overline{\text{H}_2\text{O}}$$

The ammonium chlorozincate and any undecomposed ammonium chloride melt and flow away (hence the name "flux") from the advancing solder. Ammonium nitrate is a valuable high explosive. It is extremely insensitive, requiring a powerful detonator, but is as powerful as any dynamite. This was demonstrated by the devastating explosion of the freighter *Grandcamp*, laden with ammonium nitrate, at Texas City in 1947. (Fig. 24.4.) Explosives deficient in oxygen, such as TNT, are sometimes mixed with NH_4NO_3 to advantage, because it has an excess of oxygen. The use of NH_4Cl in dry cells has been mentioned.

Reactions in Liquid Ammonia

Ammonia is strikingly similar to water in many respects. Both substances are simultaneously weak acids and weak bases. Both associate by means of hydrogen bonds and therefore have extraordinarily high specific heats and heats of vaporization. Both molecules are unsymmetrical in such a way as to make them polar; both are therefore ionizing solvents for salts. Ammonia is a poorer solvent for inorganic salts than water is, but makes up for this by dissolving many organic substances which are insoluble in water. The resemblances between water and ammonia suggested to E. C. Franklin that chemical reactions might take place in anhydrous liquid ammonia as a solvent as well as they do in water. He found this to be the case. All types of reaction that are familiar in water occur in liquid ammonia.

Precipitation reactions may go in surprising directions, owing to differing relative solubilities in the two solvents. For example, silver chloride is soluble in NH_3, but sodium chloride is not and can be precipitated from it.

$$Ag^+ + Cl^- + Na^+ + NO_3^- \xrightarrow{NH_3} Ag^+ + NO_3^- + \underline{NaCl}$$

Ammonia is more basic than water; therefore some acids which are weak (establish equilibria with H_3O^+ ions) in water solution are strong (react completely to form the NH_4^+ ion) in ammonia solution. The ammonium ion is of course the strongest acid that can exist in liquid ammonia, corresponding to the hydronium ion in water. A typical neutralization reaction in liquid ammonia is:

$$NH_4^+ + NO_3^- + Na^+ + NH_2^- \longrightarrow Na^+ + NO_3^- + 2\ NH_3$$

The amide ion is the strongest possible base in NH_3 just as the hydroxide ion is in water.

At the time that Franklin was pioneering in this field and inventing the techniques that enabled him and others inspired by him to handle a solvent that boiled at $-40°$ C., the chemical world was thoroughly under the influence of Arrhenius. It believed with him that the hydrogen ion (thought of as a free proton) was responsible for all acid properties, and that no substance was really an acid until it had ionized. It accepted his argument that the hydroxide ion was the only base; i.e., that the CO_3^{--} ion, for example,

NITROGEN AND ITS COMPOUNDS

was not a base but only *produced* a base by hydrolysis. Franklin's work with the NH$_4^+$ ion in ammonia helped show the true nature of the "H$^+$" ion in water (namely, that it is actually the H$_3$O$^+$ ion) and laid the foundation upon which Brønsted generalized the concept of bases.

OTHER HYDROGEN-NITROGEN COMPOUNDS

The fact that hydrogen and oxygen combine to form two compounds, H$_2$O and H$_2$O$_2$, should lead us to investigate the possibility of hydrogen-nitrogen compounds other than ammonia. The most important of these complex inorganic H—N compounds is *hydrazine*, N$_2$H$_4$. When a mixture of K$_2$SO$_3$, NO, H$_2$O, and Na—Hg amalgam is heated, hydrazine hydrate, N$_2$H$_4$·H$_2$O (or N$_2$H$_5$OH), is formed. If the hydrate is heated in the presence of barium oxide, hydrazine vaporizes and condenses as a white solid which melts at 1.4° C. N$_2$H$_4$ fumes strongly in moist air and forms the hydrate.

$$\begin{array}{ccc} \text{H H} & \text{H} & \text{H H} \quad \text{H} \\ \text{H:N:N:} + \text{H:O:} & \longrightarrow & \text{H:N:N:H:O:} \\ \text{H} & & \text{H} \end{array}$$

This solution is weakly alkaline. Hydrazine may be considered to be ammonia with one of the hydrogens replaced with an *amido group*. (H—NH$_2$ and H$_2$N—NH$_2$.) The similarity between hydrazine hydrate and ammonium hydroxide is evident from the above electronic formula. The systematic name for the hydrate is hydrazinium hydroxide. It ionizes in the same way as does ammonium hydroxide, to the hydrazinium ion and the hydroxide ion.

$$\text{H}_2\text{N} \cdot \text{NH}_3\text{OH} + \text{H}^+ + \text{Cl}^- \longrightarrow \text{H}_2\text{N} \cdot \text{NH}_3^+ + \text{Cl}^- + \text{H}_2\text{O}$$

However, salts like hydrazinium chloride are more commonly called "hydrazine hydrochloride," etc., and written N$_2$H$_4$·HCl. (The dot is noncommittal as to the nature of the attachment.)

Hydrazoic acid is obtained by reacting hydrazine hydrate and cold nitrous acid together.

$$\text{N}_2\text{H}_5\text{OH} + \text{HNO}_2 \longrightarrow \text{HN}_3 + 3\,\text{H}_2\text{O}$$

The electronic formula of *azide ion* is :N::N::N:$^-$. The acid and all of its heavy metal salts are violently explosive. Lead azide, Pb(N$_3$)$_2$, is used as a detonator.

Hydroxylamine, NH$_2$OH, may be considered ammonia in which an OH group has replaced one hydrogen. (NH$_2$—H, NH$_2$—OH.) It can be prepared by reducing nitric oxide with tin, in acid solution.

$$2\,\overline{\text{NO}} + 3\,\underline{\text{Sn}} + 8\,\text{H}^+ + 8\,\text{Cl}^- \longrightarrow 2\,\text{HONH}_3^+ + 3\,\text{Sn}^{++} + 8\,\text{Cl}^-$$

The stannous ions are precipitated as SnS by means of H₂S. The solution is evaporated to dryness and the hydroxylammonium chloride (hydroxylamine hydrochloride) recrystallized from alcohol. The free base can be obtained by treating the salt with NaOH and extracting with ether.

$$\text{H:\ddot{O}:\ddot{N}:H}^+ + Cl^- + Na^+ + OH^- \longrightarrow \text{H:\ddot{O}:\ddot{N}:} + Na^+ + Cl^-$$

(with H substituents on N)

The ordinary way of writing the formula for hydroxylamine, NH₂OH, is deceptive, because it implies a similarity to ammonium hydroxide. The electronic formula in the equation should make it plain that there is no likeness. The oxygen in NH₂OH shares electrons with the nitrogen; that in NH₄OH does not. The weak basic properties of hydroxylamine are due to the lone electron pair on the nitrogen, not to any ionization of the HO group. Hydroxylamine salts are frequently used as reagents in organic chemistry. They are powerful reducing agents.

OXIDES OF NITROGEN, OXY-ACIDS, AND OXY-SALTS

Since nitrogen has valences of $+1$, $+2$, $+3$, $+4$, and $+5$, there are five oxides of nitrogen. Not all of these dissolve in water and form corresponding acids. The two common acids, HNO₂ and HNO₃, contain nitrogen with a valence of $+3$ and $+5$ respectively. Some of the properties of the oxides are shown in Table 24.1.

TABLE 24.1. OXIDES OF NITROGEN

Name of Oxide	Formula	Valence	Physical Properties
Nitrous oxide	N₂O	+1	Colorless; B.P., −89.5° C.; 1.3 ml. dissolve/ml. H₂O
Nitric oxide	NO	+2	Colorless; B.P., −151° C.; 0.07 ml. dissolve/ml. H₂O
Nitrogen trioxide	N₂O₃	+3	Blue liquid, red-brown gas; B.P., 3.5° C.; very soluble in H₂O
Nitrogen tetroxide (di) (per)	NO₂ or N₂O₄	+4	Yellow liquid, red-brown gas; B.P., 21.3° C.; decomposes in H₂O (At low temperature NO₂ polymerizes to colorless N₂O₄.)
Nitrogen pentoxide	N₂O₅	+5	White solid; M.P. 30° C.; very soluble in water

Nitrous Oxide

Nitrous oxide is prepared by heating ammonium nitrate as shown in Fig. 24.5.

$$\underline{NH_4NO_3} \longrightarrow \overline{N_2O} + 2\ \overline{H_2O}$$

NITROGEN AND ITS COMPOUNDS

Great care must be taken in heating NH_4NO_3, for the reaction is exothermic and may become explosive. Nitrous oxide decomposes with the liberation of heat.

$$2 \overline{N_2O} \longrightarrow 2 \overline{N_2} + \overline{O_2} + 36{,}000 \text{ cal.}$$

That N_2O is a good oxidizing agent is shown by the fact that a glowing splint will burst into flame in the gas.

The popular name for nitrous oxide is "laughing gas" because people under its influence frequently become hysterical. Sir Humphry Davy observed that mice placed in the gas first became greatly excited and then dropped unconscious, but soon revived upon being placed in fresh air and were none the worse.[3] N_2O is still used as an anesthetic for minor operations, but it must be mixed with oxygen because the human body cannot utilize the oxygen in the gas. Most people have no harmful after-effects from it.

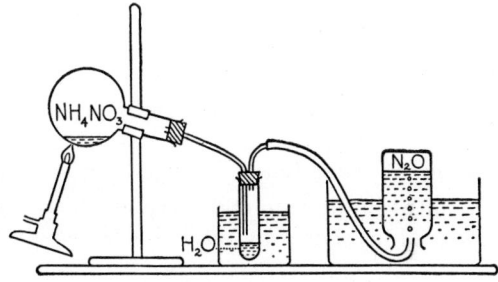

FIG. 24.5. Preparation of nitrous oxide.

Nitric Oxide

Nitric oxide is produced commercially in the course of the Ostwald process (page 417) by the careful oxidation of ammonia by air in the presence of a catalyst.

$$4 \overline{NH_3} + 5 \overline{O_2} \longrightarrow 4 \overline{NO} + 6 \overline{H_2O}$$

A little NO is produced naturally in the atmosphere by electrical storms. A more convenient method of preparing NO in the laboratory is to use dilute nitric acid and copper, with a little copper sulfate in the flask to catalyze the reaction.

$$3 \underline{Cu} + 8 H^+ + 8 NO_3^- \longrightarrow 3 Cu^{++} + 6 NO_3^- + 2 \overline{NO} + 4 H_2O$$

Nitric oxide also decomposes with the liberation of heat, but will *not* support the combustion of a glowing splint, although burning phosphorus will continue to burn in it. NO, like N_2 and O_2, is unexpectedly stable on account of a triple bond. The only sign of the presence of an odd electron is that NO has

---

[3] The story is told that Sir Humphry and some of his friends decided to try the gas on themselves. They agreed that as soon as one man became unconscious, the others would carry him out into the fresh air; when he revived he would describe his sensations. All of them huddled around the dish which contained the ammonium nitrate. But there was one flaw in their experiment—they all became hysterical at the same time.

one unit of magnetic susceptibility. Nitric oxide combines readily with molecular oxygen at room temperature to form red-brown nitrogen dioxide, in which the effects of the odd electron are plain enough (its color, reactivity, and ability to polymerize; see below).

$$2\ \overline{NO} + \overline{O_2} \longrightarrow 2\ \overline{NO_2}$$

Nitric oxide coordinates readily with the ferrous ion, probably displacing one of four water molecules:

$$Fe(H_2O)_4{}^{++} + SO_4{}^{--} + \overline{NO} \rightleftarrows Fe(H_2O)_3NO^{++} + SO_4{}^{--}$$

The nitrosylferrous ion has a strong, dark brown color and serves to identify substances from which NO can be produced.

Nitrogen Trioxide

If nitrogen dioxide and nitric oxide are mixed, some nitrogen trioxide is produced, as shown by the following equilibrium:

$$\overline{NO_2} + \overline{NO} \rightleftarrows \overline{N_2O_3}$$

Heat decomposes N_2O_3 into NO and NO_2. Since N_2O_3 is the anhydride of nitrous acid, a convenient means of making it is to prepare the acid and heat it until it decomposes into water and nitrogen trioxide. The cheap salt, sodium nitrite, is usually used as the initial material.

$$2\ \underline{NaNO_2} + H_2SO_4 \xrightarrow{\Delta} \underline{Na_2SO_4} + 2\ HNO_2$$
$$2\ HNO_2 \longrightarrow \overline{H_2O + N_2O_3}$$

Nitrogen Dioxide

There is an interesting difference in the reaction between copper and nitric acid, depending upon the strength of the acid. With dilute HNO_3, nitric oxide is liberated; NO_2 is produced with concentrated HNO_3.

$$\underline{Cu} + 4\ H^+ + 4\ NO_3{}^- \longrightarrow Cu^{++} + 2\ NO_3{}^- + 2\ \overline{NO_2} + 2\ H_2O$$

Red-brown NO_2 escapes from the solution. Probably nitric oxide forms first and is then oxidized to NO_2 by HNO_3. Remember that this gas is *very toxic*; never allow it to escape into an open room. X-ray films are usually cellulose nitrate, and they liberate nitrogen dioxide if they catch on fire. (This was responsible for a horrible X-ray film disaster at the Cleveland, Ohio, Clinic in 1929, in which many doctors, nurses, and patients lost their lives.)

A laboratory method for preparing NO_2 is by heating lead nitrate. The escaping gases are $\frac{4}{5}$ NO_2 and $\frac{1}{5}$ O_2.

$$2\ \underline{Pb(NO_3)_2} \xrightarrow{\Delta} 2\ \underline{PbO} + \overline{4\ NO_2} + \overline{O_2}$$

Nitrogen dioxide is produced commercially by the oxidation of nitric oxide with oxygen.

At low temperatures NO_2 polymerizes or associates into N_2O_4, which is colorless. The liquid is almost entirely N_2O_4, and has only a light yellow color. Just above the boiling point the gas is a mixture of the two molecular species; as the temperature rises the dissociation into NO_2 increases and the color becomes darker brown.

Nitrogen dioxide may act either as an oxidizing or a reducing agent, since the nitrogen in it has one of the intermediate valences of that element. In its most useful reaction it does both; that is, it disproportionates. This occurs when the gas is led into water.

(cold) $\quad H_2O + 2\ \overline{NO_2} \rightleftarrows H^+ + NO_3^- + HNO_2$

(hot) $\quad H_2O + 3\ \overline{NO_2} \rightleftarrows 2\ H^+ + 2\ NO_3^- + \overline{NO}$

The second equation represents the final reaction in the manufacture of the extremely useful nitric acid. The reversibility of this reaction will explain, after a little study, why it is impossible for NO to be evolved when concentrated HNO_3 is used as an oxidizing agent, or NO_2 when the nitric acid is dilute. It also explains why the gas in the top of bottles of concentrated nitric acid is likely to be yellow.

Nitrogen pentoxide, N_2O_5, is formed by dehydrating nitric acid with P_2O_5. It has no uses.

Nitrous Acid and Its Salts

Nitrous acid 100 per cent pure is so unstable that it has never been prepared. The acid is available in dilute solutions, but even these are not stable. The acid and its salts are used in the manufacture of organic dyes.

The two most common nitrites in the chemical laboratory are $NaNO_2$ and KNO_2, which are stable salts. $NaNO_3$ may serve as a source of oxygen and $NaNO_2$.

$$2\ \underline{NaNO_3} \xrightarrow{\Delta} 2\ \underline{NaNO_2} + \overline{O_2}$$

$NaNO_2$ may be prepared by bubbling a mixture of NO and NO_2 (equivalent to N_2O_3) into a solution of NaOH.

$$\overline{NO} + \overline{NO_2} + 2\ Na^+ + 2\ OH^- \longrightarrow 2\ Na^+ + 2\ NO_2^- + H_2O$$

Sodium nitrate is easily reduced to sodium nitrite by being heated with metallic lead.

$$\underline{Pb} + \underline{NaNO_3} \longrightarrow \underline{PbO} + \underline{NaNO_2}$$

The presence of the nitrite ion in drinking water indicates pollution; bacteria commonly found in sewage can reduce NO_3^- to NO_2^-. The nitrite ion in acid solution will reduce MnO_4^- to Mn^{++}, but will oxidize the iodide ion to free iodine. Can you write the equations? If acid is required, use sulfuric acid in the first reaction, hydrochloric in the second. What oxidizing or reducing action could these two acids show if used in the reverse way?

Nitric Acid

Nitric acid has been known for many years; the alchemists called it *aqua fortis* because it was such a powerful oxidizing agent. The various commercial methods for the preparation of nitric acid are discussed under nitrogen fixation. The easiest method for preparing it in the laboratory is to distill it from a mixture of sodium nitrate and sulfuric acid in an apparatus like that shown in Fig. 24.6. Because nitric acid destroys cork and rubber easily, an all-glass apparatus is preferable. Nitric acid is a low-boiling acid, B.P. 86° C., whereas sulfuric acid is a high-boiling acid; therefore HNO_3 distills from the solution in preference to H_2SO_4.

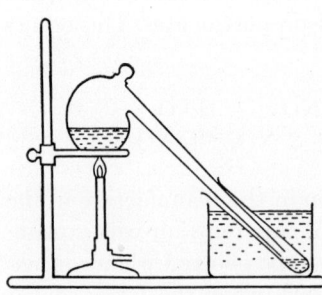

Fig. 24.6. Preparation of nitric acid.

$$NaNO_3 + H_2SO_4 \xrightarrow{\Delta} NaHSO_4 + HNO_3$$

Some nitric acid is decomposed by heat,

$$4\ HNO_3 \longrightarrow 2\ H_2O + 4\ NO_2 + O_2$$

hence the solution obtained upon distillation is colored with the red-brown NO_2. Sunlight catalyzes the decomposition of nitric acid.

Nitric acid is a strong acid and an excellent oxidizing agent. These are its two outstanding *chemical properties*, and both of them are often illustrated in a single chemical reaction.

Many spectacular experiments show that nitric acid is a powerful oxidizing agent. If a few milliliters of concentrated HNO_3 are added to a pile of sawdust, the oxidation is so rapid that the sawdust bursts into flame. Bottles of nitric acid were formerly packed in sawdust for shipment, but because of the fire hazard an inert material is now used. If a small piece of woolen cloth is placed in the mouth of a test tube containing a few milliliters of HNO_3 and heat is applied, the cloth will ignite when the acid boils. A glowing splint or charcoal thrust into concentrated HNO_3 burns brightly. Beware of splattering the hot acid, because nitric acid burns on the body may be serious. Apply a paste of $NaHCO_3$ to such burns. Dilute HNO_3 stains the skin yellow as a result of complicated reactions with the protein.

Two equations given previously for the preparation of NO and NO_2 illustrate the oxidizing property of nitric acid. Hydrogen sulfide is oxidized to sulfuric acid by concentrated HNO_3.

$$\overline{H_2S} + 8\ H^+ + 8\ NO_3^- \longrightarrow H^+ + HSO_4^- + 8\ \overline{NO_2} + 4\ H_2O$$
concentrated

If dilute acid is used, the oxidation is carried only to free sulfur.

$$3\ H_2S + 2\ H^+ + 2\ NO_3^- \longrightarrow 3\ \underline{S} + 4\ H_2O + 2\ \overline{NO}$$
dilute

The carbon in organic matter can be oxidized to CO_2 and the element phosphorus to phosphoric acid by concentrated nitric acid.

The action of nitric acid upon metals depends upon the concentration, as we have seen. With concentrated HNO_3, if any action at all occurs, NO_2 will be formed. The vigor of the reaction depends upon the activity of the metal. Gold and platinum do not react at all unless the chloride ion is present (page 337) to remove the product. Silver reacts smoothly, and magnesium almost explosively. With dilute nitric acid an interesting array of possibilities exists. With the less active metals the nitric acid is reduced to NO, as illustrated with copper on page 405. Metals above hydrogen in the E.C.S. can reduce the nitrogen to still lower valences. (Indeed, all the different valence compounds of nitrogen except N_2O_3 have been observed in such reactions. N_2O_3 probably forms but decomposes into NO and NO_2.) Hydrogen is also formed, for HNO_3 is a strong acid; but *hydrogen gas does not escape from the solution* when the metal is less active than magnesium, because as soon as the gas is produced it reacts with more nitric acid.

$$3\ \overline{H_2} + 2\ H^+ + 2\ NO_3^- \longrightarrow 2\ \overline{NO} + 4\ H_2O$$

in the case of zinc and dilute nitric acid, no gas is evolved; evidently the zinc reduces still further any NO that is produced by the action of hydrogen. Tests show the presence of the ammonium ion. Accordingly the equation is:

$$4\ \underline{Zn} + 10\ H^+ + 10\ NO_3^- \longrightarrow 4\ Zn^{++} + NH_4^+ + 9\ NO_3^- + 3\ H_2O$$

Nitric acid reacts with many organic compounds such as glycerol, benzene, toluene, cellulose, phenol, etc. These reactions are discussed in connection with organic chemistry (pages 702, 705, and 707).

Nitrates

Nearly all the nitrates are soluble in water; one of the few exceptions is the basic salt known in medicine as bismuth subnitrate, formed by the hydrolysis of $Bi(NO_3)_3$. The reaction is:

$$Bi^{+++} + 3\ NO_3^- + 2\ H_2O \longrightarrow \underline{BiONO_3 \cdot H_2O} + 2\ H^+ + 2\ NO_3^-$$

The formula of bismuth subnitrate could equally well be written $Bi(OH)_2NO_3$, but it is possible that some of the oxygen atoms link the bismuth ions together.

Nitrates decompose in several different ways. The decomposition of NH_4NO_3, $NaNO_3$, and $Pb(NO_3)_2$ has already been discussed. The decomposition of $Cu(NO_3)_2$ is similar to that of $Pb(NO_3)_2$. (Metal nitrates above barium in the E.C.S. decompose into nitrites and oxygen; those from barium to hydrogen yield the oxide, NO_2, and O_2; those below antimony yield the metal, NO_2, and O_2.) Many organic nitrates and nitro compounds decompose explosively. *Amitol*, a powerful explosive, is a mixture of NH_4NO_3 and T.N.T. (trinitrotuluol). Another explosive, *ammonal*, contains powdered aluminum and NH_4NO_3, and black gunpowder contains charcoal, sulfur, and KNO_3.

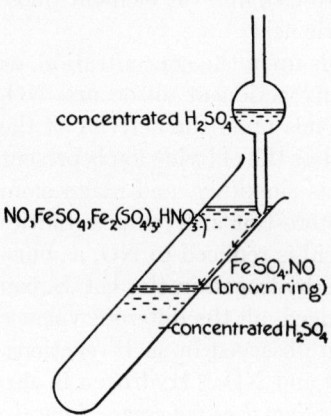

FIG. 24.7. The brown-ring test for nitrates.

Test for the Nitrate Ion. Since practically all the nitrates are water-soluble, precipitation reactions cannot be used to identify the NO_3^- ion. The most common test involves the use of ferrous sulfate as a reducing agent, and concentrated sulfuric acid to furnish the H^+ ion. About 3 or 4 ml. of a solution of $FeSO_4$ are added to a test tube containing the solution being tested. The tube is inclined, and some concentrated sulfuric acid is carefully poured into it. This forms the bottom layer; its high specific gravity makes possible the formation of a boundary layer between the two liquids. A brown ring forms at the junction if nitrates are present (Fig. 24.7), the brown color being due to the unstable addition compound of nitric oxide and ferrous ion.

$$K^+ + NO_3^- + 3\ Fe^{++} + 3\ SO_4^{--} + 7\ H^+ + 7\ HSO_4^- \longrightarrow$$
$$K^+ + 3\ Fe^{+++} + 10\ HSO_4^- + \overline{NO} + 2\ H_2O$$
$$Fe^{++} + NO \longrightarrow FeNO^{++}\ (brown)$$

Nitrites give the same test because they too yield NO under these conditions. If iodides or bromides are present the resulting color (what is it?) interferes with this test.

Cyanides and Cyanates

Sodium cyanide, NaCN, can be prepared by heating carbon, nitrogen, and sodium carbonate together.

$$Na_2CO_3 + 4\ \underline{C} + \overline{N_2} \longrightarrow 2\ \underline{NaCN} + \overline{3\ CO}$$

NITROGEN AND ITS COMPOUNDS

The free acid, called *hydrocyanic* or *prussic acid*, is obtained by treating NaCN with sulfuric acid.

$$Na^+ + CN^- + H^+ + HSO_4^- \longrightarrow Na^+ + HSO_4^- + \overline{HCN}$$

Hydrocyanic acid is also produced by the Castner process, in which NH_3, metallic sodium, and charcoal are heated together. HCN boils at 26° C. It is very soluble in water, forming a weak but *extremely toxic acid*. Even the sodium salt hydrolyzes in water and liberates hydrogen cyanide gas. This gas is used as a fumigant on ships. It will destroy plant life. NaCN is used by biologists to kill insects which they have collected as specimens.

The cyanide ion has the same number of electrons and the same structure as the nitrogen molecule, $:C:::N:^-$. The triple bond holds the atoms so close together that they behave much like a single atom. A monatomic univalent anion would be a halide ion; the cyanide ion is so much like the halide ions (its place is near F^-) that it is called a pseudo-halide. The resemblance extends even to the formation of a compound analogous to a diatomic molecule, e.g., Cl_2, of a free halogen. Mercuric cyanide, $Hg(CN)_2$, decomposes upon being heated; the colorless and extremely poisonous gas, cyanogen, $(CN)_2$ is liberated.

$$Hg(CN)_2 \xrightarrow{\Delta} Hg + \overline{(CN)_2}$$

Again like the halide ions, the cyanide ion coordinates with many cations (indeed, with practically all the transition metal cations) to form complexes. Many of these are of great commercial importance. Native silver and gold, in particles too small to be recovered mechanically, can be leached cheaply from finely ground ore by the use of NaCN solution.

$$4\,\underline{Au} + O_2 + 8\,Na^+ + 8\,CN^- + 2\,H_2O \longrightarrow 8\,Na^+ + 4\,OH^- + 4\,Au(CN)_2^-$$

This reaction is similar to the solution of gold by aqua regia, O_2 playing the part of the HNO_3 and CN^- that of the Cl^-. The equation for the solution of silver is obtained from the above by replacing Au by Ag. The cyanide complexes of many metals, including silver, gold, copper, zinc, cadmium, nickel, and cobalt, are useful in electroplating baths. Their low ionization constants enable them to keep the concentration of the metal ion low while providing an ample reserve supply. A low concentration of the ion being plated enables a higher voltage to be used, resulting in a smooth, tightly adhering coating. Other important cyanide complexes include the ferricyanide ion, $Fe(CN)_6^{---}$, from Fe^{+++}, and the ferrocyanide ion, $Fe(CN)_6^{----}$, from Fe^{++}. Sodium ferricyanide, known commercially as red prussiate of soda, is used in making blueprint paper (page 611). "Yellow prussiate of potash," Prussian blue, is made from "yellow prussiate of potash," potassium ferrocyanide.

The *cyanate ion*, OCN^-, is formed by the oxidation of the cyanide ion. Its electronic formula is $:\overset{..}{O}::C::\overset{..}{N}:^-$. The first organic compound ever synthesized in the laboratory was made in 1828 from ammonium cyanate, $NH_4(OCN)$, when by heating some of it Wöhler converted it into the organic compound urea, $H_2N-\overset{\overset{O}{\|}}{C}-NH_2$.[4] Sulfur can be substituted for oxygen in the cyanates. $K(SCN)$ is called potassium thiocyanate. Both OCN^- and SCN^- are pseudo-halides. The latter, for example, readily replaces some or possibly all of the water molecules in the hydrated ferric ion, $Fe(H_2O)_6^{+++}$, forming $Fe(SCN)_6^{---}$ (or perhaps some intermediate ion; the formula is not yet settled), which has an intense brownish red color. One p.p.m. of the Fe^{+++} ion can be identified in this way. The cyanates and thiocyanates are not nearly as toxic as the cyanides.

FIXED NITROGEN AND ITS USES

The following ten elements have long been considered essential to plant growth: carbon, hydrogen, and oxygen, which are obtained from the air and water; and phosphorus, sulfur, nitrogen, potassium, calcium, iron, and magnesium, which are supplied by the soil. Within the past few years this list has been expanded to include manganese, copper, zinc, and boron. Soils vary greatly in their composition. Cropping, leaching, and erosion remove from them many of these essential elements—nitrogen, phosphorus, and potassium in particular. Government estimates indicate that 250,000 tons of nitrogen, 350,000 tons of phosphoric acid, and 3,500,000 tons of potash (calculated as K_2O) annually are leached from the soils of this country; and that the total annual losses from cropping, leaching, and erosion are at least 5,000,000 tons of nitrogen, 3,000,000 tons of phosphoric acid, and 28,000,000 tons of potash. These losses are made up by the addition of fertilizers to the soil.

Of the few nitrogen compounds which were known in the early days, saltpeter (KNO_3) was the most important. As long as a thousand years ago it was prepared in China and India by piling up manure, adding lime and wood ashes which are rich in potassium carbonate, letting the mixture stand a year or so, and finally leaching out the potassium nitrate. The amount of nitrogen in the earth's crust is negligible compared with that in the atmosphere. The amount of free nitrogen above one square mile of the earth's surface—four million billion tons—is sufficient to supply the world's needs for ten years; therefore the supply of free nitrogen is inexhaustible.

Plants cannot use free nitrogen and most plants cannot convert it into useful compounds. Since we as human beings are dependent directly or indirectly upon plant life, the fixation of sufficient atmospheric nitrogen to produce plant growth is vital to us. The rapid increase in the world popula-

[4] See p. 714.

tion from 1800 to 1900 led scientists to predict that there would be a world famine unless some method of nitrogen fixation was discovered. Methods of fixing nitrogen have been developed until today as much fixed nitrogen is produced as is required for fertilizers and for the chemical industries. Next to fertilizers, the most important use of fixed nitrogen is in the manufacture of explosives which are indispensable in peacetime as well as war; without them the Panama Canal could not have been built. Combined nitrogen is used in the manufacture of many organic dyes, rayon, drugs, and plastics such as pyroxylin and celluloid.

It thus becomes evident that the manufacture of fixed nitrogen is one of the most important industries in the world. Scientists have attacked this problem from several angles and, as a result, fixed nitrogen can now be obtained by several processes, among which are the following:

1. Mine fixed nitrogen from the earth.
2. Cultivate low forms of plant life which are capable of fixing nitrogen.
3. Decompose nitrogenous material, such as coal and shale, and produce ammonia.
4. Combine calcium carbide with nitrogen and hydrolyze the product formed (cyanamide process).
5. Combine nitrogen and hydrogen to form ammonia and oxidize it to nitric acid.
6. Combine nitrogen and oxygen to form the lower oxides of nitrogen which are easily oxidized.

Mining Fixed Nitrogen

In the desert region along the mountains in Chile is a strip of saltpeter, $NaNO_3$, some 200 miles long, two miles wide, and from one to twelve feet thick. This deposit is thought to have been formed from the decomposition of the excreta of birds and of other organic matter; it may also have been leached from the mountainsides. There are some deposits in the desert regions of the United States, and in Tennessee; some of our caves—the Mammoth Cave, for example—contain deposits formed from the refuse of bats and other animals.

From 1880 to 1915 Chile's production of natural sodium nitrate represented well over 50 per cent of the world output of chemical nitrogen, but the approximately two million tons mined each year constitute only 5 to 10 per cent of the world demand. Furthermore, at this rate of production, this deposit will be exhausted during the present century. *All the natural deposits of nitrates in the world cannot supply the demand for fixed nitrogen.*

Fixed Nitrogen from Low Forms of Plant Life

About 20 pounds of nitrogen per acre per year are supplied by bacteria such as *Azobacter chroococcum* and *Clostridium pasturianum*, which live free in the soil. Of much greater importance are the *Rhizobium radicicola*, which are capable of producing between 60 and 100 pounds of fixed nitrogen per acre per year, and which live in nodules on the roots of leguminous plants such as alfalfa and clover. The principle of crop rotation is based upon the fact that leguminous crops increase the fixed nitrogen reserve of the soil. Scientists have attempted to produce a fertilizer from low forms of plant life. Some algae, for example, are efficient nitrogen fixers, and the dried plants are rich in nitrogen. Thus far, however, the process has not been profitable.

Destructive Distillation of Coal

As early as 1848, inorganic fertilizers obtained as a by-product from the destructive distillation of coal were added to the soil. When coal is heated in

FIG. 24.8. Ingots of cyanamide as they reach the fixation ovens. (Courtesy, North American Cyanamide, Ltd., Niagara Falls, Canada.)

the absence of air, many chemical compounds are produced, among them ammonia gas (NH_3). This is usually caught in water and then neutralized with a solution of sulfuric acid. About 20 pounds of $(NH_4)_2SO_4$ are produced from one ton of coal; in the United States, over three-fourths of a million tons are produced annually from this source.

The Cyanamide Process for Fixing Nitrogen

We saw above that Na_2CO_3, carbon, and nitrogen, when heated together, yield sodium cyanide.

$$Na_2CO_3 + 4\ C + N_2 \longrightarrow 2\ NaCN + \overline{3\ CO}$$

NITROGEN AND ITS COMPOUNDS

Ammonia can be produced by the hydrolysis of cyanides, but the preparation of the cyanides is too expensive. As a result of the work on cyanides, the German chemists, Frank and Caro, developed the cyanamide process in 1895. This process consists essentially in passing pure nitrogen over powdered calcium carbide at about 1100° C., and is speeded up by the presence of calcium chloride or of fluorspar. The calcium carbide is prepared by calcining calcium carbonate to obtain lime, which is then heated with carbon in an electric furnace to produce CaC_2. When CaC_2 and nitrogen are heated together, calcium cyanamide, $CaCN_2$, is formed; this is hydrolyzed with 3 per cent NaOH and steam under pressure. The ammonia is then neutralized with acids or oxidized to nitric acid. The raw materials needed for the production of ammonia by this process are limestone, coal, and liquid air from which pure nitrogen can be obtained. For economy of operation, cheap electricity must also be available for the electric furnaces. The equations for the reactions are:

$$CaCO_3 \xrightarrow{\Delta} CaO + CO_2$$

$$CaO + 3\ C \xrightarrow{\Delta} CaC_2 + CO$$

$$CaC_2 + N_2 \text{ (from liquid air)} \xrightarrow{1100°} CaCN_2 + C.$$

$CaCN_2$ is written $Ca^{++}(:N::C::N:)^{--}$.

$$3\ H_2O + CaCN_2 \xrightarrow[\text{steam}]{\text{NaOH}} CaCO_3 + 2\ NH_3$$

During the First World War the demand for nitrogen compounds was so large that the government built an $80,000,000 cyanamide plant at Muscle Shoals, Alabama, which was capable of fixing 40,000 tons of nitrogen per year. It was never operated because it was obsolete before it was ready. The cyanamide plants at Niagara Falls, Canada, of twice that capacity, still operate successfully because of cheap current and because of other uses for their product. They do not produce ammonia.

Calcium cyanamide is used as a fertilizer. A series of hydrolysis reactions, catalyzed by the inorganic and organic substances of the soil, releases ammonia.

$$2\ CaCN_2 + 2\ H_2O \longrightarrow Ca(HCN_2)_2 + Ca(OH)_2$$
$$\text{(an acid salt)} \quad \text{(neutralizes soil acidity)}$$

$$2\ Ca(HCN_2)_2 + 2\ H_2O \longrightarrow (CaOH)_2CN_2 + 3\ H_2CN_2 \text{ (free cyanamide)}$$

$$H_2CN_2 + H_2O \longrightarrow H_2N-\overset{\overset{O}{\|}}{C}-NH_2 \text{ (urea)}$$

$$(NH_2)_2CO + H_2O \longrightarrow 2\ NH_3 + CO_2$$

Crystalline urea is also produced on a commercial scale, but by a different process. It is prepared by heating carbon dioxide and an excess of ammonia at 135° C. under pressure in the presence of catalysts which act as dehydrating agents. As a fertilizer, it is richer in nitrogen content than any others. Most of the urea produced in the United States is used in the manufacture of other products such as resins. A total of over 200 tons of urea is produced per day by the industrial plants of the United States.

The Haber Process for the Synthesis of Ammonia[5]

As early as 1850 chemists knew that traces of ammonia could be produced by passing nitrogen and hydrogen through a hot iron pipe, and many worked on this process. The German chemist, Fritz Haber, finally developed it on a commercial scale in 1905. After trying many catalysts in the iron reaction chambers, he discovered that osmium, uranium, and uranium carbide were much better for this purpose than iron, chromium, and nickel. By 1913, the process was on a commercial basis and a plant with a capacity of 10,000 tons per year had been built at Oppau.

Pure hydrogen and nitrogen are necessary for the synthesis of ammonia by the Haber process. Some of the hydrogen is produced commercially by passing carbon monoxide and steam at a slight pressure over chromium oxide, ferric oxide, or thorium catalysts at 500° C.

$$\overline{CO} + \overline{H_2O} \longrightarrow \overline{H_2} + \overline{CO_2}$$

The CO_2 is scrubbed out with a caustic solution. The nitrogen is supplied by a Linde liquid-air plant. The reaction between N_2 and H_2 is exothermic.

$$\overline{N_2} + 3\,\overline{H_2} \longrightarrow 2\,\overline{NH_3} + 24{,}400 \text{ cal.}$$

According to the Le Chatelier Principle, the reaction should be carried out at a high pressure and a low temperature. Four volumes of gases are converted into two volumes; therefore pressure shifts the equilibrium from left to right. Since the reaction is exothermic, heat shifts the equilibrium from right to left. At a low temperature the yield is small and at high temperatures the ammonia decomposes too rapidly. The solution of this problem depended upon finding a catalyst which would greatly decrease the time required for an equilibrium to be established. Carbon-free chromium steel must be used in the construction of the reaction chamber because hydrogen diffuses very rapidly through ordinary steel. A pressure of 200 atm. was used in the first Haber plants, but some of the newer plants operate at pressures of 1000 atm., and the temperature is maintained at 400° to 600° C. Uncombined gases are recirculated. Fig. 24.9 shows the fundamental steps in

---

[5] Without this process, the First World War could never have lasted for years; in fact, many people believe that the war would never have begun, inasmuch as Germany, prior to the discovery of this process, was directly dependent upon other nations for her fixed nitrogen and therefore indirectly for her explosives.

the process. Many modifications of the Haber process are now in use. The *Claude process* operates at a pressure of 1000 atm. C. The *Casale Italian process* operates at 500° C. and 600 atm.; the gases are recirculated and the ammonia recovered is reported to be 15 per cent per cycle. The *Fauser Italian process* operates at 200 atm. and 500° C., the hydrogen being produced

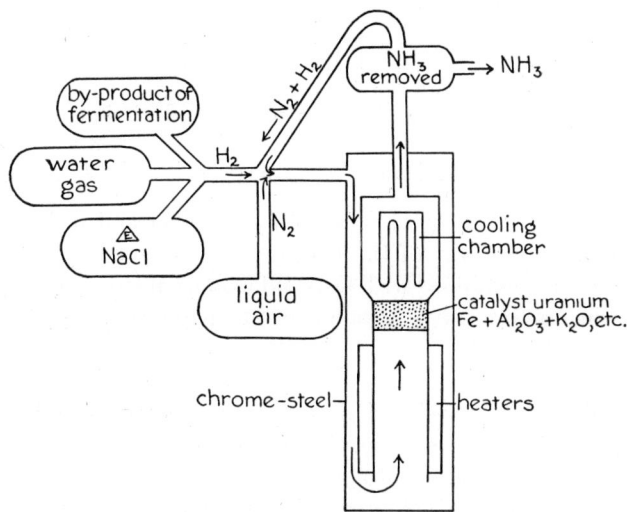

FIG. 24.9. Fundamental steps in the manufacture of ammonia by the Haber process. Great care is necessary in purifying the hydrogen and nitrogen because carbon monoxide, sulfur compounds, etc., poison the catalysts. The ammonia is liquefied by means of pressure and is removed from the system. Hydrogen is obtained from water gas or as a by-product in the manufacture of sodium hydroxide.

electrolytically. *The American process*, developed by the Fixed Nitrogen Laboratory of the U. S. Department of Agriculture, operates at 300 atm. and 475° C. Iron oxide granules mixed with potassium and aluminum oxides are used as a catalyst, and the recovery of ammonia per cycle is about 20 per cent.

Both nitrogen-fixation processes yield compounds in which the valence of the nitrogen is -3, whereas there is a huge demand for nitric acid. Fortunately, ammonia can be converted to nitric acid by a method known as the *Ostwald process*. Ammonia can be burned in air in the presence of a catalyst; platinum has been found excellent for this purpose. An aluminum chamber containing platinum gauze is used for the reaction. The gauze is heated to about 700° C. by an electric current, and NH_3 and air in the ratio of 1 to 10 are then passed through the chamber. The reaction is exothermic; therefore as soon as it begins, the current is shut off. A constant temperature can be maintained by adjusting the volume of air; if it is too high, the oxides of nitrogen will decompose. The first reaction, which requires contact for only a fraction of a second, is the conversion of ammonia into nitric oxide.

$$4\ NH_3 + 5\ O_2 \longrightarrow 4\ NO + 6\ H_2O + 200{,}000\ \text{cal. (approx.)}$$

The nitric oxide immediately combines with more oxygen, yielding nitrogen dioxide

$$2\ NO + O_2 \longrightarrow 2\ NO_2$$

The nitrogen dioxide reacts with warm water, and nitric oxide is liberated.

$$3\ NO_2 + H_2O \longrightarrow 2\ HNO_3 + NO$$

The nitric oxide is returned to the reaction chamber and recirculated. Once nitric acid is prepared, any of the nitrates can be produced from it. Many ammonia plants are equipped with Ostwald oxidation units which convert the nitrogen of the air to nitrates in one continuous process.

Other Processes

Some nitric oxide is produced during thunderstorms by the passage of lightning through the atmosphere. Scientists tried for many years to duplicate nature's method, and eventually succeeded; but the success was short-lived, for the arc process, which was once thought to be the most probable method of fixing nitrogen, is obsolete today because ammonia can be produced so economically by the Haber process. The arc process depends upon the endothermic reaction:

$$N_2 + O_2 + 43{,}200\ \text{cal.} \rightleftarrows 2\ NO$$

It was carried out by blowing air through an electric arc at 3500° C. by Birkeland and Eyde in Norway for nearly forty years.

The Serpek process depended upon the reactions:

$$Al_2O_3 + 3\ C + N_2 \longrightarrow 2\ AlN + 3\ CO$$

$$AlN + 3\ H_2O \longrightarrow Al(OH)_3 + NH_3$$

It never became of much importance.

A new process with interesting possibilities was developed at the University of Wisconsin under Dr. Farrington Daniels. The research was a war project sponsored by the Office of Scientific Research and Development. It was found that when hot air was blown through a "stove" filled with pebbles previously heated white-hot, a small amount of NO was formed and immediately oxidized to NO_2. The NO_2 was concentrated by absorption with silica gel (page 461) and then converted into nitric acid. The simplicity of the process is attractive, but it is doubtful if the energy requirements can be met at low enough cost to make it practical. At least, that must have been the conclusion of the companies which considered the Daniels process but finally committed themselves to new ammonia plants in 1948.

Production of Fixed Nitrogen

Before World War II Germany led the world both in total production of fixed nitrogen and in size of individual plants. The largest ammonia plant in the world was at Merseburg; in 1934 it had a capacity of 715,000 tons of nitrogen a year, which was about equal to the total synthetic production of the United States. During the war our government built ammonia plants whose capacity totaled 800,000 tons of nitrogen a year. Most of this was used as fertilizer, our consumption of which doubled during the war. Contrary to the expectations of many, it has been necessary for the United States to continue ammonia production at full capacity. In the year 1946–1947 the world's production of fixed nitrogen, some 4,000,000 tons, still fell a million tons short of meeting the need for fertilizer. All the other sources of fixed nitrogen are now small compared with synthetic ammonia. In 1944 our production of ammonium sulfate and ammonia from coke amounted to about 200,000 tons of nitrogen; the entire output of cyanamide at Niagara Falls was equivalent to 80,000 tons more; and the half million tons of sodium nitrate we imported from Chile in 1946 contained only about as much nitrogen as did the Canadian cyanamide just mentioned.

QUESTIONS AND PROBLEMS

1. List the elements in the nitrogen family. Sketch the planetary electrons for each of these elements.
2. Is the gas obtained by removing water vapor, carbon dioxide, and oxygen from the air lighter or heavier than *pure* nitrogen?
3. Since nitrogen and oxygen combine when there is a flash of lightning, why does the reaction not go to completion and thus use up all the oxygen in the air?
4. Balance the equation:

$$NH_3 + CuO \longrightarrow$$

   Is ammonia an oxidizing or a reducing agent in this reaction?
5. What is the smallest amount of water which should be added to dissolve the salt formed if 16 g. of NH_4Cl are used with $NaNO_2$ to prepare pure nitrogen? (35.7 g. of NaCl dissolve in 100 cc. of H_2O at 0° C. Assume the temperature to be 0° C.)
6. What weight of urea is required to produce 45 l. of gases at S.T.P. by hydrolysis?
7. Start with nitrogen and show by equations how one compound of each valence of nitrogen could be formed.

8. Is ammonia gas toxic? How does it compare with other gases?
9. How are amides prepared?
10. What are complex ions of ammonia?
11. Show by equations the heat decomposition of each of the following: NH_4Cl, $(NH_4)_2Cr_2O_7$, NH_4HCO_3, NH_4NO_2, NH_4NO_3. If the gases which escape are collected at 0° C., which salt liberates the greatest volume of gas per gram of salt used?
12. If there are only 10 g. of copper in the laboratory and you wish to prepare the *greatest possible volume of oxides* of nitrogen by the action of copper on nitric acid, will you use dilute or concentrated HNO_3? Why?
13. List the oxides of nitrogen in order of stability.
14. What precautions should you remember in using concentrated nitric acid? Are any of the oxides of nitrogen poisonous? What is aqua regia?
15. How do we account for the fact that concentrated nitric acid and magnesium fail to liberate hydrogen?
16. List some properties and uses of cyanides.
17. A gas is known to be He, H_2, O_2, N_2, N_2O, NO, NO_2, Cl_2, NH_3, or Br_2; how would you identify it?
18. Calculate the tons of nitrogen in 1 cu. mile of air. Assume that 22.4 l. of air weigh 29 g.
19. What weight of calcium cyanamide is required to produce one ton of HNO_3 of s.g. 1.43 and 74 per cent HNO_3 by weight?
20. What volume of gases at S.T.P. would be required to produce the HNO_3 specified in problem 19 by the arc process?

REFERENCES

Books

Fixed Nitrogen. Curtis, H. A. *A.C.S. Monograph 59.* Chemical Catalog Co.
Fixation of Atmospheric Nitrogen. Ernst, F. A. D. Van Nostrand Company Inc.
The Nitrogen System of Compounds. Franklin, E. C. *A.C.S. Monograph No. 68.* Reinhold Publishing Corp.

Articles

"Ammonia Synthesis." Emmett, P. H. *J. Chem. Ed.* **7,** 2571–2583 (1930).
"Developments in Nitrogen Fertilizers." Burdick, C. L. *Chem. and Met. Eng.* **40,** 638–641 (1933).
"Cyanamide Process." Lee, J. A. *Chem. and Met. Eng.* **38,** 564–567 (1931).
"Ammonia Synthesis." Mittasch, A., and Frankenburger, W. *J. Chem. Ed.* **6,** 2097–2103 (1929).
"Anhydrous Ammonia." Quinn, R. J. *Ind. and Eng. Chem.* **24,** 610–613 (1932).
"Liquid Ammonia." Watt, G. W., and Cappel, N. O. *J. Chem. Ed.* **15,** 133–142 (1938).

"Liquid Ammonia as a Solvent." Fernelius, W. C., and Johnson, W. C. *J. Chem. Ed.* **5,** 664–670, 828–835 (1928); **6,** 441–450 (1929).
"Arc Process." Braham, J. M. *Chem. and Met. Eng.* **32,** 321–322 (1925).
"Catalysts for Oxidation of Ammonia." Handforth, S. L., and Tilley, J. N. *Ind. and Eng. Chem.* **26,** 1287–1292 (1934).
"Nitric Acid." Fauser, G. *Chem. and Met. Eng.* **39,** 430–432 (1932).
"Technology of Chilean Nitrate Industry." *Ind. and Eng. Chem.* **23,** 456–462 (1931).
"Nitrate Fields of Chile." Reichart, H. L., and Schulz, H. W. *Chem. and Met. Eng.* **46,** 464–467 (1939).

» 25 «

PHOSPHORUS AND ITS COMPOUNDS

Phosphorus, the element just below nitrogen in the periodic table, is strictly a non-metal. In some respects it is quite similar to nitrogen, in that both form hydrides, a series of oxides, and halides; however, the compounds show more resemblances in characteristics than do the elements themselves.

Discovery of Phosphorus

Although the famous English chemist, Robert Boyle, discovered phosphorus independently, Brand (or Brandt—there is some question about the spelling of his name) is usually credited with its discovery. After serving as a soldier and then becoming a physician (the latter with no training), Brand married a wealthy woman and lived in luxury for several years. After her death, he squandered his money; in an attempt to regain it, he turned to alchemy, hoping to find a method of preparing gold from silver. During an experiment in 1669, he evaporated some urine to dryness and heated the residue with sand and charcoal. To his great surprise, this mixture, when distilled, yielded a substance that glowed in the dark. He tried to keep his famous discovery a secret, but word of it spread like fire; phosphorus was soon on the market, and the "wonderful shining pills" were being used in medicine.

Phosphorus ignites so readily in the atmosphere that one of the first tasks was to find an easy way of collecting it as it was distilled. Placing the opening of the retort under a receiver containing water soon proved to be the best way.

Occurrence of Phosphorus

Though phosphorus is widely distributed in nature, it is never found in a free or uncombined state because of its great affinity for oxygen. With only few exceptions it is present only in the form of phosphates, of which a large number have been identified. Bone ash is about 83 per cent calcium phosphate, $Ca_3(PO_4)_2$. This salt, which is also known as phosphorite, is found in fossil deposits; important phosphorite mines are located in Tennessee, Florida, Montana, Utah, and Idaho. Apatite, $Ca_5(PO_4)_3F$, is also found in nature, some of the largest deposits being located in Canada. Extensive phosphate mines have recently been opened in Russia, and an enormous deposit of high-grade apatite is being developed on the Kola Peninsula in the Arctic Circle. The total deposits of phosphate rocks in the United States are about 6,500,000,000 tons; the deposits in Idaho are estimated at 5,000,000 tons, and those in Florida at 500,000,000 tons. At the present rate of mining in this country, these deposits will last about 2000 years. World deposits are at least three times our own total deposits, although no accurate estimates are available for South America, Canada, or Russia. The yearly production of phosphate rock throughout the world is about 8,000,000 tons, most of which is consumed in the fertilizer industry.

Since phosphorus is a constituent of protein, it is present in urine; this explains why Brand obtained it from this source. Muscle and brain tissue are also rich in phosphorus. Its total content in the body is between 30 and 40 g. at birth and about 1600 g. in middle age. Meat, milk, fish, nuts, and egg yolk are rich in protein and hence in phosphorus compounds.

Preparation of Phosphorus

The preparation of phosphorus is so difficult that it is usually not prepared in experiments in general chemistry; that required in the laboratory is purchased. The same chemicals are used today in the commercial preparation of phosphorus as Brand used nearly 300 years ago; however, the source of these chemicals is different. If calcium phosphate, sand, and coke are heated together in an electric furnace, phosphorus will distill from the mixture, but the temperature must be higher than the melting point of sand. The equation for the reaction can be written in steps, the first of which is probably the following equilibrium:

$$2\ Ca_3(PO_4)_2 + 6\ SiO_2 \rightleftharpoons 6\ CaSiO_3 + 2\ P_2O_5$$

As soon as any P_2O_5 is formed it is reduced to phosphorus.

$$2\ P_2O_5 + 10\ C \longrightarrow 10\ CO + P_4$$

or $\quad 2\ Ca_3(PO_4)_2 + 6\ SiO_2 + 10\ C \longrightarrow 6\ CaSiO_3 + 10\ CO + P_4$

Phosphorus is written P_4 because the density of the gas up to 1500° C. indicates that it is tetratomic. As the mixture is heated to a high temperature by an electric arc, the phosphorus distills off and can be pumped from one place to another in heat-jacketed lines. Most furnaces are so equipped that the mixture is fed into the furnace continuously, the calcium silicate being removed as a molten slag from the bottom of the furnace.

Phosphorus, like sulfur and oxygen, can be prepared in allotropic forms, there being three—white, red, and black—for phosphorus. White phosphorus is always produced by the procedure just described. If it is heated to between 230° and 300° C. in the absence of air, it changes to the red allotropic form. When red phosphorus is distilled, the vapors condense to the usual white form. White phosphorus exposed to sunlight soon becomes coated with red phosphorus and has a yellow color. The unusual black form is made by putting white phosphorus under a pressure of seven tons per square inch at 200° C.

Physical and Chemical Properties of White Phosphorus

As ordinarily prepared, white phosphorus is a wax-like substance which melts at 44° C. and boils at 287° C. It is heavier than water (s.g. 1.83 at room temperature). It is insoluble in water, but dissolves in carbon disulfide, from which it crystallizes in rhombic dodecahedra. It is very soluble in the phosphorus halides, and slightly soluble in the organic compounds, alcohol, ether, benzene, glycerine, and fused stearic acid.

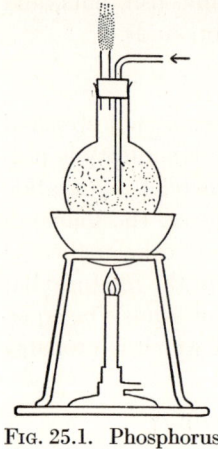

FIG. 25.1. Phosphorus glow.

Phosphorus differs decidedly from nitrogen in activity, for it combines readily with many metals and non-metals. Fragments of phosphorus ignite in air at 35° C. The typical phosphorus glow (Fig. 25.1) may be produced by putting a few pieces of yellow phosphorus in the bottom of a flask and filling it with glass wool. The flask is heated on a water bath and carbon dioxide forced in; the glow appears as the CO_2 sweeps the phosphorus vapor into the air. The flame is so cool that it will not ignite a match head or burn the fingers. Moist phosphorus oxidizes rapidly in air and produces white fumes of phosphorus pentoxide, P_2O_5. It is claimed that *absolutely* dry phosphorus can be distilled in pure oxygen. (There are so many theories pertaining to phosphorescence that none of them will be discussed here.) Never pick up a piece of white phosphorus with your fingers, for phosphorus burns are extremely painful and the heat of the hand is sufficient to ignite it.

White phosphorus is very poisonous, 0.1 g. being sufficient to cause death. It is absorbed slowly by the liver and blood; hence the symptoms of acute poisoning may not appear for several hours after it has been swallowed. In spite of its toxicity it is used as a stimulant for the nervous system, and phosphorus ointments are used for certain skin diseases.

Physical and Chemical Properties of Red Phosphorus

The change from white to red phosphorus involves an increase in specific gravity from 1.83 to 2.34, and also a loss of energy in the form of heat; thus the red form burns with a smaller heat of combustion. Both forms, when burned, produce a dense white smoke of solid particles of P_2O_5. Red phosphorus is microcrystalline, not soluble in any solvent, and not poisonous; it must be heated to 240° C. before it ignites.

The differences between white and red phosphorus are explained by their different molecular structures. The P_4 molecule of yellow phosphorus is tetrahedral. Imagine a triangular pyramid with a phosphorus atom at each vertex and an electron pair on each edge, and you have a good picture of it. Each P atom has one covalent bond to each of the other three atoms in the molecule, and one unshared electron pair. Although fairly complicated, this molecule is symmetrical and not very heavy (it weighs $\frac{3}{4}$ as much as a Br_2 molecule); hence it is not surprising to find it very volatile. Phosphorus atoms are less electrophilic than the smaller nitrogen atoms; therefore bonds in the P_4 molecule break at a moderate temperature. The situation is like that with molten sulfur, and the result is similar. However, since the covalence of phosphorus is 3 instead of 2, the giant molecules which form are three-dimensional tangles instead of simple chains. These giant molecules of red phosphorus cannot dissolve in solvents, and they evaporate only when the temperature is high enough to rupture covalent bonds and fling off fragments. The chemical reactivity is low for the same reason.

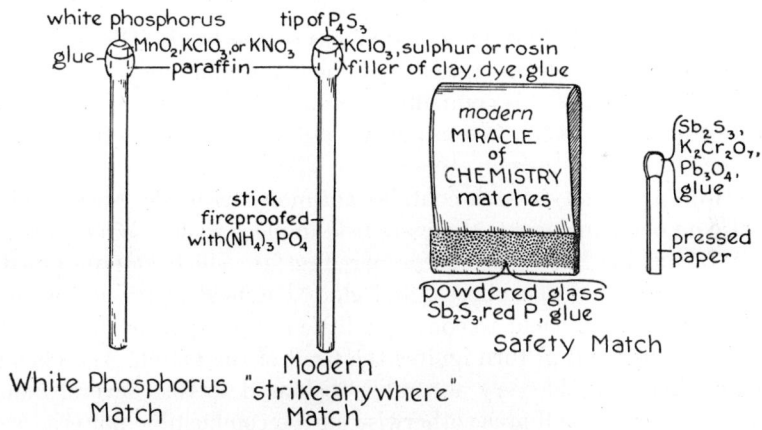

FIG. 25.2. Preparation of matches.

Uses of Phosphorus

Besides its use in medicine already mentioned, phosphorus is used in making special phosphorus alloys, many useful phosphorus compounds, and rat poisons; as a smoke screen and incendiary in chemical warfare; and in the manufacture of matches.

Friction matches, which have been in use for over a century, are one of the many modern conveniences made possible by the application of chemistry. White phosphorus was formerly used in the head of the "strike-anywhere" match. The workers in match plants were necessarily exposed day after day to phosphorus vapors, and usually succumbed to a disease called "phossy jaw," or decay of the lower jaw bone. It was not until 1913 that the United States government passed laws levying so heavy a tax on the manufacturers of these matches that this kind of match was driven out of existence. Fig. 25.2 shows the constituents of the white phosphorus match, the present "strike-anywhere" match, and the safety match. In the old match, a little friction ignited the white phosphorus, this in turn ignited the paraffin in the presence of an oxidizing agent, and the paraffin ignited the wood. Glue held the oxidizing agent and phosphorus in place and also protected the phosphorus from being oxidized by the air. The wood of the "strike-anywhere" match is first dipped in a fireproofing agent so that the lower part of the stick will not burn readily, and the other end of the stick is then dipped in paraffin. The head of the match contains an oxidizing agent such as $KClO_3$, a substance like sulfur or rosin which oxidizes readily, a filler of clay or infusorial earth, an aniline dye to give it a distinctive color, and a binding material of casein glue. When the head is nearly dry, a tip of phosphorus trisulfide, P_4S_3 (also called phosphorus sesquisulfide), is applied. When the match is rubbed against a rough surface, the heat of friction ignites the P_4S_3, which decomposes and burns at a low temperature and, in the presence of oxidizing agents, ignites the paraffin.

The patent controlling the use of P_4S_3 was owned by the Diamond Match Co. When the objection was raised that the law forbidding the use of white phosphorus would give this company a monopoly, the company promised to dedicate the patent to the free use of the public if the law was passed, and did so.

The tip of the safety match contains antimony trisulfide, Sb_2S_3, and possibly also an oxidizing agent; these are held in place with casein or glue. The package of matches has a specially prepared surface which contains powdered glass for friction, red phosphorus, and glue. The heat of friction when the match is struck is sufficient to convert a little red phosphorus into the white form; this ignites and in turn ignites the head of the match. The chemicals on the surface must be very accurately balanced so that several matches can be struck on a small area; otherwise all the combustible material would burn off when a single match was struck.

Hydrogen Compounds of Phosphorus

Phosphorus forms hydrides such as $(PH_2)_2$, $(P_4H_2)_3$, and PH_3; of these, phosphine, PH_3, is the only important one. Note its similarity in formula to ammonia, NH_3. Fig. 25.3 shows two methods of preparing this gas. Calcium phosphide, Ca_3P_2, can be obtained by heating phosphorus and calcium together under petroleum. If the red-brown phosphide is added to water, phosphine is liberated. The reaction between calcium phosphide and water is very similar to that between magnesium nitride and water.

$$\underline{Mg_3N_2} + 6\ H_2O \longrightarrow 3\ \underline{Mg(OH)_2} + 2\ \overline{NH_3}$$

$$\underline{Ca_3P_2} + 6\ H_2O \longrightarrow 3\ \underline{Ca(OH)_2} + 2\ \overline{PH_3}$$

Phosphine is not as stable as ammonia; the formation of a stable hydrogen compound is a characteristic of a typical non-metal, and phosphorus is not as strongly non-metallic as nitrogen. (Recall the discussions in Chapter 7 regarding the increasing metallic nature of the elements as we progress down a given subgroup.) Phosphine is much more easily oxidized than ammonia; being less electrophilic than nitrogen, it is more willing to share electrons with the violently electrophilic oxygen.

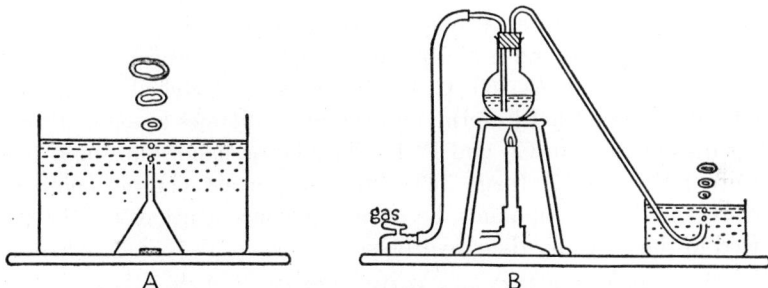

FIG. 25.3. *A*, phosphine from calcium phosphide; *B*, phosphine from phosphorus and sodium hydroxide.

Phosphine can be produced, along with traces of P_2H_4, by the disproportionation of phosphorus in contact with sodium hydroxide solution. A few pieces of white phosphorus are placed in a 500-ml. flask containing 200 ml. of 40 per cent NaOH solution, and the apparatus is connected as shown in Fig. 25.3B. All the air in the flask must be displaced with illuminating gas *before* heat is applied, or an explosion will occur. Absolutely pure PH_3 does not ignite on coming in contact with air, but P_2H_4 is spontaneously inflammable. As the bubbles of gas reach the surface of the water and break, the P_2H_4 catches fire and ignites the other gases; there is a puff of yellow flame, and a smoke ring of P_2O_5 floats upward.

$$6\ \underline{P} + 4\ Na^+ + 4\ OH^- \longrightarrow \overline{P_2H_4} + 4\ Na^+ + 4\ H_2PO_2^-$$

$$4\ \underline{P} + 3\ Na^+ + 3\ OH^- \longrightarrow \overline{PH_3} + 3\ Na^+ + 4\ H_2PO_2^-$$

The fact that the phosphine does not dissolve to any great extent in water shows that it is a much weaker base than ammonia. It cannot react with such a weak acid as water, but does take a proton from a strong acid.

$$\overline{PH_3} + \overline{HCl} \longrightarrow \underline{PH_4Cl}$$

Correspondingly, the *phosphonium ion*, PH_4^+, is a much stronger acid than ammonium ion. The latter yields only a few protons to water, whereas phosphonium salts hydrolyze completely.

$$PH_4^+ + Cl^- \xrightarrow{H_2O} H^+ + Cl^- + \overline{PH_3}$$

Halides of Phosphorus

All the halogens combine directly with phosphorus to form halides of the types PX_3 and PX_5. The former are typical covalent compounds; PF_3 is a gas, PCl_3 and PBr_3 are liquids, and PI_3 is a low melting-point solid. In PF_5, phosphorus has a valence layer of ten electrons; the substance is a gas. PCl_5 behaves as though it were a salt, having the ions PCl_4^+ and Cl^- and being a solid at room temperature. Apparently there is not quite enough room for five chlorine atoms around a phosphorus atom at the proper distance for a normal covalent bond. At 160° C. the bonds have stretched enough to let the molecule assume the PF_5 form, and the PCl_5 sublimes as a gas. However, it easily dissociates into Cl_2 and PCl_3. Phosphorus halides are used to prepare pure HBr and HI (page 333) and also certain organic compounds. Never breathe these compounds, because high concentrations of HCl will be produced in the lungs by their hydrolysis.

$$PCl_3 + 3\ H_2O \longrightarrow H_3PO_3 + 3\ H^+ + 3\ Cl^-$$

A bottle of PCl_3 fumes in the air as soon as the stopper is removed.

Oxides of Phosphorus, Oxy-acids and Their Salts

Unlike nitrogen, phosphorus combines readily with oxygen. Only two of the several oxides are of commercial importance.

Oxides of Phosphorus. The two important stable oxides are P_2O_3 and P_2O_5. If phosphorus is burned in a limited amount of air, P_2O_3 will be predominant in the mixture of P_2O_3 and P_2O_5, whereas in an excess of air only P_2O_5 is formed. Since P_2O_3 is easily oxidized, it is a good reducing agent. It boils at 173° C.; the vapor is quite toxic and smells like garlic. P_2O_3 is the anhydride of phosphorous acid, H_3PO_3. P_2O_5 is very stable and is reduced only with great difficulty; therefore it is an extremely poor oxidizing agent, as is evidenced by the high temperature required to prepare phosphorus by reduction with carbon. P_2O_5 is an excellent drying agent, for it has a great affinity for water. It is the anhydride of phosphoric acid, H_3PO_4.

The molecular formulas of these oxides are double the commonly used empirical formulas. In P_4O_6 an $\ddot{\mathrm{O}}{:}$ atom has inserted itself into each edge of the P_4 tetrahedron, so that P:P is changed into $\overset{\cdot\cdot}{\underset{P\quad P}{\overset{\mathrm{O}}{\cdot\cdot}}}$ (the other electrons of the P atoms are not in the plane of the paper). In the formation of P_4O_{10} the P_4O_6 structure remains intact, but oxygen atoms seize the four lone electron pairs.

Hypophosphorous Acid and Its Salts. If barium hydroxide is substituted for NaOH in the preparation of phosphine, barium hypophosphite is formed. The addition of H_2SO_4 to the solution liberates the free acid, which can be concentrated by careful evaporation.

$$Ba^{++} + 2\ H_2PO_2^- + H^+ + HSO_4^- \longrightarrow \underline{BaSO_4} + 2\ H_3PO_2$$

On being heated, the acid decomposes into H_3PO_4 and PH_3, according to the equation:

$$2\ H_3PO_2 \longrightarrow H_3PO_4 + \overline{PH_3}$$

Both the acid and its salts are powerful reducing agents, an example of their action being the reduction of $AgNO_3$ to metallic silver. The reactions of H_3PO_2 indicate that it is *monobasic*, only one of the hydrogens being replaceable with a metallic ion; therefore its electronic formula is:

$$\begin{array}{c} H \\ H:\!\overset{..}{\underset{..}{O}}\!:\!\overset{..}{\underset{..}{P}}\!:\!\overset{..}{\underset{..}{O}}: \\ H \end{array}$$

(The valence of phosphorus in this compound is plus one.) Hydrogens attached directly to the non-metal are not replaceable in simple neutralization reactions, but they do have reducing properties. Some of the hypophosphites are used medicinally as tonics.

Phosphorous Acid and Its Salts. Phosphorus trioxide dissolves in water to form phosphorous acid, H_3PO_3. The easiest method of preparing the acid in the pure state is by the hydrolysis of phosphorus trichloride. The HCl is removed by boiling the solution. As in the case of hypophosphorous acid, the ordinary formula is deceptive in suggesting that the acid is tribasic. The electronic formula shows plainly that it is dibasic.

$$\begin{array}{c} :\!\overset{..}{O}\!: \\ H:\!\overset{..}{\underset{..}{O}}\!:\!\overset{..}{\underset{..}{P}}\!:\!\overset{..}{\underset{..}{O}}\!:H \\ H \end{array}$$

Phosphorous acid is a weak acid, forming such salts as NaH_2PO_3 and Na_2HPO_3, some of which are used medicinally.

Phosphoric Acids. On page 336 we learned that non-metallic oxides were acid anhydrides because of the ease with which they add water hydrolytically wherever an oxygen atom is bound to two non-metal atoms. In the case of the oxides of phosphorus there are obviously several possible steps in this process, for there are four dicovalent oxygen atoms in the molecule. In discussing them we shall use P_4O_{10} only. P_4O_6 behaves the same way, but the resulting acids are of no real interest.

The first step in the addition of water to P_4O_{10} is the breaking of a single P–O–P linkage in the tetrahedron, forming $H_2P_4O_{11}$.

If exactly two mols of water are added to one of P_4O_{10}, a white transparent solid called "glacial phosphoric acid" is formed; it can be melted and cast into sticks. (The word "glacial" refers to the ice-like appearance.) The empirical formula is HPO_3, but the molecular formula is *not* $H_4P_4O_{12}$, even though only enough water has been added to break two of the P–O–P linkages. The hydrolysis of these two linkages lets the molecule flatten out into a plane, thus:

$$\begin{array}{c} \ddot{:}\ddot{O}\ddot{:}\quad\ddot{:}\ddot{O}\ddot{:} \\ H\!:\!\ddot{O}\!:\!P\!:\!\ddot{O}\!:\!P\!:\!\ddot{O}\!:\!H \\ \ddot{:}\ddot{O}\ddot{:}\quad\ddot{:}\ddot{O}\ddot{:} \\ H\!:\!\ddot{O}\!:\!P\!:\!\ddot{O}\!:\!P\!:\!\ddot{O}\!:\!H \\ \ddot{:}\ddot{O}\ddot{:}\quad\ddot{:}\ddot{O}\ddot{:} \end{array}$$

But this ring quickly breaks, yielding a chain, on one end of which is an atom with only six valence electrons. Here again is a situation like the one which resulted in the formation of elastic sulfur, and the same thing happens. The units join each other, forming enormously long chains. This acid, $(HPO_3)_x$, reacts immediately with more water when dissolved, but its sodium salt can be obtained by driving off water from NaH_2PO_4. It is called sodium metaphosphate.

The addition of three mols of water to a mol of P_4O_{10} under the proper conditions yields tetraphosphoric acid by hydrolyzing one of the P–O–P linkages in the ring shown above. The use of $H_6P_4O_{13}$ as a catalyst in certain organic reactions has been patented.

If four mols of water are added to one of P_4O_{10}, or if glacial phosphoric acid is dissolved in water, pyrophosphoric acid is formed.

$$\underline{P_4O_{10}} + 4\ H_2O \longrightarrow 2\ H_4P_2O_7$$

On long standing, and in the presence of an excess of water (or more quickly if a trace of HNO_3 is added as a catalyst), orthophosphoric acid forms.

$$H_4P_2O_7 + H_2O \longrightarrow 2\ H_3PO_4$$

This is equivalent to adding six mols of water to one of P_4O_{10}. Since the P_4 complex finally broke in two on the addition of the fourth mol of water, there can be no question of adding *one* more. The structure of orthophosphoric acid is

$$\begin{array}{c} \ddot{:}\ddot{O}\ddot{:} \\ H\!:\!\ddot{O}\!:\!P\!:\!\ddot{O}\!:\!H \\ \ddot{:}\ddot{O}\ddot{:} \\ H \end{array}$$

PHOSPHORUS AND ITS COMPOUNDS

There are now no more oxygen atoms with a covalence of two; so the addition of another water molecule could take place only by the enlargement of the valence layer of P to 10 electrons. Third-period elements do not appear to be large enough to do this in any of their compounds with oxygen; there is no H_5PO_5. The oxidation number of phosphorus is +5 in phosphorus pentoxide and in all the acids obtained by hydrating it; hence all these acids are phosphoric acids. However, if "phosphoric acid" is used without qualification, it means orthophosphoric acid to everyone. Ortho- and pyrophosphoric acids are among the strongest of the weak acids, being slightly stronger than the bisulfate ion.

The ortho-, meta-, and pyrophosphoric acids, and also the soluble salts of these acids, can be differentiated from one another by certain chemical properties. How can a white salt which is one of the following be identified: $NaPO_3$, Na_3PO_4, or $Na_4P_2O_7$? If the tests listed in Table 25.1 were made, the results indicated would be obtained.

TABLE 25.1. TESTS FOR THE IDENTIFICATION OF THE ORTHO-, META-, AND PYROPHOSPHATE RADICALS

	$[PO_3^-]$	$[P_2O_7^{----}]$	$[PO_4^{---}]$
Add $AgNO_3$ to neutral solution	$AgPO_3$ white insoluble	$Ag_4P_2O_7$ white insoluble	Ag_3PO_4 insoluble yellow
Add a clear solution of egg albumin[a]	Protein is coagulated	No coagulation	No coagulation
$MgCl_2$ and NH_4OH	No precipitate	No precipitate	$MgNH_4PO_4$ white
$(NH_4)_2MoO_4$ and HNO_3	No precipitate	No precipitate	$(NH_4)_3PO_4 \cdot$ 12 MoO_3 yellow

[a] The solution must contain the free acid.

The equations for the formation of ammonium phosphomolybdate and magnesium ammonium phosphate are as follows:

$$H_3PO_4 + 24\ NH_4^+ + 12\ MoO_4^{--} + 21\ H^+ + 21\ NO_3^- \longrightarrow$$
$$(NH_4)_3PO_4 \cdot 12\ MoO_3 + 21\ NH_4^+ + 21\ NO_3^- + 12\ H_2O$$

$$Mg^{++} + 2\ Cl^- + 3\ NH_4OH + H_3PO_4 \longrightarrow$$
$$MgNH_4PO_4 + 2\ NH_4^+ + 2\ Cl^- + 3\ H_2O$$

The first precipitate is always produced in the presence of an excess of nitric acid, and the second in an excess of ammonium hydroxide.

Pentavalent Phosphorus Salts. Since it is possible to replace all or any part of the replaceable hydrogen of an acid, there are many pentavalent phosphorus salts; the list becomes even larger because of the great number of salt hydrates. The most important of the salts are those of orthophosphoric acid, all of which form several hydrates.

Salts of Orthophosphoric Acid. The three sodium salts of orthophosphoric acid in the following list are the most important derivatives of the acid.

Na_3PO_4, trisodium phosphate (tribasic phosphate)
Na_2HPO_4, disodium monohydrogen phosphate (dibasic phosphate)
NaH_2PO_4, monosodium dihydrogen phosphate (monobasic phosphate)

These compounds are prepared by the complete or partial neutralization of H_3PO_4 with sodium hydroxide. Several hydrates may be formed, depending upon the temperature and the method of crystallization from the water solution.

The dihydrogen phosphate ion is a weak acid, slightly weaker than carbonic acid; it is familiar in plain carbonated water. (Its use as an acid in baking powder has already been mentioned.) The monohydrogen phosphate ion is therefore mildly basic, slightly more so than the bicarbonate ion. Solutions containing it must also contain a little dihydrogen phosphate ion, by hydrolysis.

$$2\ Na^+ + HPO_4^{--} + H_2O \rightleftarrows 2\ Na^+ + H_2PO_4^- + OH^-$$

The monohydrogen phosphate ion is also, as its formula suggests, an acid. It is a very weak one, almost as weak as the bisulfide ion; but a solution of Na_2HPO_4 contains an appreciable amount of PO_4^{---} because of the ionization of HPO_4^{--}. (The ability of mixture of phosphates to serve as buffer salts was discussed on page 240, which should be reviewed.) Mixtures of $(NH_4)H_2PO_4$ and $(NH_4)_2HPO_4$ are valuable constituents of culture media in which bacteria and yeasts are grown. The mixture serves both as a buffer and as a source of the nitrogen and phosphorus essential for plant growth. Nearly all culture media contain phosphates in one form or another.

Phosphates containing either H or NH_4 in the formula decompose on heating. For example:

$$2\ Na_2HPO_4 \xrightarrow{\Delta} Na_4P_2O_7 + \overline{H_2O}$$
$$NaNH_4HPO_4 \xrightarrow{\Delta} NaPO_3 + \overline{H_2O} + \overline{NH_3}$$

Reactions of this type offer convenient means of preparing pyro- and metaphosphates.

The phosphate ion is a fairly strong base. A 0.1 N solution of Na_3PO_4 has a pH of 12, being about 10 per cent hydrolyzed.

$$3\ Na^+ + PO_4^{---} + H_2O \longrightarrow 3\ Na^+ + HPO_4^{--} + OH^-$$

Trisodium phosphate ("TSP") is a "heavy chemical"; that is, it is bought by individual users in carload lots. In water softeners it does triple duty; it softens the water by precipitating insoluble $Ca_3(PO_4)_2$, raises the pH to the point at which soap is most effective, and aids in dispersing grease and dirt into particles of colloidal dimensions so that they can be rinsed away. The ability to act as a dispersing agent leads to curiously diverse uses for this salt. It helps prevent the separation of drops of oil from cheese and ice cream, and holds in suspension the heavy $BaSO_4$ particles in the "driller's mud" that counterbalances the weight of a half-mile rotary drill in an oil well.

Salts of Pyrophosphoric Acid. Since pyrophosphoric acid is tetrabasic, we might expect four different sodium salts; but only two have as yet been prepared. The normal salt is $Na_4P_2O_7$; the other is the dibasic salt, $Na_2H_2P_2O_7$. The uses of these salts are similar to those of the corresponding sodium orthophosphates. Differences in acid or base strength may decide the question of which to use in a particular case.

Salts of Metaphosphoric Acid. Sodium metaphosphate, $Na_x(PO_3)_x$, is practically insoluble in water on account of the large size of the anion. It is used as an opacifying agent in ceramic glazes. If it is carefully heated to about 700° C., it can be transformed into an easily soluble variety with the same empirical formula. This substance is called sodium hexametaphosphate because the anion consists of a ring of six PO_3^- units. This substance is sold as a water softener under the trade name of Calgon. Two Ca^{++} or Mg^{++} ions can get *inside the ring*, and are held there so tightly as to suggest that some kind of coordination takes place, forming a complex ion $[Ca_2(PO_3)_6]^{--}$. $Na_6(PO_3)_6$ is an interesting water softener in that no precipitate is formed; it can even dissolve $CaSO_4$ scale that has already been deposited by hard water in pipes. The hexametaphosphate ion possesses the typical phosphate ability as a dispersing agent; one or two p.p.m. of it can prevent the precipitation of red $Fe(OH)_3$ from water containing a little iron.

Phosphorus Compounds in the Fertilizer Industry

It is difficult to distinguish between soluble and insoluble phosphates, available and unavailable forms of phosphoric acid, and natural and manufactured fertilizers because so many of the phosphorus compounds used in the fertilizer industry are border line cases.

Water-soluble phosphates include ordinary acid phosphate, double superphosphate, and ammonium phosphate.

Available phosphates include both the products and by-products of industrial processes, such as steamed or degreased bone, basic slag, dicalcium phosphate, and other manufactured phosphates. These phosphates are only slightly soluble in water, but they are soluble in neutral ammonium citrate or in a 2 per cent citric acid solution. (One specification for a phosphate fertilizer is the amount of "citrate-soluble phosphate" in it.)

Natural phosphates include raw bone, guano, and the phosphate rocks. All are practically insoluble in water; soil conditions make them slowly available. These phosphates are considered inferior to factory-converted ones. In many foreign countries all bones are saved for use as fertilizer; the garbage plants of large cities recover bones from the waste and sell them for this purpose. The grease is removed before the bones are pulverized. The guano deposits found on certain islands off the coast of Peru were formed by bird excrements and contain from 18 to 29 per cent P_2O_5 as phosphates. The deposits of phosphate rock throughout the world have already been mentioned.

Basic slag is by far the greatest source of one so-called available phosphate for fertilizer purposes. It contains from 11 to 23 per cent P_2O_5, and is a by-product of steel manufacture in both the Bessemer and the open-hearth processes. It was first produced as a waste in the processing of high-phosphate iron ores; but its use as a fertilizer had been discovered by 1880, and from then on it was a valuable by-product. Europe normally produces about 4,000,000 tons of basic slag per year, about 60 per cent of which is used in Germany. Some 25,000 tons are produced annually at the Birmingham, Alabama, steel mills.

Phosphate rock is made available for fertilizer use by treating it with acid, converting the PO_4^{---} ion to $H_2PO_4^-$. This is the largest single use of sulfuric acid.

$$\underline{Ca_3(PO_4)_2} + 2\ H^+ + 2\ HSO_4^- \longrightarrow 2\ \underline{CaSO_4} + \underline{Ca(H_2PO_4)_2}$$

Dilute acid is used, the amount of water being calculated so as to produce a dry product after aging. Part of the water is evaporated off by the heat of reaction; the rest is absorbed as water of crystallization by both components of the mixture. With no attempt at separation, the mixture of useless gypsum, $CaSO_4 \cdot 2\ H_2O$, valuable acid phosphate, $Ca(H_2PO_4)_2 \cdot H_2O$, and accidental impurities in the original rock (amounting to about 11 per cent of the finished product) is sold as "superphosphate." Eight million tons of it were produced in the United States in 1944.

As originally sold, superphosphate contained only 15 per cent P_2O_5. It seemed ridiculous to pay freight on 85 per cent of useless material; consequently when phosphoric acid became commercially available, some fertilizer manufacturers began to substitute it for H_2SO_4 in treating the phosphate rock.

$$\underline{Ca_3(PO_4)_2} + 4\ H_3PO_4 \longrightarrow 3\ \underline{Ca(H_2PO_4)_2}$$

This product could be prepared to contain 45 per cent P_2O_5; hence it was called triple superphosphate. Only a relatively small amount of it is sold (325,000 tons in 1944); but because of its competition, improvements have been made in the process of preparing ordinary superphosphate which have brought its average P_2O_5 content up to 18 per cent. The newer material is now more often called "double" rather than "triple" superphosphate.

Two competing processes are used at present in the commercial production of phosphoric acid for fertilizers: the wet process and the thermal process. *In the wet process* the phosphatic material is finely pulverized and treated with sulfuric acid. (All grades of sulfuric acid can be used.)

$$\underline{Ca_3(PO_4)_2} + 3\ H^+ + 3\ HSO_4^- \longrightarrow 3\ \underline{CaSO_4} + 2\ H_3PO_4$$

PHOSPHORUS AND ITS COMPOUNDS

Phosphoric acid is filtered from the insoluble calcium sulfate and then neutralized with ammonia either alone or with potassium hydroxide, or used to prepare double superphosphate. Cheap and easily installed equipment cuts down the cost of production, which is important, since the by-product, calcium sulfate, is of no commercial value.

The thermal process was described on page 423. The electric furnace is steadily becoming more important in industry, but is not able to compete with the blast furnace in making P_2O_5 except where electricity would otherwise go to waste. The Tennessee Valley Authority is conducting large-scale electric furnace operations in an endeavor to make improvements and develop new processes.

Once phosphorus is obtained, it can be converted into P_2O_5, from which phosphoric acid and salts are made. Calcium metaphosphate can be prepared by heating $Ca_3(PO_4)_2$, CO_2, and phosphorus together at 800° C. It contains about 60 per cent available P_2O_5 for plant growth.

$$P_4 + 10\ CO_2 + Ca_3(PO_4)_2 \xrightarrow[800°]{\Delta} 3\ Ca(PO_3)_2 + 10\ CO$$

Most phosphate rock contains 3 to 4 per cent fluorine, some of which is volatilized in the superphosphate process and recovered as fluosilicates. Sodium fluosilicate, a by-product of the phosphate industry, is used in laundries, the manufacture of enameled ware, and as an agricultural poison.

A list of phosphate fertilizers now available in the United States would include blast furnace slag, calcined phosphate rock, KPO_3, ammoniated phosphates, magnesium ammonium phosphate, and urea phosphate $(H_3PO_4 \cdot CO(NH_2)_2)$.

Other Uses of Phosphorus Compounds

The uses for phosphorus compounds are still expanding: phosphorus steels, phosphoric acid in soft drinks and clarifying sugar solutions, weighting silk, fireproofing, cleansers, baking powders, etc. The annual phosphate rock tonnage in the United States is around the five-million mark.

QUESTIONS AND PROBLEMS

1. Account for the early discovery of phosphorus.
2. What volume of H_3PO_4 of s.g. 1.69 and 85 per cent H_3PO_4 by weight can be prepared from one ton of $Ca_3(PO_4)_2$ if the process is 88 per cent efficient?
3. Compare the properties of red and white phosphorus. How many examples of allotropism can you list?
4. Make a list of ways to start a fire without using matches.
5. List the following in order of increasing pH: Na_2HPO_4, H_3PO_4, NaH_2PO_4, and Na_3PO_4.

6. Write the structural formulas for: NaH_2PO_2, $NaPO_3$, H_3PO_3, Na_3PO_4, $Na_4P_2O_7$, Na_2HPO_4, and Na_2HPO_3.
7. An unknown contains PO_3^-, $P_2O_7^{----}$, or PO_4^{---}; how would you identify it?
8. What are buffer salts?
9. Show by equations the heat decomposition of $MgNH_4PO_4$, Na_2HPO_4, NaH_2PO_4, and $NaNH_4HPO_4$.
10. Outline two commercial methods for the preparation of phosphate fertilizers.

REFERENCES

Books

A Comprehensive Treatise on Inorganic and Theoretical Chemistry. Mellor, J. W. Vol. VIII, 1058–1061 (Matches).

Articles

"Phosphorus for Progress." Kirkpatrick, S. D. *Chem. and Met. Eng.* **44,** 644–650 (1937).
"Phosphorus." Davis, T. L. *J. Chem. Ed.* **4,** 1105–1113 (1927).
"The Raw Materials for Phosphate Fertilizer." Waggaman, W. H., and Easterwood, H. H. *Chem. and Met. Eng.* **29,** 393–398 (1923).
"Phosphoric Acid Electrically Made at Wilson Dam." Curtis, H. A. *Chem. and Met. Eng.* **42,** 320–324 (1935).
"Our Phosphate Reserves." Waggaman, W. H. *Chem. and Met. Eng.* **46,** 66–68 (1939).
"Sodium Metaphosphate in Mechanical Dishwashing." Schwartz, C., and Gilmore, B. H. *Ind. and Eng. Chem.* **26,** 998–1001 (1934).
"What's New in Phosphorus." Killeffer, D. H. *Ind. and Eng. Chem.* **30,** 967 (1938).
"Sodium Metaphosphate in Dish Washing." Hall, G. O., and Schwartz, C. *Ind. and Eng. Chem.* **30,** 23 (1938).
"The Family of Phosphates." Logue, Paul. *Chem. Ind.* **49,** 303 (1941).
"Industrial Uses of Phosphates." Logue, Paul. *J. Chem. Ed.* **23,** 529 (1946).

» 26 «

ARSENIC, ANTIMONY, AND BISMUTH

The nitrogen subgroup of Group V in the periodic table contains the five elements, nitrogen, phosphorus, arsenic, antimony, and bismuth. Their atomic weights and metallic properties increase in the order just listed. Nitrogen and phosphorus are strictly non-metallic, arsenic is border-line, antimony has many metallic properties, and bismuth might equally well be discussed in the chapters dealing with the metals. This transition in properties within a subgroup has been noted with the halogens, F–Cl–Br–I, and the sulfur subgroup, O–S–Se–Te. Since Group VII began with the most electrophilic of all elements, and since the element with atomic number 98 is not available for examination, it is natural that metallic properties are barely indicated in iodine (dark color and semi-metallic luster). Tellurium, the fourth main-group element in Group VI, is metallic in appearance but mainly non-metallic in properties. Here again the last element in the family, polonium, is too rare for ordinary general study. For these reasons Groups VII and VI are not well suited for a detailed discussion of the way increasing atomic radii diminish the non-metallic properties and introduce metallic properties in elements in a given family. Group V, however, begins with an element not so violently electrophilic as fluorine or oxygen, and the fifth element is common enough. Accordingly this transition is easily observed in this family. Careful attention should be paid to all the indications of it. For ease in comparison, the properties of nitrogen and phosphorus and their compounds are listed in Table 26.1, along with those of the remaining elements and their compounds.

ARSENIC

A substance which the early Greeks and Romans called arsenic in reality consisted of the poisonous sulfides, orpiment and realgar. Albert the Great

(1193–1280) is usually considered the first one to have isolated the element; he heated soap and arsenic sulfide together. In 1649 Schroeder published methods for preparing arsenic by decomposing orpiment, As_2S_3, and by reducing arsenious oxide, As_2O_3, with charcoal. Lavoisier distinguished clearly between the element and its oxide when he clarified the concept of a "calx" or ash of an element. The earliest records indicate that women used the sulfide to "paint" their faces. Arsenic compounds were widely used in medicine for skin diseases. The high toxicity of the oxide and the fact that it was white and could therefore be mixed with food without detection made it a popular poison. Arsenic is the most toxic of the nitrogen sub-

TABLE 26.1. PROPERTIES OF THE ELEMENTS AND COMPOUNDS OF THE NITROGEN SUBGROUP

	Nitrogen	(White) Phosphorus	(Crystalline) Arsenic	Antimony	Bismuth
Atomic weight	14.008	31.02	74.91	121.76	209
Melting point °C.	−209.8	44.1	814 at 36 atm.	630.5	271
Boiling point °C.	−195.8	280	Subl. 615	1440	1450
Color	Colorless gas	White, red	Gray	Tin white	Silver white
Density	28/22.4 g./l.	1.82	5.7	6.68	9.8
Formula of a metallic compound	Ca_3N_2	Ca_3P_2	Forms alloys	Forms alloys	Forms alloys
Hydrogen compound	NH_3	PH_3	AsH_3	SbH_3	BiH_3
Stability	Very stable	Stable in absence of air	Dec. at 230°	Dec. at 150°	Very unstable
Trivalent oxide	N_2O_3	P_2O_3	As_2O_3	Sb_2O_3	Bi_2O_3
Solubility[a]	Very soluble	Very soluble	Insoluble	Insoluble	Insoluble
Pentavalent oxide	N_2O_5	P_2O_5	As_2O_5	Sb_2O_5	Bi_2O_5
Solubility[a]	Very soluble	Very soluble	59 g./100 g.	0.3 g./100 g.	Insoluble
Halide	NCl_3	PCl_3	$AsCl_3$	$SbCl_3$	$BiCl_3$
Hydrolysis	Explodes 93°	Complete	Sl. reversed by conc. HCl	Reversed by 6 N HCl	Reversed by 3 N HCl
Pentavalent halide	—	PCl_5	$AsCl_5$	$SbCl_5$	—
Hydrolysis in water	—	Complete	Complete	Sl reversed by conc. HCl	—

[a] Non-metal oxides which are soluble in water form acids.

group elements, a fatal dose being between 0.06 and 0.18 g. It is used medicinally in smaller concentrations to increase the blood count and strengthen respiration; the body can build up a tolerance for four times a fatal dose.

Occurrence

Arsenic is found free in small quantities; it is found combined in the form of arsenides of iron, cobalt, and nickel, but it occurs chiefly in the form of sulfides, orpiment (As_2S_3), realgar (As_2S_2), and mispickel or arsenopyrites (FeAsS). In Colorado, Utah, and Montana it is obtained as a by-product of the copper and lead industries; it is recovered from arsenopyrites as a by-product of the nickel and copper industries at Ontario, Canada.

The world production of arsenic has greatly increased during the past ten years, although few new uses have developed. Crude arsenic sells for about 4 cents per pound. Our domestic production of white arsenic, As_2O_3, is about 22,000 tons; in 1945 we imported about 13,000 tons from Mexico, Sweden, Japan, and Belgium. Sweden could more than supply the world's needs from a gold-silver ore containing nearly 10 per cent arsenic. So much by-product arsenic had been produced that storing the excess created a problem; yet during World War II, transportation difficulties produced a serious deficit in our country.

Preparation of Arsenic

Arsenic is easily prepared in the laboratory by heating As_2O_3 and carbon together.

$$As_2O_3 + 3\ C \xrightarrow{\Delta} 2\ As + \overline{3\ CO}$$

Arsenopyrite decomposes into ferrous sulfide and arsenic.

$$FeAsS \xrightarrow{\Delta} FeS + As$$

During the roasting of ores which contain arsenic, the arsenic compounds are converted into As_2O_3, which sublimes at 315° C. and condenses in the flues. In precipitating it, Cottrell precipitators are always used to prevent the dust from escaping into the atmosphere.

Properties of Arsenic

Arsenic is a gray, crystalline, brittle solid which has a metallic appearance. If heated to 615° C., it sublimes and produces a yellow poisonous vapor that smells like garlic. At lower temperatures its formula, as determined by vapor density measurements, is As_4, and at higher temperatures it is As_2.

There are three *allotropic forms of arsenic*. The sudden cooling of arsenic vapors produces a *yellow* crystalline form which resembles flowers of sulfur and is likewise soluble in carbon disulfide. *Black* arsenic is obtained when arsenic vapor is cooled slowly; it may condense on a cold surface as a black mirror. If arsenic is produced in large quantities and cooled slowly, a *gray* crystalline mass is formed.

Arsenic combines readily with many other elements, both metals and nonmetals. It is oxidized slowly in moist air to As_2O_3. Hydrochloric acid dissolves arsenic in the presence of air, probably because As_2O_3 is formed first. Oxidizing acids such as nitric acid convert arsenic into soluble arsenic acid, H_3AsO_4.

$$3\ As + 5\ HNO_3 + 2\ H_2O \longrightarrow 3\ H_3AsO_4 + \overline{5\ NO}$$

Arsenic is also soluble in fused alkali.

$$2\ As + 6\ NaOH \xrightarrow{\Delta} 2\ Na_3AsO_3 + \overline{3\ H_2}$$

If powdered arsenic is sprinkled into chlorine gas, it catches fire and burns, forming the trichloride. Arsenic combines readily with sulfur to form sulfides and with metals to form arsenides. Arsenic is not sufficiently metallic to replace hydrogen from HCl. A solution of the oxide in water has slightly basic properties.

Uses of Arsenic and Its Compounds

Alloyed with copper, arsenic increases resistance to corrosion and raises the annealing temperature; this latter accounts for its use in automobile radiators assembled by soldering. Arsenical copper is used in the plates and staybolts of locomotive fireboxes. Lead shot, lead-antimony alloy anodes, muntz metal (60 per cent Cu, 40 per cent Zn), speculum metal for the mirrors of reflecting telescopes, and lead-tin bearings all contain some arsenic (usually less than 1 per cent). The use of arsenic in the manufacture of lead shot is interesting, for in addition to increasing the hardness of the shot it aids in the formation of perfectly spherical particles. If, after the droplets of molten lead fall through the screen, they cool too quickly, they cannot be rotated sufficiently to form perfect spheres. The addition of about 0.5 of 1 per cent of arsenic to the molten lead prevents their cooling too rapidly. About 100 tons of arsenic are used per year in the United States.

Arsenic compounds have a wide variety of uses. Because of the toxic nature of the element, about 80 per cent of the compounds produced are used as insecticides, weed killers, wood preservatives, cattle and sheep dips, and in drugs. The most important insecticide, calcium arsenate, $Ca_3(AsO_4)_2 \cdot 3\ H_2O$, is used in large quantities in the southern states to fight the boll weevil. Lead arsenate, $Pb_3(AsO_4)_2$, is second in importance as an insecticide, being used either alone or mixed with other toxic materials. Sodium arsenate, $Na_3AsO_4 \cdot 12\ H_2O$, is used in manufacturing lead arsenate and printing inks, as an insecticide, and as a mordant in dyeing. Sodium arsenite, $NaAsO_2$, is used in antiseptics and insecticides, and in dyeing textiles and preserving hides. About 30,000 tons of As_2O_3 are used each year in insecticides, and solutions of it are used to combat the grasshopper menace in the Middle West. It is a good weed killer and is also used to kill green timber when land is being cleared.

The two chief objections to the use of arsenic compounds as insecticides are their high cost and the possibility of being poisoned by food sprayed with them. (For many years chemists have been trying to develop new insecticides, organic in nature, which will be toxic to insects but not harmful to human beings in the concentrations necessary in spraying.)

Salvarsan and neosalvarsan are *complicated organic arsenic compounds* which are used as specific cures for syphilis and relapsing fever. Ehrlich produced arsphenamine or salvarsan on his six hundred and sixth attempt to prepare a compound which would cure syphilis; hence its common name, "606."

Arsine

Arsine, AsH_3, corresponds in formula to NH_3 and PH_3, and is a gas at room temperature. It is toxic in such small concentrations that its "garlic odor" is hardly sufficient warning of its presence. It neither dissolves in water nor forms salts as does ammonia. It decomposes at 230° C. into hydrogen and arsenic. It burns readily, forming water and arsenic.

A delicate test, known as the *Marsh test*, has been developed for detecting the presence of arsenic in the internal organs of humans; it is equally applicable for fruit, etc., sprayed with arsenic. This test depends upon the easy formation and decomposition of arsine; zinc reduces arsenic compounds to arsine. The suspected material is placed in a flask as shown in Fig. 26.1, and a few grams of arsenic-free mossy zinc and some water are added. A drying tube containing calcium chloride is attached to the stopper of the flask, and a second drying tube, empty, is attached to the first one. Hydrochloric acid (also arsenic-free) is added to the flask through a thistle tube. HCl and zinc react to liberate hydrogen, which carries with it any arsine which is simultaneously produced. The second tube is heated near the outlet, and any arsine which is present decomposes into hydrogen and arsenic. A bright metallic black-brown mirror gradually forms beyond the flame if there is the slightest trace of arsenic. (Even a few milligrams of arsenic per bushel of apples can be detected by the Marsh test.)

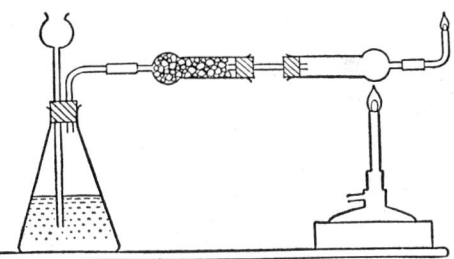

FIG. 26.1. The Marsh test for arsenic.

$$As_2O_3 + 6\ \underline{Zn} + 12\ H^+ + 12\ Cl^- \longrightarrow 2\ \overline{AsH_3} + 6\ Zn^{++} + 12\ Cl^- + 3\ H_2O$$
$$\xrightarrow{\Delta} 2\ \underline{As} + 3\ \overline{H_2}$$

Arsine is a reducing agent and will reduce the silver ion.

$$6\ Ag^+ + 6\ NO_3^- + \overline{AsH_3} + 3\ H_2O \longrightarrow 6\ H^+ + 6\ NO_3^- + H_3AsO_3 + 6\ \underline{Ag}$$

Metallic arsenides hydrolyze with the liberation of arsine. The reaction between zinc arsenide and water is similar to that between Mg_3N_2 and water.

$$\underline{Zn_3As_2} + 6\ H_2O \longrightarrow 2\ \overline{AsH_3} + 3\ \underline{Zn(OH)_2}$$

Metals do not form gaseous hydrogen compounds at all; hence the decreased willingness of arsenic to combine with hydrogen (lower stability and lower basicity of AsH_3), as compared with the preceding elements in the family, is evident of its approach to metallic properties.

Oxides of Arsenic

The common arsenic oxide of commerce is the trioxide, As_2O_3, known commercially as white arsenic, or simply "arsenic." It sublimes at a low temperature, and investigation of the vapor density shows the formula to be As_4O_6, as might be expected. It is usually purified by sublimation. The somewhat metallic property of arsenic is shown by the fact that the pentoxide, As_2O_5, is prepared not by heating the lower oxide in air, but by evaporating a solution of arsenic acid. Heat tends to cause the higher oxides of metals to decompose into the lower oxides. The solution of As_2O_3 is easily oxidized with nitric acid, chlorine water, and other good oxidizing agents.

$$\underline{As_2O_3} + 2\ H^+ + 2\ NO_3^- + 2\ H_2O \longrightarrow \overline{N_2O_3} + 2\ H_3AsO_4$$
$$\underline{As_2O_3} + 2\ Cl_2 + 5\ H_2O \longrightarrow 4\ H^+ + 4\ Cl^- + 2\ H_3AsO_4$$

As_2O_5 is a deliquescent white solid which will liberate oxygen if heated red hot. Whereas As_2O_3 is almost insoluble in water, the pentoxide is quite soluble. This difference in solubility is caused by the greater tendency of the pentoxide to react with water to form an acid. The lowered acid-forming ability of arsenic is another evidence that it is less electrophilic (and thus more nearly metallic) than N and P. This is not as noticeable in the pentoxide as in the trioxide; the higher oxide of an element is always more acidic than the lower, because it has lost more electrons (see K_1 relationships below).

Arsenious Acid and Its Salts

The water solution of As_2O_3 is called arsenious acid (or frequently, arsenous acid). Because of the very low solubility of As_2O_3 in water, the acid might be expected to be quite weak. It is weaker with respect to the concentration of hydrogen ions than even a solution of hydrogen sulfide. Ortho-, meta-, and pyroarsenious acids are believed to exist *in solution* because salts of all three have been prepared. Sodium metaarsenite, $NaAsO_2$, is used as an insecticide. Insoluble orthoarsenites such as Ag_3AsO_3 are easily prepared. Two important copper arsenites are Scheele's green and Paris green, both used as insecticides and to a lesser extent as green pigments. The use of Scheele's green as a pigment in wall paper is forbidden by law because it decomposes and liberates arsine. Scheele's green, copper hydrogen arsenite ($CuHAsO_3$), is precipitated when $CuSO_4$ and Na_3AsO_3 are mixed. Paris green, $Cu(C_2H_3O_2)_2 \cdot Cu_3(AsO_3)_2$, a double salt of cupric acetate and arsenite, is obtained by boiling arsenious oxide and basic copper acetate together. Many of the metallic arsenites are insoluble in water. Trivalent arsenic compounds are all reducing agents and can be oxidized to the equivalent pentavalent compounds by suitable oxidizing agents.

Arsenic Acid and Its Salts

Arsenic acid is easily prepared by the oxidation of As_2O_3 with nitric acid. $(H_3AsO_4)_2 \cdot H_2O$ can be obtained as a crystalline solid by evaporating solutions of arsenic acid. A water solution of H_3AsO_4 is a much stronger acid than H_3AsO_3.

$$\frac{[H^+][H_2AsO_4^-]}{[H_3AsO_4]} = 5 \times 10^{-3}. \quad \frac{[H^+][H_2AsO_3^-]}{[H_3AsO_3]} = 6 \times 10^{-10}$$

$$\frac{[H^+][C_2H_3O_2^-]}{[HC_2H_3O_2]} = 1.86 \times 10^{-5}$$

As can be seen from these ionization constants, arsenic acid is stronger than acetic acid.

Salts of ortho-, meta-, and pyroarsenic acids have been prepared. The use of arsenates as insecticides has been mentioned. Two insoluble arsenates, both very similar to the corresponding phosphorus compounds, are used in the analytical detection and determination of the arsenate radical. Ammonium arsenomolybdate, a yellow insoluble salt of the formula $(NH_4)_3AsO_4 \cdot 12\ MoO_3$, and the white crystalline salt, $MgNH_4AsO_4$, which on heating leaves a residue of magnesium pyroarsenate, $Mg_2As_2O_7$, are prepared by reactions exactly analogous to those for the phosphates (page 431).

Halides of Arsenic

Arsenic combines directly with all the halogens. The halides hydrolyze readily. Insoluble As_2O_3 is obtained by the hydrolysis of $AsCl_3$.

$$2\ AsCl_3 + 6\ H_2O \rightleftarrows 2\ As(OH)_3 + 6\ H^+ + 6\ Cl^-$$
$$\longrightarrow As_2O_3 + 3\ H_2O$$

Concentrated (12 N) HCl is required to produce any reversal of this hydrolysis, but the hydrolysis of halides of typical non-metals cannot be reversed at all. $AsCl_3$, like PCl_3, fumes strongly in moist air. When the amount of water is limited, the crystalline hydroxychloride forms.

$$AsCl_3 + 2\ H_2O \rightleftarrows 2\ H^+ + 2\ Cl^- + \underline{AsCl(OH)_2}$$

These halides are not important compounds.

Sulfur Compounds of Arsenic

Several sulfur compounds of arsenic are found in nature but are of little importance except as sources of arsenic. They can be prepared in the laboratory by the direct union of arsenic and sulfur in the calculated proportions.

The mineral, *realgar*, or *arsenic disulfide* (As_2S_2), is red or orange-yellow in color; it burns readily in air, forming SO_2 and As_2O_3, and is used in pyrotechnics. The brilliant white Bengal fire is produced by mixing As_2S_2, KNO_3, and sulfur in the ratio of 2:27:7.

Yellow *arsenic trisulfide*, As_2S_3, is mined as the mineral, orpiment, and is an important source of arsenic. If H_2S is added to a solution of arsenious acid, yellow insoluble As_2S_3 is formed.

$$2\ H_3AsO_3 + 3\ H_2S \longrightarrow \underline{As_2S_3} + 6\ H_2O$$

It is easily prepared in the colloidal state (page 301). Arsenic trisulfide is also formed by the reaction of arsenic trichloride and hydrogen sulfide.

$$2\ AsCl_3 + 3\ H_2S \longrightarrow \underline{As_2S_3} + 6\ HCl$$

Although this reaction might be expected to go from right to left, it does not, because arsenic trisulfide is insoluble in HCl. H_2S in an acid solution is used as a precipitating agent for several metallic ions.

Arsenic pentasulfide is not found in nature but is easily prepared in the laboratory as a yellow precipitate by adding H_2S to soluble pentavalent arsenic compounds. It is precipitated in concentrated solutions of hydrochloric acid.

$$2\ H_3AsO_4 + 5\ H_2S \longrightarrow \underline{As_2S_5} + 8\ H_2O$$
$$2\ AsCl_5 + 5\ H_2S \longrightarrow \underline{As_2S_5} + 10\ HCl$$

Thioacids and Salts of Arsenic

The concept of thio compounds is quite simple if we keep in mind the fact that sulfur is just below oxygen in Group VI and should therefore have many similar properties. We saw before (page 385) that sulfur can take the place of some of the oxygen atoms in certain compounds; this same property is shown by the arsenic compounds.

As_2O_3, arsenic trioxide	H_3AsO_3, arsenious acid	Na_3AsO_3, sodium arsenite
As_2S_3, arsenic trisulfide	H_3AsS_3, thioarsenious acid	Na_3AsS_3, sodium thioarsenite
As_2O_5, arsenic pentoxide	H_3AsO_4, arsenic acid	Na_3AsO_4, sodium arsenate
As_2S_5, arsenic pentasulfide	H_3AsS_4, thioarsenic acid	Na_3AsS_4, sodium thioarsenate

If As_2S_3 is treated with a solution of Na_2S, the reaction is similar to that between As_2O_3 and Na_2O.

$$3\ \underline{Na_2O} + \underline{As_2O_3} \longrightarrow 6\ Na^+ + 2\ AsO_3{}^{---}$$
$$3\ \underline{Na_2S} + \underline{As_2S_3} \longrightarrow 6\ Na^+ + 2\ AsS_3{}^{---}$$

Ammonium sulfide in place of Na_2S reacts similarly.

$$6\ NH_4{}^+ + 3\ S^{--} + \underline{As_2S_3} \longrightarrow 6\ NH_4{}^+ + 2\ AsS_3{}^{---}$$

Pentavalent arsenic compounds react in the same manner.

$$6 \text{ NH}_4^+ + 3 \text{ S}^{--} + \underline{\text{As}_2\text{S}_5} \longrightarrow 6 \text{ NH}_4^+ + 2 \text{ AsS}_4^{---}$$

If the trisulfide of arsenic is treated with a solution of a polysulfide, a trivalent arsenic is oxidized to the pentavalent state.

$$\underline{\text{As}_2\text{S}_3} + 6 \text{ Na}^+ + 3 \text{ S}_x^{--} \longrightarrow 6 \text{ Na}^+ + 2 \text{ AsS}_4^{---} + \text{ free sulfur}$$

$$\underline{\text{As}_2\text{S}_3} + 6 \text{ NH}_4^+ + 3 \text{ S}_x^{--} \longrightarrow 6 \text{ NH}_4^+ + 2 \text{ AsS}_4^{---} + \text{ free sulfur}$$

These reactions are used in the separation of insoluble arsenic, antimony, and tin sulfides from other sulfides which are not soluble in Na_2S and $(NH_4)_2S$ and therefore do not form soluble thiosalts.

ANTIMONY

Antimony must have been recognized as a pure substance almost 5000 years ago, for in 3000 B.C. Egyptian women used the orange pigment (the sulfide) for painting their eyebrows. A vase in the Louvre found in the ruins of Tello (*c.* 100 B.C.) consists of nearly pure metallic antimony. Compounds of antimony were often used as early medicines. The characteristics of the element were described in detail in *Triumphal Chariot of Antimony*, a book by Basil Valentine, who was reputedly a fifteenth-century Benedictine monk. However, Valentine is now believed to have been a mythical character; the real author was apparently Johann Tholde, who wrote in German and claimed to have translated Valentine's articles from the Latin.

Occurrence

About 50 per cent of the antimony produced in the world came from the Province of Hunan in China before World War II. Bolivia and Mexico ranked next, and the former was able to expand its production sufficiently to take care of war needs. The price advanced only about a cent from the controlled 15 cents a pound in the Hunan antimony syndicate. The United States consumption was 23,750 tons in 1944. The chief antimony ore is stibnite, Sb_2S_3. The element is obtained as a by-product in the mining of several other ores. Part of our supply is recovered from scrap metal.

Preparation and Properties of Antimony

Antimony is prepared by reducing the sulfide with iron:

$$Sb_2S_3 + 3 \text{ Fe} \longrightarrow 2 \text{ Sb} + 3 \text{ FeS}$$

or by roasting the sulfide, converting it into the oxide, and then reducing the oxide with carbon. If some of the oxide is mixed with charcoal in a test tube and heated, antimony is readily produced. It expands slightly on cooling from the molten state and forms large silver-white crystals which are very brittle. The element is a poor conductor of electricity, an indication that it is a border-line metal.

Antimony is not oxidized in the air and it is insoluble in dilute acids, such as hydrochloric acid. It is soluble in concentrated H_2SO_4, forming $Sb_2(SO_4)_3$. This is metallic behavior, for the product is a salt. Nitric acid dissolves antimony but oxidizes it to the higher and more acidic valence state; antimonic acid is formed and precipitates immediately as a white powder. This is non-metallic behavior, but the insolubility of the acid is an indication of weakness. Aqua regia attacks antimony and forms $SbCl_5$, which is *not* a salt (M.P. 3° C.).

COMPOUNDS OF ANTIMONY

Antimony combines readily with the non-metals oxygen, sulfur, phosphorus, and the halogens; some of the resulting compounds behave as though the antimony were metal, some as though it were a non-metal, and some behave both ways. With metals antimony produces alloys, many of them very useful; alloy formation is a metallic characteristic. The hydrogen compound of antimony is similar to the hydrogen compounds of the non-metals.

Stibine

The hydrogen compound of antimony, stibine, SbH_3, is prepared by the same procedure as arsine, AsH_3. Like arsine, it is poisonous. The Marsh test can be used for antimony; but since stibine is even less stable than arsine, it is decomposed and deposits antimony *before* it reaches the hottest part of the tube. As a confirmatory test, a Marsh test mirror is treated with a hypochlorite solution which dissolves arsenic but not antimony. Other tests are based on the following differences in properties: antimony is soluble in tartaric acid and arsenic is not; the arsenic residue turns yellow in the presence of $(NH_4)_2S$, and the antimony residue turns orange.

Oxides and Acids of Antimony

The most easily prepared oxide is the trioxide, Sb_2O_3, which is always formed when an antimony ore is roasted. A little Sb_2O_4 may also appear, but this oxide is of no importance. Antimony pentoxide, Sb_2O_5, like As_2O_5, is prepared by oxidizing H_3SbO_3 with nitric acid or a similar agent and then dehydrating the antimonic acid, H_3SbO_4. That ortho-, meta-, and pyroacids exist in solution is demonstrated by the fact that such salts as Na_3SbO_3, $NaSbO_2$, and $Na_4Sb_2O_7$ have been prepared. Antimonous acid could just as well be written $Sb(OH)_3$ and called antimony hydroxide, for it is a weak base as well as a weak acid.

$$\underline{Sb(OH)_3} + 3\ H^+ + 3\ Cl^- \longrightarrow Sb^{+++} + 3\ Cl^- + 3\ H_2O$$
$$\underline{H_3SbO_3} + 3\ Na^+ + 3\ OH^- \longrightarrow 3\ Na^+ + SbO_3^{---} + 3\ H_2O$$

ARSENIC, ANTIMONY, AND BISMUTH

Both these reactions are reversible but go to completion in the presence of 6 N base or acid. On page 218 was given an example of a hydroxide which can behave as an acid when in contact with a base, and as a base when in contact with an acid. The three reversible hydrolysis reactions on that page would all go to completion to the left on the addition of 3 N HCl, and the reactions could be summed up in the equation:

$$\begin{bmatrix} H_2O & _{+++} & OH^- \\ H_2O & Al & OH^- \\ H_2O & & OH^- \end{bmatrix}^\circ + 3\,H^+ + 3\,Cl^- \longrightarrow \begin{bmatrix} H_2O & _{+++} & OH_2 \\ H_2O & Al & OH_2 \\ H_2O & & OH_2 \end{bmatrix}^{+++} + 3\,Cl^-$$

The reaction of aluminum hydroxide with sodium hydroxide was mentioned, but the equation was not given.

$$\begin{bmatrix} H_2O & _{+++} & OH^- \\ H_2O & Al & OH^- \\ H_2O & & OH^- \end{bmatrix} + Na^+ + OH^- \longrightarrow Na^+ + \begin{bmatrix} H_2O & _{+++} & OH^- \\ -HO & Al & OH^- \\ H_2O & & OH^- \end{bmatrix}^- + H_2O$$

If the water of hydration is neglected (as is customary) and the formulas are written in the conventional manner, these equations are seen to be similar to those just written for antimony.

$$\underline{Al(OH)_3} + 3\,H^+ + 3\,Cl^- \longrightarrow Al^{+++} + 3\,Cl^- + 3\,H_2O$$
$$\underline{H_3AlO_3} + Na^+ + OH^- \longrightarrow Na^+ + AlO_2^- + 2\,H_2O$$

The formula for sodium aluminate differs from that for sodium antimonite because aluminum hydroxide is a monobasic acid, whereas antimony hydroxide is a tribasic acid, an evidence that Sb is less metallic than Al. The degree of hydration of Sb^{+++} is not known; the analogy with the behavior of aluminum may conceivably be only formal. The older assumption, still held by many, was that the hydroxide was able actually to lose both H^+ and OH^- ions.

$$3\,H^+ + SbO_3^{---} \rightleftarrows \underline{H_3SbO_3} \equiv \underline{Sb(OH)_3} \rightleftarrows Sb^{+++} + 3\,OH^-$$

(The identity sign, $\equiv$, means that the two formulas are merely different ways of writing the same substance.)

Amphoterism

A neutral hydroxide which is both an acid and a base is said to be *amphoteric* (Greek, = both). The term is extended to oxides and sulfides, but not customarily to water or ions; however, it is customary to say that antimony and aluminum are amphoteric, meaning that their hydroxides are. The amphoteric elements which show, although weakly, both metallic and non-metallic properties lie near the zigzag line drawn in the periodic table (page 83). Arsenic, on the non-metallic side of the line, is much more non-metallic than metallic. Nevertheless, it is amphoteric to the extent that the hydrolysis of $AsCl_3$ is reversible. Other important amphoteric elements are lead, tin, and zinc. If an element has two valences it may be acidic in its higher and amphoteric in its lower valence, or amphoteric in its higher and basic in its lower valence. All amphoteric hydroxides are nearly insoluble.

Salts of Antimony

Antimony trichloride, $SbCl_3$, was prepared by the alchemists by distilling the solution obtained when Sb_2S_3 is dissolved in hydrochloric acid. They called it "butter of antimony" because it looked like butter. The addition of $SbCl_3$ to water yields a white precipitate of $SbOCl$ which is called either antimonyl chloride or antimony oxychloride. The basic chloride which probably forms first loses a molecule of water.

$$SbCl_3 + 2\ H_2O \longrightarrow Sb(OH)_2Cl + 2\ H^+ + 2\ Cl^-$$
$$ \longrightarrow SbOCl + H_2O$$

Although $SbCl_3$ is written above in the un-ionized form, as the halides of the lighter members of the family have been in preceding equations, this is actually a border-line case. The hydrolysis is easily reversible (6 N HCl) and the strongly acid solution may well contain Sb^{+++} ions. Further evidence that $SbCl_3$ comes between typical salts and covalent compounds is furnished by its physical state; it is a solid, but a soft one with a low melting point (76° C.).

Thio compounds analogous to those of arsenic are formed by antimony, a further example of its amphoteric behavior. Thus insoluble Sb_2S_3 dissolves in ammonium polysulfide and forms ammonium thioantimonate.

$$Sb_2S_3 + 6\ NH_4^+ + 3\ S_x^{--} \longrightarrow 6\ NH_4^+ + 2\ SbS_4^{---} + (3x - 8)\ S$$

If Sb_2O_3 and cream of tartar—potassium bitartrate, $(KHC_4H_4O_6)$—are boiled together, soluble potassium antimonyl tartrate, or *tartar emetic*, is formed. This compound is used medicinally to induce sweating and vomiting. It crystallizes out with one molecule of water of crystallization; the formula of the solid is usually written $[K(SbO)C_4H_4O_6]_2 \cdot H_2O$, but the complete formula with the exception of the potassiums may represent a single complex divalent anion.

Uses of Antimony and Its Compounds

Over half the antimony consumed in the United States is used in the manufacture of storage batteries, cable coverings, bearing metals, and type metal. Much of this antimony is recovered and used again. It increases the tensile strength of the antimonal-lead in storage batteries; the alloy may contain as much as 12 per cent antimony. The "hard" lead used in making bullets and shrapnel contains 12 to 15 per cent antimony. Stopcocks in sulfuric acid lines are made of alloys of antimony. Many uses of the element are based on the fact that antimony, unlike most metals, expands on solidifying. For example, 15 to 30 per cent antimony in type metal gives an alloy of Sb–Pb–Sn which, because of this expansion property, gives a sharp outline to the solidified type. Telephone cables are covered with a Pb–Sb alloy containing about 1 per cent antimony, and bearing metal for automobiles frequently contains an antimony alloy.

The dull rust-proof finish on a gun barrel is obtained by rubbing the barrel with "butter of antimony," $SbCl_3$. Antimony sulfide is used in giving a yellow tint to enamel and glass and in making red rubber. Since it burns readily, it is used in making matches (page 425), in pyrotechnics, and in primers for cartridges. Tartar emetic, $K(SbO)C_4H_4O_6$, is used both as a mordant in dyeing and in medicine. Antimony fluoride is recommended as a mothproofing agent for fabrics.

BISMUTH

With bismuth, which is at the bottom of the N–P–As–Sb–Bi subgroup, the transition from non-metal to metal is practically complete, for nearly all its properties are metallic. Bismuth pentoxide is very slightly acidic in water solution. There are few compounds of pentavalent bismuth.

Occurrence

Bismuth was apparently first recognized as an individual substance by the Orientals; for many years it was confused with lead and tin. The early miners believed that there were three kinds of lead (ordinary lead, tin, and bismuth) and that all of these would eventually turn into silver. Since bismuth most resembled silver, they often called it "unfinished silver." In 1753 C. J. Geoffroy proved that bismuth was a specific metal.

Bismuth, the least abundant element of the nitrogen subgroup, is found free in nature, and as the sulfide, Bi_2S_3, the telluride, Bi_2Te_3, and the oxide, Bi_2O_3. Most of it is obtained as a by-product from lead, copper, tin, silver, and gold ores. In 1944 the United States consumed about a million and a half pounds of bismuth, more than a million pounds of which was produced here from the electrolytic refining of lead and other metals. Other producers included Peru, Bolivia, Spain, Canada, and Australia. Bismuth sells for about $1.00 a pound.

The source of the bismuth determines the process used to obtain it. An ore rich in bismuth is heated with carbon in a sloping furnace; the molten bismuth flows to the lower end of the furnace. If bismuth is an impurity in another ore, such as galena, PbS, the bismuth separates at the anode during the electrolytic refining process of the lead.

Properties of Bismuth

In the solid state bismuth is tin-white and has a definite metallic luster. Its property of expanding about 3.2 per cent on cooling, and its melting point of 271° C. make it of particular value in alloys. It is a poor conductor of electricity. It is diamagnetic, that is, repelled by both poles of a magnet.

Bismuth burns readily with oxygen to form the trioxide, Bi_2O_3. At low temperature a coating of Bi_2O_3 protects the rest of the metal from rapid oxidation. Bismuth combines directly with the halogens and sulfur. It is below hydrogen in the E.C.S. and can therefore be dissolved only with oxidizing acids such as HNO_3 and H_2SO_4. It dissolves in HCl if air is present (probably the oxide forms first). Its more metallic property is indicated by its reaction with HNO_3. Although acids were formed by the action of HNO_3 on both arsenic and antimony, metallic salts are formed with bismuth.

An alloy of magnesium and bismuth treated with HCl produces hydrogen and a trace of extremely unstable bismuthine, BiH_3. This was proved by Paneth by means of the technique of radioactive *tracers*, which he invented. For over a century attempts to prepare BiH_3 had proved futile. Many different sets of conditions had been tried; no one knew which one had come nearest to producing a detectable amount of the gas. Paneth added a very small amount of a radioactive isotope of bismuth to his ordinary bismuth and tested the issuing hydrogen for radioactivity with a Geiger counter. As soon as the counter began to click he knew that BiH_3 was being formed. Varying the conditions, he judged by the rate of clicking which changes were improvements, and eventually obtained enough BiH_3 to give a chemical test.

Compounds of Bismuth

The important oxide of bismuth is Bi_2O_3. It can be oxidized to bismuth pentoxide with vigorous oxidizing agents. Bismuth salts stay in solution only in the presence of excess acid.

Bismuth trichloride and bismuth trinitrate are two important salts. The hydrolysis reactions are the same as those for the production of SbOCl. However, the loss of water from $Bi(OH)_2Cl$ requires heat. The resulting bismuthyl chloride, or bismuth oxychloride, BiOCl, is known to the trade as "pearl white." It is used as a pigment and in face powders. If these face powders are treated with HCl and H_2S is added, black Bi_2S_3 is precipitated. Bismuthyl nitrate, similarly prepared, is usually known as bismuth subnitrate. It is used medicinally for the treatment of gastric ulcers and also in skin ointments. In 1944 nearly 300 tons of bismuth went into pharmaceutical preparations. The hydrolysis of bismuth compounds is easily reversed by an excess of dilute acid (3 N HCl).

ARSENIC, ANTIMONY, AND BISMUTH

Ammonium hydroxide reacts with bismuth salts to form white bismuth hydroxide which, on losing water, forms the insoluble bismuthyl hydroxide.

$$Bi(OH)_3 \longrightarrow BiO(OH) + H_2O$$

This can be reduced to the metallic state by divalent tin in alkaline solution, a reaction which is used in detecting the presence of bismuth. The addition of NaOH to stannous chloride first precipitates stannous hydroxide:

$$Sn^{++} + 2\ Cl^- + 2\ Na^+ + 2\ OH^- \longrightarrow Sn(OH)_2 + 2\ Na^+ + 2\ Cl^-$$

which, being amphoteric, dissolves in an excess of NaOH.

$$Sn(OH)_2 + 2\ Na^+ + 2\ OH^- \longrightarrow 2\ Na^+ + SnO_2^{--} + 2\ H_2O$$

Sodium stannite reduces BiO(OH) and black[1] bismuth forms.

$$6\ Na^+ + 3\ SnO_2^{--} + 2\ BiO(OH) \longrightarrow 2\ Bi + 6\ Na^+ + 3\ SnO_3^{--} + H_2O$$

Bi_2O_3 is used in certain optical glass, in enamels, and as a paint pigment. $BiCl_3$ is added to creosote and oils to make them less inflammable.

Bismuth can be separated from arsenic and antimony because Bi_2S_3 is not soluble in alkali sulfides and does not form thiosalts, further evidence that arsenic and antimony are more acidic than bismuth.

Uses of Metallic Bismuth

One hundred and twenty tons of bismuth (43 per cent of the amount used in the United States) went into the manufacture of low melting-point alloys, solders, and bearing metals in 1944. Bismuth alloys have low melting points and do not shrink at the freezing point. The composition and melting points of a few bismuth alloys are given in Table 26.2. (For a more complete discussion of alloys, see page 496.)

If *pure* metals are used, the physical properties of the alloys will remain constant for many years. Bismuth alloys are important in the manufacture of fusible solders for automatic fire extinguishers. All the many sprinkler designs on the market depend upon the solder being sufficiently strong to hold the plug in place and still having a low melting point. The alloy used depends upon the temperature of the room in which the sprinkler head is placed. Fig. 26.2 shows one type of fire sprinkler.

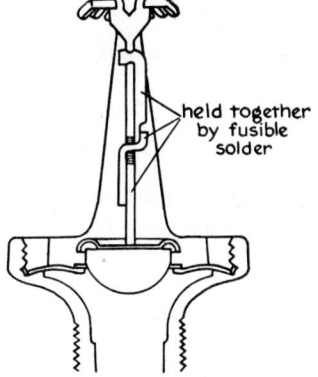

FIG. 26.2. A fire sprinkler.

[1] All finely divided metals are black.

TABLE 26.2 Composition and Melting Points of Bismuth Alloys

Name of Alloy	Bi	Pb	Sn	Cd	Melting Point
Neuton's	50	31.25	18.75		94.5
Rose's	50	27.10	22.9		95.0
D'Arcet's	50	25.0	25.0		94.0
Wood's	50	25.0	12.5	12.5	65.0
Lipowitz's	50	26.9	12.78	10.4	65.0

(Percentage of Each Element)

QUESTIONS AND PROBLEMS

1. Compare the stabilities of the hydrides of the nitrogen group. Which hydride is most important?
2. Compare the properties of the halides of nitrogen, phosphorus, arsenic, antimony, and bismuth.
3. a. List two uses of arsenic, antimony, and bismuth.
   b. Write the structural formulas of compounds to show the valences of these elements.
4. What volume of NO at S.T.P. can be obtained by using 25 g. of arsenic?
5. What is meant by amphoterism? Illustrate.
6. K_I for the first H^+ of H_3AsO_4 is 5×10^{-3}. What is the pH of a solution which contains 28 g. per liter of H_3AsO_4?
7. How many grams of sodium thioantimonate can be prepared from 1 g. of antimony?
8. How would you distinguish between the following groups of substances?

As	As_2O_3	AsH_3	As_2S_3	$BiO(OH)$
Sb	Sb_2O_3	SbH_3	As_2O_3	Bi_2S_3
Bi	Bi_2O_3	PH_3	Na_3AsO_4	$Bi(NO_3)_3$

9. What weight of bismuth can be reduced with 1 molecular weight of sodium stannite?
10. List the uses of arsenic, antimony, bismuth, and their compounds which indicate their importance in your home.

REFERENCES

Articles

"Arsenic in Alloys." Wegner, K. H. *Met. and Alloys* **3**, 116–118 (1932).
"Arsenic." Tyler, P. M., and Petar, A. V. *Trans. Electrochem. Soc.* **61**, 125–130 (1932).
"Bismuth Alloys." Thompson, J. G. *Met. and Alloys* **2**, 92–94 (1931).
"Uses of Bismuth." Smith, W. C. *Met. and Alloys* **2**, 236 (1931).

» 27 «

SILICON AND ITS COMPOUNDS

The first element in Group IV of the periodic table is carbon; if the nonmetals were being considered in order, carbon should be discussed in this chapter. However, carbon and its compounds constitute a different field of chemistry called organic chemistry, and will be discussed in a later chapter. Boron is like silicon in so many of its properties that, although it is the first element in Group III, the next chapter will be devoted to boron and its compounds.

SILICON

Occurrence

Although silicon is never found free in nature, its compounds are so numerous and so widely distributed in the earth's crust that the supply of this element is abundant. Silicon constitutes about 28 per cent of the earth's crust and is a very important element in the mineral kingdom; in fact, it is the central element of this kingdom, just as carbon is the central element of the plant and animal kingdom. Most of the silicon occurs in nature as silica, SiO_2, either free or combined. Combined silicates are numerous and complicated in structure.

Preparation of Silicon

In 1809 Davy attempted unsuccessfully to obtain pure silicon by the electrolysis of silicon dioxide and also by the reduction of SiO_2 with potassium. In 1823, J. J. Berzelius produced the element by reducing potassium fluosilicate, K_2SiF_6, with potassium.

$$K_2SiF_6 + 4 K \longrightarrow 6 KF + Si$$

He named the element "Kunsel," but it is now called silicon.

A convenient laboratory procedure for the preparation of silicon is to heat magnesium and pure quartz (SiO$_2$) in a crucible lined with magnesium oxide. As soon as the crucible is heated to a bright red heat, the reaction proceeds with brilliant incandescence.

$$SiO_2 + 2\ Mg \longrightarrow 2\ MgO + Si + \Delta$$

The crucible and its contents are cooled and the MgO is dissolved out with HCl. Any SiO$_2$ which has not reacted is removed as volatile SiF$_4$ by being treated with hydrofluoric acid. Further purification is required to obtain pure silicon. Aluminum and other active metals can be substituted for magnesium. Silicon tetrachloride can be reduced with sodium. Of commercial significance is the fact that silica can be reduced with carbon in an electric furnace; however, the difficulty here is that carbon tends to react with silicon at high temperatures and form silicon carbide.

Properties of Silicon

Silicon occurs in brown amorphous and black crystalline forms which differ only in the size of particles, not in the crystalline lattice. Amorphous silicon is obtained by all the usual reduction processes. The crystalline form can be obtained by many methods, as for example, by dissolving the amorphous form in molten aluminum and then cooling it. Crystalline silicon is harder than glass, melts at 1400° C. and conducts electricity fairly well.

The element is insoluble in acids but dissolves readily in alkali, liberating hydrogen.

$$2\ Na^+ + 2\ OH^- + H_2O + \underline{Si} \longrightarrow 2\ \overline{H_2} + Na_2SiO_3\ \text{(colloidal)}$$

Silicon and sodium hydroxide are efficient for transporting "potential hydrogen gas," only 28 g. of silicon being required to liberate 4 g. of hydrogen. In spite of the high cost of silicon, this procedure was used to some extent during World Wars I and II. Silicon can be dissolved by fusion with sodium carbonate.

$$Na_2CO_3 + Si \xrightarrow{\Delta} Na_2SiO_3 + C$$

Silicon differs from carbon in that it combines with oxygen only slowly even at a high temperature. A coating of SiO$_2$ on the surface of the silicon stops the exothermic reaction, which otherwise would be rapid.

Uses of Silicon

One important use of silicon is found in the steel industry. The addition of silicon to low-carbon steel increases its elastic limit slightly and markedly increases its resistance to wear. It also makes the steel more fusible. Ordinary steel usually contains less than 0.03 of 1 per cent silicon; steel castings contain about 0.25 of 1 per cent.

SILICON AND ITS COMPOUNDS

Silicon steel is made by heating steel containing 2.5 to 4 per cent silicon to 1000° C., cooling, reheating to 800°, and cooling. It is known as low-hysteresis steel and is used in making the cores of electrical transformers. (Hysteresis is the tendency of a magnetic material to retain its magnetism. Residual magnetism is detrimental to the efficiency of transformers, etc.) Not all the silicon in silicon steel is iron silicide.

Duriron is an alloy which contains about 14 per cent silicon. It is hard, brittle, and so resistant to corrosion that it can be used for the condensing units of nitric acid plants.

The Hydrosilicons and the Silicones

An atom with four valence electrons is particularly adapted to forming long chain-shaped molecules, thus:

$$\cdot \dot{C} \cdot + \cdot \dot{C} \cdot + \cdot \dot{C} \cdot + \cdot \dot{C} \cdot \longrightarrow \cdot \dot{C} : \dot{C} : \dot{C} : \dot{C} \cdot , \text{ and so on.}$$

Such a skeleton could be "finished up" at any point by the addition of a hydrogen or halogen atom, that is, an atom which had one electron to share and which could complete its own valence layer by gaining one electron. In the case of carbon such compounds are stable, important, and almost innumerable. One example, the palmitate ion, has already been mentioned (page 288); the last pages of this book are devoted to an introduction to some of the others. Compounds which contain only carbon and hydrogen are called hydrocarbons; the simplest of them is methane, CH_4 (natural gas). Octane, C_8H_{18}, is familiar as a constituent of gasoline. All of them are combustible, but have ignition temperatures of several hundred degrees.

The Hydrosilicons. As would be expected, hydrosilicons exist. However, only a few of the simpler ones have been prepared, for beyond silicohexane, Si_6H_{14}, the difficulties in preparing them become almost insuperable. The trouble is not instability, although they are less stable than the corresponding hydrocarbons; it is the enormous affinity of silicon for oxygen. If silane is prepared similarly to bismuthine:

$$\underline{Mg_2Si} + 4\ H^+ + 4\ Cl^- \longrightarrow 2\ Mg^{++} + 4\ Cl^- + \overline{SiH_4}$$

each bubble ignites at the surface and forms smoke rings similar to those formed when phosphine burns.

$$\overline{SiH_4} + 2\ \overline{O_2} \longrightarrow \underline{SiO_2} + 2\ \overline{H_2O}$$

More complex hydrosilicons hydrolyze vigorously on contact with the slightest trace of water, liberating hydrogen.

$$\overline{Si_2H_6} + 6\ H_2O \longrightarrow 2\ \underline{H_2SiO_3} + 7\ \overline{H_2}$$

It is easy to see why the hydrosilicons are of only theoretical interest at the present time.

The Silicones. The oxidational difficulties of working with the hydrosilicons prove that the Si–O bond is much more stable than the Si–Si bond. It has also been found that the Si–C bond is much more stable than the Si–H bond. These facts are the basis of a new industry that had its inception during World War II and promises to be as important in peacetime as it was during the war—the manufacture of a whole new series of compounds called *silicones*. The silicones are compounds whose molecules are chains composed of *alternate Si and O atoms*.

Preparation of Silicones. Methyl chloride, CH_3Cl, reacts readily with silicon which has been alloyed with a little copper as a catalyst. In effect, the molecule breaks into two fragments, a chlorine atom, $:\ddot{C}l\cdot$, and a methyl radical, $H:\ddot{C}\cdot$ (with H above and below), both of which unite with silicon, $\cdot\dot{S}i\cdot$; this is repeated and dimethylsilicon dichloride is formed.

$$\begin{array}{c} H \\ H:\ddot{C}:H \\ :\ddot{C}l:Si:\ddot{C}l: \\ H:\ddot{C}:H \\ H \end{array}$$

The bonds between the silicon atoms and the methyl groups are quite stable; those with chlorine are subject to hydrolysis like any other non-metal halide. Hydrolysis replaces the chlorines with $-OH$ groups (HCl escapes). Immediately a process called *condensation* sets in; $-OH$ groups on adjoining molecules react, liberating water and leaving the two Si atoms attached to one oxygen.

$$\begin{array}{cc} H & H \\ H:\ddot{C}:H & H:\ddot{C}:H \\ H:\ddot{O}:Si:\ddot{O}:\boxed{HH:\ddot{O}:}Si:\ddot{O}:H \\ H:\ddot{C}:H & H:\ddot{C}:H \\ H & H \end{array}$$

By governing the conditions the condensation may be made to produce rings of various sizes or chains of any desired length (thousands of molecular units in one chain are usual).[1] Furthermore, by using a chosen proportion of methylsilicon trichloride, any desired number of cross links may be produced between chains. Products having the physical properties of oils, rubbers, and

---

[1] The empirical formulas approximate $(CH_3)_2SiO$. The similarity of this to the formula for acetone, a *ketone* (page 700), is responsible for the name "silicone."

resins can be thus produced. Chemically, they are much more stable against both heat and oxygen than the corresponding carbon compounds.

Uses of Silicones. The surface of porcelain is covered with a tightly adsorbed layer of water molecules. This water reacts readily with the vapor of dimethylsilicon dichloride, and is thus replaced by a monomolecular silicone layer that adheres just as tightly. The outer surface of this new layer, being composed of methyl groups, is similar to the surface of a piece of paraffin or a layer of oil, and is equally water-repellent. The radios of high-altitude bombers used to be put out of operation on their return to sea level by the condensation of a conducting film of water on the cold porcelain cores of certain coils which shorted the coils. Treatment of the porcelain as described above eliminated this trouble.

Silicone rubber gaskets, replacing asbestos ones, made big naval searchlights airtight against the intrusion of moist sea air which had been corroding the reflectors. Ordinary rubber melted in the heat of the searchlight and could not be used.

Silicone liquids in the hydraulic systems of planes retained satisfactory viscosity at temperatures so low that standard hydraulic fluid became stiff, and when it was so hot that the regular liquid became water-thin and leaked out.

Silicone varnishes are such excellent insulators and so heat-resistant that wiring thus insulated enabled motors to work under overloads that would have set fire to the insulation used previously. The superfortresses would have been overloaded beyond successful operation with their multitude of remote-control electric motors had not silicone insulation halved the motor size.

A whole new field of chemistry and technology has been opened up by the development of silicones.

Silicon Halides

The halogens combine with silicon to form several halides, of which silicon tetrachloride, $SiCl_4$, and silicon tetrafluoride, SiF_4, are of importance at present. SiI_4 is a solid, $SiCl_4$ a liquid, and SiF_4 a gas at room temperature. $SiCl_4$ melts at $-70°$ and boils at $57.6°$ C.; a bottle of it fumes strongly in moist air.

$$SiCl_4 + 4\,HOH \longrightarrow \underline{H_4SiO_4} + \overline{4\,HCl}$$

$SiCl_4$ alone was used during the First World War to produce a smoke screen; a better method is to use it in combination with NH_3 because the HCl liberated combines with NH_3 to form NH_4Cl, and thus two white solids are produced simultaneously.

SiF_4 can be prepared by the reaction between fluorine and silicon, but this is a difficult method. A much easier one is to add hydrofluoric acid to silica or a silicate; this forms the colorless gas, SiF$_4$. HF cannot be kept in a glass bottle because SiO$_2$, although insoluble in HCl, reacts vigorously with HF.

$$SiO_2 + 4\ HF \longrightarrow \overline{SiF_4} + 2\ H_2O$$

Calcium silicate also reacts with HF.

$$\underline{CaSiO_3} + 6\ HF \longrightarrow \underline{CaF_2} + \overline{SiF_4} + 3\ H_2O$$

As soon as SiF$_4$ comes in contact with moisture it hydrolyzes; insoluble gelatinous silica is formed in a water solution, together with HF. The reaction of HF with SiF$_4$ to form H$_2$SiF$_6$, fluosilicic (or hydrofluosilicic) acid, and the use of sodium fluosilicate as an insecticide and a laundry "sour" were described on page 339. Na$_2$SiF$_6$ is nearly 600 times as soluble in water as K$_2$SiF$_6$; thus to separate K$^+$ from Na$^+$, H$_2$SiF$_6$ is used in analytical chemistry as a precipitating agent for the potassium ion. None of the alkali metals, alkaline-earth metals, or rare earth metal ions are very soluble in the presence of the (SiF$_6$$^{--}$) ion.

Silicon Carbide

The one important silicon-carbon compound, carborundum, SiC, was accidentally discovered by Acheson in 1891. The furnaces in which it is prepared at Niagara Falls are made of fire brick and are 16'×5'×5'. The ends of the beds are 2 ft. thick; they carry the terminals, each of which consists of about 60 carbon rods 30 in. long and 3 in. in diameter. Only the ends of the bed are permanent; the sides are built up as the charge is added. The furnace is half filled with charge which does not touch the terminals. Between the electrodes is a cylindrical core 21 in. in diameter composed of small pieces of coke; the current passes through the core and produces numerous arcs and a high temperature (about 3000° C.). A charge 8 ft. high is piled over the core; the charge weighs about 15 tons and consists of coke, sand, sawdust, and salt in the ratio of 34.2:54.2:9.9:1.7. The salt serves as a flux and the sawdust makes the mixture more porous. The CO produced in the reaction burns at the top of the furnace.

$$SiO_2 + 2\ C \longrightarrow Si + \overline{2\ CO}$$
$$Si + C \longrightarrow SiC$$

A charge is usually left in the furnace for 36 hours. About 6700 lb. of carborundum and 5000 lb. of amorphous silicon carbide are obtained from each charge. The product is dug out of the furnace and then ground, washed, and graded. Carborundum varies in color from dark green to black; the absolutely pure product is colorless.

Carborundum is made into wheels and hones, or powdered and applied to paper, and is used chiefly as an abrasive. It is more expensive than emery, but also more effective. It can be used instead of diamonds for drill heads, since it is nearly as hard as diamond. It is an excellent refractory material for furnaces, and is also used as a resistor in numerous electrical appliances. Without carborundum the vast number of precision-made automobiles produced each year could not be made. Several thousand tons of carborundum are produced annually; the cost to the consumer is 15 cents per pound.

Other Non-metallic Compounds of Silicon

Silicon combines with sulfur to form SiS_2 which hydrolyzes readily. Silicon nitrides are obtained by passing nitrogen over hot silicon. Silicon borides, SiB_3 and SiB_6, are produced in an electric furnace and are extremely hard. Oxides of silicon will be discussed in later paragraphs.

Compounds of Silicon and Metals

Silicon combines with several metals to form silicides. Magnesium silicide, Mg_2Si, has already been mentioned. Other silicides are those of calcium, iron, and cobalt (Ca_2Si, $FeSi$, and $CoSi$).

Silicon Dioxide

The most important compound of silicon is silicon dioxide, SiO_2 (silica, quartz, rock crystal), very pure deposits of which are found in nature. Quartz, the beautiful crystalline form of silica, is an important constituent of the earth's crust; geologists estimate that igneous rocks are about 12 per cent quartz.

Many semi-precious stones such as the amethyst, bloodstone, opal, agate, onyx, and jasper are nearly pure quartz. Traces of impurities give these stones their beautiful colors. The opal is an extremely interesting form of quartz, for its lovely colors are due not to impurities but to diffraction of light caused by tiny fissures crossing the crystal in all directions. Many of the hitherto "semi-precious stones" are no longer expensive because they can be made in the laboratory.

Pure quartz softens at 1700° C. and at this temperature it can be molded into test tubes, beakers, crucibles, etc. Quartz has such a low coefficient of expansion that a quartz test tube can be heated to the maximum temperature of a Bunsen burner and quickly dropped into water without cracking. Quartz is resistant to all chemical agents except hydrofluoric acid, strong alkali solutions, and alkaline fusion mixtures.

Two types of quartz are used for chemical apparatus: vitreous or opaque quartz and clear quartz. Vitreous quartz apparatus is made by fusing quartz and pressing it into the desired shape without removing air and water bubbles from it. It is difficult to remove air entrapped in quartz because the quartz is so viscous; but it can be done by placing molten quartz under a high vacuum which will slowly pump out the air bubbles. If the material is then cooled under pressure, the remaining gas is compressed to such a small volume that the quartz is practically clear.

Quartz allows ultraviolet light to pass through it and is therefore superior to ordinary glass for many purposes, as for example, for windows in sunrooms of hospitals. The bulb or tube of the mercury vapor ultraviolet lamp is made of quartz.

Kieselguhr or diatomaceous earth is composed of the skeletons of diatoms, infusoria, sponges, and other forms of aquatic life. This material, which is nearly pure silica, is so finely divided that it is not gritty; hence it is used in some scouring soaps, metal polishes, etc. It is also used as a filtering medium for the removal of coloring material from petroleum.

Although we may take considerable silica into our bodies along with our food, only minute traces remain. However, silica breathed into the lungs as dust remains and produces silicosis. Human hair and teeth contain silica. The feathers of some birds contain as much as 40 per cent silica, and it is present in straw, bamboo, and other plant fibers.

Whereas carbon forms two oxides which are gases at room temperature, both SiO_2 and SiO (silicon monoxide) are solids. SiO is prepared by reducing SiO_2 with carbon. It is brown in color and is used as a pigment.

At ordinary temperatures CO_2 will replace SiO_2 from some compounds, but at higher temperatures SiO_2 will replace CO_2. The glass industry is based on this important fact.

One of the recent uses of SiO_2 is in the manufacture of mineral or rock wool. This fibrous material, which is an excellent insulating and sound-proofing substance, is made by forcing steam at high pressure against a thin stream of molten rock.

The Structure of Silica. Whereas carbon forms two oxides which are gases at room temperature, silicon dioxide, as we have seen, is a high-melting solid. This seems strange at first glance, because carbon and silicon are consecutive members of Group IV in the periodic system. The reason is a peculiarity due to the small size of carbon, not to anything unusual in the behavior of silicon. The ability of carbon, nitrogen, and oxygen to form multiple covalent bonds has already been mentioned in connection with the latter two elements; silicon does not display this ability to any important extent. The electronic formulas of carbon dioxide and carbon monoxide, respectively, $:\!\ddot{O}\!::\!C\!::\!\ddot{O}\!:$ and $:\!C\!:::\!O\!:$, explain the small size and consequent volatility of the molecules. Since double bonding is impossible in silicon dioxide, the valence octet of the silicon cannot be completed in a single SiO_2 unit, $:\!\ddot{O}\!:\!Si\!:\!\ddot{O}\!:$, and the silicon attaches itself to an electron pair in each of two other similar units. But the silicon in these two units is subject to the same necessity; hence the process repeats itself indefinitely. A whole crystal of quartz is thus a single giant molecule. In it each silicon atom is covalently bound to four oxygen atoms tetrahedrally arranged around it. Each oxygen atom is a part of two

SILICON AND ITS COMPOUNDS

such tetrahedra. The three-dimensional structure thus built up is composed of six-membered rings, made up of alternate Si and O atoms, with the Si atoms in one plane and the O atoms in a parallel plane at a little distance. The rings fit into each other at such angles that four adjacent ones enclose a somewhat tetrahedral cell of empty space. It is easy to understand why quartz is not a gas.

Silicic Acid

Silicon dioxide does not react with water to form silicic acid, but does form soluble silicates when treated with alkali hydroxides at high temperatures. Silicic acid is very weak and very insoluble; so it can be easily prepared by treating sodium silicate with an acid. The product thus obtained is probably metasilicic acid.

$$2\ Na^+ + SiO_3^{--} + 2\ H^+ + 2\ Cl^- \longrightarrow 2\ Na^+ + 2\ Cl^- + \underline{H_2SiO_3}$$

Orthosilicic acid, H_4SiO_4, may possibly be obtained by the hydrolysis of silicon tetrafluoride, SiF_4, but loses water upon exposure to air. When a soluble silicate is acidified the silicic acid appears first as a colloidal solution which soon gets to a gel. This gel is believed to be a tangled structure of endless polymers of H_2SiO_3:

$$\begin{array}{ccc} H & H & H \\ :\!O\!: & :\!O\!: & :\!O\!: \\ :\!O\!:\!Si\!:\!O\!:\!Si\!:\!O\!:\!Si \\ :\!O\!: & :\!O\!: & :\!O\!: \\ H & H & H \end{array}$$

Ions can move freely in the water which occupies the relatively large spaces between the fiber-like molecules of silicic acid. Diffusion will remove the dissolved salts completely if the gel is crumbled and soaked in many changes of water. If the gel is dried the acid itself is dehydrated to silica simultaneously with the evaporation of the free water. The material shrinks and becomes too hard to alter its shape any further, long before the drying is completed. As a result, the particles, although glassy in appearance, actually have a submicroscopic sponge-like structure which gives them an enormous surface area. Most of the silicon atoms in this surface have incomplete valence octets and are therefore surrounded by strong force fields which give the surface extraordinarily good sorbent powers. This dried material—called, curiously enough, *silica gel* (although it is no longer a gel)—is an important commercial product that is used to remove moisture or vapors of volatile solvents from air. The sorbed material can be driven off by simple heating (and recovered if valuable), leaving the gel as good as new. A more porous or chalky type of gel can be made by using ferric chloride instead of hydrochloric acid. One of these chalky gels has been found to sorb benzene vapors to over 1.5 times its own weight. Airplane motors were kept free from rust on sea voyages during the recent war by the use of silica gel to remove the water vapor from the air inside their air-tight Pliofilm wrappers.

Silicate Minerals

In all naturally occurring silicate minerals, each silicon atom is the center of a tetrahedron of oxygen atoms, to each one of which it is covalently bound. In *quartz*, as previously stated, each oxygen atom is a part of two tetrahedra; if there are metal ions in the mineral, the electrons which they furnish may permit some of the oxygen atoms to have a covalence of only one. In the limiting case metals have furnished four electrons for each silicon atom, and each oxygen atom is a part of one tetrahedron only.

$$\begin{array}{c} :\!\ddot{O}\!: \\ :\!\ddot{O}\!:\!\ddot{S}i\!:\!\ddot{O}\!: \\ :\!\ddot{O}\!: \end{array}$$

Minerals containing this unit are called orthosilicates. Among them are zircon, olivine, and the garnets. *Zircon* is $ZrSiO_4$. In an *olivine* the Zr^{++++} is replaced by two divalent ions, such as Mg^{++} or Fe^{++}. In the *garnets* half of the positive charges are furnished by divalent ions (including Ca^{++} in this case) and half by trivalent ions (Al^{+++}, Fe^{+++}, and Cr^{+++}).

Metasilicates, like metaphosphates, have anions with the empirical formula SiO_3^{--}, composed of either rings (three-, four-, or six-membered) or endless chains of tetrahedra. In the latter case the cations, distributed regularly along the chain, may hold it practically straight while rendering its surface nearly neutral.[2]

When well crystallized, minerals with this type of structure can be easily separated into fibers so fine as to be flexible. They are collectively known as *asbestos*.

In another interesting class of minerals the anions consist of infinite

[2] Each O in the formula has a complete octet, but only shared pairs of electrons are shown by a diagonal line. The charges on the anion may be considered as localized on the singly covalent O atoms because these atoms have 6 unshared electrons of their own + a half share in a bonding pair.

SILICON AND ITS COMPOUNDS

sheets of silicon-oxygen tetrahedra, each of which is a member of three contiguous rings. The empirical formula of this anion is $Si_2O_5^{--}$. (Each ring has $\frac{1}{3}$ of each of 6 Si, $\frac{1}{2}$ of each of 6 O, and all of 2 O.)

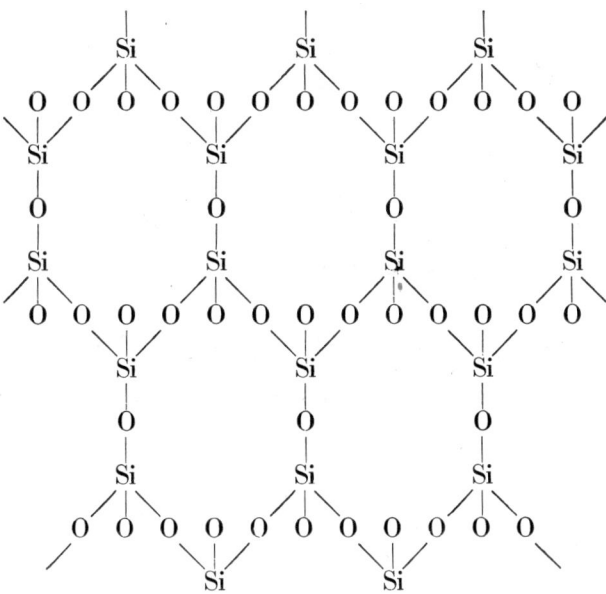

In *talc* there is an OH⁻ ion in the center of each ring and the negative sheets are held together in pairs by a layer of Mg^{++} ions between them; in a typical *clay* mineral there is a layer of Al^{+++} ions (only two-thirds as many, of course) instead of the Mg^{++}. In the *micas* one-fourth of the silicon atoms are replaced by aluminum atoms, which act non-metallically and show the same four covalent bonds as silicon. Since the atomic number of aluminum is one less than that of silicon, each aluminum atom which thus takes the place of a silicon atom calls for one more ionic positive charge. This is furnished by a layer of alkali metal ions between each pair of double sheets. It is easy to see why these minerals are all laminar in nature. Cleavage takes place easily and very accurately between the neutralized double sheets.

Still other rocks have a three-dimensional anion skeleton resembling the quartz structure, the negative charge being the result of the replacement of some of the silicon atoms by aluminum, as mentioned in the preceding paragraph. In the *feldspars* one-fourth of the silicons have been thus replaced; sodium or potassium ions equal in number to the aluminum atoms occupy the cells. Feldspar is a common constituent of granite. The replacement of one-third of the silicon by aluminum produces a *zeolite*. In the zeolites the smaller amount of nuclear charge in the anion lattice lengthens the covalent bonds between its atoms. The cells are so much larger than in quartz or even feldspar that water can penetrate everywhere within a crystal. The positive ions can diffuse from cell to cell or, if others diffuse at the same time, leave the cells and go into the surrounding solution. Cations with charges greater than $+1$ are held much more strongly within the alumino-silicate anion than are sodium ions. If water containing Ca^{++} or Mg^{++} ions (hard water) is allowed to seep through a bed of sodium zeolite granules, every divalent cation that wanders into one of the passages in the zeolite will be held there and will release an equivalent number of sodium ions into the moving water. The effluent will be soft water. The Ca^{++} and Mg^{++} ions are not absolutely fixed in the zeolite structure; they merely diffuse much more slowly than do the Na^+ ions. After the water softener has exhausted its cation exchange[3] power by replacing all its Na^+ by di- or trivalent cations, the original zeolite can be regenerated by soaking the material in saturated NaCl brine. During this process any Ca^{++} ion (for example) which wanders out of the zeolite becomes lost in the swarm of Na^+ ions and never goes back. The situation is essentially the same as that involved when ammonia is added to a suspension of a precipitate of silver chloride to remove from the field of action each Ag^+ ion that succeeds in dissolving away from the crystals.

Sodium Silicate

The most important synthetic silicate is sodium silicate, Na_2SiO_3, which is known to the trade as *water glass*. It is prepared commercially by either of two methods: fusing sand with sodium carbonate or heating it with concentrated sodium hydroxide under pressure.

$$SiO_2 + Na_2CO_3 \xrightarrow{\text{fuse}} Na_2SiO_3 + \overline{CO_2}$$

$$SiO_2 + 2\ NaOH \xrightarrow[\text{pressure}]{\Delta} Na_2SiO_3 + \overline{H_2O}$$

The common sodium metasilicate on the market is a thick syrupy solution, but solutions of almost any desired ratio of $Na_2O:SiO_2$ can be purchased.

The many uses for sodium silicate undoubtedly account for its being sold in so many different forms. One semi-solid form can be rolled into a round ball which will bounce. The pentahydrate, $Na_2SiO_3 \cdot 5\ H_2O$, is a crystalline solid which is very soluble in water. Sodium silicate is used in solution as an egg preservative. Because it is cheaper than glue, it is used as a substitute in the making of cardboard boxes and other shipping containers. It is used to prevent corrosion in water mains because the insoluble silicates precipitate and form a protective coating. Cheap soaps contain Na_2SiO_3 as a filler and binder, and many cleansers contain it. Water glass serves as the binder of artificial stone. Sodium silicate is a fairly good fireproofing agent. Nearly a half million tons of sodium silicate are manufactured each year.

[3] Commonly called "base exchange."

THE GLASS INDUSTRY

Glass-making is one of the oldest chemical industries and one in which great progress was made by chance methods. Only within recent years has this industry been put on a scientific basis and even now many data are still lacking.

No one knows how the art of making glass originated, but glass was made more than 5000 years ago. The oldest record of it is Egyptian and dates back to 3200 B.C. Sand from the banks of the Nile and alkalis from the nearby deserts furnished the raw materials. At first the Egyptians used glass to cover or glaze articles made from clay; but by about 2000 B.C. articles were made of glass itself. A glass goblet dating from 1490 B.C. and bearing the name of one of the Pharaohs is still in existence. Glass-blowing dates back to 250 B.C. When Caesar Augustus conquered Egypt in 23 B.C. he required the conquered people to pay taxes in the form of glassware, and later many Egyptian glass workers were brought to Rome. From there the glass industry spread to Gaul, Spain, Britain, and the Rhine provinces, but was almost lost when the barbaric tribes from the north swept down and destroyed the Western Roman Empire.

China learned the secret of making glass in the fifth century. By 1200 A.D. the industry had shifted to Venice, where it thrives to this day. The use of glass in mirrors and ornamental objects, the making of colored and enameled glass and lace and net glass, and the art of cutting glass with diamond are some of the contributions made by the Venetian glassmakers. Window glass was being made in England by 1557, and her glass industry thrived from then on. The German alchemist, Kunckel, developed a ruby glass about 1680 but died without passing on his secret. This glass is now made by adding gold to the molten glass.

The first glassworks in the United States was begun at Jamestown, Virginia, but the Indian massacre of 1622 prevented its completion. The first plant to operate was built by Robert Hewes of Boston at Temple, New Hampshire, in 1780. Mr. Hewes presented to Harvard University the large circular plate which was the first article made.

An important development in the glass industry occurred during the First World War, when in 1917 the Corning engineers developed Pyrex glass. Hitherto, high-grade glassware which had a low coefficient of expansion and a high melting point had to be imported from Jena, Germany. The Pyrex glass not only made it unnecessary to import the German glass, but was actually superior to the imported glass.

Although glass has many very desirable properties, it is not malleable.[4]

[4] According to an old story, a Roman architect discovered malleable glass and made a cup from it. As he was presenting the cup to Caesar, he purposely dropped it. Although dented, it did not break, and a few taps with a hammer restored it to its original shape. Instead of the expected reward of riches and power, the architect was put to death because Caesar thought the invention dangerous to the Roman glass industry.

An organic malleable glass is known today, but no inorganic malleable glass is known as yet; the possibility is doubtful.

Composition of Glass

Glass is a transparent or translucent resonant substance which is usually considered to be a supercooled liquid. Among the many kinds of glass is that made from the single element, selenium; that made from a pure oxide like SiO_2 (quartz), and that made from complicated mixtures of metallic and non-metallic oxides and other compounds. The composition of glass has changed but little during the centuries. Analysis of modern window glass and some transparent glass made in Egypt in 1400 B.C. showed the following constituents:

	Egyptian Glass, 1400 B.C.	Modern Window Glass
Silica	63 per cent (approx.)	69 per cent (approx.)
Lime and magnesia	12 per cent (approx.)	9 per cent (approx.)
Soda and potash	23 per cent (approx.)	18 per cent (approx.)
Alumina, ferric oxide, etc.	2 per cent (approx.)	4 per cent (approx.)

The many classifications of types of glass are based on either its composition or its uses. It was formerly customary to find a use for new kinds of glass as they were developed, but modern science frequently reverses this procedure. When a demand arises for a particular type of glass, this glass is synthesized in the laboratory. The approximate number of metallic atoms per hundred silicon atoms in some common glasses is given in Table 27.1

TABLE 27.1. COMPOSITION OF COMMON GLASSES

	\multicolumn{7}{c}{Relative Numbers of Atoms of}
	K	Na	Ca	Pb	Al	Fe	Si
Bottle glass	25		100		50	25	100
Window glass		50	42				100
Plate glass		67	17				100
White glass	33		17				100
Flint glass	60			45			100
Paste glass	37			56			100

These ratios emphasize the fact that innumerable mixtures of metal and non-metal oxides can be fused into a substance which has the properties of glass. The arrangement of molecules in glass is still unknown.

The purest sand used in the American glass industry is disintegrated quartz rock which comes from Lanesborough, Massachusetts. For CaO, either lime or limestone may be used. Wood ashes were formerly the source of K_2O, and ashes of sea plants the source of Na_2O; but these are now obtained as products of the salt industry. Pb_3O_4 is used in preference to PbO because the excess oxygen aids in burning out carbonaceous material. Waste glass,

SILICON AND ITS COMPOUNDS

called cullet, is added to promote fusion and the union of the silica and bases.

For the most part, glass is a mixture of alkali and silica, for only this combination provides both a low melting point and durability. It is possible to make alkali-free inorganic glasses which have valuable chemical and electrical properties; for example, it is difficult to melt them. Silica-free inorganic glasses lack durability. Silicate glasses are frequently divided into four groups: *lime*, *lead*, *borosilicate*, and *colored*.

Lime glass, which excels all other glass in tonnage, is used for window and plate glass and containers. It is made by fusing lime, soda, and sand. The soda acts as a flux, but it also makes the finished product more water-soluble and greatly increases the coefficient of expansion. Magnesia, MgO, is sometimes substituted for lime. Equal parts of these oxides produce a glass with a low melting point. Minute quantities of Al_2O_3 are sometimes substituted for SiO_2.

Lead glass contains lead oxide and has a low melting point, a long working range, and a high electrical resistance. It is satisfactory for light bulbs, and its high index of refraction and brilliancy makes it ideal for cut glass and certain optical lenses.

Borosilicate glass is resistant to chemical attack and to heat shock. The discovery of the improvement in ordinary glass resulting from adding B_2O_3 was made by Schott of the great Jena glass works. A Jena borosilicate glass containing zinc oxide instead of lime was the standard chemical glass before World War I. Pyrex heat-resistant glass, which has replaced it, contains 81 per cent silica and 12 per cent B_2O_3, and practically no Group II oxides. Its softening point is so much higher than that of soft glass that an oxygen-fed blast lamp is needed to work it. It expands only slightly with an increase in temperature and therefore can be used for cooking utensils. The development of new methods for producing B_2O_3 should make this glass even cheaper.

Nearly all glass is *colored* because of impurities in the sand. For example, iron gives glass a green tint which can be neutralized with manganese dioxide or selenium. If highly colored glass is desired, metal oxides are usually added to the molten mix. Cobalt, copper, and chromium oxides produce the colors at the purple-blue-green end of the spectrum. Red is obtained with gold, copper, and selenium. White and opal are produced by the addition of phosphates and fluorides. Manganese, iron, titanium, cerium, uranium, and vanadium are among the many metals used to produce specific colors. It is extremely difficult to secure an exact match of the color in two different batches of glass.

Optical Glass

Optical glass is used in the lenses of glasses, cameras, microscopes, and telescopes. Some of the newer optical glass contains a variety of chemicals,

Corning Glass Works Photo

FIG. 27.1. The largest solid piece of glass ever cast by man looked much like a huge cake of ice after cooling. This 200-inch telescope mirror disk is large enough for more than 100 men to stand upon it. The circular opening in the center, 40 inches in diameter, is for the passage of light rays. Supporting the disk is the bottom of the great mold mounted on the carriage of the 60-ton locomotive hoist which moved it from the annealing kiln. The disk was poured at Corning, New York, on December 2, 1934; its dimensions as poured were 200 inches in diameter, 27 inches thick, 20 tons in weight, 218 square feet surface area.

Corning Glass Works Photo

FIG. 27.2. The completed ceramic mold for the 200-inch disk with cores in position. The large central core produced the 40-inch hole required in the center of the disk. The remaining system of cores produced the ribbed structure of the disk.

including barium, boron, aluminum, and zinc oxides. Flint or lead glass, frequently used in optical instruments, contains up to 70 per cent by weight of lead oxide. Flint glass is cut into desired shapes with grinding wheels and then polished.

Photo by Robert Yarnall Richie

FIG. 27.3. The 200-inch telescope disk, showing the geometrically cored pattern on its under side. These hollows and ribs of glass lighten the weight of the 20-ton disk and provide a means of supporting it in the telescope. Standing in front are the two men who made the disk, Dr. George V. McCauley (left), physicist in charge of disk-making at the Corning Glass Works, and Dr. J. C. Hostetter, director of development and research.

Prior to 1912 we purchased nearly all our optical glass abroad; but an American concern, the Bausch and Lomb Optical Company, now produces the finest and most uniform optical glass in the world. It is characterized by its homogeneity, great transparency, and high index of refraction.

The manufacture of the famous 200-inch glass reflector by the Corning Glass Company for the great telescope at the Palomar Observatory was truly a remarkable achievement in the art of handling glass. It is estimated that a billion new stars can be seen with this telescope.

Other Special Glasses

There have been many improvements in the glass industry within recent years, and the new products developed have contributed materially to our comfort. The industry itself has expanded, there now being over 200 plants concerned with the manufacture of glass and its products. Nearly 100,000 people are employed in the industry, and the output is valued at about $300,-

FIG. 27.4. Charging glass-melting furnace.

000,000 per year. Among the various forms in which glass is now available are the following:

Wire glass contains wire embedded in the molten glass. In case of fire, the wire holds the glass together even though the glass itself has softened. Such glass does not break easily.

Invisible glass has a light transmission of 99.6 per cent. It is produced by evaporating exceedingly thin films ($\frac{1}{4}$ the wave length of green light) of fluorides of the alkali and alkaline earth metals onto the glass surface. Glass which is almost invisible can be produced by dipping glass in certain organic compounds which form a film some 40 to 50 molecules thick.

Safety glass was discovered by an accident. A French chemist noticed that a glass bottle which had contained collodion "starred" but did not shatter when it was accidentally dropped on the floor, and this gave him a clue to a way of preventing glass from shattering. The laminated safety glass of today is made by placing a suitable plastic between plates of glass and then "gluing" all of it together by heat and pressure.

The composition of the *Carrara and black glass* made by the Pittsburgh Plate Glass Company approaches in general that of plate glass, but includes certain special chemicals. Carrara glass does not stain and it takes various finishes well.

Fibrous glass is quite flexible. The bulk or insulation type is known as insulating wool. One of the most recent developments in this field is the making of filter cloth from glass yarn. Glass cloth is also used as reinforcement for plastic.

Tempered glass, made by sudden cooling, is stronger and more flexible than plate glass; when broken, it crumbles rather than shatters, and it will crumble if tapped lightly in a certain way. It is used when bullet-proof glass is required.

Vycor glass is made from Pyrex glass by dissolving out all the metallic oxides by means of long treatment with concentrated nitric acid, after the desired object has been shaped from it. The slightly porous glass is then heated until it becomes clear again; it shrinks about 10 per cent in the process. It contains about 96 per cent silica and has very nearly the properties of quartz glass, but is much cheaper.

Neodymium glass is used for glass-blowers' goggles because it selectively cuts off the dazzling yellow sodium light from the heated glass without having much effect on other light.

Low silica glasses include a new borotantalate-tungstate optical glass that contains thorium and lanthanum and a maximum of 10 per cent silica. Its high combined refractive and dispersive index permits new achievements in lense design. An aluminum phosphate glass which absorbs infra-red rays contains no silica.

THE CEMENT INDUSTRY

Cement is a fine gray powder which will harden under water and yet withstand temperatures that melt steel. It is used to bind hard material together into a stone-like substance called concrete. Sand, crushed rock, and pebbles are usually mixed with cement in making concrete. Concrete has one outstanding advantage over other construction materials in that it can be easily molded into any shape.

The ancient Egyptians used a crude cementing material in building the Pyramids; and a cement which would harden under water was used in a 70-mile aqueduct built by the Carthaginians and still in existence. The Romans used volcanic dust mixed with slaked lime as a cement. An English engineer, John Smeaton, faced with the task of making a suitable foundation for a lighthouse in 1756, discovered that a calcined mixture of a certain limestone and clay could be made to harden under water.

The real founder of the modern cement industry was a mason, Joseph Aspdin of Leeds, who in 1824 patented a cement made by burning and pulverizing an artificial mixture of slaked lime and clay. Because blocks made from this cement resembled the famous Portland building stone, it was called Portland cement. Shortly thereafter deposits of rock from which an excellent cement could be made were found in New York State.

Fig. 27.5. Castle of St. Angelo in Rome, built in 138 A.D. The structure is reinforced concrete. (Courtesy, Portland Cement Assoc.)

Portland cement is defined by the American Society for Testing Materials as "the product obtained by finely pulverizing clinker produced by calcining to incipient fusion an intimate and properly proportioned mixture of argillaceous and calcareous materials, without the addition of anything subsequent to calcination excepting water and calcined or uncalcined gypsum." From this definition it is clear that many combinations of materials can be used, such as cement rock and limestone, limestone and clay or shale, limestone and blast furnace slag, and marl and clay. Clay is typically argillaceous and limestone is calcareous. Cement rock, which contains the necessary substances in about the right proportions, is found chiefly in Pennsylvania.

SILICON AND ITS COMPOUNDS

Table 27.2 gives the approximate proportions of raw materials used in making cements.

TABLE 27.2. APPROXIMATE COMPOSITION OF SUBSTANCES USED IN MAKING CEMENTS
(In per cent by weight)

	British	Egyptian	Lehigh	Quick Hardening
Silica	52	27	18	4
Ferric oxide	5	4	8	8
Alumina	14	0.4	—	30
Lime	10	28	38	31
Magnesia	0.5	2	2	—
Carbon dioxide	12	17	32	24
Alkali	4	8	trace	1
Water	—	10	4	—

FIG. 27.6. Explosives and cement were essential in the construction of Hoover Dam. (Courtesy, Hercules Powder Co.)

To secure intimate fusion, the raw materials are usually pulverized in ball mills and then burned in a rotary kiln. The kiln is between 8 and 13 ft. in diameter and from 150 to 340 ft. long, and rotates on roller bearings at about one revolution per minute. Powdered coal, fuel oil, or gas burning at the end of the kiln shoots flames 40 ft. long into it. The pulverized raw materials are fed into the upper end of the kiln, and remain in the kiln for two hours. Increasing heat is applied, and water and carbon dioxide are driven off. Finally the material fuses into clinkers which are air cooled at the exit. They are then mixed with not more than 3 per cent gypsum (this controls the rate of hardening of the cement), pulverized so finely that the cement will flow through a sieve that will retain water, and then sacked.

The chemistry of the hardening of cement is not well understood at present. Calcium aluminates, calcium silicates, silicic acid, calcium hydroxide, and other compounds are known to be formed when water is added to the cement. Because of the insolubility of these compounds, considerable time might be required for a series of such reactions and crystallizations to reach equilibrium. The following equation for the hydrolysis of tricalcium aluminate is an example of the reactions:

$$Ca_3(AlO_3)_2 + 6\ HOH \longrightarrow 3\ Ca(OH)_2 + 2\ Al(OH)_3$$

The initial set of cement which occurs within three hours after the addition of water is thought to be in part due to the above reaction. As the hydration

Fig. 27.7 At left, working cement. At right, stiff, medium, and wet mixtures of concrete. (Courtesy, Portland Cement Assoc.)

and crystallization continue, the grains of rock and sand are held together in a firm solid network. Certain cements take nearly a month to harden. Some of the hydration, hydrolysis, and neutralization reactions are exothermic, for heat is evolved when the water and cement are mixed. An elaborate cooling system was built into Hoover Dam to carry away this heat and thereby hasten the setting of the structure. Although 4 to 8 gallons of water are used per sack of cement, only about 2.5 gallons combine chemically. The rest evaporates; slow evaporation is preferable.

Quick-hardening cement has a high content of Al_2O_3. In one day it develops a tensile strength equal to that of Portland cement aged for four weeks. Steel wire and bars placed in the cement-sand mixture increase the tensile strength of the concrete. The short life of the average concrete highway is sufficient evidence of the need for further scientific research in this industry.

Early in the "Concrete Age" a large number of enthusiasts decided to get rich by building cement plants. Plants were constructed in thirty-three states at a capital expenditure of over $700,000,000. The 151 of them now in operating condition have a capacity of 240,000,000 barrels annually and would probably employ 45,000 men to produce that quantity. Actually, in 1942, the peak year of war construction, they produced 182,800,000 barrels; in 1944, production had dropped to 38 per cent of capacity. Employment is approximately proportional to production.

Fig. 27.8. Making a plate. (Courtesy, Onondaga Pottery Co., Syracuse, N. Y.)

THE CERAMIC INDUSTRY

The making of bricks, pottery, and other clay products is another long-established industry; museums throughout the world contain many fine collections of ancient pottery. Ceramics includes the making of products by shaping wet clay (with or without the addition of other substances) and drying it by sun-baking or firing it in kilns. Clays result from the weathering of feldspars, such as $KAlSi_3O_8$, $NaAlSi_3O_8$, and $H_2Al_2(SiO_4)_2 \cdot H_2O$.

Feldspar + CO_2 + H_2O ⟶ alkali carbonates + sand + aluminum silicate
(clay)

Some good deposits of china clay are found in Georgia and Florida. The composition of the clay determines its use in the industry. The percentage composition of china clay is approximately SiO_2, 47; Al_2O_3, 37; iron oxides, traces; alkalis, traces; water, 13.

The wet clay mixture, called the "slip," is molded on a turntable called a "jigger." The molded product is partly dried and then placed in the kiln where it is baked at a temperature of about 1200° C.; it shrinks about 10 per cent in the kiln. Glazing consists of coating the article with a mixture of oxides and then reheating it. Glazes contain borax, zinc oxide, silica, tin oxide, titanium dioxide, etc. One of the greatest difficulties in making glazed ware is preparing a glaze which will have the same coefficient of expansion as the part being glazed. Colored ware is produced by means of inorganic oxides; for example, cobalt oxide applied under the glaze gives a blue, chromium oxide a green, and uranium oxide a black color.

FIG. 27.9. Placing ware for glost fire. Cut section in center shows arrangement for biscuit fire; that on right, for glost fire. (Courtesy, Onondaga Pottery Co., Syracuse, N. Y.)

Fused silicate coatings which are applied to metal are called *vitreous enamels*. Feldspar, fluorspar, cryolite, silica, and other chemicals are fused and drawn off into water; this produces a friable product, called "frit." The frit is pulverized, made into a paste, applied to the metal surface, and baked on. Usually more than one coat of enamel is required for a smooth surface. The use of enamel on refrigerators, stoves, office equipment, etc., is indicative of the fact that vitreous enamelware is a valuable product. *Porcelain* is made from a mixture of kaolin and feldspar.

QUESTIONS AND PROBLEMS

1. Is silicon a metal or a non-metal? How is it prepared from sand?
2. What volume of SiH_4 can be prepared from 12 g. of SiO_2? What volume of hydrogen can be obtained by the action between two molecular weights of NaOH and 1 g. of silicon?
3. Write equations for the etching of glass.
4. Which elements should have properties similar to those of silicon?
5. By means of compounds, show the importance of silicon in the mineral kingdom.
6. What is a "silica gel"? Is silicic acid soluble in water?
7. How is sodium silicate prepared?
8. How would you distinguish between Pyrex, quartz, and soft glass? What are some of the new developments in the glass industry?
9. Suggest a reason for the setting of cement. Is the process exothermic or endothermic?
10. What is porcelain? Vitreous enamel?
11. What type of coloring agent is used in the pottery industry?
12. A sample is either SiO_2, Na_2SiO_3, cement, or china clay; how would you identify it?

REFERENCES

Books

Properties of Glass. Morey, G. W. Reinhold Publishing Corporation.
A Practical Course in Concrete. Giese, H. Portland Cement Assoc. 33 W. Grand Ave., Chicago, Ill.

Articles

"Silicon Carbide." Boyer, J. A. *Met. and Alloys,* **10,** 8–12 (1939).
"Glass. Non-Metallics in the Chemical Industry." Rohrman, F. A. *J. Chem. Ed.* **14,** 353–359 (1937).
"Composition and Properties of Glass." Morey, G. W. *J. Chem. Ed.* **8,** 421–441 (1931).
"Sodium Metasilicate." Vail, J. G. *Chem. and Met. Eng.* **37,** 736–740 (1930).
"The Quest for Hard Materials." Tone, F. J. *Ind. and Eng. Chem.* **30,** 232 (1938).
"Portland Cement." *Chemistry and Industry* **2,** 261–278.

» 28 «

BORON AND ITS COMPOUNDS

Boron is considered immediately after silicon because it gives us a good opportunity to observe a *diagonal* relationship that exists between the two eight-element periods of the periodic system. In many ways boron and silicon are more alike than either of them is like the adjacent element in its own family. This is because they are about equally electrophilic. The smaller number of valence electrons tends to make boron more metallic than silicon, but this is counterbalanced by its smaller size, which acts in the opposite direction. Of course valence similarities run vertically in the periodic table, but it is difficult to see much resemblance between boron, a non-metal, and aluminum *when the latter is behaving as a metal*. Such resemblance as aluminum shows to boron is confined to cases when the aluminum is acting as a non-metal.

Occurrence

The element boron constitutes slightly less than 0.001 of 1 per cent of the earth's crust; it is present in some silicate minerals. Boron compounds are widely distributed in nature, chiefly in old lake beds, borax marshes or dry lakes, volcanic vapors, hot springs in volcanic regions, and marine borates; but workable deposits of these compounds are rare. Boron is always found in the combined form as boric acid and borates. The important borate minerals of the United States are borax, $Na_2B_4O_7 \cdot 10\ H_2O$; ulexite, $NaCaB_5O_9 \cdot 8\ H_2O$, kernite, $Na_2B_4O_7 \cdot 4\ H_2O$, and colemanite, $Ca_2B_6O_{11} \cdot 5\ H_2O$. These complex anion formulas suggest those of the silicates.

Borax was relatively scarce until the latter part of the 19th century, when borax crystals were found in the mud of a lake in Lake County, California. Ulexite was discovered later in some marshes in Nevada. The discovery of borax in Death Valley, California, by Aaron Winters and his wife in 1880 was the beginning of the borax industry in the United States. The first borax was drawn by 20-mule-team caravan 165 miles to the nearest railroad.

BORON AND ITS COMPOUNDS

Fig. 28.1. Transporting borax from the mines in Death Valley to the rail head. (Courtesy, Dane Packwood, Los Angeles.)

Colemanite is the chief deposit in the old lake beds of Death Valley. The recently discovered deposits in the Mojave Desert are mainly kernite. The borax marsh deposits of Nevada, Oregon, and California consist chiefly of ulexite. The vapors of volcanoes in Tuscany, Italy, contain boric acid, as do also the hot springs in Italy, Chile, and California. The complex salt deposits of Stassfurt, Germany, which are regarded as being of marine origin, contain a mixture of magnesium borate and magnesium chloride.

© *Spence Air Photos*

FIG. 28.2. Mining and milling plant at Boron, California. (Courtesy, Pacific Coast Borax.)

The successive discarding of one mineral for another as a source of boron compounds in the United States is interesting. From 1864 to 1872 native borax was obtained from lake muds, and from 1872 to 1887 most of it came from the salt marshes; but these sources were discarded with the discovery of the deposits of colemanite. This source was discarded in turn with the discovery of high-grade deposits of borax and kernite and the successful extraction of borax from the Searles Lake brine in 1925.

To obtain borax from colemanite, $Ca_2B_6O_{11} \cdot 5\ H_2O$, the compound must first be calcined and then boiled with a sodium carbonate solution. Borax can be obtained as a precipitate by evaporating the solution which is filtered from the insoluble calcium carbonate. However, the use of Na_2CO_3 makes this process very expensive. The preparation of both potash and borax from the Searles Lake brine now furnishes us with cheaper borax.

The United States produces about 95 per cent of all the borates mined throughout the world. Our consumption of borax is nearly 300,000 tons per year, and in normal times we export an additional 100,000 tons or more.

Discovery and Preparation of Boron

Gay-Lussac and Thenard prepared boron in 1808 by heating potassium and B_2O_3 together. Any of the alkali or alkaline earth metals can be used as a reducing agent. If magnesium and boron trioxide are heated together in a furnace until the iron container becomes dull red, an extremely vigorous exothermic reaction occurs suddenly.

$$3\ Mg + B_2O_3 \longrightarrow 3\ MgO + 2\ B + \Delta$$

Dissolving the magnesium oxide in hydrochloric acid leaves boron which is fairly but not absolutely pure, because magnesium boride also forms. Boron can also be prepared by electrolyzing fused mixtures containing boron compounds; but thus far this method has been unsuccessful on a commercial scale. Very pure boron is obtained by reducing boron trichloride with hydrogen.

Physical and Chemical Properties of Boron

As usually prepared, boron is a grayish-brown amorphous powder; the crystalline form can also be made. Boron is soluble in oxidizing acids such as HNO_3 and H_2SO_4, the boron being oxidized to boric acid. It is extremely difficult to oxidize boron with oxygen because a surface film of B_2O_3 forms that protects the element from further oxidation. Boron melts at 2300° C.

Fused boron has a high electrical resistance. Boron differs from most substances in that this property decreases with an increase in temperature; therefore attempts have been made to use it in overload relays in electric circuits and for igniter points in certain rectifier tubes. Several boron alloys have been recommended for use in the steel industry, and it is probable that extremely tough steels containing it may be of commercial importance.

Compounds of Boron and Metals

Boron combines with several metals to form borides such as magnesium boride, Mg_3B_2, calcium boride, CaB_6, and manganese boride, MnB_6. Some of these compounds are used in the oxidation and degasification of molten metal.

Magnesium boride reacts with acids and evolves a mixture of boron hydrides. B_2H_6 is a gas that can be liquefied at $-87°$ C. Hydrides of such high molecular weight as $B_{10}H_{14}$ have been prepared, but none of them are of any general importance at present.

Compounds of Boron and Non-metals

The most important compounds of boron and non-metals contain oxygen; they will be discussed in later paragraphs. Boron halides such as BCl_3 are prepared by the direct union of the elements. Boron combines readily with nitrogen to form boron nitride, BN, a white powder that is quite stable. (This is one of the impurities in the boron prepared by fusion methods.) B_2S_3 is formed by the union of boron and sulfur. None of these compounds are of any importance. Boron carbide, however, is both interesting and useful.

Boron carbide is prepared by heating a mixture of completely dehydrated boric oxide and very pure carbon in an electric resistance furnace to 2450° C., at which temperature the product melts. The reaction is:

$$2\ B_2O_3 + 7\ C \longrightarrow B_4C + 6\ \overline{CO}$$

The formula B_4C is the empirical formula of a giant molecule extending throughout each crystal, in which all the atoms are held to their nearest neighbors by covalent bonds. On account of its extremely compact, strongly bonded structure, boron carbide is the hardest of all manufactured substances. It is used for the nozzles of sand-blasting apparatus, which must stand a terrific abrasive action, for extrusion dies for abrasive rods, and for the contact points of precision gauges, dial indicators, and micrometers. A boron carbide plug gauge has been used to test more than a million holes without losing its accuracy; in the same service ordinary steel gauges were worn beyond permissible limits in testing a thousand holes. Harder than silicon carbide, boron carbide powder is used to produce a smoother finish and sharper edges on tungsten carbide tools which have been rough-ground with silicon carbide, and in piercing and finishing tungsten carbide drawing dies. Intrinsically it is about one-quarter as good as diamond powder, and costs only one-hundredth as much.

Boron Trioxide and Boric Acid

The only important oxide of boron is B_2O_3, which is prepared by the dehydration of boric acid, H_3BO_3. B_2O_3 is a white compound which melts at 577° C. to a thick, viscous, glass-like substance. It readily takes on water from the atmosphere. Considerable B_2O_3 is always vaporized when boric acid is heated in an attempt to dehydrate it completely. B_2O_3 is used in the glass and ceramic industries.

Boric acid is usually prepared in the laboratory by acidifying a hot solution of borax with HCl or H_2SO_4 and then cooling the mixture. H_3BO_3 is over ten times as soluble at 100° C. as it is at 0°. (At 0°, 2.59 g. of H_3BO_3 dissolve in 100 g. of water.) As the solution cools, flakes of boric acid crystallize and are filtered from the mother liquor and dried.

$$5\,H_2O + 2\,Na^+ + B_4O_7^{--} + H^+ + HSO_4^- \longrightarrow 2\,Na^+ + SO_4^{--} + 4\,H_3BO_3$$

If orthoboric acid is heated to 100° C. metaboric acid forms; at a higher temperature tetraboric (or pyroboric) acid forms. Further heating results in the formation of B_2O_3.

$$4\,H_3BO_3 \xrightarrow[100°]{\Delta} 4\,HBO_2 + 4\,H_2O$$
$$\xrightarrow[150\text{-}200°]{\Delta} H_2B_4O_7 + H_2O$$
$$\xrightarrow{\Delta} 2\,B_2O_3 + H_2O$$

Boric acid will not liberate CO_2 from metal carbonates and has only slight action on metals.

Boric acid is a solid at room temperature; crystals of it have a slippery feeling. It is present in borated talcum powder. Taken internally, boric acid is a poison; therefore its use as a preservative in smoked meats, sausage, fish, dairy products, and other foods is now almost entirely prohibited. It is used externally as a mild antiseptic. Dilute solutions can be used as an eyewash because the pH of these solutions is only slightly less than 7. A shocking number of babies have died of boric acid poisoning in both hospitals and homes, because boric acid solution was mistaken for boiled water or lime water; the solution should always be plainly marked POISON. Boric acid is used in cements capable of taking a polish, in laundry starch glazes, in the sterilization of hides, as a welding flux, and as a fireproofing agent. Boric acid is known popularly as *boracic acid*.

Salts of Boric Acid

Borax, $Na_2B_4O_7 \cdot 10\,H_2O$, is the most important salt of boric acid. It can be made by the neutralization of boric acid with sodium hydroxide, but this procedure is usually unnecessary because the salt is mined in large quantities as one of its several hydrates. Since borax is formed by the neutralization of a weak acid and a strong base, a solution of it is strongly basic. Kernite, $Na_2B_4O_7 \cdot 4\ H_2O$, is the chief source of borax in this country. Kernite dissolves so slowly in water that it is unsatisfactory for many purposes; this difficulty is overcome by heating kernite with steam under pressure, thus producing the more rapidly soluble $Na_2B_4O_7 \cdot 10\ H_2O$. A white porous fluffy mass results when borax is heated until it is dehydrated.

Borax is sold on the market as anhydrous $Na_2B_4O_7$, or the penta- and decahydrates of this compound. Borax is widely used commercially. It constitutes about 25 per cent of the composition of enamels. Borax and boric oxide are used as fluxes in making glazes for ceramic products. From 15 to 50 parts of granulated borax are added per 1000 parts of sand in making common glass. Borax is used as a flux to free metallic surfaces of oxide films before welding and brazing operations, and solutions of borax and soap are used in alkaline baths to clean metal surfaces before they are plated. It is used in the tanning industry to neutralize the acidity of tanned leather. About 10 or 15 lb. of borax to 1000 gal. of water are used to hasten the cleansing and softening of hides and skins. It is used in the cleansing of fabrics in the textile industry and in the control of the pH of spinning baths. The addition of borax to dextrin or casein (the coating on glazed or enameled paper) prevents excess hydrolysis of the adhesives. Borax is also used as the solvent for casein and, in the manufacture of playing cards and similarly coated board, as a solvent for shellac; it also prevents mold growths in the paper. Packers of citrus fruits use a 5 per cent solution as a wash to prevent blue mold and decay. Calcium tetraborate is insoluble; hence borax is used as a water softener. Its detergent properties make it a common constituent of the solution used for washing milk bottles, etc. Several soap preparations on the market are mixtures of soap and borax.

If a platinum wire is warmed and dipped into some powdered borax and heated again, a glass-like borax bead forms. These beads take on characteristic colors if they are dipped in certain metal salts and reheated. Borax may be considered as consisting of two molecules of sodium metaborate and one of boric oxide. The latter plus metallic oxides produces colored borates.

$$Na_2B_4O_7 \longrightarrow 2\ NaBO_2 + B_2O_3$$
$$B_2O_3 + \text{metallic oxide} \longrightarrow \text{colored borates (beads)}$$

Sodium metaborate can be made by fusing together Na_2SO_4 and B_2O_3.

$$Na_2SO_4 + B_2O_3 \longrightarrow 2\ NaBO_2 + \overline{SO_3}$$

Sulfur trioxide is much more volatile than B_2O_3. $NaBO_2$ may also be prepared by neutralizing HBO_2 with $NaOH$. The crystalline salt has the formula $NaBO_2 \cdot 4\ H_2O$, and effloresces in the atmosphere. A water solution of it has a pH of 10.8; this makes it a little more alkaline than borax.

Sodium "perborate," $NaBO_2 \cdot H_2O_2 \cdot 3\ H_2O$, is a strong oxidizing or bleaching agent, for hydrogen peroxide is liberated when water is added. As a tooth powder it is a specific against Vincent's angina, or trench mouth, but should be used only according to a doctor's instructions. It is prepared by electrolyzing a mixture of borax and sodium hydroxide. The salt thus formed is only slightly soluble in cold water.

Tests for the Borate Radical

The free acid is liberated from borates by the addition of HCl. If turmeric paper is dipped into a solution containing free boric acid and then dried, the paper turns dark red.

A more spectacular test for the borate radical is to moisten the solid sample with concentrated sulfuric acid, add alcohol, and warm; the vapors escaping from the mixture will ignite. An acid solution of boric acid reacts with alcohol and forms tri-ethyl borate $(C_2H_5)_3BO_3$. This gas is fairly volatile and burns with a characteristic green flame.

$$3\ C_2H_5OH + H_3BO_3 \xrightarrow[\text{dehydrating agent}]{H_2SO_4} (C_2H_5)_3BO_3 + 3\ H_2O$$

Boron in Plant Growth

Boron is essential to plant growth, but the concentration used in culture media to produce normal growth is less than one part per million. Even slightly higher concentrations are fairly toxic. Boron is present in some irrigation waters coming from wells and it accumulates in waters which flow over soil containing boron compounds. Boron compounds in irrigation water accumulate in the soil; hence ill effects may not appear until after several seasons of cultivation. Boron compounds concentrate in the leaves of plants and cause them to turn yellow. Alfalfa and sugar beets will thrive in soil that contains sufficient boron compounds to destroy deciduous fruits and grapes. The problem warrants considerable study if our national policy is to be the encouragement of more irrigation farming in the West and Southwest.

QUESTIONS AND PROBLEMS

1. What weight of borax can be prepared from one ton of colemanite? What weight of B_2O_3? What volume of 0.01 molar H_3BO_3?
2. A substance is boron, silicon, bismuth, or lead; how would you identify it?
3. Of what commercial use is boron carbide?
4. Show by step equations the heat decomposition of boric acid.
5. What weight of sodium metaborate can be prepared from 1 lb. of B_2O_3?
6. List some uses of borax.

BORON AND ITS COMPOUNDS

7. Which of the following are metals? Non-metals? What general statements based upon the positions of these elements in the periodic table can you make? (Refer to the long periodic table, page 82.)

GROUP IN THE PERIODIC TABLE

0	I A	II	III A	IV A	V A	VI A	VII A	VIII
He	H		B	C	N	O	F	
Ne	Li			Si	P	S	Cl	
A	Na				As	Se	Br	
Kr	K				Sb	Te	I	
Xe	Rb				Bi			
Rn	Cs							

Summarize the properties of these elements under several headings, such as method of preparation, properties of oxides, properties of hydrides, etc.

8. The following exercises summarize the many examples thus far given. Can you do them?

a. Determine the molecular weight of a compound.

b. Determine the formula of a compound, knowing the percentage composition.

c. Determine the percentage of an element in a compound.

d. Given the weight per liter and the percentage composition of a gas, determine its formula.

e. Weight-weight problems. Given so many grams of x, how many grams of y will be formed?

f. Weight-volume problems. Given so many grams of x, how many liters of y will be formed?

g. What is the significance of S.T.P., 22.4 l., °C., 760 mm., cc., ml., M, N, G.M.V., G.M.W., kilo, H_F, H_V, specific heat, K_I, K_E, K_{sp}, pH, 0° A., F, V, A, $\triangle$, and s.g.?

h. Convert a volume of gas at one temperature and pressure to another temperature and pressure, thus applying the laws of Boyle, Charles, and Dalton.

i. Compare the rates of diffusion of gases.

j. What is the significance of boiling point and freezing point, changes due to the addition of electrolytes and non-electrolytes? Molal solutions?

k. Given the molarity and degree of dissociation, calculate K_I.

l. Given the solubility, calculate K_{sp}.

m. Given the K_{sp}, calculate the solubility.

n. Given the pH and normality, calculate K_I.

o. Given K_I and normality, calculate the pH.

p. Given amperage and time, calculate grams deposited; or given any two of these, calculate the third.

q. Given specific gravity and percentage composition, calculate the normality; or given any two, calculate the third.

r. Determine the milliliters of one substance of known normality required to neutralize a definite volume of another substance of known normality; or given any three of these, calculate the fourth.

REFERENCES

Books

Properties of Glass. Morey, G. W. Reinhold Publishing Corporation. 227, 272, 300, 370.

Articles

"The Discovery of Boron." Weeks, M. E. *J. Chem. Ed.* **9**, 1389-1394 (1932).
"Borax Industry in S. California." Dingley, W. F. *J. Chem. Ed.* **8**, 2113–2125 (1931).
"Borax." Turrill, P. L. *J. Chem. Ed.* **9**, 1319–1324 (1932).
"Pyrex." Curtiss, W. N. *Ind. and Eng. Chem.* **14**, 336–337 (1922).
"The Many-Sidedness of Glass." Sullivan, E. C. *Ind. and Eng. Chem.* **21**, 177–180 (1929).
"Boron, a Review." Schaller, W. T. *Am. Inst. Mining and Met. Eng.* 149–162 (1937).
"Manufactured Abrasives, Old and New." Ridgway, Raymond R. *Chem. and Eng. News* **21**, 858 (1943).
"Developments in Glass." Taylor, A. S. *Illum. Eng.* **39**, 369–372 (1944).
"Crystals from Portland Cement Hydration, an Electron Microscope Study." *Ind. and Eng. Chem.* **35**, 1178 (1943).

» 29 «

CHARACTERISTICS OF THE METALS

In a general way you are familiar with the properties of metals, and you could probably list the outstanding properties of metals and non-metals, but you would find that there are exceptions in nearly every respect. This is partly because the most familiar metals are not always the most typical, and partly because elements that are intermediate between the extreme metals and the extreme non-metals may have properties that do not, without explanation, seem to be intermediate. Some special factors are also introduced by the incomplete electron layers in the transition elements. We have already studied the extreme metals (Chapter 22) and the typical and some less typical non-metals. Let us review and compare some of their important physical and chemical properties. These are summarized in Tables 29.1 and 29.2.

TABLE 29.1. PHYSICAL PROPERTIES OF METALS AND NON-METALS

	Metals	Intermediates	Non-Metals
Molecular size	Monatomic	Giant	Moderate
Boiling point	Medium	High	Low
Density	Low to medium	Medium to very high	Low to high
Luster	High	Varies	Poor reflectors
Color of powder	Black	Strong to black	None to strong
Hardness	Low	High	Low
Malleability	High	All degrees	Brittle
Conductivity	High	All degrees	Low

The fundamental difference between non-metals and metals is that the former have more valence electrons and hold onto electrons much more tightly than the latter. How is this simple factor responsible for the facts shown in Table 29.1?

Molecular Size. The extreme non-metals are strongly electrophilic and have plenty of electrons to form small to moderate-sized molecules, in which all the octets are completed by the establishment of a reasonable number of covalent bonds. These covalent bonds are very strong. The extreme metals have too few electrons to form any complete octets; therefore individual atoms are the units. The intermediate elements, having fewer valence electrons than the extreme non-metals, have to form more bonds to complete their octets, and these bonds are weaker because the elements are less electrophilic. Moderate-sized molecules are possible, but there is a great tendency for the bonds to break and re-form in such a way as to join molecules indefinitely, making giant molecules.[1] In the case of metals the bond strength has weakened to such a point that although bonds may be thought of as forming momentarily in all directions, they break again instantly.

Boiling Point. To separate the molecules of a non-metal from each other as it boils, only the small van der Waals forces must be overcome. Accordingly the melting and boiling points are low. The forces between the atoms of metals are higher, because there are unpaired electrons; hence the melting and boiling points are higher. In the intermediate elements, with their giant molecules, melting is very difficult and evaporation involves the actual breaking of covalent bonds that are enormously stronger than van der Waals forces. Frequently intermediate elements do not melt but sublime at temperatures high enough to shake off fragments from the giant molecules.

Density. In any family of elements the density increases with atomic weight. The typical metals have relatively large atomic volumes because the small charge of the kernel permits the valence electrons to have very large orbits. The smaller non-metal molecules are not tightly packed because their electrons are too well coupled to have appreciable van der Waals forces. With increasing atomic size and weight, the coupling becomes poorer, the van der Waals forces increase, and the molecules are packed tightly enough together so that the density is considerable. Iodine is nearly twice as dense as aluminum. In the more non-metallic intermediate elements all the atoms are closer together than *molecules* can be brought; so even the lightest of them compares in density with the heaviest of the extreme metals in Groups I and II. The more metallic intermediate elements and the less extreme metals are held together by strong forces arising from incompletely filled electron shells; this leads to the highest of all densities.

Luster. The ability to reflect light increases as the electrons are more loosely held in the atom or molecule. The same is true of the ability to absorb light, which results in *color*.

Hardness. The hardness of a substance is governed largely by the same considerations that affect its boiling point.

Malleability. The ability to be deformed beyond the elastic limit without breaking is one of the most characteristic of metallic properties. It is due to a combination of two factors: (1) The molecules are of minimum size,

[1] Examples are: S_μ, red phosphorus, and gray arsenic. An unstable yellow arsenic is As_4.

i.e., monatomic, providing a maximum number of planes of flow along which slippage can take place in nearly any direction. (2) Every molecule, being a neutral atom with unpaired electrons, attracts all its neighbors equally and strongly; this prevents separation as they move past each other.

Conductivity. The highly characteristic metallic property of conductivity is due to the multiplicity of empty valence orbits which permits electrons almost complete freedom of motion from atom to atom.

TABLE 29.2. CHEMICAL PROPERTIES OF METALS AND NON-METALS

	Metals	Intermediates	Non-Metals
Type of ion	Positive	Both	Negative
Covalent bonds	None	Moderate	Strong
Element + acid	H_2 + cation	No reaction	No reaction
Element + base	No reaction	H_2 + anion	Disproportionates or O_2 + anion
Element + H_2	Cation + H^- or no reaction	Indirect formation of unstable covalent compound	Stable covalent compound
Oxide + water	Cation + OH^-	Insoluble	H^+ + anion
Chloride	Hard salt	Low-melting solid or liquid	Gas or liquid
Chloride + H_2O	Ions, no reaction	Hydrolyzes reversibly	Hydrolyzes completely
Hydroxide	Base	Amphoteric	Acid
Redox behavior	Reducing agent	Both, weakly	Oxidizing agent

All the material in Table 29.2 has been so thoroughly discussed in preceding chapters that no further explanation should be necessary here.

Occurrence of the Metals in Nature

Ores are the natural substances from which metals are extracted; and frequently more than one type of ore is used as a commercial source of a metal. We should not expect to find large concentrations of any very soluble metal compound near the earth's surface; or, stated the other way, it is only logical that metal ores should be insoluble. Since most metals form several different insoluble compounds, many chemical combinations of metallic ions with other elements or radicals are possible.[2]

In discussing the relative abundance of the elements (page 13), we saw that oxygen and silicon make up about 74 per cent of the earth's crust, with aluminum, iron, calcium, sodium, potassium, and magnesium next in order. Of these six, only iron has been of commercial importance as an element for as long as fifty years. An element may be abundant and yet have few uses as an element. On the basis of abundance, the element aluminum should be the cheapest of the metals; that it is expensive is due to the cost of the process

[2] Review Chapter 16 on the properties of ions, for that chapter gives a clue to the form in which metals are found in nature. The list would include *native metals, oxides, sulfates, sulfides, carbonates, halides, silicates,* etc.

which must be used to obtain it from its ores. Juggling the value of the dollar gives the prices of gold and silver artificial values. A vast store of both these metals has been created in this country for reasons unconnected with their usefulness. Prices for metals change rapidly as new methods of mining, new ores and metallurgical procedures, and new uses or substitutes are developed.

Classification of Metals

For convenience in studying their properties, the metals may be classified on other bases than that used in the periodic table; but the position of the element in the periodic table is of some importance in such classifications.

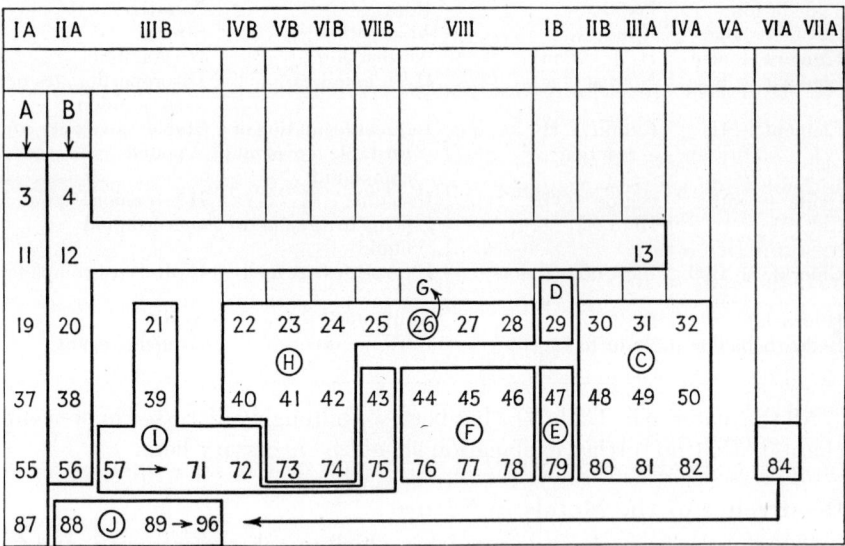

FIG. 29.1. A classification of the metals for convenience in studying their properties

The classification shown in Fig. 29.1 includes the following groups:

- A. The alkali metals
- B. Aluminum and the alkaline earth metals
- C. The soft metals
- D. Copper
- E. Gold and silver
- F. The platinum metals
- G. Iron
- H. Metals frequently used with iron
- I. Less familiar metals
- J. Radioactive metals

A. All the alkali metals are prepared by the electrolysis of fused compounds in the absence of water. These metals were discussed in Chapter 22.

B. All the alkaline earth metals—beryllium, magnesium, calcium, strontium, and barium in Group IIA and aluminum in Group IIIA of the periodic table—are prepared commercially by the electrolysis of fused non-aqueous solutions or by reduction with the alkali metals. The elements are never produced in aqueous solutions.

C. The metallurgy of each of the *common* soft stable metals—zinc, cadmium, and mercury in Group II B, and tin and lead in Group IV A—is sufficiently alike so that these elements can be studied together.

D. Copper is such an important element that it is discussed in a separate chapter. It has much in common with silver and gold, which are also in Group I B.

E. Gold and silver are found in similar forms in nature, their metallurgical processes are similar, and they have many kindred uses.

F. The six platinum-like metals in Group VIII—platinum, iridium, osmium, palladium, rhodium, and ruthenium—also have much in common.

G. Iron is so important that its properties, metallurgy, and uses are treated in a separate chapter.

H. Although nearly all the metals may in time be widely used with iron, the following are now frequently used with iron and may be considered together: titanium and zirconium in Group IV B; vanadium, columbium, and tantalum in Group V B; chromium, molybdenum, and tungsten in Group VI B; manganese in Group VII B; and cobalt and nickel in Group VIII. Many steels known to the trade contain these metals in concentrations varying from less than one to several per cent.

I. The twenty elements listed together as "the less familiar metals" constitute one of the most interesting groups of all, because so much is yet to be learned regarding their properties. Some of these metals are of importance now; and it is almost certain that, as our knowledge of them increases, new uses will be developed that will make some of them even more important.

J. The radioactive property of uranium, protactinium, thorium, actinium, radium, polonium, plutonium, neptunium, americium, and curium warrants their being treated together.

FUNDAMENTAL PRINCIPLES OF METALLURGY

Before discussing the metallurgy of any one of the metals, it is advisable to consider some of the fundamental principles of metallurgy. The term "metallurgy" includes all the various processes used in securing metals from their ores. Many ores contain so much inert worthless material that *preliminary treatment* is required to concentrate the valuable metal. The second step involves *pyro-*, *hydro-*, and *electrometallurgical processes*, after which the metal can be obtained in the free state. The metallurgist is also in charge of the processes by which the quality of the metal is improved; this is called *refining*. These processes include the addition of other metals to produce alloys, and of carbon and phosphorus to steel, and of silicon to steel and aluminum. A metallurgist is also an authority on the many mechanical treatment processes for metals, such as hot and cold rolling, drawing, etc.

Mining

Many metal ores are found far below the surface of the earth, and frequently only a streak of ore is mined. Because this may zigzag through the surrounding rock, deciding on the location of the shaft is a real problem, for

Fig. 29.2. The Nevada-Massachusetts Company camp at "Tungsten," Nevada, near Mill City, Nevada. (Courtesy, American Tungsten Association.)

the maximum amount of ore must be mined and yet the number of horizontal tunnels must be kept to a minimum. The ideal situation would be that in which the shaft is sunk through the center and to the bottom of a deposit, the miners starting at the bottom and working their way *upward*.

Holes are drilled in the rock, filled with explosives, and fired. The waste rock and the ore are separated by hand, and the waste is left at the bottom of the shaft whenever possible. The ore is loaded on miniature trains which in the newer mines are pulled through the shaft with electric engines, and transported to the bottom of the shaft, where it is loaded into ore buckets and hauled to the surface. Men and tools are also hauled up and down the shaft in these ore buckets.

Temperatures in deep mines are so high that anyone unaccustomed to the

CHARACTERISTICS OF THE METALS

environment nearly suffocates. The temperature increases about one degree Fahrenheit for every hundred feet of descent. In modern mines, great air-conditioning units are used to produce a comfortable working temperature; in the older mines, the men work in front of a strong blast of air which is forced in.

As in other industries, the number of miners in one mine varies from one-man enterprises to those like the Anaconda Copper plant, which employs

FIG. 29.3. Gold and silver mine near Chloride, Arizona.

thousands. Small mines cannot afford to carry through the processes of smelting and refining, and usually sell their crude ore to the larger companies; but some small mines which are operated by 10 to 40 men give the ore preliminary treatment and sell only ore concentrates.

Preliminary Treatment of Ores

Preliminary treatment is essential in concentrating the metal ore so that the smelting and other processes can be done efficiently, but usually none of the metal is produced. Metal ore is usually dispersed through the rock in a thin streak or small granules. The first step in the process is to separate the ore from the rock; this is done by putting the rock through large crushers which can handle rocks weighing over 100 pounds. The rock goes from one crusher to another until the particles are quite small; it is finally reduced to dust by grinders and ball mills.

The metal ore must now be separated from the rest of the dust, or concentrated. Many different properties are considered in selecting the procedure for this purpose. The oldest process is based on the fact that metal ores are heavier than the siliceous substances with which they are associated;

therefore, if the powder is stirred in water, the metal particles will settle more rapidly than the rock particles. All sorts of mechanical devices are used to produce this separation into tailings, or waste material, and an ore concentrate; however, the air separation process used in the large-scale cleaning of cereal is not practical.

Electrostatic separation is based on the fact that substances with unlike charges of electricity attract each other, whereas substances with like charges repel each other. If a mixture of good and poor conductors, such as metallic sulfides and sandstone, falls on a highly charged surface, the good conductors take the charge of the surface and are then repelled from it. Because the ore must be dry for this process, the dust problem is serious.

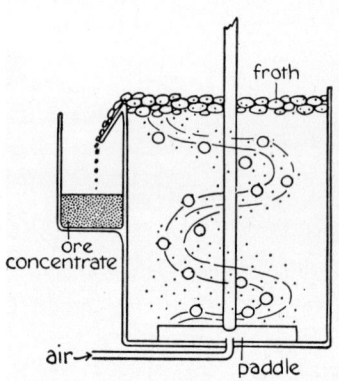

FIG. 29.4. Ore flotation.

The ore flotation process, which is extremely important at present, is applicable to many ores and creates no dust problem because the ore must be wet. This process (Fig. 29.4) depends upon the addition of a chemical to the finely pulverized ore; a froth forms when air is blown through the wet mixture. Many non-soluble oils such as pine, creosote, eucalyptus, and camphor are used for wetting; varying the wetting agents makes it possible to float first one mineral and then another. The wet valuable ore is carried to the surface; silica and other nonmetallic constituents remain suspended in the liquid. As the froth comes to the surface a paddle wheel brushes it off into another container. Acid is added to break the froth, and the mineral is then filtered on vacuum rotary filters covered with a special canvas. A scraper on one side of the filter dislodges the sticky concentrate.

When the water is removed at a temperature of 100° C., the process is called drying. Frequently the temperature is sufficiently high to induce chemical reactions; for example, carbonates may be decomposed into oxides and carbon dioxide be liberated. This is called calcination. Roasting, or heating in the presence of air, usually refers to the process of converting sulfide ores into oxides or sulfates. A dry concentrated mineral composed of these metal oxides or sulfates is available for the smelting processes. The flue gas may contain, in addition to sulfur dioxide and carbon dioxide, numerous other volatile materials. Many plants now recover valuable by-products from the flue gas. Thus, sulfur dioxide is oxidized to sulfur trioxide and converted into sulfuric acid; arsenic, antimony, and selenium are precipitated with Cottrell precipitators.

Pyro-, Hydro-, and Electrometallurgical Processes

To produce a metal from a metallic compound, it is necessary to reduce the metallic ion. This can be done in the fused state, in water solution by means of chemicals alone, or in either state with an electric current. The chemical properties of the metal compound and the metal, as well as the expense, determine the procedure.

Pyrometallurgical Processes. There is some confusion regarding the term *smelting*. In its broadest sense, it includes all the heat processes—calcination, roasting, and reduction—that is, heat treatment involving chemical change and melting. Some scientists restrict the term to the extraction of a metal in the fused state.

The stone or earthy substance associated with metallic ore is called the *gangue*. This must be separated from the molten metal; to do this, another impurity called a *flux* is frequently added. Thus, if sand is mixed with the metal, lime is added, the SiO_2 and CaO fusing to form calcium silicate.

$$CaO + SiO_2 \longrightarrow CaSiO_3$$

This material is not miscible with the fused metal; and since its density differs from that of the metal, it forms a separate layer in the furnace. The molten waste material is called the *slag*.

Carbon is the most important reducing agent used in the smelting process, because it is the cheapest and also the most abundant one available inasmuch as coal deposits are widely distributed in the United States. Coal is the source of the coke required for the metallurgical processes. Sulfide ores are first roasted to yield the metal oxides; and these are then reduced with carbon.

Metal sulfide + oxygen $\longrightarrow$ metal oxide + sulfur dioxide
Metal oxide + carbon $\longrightarrow$ metal + carbon monoxide

Carbonates are calcined to the metal oxides and then reduced with carbon. Oxides are reduced without any previous heat treatment. Only rarely are metals found free in nature in such quantity that they can be melted and drained from the gangue.

Hydrometallurgical Processes. All the chemical reactions used in concentrating the metal, as such, in water solution are called hydrometallurgical processes. Potassium cyanide, KCN, is used in extracting gold and silver from low-grade ores. Some copper ores are left in the open until they "weather" sufficiently to form copper sulfate; this is then extracted with water.

The use of mercury to recover gold and silver by amalgamation is very old. The ore was roasted, and vinegar, mercuric chloride, copper sulfate, and mercury were added. The mixture was then ground, and the silver and gold were recovered by distilling the amalgam. Gold is sometimes recovered by adding chlorine water which reacts with gold and forms soluble gold chloride. The metal is then precipitated with scrap iron or some other reducing agent.

Electrometallurgical Processes. There are two types of electrometallurgical processes: those in which the metal can be precipitated electrolytically from water solution, and those in which the metal can be deposited only in the absence of water. The dry materials are poor conductors of electricity; hence they must be fused and then electrolyzed. The alkali metals, alkaline earth metals, aluminum, cerium, and the rare earth metals are among those which cannot be obtained in the metallic state by electrolysis of water solutions. The amperage determines the quantity of metal produced in a unit time. The voltage is extremely important, for its proper control makes possible the selective electrodeposition of the metals. A certain minimum voltage is required for each metal to be deposited by electrolysis. For example, if two or more metallic ions which deposit at different voltages are present in one solution, the metal which is most easily deposited will be obtained in the metallic state with the lowest voltage. Elaborate care is also necessary to control the composition and temperature of the electrolytic bath. The cathode should be made of some material that is easily separated from the metal being deposited. The cheapest one possible is used, for once it is coated over with the metal, its composition makes little difference.

Refining of Metals

In most cases, smelting and other metallurgical processes yield impure metal; it may contain other metals, slag, dissolved gases, or other impurities. If pure metal is required, it must be refined. Some refining processes are very complicated; others are quite simple. Mercury and zinc can be separated from lead by distillation. Tin is frequently refined by a simple process: the temperature of the furnace is increased just enough to melt the tin, and the pure metal runs down the sloping hearth. Gold, silver, and platinum can be separated from more active metals by being heated in a blast of air, for the noble metals are not oxidized by this treatment.

Electrolysis is the most important refining process. Its use for this purpose will be discussed more fully in the chapter on copper and its compounds. Electrolytic refining can be used for both water solutions and fused electrolytes, but cheap electricity is essential for its commercial success. The bath contains a salt of the metal. The impure metal, as the anode, goes into solution and deposits on the cathode. Metal nearly 100 per cent pure can be thus obtained, although it is sometimes necessary to repeat the electrolytic process, the cathode of the first electrolysis being used as the anode for the next.

ALLOYS

"Alloy" is a term with which everyone is more or less familiar. The use of alloys dates back to prehistoric times, as witness the "Bronze Age"—bronze is an alloy of copper and tin. Silver and copper coins, watches, gold rings, dental fillings, the nails in shoe heels, and fountain pen points—all are alloys. (The use of bismuth in automatic fire sprinklers, antimony in type metal, etc., has already been mentioned.) Only rarely are pure metals suitable for industrial purposes; an alloy is much better in most cases. An alloy is prepared by melting two or more metals together. Although from a theoretical point of view the number of possible alloys is almost limitless, many of these have not been prepared because no commercial application has as yet been found for them.

Pure metals crystallize in definite crystal systems. Rolling, drawing, and other mechanical processes by which metals are worked cause a slippage along the crystal planes, and frequently a change in such physical properties as hardness, etc. All sorts of variations in physical and chemical properties are evident in metals which are alloyed.

Types of Alloys

What is an alloy? Is it a solution? A compound? A mixture? Can we go further than saying that an alloy is the product obtained by cooling a fused mixture of two or more metals? If we had methods of separating an alloy into the components present in the solid state, we could determine the composition of each component. Our first answer to such a question as: "What can happen when metals are melted together?" is that either they will combine and form compounds, or they will not. Because two metals cannot form three or four hundred compounds, we must expand our answer to include compounds which also contain some uncombined metal. A fourth possibility immediately comes to mind. From our study of solutions we know that some substances, such as alcohol and water, are miscible with each other in all proportions at all temperatures between the boiling and freezing points of the solvent, whereas the solubility of other substances varies greatly with the temperature. Could not metals in the solid state show similar properties? Alloys may be classified in four groups: *chemical compounds, chemical compounds intermingled with an excess of one constituent, a solid solution,* and *a solid solution with an excess of one constituent.* There are also border-line alloys.

Since there are so many types of alloys, we can easily appreciate the difficulty in identifying the one obtained by fusing two or more metals. Microscopic examination is an excellent method of identifying an alloy. The surface of the alloy is polished and then treated with certain chemicals which differentially attack it, and the various crystal formations are then examined with a microscope.

Freezing Points of Alloys

The cooling of salt-ice mixtures gives a clue to what happens when an alloy cools. When a dilute salt solution is cooled, ice crystals form first; the remaining solution becomes more and more concentrated with salt until a point is reached at which both salt and water crystallize together. The milky streak in the center of a large cake of ice is due to the high salt content of the last portion that froze. When a saturated salt solution is cooled, salt crystallizes out until the freezing point of the solution is reached; further cooling results in the complete solidification of both salt and water. Regardless of whether the salt solution is dilute or saturated, the temperature required for complete solidification is the same. This constant temperature at which the mixture freezes is called the *eutectic temperature*, and the mixture is called a *eutectic mixture* (from the Greek, meaning "easily melted"; the eutectic mixture is the one with the lowest melting point). These statements are illustrated in Fig. 29.5. A mixture of salt, ice, and salt water is at equilibrium at $-21.1°$ C.

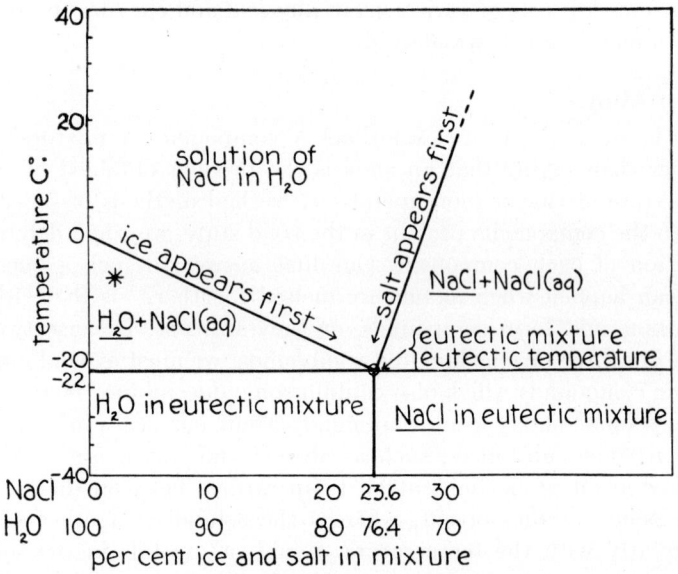

FIG. 29.5. Eutectic mixture. The eutectic mixture contains 23.6 per cent salt and 76.4 per cent water. It freezes at $-22°$. The drawing is divided into five compartments. The states of the constituents at these temperatures are given. At the point marked * (temperature $-6°$, 2 per cent salt and 98 per cent water), water crystals are present in a salt solution. The melting point of NaCl is $805°$ C. By regulating temperature and concentration, any of these five may exist in equilibrium: salt in water; ice in an unsaturated salt solution; ice in a eutectic mixture; salt in a saturated salt solution; and salt in a eutectic mixture.

Metals which do not form compounds and are mutually soluble in the liquid state have temperature-percentage composition curves similar to the water-salt curve in Fig. 29.5. Lead-antimony alloys are a common example (Fig. 29.6). Lead melts at $327°$, and antimony at $630°$ C. The eutectic mixture melts at $247°$ C.; it is 88 per cent lead and 12 per cent antimony. Crystals of antimony are in equilibrium with liquid lead-antimony at the temperature and percentage composition indicated by the asterisk in the figure. Not all alloy diagrams are as simple as that of lead-antimony; on the contrary, many of them are very complicated. This one merely illustrates those used by the metallurgist.

The physical characteristics of an alloy are determined not only by the percentage composition but also by the arrangement of the constituents in the solid state. Alloys are sometimes quenched or cooled quickly to prevent normal crystallization from occurring. The properties of some alloys can be changed by rapid or slow cooling. The structure of alloys sometimes changes after they have been used; for example, the metallurgist may account for the sudden snapping of a metal spring on a car by the fact that the crystallization of the constituents has changed from that present originally in the alloy.

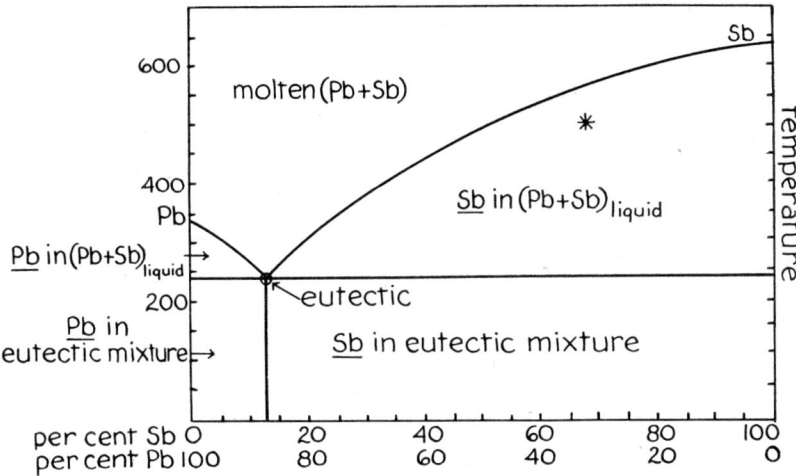

Fig. 29.6. Melting-point curves of mixtures of antimony and lead. (Temperature in degrees C.)

Some Common Alloys

The average composition and uses of a few of the more common alloys are given in Table 29.3. However, variations may be made in the composition. Handbooks of chemistry, *International Critical Tables*, and the handbook of the American Society for Metals contain extensive lists of the trade names, composition, and properties of alloys.

The elements used for low-melting alloys are all grouped closely together in the periodic table. They can be bracketed in a group as follows (melting points of the elements in ° C. are given below their symbols):

Cu	Zn	Ga	Ge	As
1083	419	30	958	814 at 36 atm.
Ag	Cd	In	Sn	Sb
960	321	155	232	630
Au	Hg	Tl	Pb	Bi
1063	−39	303	327	271

Alloys of gallium and indium which melt at as low as 16° C. have been made. Their use for surgical casts and fingerprinting has been suggested.

TABLE 29.3. ALLOYS

Name	Percentage Composition	Uses
Babbitt metal	Sn, 90; Sb, 7; Cu, 3	Bearings
Brass	Cu, 67; Zn, 33 (Wide range)	Sheets, tubing, plumbing
Chromel	Ni, 60; Cr, 40	Resistance wire
German silver	Cu, 60; Zn, 25; Ni, 15 (Wide range)	Tableware, jewelry
Magnalium	Al, 70; Mg, 30	Scientific instruments
Monel metal	Ni, 68; Cu, 28; Fe, 2 (Traces Si, Mn, C)	Corrosion resistant
Pewter	Sn, 74; Pb, 6–20	Table utensils, etc.
Solder	Pb, 67; Sn, 33 (Highly variable)	Plumber's solder
Type metal	Pb, 70; Sb, 18; Sn, 10; Cu, 2	Printer's type
Wood's metal	Bi, 50; Pb, 25; Sn, 12.5; Cd, 12.5	Fusible plug for automatic sprinklers
Iron Alloys		
Duriron	Fe, 84; Si, 14.8; C, 0.85; Mn, 0.35	Corrosion resistant, too hard to machine, brittle
Stainless steel	Fe, 73.5; Cr, 18; Ni, 8; Mn, 0.35; C, 0.15	Strong, corrosion-resistant even at high temperature
High speed tool steel	Fe, 76; W, 18; Cr, 4; V, 1; C, 0.7	Keeps temper at red heat

Airplanes, railroads, automobiles, factories, home appliances, farm implements, hospital equipment, and almost every other mechanical contrivance are made of alloys. Probably the most important recent advancement in the manufacture of alloys has been decreasing their weight and increasing their tensile strength; no giant airliners could be made if no light alloys were available.

QUESTIONS AND PROBLEMS

1. Compare the physical and chemical properties of a typical metal and a typical non-metal.
2. Why are certain metal salts found more frequently than others?
3. Aluminum compounds are more abundant than iron compounds, but aluminum is the more expensive of the two. Explain.
4. Outline the fundamental steps of metallurgy.
5. What is a flux? A slag?
6. What are alloys? List a few common types.
7. List ten alloys found in the home.

8. Study Fig. 29.1 carefully, and list the elements to be discussed in each of the following chapters. How many of these elements are displayed in your chemical laboratory? Compare the current price of each element per pound with the price per volume (your instructor will help you to find current prices). How many of these metals had you seen before? Can you suggest uses for them?

REFERENCES

The journal *Metals and Alloys* contains many articles on metals and alloys and has an excellent abstract section. Refer to it first when looking up recent material pertaining to the metals. It is published by the Reinhold Publishing Corporation at East Stroudsburg, Pennsylvania, and is now in its 27th volume.

Books

Principles of Metallurgy.   Liddell, D. M.   McGraw-Hill Book Company, Inc.

Articles

"Nature of the Metallic State."   Fernelius, W. C., and Robey, R. F.   *J. Chem. Ed.* **12,** 53–68 (1935).

» 30 «

THE ALKALINE EARTH METALS; ALUMINUM

Compounds of beryllium, magnesium, calcium, strontium, and barium in Group II and aluminum in Group III have been used commercially for many years. As metals, they remained laboratory curiosities until developments in metallurgy lowered the processing cost to such extent that their use became practical. Aluminum is included in this chapter because its high position in the E.C.S. makes its metallurgy similar to that of the active Group II elements. Chemically, by the diagonal relationship mentioned at the beginning of Chapter 29, aluminum is similar to beryllium, both being amphoteric. Beryllium and magnesium are treated here for the same reason. Chemically, they might as well be considered with zinc, cadmium, and mercury, for many properties of these five elements are similar. Strictly speaking, only calcium, strontium, and barium are alkaline earth metals (magnesium is on the border line). In the terminology of the alchemists an "earth" was a substance physically resembling clay. The oxides and hydroxides of all these elements have this resemblance, but only those of the last-mentioned elements are soluble enough to give an *alkaline* (basic) reaction. Although radium is an alkaline earth metal, it is more conveniently classified with the radioactive elements.

Occurrence

The alkaline earth metals and aluminum are extremely active and therefore are not found free in nature. The chief source of *beryllium* and its compounds is beryl, $Be_3Al_2Si_6O_{18}$, a beryllium aluminosilicate. Aquamarine and emerald, both valued as gems, are varieties of beryl. Most of the deposits consist of a small quantity of beryl mixed with large amounts of other silicates, but gigantic single crystals have been found. In 1944 a crystal 28 feet long yielded $61\frac{1}{4}$ tons of beryl. Some is mined in the New England States, South Dakota, Colorado, and Nevada, but most of it is imported from British India and Argentina. (Beryllium is called glucinum in England.)

THE ALKALINE EARTH METALS; ALUMINUM

Metallic *magnesium* is obtained from soluble salts or magnesite, $MgCO_3$. The former are more important. The pre-war importance of Germany in the production of magnesium was due to the great Stassfurt deposits of carnallite, $KCl \cdot MgCl_2 \cdot 6\ H_2O$, although these were worked primarily for their potassium content. In the United States the only company producing magnesium before the war was the Dow Chemical Company, which obtained it from brine from their salt wells at Midland, Michigan. During World War II, thirteen new plants were built in the United States; they made use of magnesite, dolomite, $MgCO_3 \cdot CaCO_3$, brucite, $Mg(OH)_2$, and, most important, sea water. The two sea-water plants, built by Dow, will probably continue in operation. Other important natural magnesium minerals are asbestos, $CaMg_3(SiO_3)_4$; soapstone or talc, $Mg_3(Si_2O_5 \cdot OH)_2$; meerschaum, $Mg_2Si_3O_8 \cdot 2\ H_2O$; and serpentine, $Mg_3Si_2O_7 \cdot 2\ H_2O$. Many ground waters contain magnesium sulfate; and deposits of brucite, $Mg(OH)_2$, are found in Nevada. Chlorophyll, the green coloring material of plants, contains magnesium.

Calcium, the element fifth in abundance in the earth's crust, is an important constituent of many rocks. Over twenty common calcium minerals are found in nature; a few of the more important ones are limestone, $CaCO_3$; gypsum, $CaSO_4 \cdot 2\ H_2O$; apatite $Ca_5(PO_4)_3F$; fluorspar, CaF_2; and dolomite. The importance of apatite in the phosphate fertilizer industry has already been discussed. These compounds are so widely distributed in nature that few nations lack calcium.

The two important sources of *strontium* are celestite and strontianite. Celestite, which contains about 96 per cent $SrSO_4$, is more important than strontianite, which is 90 per cent $SrCO_3$; both also contain $CaCO_3$, Al_2O_3, SiO_2, and other impurities. The best-known deposits are located in England and Germany; all our supply of the strontium minerals is imported.

Barium occurs most commonly in nature as barium sulfate, $BaSO_4$, or barite. Barite is also called heavy spar. Its density, 4.5, is greater than that of many metals. The name barite comes from a Greek word meaning heavy. Barium carbonate, or witherite, as it was called after its discoverer, Dr. Withering, was discovered in an abandoned lead mine in England in 1783 and was at one time the most important source of barium compounds. Large and commercially important deposits of barite are found in at least twenty states in the United States. Although the Arkansas mines were opened only in 1941, their 260,000-ton production now somewhat exceeds that of Missouri. The total United States production in 1945 was 700,000 tons.

Since *aluminum* constitutes about 8 per cent of the earth's crust and is thus the most abundant metal, we should naturally expect it to be the cheapest; but the cost of the metallurgical processes makes it expensive. Micas, feldspars, and clay contain aluminum, but the only ore which is important as a source is bauxite, $Al_2O_3 \cdot 2\ H_2O$. There are large deposits of this ore in France and in British and Dutch Guiana. Most of the bauxite used in the United States came from Guiana, although some was mined here, mostly in Arkansas. The wise policy of the Aluminum Company of America, to buy high-grade bauxite abroad and keep the deposits here in reserve, paid off in terms of national security during the war. However, such inroads were made into our reserves that the development of methods for using lower-grade minerals has become essential. It is already possible to use clay, the commonest aluminum mineral, but this process is probably not cheap enough to produce the metal at the present record low price of 15 cents per pound. Wyoming alunite, $KAl(SO_4)_2 \cdot 2\ Al_2O_3 \cdot 3\ H_2O$, has been experimented upon, but the supply does not seem to be unlimited. Many aluminosilicate minerals have been mentioned previously. An additional aluminum mineral of interest is cryolite, Na_3AlF_6; its use in the production of aluminum will be described in a later paragraph. The natural supply having become inadequate, this mineral is now being supplemented by synthetic cryolite.

Discovery

Compounds of the alkaline earth metals and aluminum were recognized prior to the actual isolation of the elements; the latter was impossible until the principles of electricity were understood. Once an electric current was available, fused compounds of the metals could be decomposed. Thus active potassium prepared by electrolytic reactions could be used as the reducing agent. Sir Humphry Davy was able to isolate several of these elements in a short time by means of an electric current. He added mercuric oxide to the alkaline earth oxide and fused the mixture with electricity, thus forming mercury amalgams. When he distilled the mercury from the amalgam, he obtained the pure metal. Unless these metals are kept away from oxygen during the heating process, they will ignite and burn.

Metallurgy

The preliminary treatment given the ore depends upon the type of ore and the impurities it contains. This preliminary treatment is sometimes very complicated.

Beryllium. The production of beryllium does not differ in principle from that of the more important metal, magnesium. An essential to efficient production only recently achieved was the carrying out of the electrolysis at a temperature above the rather high melting point of Be (1350° C.), so that the metal could be obtained in massive form instead of loose powder.

Magnesium. In 1939 the Dow Company was operating, at some 10 per cent beyond its rated capacity, a magnesium plant; the raw material for it was $MgCl_2$ obtained from the mother liquors left after crystallizing NaCl from the brine from the company's Michigan salt wells. $MgCl_2 \cdot 6\ H_2O$ was separated by cooling the liquor (the solubility of NaCl is little affected by temperature); then it was dehydrated. The small amounts of NaCl and

THE ALKALINE EARTH METALS; ALUMINUM

CaCl$_2$ contaminating it were unobjectionable; in fact more was sometimes added to lower the melting point of the anhydrous MgCl$_2$, which was then electrolyzed (Fig. 30.1). Bars of graphite suspended in the salts serve as anodes, and the cast-steel pots serve as cathodes. The container is heated externally, and the magnesium produced floats to the surface of the bath whence it is dipped out. The chlorine produced at the anodes must never come in contact with the magnesium. A diagram of the cell is shown in Fig. 30.2. Foreseeing the war, the Dow Chemical Company doubled the

Fig. 30.1. Banks of cells in the magnesium cell building. (Courtesy, Dow Chemical Co.)

size of their plant in 1940 and in 1941 increased it as much again, to a total capacity of 18,000,000 pounds per year. A limit to the size of their Michigan operations was set by the fact that the magnesium chloride was a by-product of the salt industry. Only $3\frac{1}{2}$ per cent of the brine was MgCl$_2$. By this time the urgency of the situation was apparent to all, and the government was having new magnesium plants built in a dozen locations. One, with a capacity equal to the total capacity of the expanded Michigan plant, was put into operation by the Dow Company at Freeport, Texas, that same year; its capacity was doubled in 1942. This plant obtained its magnesium from sea water. Sea water contains only 0.13 of 1 per cent of Mg^{++}, but a cubic mile of it would last the expanded Freeport plant for two centuries.

The sea-water process is as follows. Oyster shells dredged up from a vast deposit are burned to lime with natural gas (page 522). This lime is used to bring the pH of the strained sea water to 11, whereupon Mg(OH)$_2$ precipitates and is settled out.

$$Ca^{++} + 2\ OH^- + Mg^{++} + 2\ Cl^- \longrightarrow \underline{Mg(OH)_2} + Ca^{++} + 2\ Cl^-$$

In another section of the plant, NaCl is electrolyzed to provide Cl_2, which is burned in natural gas forming HCl to convert the $Mg(OH)_2$ into $MgCl_2$ for the magnesium cells. Since the electrolysis of $MgCl_2$ yields chlorine, only enough NaCl had to be electrolyzed to make up the losses. (The accompanying NaOH was sold.)

$$2\ \overline{CH_4} + \overline{O_2} + 4\ \overline{Cl_2} \longrightarrow 2\ \overline{CO} + 8\ \overline{HCl}$$

A plant was built at Permanente, California, which was designed to produce 24,000,000 pounds of magnesium a year by the Hansgirg process.

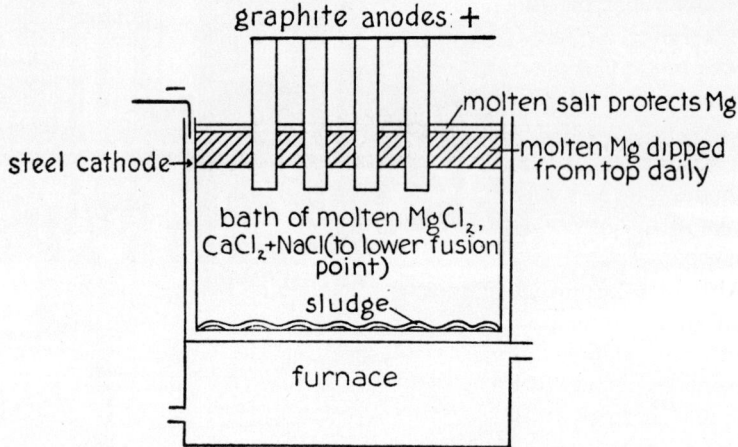

FIG. 30.2. Electrolytic production of magnesium.

MgO obtained from $MgCO_3$ was reduced by carbon in a fuel-fired furnace at a very high temperature. The metallic vapor distills from the solid mixture and is condensed from the furnace gases to a fine powder, which is filtered out. This must be redistilled in a current of inert gas, liquefied, and cast into ingots. In Austria and later in Germany hydrogen was used as the gas which is chemically inert to magnesium; however, the cost was considerable and there were a number of disastrous explosions. At Permanente natural gas was used; it could be burned as fuel later, instead of being purified and recirculated. Even then many difficulties were encountered and, although put into operation in 1941, the plant had reached only 80 per cent of its designed capacity in 1943. Other thermal reduction plants, using ferrosilicon as the reducing agent in an electric furnace, also had engineering difficulties. However, nine of the thirteen new plants had exceeded their planned capacity early in 1943. The plan was to increase the 1939 capacity 87-fold, but the need proved to be less than anticipated. By the time production reached

41,000,000 pounds per *month* ($73\frac{1}{2}$ times 1939 production), an enormous stockpile had accumulated; so in 1944 production was cut back to one-sixth of the capacity at that time. The cost of production of magnesium during the war ranged from $11\frac{1}{2}$ to $57\frac{1}{4}$ cents a pound.

Calcium, Barium, and Strontium. The present demand for metallic calcium is much greater than that for barium; very little metallic strontium is produced. Calcium is prepared by electrolyzing molten anhydrous $CaCl_2$. Carbon anodes are placed just inside the edges of the furnace and a hollow iron cathode is suspended in the center of the fused salt; the cathode is cooled by water which passes through it. Metallic calcium deposits on the metal cathode. As soon as there is a good deposit, the electrode is raised slowly, and the calcium then serves as the cathode. The hot metal must be kept in an inert atmosphere.

Although barium and strontium can be prepared by the electrolysis of fused salts, the present procedure is different. Metallic barium is produced by heating a mixture of barium oxide and aluminum in a bomb, or metal container, in an electric furnace. A vacuum of 0.001 to 0.003 mm. is applied to the bomb, and the temperature is raised to 950° or 1000° C. There is an equilibrium reaction.

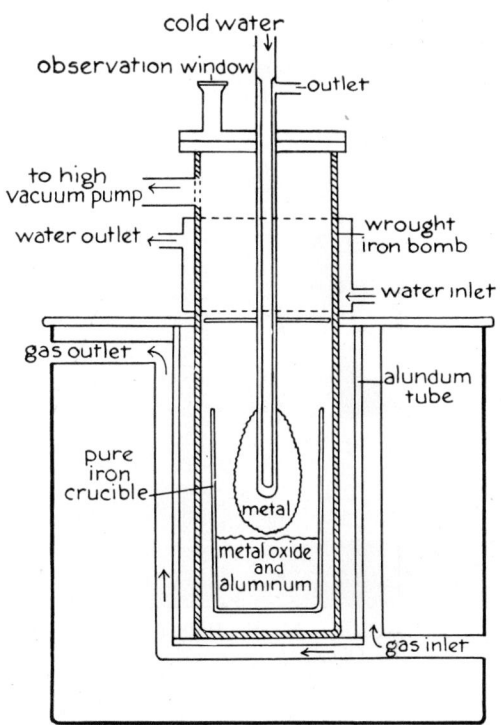

FIG. 30.3. Furnace for production of barium.

$$3\ BaO + 2\ Al \rightleftarrows Al_2O_3 + 3\ Ba$$

Since barium has the higher vapor pressure, it distills and is condensed on a cold surface. It is cooled in the presence of argon gas, because the active barium would react with either oxygen or nitrogen in the air. The apparatus used by King Laboratories in Syracuse, New York, is shown in Fig. 30.3. Strontium and calcium can also be prepared by this method.

Aluminum. The first aluminum ever produced sold for about $160 per pound; opera glasses made of this metal were at one time more expensive than silver ones. When, in 1854, Deville, a French chemist, used sodium as the reducing agent, this reduced the price from its current level of $100 a pound; by 1886 it had dropped to $8 a pound. With the development of the Castner cell, whereby sodium could be produced more cheaply, the price of aluminum dropped to $4 per pound.

Charles M. Hall, while a student at Oberlin College, decided to devote himself to finding an even cheaper method of producing aluminum. He concluded that, in spite of the failure of others to electrolyze Al_2O_3, it was this method which would eventually be successful. However, it is difficult to melt Al_2O_3, and until melted it does not conduct an electric current and cannot be electrolyzed. Therefore he had to find a substance which, in the molten state, would dissolve Al_2O_3; and in cryolite, $3\ NaF \cdot AlF_3$, he found it. He obtained the high-potential direct current he needed by making his own batteries. On February 23, 1886, when he was only 22, Hall proudly showed his sisters a button of metallic aluminum which he had made by fusing cryolite in a graphite crucible and passing an electric current through it. Hall's patents were bought by the Pittsburgh Reduction Company in 1888 after several other concerns had turned them down, and aluminum was soon being produced in greater quantities at a lower price than ever before. Hall's patent barely preceded the Frenchman Heroult's attempt to patent the same process; he himself had discovered it, working independently. The Aluminum Company of American (successor to the Pittsburgh Reduction Company) was, until World War II, the only producer of aluminum in the United States. This was largely because they had had to work so hard to persuade a reluctant industrial world to use the new metal. They were forced to learn so much about its production and properties that when people realized that Alcoa had a good thing it seemed hopeless to try to compete. Our aluminum production capacity was expanded sevenfold during the war from the 1939 figure of 327,000,000 pounds. Although most of the new plants were built and operated by Alcoa, the latter's "know-how" was made freely available to Reynolds, the other operating company. Reynolds plans to continue operating its war-built plant of 170,000,000 pounds capacity. As in the case of magnesium, the production of aluminum soon outran even war needs. The first cut-back was made in December, 1943, and a year later the ex-

FIG. 30.4. Charles Martin Hall. (Courtesy, Oberlin College.)

panded industry was operating at less than half capacity. During the war, costs of aluminum ranged from 10.6 to 15.4 cents a pound, depending largely upon the cost of alumina and electric power at the different plants, since only the one process was used.

High-grade bauxite contains only a small fraction of 1 per cent of impurities, but during the war much low-grade material had to be used. The chief

Photo by Margaret Bourke-White

Fig. 30.5. Filtering sodium aluminate through a large filter press. (Courtesy, Aluminum Co. of America.)

impurities are iron oxide and combined silica; they are removed by the Bayer process. The bauxite is treated with lime and soda ash (the equivalent of NaOH solution) under steam pressure in steel containers. The iron oxide, traces of titanium oxide, and most of the silica remain as a red mud; the bauxite dissolves as sodium aluminate.

$$2\ Na^+ + 2\ OH^- + \underline{Al_2O_3 \cdot 2\ H_2O} \longrightarrow 2\ Na^+ + 2\ AlO_2^- + 3\ H_2O$$

The basic solution is then neutralized sufficiently with CO_2 to reprecipitate aluminum hydroxide.

$$2\ Na^+ + 2\ AlO_2^- + H_2CO_3 + 2\ H_2O \longrightarrow 2\ Na^+ + CO_3^{--} + 2\ \underline{Al(OH)_3}$$

A little freshly precipitated aluminum hydroxide is added to seed the mixture and start crystallization. This preliminary treatment is given in large plants near the coal fields, such as those at East St. Louis and Mobile. The purified material is dried and shipped to points where cheap electricity is available, such as Massena and Niagara Falls, New York, Alcoa, Tennessee, and Badin, North Carolina.

FIG. 30.6. A giant precipitator. (Courtesy, Aluminum Co. of America.)

Bayer-process "red mud" contains, in addition to the iron oxide which gives it its color and the $CaCO_3$ formed when the soda is causticized, a mixture of sodium and calcium aluminosilicates. For every pound of SiO_2 which was present in the original bauxite, about a pound *each* of alumina, lime, and soda is carried into the red mud. This is a serious waste and limits the silica content of the bauxite to a maximum of 7 per cent. Since most bauxite has more than 7 per cent silica rather than less, research was pushed and led to

Photo by Margaret Bourke-White
Fig. 30.7. Calcining of aluminum hydroxide in a rotary kiln. (Courtesy, Aluminum Co. of America.)

the discovery of a method of recovering most of the values from the red mud. A mixture of the mud, soda ash, and quicklime is sintered (heated to incipient fusion) and ground. The resulting $NaAlO_2$ is leached out with water. On precipitating $Al(OH)_3$ from this with CO_2, nearly two-thirds of the sodium carbonate used is recovered. By using this process with the Bayer process it is possible to use bauxite containing up to 13 per cent SiO_2, and recover 95 per cent of the contained alumina (instead of 80 to 85 per cent) at a lower cost for reagents.

The purified alumina is dissolved in the fused cryolite bath in the electrolytic plants. The electrolysis chambers are large rectangular iron cells, like that shown in Fig. 30.8; they are lined with carbon to prevent metallic aluminum from coming in contact with the iron. The anodes are made from low-ash petroleum coke, and a row of them extends into the electrolyte. As the electrodes are used up, any impurities in the anodes fall to the bottom and contaminate the aluminum. Oxygen of the alumina combines with the carbon of the anodes.

$$2\ Al_2O_3 \longrightarrow 4\ Al + 3\ O_2$$
$$3\ O_2 + \text{carbon anodes} \longrightarrow CO + CO_2$$

The bath is kept at about 1000° C., and a thin scum of bauxite usually floats on its surface. The molten aluminum is tapped from the bottom of the cell every two or three days.

About 0.6 of a pound of carbon electrode, 2 pounds of bauxite, 0.1 of a pound each of cryolite and fluorspar, and 10 kilowatt-hours of electrical energy are used in producing one pound of aluminum. Maintenance costs on the cells are high; when possible, the plant which manufactures the electrodes is located nearby. If it is necessary to shut down the plant, the electrolyte solidifies, and the pots have to be cleaned out with a pick and shovel.

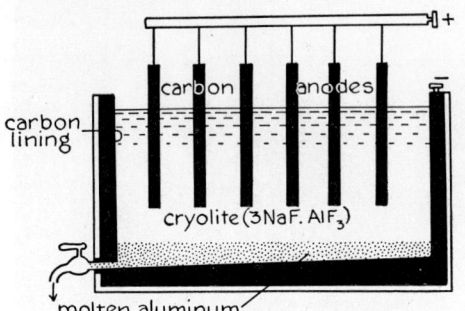

FIG. 30.8. Electrolytic production of aluminum.

If greater purity than 98 or 99 per cent is required, the aluminum obtained by the Hall process is further refined electrolytically by the Hoopes process. In this process the cell is the anode and has a copper bottom. Molten aluminum is poured in. Above it is a layer of fused fluorides which serve as the electrolyte; however, they are so mixed that their density is greater than that of the molten aluminum. Aluminum cathodes are suspended in the bath. When the current passes through, the aluminum goes from the bottom of the cell to the fused salt layer and then plates out at the top; impurities settle to the bottom. Aluminum 99.9 per cent pure can be made by the Hoopes process.

Physical and Chemical Properties

When freshly prepared, all the alkaline earth metals and aluminum have a bright white metallic luster. Barium, calcium, magnesium, and strontium tarnish rapidly in the air and therefore are usually kept in tin cans that can be closed tightly. Beryllium and aluminum tarnish or oxidize more slowly, and the surface film protects the metal from further oxidation, whereas the film on calcium, barium, and strontium flakes off as fast as it forms. The

THE ALKALINE EARTH METALS; ALUMINUM

densities of the metals vary from 1.55 for calcium to 3.5 for barium; aluminum has a density of 2.7. All are good conductors of electricity. Beryllium is hard and brittle (it will scratch glass); aluminum is so brittle at high temperatures that it can easily be powdered; all the others are ductile and malleable. Their melting and boiling points are as follows:

	Be	Mg	Ca	Sr	Ba	Al
M.P.	1350	651	810	800	850	660
B.P.	1500	1110	1170	1150	1140	1800

Calcium, barium, and strontium react with cold water, liberating hydrogen and forming bases. The latter are not very soluble in water, but the degree of dissociation is high. Magnesium reacts readily with steam to liberate hydrogen and form MgO. As far as chemical properties are concerned, beryllium lies between magnesium and aluminum. It reacts very slowly with hot water. Aluminum dipped into a solution of mercuric chloride displaces mercury, and aluminum amalgam forms; this liberates hydrogen from water. BeO, MgO, and Al_2O_3 are practically insoluble in water. $Al(OH)_3$ and $Be(OH)_2$ are both insoluble in water and amphoteric in nature. The metals are readily soluble in non-oxidizing acids, hydrogen being liberated. Both beryllium and aluminum dissolve readily in sodium hydroxide with the liberation of hydrogen.

$$2\ \underline{Al} + 2\ Na^+ + 2\ OH^- + 2\ H_2O \longrightarrow 2\ Na^+ + 2\ AlO_2^- + 3\ \overline{H_2}$$

$$\underline{Be} + 2\ Na^+ + 2\ OH^- \longrightarrow 2\ Na^+ + BeO_2^{--} + \overline{H_2}$$

These reactions may each be considered as the sum of two other reactions, the first being the liberation of H_2 from water by the metal, the second being the solution by the sodium hydroxide of the insoluble amphoteric hydroxide resulting from the first (see page 447). Neither metal can come into contact with water to react with it until the protecting oxide coating has been removed.

Uses of the Free Metals

The alkaline earth metals and aluminum rank in the following order as far as their commercial importance as metals is concerned: aluminum, magnesium, beryllium, calcium, barium, and strontium.

Barium alloyed with magnesium or aluminum and stamped into metal containers is used as a "getter" to combine with and remove the last trace of gases from radio tubes. The "getter" is placed in the radio tube, which, after being subjected to a high vacuum and sealed, is then heated in an induction furnace. Barium is also used as a scavenger in the refining of copper; small amounts of it increase the electrical conductivity of the copper. Barium alloys and compounds are noted for their high thermionic electron emission. Its alloys are used in spark-plug points. One alloy, known as

Frary metal and used in bearings, contains 98 per cent lead and about 2 per cent calcium and barium; it is prepared by electrolyzing a mixture of $CaCl_2$ and $BaCl_2$, with molten lead as the cathode. About two tons of barium are produced annually in the United States, and the metal which used to sell for a dollar a gram is now worth about $7 a pound.

The production of *strontium* experienced a considerable spurt during the war because it is used in tracer bullets; important peacetime uses are still to be found. It has been used to some extent as a "getter."

Calcium was used in large quantities during the war as a reducing agent for the production of zirconium, vanadium, and other metals used in special alloys. These uses may continue. Between the two World Wars the cost of calcium fell from $20 a pound to $1, and production reached 25 tons annually. The price rose to $1.85 a pound in 1944 and the production at least doubled. Two million pounds of Ca-Si alloy were imported in 1941, before our own production could be expanded.

Metallic calcium is used as a scavenger to remove oxygen and sulfur from ferrous alloys (particularly stainless steel), as a dehydrating agent in the treatment of oils and alcohols, and as a powerful reducing agent for many metal oxides. The presence of small amounts of bismuth in lead interferes with its electrolysis; this difficulty is overcome by adding metallic calcium to molten lead. Lead containing small amounts of calcium is used for the plates of some storage batteries. Since metallic calcium combines with both nitrogen and oxygen, it can be used to produce high vacuums. An alloy of lead (0.6 of 1 per cent each of Ca and Na, 0.04 of 1 per cent Li, and the remainder Pb) is used as a bearing metal on the German State Railways. Another alloy which contains 11 to 12 per cent calcium and 88 to 89 per cent aluminum is used as a deoxidizing alloy in England. Calcium is now used in many nickel, chromium, and selenium steels to improve the grain structure of the alloy.

Beryllium has a unique use as "windows" in X-ray tubes; for this use its low atomic number is responsible. The absorption of X rays by materials through which they pass is proportional to the atomic numbers of all the atoms encountered. Beryllium is therefore much more transparent to X rays than glass is. The metal, in contrast to lithium, is hard and resistant to the atmosphere. Its major and indispensable use, however, is as a beryllium-copper alloy in springs such as those used for the indicating hands of airplane instruments. A mere 1 or 2 per cent of beryllium produces an astonishing change in the properties of copper. The alloy has a temper like steel and is corrosion-resistant. Most important, its fatigue resistance surpasses that of steel about as much as that of steel does that of copper. If any piece of metal is bent back and forth a sufficient number of times, cracks form along the lines of the crystal grains and presently, even when no more force is applied than it has withstood many times before, it breaks "from fatigue." The almost infinite fatigue resistance of the beryllium alloy makes it ideal

THE ALKALINE EARTH METALS; ALUMINUM

for use in places where it is subjected to continuous heavy vibration, as in airplanes. Its cost of $20 a pound is unimportant here but limits its use in tools, where its non-sparking quality makes it valuable when there is danger of igniting explosive gases.

Magnesium, which was first used in pyrotechnics and for military signaling, is an excellent deoxidizer in the metallurgical treatment of other metals.

Fig. 30.9. Reconstruction of Smithfield St. Bridge, Pittsburgh. Note that one man is carrying a large piece of aluminum. (Courtesy, Aluminum Co. of America.)

Photographers' flashlight bulbs contain it or its alloys, and the latter have long been used in the manufacture of vacuum cleaners for the home. Because magnesium alloys are light and easily machined, many new uses have recently been developed, as in aviation, where they are used for crankcases, oil pans, blower sections, landing wheels, fittings, etc. The alloys are known to the trade by such names as magnalium, Dowmetal, Elektron, etc. The density of magnesium, 1.74, is less than that of any other structural metal. Dowmetal H, with less than one-fourth the weight, has a tensile strength almost equal to that of cast iron and half that of annealed cast steel. At 22 cents per pound, it costs $25 per cubic foot, a little less than aluminum at 15 cents per pound. In view of its low cost (page 507) and the limitless supply, it would seem that this low-density, strong, corrosion-resistant metal is likely to invade much of the field now occupied by aluminum and steel as soon as the techniques of using it become familiar.

Aluminum was first used in large quantities in 1914, in the manufacture of cooking utensils. At present, however, this use accounts for only about one-seventh of its peacetime production. Aluminum is making progress as a structural material. The 350 tons of it used in resurfacing an old bridge (Fig. 30.9) reduced the load on the trusses by 750 tons. Aluminum bodies on trucks increase the pay load, for most states limit the weight of trucks.

Wood was used exclusively for railroad coaches and freight cars until 1907, when the first all-steel Pullman car was exhibited. The replacement of steel by aluminum began in 1934 when the Union Pacific broke all former transcontinental speed records with a six-car aluminum streamliner which weighed only 210 tons—about 500 tons less than a steel train. (However, not all streamliners are aluminum. Modern stressed-skin construction with thin sheets of stainless steel, taking full advantage of its enormous tensile strength, has also produced great weight-saving.) Many tank cars and some freight cars are also made of aluminum. Its use in automobile engines and airplane construction is too familiar to need emphasis. A factory-made house of aluminum, in which airplane construction and fabrication methods are used, is light enough to be shipped almost anywhere.

Aluminum stranded around a steel core competes with copper as a conductor of electricity for power lines; over half a million miles of these wires are now in use. Because of their insufficient tensile strength, pure aluminum wires require a great many poles and supports. Per unit cross section, copper is 1.5 times as efficient as aluminum as a conductor of electricity, but on a weight basis aluminum is twice as efficient.

In one type of rectifier for charging storage batteries from an alternating current, aluminum is used as the anode plate. This dips into a water solution of alkali carbonates, borates, etc.; and as oxygen is released at the anode the aluminum plate quickly becomes covered with insoluble Al_2O_3, a non-conductor. From then on, electrical impulses travel only in one direction.

Aluminum can be rolled and hammered into very thin sheets under suitable temperature conditions. This foil has many uses. As a wrapping material it competes with all other similar substances, being used for candy bars, cigarettes, soap, etc. Shaving cream, tooth paste, and similar products are packaged in collapsible aluminum tubes.

Aluminum is also available as a powder. However, grinding or polishing any of the active metals is always dangerous because the heat of friction may ignite the material; it should therefore be done in an inert atmosphere. Aluminum powder is used in the manufacture of paints, and as a metallized wrapper. Aluminum paints are attractive, resist corrosion, and reflect heat; this last property makes them popular for use on gasoline storage tanks.

Peel off the metallized wrapper from a stick of chewing gum, dissolve it in hydrochloric acid, and neutralize with ammonium hydroxide; if aluminum powder was used in the paper, a white precipitate of $Al(OH)_3$ will appear. Probably the paper was first coated with resin dissolved in alcohol; aluminum powder was then sprinkled on it, and the sheet was pressed or rolled. Foil pressed against paper can be used the same way.

Because of its efficiency in reflecting ultraviolet radiations, aluminum is being used on the reflecting surface of the large telescope at Mount Palomar, California.

Very pure aluminum produced by the Hoopes process is much more resistant to corrosion than are its stronger alloys. Putting a plate of pure aluminum on either side of a thicker one of duralumin made it possible to roll them out into a single sheet of metal that has the strength of the alloy and the resistant surfaces of the pure metal. This "Alclad" was so successful that the method has been greatly extended and is now used for different purposes. For example, where only surface resistance to corrosion is needed (and not high strength), plain steel can be cladded (sic!) with stainless. The stainless-clad steel is much cheaper than pure stainless of any considerable thickness.

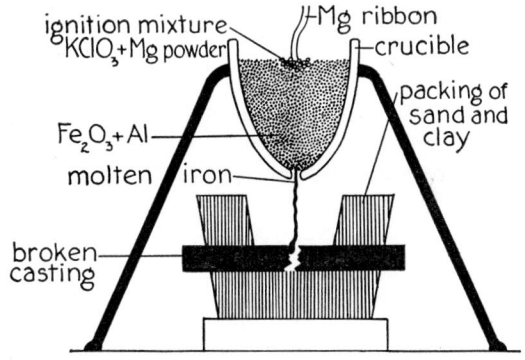

FIG. 30.10. Thermite welding. Molten iron drips from the crucible. A slag of Al_2O_3 floats to the top.

Since the world's supply of tin will probably soon be exhausted, many attempts have been made to coat iron with aluminum. Dr. C. G. Fink, of Columbia University, has done this by reducing the oxide film on iron with hydrogen and then dipping the iron into molten aluminum; in this way a film of aluminum is deposited on the iron.

The value of metallic aluminum as a reducing agent was first emphasized by Goldschmidt, who noted that powdered aluminum would reduce many metal oxides to the metallic state. The heat of the reaction is very high, a fact on which the thermite welding process is based. Fig. 30.10 shows the apparatus for welding a broken casting by this process. In the formation of one molecular weight of Fe_2O_3 from the elements, 192,200 calories of heat are liberated. The heat of formation of Al_2O_3 is 399,000 calories.

$$2\ Fe + 3\ O \longrightarrow Fe_2O_3 + 192{,}200 \text{ cal.}$$
$$2\ Al + 3\ O \longrightarrow Al_2O_3 + 399{,}000 \text{ cal.}$$
$$Fe_2O_3 + 2\ Al \longrightarrow 2\ Fe + Al_2O_3 + 399{,}000 - 192{,}200 = 206{,}800 \text{ cal.}$$

The heat liberated is sufficient to melt and weld the broken steel. The use of aluminum as a scavenger in the purification of other metals is another application of the thermite reaction. Thermite has been used to break ice jams on rivers.

An aluminum-dust blowpipe for welding has recently been placed on the market. The metal dust and oxygen burn, producing a very high temperature.

Because aluminum is the cheapest of the active metals that can be handled as a powder at room temperature without oxidizing too rapidly, it is used to reduce oxides of the more expensive metals to the metallic state. Molybdenum, tungsten, and other metals are produced commercially in this way.

COMPOUNDS OF BERYLLIUM

The only manufactured beryllium compound of commercial importance is *beryllium oxide*, BeO, which is used as a superrefractory in lining furnaces. It melts at about 2500° C., has a low density, and retains its electrical resistance properties even at high temperatures. The United States production is 100 to 200 tons a year. About half that weight of natural beryl is ground annually and used in pottery and ceramics. Beryllium forms the usual divalent salts. The insoluble hydroxide is amphoteric.

COMPOUNDS OF MAGNESIUM

Several compounds of magnesium are widely used, the three most important natural ones being the sulfate, the chloride, and the carbonate.

Magnesium Sulfate

Large deposits of $MgSO_4$ are located in Stassfurt, Germany. There are deposits of both kieserite, $MgSO_4 \cdot H_2O$, and epsomite, $MgSO_4 \cdot 7 H_2O$, in the western United States, and some of the ground-water supplies in the Dakotas and other states contain considerable $MgSO_4$. This salt is very soluble in water and has a rather bitter taste. It is used medicinally as a purgative under its trade name, Epsom salts. Commercially it is used as a filler in cotton goods and in dyeing and tanning.

Magnesium Chloride

Many water supplies and nearly all salt brines contain $MgCl_2$. The concentration in the salt brine at Midland, Michigan, is sufficiently high to make this brine a satisfactory source of metallic magnesium. The Stassfurt deposits contain the double salt, carnallite, $MgCl_2 \cdot KCl \cdot 6 H_2O$, which is a source of both potassium and magnesium. The deliquescent nature of $MgCl_2$ makes it particularly objectionable in table salt, and waters containing it must be softened before being used in steam boilers because it hydrolyzes and liberates free hydrochloric acid. The salt is used in making magnesia cements. Fillers of all kinds—for example, stucco and wall plasters—are made from a mixture of $MgCl_2$ and MgO, for in the presence of water they form a hard insoluble basic chloride.

Magnesium Carbonate

Magnesium carbonate is found in nature as the normal carbonate, magnesite. If excess CO_2 is bubbled into a suspension of $Mg(OH)_2$, the acid carbonate, $Mg(HCO_3)_2$, is formed. It is water-soluble and is present in many water supplies. $MgCO_3$ is frequently mixed with about 15 per cent asbestos to form a light, porous insulating material used for wrapping hot-water tanks, etc. Tons of $MgCO_3$ are used in making linings for the open-hearth furnaces of the steel industry. It is also used in some tooth and face powders.

Magnesium Silicates

Several valuable magnesium silicates are found in nature, at least two of which are in use in nearly every chemical laboratory. Talc, $Mg_3(Si_2O_5 \cdot OH)_2$, has a smooth, almost greasy, feeling. When finely pulverized, it is used in talcum powders. "Steatite," from which some crayons are made, is pulverized talc which is pressed into sticks. The soapstones used as bed warmers before the days of electric heating pads and in fireless cookers are magnesium silicate. The table tops and sinks in chemical laboratories and most basement laundry tubs are frequently made of alberene, another form of magnesium silicate.

Asbestos, $CaMg_3(SiO_3)_4$,[1] used as a filtering medium in every chemical laboratory, occurs in nature in long flexible fibers which are broken up, then washed with acid and water, and, in a water suspension, caught on porous plates. Many precipitates are filtered in crucibles which contain asbestos, and it is a constituent of many fireproofing coverings, gaskets, packings, etc. A mixture of asbestos and graphite is used in brake linings for cars. Transite board is made by mixing asbestos and Portland cement and pressing them together. Although it is hard on a saw, the material is fireproof and acid-resisting; electrical resistances are frequently wound on it. Many buildings are decorated with serpentine. Dry meerschaum is called sea froth because it floats on water.

Magnesium Oxide and Magnesium Hydroxide

MgO is prepared by calcining or heating $MgCO_3$ to between 350° and 600° C.; even at the latter temperature some CO_2 may remain. The oxide is light and fluffy and slakes or reacts with water to form $Mg(OH)_2$. Suspended in water, it is sold as "milk of magnesia"; it neutralizes acidity and serves as a mild laxative. If MgO is heated to 1500° C., a very dense oxide is formed which is insoluble in water. (Burn a magnesium ribbon and try to dissolve the ash in water.) This oxide, which melts at about 2800° C., is used in furnace linings. MgO can also be prepared by reducing non-metal oxides with magnesium.

[1] One of several, see page 462.

$$SiO_2 + 2\ Mg \longrightarrow 2\ MgO + Si$$
$$CO_2 + 2\ Mg \longrightarrow 2\ MgO + C$$

The fact that magnesium burns in CO_2 shows that it is a powerful reducing agent.

Gelatinous $Mg(OH)_2$ is easily prepared in the laboratory by adding NH_4OH or $NaOH$ to $MgSO_4$.

$$Mg^{++} + SO_4^{--} + 2\ Na^+ + 2\ OH^- \longrightarrow \underline{Mg(OH)_2} + 2\ Na^+ + SO_4^{--}$$

The hydroxide is so insoluble that magnesium could be determined quantitatively by filtering the hydroxide and igniting it; but because of the gelatinous nature of the precipitate other methods are used. $Mg(OH)_2$ cannot be precipitated with NH_4OH if NH_4Cl is also present, for, because of the common (NH_4^+) ion, the NH_4Cl depresses the concentration of (OH^-) ions to such an extent that no $Mg(OH)_2$ forms.

Magnesium Ammonium Phosphate

The magnesium ion is one of the last to be separated from a mixture in qualitative analysis. It is not precipitated with hydrogen sulfide in either an acid or a basic solution, and, as just mentioned, the hydroxide is soluble in the presence of an excess of NH_4Cl. If disodium hydrogen phosphate and NH_4OH are added to a solution containing Mg^{++}, insoluble magnesium ammonium phosphate precipitates.

$$Mg^{++} + 2\ Cl^- + 2\ Na^+ + HPO_4^{--} + NH_4OH \longrightarrow$$
$$\underline{MgNH_4PO_4} + 2\ Na^+ + 2\ Cl^- + H_2O$$

The precipitate crystallizes so slowly that it cannot be filtered for from four to six hours. In quantitative analysis $MgNH_4PO_4$ is ignited and weighed as the pyrophosphate.

$$2\ MgNH_4PO_4 \xrightarrow{\Delta} Mg_2P_2O_7 + \overline{2\ NH_3} + \overline{H_2O}$$

The Mg^{++} ion is used as a precipitating agent for the phosphate radical in determining PO_4^{---} in fertilizers, etc. The solution used for this purpose is called "magnesia mixture," for it is a single reagent that contains $MgCl_2$, NH_4OH, and NH_4Cl. Can you write chemical equilibria which illustrate the solubility of $Mg(OH)_2$ in NH_4Cl?

For uses of *magnesium perchlorate*, see page 349.

COMPOUNDS OF CALCIUM

Calcium compounds are essential for both plant and animal growth. In some parts of the United States, farmers still "burn" or heat limestone in lime kilns to convert it into calcium oxide, CaO, which they then apply to the soil. The role of calcium in human metabolism is very important. Milk and other foods rich in calcium are recommended for the production of strong bones and good teeth; but other factors, such as calciferol (vitamin D) and perhaps a trace of fluoride ion, are also essential.

Calcium Nitride and Calcium Hydride

Heating metallic calcium in the presence of hydrogen and nitrogen forms the hydride, CaH_2, and the nitride, Ca_3N_2. Both of these solids hydrolyze readily. "Hydrolite," as calcium hydride is known commercially, was used during the war as a convenient way of transporting hydrogen.

$$CaH_2 + 2\ H_2O \longrightarrow Ca(OH)_2 + \overline{H_2}$$

The nitride hydrolyzes to produce ammonia gas.

$$Ca_3N_2 + 6\ H_2O \longrightarrow 3\ Ca(OH)_2 + 2\ \overline{NH_3}$$

Do you think this would be a good process for the commercial production of ammonia?

Calcium Carbonate

The most important calcium compound is limestone, $CaCO_3$. There are deposits in all parts of the world, and it is found in many different forms such as pearls, corals, and marble. Seashells and egg shells are rich in $CaCO_3$. Deposits of marl contain both clay and limestone. The chalk deposits along the coasts of the British Isles were formed from the skeletons of marine animals, and some deposits in the ocean have been produced by the decomposition of calcium bicarbonate. The CO_2 is taken up during the rapid growth of algae and other forms of plankton; algae shift the equilibrium from left to right.

$$Ca^{++} + 2\ HCO_3^- \rightleftarrows CaCO_3 + H_2O + CO_2$$

Deposits of dolomite, the double salt, $CaCO_3 \cdot MgCO_3$, are also quite common.

The two crystalline forms of $CaCO_3$ are aragonite and calcite; different forms of the latter are known as oriental alabaster, onyx, Iceland spar, and dogtooth spar. The beautiful Jupiter Terrace at Yellowstone National Park was formed as a result of the release of CO_2 from water escaping from the Mammoth Hot Springs; the water contains $Ca(HCO_3)_2$. The reaction is the same as that given above, except that here the escape of the CO_2 is due to the release of pressure. One of the most awe-inspiring sights in America is the Carlsbad Caverns in New Mexico, another product of the carbonate-bicarbonate equilibrium. Here you may walk miles underground; one cave is 4000 feet long, 625 feet wide, and 350 feet high. There are thousands of stalagmites and stalactites which have been over 200 million years in the making; impurities in the deposits give them all the colors of the rainbow. Some of the stalagmites are many feet in diameter.

$CaCO_3$ is nearly insoluble in water. If water is saturated with $Ca(OH)_2$ and CO_2 is then bubbled into it, a white precipitate of $CaCO_3$ forms. Bubbling your breath through a little $Ca(OH)_2$ will also produce the precipitate.

$$Ca^{++} + 2\ OH^- + CO_2 \longrightarrow \underline{CaCO_3} + H_2O$$

If more CO_2 is added to the solution, the soluble bicarbonate is formed.

$$\underline{CaCO_3} + H_2O + CO_2 \rightleftarrows Ca^{++} + 2\ HCO_3^-$$

FIG. 30.11. Temple of the Sun in Carlsbad Cavern, New Mexico.

This reaction is reversible. The use of $CaCO_3$ as a source of CO_2 in the Solvay process has already been discussed. The detrimental effect of calcium ions in water supplies was discussed in Chapter 20, together with the common methods of water softening.

Calcium Oxide and Calcium Hydroxide

The chief sources of calcium oxide, CaO, in the United States are limestone, oyster shells, and calcareous marl. CaO is known commercially as quicklime, lime, unslaked lime, stone lime, and dead-burned lime. Dead-burned lime is obtained by heating limestone to a higher temperature than that required to free the CO_2; the traces of silicates are fused and this lime is nearly insoluble in water.

The burning of limestone is an important industry in Ohio, Pennsylvania, West Virginia, and Missouri. Although these four states produce about 50 per cent of the lime, some is produced in nearly all the others. In the early days, all the lime was burned in batch kilns, but the process is now continuous. The decomposition of calcium carbonate is a true equilibrium reaction.

Some substances do not decompose to any extent at a temperature lower than that of complete decomposition. Calcium carbonate produces a measurable vapor pressure of CO_2 at 550° C., and at about 900° its vapor pressure is 1 atm. Lime kilns are operated at 900° to 1000° C. so that the CO_2 will be driven off rapidly and not recombine with calcium oxide.

There are two types of lime kilns: the vertical (Fig. 30.12) and the rotary (Fig. 30.13). Vertical lime kilns are frequently about 50 ft. high and 10 to 15 ft. in diameter. Powdered coal, oil, and gas have largely taken the place of coal and wood as fuel. The air carried by the fuel gases as they pass through the limestone sweeps out the carbon dioxide. The 400-ft. rotary kiln of the Chemical Lime Co. at Bellefonte, Pennsylvania, can produce 200 tons of lime per day. The maximum temperature in the kiln is about 1200° C., and about three hours elapse from the time the limestone enters the kiln until it is discharged as calcium oxide. If carefully calcined, limestone shrinks little on being heated and forms a porous product.

Burned limestone or calcium oxide crumbles readily in the presence of water; sufficient heat may be liberated from this reaction to make water boil.

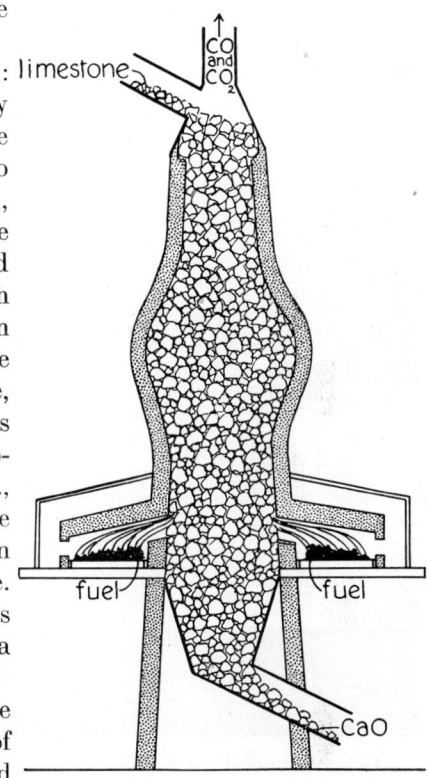

FIG. 30.12. Vertical limestone kiln.

$$CaO + H_2O \longrightarrow Ca(OH)_2 + 15{,}500 \text{ cal.}$$

The process of adding water to lime is called "slaking." Unslaked lime is a potential fire hazard, and the heat liberated during its hydration makes it disagreeable to handle. If lime is exposed to air, it becomes "air-slaked" and reverts to calcium carbonate.

Since CaO will react with SiO_2 at high temperatures to form $CaSiO_3$, it is used in the steel industry to remove SiO_2 from the iron ore. Dolomite lime ($MgO \cdot CaO$) is frequently used for this purpose, for MgO also reacts with SiO_2.

If just enough water is added to calcium oxide to react, molecule per molecule, a white powder, $Ca(OH)_2$, called hydrated lime, is formed. This is much easier to handle and the fire hazard of storing CaO is thus eliminated.

Calcium hydroxide is the cheapest of all bases; an equivalent amount of ammonia costs ten times as much; of soda ash, thirty times; and of sodium hydroxide forty times.

Only 1.85 g. of Ca(OH)$_2$ dissolve in 1 l. of water at room temperature; the resulting solution is highly ionized and therefore quite basic. One objection to its use as a base in chemical industries is its low solubility, but some industries can overcome this by using a suspension of lime called milk of lime. Limewater, a saturated solution of Ca(OH)$_2$, is used with linseed oil for sunburn.

FIG. 30.13. A typical rotary dryer. (Courtesy, Struthers Wells, Titusville, Pa.)

Mortar is made by mixing slaked lime, sand, and water. Calcium hydroxide forms first, and this, in turn, reacts with the CO$_2$ of the air to form calcium carbonate: the water evaporates into the air. A thick wall made of mortar would take many years to harden; some walls built over 1000 years ago have not yet reached their maximum strength. Plaster is mortar containing hair to serve as a binder. To speed up the drying of plaster, charcoal burners are often placed in newly plastered rooms to increase the concentration of carbon dioxide in the air and decrease the humidity. Some of the new sound- and heat-insulating materials are made by molding together powdered silica dust, lime, and water.

Six million tons of lime are used annually in the United States. The building trade normally consumes a million tons, and agriculture nearly half that. Lime is important as a fertilizer and in the neutralization of acid soils, in metallurgy, in the manufacture of paper and glass, in water softening, tanning, and sugar refining. It is used in the intermediate steps in the manufacture of calcium carbide, CaC_2, calcium cyanamide, $CaCN_2$, and many other chemicals. Its use in the cement industry was discussed on page 474.

Calcium Sulfate

On the basis of annual production, calcium sulfate is next in importance to the oxide. Between 3 and 5 million tons of gypsum, a dihydrate, $CaSO_4 \cdot 2\,H_2O$, are mined annually in the United States. Other polymorphic forms of calcium sulfate are the minerals alabaster, satin spar, and selenite. Anhydrous calcium sulfate occurs as anhydrite. The most important producers of gypsum in this country are New York, Michigan, Iowa, and Texas. It is used to retard the setting of cement, and also as a filler in paints and paper, in fertilizers (farmers call it "land plaster") and crayons. (Many blackboard crayons labeled "chalk" consist of powdered gypsum pressed into sticks.)

Gypsum is one of the constituents responsible for the hardness of water; about 2.2 g. will dissolve in 1 l. of water. It loses three-quarters of its water of hydration at 128° and all of it at 163° C. Plaster of Paris, $(CaSO_4)_2 \cdot H_2O$, is made by heating gypsum between these two temperatures.

$$2\,CaSO_4 \cdot 2\,H_2O \xrightarrow[128°]{\Delta} (CaSO_4)_2 \cdot H_2O + 3\,H_2O$$

Because of the small demand for the completely dehydrated product, the temperature of the dehydrating units is carefully controlled. Plaster of Paris is used in making molds and statues, and in filling in cracks in plaster. Large quantities of it are used in the finishing coat of plaster on the walls of buildings for it sets very rapidly, becoming quite hard in 10 or 15 minutes. It is valuable in the metallurgical industries because it expands slightly on solidifying and therefore takes a sharp impression of the mold. Surgical casts and dental impressions are made of plaster of Paris. It is used in the building industry. Combined with wood pulp, it is used in making wallboard, and, mixed with straw and other plant fibers, in making inexpensive wall partitions; some types of stucco contain lime, plaster of Paris, and glue (which retards the rate of setting). Completely burned or dehydrated gypsum is used in some floor and hard-finish plasters and for imitation marble decorations. The product obtained by the careful dehydration of gypsum is known to the trade as "drierite." It is used as a drying agent for gases and liquids, and can be dehydrated and used again.

Calcium Chloride

It has been difficult to find sufficient uses for $CaCl_2$, for 5 million tons of it are produced each year by the Solvay soda process alone, and all salt brines contain it. Its present uses are described on page 354.

$CaCl_2$ crystallizes from solution as the hexahydrate, $CaCl_2 \cdot 6\,H_2O$. These crystals melt at 30° and are completely dehydrated at 200° C. A mixture of snow and $CaCl_2 \cdot 6\ H_2O$ is used to obtain temperatures of $-40°$ and lower. The deliquescent monohydrate, $CaCl_2 \cdot H_2O$, is the compound most frequently used as a drying agent in chemical laboratories. Anhydrous $CaCl_2$ dissolves in water with the liberation of heat.

Calcium Sulfite and Calcium Bisulfite

The use of calcium bisulfite in the paper industry was described on page 375. Since the solubility of $CaSO_3$ is only about 40 mg. per liter, it precipitates from any solution containing the calcium and sulfite ions. Like $CaCO_3$, which is soluble in the presence of H_2CO_3, $CaSO_3$ is soluble in the presence of H_2SO_3. The soluble bisulfite is prepared by bubbling SO_2 gas into limewater.

$$Ca^{++} + 2\ OH^- + H_2SO_3 \longrightarrow \underline{CaSO_3} + 2\ H_2O$$

$$\underline{CaSO_3} + H_2SO_3 \longrightarrow Ca^{++} + 2\ HSO_3^-$$

The bisulfite is produced in some plants by the direct reaction of limestone and sulfurous acid.

$$\underline{CaCO_3} + 2\ H_2SO_3 \longrightarrow Ca^{++} + 2\ HSO_3^- + H_2O + \overline{CO_2}$$

Other Calcium Compounds

Calcium is determined quantitatively in the laboratory by precipitating the calcium ion as the insoluble calcium oxalate in an alkaline solution and then igniting the calcium oxalate to CaO, which is weighed.

$$2\ NH_4^+ + C_2O_4^{--} + Ca^{++} \longrightarrow \underline{CaC_2O_4} + 2\ NH_4^+$$

Can you suggest uses for calcium fluoride, borate, phosphate, nitrate, acetate, chlorate, and silicate? The index lists several other calcium compounds which were discussed in connection with the non-metals.

COMPOUNDS OF STRONTIUM

About 2000 tons of strontium ores are imported each year into this country. Strontium is used in tracer bullets. *Strontium nitrate*, $Sr(NO_3)_2$, is one of the compounds in the mixture used for red signal flares. "Red fire" contains about 57 per cent $Sr(NO_3)_2$, 29 per cent $KClO_3$, 12 per cent shellac or gum, and 2 per cent sulfur; its beautiful carmine flame can be produced in the laboratory by heating a mixture of sugar, potassium chlorate, and strontium nitrate on an asbestos mat. The nitrate and other strontium salts are prepared from the sulfide, which is formed by reducing the sulfate with hot carbon. *Strontium oxide* can be prepared by heating either $Sr(NO_3)_2$ or $SrCO_3$. The oxide is slightly soluble in water and liberates heat as it dissolves. *Strontium hydroxide* is used in the purification of beet sugar because the sugar cannot be separated by simple crystallization. Sugar reacts with warm $Sr(OH)_2$ to form crystalline strontium disucrate. These crystals are filtered from the mother liquor and dissolved in more $Sr(OH)_2$; upon the addition of CO_2, the insoluble $SrCO_3$ precipitates. The sugar is then crystallized from the remaining solution by vacuum evaporation of the water present. Some strontium compounds are used to a limited extent in medicine. Strontium salicylate is used for rheumatism, and the bromide as a nerve sedative.

COMPOUNDS OF BARIUM

Nearly all our barium chemicals were formerly imported from Europe; but since the First World War the barium industry has developed on both the Atlantic and Pacific coasts. Barite, $BaSO_4$, known commercially as barytes, is found in veins and seams, and must be washed free of earth and clay. More than half the amount mined (400,000 tons in 1945) is finely ground and used by oil drillers to increase the density of the liquid "mud" with which they fill deep well bores to help buoy up the heavy drilling tool. The first step in the manufacture of other barium salts is the reduction of the insoluble $BaSO_4$ with carbon; this produces the "black ash" or soluble barium sulfide, which contains some carbon. BaS has some use as a fungicide, but most of it is used in the making of other compounds.

Lithopone is a white paint pigment made by reacting soluble BaS and $ZnSO_4$ (obtained by dissolving waste ZnO and scrap zinc in H_2SO_4) to form the insoluble salts $BaSO_4$ and ZnS. Although it tends to darken in bright sunlight, lithopone is an excellent, cheap indoor paint pigment. It is also used extensively to coat fabrics and textiles, and in linoleums and felt-base floor coverings. About 150,000 tons are consumed annually in the United States.

Reprecipitated barium sulfate, called "blanc fixe," is next in importance, approximately 30,000 tons being used each year. At first, it was only a by-product in the production of hydrogen peroxide, but the demand is great enough so that it is now produced by the reaction of BaS with Na_2SO_4.

$$Ba^{++} + S^{--} + 2\ Na^+ + SO_4^{--} \longrightarrow \underline{BaSO_4} + 2\ Na^+ + S^{--}$$

It is used as a filler (to bring the solids content of the paint film up to the value yielding the greatest durability) in paints in which titanium dioxide, TiO_2, is the white pigment. It is also used in the paper industry to absorb the oil from the printing ink, and in the automobile tire industry to increase the aging quality of the rubber and its resistance to abrasion. Pure $BaSO_4$ has been used for many years by the medical profession in connection with X rays, for X-ray pictures can be taken of the stomach and intestinal tract after the patient has swallowed some $BaSO_4$.

Barium Carbonate

The natural carbonate, witherite, is not mined in the United States, but some is imported. $BaCO_3$ is prepared by the precipitation of Ba^{++} from BaS with CO_2. About one-half of our 30,000-ton annual production is used by the ceramic industry for products ranging from optical glass to common brick; another 20 per cent is used in making enamels, and another 20 per cent in making case-hardened steel. Some $BaCO_3$ is used in water softening and it has been recommended for the extermination of rats and such leaf-eating insects as the Mexican bean beetle. Its use in the manufacture of brick and clay depends upon the reaction of either soluble $CaSO_4$ or $MgSO_4$ with $BaCO_3$.

$$\underline{BaCO_3} + CaSO_4 \longrightarrow \underline{CaCO_3 + BaSO_4}$$

$CaSO_4$ and $MgSO_4$ form a scum which appears as an objectionable coating on clay products after they have been heated.

Barium Oxide

Barium oxide (baryta) may be prepared by heating $Ba(NO_3)_2$ which melts at 592° C. and decomposes at a slightly higher temperature.

$$2\ Ba(NO_3)_2 \longrightarrow 2\ BaO + 4\ \overline{NO_2} + \overline{O_2}$$

Because of the high cost of $Ba(NO_3)_2$, most of the BaO is produced by the decomposition of $BaCO_3$. This compound decomposes at 1450° C., but the reaction is slow because of the great tendency of BaO to recombine with CO_2. To shift the equilibrium from left to right, carbon is mixed with the $BaCO_3$; this reacts with carbon dioxide to form carbon monoxide.

$$BaCO_3 \rightleftarrows BaO + \overline{CO_2}$$
$$\hookrightarrow + C \longrightarrow \overline{2\ CO}$$

Barium oxide is used in the manufacture of metallic barium and in the preparation of $Ba(OH)_2$ and BaO_2. Because of its tendency to react with water it is used as a drying agent; it is frequently used to dry chemicals which are kept in desiccators or glass jars. It can be regenerated quite easily providing it is kept away from CO_2 and SO_3.

Barium Hydroxide

$Ba(OH)_2$ is the most soluble of the alkaline earth hydroxides. Its solution is called baryta water. It is used in removing the last traces of carbonates from sodium hydroxide, in purifying sugar, in softening water, and in analytical work when a base must be entirely free of carbon dioxide or when soluble carbonates formed during the titration interfere with the sharpness of the end point. Great care is required to prepare an absolutely clear solution of $Ba(OH)_2$.

THE ALKALINE EARTH METALS; ALUMINUM

Of its several hydrates, $Ba(OH)_2 \cdot 8\ H_2O$ is the one used in water purification. It is sold in a white crystalline form and can be shipped in paper sacks.

Other Barium Compounds

Barium peroxide, BaO_2, was formerly used as the principal oxygen carrier in manufacturing hydrogen peroxide (page 133), but cheap electrolytic processes are now displacing this process. *Barium chloride* is usually sold as the dihydrate, $BaCl_2 \cdot 2\ H_2O$; it is used as a precipitating agent for the sulfate radical and in the tanning of white kid leather. *Barium perchlorate*, $Ba(ClO_4)_2$, is sold as "desicchlora" and is a drying agent for gases; but serious explosions may result if it is used with organic gases which liberate free $HClO_4$. *Barium fluosilicate*, $BaSiF_6$, is one of the newer insecticides on the market. *Barium fluoride* is used both as an antiseptic and in making enamels. Barium salts, particularly the nitrate and chlorate, are used in pyrotechnics to produce green-colored flames.

COMPOUNDS OF ALUMINUM

The discussion of aluminum silicates (page 463) indicated the importance of these compounds in the ceramic and cement industries. Bauxite is the most important ore mined as a source of aluminum. *Fuller's earth* is a clay which years ago was used in "fulling" or removing grease from wool; hence its name. About 300,000 tons of this clay are mined per year, and it is used as a sorbent in many industries, the petroleum industry in particular. Sulfates, chlorides, and oxides are the most important aluminum compounds. Aluminum is trivalent in all its compounds. The hydroxide is amphoteric and reacts to form compounds of Al^{+++} and AlO_2^- (aluminates). Litmus paper is red in salt solutions of Al^{+++} and blue in solutions of soluble aluminates.

Aluminum Hydroxide and Aluminum Oxide

Pure aluminum hydroxide, as first formed, is a white gelatinous precipitate which is soluble in both acids and bases. These reactions were discussed on pages 218 and 447 (review them in this connection). Insoluble aluminum hydroxide can be precipitated by adding NH_4OH to a solution containing Al^{+++}.

$$Al^{+++} + 3\ Cl^- + 3\ NH_4OH \longrightarrow \underline{Al(OH)_3} + 3\ NH_4^+ + 3\ Cl^-$$

An excess of the precipitant may be added if desired, for NH_4OH is too weak a base to react with the weak acid $Al(OH)_3$. On the other hand, in preparing $Al(OH)_3$ by adding HCl to an aluminate,

$$H_2O + Na^+ + AlO_2^- + H^+ + Cl^- \longrightarrow \underline{Al(OH)_3} + Na^+ + Cl^-$$

care must be taken to add only the correct amount of acid. (Why?) In forming the gelatinous precipitate of aluminum hydroxide used in water purification to carry down dirt and bacteria, any amount of carbonic acid may be used to react with the NaAlO$_2$ (if this is the salt used), because H$_2$CO$_3$ is too weak an acid to react with the weak base, Al(OH)$_3$.

The paper and fabric industries use aluminum hydroxide as a filler and mordant. Some dyes will not hold fast to paper or cloth, but will form an insoluble, brilliantly colored compound with Al(OH)$_3$. When this substance is precipitated *within* the fibers it can still be dyed. Any substance so used is called a *mordant*, from the French word *mordre*, to bite, because it seems to make the dye *bite* into the fabric and hold tight. In using Al(OH)$_3$ as a mordant, the dyer first soaks the cloth in a solution of aluminum acetate, then steams it. The steam carries away the volatile acetic acid which is formed by hydrolysis (i.e., by the reaction of the base, the acetate ion, with the acid, the hydrated aluminum ion; see page 218) and sends the reaction to completion.

$$Al^{+++} + 3\ C_2H_3O_2^- + 3\ H_2O \longrightarrow \underline{Al(OH)_3} + 3\ \overline{HC_2H_3O_2}$$

In this way the precipitate is formed *inside* the fibers.

If the aluminum hydroxide is simply precipitated in the presence of the dye, the colored compound is called a *lake* and may be used as a pigment.

That molecules of Al$_2$O$_3$ (obtained from the dehydration of Al(OH)$_3$) are rearranged is shown by the fact that a soft white powder of Al$_2$O$_3$, which is readily soluble in acids, is obtained by igniting Al(OH)$_3$ at a low temperature. A dense product (s.g. about 4), which is practically insoluble in acids, is obtained by heating Al$_2$O$_3$ at a high temperature. It is prepared commercially by fusing bauxite in electric furnaces; its trade name is alundum. Alundum is used as an abrasive, and competes with the native crystalline ores, corundum and emery; these are crystalline forms of aluminum oxide and rank next to diamond in hardness. Many transparent forms of corundum are valued as gems; sapphire and ruby are the commonest. When the term "oriental" is prefixed to the name of a gem, it means that it is actually corundum but has a color like that of the gem named. Thus amethyst is purple quartz, but "oriental" amethyst is purple corundum; topaz contains Si and F, but "oriental" topaz is yellow corundum. The beautiful colors of these gems are due to traces of colored oxides. Transparent corundum crystals that weigh ounces are now prepared by melting alumina in an oxyhydrogen flame. They are used for jeweled bearings in watches and, when colored to taste, as inexpensive gems. The color of the ruby is easily approximated and occasionally equaled. The resulting stone is a true synthetic ruby but it still brings a trivial price compared with the natural stone even though the only way to distinguish them is by a microscopic examination of the imperfections present in both. Aluminum hydroxide dehydrated by a carefully controlled process is an excellent dehydrating agent that is easily regenerated by heating. It is known as "activated alumina" and serves also as a catalyst in organic dehydration reactions, such as the conversion of ethyl alcohol, C_2H_5OH, to ethylene, C_2H_4 (page 673).

Aluminum Sulfate and the Alums

The method used in manufacturing $Al_2(SO_4)_3$ depends upon the requirements of the particular industry. If the sulfate must be iron-free, reprecipitated Al_2O_3 (like that used in manufacturing metallic aluminum) is used as the initial material and is dissolved in sulfuric acid. If traces of iron, etc., are not objectionable, clay is used as the initial material. Evaporating the solution produces crystals of $Al_2(SO_4)_3 \cdot 18\ H_2O$, tons of which are used in water purification. It is known as filter alum, although actually it is *not* an alum. It hydrolyzes in water.

$$2\ Al(H_2O)_6^{+++} + 3\ SO_4^{--} + 6\ H_2O \longrightarrow 2\ \underline{Al(H_2O)_3(OH)_3} + 6\ H_3O^+ + 3\ SO_4^{--}$$

If the water is not alkaline enough to send the hydrolysis to completion as indicated, lime or sodium aluminate, which neutralizes the acid, is added. Aluminum sulfate is also used as a sizing agent in paper making and as a mordant in dyeing.

Beautiful octahedral crystals of $KAl(SO_4)_2 \cdot 12\ H_2O$, potassium aluminum sulfate, are obtained when the salt crystallizes from a solution of equal molecular quantities of K_2SO_4 and $Al_2(SO_4)_3$. This sulfate is known as potash alum or, more commonly, alum. That it is a double salt and not a complex salt is shown by the fact that the only ions present in water solution are K^+, Al^{+++}, and (SO_4^{--}). It can be used as a substitute for filter alum; the "alum" used in some baking powders is really sodium aluminum sulfate, made by drying soda alum, $NaAl(SO_4)_2 \cdot 12\ H_2O$.

There are many double salt duodecihydrates that are called alums. Various monovalent ions can be substituted for K^+, and various trivalent ions for Al^{+++}. A few examples are:

>General formula, $M^+M^{+++}(SO_4)_2 \cdot 12\ H_2O$
>$KAl(SO_4)_2 \cdot 12\ H_2O$, Potash alum
>$NaAl(SO_4)_2 \cdot 12\ H_2O$, Sodium alum
>$NH_4Fe(SO_4)_2 \cdot 12\ H_2O$, Ferric ammonium alum
>$KCr(SO_4)_2 \cdot 12\ H_2O$, Chrome alum
>$NH_4Al(SO_4)_2 \cdot 12\ H_2O$, Ammonium alum

The formulas for these compounds are sometimes written

$$K_2SO_4 \cdot Al_2(SO_4)_3 \cdot 24\ H_2O.$$

Compounds such as these, which crystallize in the same crystal system, are called *isomorphous* substances. K_2SO_4 could not be separated from $Al_2(SO_4)_3$ by fractional crystallization, nor could the various alums be separated from each other.

Aluminum Chloride

Pure anhydrous AlCl₃ is prepared by the direct union of chlorine and aluminum, or by passing chlorine gas over a hot mixture of bauxite and carbon. The hydrate, AlCl₃·6 H₂O, is obtained by adding HCl to Al(OH)₃ and evaporating the solution. The ease with which aluminum chloride hydrolyzes makes it impossible to obtain anhydrous AlCl₃ by heating the hydrate, for HCl is liberated and the final product is Al₂O₃. We saw earlier that MgCl₂ reacts similarly.

Pure AlCl₃ is a white solid which sublimes at 178° C. and fumes strongly in moist air; it is used in preparing many organic compounds. Some years ago, it was discovered that large petroleum molecules could be broken down or "cracked" into smaller ones in the presence of anhydrous AlCl₃; this is the basis of one commercial method for cracking petroleum.

Aluminates

An excellent base useful in the precipitation of either filter alum, as just mentioned, or chlorinated copperas (page 286) is sodium aluminate, NaAlO₂, because it adds to the precipitate. At the same time that the aluminate ion takes up a proton, it hydrates itself to aluminum hydroxide, Al(H₂O)₃(OH)₃. Writing the equation in the conventional manner (i.e., ignoring the water of hydration), we have:

$$2\ Al^{+++} + 3\ SO_4^{--} + 6\ Na^+ + 6\ AlO_2^- + 12\ H_2O \longrightarrow$$
$$8\ \underline{Al(OH)_3} + 6\ Na^+ + 3\ SO_4^{--}$$

$$Fe^{+++} + SO_4^{--} + Cl^- + 3\ Na^+ + 3\ AlO_2^- + 6\ H_2O \longrightarrow$$
$$\underline{Fe(OH)_3} + 3\ \underline{Al(OH)_3} + 3\ Na^+ + SO_4^{--} + Cl^-$$

As a rule the water is usually naturally alkaline enough so that it is not necessary to add such a large proportion of the aluminate. Aluminates are used in making lake colors and sizing paper. Aluminum hydroxide is a monobasic acid only; no salt such as Na₃Al(OH)₆ (or, as it would be written on the dry basis, Na₃AlO₃) exists. However, the fluoride ion is able to replace both water molecules and OH⁻ ions from aluminum hydroxide, forming stable fluoaluminates. Sodium fluoaluminate is used both as a replacement for natural cryolite in the metallurgy of aluminum, and as an insecticide.

$$3\ Na^+ + 3\ HF_2^- + \underline{Al(OH)_3} \longrightarrow \underline{Na_3AlF_6} + 3\ H_2O$$

THE SEPARATION OF THE ALKALINE EARTH METALS AND ALUMINUM

Calcium, barium, and strontium salts give specific flame tests (barium, green; strontium, carmine red; calcium, yellow red). Spectroscopic tests are being used increasingly to identify compounds quickly.

The actual separation of the alkaline earth metals and aluminum depends

THE ALKALINE EARTH METALS; ALUMINUM

upon differences in the solubility of their compounds. If a solution contained ions of all these elements, their separation would depend first upon group separations and finally on further separation within each group. To illustrate this separation, let us assume that all six elements are present as nitrates in a single solution. Be(OH)$_2$ and Al(OH)$_3$ are insoluble in an alkaline solution containing the ammonium ion. Therefore adding NH$_4$OH and NH$_4$NO$_3$ will result in a separation into two groups: precipitates of the hydroxides of beryllium and aluminum, and a solution of the other four ions.

The separation of aluminum and beryllium is both complicated and dangerous. They can be separated by dissolving the hydroxides in concentrated hydrochloric acid and then saturating the solution with HCl gas; ether is added to the solution to decrease the solubility of the AlCl$_3$·6 H$_2$O which precipitates. The dangers include the fire hazard from ether and the danger of breathing anhydrous HCl gas; an extremely complicated filtration system is also necessary.

The other four elements are quite easily separated, for all of them are precipitated as the carbonates by the addition of (NH$_4$)$_2$CO$_3$ and alcohol. (They are less soluble in an alcohol solution than in water.) The precipitates are dissolved in acetic acid, and ammonium acetate and potassium chromate (NH$_4$C$_2$H$_3$O$_2$ and K$_2$CrO$_4$) are then added. Barium chromate, which is insoluble in acetic acid solution, is filtered from the other three. Strontium chromate, SrCrO$_4$, is insoluble in a basic solution; therefore the filtrate from the barium separation is made alkaline with NH$_4$OH and the SrCrO$_4$ is then filtered. The filtrate contains Ca^{++} and Mg^{++} ions. On the addition of (NH$_4$)$_2$C$_2$O$_4$, insoluble calcium oxalate, CaC$_2$O$_4$, precipitates. After this has been filtered, the magnesium ion can be precipitated by adding disodium hydrogen phosphate. Magnesium ammonium phosphate, MgNH$_4$PO$_4$, is insoluble in an alkaline solution. The separation of these six elements, in outline form, is as follows, underlining being used to indicate precipitates:

QUESTIONS AND PROBLEMS

1. Does aluminum belong to the alkaline earth group of metals?
2. Plot the densities of the metals discussed in this chapter against their atomic weights.
3. Why are these metals so expensive?
4. Is it probable that beryllium will ever be an important metal? What are its most valuable properties?
5. What weight of 89 per cent pure bauxite is required to produce one ton of aluminum? Assuming 100 per cent efficiency, how many Faradays will be required to deposit the aluminum electrolytically? If the gases escaping from the anode are half CO and half CO_2, what volume of gases will be liberated?
6. Does aluminum have any amphoteric properties? If so, indicate with equations.
7. What weight of ice at 0° C. could be melted by the heat liberated when 160 g. of Fe_2O_3 are reduced by the thermite reaction? How does aluminum serve as a scavenger in the steel industry?
8. What weight of $MgNH_4PO_4$ can be precipitated with 14.2 g. Na_2HPO_4? What weight of $Mg_2P_2O_7$ could be produced from the $MgNH_4PO_4$?
9. What volume of hydrogen can be obtained from 20 g. of each of the following by the reactions indicated?

$$CaH_2 + HOH \longrightarrow$$
$$Be + NaOH \longrightarrow$$
$$Mg + steam \longrightarrow$$
$$Al + NaOH \longrightarrow$$
$$Zn + HCl \longrightarrow$$

10. How is lime obtained from limestone? What weight of limestone must be used to obtain 5,600,000 tons of lime?
11. What is the freezing point of a saturated solution of $Ca(OH)_2$? (Assume 100 per cent effective dissociation.)
12. What weight of water should be added to 145 g. of plaster of Paris to form gypsum? Would you recommend a little less or a little more than the theoretical amount of water for a plaster cast? Why?
13. If $CaCl_2 \cdot 6 H_2O$ is placed in the desert, what happens?
14. A white solid is one of the following: Al_2O_3, $CaSO_4$, CaC_2O_4, $MgCl_2$, $Sr(NO_3)_2$; how would you identify it?
15. What are alums?

16. Solubility product data are important. Look up the solubility products of BaSO$_4$, CaSO$_4$, and SrSO$_4$. To precipitate each of these from solutions of 0.005 molar Ba^{++}, Ca^{++}, and Sr^{++}, respectively, what should be the molar concentration of SO$_4{}^{--}$ in these solutions?

REFERENCES

Articles

"Beryllium," in *Ency. Brit. Year Book*, 1946, article on metallurgy.

"Magnesium." Murphy, W. J. *Chem. Ind.* **49,** 618 (1941).

"Magnesium." Killefer, D. H. *News Ed.* **19,** 1189 (1941).

"Wartime Aluminum and Magnesium Production." Klagsbrunn, H. A. *J. Ind. and Eng. Chem.* **37,** 608 (1945).

"Alumina from Clay by the H$_2$SO$_4$ Process." *Chem. and Met.* **52,** 105 (Jan. 1945).

"Bayer Process Red Mud Treated for Alumina Recovery." *Ibid.*, p. 106.

"Barium in Radio Tubes." Umbreit, S. *Metals and Alloys* **6,** 273–279 (1935).

"Preparation of Strontium and Barium." Ray, K. W. *Metals and Alloys* **1,** 112–114 (1929).

"Aluminum, the Story of Aluminum." Holmes, H. N. *J. Chem. Ed.* **7,** 233–244 (1930).

"Aluminum in Industry." Frary, F. C. *Ind. and Eng. Chem.* **26,** 1231–1237 (1934).

"Man-Made Gems." Wade, F. B. *J. Chem. Ed.* **8,** 1015–1026 (1931).

"Alkali Metals as Deoxidizers." Schumacher, E. E., *et al.* *Metals and Alloys* **1,** 714–717 (1929).

"Newer Developments in Beryllium." Sawyer, C. B., and Kjellgren, B. R. *Ind. and Eng. Chem.* **30,** 501 (1938).

» 31 «

ZINC, CADMIUM, MERCURY, TIN, AND LEAD

Zinc, cadmium, and mercury are in Group II B of the periodic table, and tin and lead are in Group IV A. They are all soft metals. Mercury is the softest, for it is a liquid at room temperature. Tin and cadmium are the hardest. These metals are more easily obtained from their compounds than any of those thus far discussed. Since they occur in nature in many different forms, several metallurgical processes are used in producing them.

Occurrence

There are so many ores of these metals that only a few of the more important ones will be discussed. *Zinc* ores are found in every state in this country, and the metal is produced in 23 states. The most important zinc-producing regions of the United States are New Jersey, Illinois, Virginia, Kansas, the famous Joplin district in Missouri, and Oklahoma. Zinc and lead ores occur together in many places. Igneous or volcanic rocks contain zinc, lead, and copper. PbS and CuS are insoluble in an acid solution and therefore were precipitated in acid waters. Zinc sulfide is soluble in an acid solution but not in a basic solution, and hence was precipitated when thermal waters passed through a limestone formation. Zinc sulfide, ZnS, is often found in limestone deposits, whereas copper ores are found in veins. ZnS has replaced the $CaCO_3$ in some fossils. Sphalerite, or zinc blende, and wurtzite are both zinc sulfides and are the more important zinc ores. Others of importance are willemite, Zn_2SiO_4; calamine, $Zn_2SiO_4 \cdot H_2O$; smithsonite, or zinc spar, $ZnCO_3$; zincite, ZnO; and franklinite, $Zn(FeO_2)_2$. The ore from the Franklin and Sterling Hill mines in New Jersey is franklinite; it also contains manganese which is used in steel and is a valuable by-product of zinc smelters.

Most of the *cadmium* produced comes from the flue dust of copper, zinc, and lead smelters, and from the electrolytic reduction of zinc ores. As this implies, cadmium ores are similar to zinc ores. The cadmium content of zinc ores is seldom as high as 3 per cent of the zinc content. Greenockite, CdS, a rare yellowish-orange mineral, is found associated with zinc blende.

Compounds of *mercury* are reduced so easily that the element is found in small amounts in the native state. The only important ore, cinnabar, HgS, is found both as the vermilion sulfide and, in the weathered deposits, as black metacinnabarite. Prior to the Civil War in Spain, that country led in the production of mercury; Italy and California are also important producers.

Tin is found in small, commercially unimportant quantities in the free state. Cassiterite, or tinstone, SnO_2, the important ore, is as hard as steel and practically infusible. The Cornwall deposits in the British Isles were the first large ones to be developed; those in the Malay region have long been more important. During World War II the Allies depended mainly upon Bolivian tin. Rich new veins were discovered in Bolivia in 1944-1945.

Lead is also sufficiently inactive to be found free in nature. Galena, PbS, is by far the most important ore, deposits being found in all parts of the world. Cerussite, $PbCO_3$, and anglesite, $PbSO_4$, are of minor importance.

Discovery

Mercury, *tin*, and *lead* in the free state were known many centuries B.C.; the Bible refers to all three of them. *Zinc* ores were used in making brass for centuries before the element was isolated. It is believed that the art of smelting these ores was first developed in India and was carried from there to China; Portuguese traders brought zinc from China a century before it was smelted in Europe. In 1746 the German chemist, Marggraf, reduced calamine with charcoal and obtained a substance whose properties differed so materially from those of copper that zinc was thereafter recognized as an element. Professor Strohmeyer of Göttingen University discovered *cadmium* in 1817, when he examined samples of zinc carbonate that had been condemned for use in pharmaceuticals because they gave a yellow precipitate with H_2S and were therefore thought to contain arsenic. He found no arsenic, but did obtain a yellow precipitate with H_2S in an acid solution. When he reduced this precipitate with carbon, a metal with a bright luster appeared; he named it cadmium, because it was associated with the zinc ore, calamine.

Metallurgy

Zinc, cadmium, mercury, tin, and lead are all easily obtained from their ores. The fact that they were known, at least in an impure state, centuries ago, makes it obvious that none of the modern scientific developments are absolutely essential in their metallurgy.

Mercury. Mercury is the easiest of all to obtain as the metal; hence the metallurgical processes are frequently carried out at the mines. Two methods are used for reducing cinnabar, HgS. In one process, HgS is heated in the air and mercury vapor and sulfur dioxide are formed.

$$HgS \xrightarrow[\text{in air}]{\Delta} \overline{Hg} + \overline{SO_2}$$

In the other process, the ore is heated with calcium oxide in a vessel from which all air is excluded; calcium sulfate, calcium sulfide, and mercury vapor are produced.

$$4\ HgS + 4\ CaO \xrightarrow{\Delta} 3\ CaS + CaSO_4 + \overline{4\ Hg}$$

In both processes, the reaction temperature is kept above the boiling point of mercury (357° C.), and a condensation apparatus is essential. Large rotary kilns are used in some plants.

Fig. 31.1. Electrolytic tank room, zinc plant. (Courtesy, Anaconda Copper Mining Co.)

Zinc. The metallurgy of zinc depends upon the ore to be processed. Typical of the electrolytic plants is that of the Anaconda Reduction Works in Montana, which is capable of producing 10,000,000 pounds per month. The ore is first concentrated by flotation; burned lime, xanthate, pine oil, and copper sulfate are used. Zinc sulfate and sodium cyanide are added to the thickened concentrate, which is rich in zinc and lead, and water is then added. The lead minerals float, but, because of the depressing action of $ZnSO_4$ and NaCN, the zinc minerals do not. The zinc concentrate is filtered and roasted in furnaces. Each furnace consists of a brick-lined steel shell 25 feet in diameter, and has seven hearths and one open dryer hearth on top. A revolving center shaft carries water-cooled arms for the dryers and hearths. The concentrate moves from the rim to the center of one hearth and then falls to the second hearth where it is scraped outward and down to the next hearth, etc. The calcined ore is leached in tanks which are arranged in series, the spent liquor discharging from one tank to another. Iron, silica, alumina, antimony, and arsenic are removed by acid leaching. Copper and

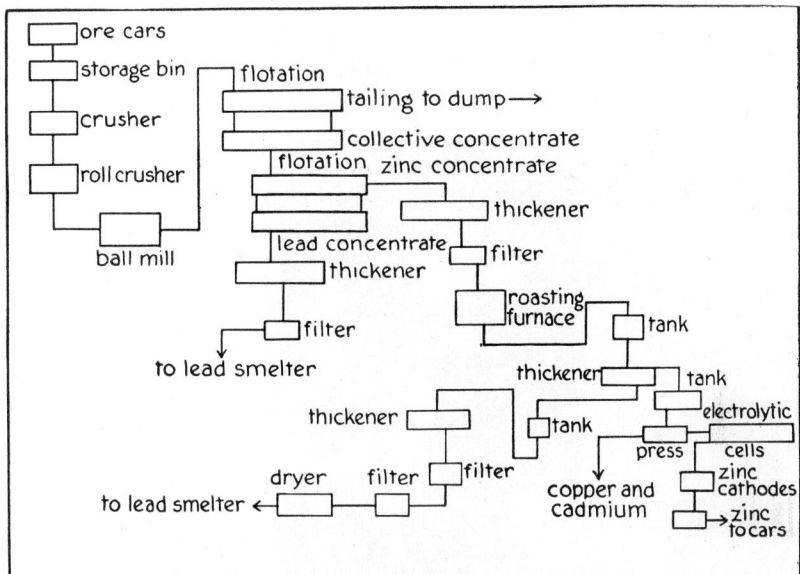

Fig. 31.2. Flow sheet in the metallurgy of zinc.

Fig. 31.3. View of a vertical retort plant for producing zinc. (Courtesy, New Jersey Zinc Co.)

cadmium are removed by adding zinc dust and then filtering the solution with a filter press. The clear filtrate is known as the electrolyte; and from it zinc is deposited electrolytically by the use of lead anodes and aluminum cathodes. The original solution is neutral, but during electrolysis the acidity increases.

This solution is returned and used again in the leaching process. Zinc is stripped from the cathodes every 24 hours. A flow sheet of the process is shown in Fig. 31.2.

The vertical retort distillation process is used by the New Jersey Zinc Company in the reduction of ores rich in zinc oxide. One difficulty with this process is the fact that zinc vaporizes readily and tends to become reoxidized. Most of the plants are small because the construction of large ones presents mechanical difficulties. Because of its high heat conductivity, silicon carbide is used as refractory. The zinc ore is pulverized and mixed with carbonaceous reducing material; a binder such as sulfite waste liquor, tar, pitch, or molasses is added; and the mixture is pressed into briquettes. These are dried and transferred to the coking ovens where they are passed through a vertical chamber, rectangular in cross section. The zinc ore is reduced and the zinc vapor is collected in the condenser; it is tapped from time to time and cast into slabs. Very pure zinc can be obtained by redistilling the impure zinc. Fractional distillation is used to separate zinc from cadmium and lead.

FIG. 31.4. Tapping a condenser. (Courtesy, New Jersey Zinc Co.)

Ores from the Joplin district are rich in zinc sulfide and can easily be concentrated by ore flotation to over 99 per cent ZnS. This ore is first roasted to remove arsenic and sulfur. (Some plants recover the sulfur dioxide and convert it into sulfuric acid.) The zinc oxide is then mixed with coal and reduced in fire-clay retorts. The furnaces have an odd appearance because each retort slopes to the outside. The receiver is sealed in with clay. From time to time, the receivers are tapped and the metal—or "spelter," as it is called—is poured into molds.

ZINC, CADMIUM, MERCURY, TIN, AND LEAD

Cadmium. No cadmium is produced as a primary product; it is always obtained as a by-product of the copper, lead, and zinc industries. Although formerly no attempt was made to separate cadmium from zinc, the current demand for cadmium makes this profitable. A process that has been recently suggested for its direct production consists of adding a cheap chloride to the roasted concentrate and volatilizing cadmium chloride along with other easily volatilized chlorides. Metallic cadmium is purified by fractional crystallization and electrolysis from aqueous solutions.

Fig. 31.5. Filter presses, zinc plant. (Courtesy, Anaconda Copper Mining Co.)

Tin. Tin ores are nearly always low grade; many that are worked do not contain over 0.5 of 1 per cent tin. The oxide of tin, SnO_2, is quite heavy and can be separated from the pulverized ore by floating away the impurities. If the ore contains sulfur or arsenic, it is roasted first; otherwise the concentrate is smelted without further treatment.

Although a few blast furnaces are used in Germany and India, most of the ore is smelted in reverberatory furnaces. One of these large furnaces in Singapore can produce 30,000 to 50,000 tons of tin per year. Another furnace, in Texas City (the only one in the United States, built during the war), now smelts all American purchases of Bolivian tin ore. In these furnaces (Fig. 31.6) the flame is reflected from the top of the furnace down on the ore. A mixture of SnO_2 ore, powdered coal, and flux is heated on the furnace floor until the tin oxide is reduced to molten metallic tin which is collected in settling basins. The tin in these basins is kept in the molten state to bring the slag to the surface. Some tin is volatilized, necessitating equipment for collecting the dust. Since the first-run slag may contain 10 to 25 per cent tin, it is returned to the furnace and resmelted.

Tin is refined by heating the crude tin just enough to melt the pure tin. The hard brittle residue which remains usually contains iron, arsenic, sulfur, lead, and 20 per cent tin, and is known as hard lead. This can be purified further.

The molten high-quality tin is further purified by stirring with poles made from green wood. The gases produced bring the impurities to the top. Another means of further purification is to pour the tin in a thin stream through the air. The high-melting metals and alloys solidify before the tin does, and oxygen of the air oxidizes some of the impurities; these are then skimmed from the surface.

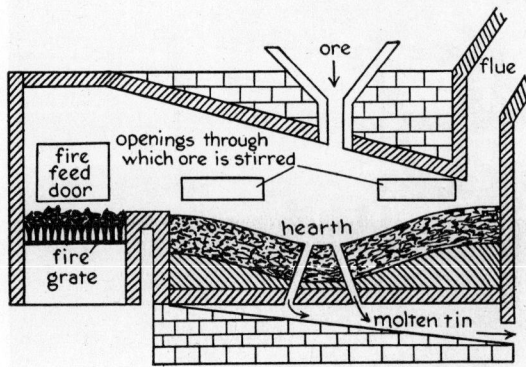

FIG. 31.6. Reduction of SnO$_2$.

Very pure tin is prepared by electrolytic refining. The tin electrolyte must contain a radical which will form an insoluble lead compound, for otherwise any lead present will plate out with the tin. Moreover, the bath must not dissolve arsenic, antimony, bismuth, or copper, traces of which are usually present. Hydrofluosilicic acid, H$_2$SiF$_6$, with sulfuric acid is satisfactory for the bath.

The detinning of tin scrap and tin cans adds to the supply of tin, about 3000 tons being obtained annually from this source in normal times (10 times that amount was obtained in 1944). Dry tin plate and tin cans are piled in large containers and chlorine gas is added. The gas attacks tin and forms liquid SnCl$_4$, but does not attack dry iron. Some of this SnCl$_4$ is used in weighting silk.

Lead. Lead is usually mined from tunnels. The Missouri deposits are from 300 to 800 feet thick and cover hundreds of acres. Seldom is an ore rich enough to be sent to the smelter without preliminary treatment; the ore worked by one large mining company is only about 3 per cent lead. The important lead ore, galena (PbS), is easily wetted with the reagents used in ore flotation processes; selective ore flotation processes have even been developed to separate galena from zinc blende. Zinc ores interfere with the metallurgy of lead to such an extent that smelter companies penalize the mining companies if the ore contains zinc. The concentrate that is shipped to the smelters contains 70 to 85 per cent lead ore.

Open-hearth, reverberatory, and blast furnaces are used in the smelting of lead ores. The open-hearth furnace is used for high-grade ores which contain only traces of other metals. Scrap lead and lead waste products are frequently resmelted in reverberatory furnaces. The blast furnace is used for low-grade ore and hence it is the most important of the three.

As a rule, part of the concentrate is roasted and then mixed with more concentrate for use as the charge in the blast furnace. Roasting at about 500° C. converts most of the metal sulfides to oxides; some of the sulfide can be converted to sulfate by very careful manipulation of the furnace.

$$4\ PbS + 7\ O_2 \longrightarrow 2\ PbO + 2\ PbSO_4 + 2\ SO_2$$

The mixture of PbO, $PbSO_4$, PbS, other metal oxides, and carbon is fed into a small blast furnace with a basic lining. The lime added as a flux combines with silica to form a fusible slag, $CaSiO_3$. Air is forced in at the bottom of the furnace, and the burning carbon produces carbon monoxide; this, with the carbon, serves as the reducing agent. With such a complicated mixture, a large number of chemical reactions must take place simultaneously; some of the more important ones are the following:

Reduction of PbO with C and CO
$$2\ PbO + C \longrightarrow 2\ Pb + CO_2$$
$$PbO + CO \longrightarrow Pb + CO_2$$

Reduction of PbO and $PbSO_4$ with PbS
$$2\ PbO + PbS \longrightarrow 3\ Pb + SO_2$$
$$PbSO_4 + PbS \longrightarrow 2\ Pb + 2\ SO_2$$

Reduction of PbS with FeO
$$Fe_2O_3 + C \longrightarrow 2\ FeO + CO$$
$$FeO + CO \longrightarrow Fe + CO_2$$
$$Fe + PbS \longrightarrow Pb + FeS$$

The iron oxide, which is an impurity, is valuable in reducing the lead ore. Three layers of slag, matte, and lead bullion sometimes form in the furnace. The slag is rich in calcium silicate. The matte contains lead, precious metals like gold and silver, and metal sulfides such as iron and copper; it is treated separately because of its possible valuable constituents. The lead bullion is pure enough for some commercial purposes but must be refined for others.

Gold and silver are removed because of their value. Copper and iron must be removed, especially if paints are to be made from the lead, for these impurities discolor paint. Antimony must also be removed, because a minute quantity hardens lead.

The Parkes process is used to remove gold, silver, and copper. This consists of adding metallic zinc and fusing the mixture. The zinc floats on the lead and dissolves the impurities. As the mixture cools, a crust forms which can be skimmed off. Frequently it is necessary to repeat the process several times. The little zinc that dissolves in the lead is oxidized by blowing steam and air through the lead bullion.

In the Betts process, an electrolytic refining method, anodes of lead bullion are suspended in a bath of fluosilicic acid and lead fluosilicate; pure sheet lead is used for the cathodes. At the voltage used in this process, active metals like iron and zinc remain in solution. The less active metallic impurities, such as copper, gold, silver, and bismuth, do not dissolve in the electrolyte; they drop beneath the anode and form the "anode mud." Although the Parkes process is the cheaper, the Betts process is widely used because many industries require electrolytic lead.

Calcium has already been mentioned as a scavenger in the purification of lead. Metallic calcium alloys with many impurities and forms a scum or dross; but if too much calcium is added, it alloys with lead and makes it brittle. Metallic calcium, as well as bismuth, can be removed by blowing chlorine through the molten metal.

Physical and Chemical Properties

Anyone who has seen lead pipe, tin cans, galvanized or zinc-coated buckets, mercury thermometers, and cadmium-plated parts on automobiles, jewelry, and tableware is familiar with the general appearance of the soft metals. Table 31.1 lists several of their properties.

TABLE 31.1. PROPERTIES OF ZINC, CADMIUM, MERCURY, TIN, AND LEAD

	Zinc	Cadmium	Mercury	Tin	Lead
Melting point, °C.	419	321	−38.87	232	327
Boiling point, °C.	907	767	356.9	2260	1620
Specific gravity	7.14	8.65	13.54	6.5–7.3	11.3
Common valences	2	2	2, 1	2, 4	2, 4
Soluble in	HCl, NaOH	HCl	HNO_3	HCl, KOH	HNO_3

Mercury is the only one which is a liquid at room temperature. The other four melt in the flame of a Bunsen burner, and all but tin and lead can be boiled with a good burner. The most common valence of all these elements is two. Oxidizing acids are necessary to dissolve mercury and lead. Tin, cadmium, and zinc are soluble in HCl, and tin and zinc are also soluble in alkalis.

One valuable property of all these elements is their ability to resist atmospheric corrosion. Although *zinc* is readily oxidized in the atmosphere, the zinc oxide formed is an efficient protective coating that prevents further corrosion; if this were not the case, zinc could not be used to protect iron. Zinc is brittle at room temperature, as may be demonstrated by the ease with which a zinc rod can be broken; it is also quite brittle at 250° C. Zinc is made in the form of sheets and wire by rolling or drawing it at a temperature of about 125° C.

Cadmium, which is just below zinc in the periodic table, is a little harder than zinc, but otherwise much like it in both physical and chemical properties.

One of the interesting properties of *mercury* is the fact that it oxidizes to

ZINC, CADMIUM, MERCURY, TIN, AND LEAD

HgO in the presence of an excess of oxygen at about 300° C. The oxide can be decomposed by heat in the absence of oxygen. If the oxide is heated in a test tube, liquid mercury will condense on the walls. Mercury is a poor conductor of electricity, with 60 times the resistance of silver. Its coefficient of expansion is nearly constant over a wide temperature range. Mercury is known to the trade as quicksilver.

Mercury alloys are called *amalgams*. The silver-white mercury-gold amalgam will form if liquid mercury comes in contact with a gold ring or a gold watch in the chemistry laboratory. An amalgam of silver, gold, and tin is used for dental fillings. The alkali metals like sodium and potassium form amalgams which are used as reducing agents. An interesting development in the use of these amalgams is in electrolytic reductions in which the cathodes are liquid mercury. The alkali ions are reduced to the metallic state at the electrode, and these active metals then serve, either directly or indirectly, as reducing agents. Some metals such as the iron group (Fe, Co, Ni) do not form amalgams; hence iron vessels can be used for distilling mercury, and it is frequently shipped in iron containers.

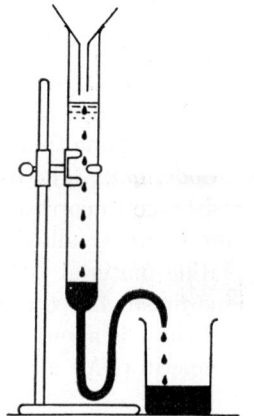

FIG. 31.7. Purification of mercury.

Mercury is used in the chemical laboratory for electrical contacts and in the leveling bulbs for measuring gases; it should be dust-free. It is purified by distillation or by allowing it to drip through a tall column of dilute nitric acid containing mercurous nitrate. The dust particles are easily wetted and remain in the water. The apparatus is shown in Fig. 31.7.

Pure *tin* is a white metal with a bluish cast. Its electrical conductivity is only about one-seventh that of silver. The metal is not affected by even moist air, but tarnishes slowly in the presence of hydrogen sulfide.

Tin is crystalline in nature. The tin "cry" heard when a piece of tin is bent is due to crystals slipping over each other. Below $-40°$ C., tin becomes an allotropic gray powder. One of the most interesting characteristics of this element is that the change to gray tin, once initiated, will continue at room temperature. It is known as "tin pest" or "tin disease," and has caused museum pieces to crumble in a short time.[1] The allotropic forms of tin are as follows:

$$\text{amorphous tin} \underset{18°}{\rightleftarrows} \text{malleable tin} \underset{161°}{\rightleftarrows} \text{brittle tin}$$

| Amorphous | Tetragonal crystals | Rhombic crystals |

[1] Among the many stories of tin disease are those of the tin pipes of an organ in Russia which crumbled, the Russian government's block tin which was found to be a powder, and the tin buttons which turned to powder just before they were to be sewed on the soldiers' uniforms.

The ordinary malleable tin is stable between 18° and 161° C. Tin is attacked by both acids and bases. An excess of hot concentrated oxidizing acids converts it to the tetravalent state.

Freshly cut *lead* has a silver-like luster, but it quickly tarnishes, the surface film protecting the metal from further corrosion. Lead is one of the softest stable metals. Lead pipes should not be used for drinking water because lead reacts with oxygen and water and forms $Pb(OH)_2$, which flakes off. This reaction is especially evident in soft waters. Lead is readily attacked by nitric acid; either nitric oxide or nitrogen dioxide is formed, depending upon the concentration of the acid.

Production and Uses

The quantities of each of these metals produced in 1920, 1930, and 1944 are shown in Table 31.2. Because of differences in density, zinc is produced in greater volume than any of the others; cadmium is the least important.

Cadmium. The uses of cadmium depend upon its low melting point and resistance to corrosion. It is used as a plating material and in the manufacture of many alloys. At one time it competed with zinc as a finishing or plating material because it gives a bright finish as compared with the dull zinc finish; but the development of bright zinc coatings and the fact that cadmium is about twelve times as expensive as zinc have removed it as a competitor. An attempt was made to popularize cadmium-plated products

TABLE 31.2. PRODUCTION OF ZINC, CADMIUM, MERCURY, TIN, AND LEAD

	World Production	U.S. Production	Cost
1920			
Cadmium	100 T.[a]	70 T.	$ 1.17 lb.
Zinc	800,000 T.	450,000 T.	.081 lb.
Mercury	86,000 F.[b]	13,000 F.	81.00 F.
Tin	137,000 T.	22 T.	.50 lb.
Lead	1,000,000 T.	480,000 T.	.08 lb.
1930			
Cadmium	5,000 T.	1,500 T.	$ .64 lb.
Zinc	1,500,000 T.	500,000 T.	.048 lb.
Mercury	110,000 F.	21,000 F.	115.00 F.
Tin	193,000 T.	16 T.	.31 lb.
Lead	1,750,000 T.	600,000 T.	.055 lb.
1944			
Cadmium	5,300 T.	4,200 T.	$ .90 lb.
Zinc	—[c]	575,000 T.	.114 lb.[d]
Mercury	—[c]	38,000 F.	100–300 F.
Tin	112,000 T.	6 T.	.52 lb.
Lead	1,907,000 T.	476,000 T.	.065 lb.

[a] T = tons (2000 lb.). [b] F = flask (76 lb.). [c] Not available. [d] Including subsidy.

to compete with silver. Cadmium alloys are used as bearings in automobiles because they can withstand higher temperatures without melting than the customary bearing metals can; it is also used in alloys for automatic fire sprinklers. One per cent of cadmium in copper increases the latter's tensile strength without greatly changing its electrical conductivity. Although the demand has increased since 1920, it is unlikely that cadmium will ever be important commercially, for it is found only as an impurity in ores of other metals, particularly zinc.

Zinc. Deposits of zinc are so widely distributed in nature that the supply of this element is considered unlimited. The fact that small mines and by-product producers of zinc can afford to sell the metal if the price rises makes its price fairly stable.

Metal zinc is used as the container and negative pole of the ordinary dry cell (page 254). Some sheet zinc is used as roofing and gutters on buildings, and for lining tanks, etc.

Although zinc can be alloyed with many metals, the most important alloy is brass; bronze and German silver are also important. Zinc alloys, suitable for making small metal parts that do not require great strength, are made by means of an efficient mass-production technique called "die casting." In automobiles the carburetor, fuel pump, speedometer, radiator grill, handles, hardware, and lighting fixtures are zinc alloys. Cash registers, adding machines, gasoline pumps, and many other machines contain zinc alloy castings. One-fourth of all the zinc produced is used for brass and castings.

Nearly half the total output of zinc is used in protecting the surface of other metals, iron in particular. The problem of suitable *metal coatings* has been given much attention by metallurgists, for our annual bill for corrosion is appalling; any automobile "graveyard" shows its effects. A surface can be protected in many ways, the following being among the more important:

1. Treat the metal surface so that it acts as a better protective agent (special heat treatment of the metal and the formation of oxide and nitride films).

2. Coat the surface with paints, varnishes, shellacs, etc. (The disadvantage here is that the surface of the metal cannot be seen.)

3. Cover the surface with a less active metal. A metal can be coated with another metal by being dipped into the molten coating, rolled in the powdered coating, or sprayed with the molten coating; the coating can also be applied electrolytically.

4. Cover the surface with a *more* active but self-protecting metal. Galvanized iron is the main example of this type of protection, the iron or steel having been coated with zinc.

The word "galvanized" is derived from the name of the great Italian scientist, Galvani, who made the first electrochemical cells. When a drop of rain water falls on a surface imperfection such as a crack or hole in a sheet of galvanized iron and touches both zinc and iron, a galvanic (i.e., electrochemical) cell is set up. The zinc is the negative electrode, the iron the positive one, and the drop of water with its dissolved CO_2, O_2, and perhaps NaCl or SO_2, is the electrolyte. This cell is short-circuited, for the poles are in contact. Electrons flow out of the zinc into the iron and H^+ ions are discharged there, forming a protective coating of H_2. At the same time the Zn^{++} ions formed from the zinc precipitate as a protective coating of basic zinc carbonate. More zinc can dissolve only as the tightly adsorbed layer of H_2 (or perhaps even monatomic H) slowly escapes from the surface of exposed iron. Since the zinc from a considerable area can send electrons to the iron at a break in the coating, the protective effect is very lasting.

If less active metal is used to protect iron (method 3), the coating must be perfect or the galvanic action will work to destroy the iron instead of to protect it. It is common knowledge how fast the iron rusts away once a nickel-plated object or a piece of tinware has begun to rust. This is because the *iron* sends electrons to the nickel or tin. The United States Government Bureau of Standards tests show that zinc offers greater protection to iron than any other commercially practical metal coating. Great improvements have been made in cleaning the metals for the hot dip or galvan-

FIG. 31.8. An operator at the shop of the Turlock Irrigation District, Turlock, California, building up wear plates from wicket gates, using Metco No. 2 stainless steel and the Mogul Metallizer. This application restores the wear plates to their original size and gives longer protection from erosion and wear. (Courtesy, Metallizing Co. of America, Inc.)

izing process. Until recently, sand-blasting equipment was usually used to free the surface from scale, iron oxide, etc.; this was followed by "pickling" or acid treatment which dissolved sufficient iron to loosen the sand grains. Sand is insoluble in most acids, but it can be washed off if first loosened; a few plants use hydrofluoric acid which dissolves sand. In the newer cleaning processes special abrasive steel is used instead of sand, and this eliminates the difficulty of removing sand from the polished product. When thoroughly cleaned, the metal is dipped into molten zinc at a temperature of 500° to 600° C. If the temperature is much higher, zinc will alloy rapidly with iron, and the resulting coating will be too thick. Small articles can be coated by rotating in a revolving drum which contains zinc. "Sherardized" iron is made by the latter process.

The zinc coating process has been improved by depositing the zinc electrolytically from cyanide solutions which contain some molybdenum. The two metals plate out together and produce a bright, shiny zinc coating.

"Metallizing," or spraying on the molten metal coating, is another recent improvement that can be used with zinc and aluminum coatings as well as with low-melting alloys. Spray guns are charged with strips of the coating metal which is melted in an electric arc, and the molten coating metal is then sprayed on the clean base metal surface (Fig. 31.8).

Mercury. For many years Spain and Italy were the chief producers of mercury, producing between them about 75 per cent of the world's supply. The United States ranks third, with a production equal to about half the domestic consumption. The ores now being mined rarely contain over 0.4 of 1 per cent of mercury. The outlook for the future is not promising. However, when World War II cut off most of our foreign supply, the skyrocketing price put a swarm of marginal one- and two-man diggings back into production. In a couple of years all our domestic needs were supplied and a stockpile equal to two years' consumption was built up; consequently the price returned to the vicinity of the old rate of $90 for a 76-pound flask and the little mines closed down.

Mercury is the best substance for use in thermometers for ordinary temperatures because its coefficient of expansion is nearly constant. It is used in the chemical laboratory in vacuum pumps, barometers, liquid seals such as connections for stirrers, and electrical contacts. Ultraviolet rays or artificial sunlight is produced in homes by means of mercury vapor lamps, and these lamps are also used to sterilize drinking water and the water in swimming pools; moreover, the discomfort due to chlorinated water is eliminated in such pools. About 25 per cent of the mercury produced is used in making the many mercury drugs on the market. The use of mercury fulminate in exploding shells makes this compound important.

In 1923, the first mercury vapor turbine engine was installed at Hartford, Connecticut. In 1936, at Pittsfield and Lynn, Massachusetts, the General Electric Co. installed heating systems, each of which consisted of a mercury boiler, a 1000-kilowatt mercury turbine, a condenser-boiler, and a steam turbine. The boilers require about 6 pounds of mercury per kilowatt-hour of capacity. (A 50,000-kilowatt plant requires 140 tons of mercury.) After the mercury vapor has been used to drive a turbine it generates steam during the condensing cycle, and the steam in turn operates a steam turbine. The mercury plants are more compact and about 50 per cent more efficient in operation than steam plants. Because of its poisonous nature, mercury vapor must be prevented from escaping in the plants; less than 1 per cent per year is lost in this way. It appears unlikely that sufficient mercury will ever be produced so that its general use in boilers will be feasible.

Metallic mercury is also used in the hardening of lead alloys containing the alkali metals, as a substitute for tin in type-metal alloys, in mercury vapor lamps for motion-picture projectors, and in some recent processes for printing photographic half tones on heavy paper. Pegging the price of gold increased the quantity of mercury used in gold-mining.

Tin. In the 1930's dire predictions were being made of the imminent exhaustion of the world's supply of tin, since no new ore deposits had been found in many years. Fortunately for the Allies, after the fall of Singapore, it was found possible to expand Bolivian tin mining enough to take care of minimum requirements. Nevertheless, even after the discoveries mentioned on page 537, the situation remains tight and the outlook for the future not too bright. The January, 1948, price of tin—94 cents a pound—reflects the present necessity of working even marginal deposits. Practically no tin is produced in the United States, but we rank first as a user, the can companies estimating that we use about 10 billion tin cans each year.

The term "tin can" does not mean that the can is made from tin; the very thin tin coating on the steel seldom amounts to over 2 per cent, by weight, of the can. Many tin cans today are coated with an organic composition which also is valuable as a protecting agent; the composition of some of these lacquers, etc., is a trade secret.

The opportune perfecting of an electrolytic method for depositing extremely thin yet perfect coatings of tin was all that prevented the wartime shortage of tin from being disastrous. It made possible the saving of two-thirds of the tin formerly used in the hot-dip process. The trouble with early attempts to electroplate tin was the annoying fact that a very thin coat of tin consisted of separate crystals of tin, with bare steel between them. The saving invention used the idea of passing the coated tin through a high-frequency alternating electric field ("electronic heating") which melted the tin crystals just long enough to permit them to flow out and coalesce before they solidified again.

Curiously, tin gives better protection to the inside of a can of tomatoes or fruit than it does to the outside. The outside protection is merely inert coating protection, whereas the inside protection is galvanic. This is because tin, although less active than iron when in contact with neutral or alkaline solutions, is more active than iron when in contact with acid. A trace of acid is added to many neutral foods when they are canned in order to take advantage of this fact.

Tin is a constituent of many alloys such as solder, pewter, bronze, and bearing metal. The quantity used in tin foil is of minor importance. Since tin can be recovered from tin scrap with chlorine gas, the exportation of tin scrap has been prohibited unless a special license is obtained. Many pieces of laboratory apparatus are made of copper coated with tin; "block tin" is frequently used for distilled water pipes.

FIG. 31.9. Lead-burner making up special hard-lead bend for acid lines. (Courtesy, Pulp Division, Weyerhaeuser Timber Co., Everett, Washington, and the Lead Industries Association.)

Lead. One of the greatest single demands for metallic lead is for the plumbing industry, because lead is strong enough to withstand the pressure of water in pipes and yet the pipes are flexible. In spite of its weight and its cost, the roofs of many buildings are coated with lead. Istanbul is called "the city of lead domes." The lead cover on the roof of the famous St. Sophia was put on between 532 and 537 A.D. and is still in good condition. Many European buildings have lead roofs. Lead was used for the roofs of the National Cathedral in Washington, D. C., the Chapel at Princeton University, and the Henry Ford Museum at Dearborn, Michigan. The United

States consumes nearly half of the world's lead and used to produce a third of it. Exhaustion of our richest veins during the war has reduced our output to a quarter of the world's supply and produced a serious shortage of lead. Most automobile storage batteries have lead plates. Both underground and suspended telephone cables are made waterproof by being covered with a sheath of lead or lead alloy. The lead chamber process for manufacturing sulfuric acid has already been discussed. Lead is used in chemistry laboratories in traps for sinks, the construction of tanks, etc.

FIG. 31.10. Lead roofs on St. Sophia, Istanbul, which were installed between 532 and 537 A.D. (Courtesy, Lead Industries Association.)

COMPOUNDS OF CADMIUM

Cadmium is divalent in its compounds. Only the sulfide and hydroxide are of any importance at the present time.

Cadmium Sulfide

Although some CdS is found in nature, most of it is produced by the precipitation of the Cd^{++} ion with H_2S in a slightly acid solution. It is bright yellow and is known to artists as "cadmium yellow." Although quite expensive, it is an excellent paint pigment because hydrogen sulfide will not change its color and it is not attacked by atmospheric oxygen.

Cadmium Hydroxide

The addition of NaOH to soluble $Cd(NO_3)_2$ produces a white gelatinous precipitate of $Cd(OH)_2$ which is easily decomposed with heat to brown cadmium oxide, CdO. The hydroxide is soluble in acids but is not amphoteric and hence does not dissolve in an excess of NaOH or KOH. It is soluble in an excess of ammonium hydroxide, but this is due to the formation of the complex cadmium-ammonia ion.

$$\underline{Cd(OH)_2} + 4\ NH_4OH \longrightarrow Cd(NH_3)_4{}^{++} + 2\ OH^- + 4\ H_2O$$

Cadmium forms many complex salts; the *cyanide*, $K_2Cd(CN)_4$, is used in electroplating.

COMPOUNDS OF ZINC

On the basis of quantities produced, the compounds of zinc are not as important as the metal. Its compounds are divalent. Zinc is usually metallic in nature, but amphoterism is shown by the fact that zinc hydroxide dissolves in NaOH to form sodium zincate, Na_2ZnO_2.

$$\underline{Zn(OH)_2} + 2\ Na^+ + 2\ OH^- \longrightarrow 2\ Na^+ + ZnO_2{}^{--} + 2\ H_2O$$

This compound is also formed when zinc reacts with sodium hydroxide. Zinc, like all the other metals discussed in this chapter, is poisonous; people are frequently poisoned by eating food that has been stored in zinc containers. Water pipes cannot be galvanized in some localities because of the corrosive action of the water.

Zinc Hydroxide and Zinc Oxide

If either sodium hydroxide or ammonium hydroxide is added to a soluble zinc salt, such as zinc nitrate, a white gelatinous precipitate is formed. An excess of either reagent dissolves the precipitate. NH_4OH in excess forms the soluble complex $Zn(NH_3)_4{}^{++}$ ion. Only about 4 mg. of zinc hydroxide dissolve per liter of water. The small quantity that is in solution is in equilibrium with the solid and with the ions H^+, $ZnO_2{}^{--}$, Zn^{++}, and OH^- on account of its reactions with water (ionization and hydrolysis, respectively), as shown by the following equations:

$$2\ H_3O^+ + Zn(OH)_4{}^{--} \rightleftarrows Zn(H_2O)_2(OH)_2 + 2\ H_2O \rightleftarrows Zn(H_2O)_4{}^{++} + 2\ OH^-$$
$$\updownarrow$$
$$\underline{Zn(H_2O)_2(OH)_2}$$

(The conventional formulas can be obtained from each of those in the equation by subtracting H_2O as many times as necessary.) Furthermore, if ammonium hydroxide is present, the NH_3 which is always in equilibrium with it will enter into the following equilibrium reaction with the zinc ion:

$$Zn(H_2O)_4^{++} + 4\ NH_3 \rightleftarrows Zn(NH_3)_4^{++} + 4\ H_2O$$

HCl, NH_4OH, and NaOH dissolve $Zn(OH)_2$. How does each of these compounds shift the equilibria shown above?

Heating zinc hydroxide converts it into the white insoluble zinc oxide, ZnO. The oxide is produced commercially by igniting the basic carbonate and by directly uniting zinc and oxygen. Zinc oxide has a yellow tinge when hot.

The importance of zinc as a paint pigment is indicated by the fact that in a typical year 60,000 tons of leaded zinc oxide, 150,000 tons of lithopone, (page 527), and 110,000 tons of zinc oxide were produced in the United States. Very pure zinc oxide is known to artists as "Chinese white"; the commercial quality is called "zinc white." Its use is recommended whenever the paint may come in contact with H_2S, since ZnS is also white. However, because its covering power is only fair, ZnO is often used only in the final coat of paint. Manufacturers of zinc oxide recommend its use as a filler in all rubber goods, linoleum, oilcloth, celluloid, etc.; tons are used as fillers in automobile tires and in white rubber goods. It is used in enamels and glazes, and in the making of white glass and white adhesive tape.

Zinc Chloride

$ZnCl_2$ can be prepared by the direct union of the elements or by the action of HCl on Zn, ZnO, $ZnCO_3$, or $Zn(OH)_2$. Its melting point is 365° C. The anhydrous salt is deliquescent and the water solution is acid to litmus. It might be expected that only ZnO would result when a solution of $ZnCl_2$ is evaporated, on account of the escape of HCl (as in the case of $AlCl_3$, page 532, and $MgCl_2$, page 518). Here, however, a new factor intervenes. The zinc ion coordinates readily with the chloride ion (page 219). As evaporation brings the $ZnCl_2$ solution toward the concentration at which the Cl^- ions will begin to take a few protons from the $Zn(H_2O)_4^{++}$ ions (or the H_3O^+ ions in equilibrium with them by hydrolysis), the Cl^- ions are already displacing H_2O molecules from the zinc ion, forming $Zn(H_2O)_3Cl^+$, etc. This decreases the Cl^- concentration and prevents the formation of any molecules of HCl. Thus:

$$Zn(H_2O)_4^{++} + 2\ Cl^- \xrightarrow{\Delta} Zn(H_2O)_3Cl^+ + Cl^- + \overline{H_2O}$$
$$\downarrow \Delta$$
$$Zn(H_2O)_2Cl_2 + \overline{H_2O}$$
$$\downarrow \Delta\ \text{(eventually)}$$
$$ZnCl_2 + \overline{2\ H_2O}$$

Water continues to evaporate even after the composition of the solution averages $Zn(H_2O)_2Cl_2$, until a melt of the anhydrous salt remains; this is cast into sticks.

A quick-setting cement of the basic chloride is made by mixing $ZnCl_2$ and ZnO with water. The chloride is used to "dissolve" cellulose; a gelatinous material is formed which can be molded into various shapes and forced through openings to make threads of cellulose. The $ZnCl_2$ is then washed out and the cellulose is regenerated. $ZnCl_2$ competes with creosote and other coal-tar products as a wood preservative, for it forms a protective surface film of cellulose-zinc chloride. $ZnCl_2$ is toxic to plant and animal life. Over 50,000 tons of $ZnCl_2$ were produced in the United States in 1943. Its percentage consumption in industry in an earlier year was as follows: soldering flux, 40; wood preserving, 24; dry-cell batteries, 14; vulcanized fiber, 11; oil refining, 4; others, 7. Recently, however, some firms have maintained secrecy regarding their consumption of $ZnCl_2$.

Zinc Sulfate

Most of the $ZnSO_4$ on the market is produced by carefully roasting or oxidizing zinc sulfide. If a water solution of $ZnSO_4$ is evaporated, crystals of $ZnSO_4 \cdot 7\,H_2O$ form; these are efflorescent in the air. The salt is known to the trade as white vitriol. Its importance in the manufacture of lithopone has already been mentioned; it is also used in the rayon industry, in ore flotation, as mordants, in the manufacture of glue, in electrogalvanizing, in preserving animal hides, and (in dilute solutions) as an antiseptic and astringent. Around 20,000 tons of the salt are produced annually.

Zinc Sulfide

Pure white ZnS is prepared by bringing together Zn^{++} and S^{--} ions in an alkaline solution—for example, adding $(NH_4)_2S$ to a soluble zinc salt. Zinc sulfide is soluble in even the low concentration of acid produced by the metathesis reactions of many zinc salts and hydrogen sulfide. The large amount of ZnS used in the paint industry is produced directly from the ores.

Zinc sulfide is added to lithopone in considerable quantities to produce a high-strength product.

Zinc Stearate

Zinc stearate is a popular antiseptic powder which is used to alleviate chafing.

COMPOUNDS OF MERCURY

Mercury compounds may be either monovalent or divalent. Mercury vapors and most of its salts are poisonous; therefore great precaution is necessary in working with the element and its compounds.

The use of mercury in medicine dates back at least to the time of Buddha (about 500 B.C.). As much as two pounds of liquid mercury were taken internally at one time to remove an intestinal obstruction. Mercury rubs were used in the 13th century for leprosy, scabies, cancer, and gout, and mercury compounds were applied externally in the treatment of syphilis in the 15th century. With the development of organic chemistry during the past fifty years, many new mercury compounds have been prepared. Some are taken internally, others are injected into the muscle tissue, and still others are applied externally.

Oxides and Hydroxides

Oxides of mercury are prepared by treating soluble salts with an alkali. Hg_2O is so unstable that HgO and mercury are formed when NaOH is added to $HgNO_3$.

$$Hg_2O \longrightarrow Hg + HgO$$

Yellow mercuric oxide, HgO, which is composed of small crystals, is obtained by adding NaOH to a solution of $Hg(NO_3)_2$. When heated, it changes to the common and less active red oxide. Mercuric oxide may also be obtained by heating $Hg(NO_3)_2$ or by directly uniting mercury and oxygen. HgO is used for diluting pigments used on porcelain and also for anti-fouling paints applied to the bottoms of ships. The barnacles are killed by the mercuric chloride or corrosive sublimate which forms when HgO comes in contact with salt water. The hydroxides are unstable.

Sulfur Compounds

The most important mercury sulfur compound is vermilion red, or artificial *mercuric sulfide*, HgS, which is made by heating mercury and sulfur together and is used as a pigment in paints, sealing wax, and even lipstick. (Basic lead chromate and artificial antimony sulfide compete with it.) Black mercuric sulfide is obtained by bubbling H_2S gas into a solution of a soluble mercuric salt. *Mercuric sulfide* is insoluble in acids and bases but soluble in alkaline sulfides.

$$2\ Na^+ + S^{--} + \underline{HgS} \longrightarrow 2\ Na^+ + HgS_2^{--}$$

Mercurous sulfide, Hg_2S, is very unstable and decomposes into mercury and HgS. *Mercuric sulfate*, which is prepared by dissolving mercury in hot concentrated sulfuric acid, is used in the preparation of HgCl and $HgCl_2$.

Nitrogen Compounds

Cold dilute nitric acid attacks mercury slowly and forms *mercurous nitrate*, $HgNO_3$. It is best prepared in an excess of mercury, because once the salt is formed, it is oxidized by the air to the mercuric state. $HgNO_3$ is the only important soluble mercurous salt. *Mercuric nitrate*, $Hg(NO_3)_2$, is usually prepared by boiling mercury in an excess of hot concentrated nitric acid. Both the mercurous and the mercuric salts hydrolyze readily, forming insoluble basic salts such as $Hg(NO_3)_2 \cdot HgO$.

Mercuric cyanide, $Hg(CN)_2$, is of interest because it liberates cyanogen on decomposing (page 411).

$$Hg(CN)_2 \longrightarrow Hg + (CN)_2$$

Insoluble *mercuric thiocyanate*, $Hg(CNS)_2$, is obtained by reacting $HgCl_2$ with KCNS. If the solid is mixed with a substance like dextrin, pressed into pellets, and ignited, it swells and looks like a snake ("Pharaoh's Serpents").

Mercury fulminate, $Hg(OCN)_2$, the most important and most dangerous nitrogen-mercury compound, is obtained as a white precipitate when mercury, an excess of nitric acid, and ethyl alcohol are warmed together. (The mercury dissolves in the nitric acid.) It is used in percussion caps to detonate dynamite or ignite smokeless powder in cartridges and shells, etc. Lead azide, $Pb(N_3)_2$, is used as a substitute for mercury fulminate.

Halogen Compounds

The most important mercury compounds are the two chlorides, mercuric chloride (corrosive sublimate), $HgCl_2$, and mercurous chloride (calomel), Hg_2Cl_2.

Mercuric chloride can be prepared by the direct union of chlorine and mercury or by distillation from a mixture of mercuric sulfate and salt.

$$HgSO_4 + 2\ NaCl \xrightarrow{\Delta} Na_2SO_4 + \overline{HgCl_2}$$

It melts at 277° C. The name "corrosive sublimate" is derived from the fact that it sublimes readily and is extremely corrosive and toxic; about 0.2 g. taken internally is fatal. A water solution of the salt is a poor conductor of electricity. This is because of the large extent to which chloride ions displace water molecules from the mercuric ion. The uncharged complex, $Hg(H_2O)_2Cl_2$, contains 99 per cent of the chloride ions. The mercuric ion is a fair oxidizing agent and hence is easily reduced. A water solution of $HgCl_2$ is an excellent germicide, a dilute solution (1:1000) being used by bacteriologists and surgeons as a hand wash after contact with pathogenic organisms. The salt is used as a fixing agent in photography, in preserving wood, and in printing calico; biologists use it to preserve anatomical specimens.

Mercurous chloride, or calomel, can be prepared in the laboratory as a white precipitate by adding a soluble chloride to mercurous nitrate.

$$2\ Na^+ + 2\ Cl^- + Hg_2^{++} + 2\ NO_3^- \longrightarrow \underline{Hg_2Cl_2} + 2\ Na^+ + 2\ NO_3^-$$

(The fact that the mercurous ion is diatomic is no more peculiar than the fact that a Group II element should have a monovalent ion at all. Its electronic formula appears to be $(Hg:Hg)^{++}$. See the following section.) Mercurous chloride is prepared commercially by distilling a mixture of mercuric chloride and mercury.

$$HgCl_2 + Hg \xrightarrow{\Delta} Hg_2Cl_2$$

It is also frequently prepared by heating NaCl, $HgSO_4$, and Hg together. The salt decomposes easily in sunlight to corrosive sublimate; for this reason it is kept in dark bottles.

$$2\ Hg_2Cl_2 \longrightarrow HgCl_2 + Hg$$

Mercurous chloride is used medicinally in treating cirrhosis and as a purgative and diuretic. Calomel is almost insoluble in the stomach and large intestine, but is attacked by the alkaline pancreatic juice in the small intestine. The mercuric ion destroys the cells of the kidneys. The white of an egg is an antidote for mercuric poisoning because the Hg^{++} ion coagulates protein.

All the other halogen salts are known, but only *mercuric iodide* is of any importance. This salt exists in two insoluble forms, red and yellow. It dissolves in an excess of KI to form the complex K_2HgI_4. A solution of K_2HgI_4 in KOH which is called Nessler's reagent (page 400) reacts with ammonia to form a highly colored colloidal solution used in detecting small amounts of ammonia quantitatively.

Organic Compounds

Within recent years many organic mercury compounds have been produced for medicinal or therapeutic use. Some of the more common ones are mercurochrome, flumerin, mercuric benzoate, mercuric salicylate, afridol, and phenyl mercuric nitrate. The latter is a strong germicide that is not particularly toxic because the mercury does not ionize to form free Hg^{++} ions. In its organic compounds mercury is covalently bound, like any non-metal; it usually shows a covalence of two. The ability to form covalent compounds is present throughout the series Be, Mg, Zn, Cd, Hg, though it is not shown by Ca, Sr, Ba, and Ra. This is one of the reasons for saying that Be and Mg might have been discussed with the subgroup elements of this family instead of with the alkaline earth metals. This ability to form covalent bonds, like the similar ability to form complex ions, is due to the high field strength at the surface of the ions. In the case of Be and Mg the field is purely electrical but is concentrated on account of the small size of the ions; in the case of the others, where the electrical field strength is diminished by the larger size, the ions have the magnetic field characteristic of ions which have more than 8 electrons in the outer layer.

COMPOUNDS OF TIN

Tin forms both divalent and tetravalent compounds and there are examples of amphoterism in each group. The divalent tin ion is slightly more metallic than Sn^{++++}. The compounds of tin are not nearly as important as the metal itself; the stannous compounds are good reducing agents and the stannic compounds are fair oxidizing agents.

Hydroxides and Oxides

The first problem that arises in connection with tin compounds is to find some that are soluble in water, and the second is to keep them in solution. Since tin is attacked by HCl, HNO_3, and NaOH, the products of these reactions are usually used to make other compounds.

$$Sn + 2\ H^+ + 2\ Cl^- \longrightarrow Sn^{++} + 2\ Cl^- + \overline{H_2}$$

$$Sn + 4\ H^+ + 4\ NO_3^- \longrightarrow H_2SnO_3 + 4\ \overline{NO_2} + H_2O$$
(concentrated)
$$\longrightarrow SnO_2 + H_2O$$

$$Sn + 2\ Na^+ + 2\ OH^- \longrightarrow 2\ Na^+ + SnO_2^{--} + \overline{H_2}$$

or $\quad Sn^{++} + 2\ \overline{Cl^-} + 2\ Na^+ + 2\ OH^- \longrightarrow Sn(OH)_2 + 2\ Na^+ + 2\ Cl^-$

$$Sn(OH)_2 + 2\ Na^+ + 2\ OH^- \longrightarrow 2\ Na^+ + SnO_2^{--} + 2\ H_2O$$

Stannous hydroxide is obtained as a white gelatinous precipitate by adding KOH or NaOH to a solution of $SnCl_2$. This hydroxide has four interesting properties: it turns black when heated, is soluble in both acids and alkalis, and is a good reducing agent in an alkaline solution. This last property is used in detecting the bismuth ion (page 451). Black stannous oxide is easily oxidized to stannic oxide.

Stannic hydroxide or *stannic acid* ($Sn(OH)_4$, H_4SnO_4, or H_2SnO_3), is prepared by the action of hot concentrated nitric acid on tin. Stannic acid has different forms, depending upon the degree of hydration and particle size; in other words, the composition of the precipitate depends upon the method of its preparation. One form (alpha form) is soluble in mineral acids and alkalis and the other (beta form) is difficult to dissolve. Because of the amphoteric nature of tin (check its position relative to the diagonal line across the periodic table), the insoluble hydroxide should be somewhat soluble in both acids and bases.

$$Sn(OH)_4 + 4\ H^+ + 4\ Cl^- \longrightarrow SnCl_4 + 4\ H_2O$$
$$H_2SnO_3 + 2\ Na^+ + 2\ OH^- \longrightarrow 2\ Na^+ + SnO_3^{--} + 2\ H_2O$$

In weighting and fireproofing silk with SnO_2 the cloth is first soaked in a solution of Na_2SnO_3 and then dried. If it were now treated with hydrochloric acid, the gelatinous precipitate of stannic hydroxide that would form on the surface would prevent the penetration of HCl to the inside of the fiber until the Sn(OH)$_4$ had been dissolved to SnCl$_4$ by the increasing concentration of acid. This difficulty is avoided, ingeniously, by using an acid too weak to react with the stannate ion at room temperature, namely, the ammonium ion. The cloth is soaked in a solution of (NH$_4$)$_2$SO$_4$; in the absence of reaction the NH$_4^+$ ions penetrate easily to every place where SnO$_3^{--}$ ions are. Then, on heating, the proton transfer takes place, the stannic acid is dehydrated, and the residual ammonia is driven off. The sodium sulfate is washed out of the cloth, leaving the insoluble stannic oxide.

$$2\ Na^+ + SnO_3^{--} + 2\ NH_4^+ + SO_4^{--} \longrightarrow \underline{H_2SnO_3} + 2\ \overline{NH_3} + 2\ Na^+ + SO_4^{--}$$
$$\hookrightarrow \underline{SnO_2} + \overline{H_2O}$$

Stannic oxide is an important mordant and several patents have been taken out for ways of depositing it on cloth. A rough check on the amount of SnO$_2$ in silk is made by weighing the piece of cloth, burning it, and weighing the ash; the SnO$_2$ usually makes up more than 50 per cent of the total weight. The stannates are mild oxidizing agents.

Stannic oxide is obtained by dehydrating the hydroxide and by burning tin. When it is heated, the white oxide turns yellow but becomes white again on cooling. SnO$_2$ is the best material known for making opaque glaze or glass. About 1000 tons of stannic oxide are used yearly in the United States; its most important use is in the manufacture of porcelain.

Halogen Compounds

The only important halogen compounds are stannous chloride, SnCl$_2$, and stannic chloride, SnCl$_4$. *Stannous chloride* is a solid salt. It is a good reducing agent and is oxidized by the oxygen of the air to a mixture of the basic chloride and stannic chloride.

$$6\ SnCl_2 + \overline{O_2} + 2\ H_2O \longrightarrow 4\ Sn\!\!-\!\!Cl\ \overset{OH}{\diagup} + 2\ SnCl_4$$

A water solution of SnCl$_2$ hydrolyzes to form insoluble stannous hydroxychloride. Thus a clear solution of SnCl$_2$ is obtained only if free HCl is present. A few pieces of metallic tin are put in the bottom of bottles of SnCl$_2$ solution to keep the solution in the stannous state. SnCl$_2$ is used as a reducing agent in organic chemistry and in the dyeing of cloth.

Stannic chloride was first obtained by distilling a mixture of tin and corrosive sublimate.

$$Sn + 2\ HgCl_2 \xrightarrow{\Delta} 2\ Hg + \overline{SnCl_4}$$

It is prepared commercially by passing chlorine gas over tin scrap. It can be made by the direct union of chlorine and stannous chloride. The pure

ZINC, CADMIUM, MERCURY, TIN, AND LEAD

substance is a liquid at room temperature, boils at 114° C. and fumes strongly in moist air.

$$SnCl_4 + 3\ H_2O \longrightarrow 4\ \overline{HCl} + H_2SnO_3$$
$$\hookrightarrow H_2O + \underline{SnO_2}$$

$SnCl_4$ is evidently not a salt but a covalently bound compound. It should not be surprising that tin behaves more like a non-metal in its higher valence than in its lower valence. $SnCl_4$ dissolves chlorine, iodine, and phosphorus, and is miscible with liquid bromine and carbon disulfide. However, even tetravalent tin has some metallic properties, as is shown by the formation of the crystalline pentahydrate, $SnCl_4 \cdot 5\ H_2O$. This compound, used as a mordant in dyeing, can be dissolved in a limited amount of water without being completely hydrolyzed.

$$SnCl_4 + H_2O \rightleftarrows Sn(H_2O)Cl_3^+ + Cl^-$$
$$+$$
$$H_2O \rightleftarrows Sn(OH)Cl_3 + H_3O^+$$
$$\hookrightarrow Sn(H_2O)_2Cl_2^{++} + Cl^- \qquad \text{etc.}$$

On the addition of a little more water, $Sn(OH)_4$ precipitates.

Sulfur Compounds

Tin dissolves slowly in dilute sulfuric acid, with the liberation of hydrogen and the formation of stannous sulfate. With concentrated sulfuric acid it forms stannic sulfate.

Stannous sulfide is a dark brown precipitate that appears when H_2S is bubbled into a solution of a stannous salt. Yellow *stannic sulfide* is precipitated from solutions of stannic salts.

Thiosalts similar to those of antimony and arsenic are produced by the action of alkaline sulfides on tin sulfides.

$$\underline{SnS} + 2\ NH_4^+ + S_2^{--}\ \text{(an oxidizing agent)} \longrightarrow 2\ NH_4^+ + SnS_3^{--}$$
$$\underline{SnS_2} + 2\ NH_4^+ + S^{--} \longrightarrow 2\ NH_4^+ + SnS_3^{--}$$

Stannic sulfide is easily precipitated by acidifying a solution of an alkali (or ammonium) thiostannate.

$$2\ NH_4^+ + SnS_3^{--} + 2\ H^+ + 2\ Cl^- \longrightarrow \underline{SnS_2} + 2\ Na^+ + 2\ Cl^- + \overline{H_2S}$$

COMPOUNDS OF LEAD

The common valences of lead are two and four, the divalent compounds being the more important. Lead shows amphoterism by forming both plumbites and plumbates.

Hydroxide and Oxides of Lead

Lead hydroxide may be obtained by carefully adding a base to a soluble lead salt. $Pb(OH)_2$ is insoluble and loses water at 130° C. The pure hydroxide is of no commercial importance. There are several oxides of lead:

Pb_2O, lead suboxide, black
PbO, lead monoxide (litharge), yellow-red
Pb_2O_3, lead trioxide, yellowish-red
PbO_2, lead dioxide, brown
Pb_3O_4, lead tetroxide, minium or red lead

The first and third of these are unimportant.

Lead monoxide or *litharge* is made commercially by heating pig lead with air in special furnaces. It is insoluble in water, but is soluble in nitric acid and sodium hydroxide.

$$\underline{PbO} + 2\ Na^+ + 2\ OH^- \longrightarrow 2\ Na^+ + PbO_2^{--} + H_2O$$

Lead glass is made by melting PbO, SiO_2, and K_2O together. Litharge is used as an accelerator in the manufacture of rubber, as a dryer in varnishes, and in assaying gold and silver. For assays, powdered litharge and charcoal are mixed with the crushed ore and the mixture is heated. The lead formed by the reducing action of carbon on PbO alloys with gold and silver and the molten mixture is poured off. When the lead is oxidized and removed, pure gold and silver remain. Lead oxide is used in glazes in the pottery industry. Litharge is used in the manufacture of lead storage batteries, and also in making certain insecticides, chrome pigments, and "Doctor solution." "Doctor solution," or sodium plumbite, Na_2PbO_2, is used in petroleum refining to remove complex organic sulfur compounds by precipitating the sulfur as insoluble lead sulfide. Na_2PbO_2 is made by agitating a solution of caustic soda and litharge at 30° C. with compressed air.

Lead dioxide is obtained by heating red lead with concentrated nitric acid, or PbO with an alkaline hypochlorite solution.

$$\underline{Pb_3O_4} + 4\ H^+ + 4\ NO_3^- \longrightarrow 2\ Pb^{++} + 4\ NO_3^- + \underline{PbO_2} + 2\ H_2O$$
$$\underline{PbO} + Na^+ + ClO^- \longrightarrow \underline{PbO_2} + Na^+ + Cl^-$$

(No oxidation or reduction takes place in the first of these equations, Pb_3O_4 contains both di- and tetravalent lead.) Lead dioxide always forms when a lead storage battery is being charged. Very pure PbO_2 can be obtained by electrolyzing a lead salt between platinum electrodes; the PbO_2 collects at the anode. That the dioxide is a powerful oxidizing agent is shown by the fact that it liberates chlorine from chlorides and oxidizes Mn^{++} to the MnO_4^- ion.

$$2\ Mn^{++} + 2\ SO_4^{--} + 5\ \underline{PbO_2} + 4\ H^+ + 4\ NO_3^- \longrightarrow$$
$$3\ \underline{Pb^{++}} + 2\ MnO_4^- + 4\ NO_3^- + 2\ \underline{PbSO_4} + 2\ H_2O$$
$$\text{purple}$$

The dioxide is used on the striking surface of safety-match boxes.

Red lead, Pb_3O_4, is prepared by roasting litharge at 400° C. If heated to 500°, it decomposes.

$$2\ Pb_3O_4 \rightleftarrows 6\ PbO + \overline{O_2}$$

Its formula may be written $PbO_2 \cdot 2\ PbO$; X-ray examination of its crystal structure shows that each layer of PbO_2 is sandwiched in between two layers having the litharge structure. In a prewar year 20,000 tons were used in the manufacture of storage batteries, and 12,000 tons in making paints. Red lead paint is used as a rust-preventing coating on structural steel. Minium was the red pigment commonly used for illumination in old manuscripts. A "miniature" was originally a painting done with minium; the meaning, small size, came later, by association.

For a discussion of the oxides of lead and the storage battery, refer to page 256.

Halogen Compounds

The divalent lead halides are salts, and are much more soluble in hot than cold water. Thus if a hot saturated solution of PbI_2 is cooled, beautiful yellow crystals of lead iodide precipitate. Lead tetrachloride is a liquid that freezes at $-15°C$. It loses chlorine just as $MnCl_4$ does, and it decomposes explosively at 105° C.

Sulfur Compounds

Both black lead sulfide and white lead sulfate are insoluble in water. If lead sulfide is carefully roasted, $PbSO_4$ will form. Lead sulfate can be prepared in the laboratory by oxidizing PbS with hydrogen peroxide.

$$\underline{PbS} + 4\ H_2O_2 \longrightarrow \underline{PbSO_4} + 4\ H_2O$$
$$\text{black} \qquad\qquad\qquad\quad \text{white}$$

The addition of sulfuric acid to any soluble lead salt produces lead sulfate. The basic sulfate is used as a paint pigment. Lead is found in nature as the lead sulfide. The sulfide is easily prepared in the laboratory by adding H_2S to a soluble lead salt; it can also be prepared by the direct union of lead and sulfur. Natural PbS is almost insoluble in all acids, but will dissolve slowly in concentrated HCl or HNO_3.

Other Compounds

Lead acetate is prepared commercially by dissolving either litharge or lead carbonate in hot dilute acetic acid; when the solution cools, crystals of the colorless trihydrate, $Pb(C_2H_3O_2)_2 \cdot 3\ H_2O$, form. It is known as "sugar of lead" because of its sweet taste; but like other soluble lead salts, it is poisonous. It is used in the manufacture of other lead compounds and as a mordant in dyeing. Paper soaked in a solution of the salt is used as a test for hydrogen sulfide, because traces of the gas turn the paper black.

Lead arsenate, $Pb_3(AsO_4)_2$, is a useful and dependable insecticide. It precipitates from the reaction of arsenic acid and litharge in the presence of acetic or nitric acid as a catalyst. It can also be prepared by adding lead acetate to sodium arsenate. The basic and dibasic arsenates are used as insecticides.

Lead nitrate, $Pb(NO_3)_2$, is obtained by dissolving lead in nitric acid. The white water-soluble crystals are used in preparing other lead compounds, as a mordant, as an oxidizing agent in matches, and as a source of nitrogen dioxide in the laboratory.

$$2\ Pb(NO_3)_2 \xrightarrow{\Delta} 2\ PbO + 4\ NO_2 + O_2$$

Lead tetraethyl, $(C_2H_5)_4Pb$, is a liquid which boils at 202° C. and is miscible with organic solvents such as petroleum. Some years ago it was discovered that adding small quantities of the liquid to gasoline raised the octane rating of the fuel and decreased the knocking that occurred when the fuel was burned in motors. Its use has made possible the operation of high-compression motors, thereby increasing efficiency and indirectly preserving our supply of crude petroleum. When lead tetraethyl burns in a motor the lead combines with the bromine of ethylene dibromide (page 673) and is volatilized as $PbBr_2$. Hundreds of tests show that the concentration of fumes from this source is not sufficiently high to be toxic to garage mechanics; carbon monoxide is a far greater hazard.

$Pb(C_2H_5)_4$ can be prepared by the action of ethyl halides on a lead-sodium alloy.

$$4\ C_2H_5Cl + 4\ NaPb \xrightarrow[\text{catalyst}]{\text{Zn}} Pb(C_2H_5)_4 + 4\ NaCl + 3\ Pb$$
$$\text{(alloy)} \qquad\qquad\qquad \text{(liquid)}$$

Lead Paints

Paint has been used for centuries both for its beauty and for the protection it gives to a surface. A good paint should have a high covering capacity, adhere firmly to the surface for a long time, and not discolor. Manufacturers of paint list the constituents under the heading of *pigment, vehicle, dryer, thinner,* and *filler*. The choice of *pigment* depends upon the atmospheric conditions to which the paint is to be exposed. A typical white paint might contain white lead, lithopone, or titanium dioxide as the pigment. The *vehicle* should dry rapidly and form a tenacious film; its drying involves its oxidation and polymerization from a liquid to a solid compound. Linseed oil is the most common vehicle, although tung and other oils are also used. Metal oxides, such as manganese, cobalt, and nickel, are used as *dryers* because they react with the oil to form metallic soaps which catalyze the drying process. The most popular *thinner* is turpentine; it evaporates and leaves a more viscous film of vehicle and pigment. Any cheap inert substance can be used as a *filler*, among the more common being limestone, gypsum, kaolin, powdered silica, barium sulfate, and asbestine. The latter, a fibrous magnesium silicate, serves a useful purpose in preventing the pigment from settling out.

Among the lead pigments are:

Red lead (and orange mineral, another form of red lead)
Basic lead carbonate (white lead)
Sublimed blue lead (mixture of $PbSO_4$, $PbSO_3$, PbS, ZnO, and carbon)
Sublimed white lead (mixture of $PbSO_4$, PbO, and ZnO)
Lead chromate
Basic lead chromate

Until recently, most of the white lead paint was made by the old "Dutch process." This process requires about 90 days for the preparation of a single batch of white lead. Thin perforated disks or buckles of metallic lead 6 to 8 inches in diameter are placed in earthenware pots which are so constructed that the buckles are kept a few inches from the bottom of the pots; and dilute acetic acid is then poured in. Spent tanbark is stacked between the pots; as it ferments, heat and carbon dioxide are liberated. The heat vaporizes the acetic acid; and this, the atmospheric oxygen, and the CO_2 all react with the lead in a complicated series of reactions whose exact nature is unknown. A complex with the acetate ion appears to play an intermediate role. The final product can be formulated $(PbCO_3)_2 \cdot Pb(OH)_2$.

The newer paint processes are modifications of the Dutch process. For example, the same reactions are used in the Carter process, but only two weeks are required. Powdered lead is placed in large rotating wooden cylinders and sprinkled with acetic acid; hot air and carbon dioxide are forced through the cylinders. In the Euston process, basic lead acetate is first made by dissolving lead in a solution of lead acetate. Electrolytic white lead is manufactured in a diaphragm cell. Pb^{++} ions are liberated from a lead anode and kept in solution, while traversing the anode compartment, by the acetate ions which it contains. The cathode compartment contains sodium carbonate solution. As the Pb^{++} ions, migrating through the porous diaphragm, meet the CO_3^{--} and OH^- ions migrating in the opposite direction, basic lead carbonate is formed. The supply of hydroxyl ions, originally produced by hydrolysis of the carbonate, is maintained by the liberation of H^+ ions at the iron cathode.

Basic lead sulfate or *sublimed white lead* is made of $PbSO_4$, PbO, and ZnO (maximum 9 per cent). In one process the native mineral, galena, is oxidized. The pure sulfate can be obtained by atomizing molten lead in excess air and sulfur dioxide.

Sublimed blue lead gets its color from the lead sulfide and carbon which are present. It is used in painting steel, for it has excellent covering power and is effective in preventing the formation of rust.

Red lead, a standard metal paint, is the second most widely used paint pigment.

Lead chromate pigments are available in many different colors. The normal chromate, $PbCrO_4$, is precipitated from a solution of a soluble lead salt by the addition of a soluble dichromate. It is brilliant yellow in color and is called medium chrome yellow. If a little sulfuric acid is added to the original mixture, some white $PbSO_4$ forms with the $PbCrO_4$ and the precipitate is known as lemon chrome yellow. Orange chrome yellow is prepared by adding NaOH to the dichromate solution. Prussian blue (ferric ferrocyanide) and lead chromate are precipitated together for the chrome green pigment. Basic lead chromate made from litharge is the orange paint which is the official color for airway markers all over the world; this paint was used for the final coat on the Golden Gate Bridge because of its brilliant, long-lasting color. Chinese scarlet is a basic lead chromate which is made from white lead.

QUALITATIVE TEST FOR THE IDENTIFICATION OF IONS OF CADMIUM, ZINC, MERCURY, TIN, AND LEAD

Tests for the presence of ions depend upon the formation of some substance that can be positively identified. Oxidation, reduction, solution, precipitation, color reactions, etc., are used.

At first, it might seem difficult to identify the ions present in a solution which might contain any one or several of these metals. However, it is really easy if we consider the reactions of these metallic ions. First of all, can Cd^{++}, Zn^{++}, Hg^+, Hg^{++}, Sn^{++}, Sn^{++++}, and Pb^{++} ions be present in one solution? The stannous ion is a good reducing agent and is oxidized by either Hg^+ or Hg^{++}.

$$Sn^{++} + 2\ Cl^- + 2\ HgCl_2 \longrightarrow Hg_2Cl_2 + Sn^{++++} + 4\ Cl^-$$
$$Sn^{++} + 2\ Cl^- + Hg_2Cl_2 \longrightarrow 2\ Hg + Sn^{++++} + 4\ Cl^-$$

Therefore the stannous ion is used as a test for Hg^+ or Hg^{++} and the mercury ions are used as a test for the stannous ion. Another test for the Hg^+ ion is to add ammonium hydroxide to the white insoluble HgCl.

$$Hg_2Cl_2 + 2\ NH_4OH \longrightarrow \underset{\text{black}}{Hg} + \underset{\text{white}}{HgNH_2Cl} + NH_4^+ + Cl^- + 2\ H_2O$$

Suppose that the solution contains only Cd^{++}, Hg^{++}, Zn^{++}, Sn^{++++}, and Pb^{++}. If sulfuric acid is added, insoluble $PbSO_4$ will form.

$$Pb^{++} + H^+ + HSO_4^- \longrightarrow \underline{PbSO_4} + 2\ H^+$$

(Other insoluble lead compounds are the black PbS and the yellow PbCrO$_4$. PbCl$_2$ is not very soluble in cold water but is quite soluble in hot water. PbS is soluble in HNO$_3$ and insoluble in (NH$_4$)$_2$S$_x$.)

If H$_2$S gas is bubbled into a slightly acid solution of the other four ions, CdS, HgS, and SnS$_2$ will precipitate and the filtrate will contain the Zn^{++} ion.

Zinc sulfide can be precipitated from a basic solution. Zn(OH)$_2$ is soluble in an excess of either NH$_4$OH or NaOH. If some zinc salt and a cobalt salt are heated on charcoal, a green mass forms which is known as "Rinmann's Green."

SnS$_2$ is the only one of the other three sulfides that is soluble in ammonium polysulfide, (NH$_4$)$_2$S$_x$.

$$\underline{SnS_2} + 2\ NH_4^+ + S_x^{--} \longrightarrow 2\ NH_4^+ + SnS_3^{--} + (x-1)\ \underline{S}$$

(SnS$_2$ is yellow. SnS is dark brown and insoluble in HCl.)

If the insoluble sulfides of cadmium and mercury are then dissolved in acid, and an excess of ammonium hydroxide is added, cadmium hydroxide, which first precipitates with the mercury, will redissolve as Cd(NH$_3$)$_4$(OH)$_2$. (CdS is yellow. HgS is black. If HgO is heated, free mercury is liberated.)

QUESTIONS AND PROBLEMS

1. Plot the melting points of the elements discussed in this chapter against their atomic weights, and also their boiling points against their atomic weights.
2. Write the formulas for compounds which will illustrate the different valences of these elements.
3. Outline one important metallurgical process for each element.
4. How could you distinguish between each of the following metals? Zn, Cd, Hg, Sn, and Pb.
5. Plot the price of these metals in cents per pound from 1915 to date.
6. If the supply of each of these metals in this country was completely exhausted today, what industries would be most affected? Can you suggest substitutes for each metal?
7. Zinc is above iron in the E.C.S. Explain the use of zinc as a protective agent for iron.
8. What volume of 2-molar MnSO$_4$ solution can be oxidized by 15 g. of PbO$_2$?
9. Ask a gasoline dealer what volume of ethylene dibromide is added to the gasoline he sells. Look up the density of C$_2$H$_4$Br$_2$ in a handbook. Calculate the weight of lead tetraethyl which should be added to the gasoline.

10. Ask a storage battery dealer for the weight of the lead pole in a battery he handles. For what length of time should this battery be capable of operating the headlights on a car? What other data do you need? What assumptions must you make to do the problem?
11. Can you devise and work a similar problem pertaining to a dry cell? (Assume that half the zinc is used.)
12. From a paint dealer find the percentage of lead compounds in a lead paint. Look up the present price of metallic lead per pound. Assume that the cost of the other constituents in the paint is negligible (this isn't true), and calculate the price per pound you pay for lead when you buy a gallon of paint.
13. Using any laboratory tests which you consider necessary, distinguish between the following pairs of substances:

$$\left.\begin{array}{l}PbS\\PbSO_4\end{array}\right\} \quad \left.\begin{array}{l}ZnS\\ZnSO_4\end{array}\right\} \quad \left.\begin{array}{l}Cd(NO_3)_2\\CdS\end{array}\right\} \quad \left.\begin{array}{l}SnO\\SnO_2\end{array}\right\} \quad \left.\begin{array}{l}HgO\\HgS\end{array}\right\} \quad \left.\begin{array}{l}PbSO_4\\ZnS\end{array}\right\}$$

$$\left.\begin{array}{l}CdS\\SnS\end{array}\right\} \quad \left.\begin{array}{l}PbCrO_4\\Cd(NO_3)_2\end{array}\right\} \quad \left.\begin{array}{l}Zn\\Sn\end{array}\right\} \quad \left.\begin{array}{l}Na_2SnO_2\\Na_2SnO_3\end{array}\right\}$$

14. Distinguish between the following terms:
    Galvanic cell—galvanize   Sherardize—metallize
    Electrolysis—electroplate   sulfide—polysulfide
    Amorphous—amphoteric   Minium—minimum

REFERENCES

Books

Tin. Mantell, Charles L. A.C.S. Monograph No. 51.
Bearing Metals. Corse, N. M. A.C.S. Monograph No. 53.
Metals and Metallic Compounds. Evans, U. R. Longmans, Green & Company.
Metallurgy of Zinc and Cadmium. Hofman, H. O. McGraw-Hill Book Company, Inc.
An Outline of Metallurgical Practice. Hayward, C. R. D. Van Nostrand Company, Inc.
Protective Metal Coatings. Rawdon, H. S. Chem. Catalogue Co.

Articles

"The Story of Zinc." Hanley, H. R. *J. Chem. Ed.* **11,** 111–113 (1934).
"Mercury Poisoning." Jordan, L., and Barrows, W. P. *Ind. and Eng. Chem.* **16,** 898–901 (1924).
"Protective Metal Coatings." Blum, William. *J. Chem. Ed.* **4,** 1477–1487 (1927).
"Mercury and Its Compounds in Ancient Times." Caley, E. R. *J. Chem. Ed.* **5,** 419–424 (1928).
"Testing House Paints for Durability." Browne, F. L. *J. Chem. Ed.* **10,** 529–538 (1933).

"Mercury Boilers—Heat Technology Turns to New Processes." *Chem. and Met. Eng.* **40**, 262–264 (1933).

"The Betts Lead Process in Practice." Fingland, J. J. *Trans. Electrochem. Soc.* **57**, 177–204 (1930).

"Cadmium. Production of Electrolytic Cadmium." Hanley, H. *Chem. and Met. Eng.* **23**, 1257–1264 (1920).

» 32 «

COPPER

The story of copper probably dates back at least to the latter part of the Stone Age when a hunter found a nugget of the metal. The oldest copper utensils in existence today are of hammered copper. The first copper ore was probably roasted accidentally when a fireplace was built near an outcropping of copper, and the first brass was also probably made accidentally from a mixture of copper ores and calamine, or $ZnCO_3$. The art was almost lost during the Dark Ages but was revived about 900 A.D.

The Egyptians knew how to hammer copper 8000 years ago. Thirteen hundred feet of 1.85-inch copper drain pipe was used in the temple of King Sa-hu-Re at Abusir, dating from about 2750 B.C. and uncovered in 1907 by the German archeologist, Ludwig Borchard. One small section of the pipe which was found intact showed on analysis 96.47 per cent Cu, 0.18 of 1 per cent Fe, 3.35 per cent S, and a trace of arsenic. The seam was not soldered but had apparently been hammered over a form.

During the last Ice Age in America, copper nuggets were broken from the exposed lodes in the Great Lakes regions and scattered southward over an area of more than 70,000 square miles. The Indians used copper for ornaments, breastplates, fishhooks, beads, and many other objects which could not be made from flint. The Indians are known to have moved boulders of nearly pure copper which weighed several tons; they are believed to have moved the three-ton Ontonagon copper boulder, now in the National Museum at Washington, D. C., about two miles.

Copper mining was recorded in Santiago province in Cuba in 1534. A mine was opened at Simsbury, Connecticut, in 1709, and one in New Jersey prior to 1719. An attempt to mine copper in the Lake Superior region in 1771 did not prove successful until 1846.

Discovery of the hardening effect of tin and the production of bronze was a great advantage in war. John Winthrop started a brass foundry in 1664,

COPPER

and pins were made from native copper at Lynn, Massachusetts, in 1666. Few people know that the Paul Revere famed for the celebrated midnight ride was an artisan in gold and silver and *the founder of the malleable copper industry in this country.* He discovered the secret process, hitherto known only in England, of making copper sufficiently malleable to be hammered hot. His foundry, started in the 1780's, had become a large enterprise by 1800, casting bronze bells and brass cannon, and manufacturing much-needed

Fig. 32.1. General view of the Anaconda Copper Plant at Anaconda, Montana. The smokestack is 585 feet high and 60 feet in diameter at the top. (Courtesy, Anaconda Copper Mining Co.)

bolts, spikes, and nails for shipbuilders. The government loaned him $10,000 with which to buy a water-power site at Canton, Massachusetts. Two years later, the Navy alone bought $93,000 worth of Revere copper and brass.

Occurrence

Besides occurring free in nature, copper in quantities sufficient to be mined is found as sulfides, oxides, carbonates, silicates, sulfates, oxychloride, sulfarsenides, and sulfantimonides. The sulfides are by far the most important, with the oxides, carbonates, sulfates, and silicates following in order. One of the finest exhibits of copper ores is the Gallagher collection at the Montana

School of Mines in Butte, Montana. The names and formulas of some of the copper ores are as follows:

Sulfides: chalcopyrite, $CuFeS_2$; bornite, $FeS \cdot (Cu_2S)_2 \cdot CuS$; covellite, CuS, chalcocite, Cu_2S.
Oxides: melaconite, CuO; cuprite, Cu_2O.
Carbonates: malachite, $CuCO_3 \cdot Cu(OH)_2$; azurite, $(CuCO_3)_2 \cdot Cu(OH)_2$.
Silicate: chrysocolla, $CuSiO_3 \cdot 2\ H_2O$.
Sulfates: chalcanthite, $CuSO_4 \cdot 5\ H_2O$; brochantite, $CuSO_4 \cdot (Cu(OH)_2)_3$.
Oxychloride: atacamite, $Cu_2Cl(OH)_3$.
Arsenic and antimony compounds: enargite, Cu_3AsS_4; tetrahedrite, $(Cu_2S)_3 \cdot Sb_2S_3$.

Fig. 32.2. Dumping an ore car. (Courtesy, Anaconda Copper Mining Co.)

Copper compounds instead of iron compounds serve as oxygen carriers in the blood of oysters and lobsters. Therefore these two sea foods provide one source of the traces of copper compounds which our bodies require.

Metallurgy

The list of important copper ores indicates such a wide variety of initial materials that we should expect several metallurgical processes to be used. Traces of valuable metals, cost of fuel and water, and purity of product required by the consumer are factors in determining the process selected.

Northern Michigan is the only part of the United States in which native copper is mined in any quantity. The metal content of the ores averages only about 1.5 per cent, and each ton contains on the average 0.006 ounce of gold and 0.25 ounce of silver. Copper sold in the market is known as Lake, electrolytic, and casting copper. Typical of the procedures in the metallurgy of copper are those used in the Lake Superior region and those of the Anaconda Copper Co. at Butte, Montana, each of which will be described.

Fig. 32.3. A converter. Three hundred tons of matte are charged at one time. (Courtesy, Anaconda Copper Mining Co.)

Lake copper ore consists of lumps of native copper dispersed in rocks, the lumps ranging from very small particles to masses weighing several tons. The ore is hoisted to the surface of the ground and crushed. It is then shipped to the concentrating mill, where the copper is separated from the gangue, or waste, by jigs, tables, and ore flotation machines. The concentrate is shipped to the smelter and melted in reverberatory furnaces; the molten copper sinks to the bottom and the waste material floats on the top and is thrown away. Air is blown through the molten copper to oxidize other impurities; any copper oxide that forms is reduced with carbon. The molten copper is then cast into billets, cakes, or ingots.

The year 1864 saw the development of the first mines in Butte, Montana, the placer gold mines. Gold mining soon proved unsuccessful and was followed by silver mining. In 1875 copper mines in that region were systematically developed for the first time, and copper mining has continued from that time to the present. To date, nearly 5,000,000 tons of the metal have been taken from this section. The city of Butte is completely undermined by the 700 miles of drifts or horizontal passages that have been constructed. The shafts extend approximately 4000 feet into the ground.

The copper ore is found as bands and streaks in quartz and altered granite. The principal ores of the Butte deposits are chalcocite, bornite, and enargite. Associated with them are iron sulfide, about 0.6 ounce of silver per 1 per cent of copper, gold so small in quantity that it has a value of about 10 cents per ton of ore, zinc sulfide or sphalerite, galena (PbS), and two manganese minerals, rhodochrosite ($MnCO_3$), and the dioxide, pyrolusite.

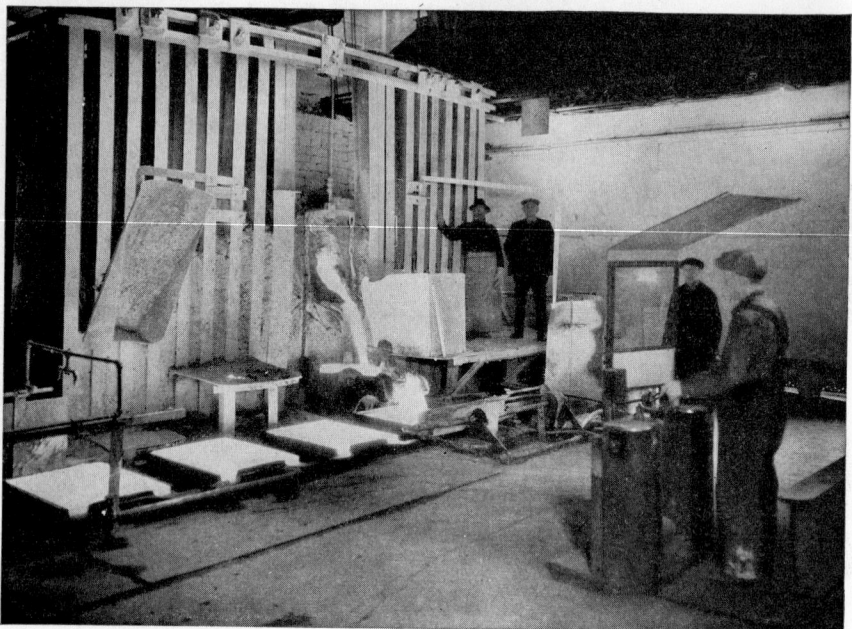

Fig. 32.4. Pouring copper anodes from refining furnace. (Courtesy, Anaconda Copper Mining Co.)

When an ore body is found in a mine, the vein is followed down as far as possible, for mining is begun at the bottom of the shaft. The rock is drilled for blasting, the holes are filled with explosives, and the charge is fired. The blasted rock is sorted by hand in the mine, only that containing streaks of copper ore being sent to the surface. The stope or excavation in the mine is timbered and filled with waste rock. The ore is hauled by electric trains to the reduction works at Anaconda, 26 miles from the Butte mines. (The water supply at Butte is insufficient for treating the ore.)

At the reduction plant, the ore is crushed to a fine powder by a series of graded crushers and grinders. The crushed ore, which contains about 5 per cent copper, is then separated into ore concentrate and tailings by the ore flotation process. The concentrate, which contains about 27 per cent copper, is roasted to remove part of the sulfur and then smelted in reverberatory furnaces. The matte from these furnaces contains about 45 per cent copper and is dumped into converters. The molten impure copper from the converters (the copper still contains gold and silver) is cast into molds and shipped to the electrolytic refineries.

Fig. 32.5. Loading copper anodes which weigh about 700 pounds. (Courtesy, Anaconda Copper Mining Co.)

The entire Anaconda works is built on the side of a mountain, the ore being hauled by trains to the bin at the top of the plant. From the time the contents of the cars are dumped into this bin until the large copper anodes weighing over 700 pounds each are made, the entire process operates by gravity. The "blister copper" anodes are about 99.3 per cent copper and contain only traces of gold, silver, and antimony.

Electrolytic refining is done where cheap electricity is available. Sheets of pure copper are used as cathodes, and "blister copper" is used as anodes, as shown in Fig. 32.6. The bath contains $CuSO_4$, H_2SO_4, and NaCl. Metallic copper goes into solution as Cu^{++} ions at the anode and plates out at the cathode. By carefully controlling the voltage, the active Zn^{++} and Fe^{+++}

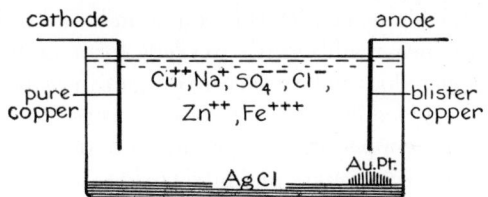

Fig. 32.6. Electrolytic refining of copper.

ions are kept in solution. Silver goes into solution as Ag$^+$ ions, but precipitates as AgCl, which forms a sludge in the electrolysis cell. The noble metals, such as gold and platinum, do not dissolve; they fall to the bottom when released from the copper. The value of the anode mud about pays for the refining. Electrolytic copper contains 99.953 per cent copper.

Sulfur dioxide from the roasting ovens is converted into sulfuric acid. Arsenic, zinc, lead, and traces of other elements are recovered by Cottrell precipitators in the 585-foot smokestack of the reduction plant. The precipitators operate at a static charge of 62,500 volts.

Physical and Chemical Properties of Copper

The commercial value of copper is based on its malleability, tensile strength, heat and electrical conductivity, and resistance to corrosion. Copper is reddish-yellow in color, but very thin films of it are green. Copper, as usually prepared, has a density of about 8.2 to 8.4, but copper with a density of 8.9 can be prepared by removing impurities. It melts at 1083° C. In electrical conductivity it ranks next to silver; but traces of arsenic (one of the most common impurities), silicon, and phosphorus lower its conductivity appreciably—an important factor in transmission lines. Brittle copper usually contains small amounts of metallic impurities such as iron and bismuth. Copper that contains oxygen is really an alloy of copper oxide and copper; the oxygen can be removed with mild reducing agents. Commercially, the molten metal is stirred with poles to remove the oxygen. The so-called oxygen-free copper now on the market is made by a process which excludes oxygen. Melting copper under a flux of magnesium prevents gas pockets and blisters from forming. As with other metals, the hardness and toughness of copper can be altered by heat treatment (annealing) and rolling, or cold working. Copper can be worked in tube mills, extruding machines, stamping mills, etc.

Copper is stable in dry air and in water. Although copper telephone and telegraph wires apparently blacken, the first film that forms is green. Analysis shows it to be $CuCO_3 \cdot Cu(OH)_2$, a basic carbonate called verdigris. Sulfides in the air react with this compound, and black copper sulfide forms. Copper combines readily with oxygen, forming both cuprous and cupric oxides. Copper does not replace hydrogen in acids. (The action of HCl on copper takes place only if oxygen is also present.) We have already discussed the use of copper in the preparation of sulfur dioxide (page 373), nitrogen dioxide (page 406), and nitric oxide (page 405).

Production and Uses of Copper

The copper-producing states listed in order of importance are Arizona, Montana, Utah, Nevada, Michigan, and Colorado. About two-fifths of our supply comes from Arizona and one-fifth from Montana. United States copper production runs from half a million to a million tons annually, and world production varies from one to nearly three million tons a year.

About 80 per cent of the total output of copper is used for copper products and 20 per cent for brass and other alloys. Manufacturers of electrical equipment, and telephone, telegraph, light, and power lines account for about 50 per cent of the output. Approximately 100,000,000 pounds are used each year as sheet or strip metal. The copper industry is hard hit during a depression in the construction and building trades. Copper sold for as low as 4.8 cents per pound in 1932 after having been 37 cents per pound in 1917. The manufacturers of beer and other alcoholic drinks use copper for their vats, stills, and condensing equipment. Copper cooking utensils have been used for centuries; but oxidation of the utensils must be prevented because copper salts are toxic.

Although lead does not alloy readily with copper, about 3 per cent lead is used with zinc and copper in leaded brass, free-cutting brass rods, and architectural bronze. Nearly all the other metals that are produced on a commercial scale are alloyed with copper. Hundreds of alloys are listed by their manufacturers under such headings as copper alloys, brasses, special brasses, bronzes, nickel silvers, cupro-nickels, etc. The composition and properties of a few of these copper alloys are given in Table 32.1.

TABLE 32.1. COPPER ALLOYS

Name	Percentage of Each Element Present in Typical Sample	Tensile Strength lbs./sq. in.	Uses
Arsenical copper	Cu, 99.6; As, 0.3; P, 0.04	60,000	Condenser tubes
Cadmium copper	Cu, 99; Cd, 1.0	80,000	Trolley wire
Beryllium copper	Cu. 98; Be, 2.0	175,000	Springs, non-sparking tools
Bronze	Cu, 90; Sn, 10	67,000	Caskets, screen cloth
Cartridge brass	Cu, 70; Zn, 30	86,000	Radiators, shells
Silicon brass	Cu, 78; Zn, 20; Si, 2.0	110,000	Fire extinguisher shells, evaporators
Naval brass	Cu, 60; Zn, 39.25; Sn, 0.75	75,000	Resistance to sea water, tube heads
Aluminum bronze	Cu, 95; Al, 5.0	105,000	Gifts, golden-colored articles
Nickel silver	Cu, 65; Zn, 20; Ni, 15	93,000	Key stock, table silver

Copper is added to our coins to harden them (nickel coin—Cu, 75; Ni, 25; silver coin—Cu, 10; Ag, 90; gold coin—Cu, 10; Au, 90).

The world reserve of copper is estimated at 100,000,000 tons, and our own reserve at only about 40,000,000 tons. The world demand has probably not yet reached its peak. Although many power lines, etc., have been built during the past twenty years, many more will be needed; copper will undoubtedly be used in new appliances for the home. Foreign countries use much less copper than does the United States. Germany experimented with the substitution of zinc and aluminum for copper during the First World War, but the result was far from satisfactory.

COMPOUNDS OF COPPER

There are both monovalent cuprous and divalent cupric compounds. Cuprous compounds are unstable and therefore of little importance. The two most common ones are Cu_2O and $CuCl$.

Hydroxides and Oxides

Cupric hydroxide is precipitated as a pale greenish-blue gelatinous substance when a base is added to a soluble cupric salt.

$$Cu^{++} + SO_4^{--} + 2\ Na^+ + 2\ OH^- \longrightarrow \underline{Cu(OH)_2} + 2\ Na^+ + SO_4^{--}$$

If ammonium hydroxide is substituted for sodium hydroxide, the precipitate which first forms redissolves and a highly colored deep-blue solution is formed

$$\underline{Cu(OH)_2} + 4\ NH_4OH \longrightarrow Cu(NH_3)_4^{++} + 2\ OH^- + 4\ H_2O$$

Because this color is apparent with even traces of copper, the ammonia test is used in detecting traces of the Cu^{++} ion.

Alkaline tartrates also dissolve $Cu(OH)_2$ and form deep-blue solutions. Fehling's solution (34.65 g. of $CuSO_4 \cdot 5\ H_2O/500$ cc. solution $+125$ g. $KOH +$ 173 g. of Rochelle salt/500 cc. solution) is to be found among the chemicals of nearly every practicing physician. It is used in detecting glucose in the urine. Reducing sugars converts the Cu^{++} ion into the insoluble red cuprous oxide, Cu_2O. The color of the precipitate indicates the amount of sugar present.

Bordeaux mixture, a popular fungicide, is made by adding slaked lime to copper sulfate, thus forming a mixture of $Cu(OH_2)$ and $CaSO_4$.

Tetra-amino cupric compounds dissolve cellulose and are used in making rayon (page 709). If $Cu(NH_3)_4(OH)_2$ is heated, ammonia is driven off. Further heating produces black *cupric oxide*.

$$Cu(OH)_2 \xrightarrow{\Delta} CuO + H_2O$$

Cupric oxide can also be prepared by heating the carbonate or nitrate or by the direct union of copper and oxygen. Copper oxide is a good oxidizing agent. The preparation of water by the reaction between CuO and hydrogen has already been mentioned (page 148). If a copper wire is held in the Bunsen flame until a coating of CuO is formed, the wire will glow brightly when held in methyl alcohol vapor; the alcohol is oxidized to formaldehyde.

$$CH_3OH + CuO \longrightarrow Cu + HCHO + H_2O$$

Cupric oxide is used in petroleum refining, in pottery glazes, inorganic analyses, and in the manufacture of copper salts.

Sulfur Compounds

Blue vitriol or *copper sulfate pentahydrate*, the most important compound, is obtained by evaporating a solution of copper sulfate. At 110° C. the salt loses four molecules of water; at 250° C. the fifth molecule is driven off, leaving white anhydrous cupric sulfate. The blue color reappears as soon as the anhydrous salt comes in contact with the moisture of the air. Organic chemists use the anhydrous salt to remove traces of water from alcohols and ethers.

Copper sulfate is used as the electrolyte in the electrolytic refining of copper, electrotyping, and electroplating. It is also used in making copper arsenic insecticides (page 442), and in controlling algae in lakes and reservoirs. Live algae are not particularly obnoxious in water supplies; but when certain ones die, they produce very disagreeable tastes and odors. Copper sulfate kills the algae before they have an opportunity to multiply. People who drink water thus treated are not poisoned by the copper because of its low concentration. Also, some is precipitated in the lake with the algae.

Black *cupric sulfide* may be prepared by the direct union of the elements or by adding H_2S to soluble copper salts.

Halides of Copper

Cuprous and cupric chlorides are the only two halide compounds of importance.

Cupric chloride is obtained by dissolving CuO in hydrochloric acid. Crystals of $CuCl_2 \cdot 2\,H_2O$ are green and deliquescent, forming a green solution in the presence of a little water. Further dilution produces the typical blue copper ion. The anhydrous salt is yellow.

Addition of copper to cupric chloride produces *cuprous chloride* as a white precipitate.

$$Cu^{++} + 2\,Cl^- + Cu \longrightarrow \underline{2\,CuCl}$$

It is soluble in an excess of hydrochloric acid and forms $HCuCl_2$. Cuprous chloride is used in some types of gas analysis apparatus to absorb carbon monoxide; the compound, $Cu(CO)Cl \cdot H_2O$, is formed.

Other Copper Compounds

Cupric acetate is used as a mordant. *Basic cupric carbonates*, $CuCO_3 \cdot Cu(OH)_2$ (malachite green) and $(CuCO_3)_2 \cdot Cu(OH)_2$ (azurite blue), are found in nature. *Cupric ferrocyanide*, $Cu_2Fe(CN)_6$, is a rose-colored insoluble complex salt that is used in the identification of the cupric ion. *Cupric cyanide,* Cu(CN)$_2$, is used in the production of cyanogen.

$$2 \text{ Cu(CN)}_2 \longrightarrow \underline{2 \text{ CuCN}} + \text{(CN)}_2$$

QUESTIONS AND PROBLEMS

1. What are the physical and chemical properties of copper which make it such a useful element?
2. Account for the early use of copper.
3. What foods should not be kept in a copper kettle? Or is copper safe for all foods?
4. If copper was not available, could any other metal be used in electric generators, or would we have to get along without electricity?
5. Copper sulfate is used to destroy algae in lakes and reservoirs; why are people who drink the water not poisoned?
6. What volume of 0.02-molar copper nitrate could be made from the copper in a penny? What other data are needed? How can you obtain these data? Does the government make a profit in producing pennies?
7. Outline the steps in the metallurgy of copper.
8. An unknown is CuS, CuSO$_4$, CuSO$_4$·5 H$_2$O, Cu(NO$_3$)$_2$, Cu$_2$Fe(CN)$_6$, or Cu(OH)$_2$; how would you identify it?
9. How is very pure copper obtained?
10. What weight of malachite green can be prepared from one ton of 99.5 per cent pure copper?

REFERENCES

Articles

"The Story of Copper." Howard, J. W. *J. Chem. Ed.* **6,** 413–431 (1929).
"Tennessee Copper." Poste, E. P. *Ind. and Eng. Chem.* **24,** 690–693 (1932).
"Production of Electrotypes." Ronneberg, C. E. *J. Chem. Ed.* **14,** 303–310 (1937).
"Copper." Anaconda Copper Mining Co., Anaconda, Mont.

» 33 «

SILVER AND GOLD

In physical and chemical properties, silver and gold are quite similar to copper; the three are in the same subgroup I B. Some of the properties of the three elements are given in Table 33.1.

TABLE 33.1. PROPERTIES OF COPPER, SILVER, AND GOLD

	Atomic Weight	Density	Melting Point	Boiling Point	Formulas of Oxides
Copper	63.57	8.92	1083	2300	Cu_2O, CuO
Silver	107.88	10.50	960.5	1950	Ag_2O, AgO
Gold	197.20	19.3	1063	2600	Au_2O, Au_2O_3

SILVER

The Latin word *argentum*, meaning *white*, was applied to silver because of its brilliant white color. The alchemists' symbol for it was derived from association with the moon and Diana, the moon-goddess. A common synonym for silver nitrate is *lunar caustic*. Silver has been highly valued for many centuries and was at one time more costly than gold. The silver mines in Asia Minor were probably worked prior to 2500 B.C.

Occurrence

Native silver and silver halides usually lie near the surface; silver sulfides, antimonides, and other complex silver compounds are found at lower depths. In many places, silver is associated with other metals. The Coeur d'Alene district of Idaho is noted for its silver, as by-product of its zinc and lead mines. Galena frequently contains as much as 1 per cent silver; most of the silver produced in Europe comes from galena mines. Two of the more important silver ores in the United States are argentite or silver glance, Ag_2S, and horn silver or cerargyrite, $AgCl$.

Metallurgy

Since silver is found associated with so many other metals, several metallurgical processes are used. The ores may be divided into two groups: those rich enough in gold and silver to make these elements most important, and those in which gold and silver are recovered as by-products in the metallurgy of other elements. In many cases, the operation of a mine depends upon a good price for the by-products.

In the *amalgamation process*, liquid mercury is used to extract the silver from the crushed ore. The crushed rock is separated from the amalgam by washing, and the mercury is separated from the silver by distillation. Insoluble sulfides are first treated with salt and a mixture of copper and iron sulfates. Of the several complicated reactions which undoubtedly take place, two of the more important are probably the following:

$$Ag_2S + CuCl_2 \rightleftarrows 2\,AgCl + CuS$$
$$AgCl + Hg \rightleftarrows HgCl + Ag$$

Lixiviation methods depend upon dissolving the silver from the ore with an aqueous solution of some salt and then precipitating the silver as the metal or the sulfide. In the cyanide process, the most important of these methods, the crushed ore is agitated and aerated in contact with a cyanide solution. The reaction of argentite ore with sodium cyanide is:

$$\underline{Ag_2S} + 4\,Na^+ + 4\,CN^- \longrightarrow 4\,Na^+ + 2\,Ag(CN)_2^- + S^{--}$$

The silver is then precipitated by bringing the solution in contact with metallic zinc or aluminum which, since they are above silver in the E.C.S., will precipitate silver from the solution.

Silver may also be obtained from silver sulfide. The ore is first roasted to convert it into the sulfate, and the silver is then precipitated by adding scrap copper.

One of the processes used to separate silver from copper and lead ores is the *Parkes process*, in which silver is separated from the metal alloy. Thus, an ore which is rich in lead and contains some silver is melted, about 1 per cent of zinc is added, and the mixture is stirred well. Silver is much more soluble in zinc than in lead and zinc is lighter than lead. Therefore zinc floats to the surface, bringing the silver with it. When the mixture is cooled, a crust of zinc forms on the surface. This is skimmed off and the zinc is distilled off to be used again in the process. This process resembles the extraction of iodine from water by means of carbon tetrachloride. If the silver contains gold and copper—as it will if these elements were present in the original molten material—it is further purified by processes to be described later.

We have seen that when such metals as zinc and copper are refined electrolytically, the noble metals deposit in the *anode mud*. The substances that will dissolve in dilute sulfuric acid are first removed from this mud. Other insoluble material is put in solution by being fused with an oxidizing agent, sodium carbonate, and sand; metal silicates form as a slag, from which the gold and silver can be separated.

The processes just described give, at best, impure silver. The further purification required is accomplished in most cases by either electrolysis or cupellation. In *electrolytic purification* the impure silver is used as the anode and pure silver as the cathode. Silver nitrate dissolved in nitric acid is used as the electrolyte. In *cupellation refining*, the impurities are either vaporized or absorbed. A silver-lead alloy containing other impurities is heated in a shallow hearth furnace with cement or some other porous material. Air blown over the hearth oxidizes lead and the other impurities which are either volatilized or absorbed in the porous lining. The silver thus obtained is cast into ingots which are called doré bullion because gold is present. The gold is separated from the silver by dissolving the silver with hot concentrated sulfuric acid; adding copper precipitates the silver from the solution.

Physical and Chemical Properties of Silver

Silver, a heavy white metal, is an excellent conductor of heat and electricity. It is harder than gold but softer than copper. It is extremely malleable and ductile. Since it is so soft it is usually alloyed with other metals for jewelry, tableware, etc.

Silverware is attacked by sulfur; for example, eggs, which are rich in this element, tarnish silver very quickly. Oxygen, hydrogen, nitrogen, and carbon do not combine directly with silver. Halogens attack it slowly, because the silver halide coating which forms protects the metal from further action.

Silver is insoluble in dilute acids and alkalis, but either concentrated nitric or sulfuric acid will dissolve it. Its solution in alkali cyanides is important in metallurgy. The equation for this reaction is usually written:

$$4\,\underline{Ag} + \overline{O_2} + 2\,H_2O + 8\,Na^+ + 8\,CN^- \longrightarrow 8\,Na^+ + 4\,Ag(CN)_2^- + 4\,OH^-$$

Production and Uses

The production of silver and gold is shown in Table 33.2.

The United States and Mexico produce a major part of the world's silver supply. Most of this used to go to India and China for jewelry and coinage, but these uses declined during the silver-buying campaign the U. S. Treasury initiated in 1934. Both the above countries were forced off the silver standard; no large currency is now based on silver. Commercial uses of silver are continually increasing. In 1944 over 80,000,000 ounces (nearly 3000 tons) were used in the United States for military and essential purposes. Before the recent war half that amount was used in the manufacture of medicinals, jewelry, and coins, and in silver plating and photography. During the war the Treasury lent several thousand tons for non-consumptive uses, such as bus bars in electrolytic plants and reaction vessels in chemical plants.

In electroplating cheaper metals, these metals serve as the cathodes and bars of pure silver as the anodes. When the anodes are immersed in a bath of the double cyanide, $KAg(CN)_2$, ionization takes place as follows:

$$K^+ + Ag(CN)_2^- \rightleftarrows K^+ + Ag^+ + 2\ CN^-$$

K_I for this reaction is very small; if the concentration of the complex ion is molar, that of Ag^+ is $2.2 \cdot 10^{-12}$. Both Ag^+ and K^+ migrate toward the cathode, but only the easily deposited silver plates out. The surface has a frosted appearance until it is polished.

TABLE 32.2. PRODUCTION OF SILVER AND GOLD IN TONS, AND VALUE IN DOLLARS PER FINE OUNCE

		World Production	U.S. Production	Value	
Silver	1920	5930	1900	$ 1.09	
	1930	8520	1740	0.385	
	1937	9310	2460	0.7735	U.S. Gov't
				0.45	Commercial
	1944	6380	1220	0.911	U.S. sells
				0.711	U.S. buys
Gold	1920	550	85	20.67	
	1930	690	78	20.67	
	1937	1190	169	35.00	
	1944	930	35	35.00	

The fact that silver may be deposited by chemical reduction is used in making silver mirrors. Glucose, formaldehyde, and Rochelle salt serve as reducing agents. If sufficient ammonium hydroxide is added to a dilute silver nitrate solution so that nearly all the Ag_2O dissolves as $Ag(NH_3)_2OH$, and an alkaline Rochelle salt solution is then added, a silver mirror will deposit on *absolutely* clean glass dipped into the solution. It is usually necessary to warm the solution to obtain a good film. *If the solution of AgNO₃ and ammonium hydroxide is permitted to dry out, it will form a very explosive silver compound.*

Compounds of Silver

Hydroxide and Oxide. Silver hydroxide cannot be isolated from water solution. Upon the addition of a base to a soluble silver salt, immediate decomposition takes place and Ag_2O forms. However, some AgOH must be present in solution, for Ag_2O in contact with water turns red litmus blue; therefore this small amount of silver hydroxide must be highly ionized. Silver oxide decomposes at 250° C. It is used to some extent to deposit yellow Ag_2SiO_3 in glass.

Black silver peroxide, Ag_2O_2, is produced by the action of ozone on metallic silver. It decomposes below 100° C. and is insoluble in water.

Silver Nitrate. $AgNO_3$ is the most important silver salt because from it nearly all the other silver compounds are made. It is prepared by dissolving silver in concentrated nitric acid. Silver nitrate is decomposed by sunlight, necessitating the use of dark bottles to store it; it decomposes when heated.

$$2\ AgNO_3 \longrightarrow 2\ Ag + 2\ NO_2 + \overline{O_2}$$

Organic matter easily reduces it; hence, if some is spilled on the hands, a black stain quickly forms. This property makes $AgNO_3$ useful as an indelible ink. It is used externally to cauterize wounds, to remove warts, and to paint ulcers.

Many organic silver compounds—for example, "argyrol," "protargol," etc.—are made by reacting silver nitrate with various proteins. These compounds are used to swab out the nose and throat and as general disinfectants.

Sulfur Compounds. *Silver sulfide* is important as a silver ore; it is insoluble in water. *Silver sulfate* is prepared by dissolving silver in concentrated sulfuric acid. It is only slightly soluble in water, but dissolves readily in sulfuric acid. The complex salt, *silver sodium thiosulfate*, is important in photography because $Na_2S_2O_3$ dissolves insoluble silver halides.

Silver Halides. *Silver fluoride* is the only halide that is appreciably soluble in water. AgCl is soluble in dilute and AgBr in concentrated NH_4OH, but even concentrated NH_4OH has no effect on AgI. Chlorides, bromides, and iodides are determined quantitatively as the insoluble silver salts; silver is also determined as the chloride. In small amounts, chlorides are determined volumetrically by using K_2CrO_4 as an indicator. AgCl precipitates first; as soon as all the Cl^- ion is used up, red Ag_2CrO_4 precipitates. The most important use of the halides is in photography.

Chemistry of Black and White Photography[1]

We seldom think of the wonderful chemical reactions involved in photography. There are five stages: (1) preparation of the film, (2) exposure, (3) developing, (4) fixing, and (5) printing.

The camera film we purchase consists of two parts, the emulsion and celluloid. The celluloid serves only as a base or support for the emulsion. A plate of glass would be equally satisfactory; in fact, it was used before the days of cellulose nitrate and acetate films, and some is still used today.

The chief methods of mixing emulsions are the acid, or boiling, and the ammonia process. Emulsions contain gelatin, a bromide, an iodide, silver nitrate, and small amounts of hydrochloric acid. Gelatin acts as a bonding material and prevents the formation of coarse grain and fogging. The effect

---

[1] The chemistry of color photography is too complicated to be included in this book.

586   TEXTBOOK OF CHEMISTRY

of grain formation is easily demonstrated by placing 10 per cent KBr in each of two cylinders, adding 10 per cent gelatin to one cylinder, and an equal volume of 5 per cent silver nitrate to each. Thick white curds of AgBr form in the aqueous solution, and a smooth cream-like substance forms in the cylinder containing the gelatin. The film always contains an excess of bromide over that required to react with the Ag$^+$ ion; this increases the speed of the film. In general, small quantities of iodides permit a greater latitude of exposure.

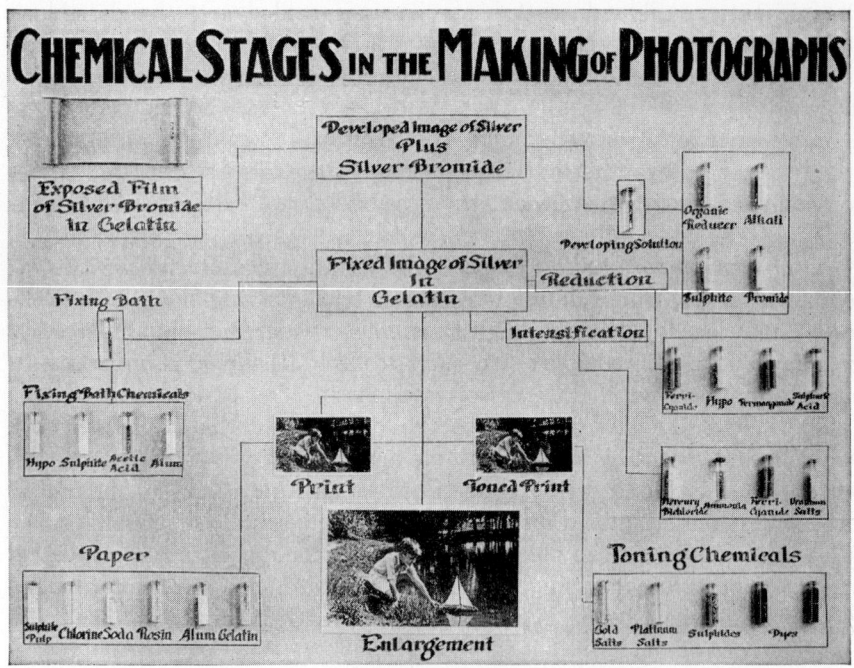

FIG. 33.1.   (Courtesy, Eastman Kodak Co.)

The chemistry of the *exposure of a film* is none too well understood even after all these years of photography. When light strikes the film through the lens of the camera, a latent image is formed on the negative or film. The film is affected by light in an amount proportional to the intensity of the light that strikes it; the entire film is affected if it is opened in broad daylight. The latent image has certain definite properties. It is normally stable and under some conditions persists for years. It deposits silver in the presence of mild reducing agents, but is destroyed by powerful oxidizing agents such as chromic and permanganic acids. It is believed that when light falls upon a crystal of silver bromide an electron is knocked out of a bromide ion, and is captured by a silver ion *if and only if* the latter is adjacent to a speck of some foreign material. Otherwise the electron is soon regained by the bromine atom. Silver sulfide is the most effective material for these sensitivity specks. It is formed automatically by the reaction of silver ions in the emulsion with sulfur compounds in the gelatin. It seems certain that as few as three quanta of light, each forming one atom of silver in this way, will somehow render a grain of AgBr developable. The light quantum which does this is used up in the process; hence if little light falls on a given area of the film, there will be many unchanged and only a few developable AgBr grains. If a hundred times as much light strikes another area, most of the AgBr grains in that area will be affected. The latent image consists of these developable grains.

The process of development consists in reducing to black metallic silver all of each grain that was struck by enough light to render it developable. If a given grain is attacked at all by the developer, it is completely blackened. Many chemicals will reduce silver halides to silver; but for a developer to be *satisfactory*, it must act only on those grains which have been struck by light. A few inorganic compounds are occasionally employed, but the developers used today are predominantly organic compounds derived from benzene, such as pyrogallol ("pyro"), hydroquinone, and *para*-methylaminophenol ("metol"). (The formulas of these compounds will be found in organic chemistry texts.) The developing solution in which the film is dipped contains, in addition to the organic developer, a base to take up the hydrogen ions liberated during the reaction, and sodium sulfite. The reason for the presence of sulfite ion was explained on page 376. After the film has been in the developer a few minutes (long enough for all the light-struck grains to be blackened but not long enough for the others to be acted upon), the film is removed and the developer remaining upon it is inactivated by dropping the film into a "short-stop" bath containing dilute acetic acid. Before the film can be exposed to light, the unchanged silver halide must be removed; otherwise it too will soon turn black.

Removing the silver halide is called fixing the film. The most common fixing agent is sodium thiosulfate, which dissolves insoluble silver halides and forms a complex silver-thiosulfate ion. The equation may be:

$$AgCl + 2\ Na^+ + S_2O_3^{--} \longrightarrow 2\ Na^+ + AgS_2O_3^- + Cl^-$$

The film is next thoroughly washed with water and can then be exposed to the light, for its surface contains only metallic silver. The brighter the object photographed, the more light is reflected from it, and the greater the intensity of the image on the film. The fixed film is called the negative; light and dark objects appear in reverse on it.

Printing is the repetition of the above four processes, with paper upon which a suitable silver halide emulsion has been deposited being used in place of the film. In *toning*, the print is dipped in a solution of a gold or platinum salt; the less active metals are precipitated on the paper and silver goes into solution. Other methods of toning are available.

GOLD

Gold is one of the oldest metals known and possibly the first one to be used by man. The word itself is thought to be derived from the Sanskrit "Jualita," from "Jual" meaning "to shine." The modern symbol, Au, comes from the Latin name, *aurum*. That the ancient Jews and Hindus were acquainted with the metal is evident from their writings; it was used as a medium of exchange in the time of Abraham. Gold ornaments have been found in the earliest Egyptian tombs. Its scarcity is made clear when we realize that all the gold thus far produced weighs less than the copper produced in one week. The ocean contains sufficient gold for each person in the world to have $15,000,000 worth of it; but all known methods for the recovery of this gold cost far more than the gold is worth. A shovelful of dirt dug up at random contains more gold than does an equal quantity of sea water.

Occurrence

Metallic gold occurs either in primary deposits in veins associated with quartz, or in secondary deposits of alluvial gold in the form of grains, dust, and even lumps. Nuggets weighing nearly 200 pounds have been found in Australia. The famous Comstock lode at Virginia City, Nevada, contained a pocket of gold which yielded about $11,000,000 worth of this precious metal in a week; needless to say, such "strikes" are rare. Gold is found associated with lead, copper, zinc, and silver ores. Only a few gold ores are known. Sylvanite, a gold-silver telluride, $(AuAg)Te_2$, is mined in Colorado.

Metallurgy

Of the world's gold output today, 90 per cent comes from lode or quartz mining and the balance from placer mining. Placer mining accounted for 87 per cent in 1847, but by 1905 this had dropped to 15 per cent. Nature has played a great part during past centuries in making placer mining possible, for valleys were formed by erosion and flats were built up. Gold, being very dense, settled to the bottom of the streams. Most placer mining today is done in the open along modern river systems, but there are some dry placers. Placer mining done by an individual is called "panning"; the miner uses a flat-bottomed pan made of stiff sheet iron. In "sluicing," a long open box in sections about 12 feet long is used; mercury sprinkled at the head of the sluice amalgamates with gold, the sand and dirt being washed away with water.

Hydraulic mining was introduced in California in 1852. An abundant water supply is required, for water under pressure is used to excavate the gravel and wash it into the large sluices; the gravel is loosened with low-grade dynamite. Gold dredging was introduced in New Zealand and Australia in 1865.

Many of the lode or quartz gold mines in the United States are quite small. The ore is crushed at the mines, and a concentrate is produced by ore flotation processes. This is sold to larger plants, the price depending on the gold and silver content as shown by analysis. Frequently two or more processes are used in obtaining all the gold from a concentrate.

In the amalgamation process, the ore is reduced and amalgamated in a stamp mill. The gold amalgam is separated from the excess mercury by filtration through leather, and the mercury is distilled. Some gold remains in the mud of the stamp mills. The waste is divided into tailings and slimes; the latter are frequently put through the cyanide process for further extraction.

Fig. 33.2. Two four-inch giants working in a placer deposit. (Courtesy, Bureau of Mines, Department of the Interior.)

Two chemical extraction processes, chlorination and cyanide lixiviation, are also used. In the chlorination process the ore is oxidized and chlorinated; this converts the metals into chlorides. The solution is filtered and the gold is precipitated with H_2S. The gold sulfide is then burned with charcoal to produce metallic gold. Bromine is even better than chlorine and some can be recovered by the action of chlorine; but it is so expensive and so much is lost that it cannot be used profitably.

In the cyanide lixiviation process, first employed on a large scale in Australia in 1888, gold is extracted with a cyanide solution and precipitated with zinc or by electrolytic reduction. Gold and silver are extracted together by this process. The hydrogen peroxide formed as an intermediate compound speeds up the process.

$$2\ \underline{Au} + 4\ K^+ + 4\ CN^- + 2\ H_2O + \overline{O_2} \longrightarrow 4\ K^+ + 2\ Au(CN)_2^- + 2\ OH^- + H_2O_2$$
$$\underline{2\ \underline{Au} + 4\ K^+ + 4\ CN^- + H_2O_2 \longrightarrow 4\ K^+ + 2\ Au(CN)_2^- + 2\ OH^-}$$
$$4\ \underline{Au} + 8\ \overline{K^+} + 8\ CN^- + 2\ H_2O + O_2 \longrightarrow 8\ K^+ + 4\ Au(CN)_2^- + 4\ OH^-$$

Of the 25 leading producers of gold in the United States, almost half are base-metal mines, producing gold as a by-product. Of those actually mining gold ore, the two leaders are the Homestake (South Dakota) and the Cripple Creek mines (Colorado). They crush their ore and remove as much gold as possible by amalgamation. The coarser sand is run into huge vats and treated for days with cyanide solutions which dissolve the remaining gold. Only a fraction of an ounce of gold is obtained per ton of ore.

Refining of Gold

The gold obtained by all these processes is impure; hence further refining is necessary. Chemical "parting" and electrolytic refining are the two procedures most frequently used.

In the chemical parting process, an alloy of gold, silver, and lead is first made; this is treated with aqua regia ($HCl+HNO_3$), which precipitates silver as AgCl. The solution is then treated with ferrous sulfate or chloride to precipitate the gold. In another parting process the granulated alloy is heated in cast-iron boilers with concentrated sulfuric acid which converts into sulfates all the metals except gold.

The electrolytic refining of gold was introduced by Watt in 1863. If the crude metal is rich in gold, the electrolyte is a hydrochloric acid solution containing $AuCl_3$, the cathode is a strip of pure gold, the anode is the impure metal, and a high-current density is used. Gold deposits on the cathode; the silver goes into solution as Ag^+ and precipitates as AgCl. If the crude ore is rich in silver, a low-current density is used, the cathode is pure silver, and the electrolyte is a solution of HNO_3 and $AgNO_3$. Silver plates out on the cathode and gold falls as a sludge beneath the anode.

Physical and Chemical Properties of Gold

Gold is a soft, yellow metal. It is more malleable than all the other metals, for it can be hammered to a fineness of 300,000 sheets per inch. It is green by transmitted light. Its electrical conductivity is about 70 per cent that of silver.

Gold has valences of $+1$ and $+3$. It is amphoteric in the higher valence. In both valences it readily forms complex ions with the halide ions and with the cyanide ion. The covalence of gold in the aurous state is 2, as can be seen from the formula of the aurocyanide ion shown in the equations for the cyanide process. Auric gold has a covalence of 4; the HCl solution of $AuCl_3$ mentioned above contains chlorauric acid, $HAuCl_4$. Sodium chloraurate, $NaAuCl_4$, frequently called sodium gold chloride, is used in gold plating. Gold is attacked by oxidizing agents such as O_2, H_2O_2, HNO_3, and Cl_2, but only in the presence of complexing agents. It is not attacked by alkalis. All gold compounds are strong oxidizing agents, but those containing gold in the anion are not as strong as the others. Gold alloys with many metals.

Production and Uses

Gold is mined in the United States in all the mountainous states west of the Mississippi, as well as in Alabama, Maryland, North Carolina, Pennsylvania, South Carolina, and Virginia. The leading mines are located in South Dakota, Colorado, California, Arizona, and Nevada. The largest gold producer in 1945 was the Utah Copper Company's copper mine at Bingham, Utah. California, with 15 per cent of our total output, was the largest producing state. Pennsylvania, with an annual output worth $50,000, is the largest producer east of the Mississippi. Undoubtedly many gold mines are still to be discovered, both in this country and in Canada and Alaska. About 53 per cent of the world's output comes from Transvaal, South Africa. Russia is rapidly developing her mines.

Prior to 1933 gold cost $20.67 per ounce; in 1933 the price was raised to $25.56, and in 1935 to $35.00. Since the price of gold is fixed by law, increased mining costs (due to higher wages and higher prices for power and supplies) cannot be met by an increase in the selling price of the product. An increase in the cost of living is the same thing as a decrease in the value of gold, and puts out of operation one gold mine after another, beginning with those with the lowest profit margins. The present outlook is poor for gold miners. Gold and silver are sold on the basis of fine or troy ounces. There are 12 troy ounces in a troy pound, the avoirdupois pound being 1.215 times as heavy as the troy pound.

Gold in the pure state is too soft for most purposes, and consequently it must be alloyed. The fineness of the gold is expressed in carats. Pure gold is 24 carats fine; 12 carat is 50 per cent pure gold and 50 per cent other metals. The lowest recognized standard is 9 carat. ("Derby gold" is an inferior quality which is worked up into ornaments and sold as real gold.) The gold in jewelry is alloyed with copper and silver. Red gold alloys are frequently treated chemically to dissolve the base metal of the alloy and leave a covering of purer gold on the surface. Rolled gold is made by applying thin sheets of the metal to a plate of alloy and rolling down the gold. White or platinum gold in jewelry is 60 parts gold and 40 parts platinum. Palladium is combined with gold for dental alloys.

Colloidal gold may be prepared in all colors of the rainbow by reducing solutions of $AuCl_3$ with formaldehyde, tartrates, and other similar agents. Such solutions are used in the diagnosis of certain diseases. The "purple of Cassius," discovered by Cassius at Leyden in 1683, is prepared by adding stannous chloride to a dilute gold chloride solution. The precipitate is used to give glass a ruby-red color and in coloring enamel and glazes.

Man has for centuries attempted to transmute base metals into gold. In one attempt, an electrical discharge was passed through mercury vapor in the hope that an occasional electron would penetrate and remain in the nucleus, thus reducing the atomic number from 80 to 79. The neutralization of one positive charge would result in the liberation of energy, providing a nuclear proton was annihilated. Although all these attempts have thus far been unsuccessful, many of the advances in chemistry can be traced directly to them. The number of fraudulent claims for the synthesis of gold are innumerable.

Compounds of Gold

Gold forms both monovalent and trivalent compounds. Aurous compounds are basic. The auric ion forms many interesting complex salts. The auric chloride on the market is usually chlorauric acid, $HAuCl_4 \cdot 4 H_2O$; the deliquescent crystals take up water rapidly when the tube is opened. $Au(OH)_3$ is obtained as an orange precipitate by adding NaOH to $AuCl_3$. Brown Au_2O_3 is obtained by heating $Au(OH)_3$. The complex aurous and auric cyanides, $NaAu(CN)_2$ and $NaAu(CN)_4$, are obtained when gold is extracted by the cyanide process and are used in electroplating.

QUESTIONS AND PROBLEMS

1. The cost of the silver in a photographic film is less than 5 per cent of the retail price of the film. Outline a chemical procedure to prove this statement true or false.
2. Start with metallic silver and write equations for the preparation of the following compounds: Ag_2S, $AgCl$, $NaAg(CN)_2$, Ag_2O, and $AgNO_3$.
3. Outline the steps in black and white photography.
4. Suggest uses for silver if it cost no more than iron.
5. Look up the K_{sp} for AgCl and calculate the weight of silver in 10 l. of solution.
6. An unknown is one of the following: Ag_2S, $AgCl$, or Ag_2O; how would you identify it? How could you clean silverware without removing any silver?
7. Ten cc. of 0.01-molar $HAuCl_4$ are added to 900 cc. of water in preparing a colloidal gold solution. The gold particles are 20 millimicrons in diameter. If they are spherical and have the same density as metallic gold, how many particles are present per cc.? How many atoms of gold does each particle contain?
8. How could you test a gold coin that you thought was counterfeit?
9. Using any tests required, distinguish between the following pairs of substances:

    Gold coin / Gold Au_2O_3 / Ag_2O $NaAu(CN)_2$ / $HAuCl_4$ Gold / Copper   Fool's gold / Magnetic oxide of iron

10. If gold were as cheap as iron, which would be more important to modern civilization? Defend your answer.

REFERENCES

Articles

"Uses of Silver and Gold and Other Precious Metals." Carter, F. E. *Ind. and Eng. Chem.* **27**, 751–755 (1935).

"Photographic Emulsions." Carroll, B. H. *J. Chem. Ed.* **8**, 2341–2366 (1931).

"Toning Prints." Maclean, M. E. *J. Chem. Ed.* **14**, 31–32 (1937).

» 34 «

THE PLATINUM METALS

The platinum metals make up two of the triads in Group VIII of the periodic table. The ruthenium, rhodium, and palladium triad is called the "light platinum group" because each of the elements in the group has a density of about twelve. The second three—osmium, iridium, and platinum—constitute the "heavy platinum group"; the density of each of these is about twenty-two. All these elements have many characteristics in common with gold and silver.

Though the records are incomplete, it is believed that the platinum metals were used several centuries B.C. The metal now called platinum was first mentioned in European literature in 1600. The word platinum is derived from the Spanish and means "little silver." The early Spanish gold-seekers disliked platinum because they could not melt or dissolve it, but they soon learned to counterfeit gold by applying a thin coat of it to platinum. This led to its importation into Spain and Portugal being prohibited. Some of the metal reached England, and in 1751 its properties were described before the London Royal Society. With the discovery of platinum in Russia in 1819, the metal soon became plentiful. Russia began coining platinum money in 1828; the coins contained about 2 per cent iridium. By 1845 platinum had become so valuable that the Russians were shipping platinum coins out of the country; hence coinage of the metal was discontinued.

Discovery

In 1803 Dr. William Wollaston, an English chemist and physicist who was secretary of the Royal Society, announced the separation of two new metals from platinum. *Palladium*, which he named in honor of the then recently discovered asteroid Pallas, he obtained when he ignited a yellow precipitate formed from the reaction between mercurous cyanide and a solution of platinum in aqua regia. Later he treated chloroplatinic acid (obtained by the action of aqua regia on platinum) with ammonium chloride and removed the platinum as insoluble ammonium chloroplatinate $(NH_4)_2PtCl_6$. He removed the palladium from the filtrate with mercurous cyanide, treated the solution containing the excess mercurous cyanide with hydrochloric acid, and evaporated it to dryness. When he washed the residue with alcohol, there remained a beautiful dark-red powder, the double chloride of a new metal which he named *rhodium*. He obtained the metal by reducing the double salt with hydrogen.

During this same period, another English chemist, Dr. Smithson Tennant, discovered and named osmium and iridium. Many chemists had believed that the black residue usually remaining when platinum was dissolved in dilute aqua regia was graphite, but Tennant suspected that it might contain a new metal. By treating this residue first with alkali and then with acid, he was able to separate two metals. He called the one *iridium* because of the various colors of its salts, and the other *osmium* because the volatile oxide OsO_4 had a most decided odor. ("Osme," in Greek, means a smell.)

In 1844, the last metal in these two triads was discovered by Professor Karl Klaus of Kazan University in Russia. He heated the osmium-iridium residue with KNO_3 in a crucible lined with MgO and extracted the residue with a large volume of water. Treating the solution with nitric acid produced a black precipitate that was rich in OsO_4. He heated the residue and distilled the volatile OsO_4; from the residue he obtained a new element which he named *ruthenium* in honor of Russia. In 1828 Professor Osann of Dorpat University claimed to have discovered ruthenium, pluranium, and polinium, but Klaus proved that the latter two did not exist.

Occurrence

The platinum metals are found in the free state and are mined on all the continents. The leading countries and their estimated production are: Canada, 317,000 ounces; Russia, 150,000 ounces; South Africa, 50,000 ounces; and Colombia, 35,000 ounces. The United States at present produces nearly 30,000 ounces annually. Most of these metals produced in the United States are obtained as a by-product of gold mining, but some are recovered by the electrolytic refining of copper, zinc, etc. Russia has produced more platinum than any other country in the world; some of the deposits are in loose watery soil. Prior to the First World War mining methods in Russia were primitive; but dredging units are now used at some surface mines. In Australia, the platinum metals are found in alluvial and beach sand deposits. Nearly all the Canadian production is a by-product of the nickel and copper mining in Ontario; the metals are refined at Acton, England.

Cost of the Platinum Metals

The platinum metals are subject to wide fluctuations in price. Prior to 1900, platinum sold for as little as $5 per troy ounce. During the five-year period 1932–1936 the maximum price for it was nearly three times the minimum. The other platinum metals varied similarly. These wide fluctuations in price are both the cause and the result of much speculation, but excessively high prices are not likely to prevail very long at any one time. It is estimated that the Acton plant alone could produce half a million troy ounces (17 tons) of the platinum metals a year if the prices were such as to make it profitable. In recent years the price of platinum has been near that of gold; our imports run over 5 tons a year. The only other metal in the group of which we import as much as a ton annually is palladium; it is worth half as much as platinum. Except for iridium, the other platinum metals sell for a little less than platinum. Owing to the difficulty of separating it, iridium costs three times as much as platinum, although osmiridium, its naturally occurring alloy with osmium, costs less than platinum.

Metallurgy

The separation of these metals is an extremely complicated process and for this reason will not be described.

Physical and Chemical Properties

A few important physical and chemical properties of the platinum metals are listed in Table 34.1.

TABLE 34.1. PHYSICAL AND CHEMICAL PROPERTIES OF THE PLATINUM METAL

	Density	Melting Point (°C.)	Boiling Point (°C.)	Order of Hardness	Valences with Oxygen	Effect of Aqua Regia	Heated with Oxygen
Ruthenium	12.10	>1950	>2700	2–3	2, 3, 4, 8	Soluble	RuO_2 RuO_4
Rhodium	12.44	1955	>2500	4	2, 3, 4	Insoluble	—
Palladium	12.16	1555	2200	5	2, 4	Soluble	PdO on surface
Osmium	22.48	2700	>5300	1	2, 3, 4, 8	Insoluble	OsO_4
Iridium	22.42	2350	>4800	2–3	3, 4	Attacked very slowly	—
Platinum	21.50	1755	>4300	6	2, 4	Soluble	—

All these elements have high boiling and melting points. They are not good conductors of electricity. They are all harder than iron, osmium being the hardest one. They all have low coefficients of expansion. All except osmium are nearly white in appearance. Rhodium, palladium, and platinum are malleable; the others are somewhat brittle. All these metals have variable valences. Osmium is the only one which combines readily with the oxygen of the air but it is also least attacked by the halogens. Ruthenium and osmium form tetroxides. Palladium and platinum sorb large volumes of hydrogen gas; the greater the surface exposed, the larger the volume of gas sorbed. Oxygen condenses on the surface of the metals; hydrogen diffuses through and actually dissolves in the metals. Hydrogen sorbed on palladium is in such an active state that it will replace from solution metals below it in the E.C.S. In his work with filaments of light bulbs, Irving Langmuir of the General Electric Co. showed that filaments of many metals sorb gases. Depending upon the degree of subdivision of the metal, palladium sorbs from 1000 to 3000 volumes of hydrogen per volume of the metal.

Uses of the Platinum Metals and Their Compounds

Neither *ruthenium* nor its compounds are of commercial importance. The total consumption of ruthenium, osmium, and rhodium constituted only 4 per cent of the total consumption of the platinum group in 1945. The volatile poisonous RuO_4 is formed when ruthenium is fused with KOH and KNO_3.

Because of its brilliance and durability, *rhodium* is often called the "diamond of the metals." It is one of the hardest of this group of metals. Because it does not tarnish, rhodium is used as a plating for jewelry and silverware and for surfacing reflectors in searchlights.

The use of *osmium* as a catalyst in the Haber process has already been discussed. The compound, OsO_4, osmic tetroxide (frequently called osmic acid, although it is not an acid), is a yellow solid which boils at about 100° C. The vapors are very poisonous. It is used as a stain in microscopic work, organic matter reducing it to finely divided black particles of the metal. Tissues harden when soaked in this hygroscopic substance.

Iridium is used to harden platinum. Most of the platinum on the market contains from 1 to 2 per cent iridium—an expensive impurity—and platinum jewelry usually contains about 10 per cent iridium. The jewelry trade consumes 75 per cent of all the iridium sold in the United States; approximately 20 per cent of the balance is used for electrical purposes. The standard meter kept in France is marked on a platinum-iridium bar; this alloy is stable and has a low coefficient of expansion.

Palladium can be beaten into thin sheets and is used in this form for decorating shoes, gloves, picture frames, etc. Because of its resistance to all forms of corrosion—it is as resistant as gold, and much less conspicuous—about 23 per cent of the total output is used in making alloys for dental work; it is also used in the manufacture of many expensive surgical tools, watches, etc. A palladium-gold alloy, sold under the trade name of "Palau," is used as a substitute for the more expensive platinum ware in chemical laboratories. During the war, when jewelers were forbidden to use platinum, much palladium was used instead. The amount so used did not fall off when platinum again became available, it amounted to about 30 per cent of all palladium sold. But the largest user of palladium is the electrical industry which in 1945 jumped to 70,000 ounces (37 per cent of the total).

Platinum is by far the most important of this group of metals. The jewelry industry uses about 50 per cent of the total output, with dentistry and the chemical and electrical industries following in order. In the chemical industry it is used as a catalyst in the manufacture of sulfuric, acetic, and nitric acids; in apparatus for distilling sulfuric acid; as an anode for electrochemical reactions; and for such laboratory equipment as anodes, blowpipe tips, combustion boats, bottles, catalytic gauze, crucibles, evaporating dishes, funnels, retorts, tongs, etc. Its coefficient of expansion is so near that of soft glass that it can be used for electrical lead-in wires for laboratory equipment and light bulbs.

Chloroplatinic acid, H_2PtCl_6, the most important compound, is produced by dissolving platinum in aqua regia. It crystallizes with six molecules of water of crystallization. A water solution is very acid; the addition of NH_4OH or KOH yields the corresponding salts. $(NH_4)_2PtCl_6$ when heated produces spongy platinum. Potassium chloroplatinate is quite insoluble in 85 per cent alcohol, and hence can be used for the quantitative separation of potassium from sodium. Platinic chloride, $PtCl_4$, is produced by heating H_2PtCl_6 in an atmosphere of HCl at 165° C.; $PtCl_2$ is formed at about 600° C. The hydroxides are prepared by adding K_2CO_3 to the corresponding platinum salts, evaporating to dryness, and extracting the KCl with acetic acid. The corresponding oxides are obtained by heating the hydroxides.

The American Platinum Works sends all users of platinum these warnings: Keep platinumware clean, bright, and smooth. Don't heat unknown substances in it. Never heat it in contact with any other metal, and never reduce metals in it. Never heat sulfides, phosphides, caustic alkalis, the alkaline earths (particularly Li_2O and BaO), nitrates, nitrites, or cyanides in it. Use no mixtures which liberate the halogens. Heat organic substances slowly, and burn carbon in presence of plenty of air. Do not let a smoky flame impinge upon platinum, and always keep it in the oxidizing portion of the burner flame. It is best to heat platinumware in electric furnaces.

QUESTIONS AND PROBLEMS

1. Plot the atomic weights of the platinum metals against their densities.
2. List the important uses of the platinum metals.
3. What precautions should be remembered in using platinumware?
4. How do we account for the ease with which hydrogen diffuses through palladium?
5. What weight of K_2PtCl_6 can be precipitated with 1 g. of H_2PtCl_6?
6. What is the peculiar characteristic of osmic acid?

REFERENCES

Articles

"Platinum Metals." Ogburn, S. C., Jr. *J. Chem. Ed.* **5,** 1371–1384 (1928).

"Discovery and History of Platinum in Russia." Menschutkin, B. N. *J. Chem. Ed.* **11,** 226–229 (1934).

"Palladium-Hydrogen." Krause, W., and Kahlenberg, L. *Trans. Electro. Chem. Soc.* **68,** 449–470 (1935).

"Rhodium Plating." Fink, C. G., and Lambros, G. C. *Trans. Electro. Chem. Soc.* **63,** 181–186 (1933).

» 35 «

IRON

Iron, cobalt, and nickel constitute one of the triads of Group VIII. Iron is the most important and most useful metal, and therefore this chapter will deal with it; the following chapter will include a discussion of the metals frequently used with it.

No one knows when or by whom iron was discovered. The charcoal from a fire built by prehistoric man on a deposit of iron ore may have reduced the ore to molten metal. In the early days of the art of smelting, a man who could produce 8 pounds of iron a day was considered a genius. Because of its importance in warfare, iron was more highly prized hundreds of years ago than either gold or silver; copper, aluminum, rubber, cellulose, etc., have become essentials in modern warfare. The chemical symbol for iron, Fe, is derived from the Latin name *ferrum*.

Occurrence

Chemically pure iron is not found in nature. Only oxygen, silicon, and aluminum are more abundant than iron; but if, as some believe, the center of the earth is a ball of iron, iron is the most abundant element in the world. Some meteorites are rich in iron, and Greenland is said to have a few small deposits of free iron. Iron is present in both plants and animals. Hemoglobin, the red coloring matter of the blood, is an iron compound that serves as the oxygen carrier of the body.

Many iron-bearing minerals are found in nature, but only a few are of commercial importance; among them are those listed in the table on page 600. Of much less importance is "fool's gold" or iron pyrites, FeS_2. A few deposits of siderite, $FeCO_3$, and ilmenite, $FeTiO_3$, are mined. There are some oölite deposits, which are primarily small particles of sand surrounded by iron oxide, but no satisfactory process of extracting the iron from this ore has as yet been found.

Name	Formula	Color	Where Found
Hematite	Fe_2O_3	Red	Widely distributed (The color of sand and clay is due to traces of it.)
Magnetite	Fe_3O_4 or $FeO \cdot F_2O_3$	Black	Adirondack region, New Jersey, Utah, Pennsylvania
Limonite	$(Fe_2O_3)_2 \cdot 3\ H_2O$	Brown	Southern Appalachian states, Missouri

Metallurgy

Little progress was made in the manufacture of iron prior to the 8th century, for in the early days sufficient heat could not be developed to melt the iron. Charcoal was used to reduce the ore to a pasty mass which was then shaped by long and repeated heatings and hammerings. Hence a forger of iron swords and armor was a man whose favor was sought by kings and nobles.

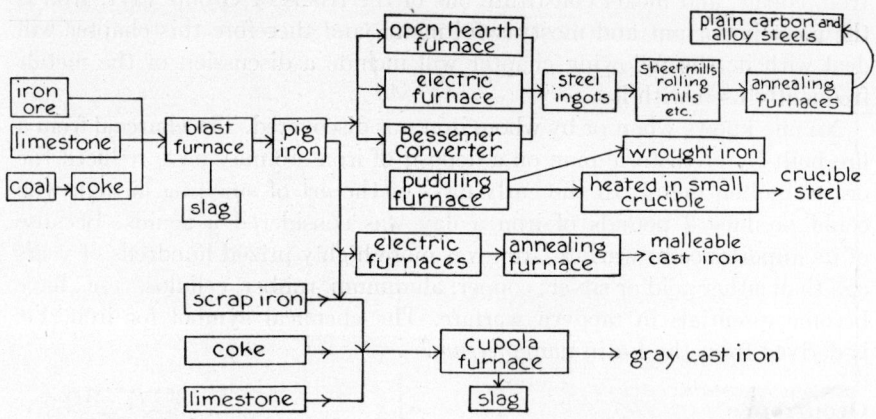

Fig. 35.1. Fundamental steps in the metallurgy of iron.

The first big advance was the invention of the blast furnace in Germany in the 15th century; after this, iron and steel were produced somewhat as we know them today. Iron ore was discovered in North Carolina in 1585 by an expedition sent from England by Sir Walter Raleigh, and the first ironworks was built near Jamestown, Virginia, in 1618. Without iron mills the colonists could never have won their freedom from England. Coke replaced charcoal in the 18th century, and the first rolling mill was established in England in 1728, thus doing away with much of the severe physical labor. One after another, rapid advances have followed in the metallurgy of iron. Bessemer converters, open-hearth processes, electric furnaces, new alloys, and modification in heat treatments have aided in making iron and steel cheaper and more common.

IRON

The fundamental steps in the metallurgy of iron are shown in outline form in Fig. 35.1. Note that five important end products are produced: (1) *plain carbon and alloy steels*, (2) *wrought iron*, (3) *crucible steel*, (4) *malleable cast iron*, and (5) *gray cast iron*.

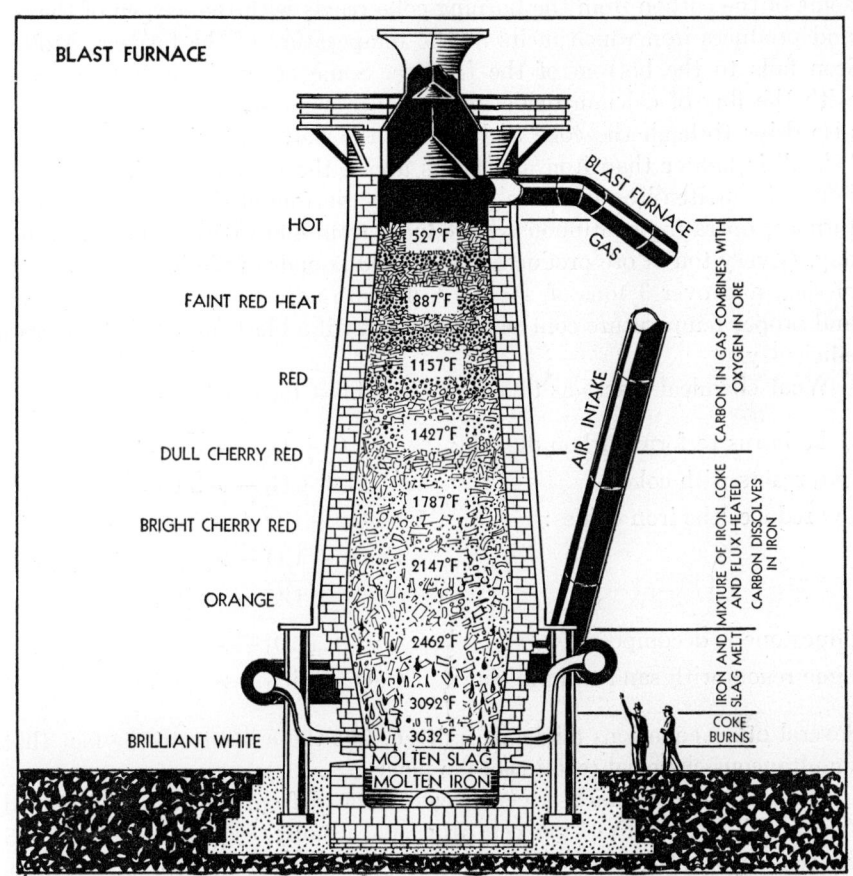

Fig. 35.2. A blast furnace. (Courtesy, General Motors Corporation.)

From Ore to Pig Iron. The *blast furnace*, a diagram of which is shown in Fig. 35.2, is the one unit through which all iron ore passes; it is the first step in the conversion of iron into steel. Iron ore as it comes from the mines contains earthy matter and many other impurities. The blast furnace has three functions: (1) It separates the earthy matter from the ore, (2) it reduces iron compounds to metallic iron, and (3) it adds carbon which gives the iron a lower melting point so that it flows readily and can be easily molded.

A blast furnace is an outer steel shell which is lined with fire brick; it is usually 100 feet high and 20 feet in diameter; it is narrow at the bottom, then widens out and tapers to the top. The charge consists of ore, coke, and limestone in the ratio of 1:0.5:0.3, and it is fed into a hopper at the top, whence it goes through a compartment called a bell. A blast of air enters through tuyeres near the bottom of the furnace. The coke fire is started and some of the carbon from the burning coke reacts with the oxygen of the ore and produces iron which melts at the temperature of the furnace. Molten iron falls to the bottom of the furnace. Some of the impurities combine with the flux of calcium oxide and produce a molten conglomerate which also drips through the coke and falls to the bottom. This mixture, called "slag," is lighter than iron and floats above the molten metal. Every few hours the molten iron is drawn off from the bottom of the furnace. A single furnace, operating continuously, produces from 400 to 500 tons of iron per day. (Every ton of ore produces about 1100 pounds of pig iron, 800 pounds of slag, and over 3 tons of gases.) A delicate adjustment of raw materials and proper temperature control are necessary if a blast furnace is to operate efficiently.

What chemical reactions take place in a blast furnace?

Coke burns to form carbon dioxide: $C + \overline{O_2} \longrightarrow \overline{CO_2} + \Delta$

CO_2 reacts with coke: $C + \overline{CO_2} \longrightarrow \overline{2\,CO}$

CO reduces the iron oxides:
$3\,Fe_2O_3 + \overline{CO} \longrightarrow 2\,Fe_3O_4 + \overline{CO_2}$
$Fe_3O_4 + \overline{CO} \longrightarrow 3\,FeO + \overline{CO_2}$
$FeO + \overline{CO} \longrightarrow Fe + \overline{CO_2}$

Limestone is decomposed: $CaCO_3 \xrightarrow{\Delta} CaO + \overline{CO_2}$

Lime reacts with sand to form slag: $CaO + SiO_2 \longrightarrow CaSiO_3$

Several other equations might be written, but these illustrate the fact that simultaneous chemical reactions take place.

The molten iron which is periodically tapped from the furnace is called "pig iron." It is 92 to 94 per cent iron, and usually also contains 3.5 to 4.5 per cent carbon, together with varying amounts of silicon, sulfur, phosphorus, manganese, etc. The liquid pig iron is cast into molds called "pigs," from which innumerable iron products are made.

Modifications in Properties of Pig Iron; Gray and White Cast Iron. Many foundries purchase pig iron, remelt it in small *cupola furnaces*, and pour the molten metal into molds to make castings. Manhole covers for sewers, frames for machines, and many parts of machinery are made of cast iron. The cupola furnace, which looks somewhat like a blast furnace, is lined with clay, and has a spout at the bottom. These furnaces hold from one to several tons of iron. Coke is dropped in from the top, and then pig iron, scrap iron, and limestone are put in on top of the coke. The coke is ignited and a blast of air is forced up through the charcoal. The iron soon melts and falls to the bottom of the furnace. The clay plug is removed from the spout, and the molten iron runs out into ladles under the spout; the spout is plugged again as soon as the ladles are filled.

The molten iron is poured into molds like that in Fig. 35.3. Hours of work precede the pouring. First a drawing of the object must be made, and then a wooden pattern. The latter is used for other patterns; the molder also uses it, since he has to build up the sand mold in sections and fit them together before the pouring can start. Foundry workers are usually classified as molders, core makers, etc.

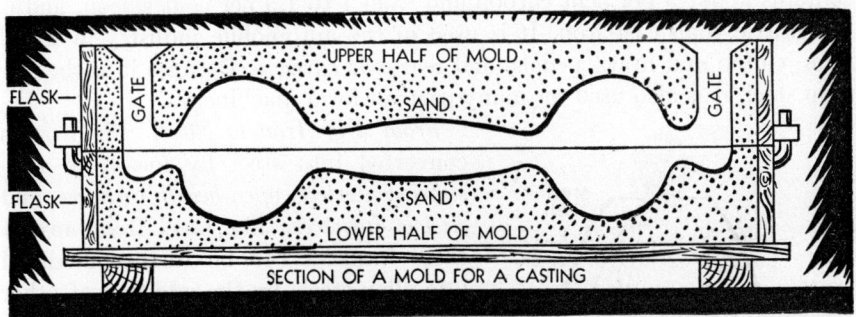

Fig. 35.3. A mold for casting. (Courtesy, General Motors Corporation.)

Gray cast iron is obtained by slowly cooling the iron in the mold, some of the carbon separating as graphite. This iron is not as hard as white cast iron; it can be made ductile by annealing. Hard, brittle *white cast iron* is obtained by cooling the molten iron in the molds very quickly. The carbon does not separate but remains distributed through the iron as cementite, Fe_3C. Pouring both white and gray cast iron is difficult, for the men must work rapidly, the sand mold often crumbles in one spot, some slag gets in with the molten iron, air pockets form, etc.

From Pig Iron to Wrought Iron. A tough form of iron is made by purifying melted pig iron in *puddling furnaces.* These are small reverberatory furnaces so constructed that heat is reflected down on the pig iron which rests on a bed of iron oxide. As the iron melts, carbon and other impurities react with the oxygen of the iron oxide, and these substances are burned out; the melting point of the iron rises from about 1100° to 1500° C. and the metal becomes plastic. A man called a "puddler" stirs the iron with a long "rabble." The molten metal is removed from the furnace in balls weighing about as much as a man can lift, and these are hammered or rolled to squeeze out most of the slag. The remaining trace of slag, distributed in the form of a thin coating around fibers of iron, is thought to be responsible for the superior resistance to corrosion exhibited by wrought iron. Where this property is not required, wrought iron is being replaced by low-carbon steel, whose manufacture is much less time-consuming. In order to retain the corrosion resistance of wrought iron prepared by the traditional process and at the same time avoid much of the costly hand labor, the Byers Company pours a fairly pure iron into a premelted slag. The iron is then gathered in much larger masses than can be rabbled and lifted by hand, and the excess slag is hammered or rolled out.

From Pig Iron to Malleable Cast Iron. Malleable iron castings are made by carefully heating either pig iron or a mixture of pig and scrap iron in air in electric furnaces and annealing the castings in special annealing furnaces. The molten metal is cooled slowly and graphite separates. Malleable iron contains about 3 per cent carbon and from 1 to 1.5 per cent silicon, and is less brittle than cast iron. It is used in the automobile industry in wheel hubs, clutch and brake pedals, and rear-axle carriers. Because it is cheaper than steel, it is also used for many parts of farm machinery.

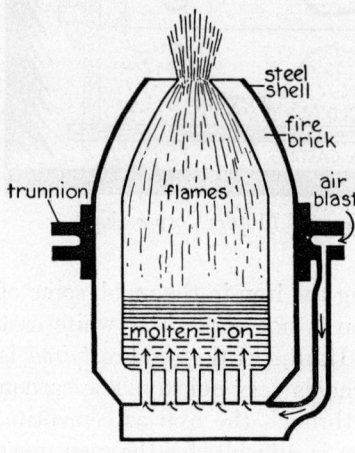

FIG. 35.4. A Bessemer converter.

From Pig Iron to Steel. Pig iron is converted into steel by means of *Bessemer converters, open-hearth furnaces*, and *electric furnaces*. The steel from any of these furnaces can be further modified into alloy steels by the addition of other metals.

The furnace which is now called the *Bessemer converter* was designed independently by William Kelly of Kentucky in 1847 and Sir Henry Bessemer of England; the latter patented the process in 1855. Kelly noticed that when air came in contact with pig iron, the metal seethed and boiled, instead of being cooled. He reasoned that the air oxidized the impurities from the metal, and that the reaction was exothermic, the heat thus produced making the metal boil. It occurred to him that the impurities could be removed if air were blown through pig iron. Bessemer had the same idea, and a special furnace called a Bessemer converter was developed.

In general appearance, this converter is a pear-shaped steel vessel lined with firebrick and so mounted that it can be tipped for pouring; it holds from 10 to 20 tons of iron. Molten pig iron is poured into the converter and a blast of air is forced up through the metal, which is at a temperature of about 1200° C. Pig iron contains about 70 pounds of carbon, 20 pounds of silicon, 15 pounds of manganese, and from 1 to 2 pounds of sulfur per ton. These impurities combine with the oxygen from the blast of air and burn, liberating sufficient heat to raise the temperature to about 1900° C. The blowing process requires between 10 and 15 minutes; workmen can tell when the process is complete by the color of the flame shooting into the sky. *No external heat is applied.*

IRON

The lining of a Bessemer converter depends upon the impurities present. If the pig iron is rich in phosphorus, P_2O_5 is formed; the lining must be basic to react with this impurity. Most of the converters in the United States are lined with siliceous substances, for our pig iron is usually low in phosphorus.

Burning the impurities out leaves iron that is too pure for many purposes. Therefore, just as the molten metal is ready to be poured, the desired amounts of carbon (enough to produce 0.1 to 1.0 per cent carbon in the

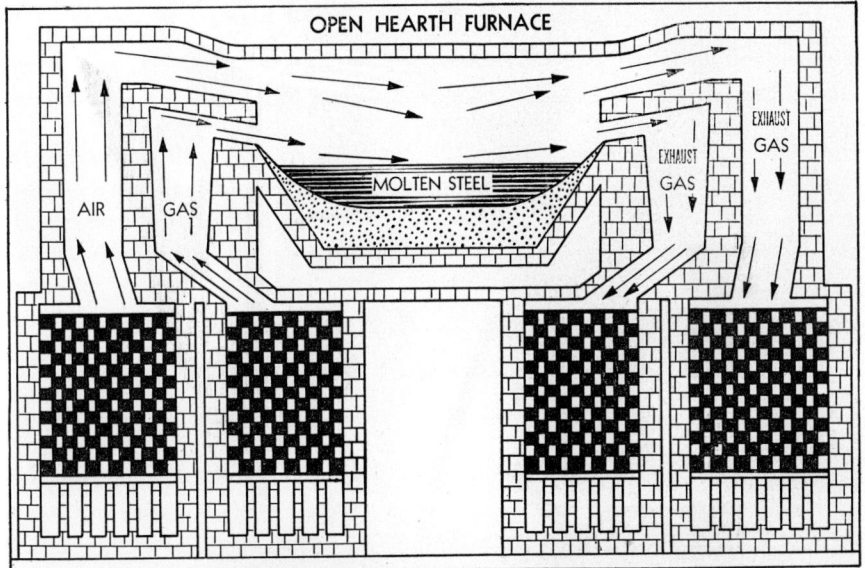

FIG. 35.5. An open-hearth furnace. (Courtesy, General Motors Corporation.)

steel), manganese, and other metals are added. Because of the vigorous aeration of the metal, much air is trapped in it, and these air pockets must be removed to prevent weak spots in the steel. Various degasifiers, including manganese, aluminum shot, ferrosilicon, iron boride, titanium, etc., are used for this purpose. Once the most important method of making steel, the Bessemer process has declined until now only about 5 per cent of our steel is Bessemer steel.

The *open-hearth process*, another method of producing steel, was developed by William Siemens of England and Pierre Martin of France; it was made necessary by the ever-increasing quantities of scrap metal on the market. A diagram of an open-hearth furnace is shown in Fig. 35.5. Externally, this furnace resembles a huge oven, and several furnaces are frequently arranged in a row. The saucer-shaped hearth may hold from a few to 250 tons of metal, and about 12 hours are required to remove the impurities from the metal. Much more accurate control is possible with these furnaces than with Bessemer converters; another distinct advantage is that iron is not blown out of the furnaces as is the case with the Bessemer converters. As a result of these advantages, open-hearth furnaces now account for more than 80 per cent of our steel capacity.

Powdered coal, oil, and gas are used as fuel, and there are two openings at the ends of the furnace through which both air and fuel may enter. To maintain a high temperature, the air which enters is preheated. (If oxygen alone

Photo by Bethlehem Steel Co.

FIG. 35.6. Tapping furnace containing high-alloy steel.

is used, only one-fifth the volume of gas need be preheated.) The metal is shielded from the direct flame, and the heat liberated from the burning gases is reflected down on the metal. Once the process is under way, the direction of the flow of gases is reversed every 15 or 20 minutes to keep the gases passing above the hearth as hot as possible. As the impurities burn out, the iron becomes hotter and hotter. Samples are withdrawn at frequent intervals and subjected to chemical test to determine the quality of the steel. Just before the steel is poured, the desired amounts of carbon and alloy metals are added.

The lining of the hearth and also the flux which is added depend upon the impurities present in the pig iron. The impurities react with the lining and the flux, producing a slag which floats on the surface. When a furnace is tapped, the molten steel is caught in ladles from which it is poured into molds. The slag is removed last and piled up as a waste material (some goes into the cement and fertilizer industries).

Electric furnaces are similar in design to open-hearth furnaces, the fundamental difference being the source of heat. They are particularly suitable to the manufacture of high-alloy steel (the open-hearth is used for low-alloy steel) and hence are of continually increasing importance. Electric furnace steel now approaches Bessemer steel in tonnage and exceeds it in value.

Crucible steel is made by reheating wrought iron, open-hearth or Bessemer steel, or scrap iron in small crucibles. The small batches in which the steel is produced enable a careful control of the temperature and the adjustment of the composition to meet the special requirements of consumers. Razor blades, kitchen and pocket knives, files, watch springs, etc., are made from crucible steel. *Cementation steel* is made by placing sheets of wrought iron between layers of carbon and heating the iron for a period at a temperature below its melting point. The carbon that diffuses into the steel hardens the surface. *Nitrided steel*, which is very hard, is made by heating sheet steel for about a day in a stream of hot ammonia gas. The ammonia which is decomposed liberates nitrogen which forms iron nitride.

The hardening and tempering or heat treatment of steel has developed into a fine art. The addition of small quantities of other elements to iron, together with proper annealing, cooling, and reheating, can produce steels with marked differences in physical and chemical properties.

Production of Iron and Steel

About a billion and a half tons of iron ore have been mined during the past quarter century in the United States, a third of it in the past five years. About 80 per cent of this now comes from the Lake Superior region. Formerly the percentage was higher, but mines in other sections of the country are being developed. World War II caused unheard-of drains upon our reserves of iron ore. Whereas production had regularly reached peaks of about 70,000,000 tons during the preceding 25 years (and a 20th-century low of 10,000,000 tons in 1932), during the war it shot up over the hundred-million mark (119,000,000 tons at one time), and is not likely soon to drop below 70,000,000 tons. The fabulous Lake region mines now contain barely a third of our reserves (a billion tons) of iron ore rich enough to ship without concentration. (Thirty-nine per cent is in the Southeast, the rest is scattered.) The United States may begin importing appreciable quantities of iron ore in another decade. However, we are in no immediate danger of becoming a "have-not" nation in regard to iron, for we have five to ten billion tons of ore which can be concentrated satisfactorily by known methods, and fifty billion more for which a method will doubtless be found. The average direct-shipping iron ore contains, in percentages, iron, 51; phosphorus <0.1; silica, 9; manganese 0.8; and moisture, 11; nearly all the rest is oxygen. It sells at the mines for about $2.70 per ton.

The 70,000,000-ton peaks mentioned above corresponded to about 45,000,000 tons of pig iron; but in 1944 our production was twice that. Pig iron sells for about $20 per ton. The price reached a high of over $43 per ton in 1922, and dropped to a low of $15 per ton in 1932. In 1936 the total world production of pig iron was about 110 million tons, of which about 30 million tons were produced by the United States. The reclaiming of scrap iron is a large industry in this country, about 61 million tons being reclaimed in 1944. Table 35.1 shows the consumption of ferrous scrap and pig iron in that year in the United States by type of furnace; the figures are taken from the *Minerals Yearbook*.

TABLE 35.1. CONSUMPTION OF SCRAP AND PIG IRON IN THE UNITED STATES IN 1944, BY TYPE OF FURNACE

Type of Furnace	Plants Reporting	Scrap Iron (1000 tons)	Pig Iron (1000 tons)
Open hearth	146	40,808	48,281
Bessemer	36	387	5,583
Electric	382	6,422	240
Cupola	2,604	7,500	3,890
Crucible	18	1	1
Puddling	6	11	28
Blast	78	3,638	—
Other types	164	2,582	2,928
Total	3434	61,349	60,951

In 1938, 3266 plants reported consumption of 21,345,000 tons of scrap iron and 18,504,000 tons of pig iron.

Physical and Chemical Properties of Iron

Iron is one of the more difficult metals to purify. In fact, not a single ounce of really pure iron had ever been prepared until very recently, when a thousand pounds or so of it was prepared as a special war project. Ordinary "pure iron" is only *high purity* iron; therefore this section will deal with the properties of high-purity iron.

Basic open-hearth iron contains about 0.222 of 1 per cent impurities. The high-purity iron used for research work is prepared electrolytically and contains about 0.03 of 1 per cent impurities. Iron prepared in Germany for experimental work by the decomposition of iron carbonyl is claimed to be only about 0.015 of 1 per cent impure.

X-ray studies prove that iron exists in three allotropic modifications; at room temperature it is called alpha iron; at intermediate temperatures, gamma; and near the melting point, delta. It crystallizes in the cubic or isometric system, but the crystal structure is changed markedly by the various heat treatments given to the metal. The density of iron is 7.87. The melting point obtained by averaging the data of eight observers is 1535° C., and the boiling point is approximately 3000°. Its tensile strength, elasticity, and hardness depend upon the method of preparation. Its coefficient of expansion is high. The volume decreases by about 5 per cent when molten iron solidifies. The rails on a railroad track expand about 0.7 of an inch per mile per degree Centigrade change in temperature. Carbon and other impurities in iron drastically affect its magnetic properties; the detrimental effect of the carbon can be counteracted by traces of nickel, cobalt, silicon, and manganese, which substitute for iron in the crystal lattice.

Iron rusts rapidly when exposed to the combined action of water and oxygen, but it does not corrode at room temperature in the presence of *dry* oxygen. The life of iron exposed to atmospheric corrosion is increased by about 50 per cent if the iron contains 0.2 of 1 per cent of copper.

The position of iron in the E.C.S. indicates that it is a relatively active metal. It burns readily in oxygen, combines with sulfur and the moist halogens, and displaces hydrogen from acids and steam. If sheet iron is left in *fuming* nitric acid for five minutes and then placed in either dilute sulfuric acid or a solution of copper sulfate, no chemical reaction takes place. The iron is said to be *passive*. If the strip is then touched with a piece of non-passive iron, this peculiar property disappears immediately.

COMPOUNDS OF IRON

Iron forms two series of compounds. The divalent or ferrous compounds are good reducing agents. The ferric or trivalent compounds are the more stable of the two series. In a few unimportant compounds such as sodium ferrite, $Na_2Fe_2O_4$, and sodium ferrate, Na_2FeO_4, iron is present in the negative radical. There are many complex iron salts. Ferrous salts are easily oxidized by atmospheric oxygen, but do not hydrolyze as readily in water solution as do the ferric salts.

Hydroxides and Oxides

In many parts of the United States water pumped from the ground contains the divalent ferrous ion, sometimes combined with the bicarbonate radical. Contact with the oxygen of the air oxidizes the iron to the ferric ion, and red insoluble ferric hydroxide precipitates. This precipitate is insoluble in both NH_4OH and $NaOH$. Pure white $Fe(OH)_2$ is also insoluble; it is seldom observed because even traces of oxygen change it to $Fe(OH)_3$.

Black *ferrous oxide*, FeO, is usually prepared by heating ferrous oxalate, FeC_2O_4, or reducing Fe_2O_3 with hydrogen. It is of no commercial importance.

Red *ferric oxide* is obtained by oxidizing pyrites, FeS_2; by igniting $Fe(OH)_3$, and by allowing iron to rust; it also forms in electrolysis reactions in which the anodes are iron. The oxide forms hydrates. Millions of tons of hematite, Fe_2O_3, are mined each year. The pure oxide is known as jeweler's rouge and Venetian red; the latter is the familiar red pigment used in cement, rubber, pottery, etc. Fe_2O_3 in a highly hydrated state is known as colloidal ferric hydroxide and is prepared by boiling a dilute solution of $FeCl_3$.

The mineral, *magnetite*, is another oxide, Fe_3O_4 (or $FeO \cdot Fe_2O_3$). The blue color of many iron products is obtained by dipping the metal in fused KNO_3, a surface film of Fe_3O_4 protecting the metal from corrosion. Fe_3O_4 is formed when steel wool is heated in oxygen.

Sulfur Compounds

Ferrous sulfide, FeS, is prepared by bubbling H_2S into an alkaline solution of a ferrous salt, and also by heating iron filings and sulfur together. Since $Fe(OH)_3$ is more insoluble than Fe_2S_3, the latter does not form when H_2S is added to a solution of ferric salts. Ferric salts oxidize H_2S to free sulfur; therefore the black precipitate formed is ferrous sulfide. Iron pyrites, FeS_2, is the only iron sulfide difficult to dissolve in acid.

Ferric sulfate, $Fe_2(SO_4)_3$, is obtained by oxidizing ferrous sulfate. It forms many alums, such as $NH_4Fe(SO_4)_2 \cdot 12\ H_2O$. The ferric salt, $Fe_2(SO_4)_3$, crystallizes with nine molecules of water and is used to a small extent in water purification.

Ferrous sulfate, the most important iron salt, is produced in large quantities by dipping iron in sulfuric acid to pickle it or remove the rust. On evaporation, $FeSO_4 \cdot 7\ H_2O$, known as green vitriol or copperas, is obtained. The pickling liquor sometimes presents a real problem, for the cost of crystallizing the salt is more than it is worth. $FeSO_4$ is frequently chlorinated and used in water purification. The salt, together with tannic acid, sulfuric acid, gum arabic as a protective agent, and often a blue dye, is used in the manufacture of black ink. The ferrous tannate is soon oxidized on the paper to black ferric tannate. Because $FeSO_4 \cdot 7\ H_2O$ is efflorescent, the double salt, ferrous ammonium sulfate, $FeSO_4 \cdot (NH_4)_2SO_4 \cdot 6\ H_2O$ (Mohr's salt), is preferred when a stable ferrous salt is required in the laboratory. This salt can be weighed in the open on an analytical balance. Mohr's salt has the further advantage that its solutions are not as rapidly oxidized by air as are those of simple ferrous sulfate. This is because of the formation of a complex sulfatoferrite ion. In ferrous sulfate considerable numbers of sulfate ions displace water molecules from the hydrated ferrous ion; the higher concentration of SO_4^{--} ions in Mohr's salt sends this process much further toward completion.

Chlorides of Iron

Iron dissolves in dilute hydrochloric acid and produces $FeCl_2$; this crystallizes as $FeCl_2 \cdot 4\ H_2O$. The pure blue-green salt is used in the laboratory as a reducing agent.

Ferric chloride, $FeCl_3$, is obtained by the action of chlorine on iron. The pure anhydrous salt is black, and it can be sublimed. The common salt is the hexahydrate. The fact that HCl escapes and the hydrated oxide forms when a solution of this salt is boiled shows that it hydrolyzes readily.

Complex Iron Cyanides

Potassium ferrocyanide was accidentally prepared years ago when iron filings, KNO_3, and nitrogenous organic matter were heated together. This salt crystallizes from water as $K_4Fe(CN)_6 \cdot 3\ H_2O$. It is a complex salt instead of a simple double salt, for a water solution of it does not give the reactions characteristic of ferrous ions. It is prepared in the laboratory by adding KCN to ferrous sulfate.

$$Fe^{++} + SO_4^{--} + 2\ K^+ + 2\ CN^- \longrightarrow \underline{Fe(CN)_2} + 2\ K^+ + SO_4^{--}$$
$$\underline{Fe(CN)_2} + 4\ K^+ + 4\ CN^- \longrightarrow \overline{4\ K^+ + Fe(CN)_6^{----}}$$

This salt can be oxidized to potassium ferricyanide, $K_3Fe(CN)_6$, by the addition of chlorine water.

Prussian blue, or laundry bluing, is prepared by adding a ferric salt to a ferrocyanide. A colloidal solution is formed.

$$4\ Fe^{+++} + 12\ Cl^- + 12\ K^+ + 3\ Fe(CN)_6^{----} \longrightarrow$$
$$\underline{Fe_4(Fe(CN)_6)_3} + 12\ K^+ + 12\ Cl^-$$

A precipitate of *Turnbull's blue* is obtained when a ferrous salt is added to a ferricyanide. Although the two blues differ in physical state, the color is the same and it is possible that they are identical in composition, the ferricyanide having oxidized the ferrous ion before precipitation occurred.

Blueprints

Paper for blueprints is soaked in potassium ferric oxalate or ferric ammonium citrate and $K_3Fe(CN)_6$ and dried in a dark room. Green ferric ferricyanide deposits in the paper. In making the blueprint, the drawing or tracing is placed over the paper and exposed to a bright light. Wherever light strikes the paper, the ferric ion is catalytically reduced by the organic matter to the ferrous ion, which reacts with potassium ferricyanide and produces insoluble Turnbull's blue. After the unchanged salt is rinsed off and the paper is dried in the light, the drawing appears as white lines against a blue background. A solution of a strong base destroys the blue color.

Determination of Iron

Large amounts of iron are precipitated as red $Fe(OH)_3$ which is then ignited and weighed. A rapid determination of iron can be made by first reducing it to the ferrous state and then measuring the volume of standard $KMnO_4$ required to oxidize the Fe^{++} to Fe^{+++}. The manganese is reduced to divalent manganese (Mn^{++}). Iron in small quantities can be determined colorimetrically. The ferric ion, $Fe(H_2O)_6^{+++}$, has a faint violet color which can be observed in ferric nitrate or ferric alum. If any of the attached water molecules ionize (which they do unless the solution is quite acid), the resulting $Fe(H_2O)_5OH^{++}$ and $Fe(H_2O)_4(OH)_2^+$ ions give the solution a color approaching that of ferric hydroxide, $Fe(H_2O)_3(OH)_3$. The replacement of water molecules by chloride ions, as in an $FeCl_3$ solution, gives a strong brown color. Thiocyanate ions, CNS^-, similarly coordinating with the ferric ions, produce an extremely intense brownish-red color which can be measured to determine the amount of iron. An excess of KCNS is used; the iron is probably in the form of $Fe(H_2O)_5CNS^{++}$ ions.

QUESTIONS AND PROBLEMS

1. Why was the development of the blast furnace so important? Is it customary to close down the furnaces of a steel mill at night?
2. Discuss the role of carbon in steel.
3. What does the use of a blast furnace accomplish? List a few of the important chemical reactions which take place.
4. What is pig iron? How is steel made from it?
5. Of what significance are furnace linings?
6. List the important physical properties of iron.
7. Start with iron and prepare the following: $FeCl_2$, $FeCl_3$, $Fe(OH)_3$, $K_4Fe(CN)_6$, and $FeSO_4 \cdot (NH_4)_2SO_4 \cdot 6 H_2O$.
8. If an unknown contains one of the compounds mentioned in question 7, how would you identify it?
9. Explain how sulfuric acid can be shipped in steel cars. Since iron reacts with steam to form Fe_3O_4 and hydrogen, how can steel boilers be used?
10. What weight of Fe_2O_3 can be obtained from 25 ml. of 0.30 molar $FeCl_2$?
11. Outline some important methods of protecting iron from corrosion.

REFERENCES
Books

Industrial Chemistry.   Rogers, Allen.   D. Van Nostrand & Company, Inc.
Chemistry in Industry.   Howe, H. E.   Chemical Foundation, Inc.

Articles

"Sources of Iron Ores."   Burchard, E. F.   *J. Chem. Ed.* **10**, 195–204, 288–296 (1933).
"Ferro-Alloys."   Burchard, E. F.   *J. Chem. Ed.* **10**, 359–368 (1933).
"Chemistry of Pig Iron."   Franklin, G. T.   *J. Chem. Ed.* **8**, 143–148 (1931).
"Alloy Steels."   Crook, W. J.   *J. Chem. Ed.* **4**, 583–595 (1927).

36

METALS USED IN THE STEEL INDUSTRY

Eleven metals in Groups IV B–VIII of the periodic table are important in the steel industry. Even though the total production of these elements is small as compared with that of iron, we would be greatly inconvenienced if we were deprived of them. They are in the transitional groups in the periodic table (page 82), and have many properties in common, as Table 36.1 shows. All of them have high melting and boiling points. Titanium is lightest and tungsten the heaviest.

TABLE 36.1. METALS USED IN THE STEEL INDUSTRY

Name	Symbol	Group	Atomic Number	Melting Point (°C.)	Boiling Point (°C.)	Density	Valence in Compounds	Uses
Titanium	Ti	IV	22	1800	>3000	4.5	2, 3, 4	Deoxidizer and carbide stabilizer in steel.
Zirconium	Zr	IV	40	1700	>2900	6.4	2, 3, 4	Removes oxygen, nitrogen, and sulfur in steel.
Vanadium	V	V	23	1710	3000	5.96	1, 2, 3, 4, 5	Steel with high tensile strength, tool steel.
Columbium	Cb	V	41	1956	>3300	8.4	3, 4, 5	Weldable high-speed tools; radio tubes.
Tantalum	Ta	V	73	2850	>4100	16.6	5	Non-corrosive steel rectifiers.
Chromium	Cr	VI	24	1615	2200	7.1	2, 3, 6	Tough corrosive-resistant alloys.
Molybdenum	Mo	VI	42	2620	3700	10.2	3, 4, 5, 6	High-fatigue load and cutting steels.
Tungsten	W	VI	74	3370	5900	19.3	2, 3, 4, 5, 6	High-speed steel.
Manganese	Mn	VII	25	1260	1900	7.2	2, 3, 4, 6, 7	Purifies iron; long-wearing steel.
Cobalt	Co	VIII	27	1480	2900	8.9	2, 3	Alloys for cutting steel.
Nickel	Ni	VIII	28	1452	2900	8.9	2, (3?)	High-strength, corrosive-resistant alloys.

COBALT (At. No. 27)

Beautiful blue cobalt pigments were used by the potters and glassmakers long before the Christian era. During the Middle Ages, Saxony was the largest producer of the cobalt compounds. Much superstition formerly surrounded cobalt mining, because the miners, believing that they had discovered silver deposits, attributed their failure to obtain the silver from the ore to the evil doings of the *Kobolds* or "subterranean gnomes." The German word *Kobold*, first applied to all metallic-looking ores which would not yield metal, was later used for cobalt.

In 1735 George Brandt, a Swedish chemist, produced metallic cobalt from its ore.

Occurrence

Cobalt is seldom found in the free state, although some metallic cobalt has been found in meteorites. The ores, of which the most important are the arsenides, arseno-sulfides, and arsenates, are always associated with other ores, the type of ores varying from one country to another. In Canada cobalt ore is present in silver-nickel ores; in Germany it is associated with bismuth; it is a by-product of copper refining in the Belgian Congo; and it is present in the manganese ores of New Caledonia. Some common cobalt ores are cobaltite, $CoAsS$; smaltite, $CoAs_2$; linnaeite, Co_3S_4; and cobalt ochre (erythrite), $Co_3(AsO_4)_2 \cdot 8\ H_2O$.

Metallurgy

The presence of arsenic, sulfur, iron, nickel, and many other metals in cobalt ores complicates the metallurgical processes, as is evidenced by the processes used at Cobalt, Ontario. The silver-arsenic-cobalt-nickel-iron ore is ground and smelted to form a spiess (a metallurgical product containing metal sulfides). The spiess is roasted to remove arsenic and convert the metals into oxides, and silver is removed from the roasted product by heating it with salt and agitating it in tanks containing sodium cyanide. Bleaching powder is added to the remaining material to precipitate black cobaltous oxide and nickel hydroxide. Many methods, some of them closely guarded secret processes, are used to obtain cobalt from the concentrated cobalt residues. The oxide may be reduced with carbon, hydrogen, carbon monoxide, aluminum (thermite), magnesium, or zinc dust. In the inexpensive Mond process, used in some plants to separate nickel from cobalt, the oxides are heated in the presence of carbon monoxide and the nickel is removed as volatile nickel carbonyl, $Ni(CO)_4$. Electrolytic methods and the distillation of cobalt amalgams are used to purify the cobalt.

Physical and Chemical Properties

Cobalt is silvery gray, magnetic, malleable, ductile, and quite stable at room temperature. It reacts with oxygen at high temperatures to form Co_3O_4 ($CoO \cdot Co_2O_3$). It is above hydrogen in the E.C.S. and reacts with non-oxidizing acids. It forms many compounds by direct union with the non-metals.

Production and Uses

Prior to 1904 most of the cobalt was produced in Sweden, Norway, and Saxony, but most of the cobalt now comes from the Belgian Congo and Northern Rhodesia. The Ontario deposits were discovered in 1904 during the construction of a railroad.

Before the First World War, the total annual output of cobalt oxide was about 250 tons; this increased to 400 tons per year during the war. Since then the demand has gradually increased until at present about 2000 tons are produced per year. The United States has never been important as a producer of cobalt, although we could produce more if necessary.

The metal is marketed in this country in three forms: rondelles (slugs about $1'' \times \frac{3}{4}''$), shot, and anodes. The producers of cobalt throughout the world have stabilized the price at about $1.60 per pound.

Cobalt is alloyed with chromium and tungsten to produce non-ferrous alloys known as "stellite." They are extremely hard, even at red heat, and are used for high-speed cutting and in the valves and valve seats of automotive and aircraft engines. "Konel" contains cobalt, nickel, and ferrotitanium, and is used as a substitute for platinum. With "alnico," an Al–Ni–Co alloy developed by the General Electric Co. in 1936, permanent magnets can be made capable of lifting 60 times their own weight. Vitallium, an alloy containing 65 per cent cobalt, 30 per cent chromium, and 5 per cent molybdenum, is used for the turbine blades of jet-propulsion gas turbines. Cobalt is used as the catalyst in a German process for the synthesis of gasoline. About half of the cobalt ore mined goes into the production of the metal and the remainder is used to make cobalt compounds.

Compounds of Cobalt

Cobalt forms two series of compounds containing Co^{++} and Co^{+++} ions. Most cobaltic salts (except the complexes) are unstable. An important use of the oxide is in the ceramic industry. Crude cobalt oxide, called "Zaffre," is heated with K_2CO_3 and white quartz to form a blue glass called "smalt." When mixed with other oxides, this produces many shades of blue, green, and violet. It is used as both an under and a surface glaze stain, and also to counteract the yellow tint of iron in white ware. *Cobalt acetates, borates, linoleates,* and *tungstates* are used as dryers in paints and varnishes.

Sympathetic ink is a solution of cobaltous chloride, $CoCl_2$; if the paper containing it is heated, the anhydrous *blue* salt forms. Crucibles in the laboratory are marked with cobaltous chloride and the color is then baked into the porcelain.

Cobalt forms many complex salts such as cyanides, ammonia complexes, ammines, nitrites, etc. One of the most important is potassium cobaltinitrite, $K_3Co(NO_2)_6$, which is insoluble and is used to separate cobalt from nickel. Soluble cobaltinitrites are used to precipitate the potassium ion from solution.

Investigations to date indicate that cobalt is essential for animal growth. Cobalt compounds fed to diseased sheep in Australia checked the deadly "enzootic marasmus," and the "bush-sickness" of New Zealand is now thought to be due to a deficiency in cobalt. Feeding experiments carried on at the University of Chicago show that cobalt compounds increase the hemoglobin content of the blood.

NICKEL (At. No. 28)

Alloys containing nickel were first used in China. A German ore resembled copper ores but yielded no copper; hence it was called *Kupfernickel*, or "false copper." The Swedish chemist, Cronstedt, studied this ore carefully in 1751 and found that it could be reduced with charcoal to a white magnetic metal which he called nickel. The fact that it was magnetic led to a general belief that the substance was only another form of iron, but it was finally proved to be an element.

Occurrence

Some metallic nickel is found in meteorites. The chief sources of it are pentlandite (Fe, Ni)S, often associated with pyrrhotite (Fe, Ni, and Cu sulfides), and garnierite $(Mg, Ni)O \cdot SiO_2 \cdot xH_2O$. The large Canadian pyrrhotite deposits lie near the surface of the ground.

Metallurgy

The ore is smelted in Bessemer or open-hearth ovens which convert it into a matte of copper and nickel sulfides. The matte is then shipped to the refineries where nickel is obtained by the Oxford process, the Mond process, or electrolysis.

The Oxford process of separation is based on differences in density. After sodium sulfate and carbon are added to the matte, it is heated to produce Na_2S. The fused mass separates into an upper layer of copper and waste, and a lower layer of nickel compounds and a trace of copper. The copper is leached out and the residue is heated to produce metallic nickel. This process is not very satisfactory because the precious metals which are present as impurities are not recovered.

In the Mond process, which has been used since 1895, carbon monoxide is passed over the ore, producing volatile nickel carbonyl, $Ni(CO)_4$, which boils at $-25°$ C. This is decomposed at $150°$, and gives metallic nickel.

In the electrolytic process, the copper is removed first by using the proper voltage and electrolyte. The nickel is then electrodeposited, the noble metals remaining in the anode mud. The only disadvantage of this process is the high power consumption.

Physical and Chemical Properties

Nickel is silver-white, hard, malleable, and magnetic. Although finely divided nickel ignites spontaneously, a surface of the highly polished metal is very resistant to atmospheric corrosion. Most of its chemical properties are similar to those of cobalt. Nickel crucibles are used for alkali fusions in quantitative analysis.

Production and Uses

There are practically no nickel deposits in the United States, although one small deposit near Lancaster, Pennsylvania, has yielded a few hundred tons of ore. About 85 per cent of the total supply of nickel comes from Sudbury, Ontario, but large deposits have been reported from Venezuela. Approximately 40 tons of ore are needed to produce one ton of metal. The world production is about 180,000 tons per year, and the metal sells at about 35 cents per pound.

The outstanding characteristic of nickel is its ability to impart great strength and corrosion resistance to alloys. Many magnetic alloys are widely used in industry. Nickel alloys are used in the automobile industry in the axles, crankshafts, gears, valves, rods, etc. Recently, nickel has been alloyed with cast iron to produce a stronger and lighter product. Nickel is essential in the manufacture of good armor plate. Nickel-clad steel and nickel alloys are used in the petroleum industry, and in the manufacture of beverages, pulp and paper equipment, etc.

A few of the more common nickel alloys are listed in Table 36.2.

TABLE 36.2. NICKEL ALLOYS

Alloy	Percentage of Element (Typical)	Uses
Monel metal	Ni, 67; Cu, 28	Kitchen sinks, fountains, etc.
Invar	Ni, 35; Fe, 64	Low-expansion metal. Seals for light bulbs; surveyors' tape.
German silver	Ni, Zn, Cu (varying content)	Jewelry, etc.
Constantan	Ni, 40; Cu, 60	Thermocouples.
Manganin	Ni, 4; Cu, 84; Mn, 12	Resistance wire.
Nichrome	Ni and Cr (varying content)	Resistance wire.
Permalloy	Ni, 78; Fe, 22	Magnetic properties. Ocean cables.
Hypernik	Ni, 50; Fe, 50	Transformer cores.
Nickel coins	Ni, 25; Cu, 75	Slot machines.

Compounds of Nickel

The only important compounds of nickel are those in which the metal is in the divalent state. (Brown nickelic hydroxide, $Ni(OH)_3$, is produced in the Edison storage battery.) Nickel forms the usual list of salts, most of which are green or blue in color and usually highly hydrated. $NiSO_4 \cdot (NH_4)_2SO_4 \cdot 6\ H_2O$ is used in nickel electroplating solutions. Green

$Ni(OH)_2$ is precipitated by the addition of NH_4OH to a nickel salt. $Ni(OH)_2$ is very slightly soluble in water and is basic. The precipitate is soluble in an excess of NH_4OH and forms dark blue complex nickelous ammonia ions.

Within recent years there has been a growing tendency to use organic compounds as specific precipitating agents for many metallic ions. The organic reagent dimethylglyoxime reacts with nickel to form a red precipitate.

$$2 \begin{array}{c} CH_3\text{---}C\text{==}N\text{---}OH \\ | \\ CH_3\text{---}C\text{==}N\text{---}OH \end{array} + Ni^{++} \longrightarrow 2\,H^+ + (CH_3CNO)_4H_2Ni$$

Nickel salts give brown borax bead tests, whereas those with cobalt are blue. NiS is precipitated from neutral or alkaline solutions. Once precipitated, it is very slowly soluble in dilute HCl.

MANGANESE (At. No. 25)

Manganese is the only common metal in Group VII. Its compounds are used more frequently in laboratory work in general chemistry than those of any other metal discussed in this chapter. Manganese is also important in the metal industries.

For years alchemists neutralized the iron color in glass with a black ore called "black magnesia." This substance was at one time believed to be the oxide of an alkaline earth metal; but Scheele disproved this in 1774 by showing that this ore would liberate chlorine from HCl, whereas the alkaline earth metals would not. That same year the Swedish chemist Gahn obtained the metal by heating the ore in a crucible with charcoal and heavy petroleum oil.

Occurrence

The ore from Caucasia, Cuba, and Brazil is black manganese dioxide or pyrolusite, MnO_2. This is the most important ore of manganese. Georgia and our western states contain small deposits of this ore. Large deposits of rhodochrosite, $MnCO_3$, are found at Butte, Montana; these can be developed if necessary. The deposits in Arkansas contain both psilomelane, an impure hydrated manganese dioxide, and braunite, $(Mn_2O_3)_3 \cdot MnSiO_3$.

Metallurgy

Manganese is required in making steel to offset the harmful effects of oxygen and sulfur, but pure manganese is unnecessary for this purpose. Most of the ore is used in making spiegeleisen (18 to 22 per cent Mn) and ferromanganese (78 to 82 per cent Mn), which the steel industry either purchases or manufactures itself. The manganese content of these two products in 1944 was 1,400,000 tons.

The pure metal can be produced by reduction with carbon as Gahn did when he discovered the element; but this always contains carbon. Purer metal is obtained by reducing MnO_2 with aluminum. Because of its high cost, the pure metal has few uses.

Physical and Chemical Properties

Manganese is gray, and quite hard and brittle. A small piece of pure metal can easily be pulverized by hitting it with a heavy hammer. Since manganese it just below aluminum in the E.C.S., it corrodes in moist air and liberates hydrogen from acids. It forms many compounds with the non-metals, including nitrides and carbides. Iron and manganese have many physical and chemical properties in common.

Production and Uses

We imported over 1,300,000 tons of manganese ores in 1944, valued at over $10,000,000, and containing about 650,000 tons of manganese. This was twice our 1925–1929 average. Cuba, Brazil, the Gold Coast, British India, and Russia rank in the order listed as exporters of this ore to the United States. Ferromanganese containing approximately 80 per cent manganese sells for about $85 per ton.

Manganese is used to make many alloys both with iron and with many non-ferrous metals. The iron alloys are characterized by their resistance to wear. Manganese bronze (Mn–Cu–Sn–Zn) resists corrosion from sea water and hence is used for propeller blades. *Manganin* wire (Mn–Cu–Ni) is used for accurate electrical measurements because its electrical conductivity changes little with temperature.

Compounds of Manganese

Manganese is in Group VII B of the periodic table and in its +7 valence has some characteristics of the halogens. Since the elements above the diagonal from the upper-left to the lower-right corner of the periodic table have many non-metallic properties, we should expect compounds in which manganese is present to be in the negative radical. Several of these compounds will be discussed in the following paragraphs. The metal has positive valences of 2, 3, 4, 6, 7. Its normal electron arrangement is 2, 8, 13, 2. We can explain the formation of compounds in which manganese has valences other than 2 by imagining a shift of electrons from the next to the outside shell to the outside shell. The gradual change in the properties of manganese compounds as the valence changes is shown by the list on the following page.

Divalent Compounds. Manganous chloride is prepared by the action of HCl on MnO_2 (page 319). This salt is stable at room temperature and is not oxidized by molecular oxygen. It reacts with a base to form the nearly insoluble $Mn(OH)_2$ from which other divalent compounds are prepared. $Mn(OH)_2$ is easily oxidized by molecular oxygen.

Trivalent Compounds. Mn_2O_3 is found in nature as the ore braunite.

Trivalent manganese compounds are prepared in the laboratory by oxidizing the Mn^{++} ion. $MnO \cdot OH$ is obtained by the action of chlorine on $Mn(OH)_2$. The salts are unstable. These trivalent compounds are unimportant.

MANGANESE COMPOUNDS

Valence	2	3	4	6	7
Formula of oxide	MnO	Mn_2O_3	MnO_2	MnO_3	Mn_2O_7
Formula of hydroxide	$Mn(OH)_2$	$Mn(OH)_3$	$Mn(OH)_4$ or H_2MnO_3	H_2MnO_4	$HMnO_4$
Acid or base	Basic	Basic	Amphoteric (inert)	Acidic	Acidic
Solubility in parts/100	0.002	Nearly insoluble	Insoluble	Soluble	Very soluble
Formula of a salt	$MnCl_2$	MnF_3	$Mn(SO_4)_2$	K_2MnO_4	$KMnO_4$
Color of ion	Pink	Violet-green	Green-brown	Very dark green	Purple
Nomenclature	-ous	-ic	-ese disulfate; also, $CaMnO_3$, calcium manganite	Manganate	Permanganate
Resembles	Fe^{++}	Fe^{+++}	Ti^{++++}	SO_4^{--}	ClO_4^-

Tetravalent Compounds. Manganese dioxide, MnO_2, which occurs in nature as pyrolusite, is the most important tetravalent compound. It is prepared in the laboratory by carefully heating $Mn(NO_3)_2$, and is used to prepare chlorine and to catalyze the decomposition of chlorates. Manganese dioxide loses oxygen when heated above 500° C., and Mn_3O_4 is formed. MnO_2 has for years been used to counteract the color of iron in glass; it is also used as a depolarizer in dry cells, about 12,000 tons having been used in 1939 for this purpose. Traces of tetravalent manganese compounds are used as paint driers.

Hexavalent Compounds. The green salt, sodium manganate, is prepared by fusing NaOH, $KClO_3$, and MnO_2.

$$3\ \underline{MnO_2} + 6\ Na^+ + 6\ OH^- + Na^+ + ClO_3^- \longrightarrow 7\ Na^+ + 3\ MnO_4^{--} + Cl^- + 3\ H_2O$$

These compounds are not important because they are unstable.

Heptavalent Compounds. Potassium permanganate is by far the most important heptavalent compound of manganese. There are several methods of preparing it.

If a solution of K_2MnO_4 is acidified, the manganate ion disproportionates.

$$6\ K^+ + 3\ MnO_4^{--} + 2\ H^+ + 2\ HSO_4^- \longrightarrow$$
$$\underline{MnO_2} + 6\ K^+ + 2\ MnO_4^- + 2\ SO_4^{--} + 2\ H_2O$$

PbO_2 is a powerful oxidizing agent and in acid solution will oxidize MnO_2

METALS USED IN THE STEEL INDUSTRY

to permanganic acid (page 562). Salts of persulfuric acid and the periodates also oxidize MnO_2 to purple $HMnO_4$. Ozone may be used to oxidize K_2MnO_4.

$$4\,K^+ + 2\,MnO_4^{--} + \overline{O_3} + H_2O \longrightarrow 4\,K^+ + 2\,MnO_4^- + 2\,OH^- + \overline{O_2}$$

Several hundred tons of various permanganates (Na, K, Ca, Zn) are used each year in the United States in dyeing, as an oxidizing agent in the chemical industry, etc. The use of $KMnO_4$ in the laboratory in the determination of iron was mentioned on page 611. The volumetric determination of a substance by means of a redox reaction is called *oxidimetry*. In this reaction the iron is reduced to the ferrous state and a $KMnO_4$ solution of known strength is then added until the purple color appears. The color will be visible with a single drop of solution in excess. The equation for this important reaction is:

$$5\,Fe^{++} + 5\,SO_4^{--} + K^+ + MnO_4^- + 4\,H^+ + 4\,HSO_4^- \longrightarrow$$
$$5\,Fe^{+++} + K^+ + Mn^{++} + 9\,SO_4^{--} + 4\,H_2O$$

The volumetric determination of hydrogen peroxide (which is oxidized to O_2) is done in a similar manner. The permanganate ion is a much less powerful oxidizing agent when used in neutral or alkaline solution, and in that case takes up only 3 electrons instead of 5. MnO_2 is precipitated. Traces of manganese compounds are essential to plant growth and in some localities are added to fertilizers.

CHROMIUM (At. No. 24)

Chromium, molybdenum, tungsten, and uranium are in one column in Group VI. Although uranium might logically be considered in this chapter because many of its properties are similar to those of the other three elements, it will be discussed with the radioactive elements.

Chromium was isolated in 1798 by a French chemist, Vauquelin. Because many of its compounds are highly colored, he named the element chromium from the Greek word *chroma*, color.

Occurrence

Although Vauquelin isolated chromium from the mineral, crocoite, $PbCrO_4$, this ore is not an important source of chromium. Nearly all of this element comes from the yellow-brown ore, chromite, $Fe(CrO_2)_2$. Chromite is a mixture, for some of the iron and chromium are frequently replaced by magnesium and aluminum. The ratio of iron to chromium in the ore determines its use; ore with a low iron content is used in refractories. Chromite is almost infusible.

Metallurgy

Metallic chromium is usually produced by one of the following methods:
1. Cr_2O_3 is heated with carbon in an electric furnace.

2. Cr_2O_3 is reduced with magnesium or aluminum by the thermite process.
3. $CrCl_3$ is reduced with sodium, potassium, or zinc.
4. A solution of chromic acid or salts of it is electrolyzed. (This method is important in electroplating steel.)

A large part of the metal used commercially is not pure, for pure metal is not required for steel alloys. The chromite ore is usually mixed with coal and reduced in an electric furnace at about 1200° C. The ferrochromium alloy thus produced contains 60 to 70 per cent chromium, 25 to 32 per cent iron, and small quantities of carbon and silicon.

Physical and Chemical Properties

Chromium is a bluish-white hard metal with a high metallic luster; it takes a brilliant polish. It dissolves slowly in cold acids and rapidly in hot concentrated hydrochloric and sulfuric acids. Concentrated nitric acid does not attack it; it is protected by a layer of its highest oxide, which is acidic. It is extremely resistant to salt water. Chromium is not attacked by sulfur compounds; hence chromium-coated metal is used in the petroleum industry and in rubber vulcanizing equipment. Oxalic acid is one of the few organic acids that attack it. Chromium compounds are toxic.

Production and Uses

The production of chromite ore in the United States is negligible compared to the 850,000 tons imported each year from South Africa, Cuba, and New Caledonia. We consume over 50 per cent of the world's production of chromium and produce less than 0.2 of 1 per cent. The most important chrome steel is the 18–8, containing 18 per cent chromium and 8 per cent nickel. Many tons of this steel were used in the Chrysler and Empire State buildings. Stainless steel is used for window fronts, entrances, elevator doors, etc.; there are over 100,000 square feet of this steel on the exterior of the Empire State Building.

Chromium plating is better than either nickel or zinc plating, for it is not attacked by sulfur, resists corrosion better, and wears longer. Articles to be chromium plated are frequently covered with a thin coat of nickel, and the chromium is then electroplated on this surface. Printing plates coated with chromium wear much better than plates not thus treated. Automobile fittings, jewelry, bathroom fixtures, etc., are chromium plated. Even aluminum can now be chromium plated.

Compounds of Chromium

Chromium has valences of 2, 3, and 6 in its compounds, a few of which are shown by table on page 623.

Divalent Compounds. Chromous compounds are prepared by reducing chromic compounds with hydrogen, zinc, or chromium. Like Fe^{++} and Mn^{++} compounds, those of Cr^{++} are good reducing agents and are easily

METALS USED IN THE STEEL INDUSTRY

Chromium Compounds

Valence	2	3	6
Formula of oxide	CrO	Cr_2O_3	CrO_3
Formula of hydroxide	$Cr(OH)_2$	$Cr(OH)_3$, $HCrO_2$	H_2CrO_4, $H_2Cr_2O_7$ (acid)
Acid-base	Basic	Amphoteric	Acid
Solubility parts/100	Insoluble	Insoluble	Very soluble
Formula of a salt	$CrCl_2$	$CrCl_3$, $NaCrO_2$	Na_2CrO_4, $Na_2Cr_2O_7$
Color of ion	Blue	Green	Yellow, red, orange
Nomenclature	-*ous*	Chrom*ic* Chrom*ite*	Chrom*ate* D*i*chrom*ate*
Resemblance	Mn^{++}	Al^{+++}	SO_4^{--}, $S_2O_7^{--}$

oxidized with atmospheric oxygen. $Cr(OH)_2$ cannot be filtered in the open because it combines with oxygen before the filtration is completed. $Cr(C_2H_3O_2)_2$ is one of the few insoluble acetates. Chromous salts do not hydrolyze in water.

Trivalent Compounds. Some Cr_2O_3 is found in nature but is rarely pure enough for commercial use. Trivalent chromium is amphoteric and the hydroxide dissolves in both acids and bases.

$$\underline{Cr(OH)_3} + 3\ H^+ + 3\ Cl^- \longrightarrow Cr^{+++} + 3\ Cl^- + 3\ H_2O$$
$$\underline{Cr(OH)_3} + Na^+ + OH^- \longrightarrow Na^+ + CrO_2^- + 2\ H_2O$$

Chromic oxide, Cr_2O_3, is easily prepared in the laboratory by igniting ammonium dichromate.

$$\underline{(NH_4)_2Cr_2O_7} \xrightarrow{\Delta} \underline{Cr_2O_3} + 4\ \overline{H_2O} + \overline{N_2}$$

A good quality of Cr_2O_3, chrome green, is the best green paint pigment known. Another chrome green is a mixture of chrome yellow and Prussian blue. Chrome yellows are compounds of lead and chromic acid. Chrome cements which are rich in Cr_2O_3 are used in building the linings of blast and annealing furnaces, electric furnaces, lime and cement kilns, etc. The advantage of these cements lies in their high fusion temperature. $Cr_2(SO_4)_3$ is used as a mordant and in electroplating baths, and its basic salt is used in tanning. Chrome alum, $KCr(SO_4)_2 \cdot 12\ H_2O$, is used as a mordant. Chromium acetate, a dye, gives the olive khaki shades.

Ferrous chromite, $Fe(CrO_2)_2$, is the most important chromium ore found in nature.

Hexavalent Compounds. Any of the hexavalent compounds can be prepared by oxidizing the di- or trivalent compounds in an alkaline solution. Chromates and dichromates are puzzling at first. The formula for potassium chromate is K_2CrO_4, and for potassium dichromate, $K_2Cr_2O_7$. If we split up the formulas and write them $K_2O \cdot CrO_3$ and $K_2O \cdot 2\ CrO_3$, we see that they differ only in ratios of K_2O to CrO_3. This idea has been illustrated in connection with acids of sulfur and phosphorus. Crystals of red CrO_3 are obtained by adding concentrated sulfuric acid to potassium dichromate. (Crystals of CrO_3 frequently form in bottles of "cleaning solution" in the laboratory.) This oxide is a powerful oxidizing agent and will ignite alcohol if the alcohol is dropped on it. (Never throw CrO_3 in the waste jars in the laboratory.) It is used principally in electroplating baths and as an oxidizing agent. The free acids, H_2CrO_4 and $H_2Cr_2O_7$, have not been prepared. The oxide, CrO_3, is sometimes called "chromic acid"; this is incorrect.

The chromates and dichromates are made from chromite ore. Soda ash, air, and heat are required in preparing Na_2CrO_4 from $Fe(CrO_2)_2$.

$$4\ Fe(CrO_2)_2 + 8\ Na_2CO_3 + 7\ O_2 \longrightarrow 2\ Fe_2O_3 + 8\ Na_2CrO_4 + 8\ CO_2$$

Chromite and sodium carbonate are fused together in the presence of air, and soluble Na_2CrO_4 is then leached from the iron oxide. Na_2CrO_4 is added to boiler water to prevent corrosion; it is also used in dyeing and in preparing many other chemicals. Potassium chromate is more expensive than Na_2CrO_4 because K_2CO_3 must be used instead of Na_2CO_3.

The corresponding dichromates are prepared by adding sulfuric acid to a solution of chromates and crystallizing the solution. The transformation of CrO_4^{--} into $Cr_2O_7^{--}$ is explained by the following equation:

$$2\ CrO_4^{--} + 2\ H_3O^+ \rightleftarrows Cr_2O_7^{--} + 3\ H_2O$$

Addition of an acid shifts the equilibrium from left to right; addition of a base shifts it back.

$Na_2Cr_2O_7$ is very important in the leather industry, some 20,000 tons being used each year. Animal hides in large churns are rotated in a solution of $Na_2Cr_2O_7$; they turn blue-green, and Cr_2O_3 deposits in the leather. (The chemistry is not well understood.) The salt is an excellent oxidizing agent.

Chrome yellows are compounds of lead and chromic acid; the color varies from light yellow to deep orange, depending upon the ratio of $PbCrO_4$ to $PbSO_4$. Lead chromate is very insoluble. $ZnCrO_4$ and $BaCrO_4$ are light yellow pigments. $ZnCrO_4$ is water-soluble and hence is not suitable for outside work.

Chrome red (American vermilion) is basic lead chromate. This brilliant scarlet pigment is used in paint for iron and steel.

MOLYBDENUM (At. No. 42)

For many years the most common molybdenum ore was thought to be graphite, but Scheele proved this to be wrong. When he put the ore in nitric acid, the reaction produced sulfuric acid and a white solid which he called molybdic acid. Because he had no suitable furnace for reducing metal ores, he sent some of the solid to Hjelm in Sweden in 1782. Hjelm mixed it with linseed oil, heated it to a high temperature in a crucible, and obtained the metal. Scheele had suggested as early as 1778 that a new element must be present in the ore. The history of molybdenum dates back even further—at least to 1300 A.D., when a Japanese sword-maker, Masamue, was producing the most beautiful and effective swords available—"the possessor of one could carve his way out of any debate with a maximum of ease and dispatch." Six hundred years later, when a German metallurgist analyzed one of these swords and found that it contained molybdenum, the development of molybdenum steels began.

Occurrence

By far the most important molybdenum ore is molybdenite, MoS_2. There are a few deposits of wulfenite, $PbMoO_4$. Traces of the element are found in plant and animal tissues.

Metallurgy and Uses

The metallurgy of molybdenum—or "moly" as it is called by miners and metallurgists—is primarily carried on by the Climax Molybdenum Corporation. In 1900, Hugh Leal, a country banker, had analyzed some blue-gray ore which a forest ranger had found at Bartlett Mountain, Colorado. The ore was identified as molybdenite. Leal patented the claims and finally leased them to what later became the Climax Molybdenum Corporation. For many years the company lost money, but gradually the steel industry discovered the wonderful properties of "moly" and at last orders began to come in. Further impetus was given to its production when the British discovered during the First World War that the Germans used it to toughen armaments. From the few tons produced in 1900, production has increased to about 15,000 tons per year in the United States, most of it from Bartlett Mountain. About 95 per cent of the world's reserve lies in this one mountain.

In mining "moly," the side of the mountain is blasted out. The ore is then crushed and MoS_2 is easily separated by ore flotation. Foreign countries buy the concentrates to avoid the tariff. Little pure molybdenum is sold on the market, calcium molybdate or ferromolybdenum being the usual forms. Both calcium molybdate and ferromolybdenum are used in the steel industry. Ferromolybdenum is made by reducing the ore in electric furnaces, and is crushed to pebble size before being added to steel and cast iron. The utilization of calcium molybdate, a cream-yellow chalky powder, greatly increased the use of molybdenum, for $CaMoO_4$ sells for about 80 cents per pound and is cheap to make. It was discovered that MoS_2 could be converted into a usable product if it was roasted in the presence of lime.

$$\begin{array}{r} 2\ MoS_2 + \overline{7\ O_2} \longrightarrow 2\ MoO_3 + \overline{4\ SO_2} \\ 2\ MoO_3 + 2\ CaO \longrightarrow 2\ CaMoO_4 \\ \hline 2\ MoS_2 + \overline{7\ O_2} + 2\ CaO \longrightarrow 2\ CaMoO_4 + \overline{4\ SO_2} \end{array}$$

Calcium molybdate is put directly into the open-hearth furnace. The CaO goes into the slag and the MoO_3 is reduced to the metal which in turn alloys with the iron.

Molybdenum steel withstands high temperature and pressure and great fatigue loads. Structural members, aircraft parts, forged auto parts, etc., are made of "moly" steels; dozens of these special steels are on the market. Molybdenum is alloyed with chromium, nickel, tungsten, manganese, and silicon. Small amounts of it are used in electron tubes, supports for tungsten lamp filaments, and furnaces with high temperature resistance. New methods are being developed for electroplating molybdenum, including plating zinc with it.

Physical and Chemical Properties

Molybdenum is not affected by air at room temperature, but combines readily with oxygen, sulfur, and the halogens when it is heated. The element is usually obtained as a powder which is pressed into rods and sintered by a current passed through the rods. They are then heated and rolled into sheets of the silver-white metal.

Compounds of Molybdenum

Of the four oxides of molybdenum, only MoO_3 is important. Molybdenum trioxide is obtained by roasting MoS_2; the oxide is the initial material for the preparation of ammonium molybdate. Ammonium hydroxide dissolves MoO_3, producing $(NH_4)_2MoO_4$, a salt used in the quantitative determination of phosphorus (page 431). Molybdenum compounds are used as catalysts in the manufacture of synthetic ammonia, sulfuric acid, phthalic anhydride, and formaldehyde; they are also used in paint pigments and enamel glazes, and as a coloring agent in glass.

TUNGSTEN (At. No. 74)

The white mineral, "tungsten" or "heavy stone," which was found in Sweden, puzzled Scheele until he proved, in 1781, that it contained lime and a solid which he called tungstic acid. The de Luyartes, two young Spanish brothers who studied chemistry under Scheele, became interested in heavy stone. They found this tungstic acid in wolframite, a brown mineral which was thought to be an iron-tin ore. When they heated the acid with charcoal to the highest temperature possible, they obtained metallic tungsten. W, the symbol for tungsten, comes from wolframite; in Germany tungsten is known as wolfram.

Occurrence

Many tungsten ores are found in nature, but only four are of commercial importance. *Wolframite*, $(Fe, Mn)WO_4$, the most important ore, has been mined with tin in at least twelve countries. *Scheelite*, CaWO$_4$, is the most important ore mined in the United States. *Ferberite*, FeWO$_4$, is mined in Bolivia and China; a deposit has been discovered at Boulder, Colorado. Of lesser importance is *hubnerite*, MnWO$_4$, found in several of the Rocky Mountain states. All tungsten deposits are located in or near mountain ranges; nearly all the tungsten produced in this hemisphere comes from the volcanic mountain chain along the Pacific Ocean.

Metallurgy and Uses

Tungsten ores are concentrated by wet gravity processes, the ore being kept in as large particles as possible to prevent its being washed away in the slime.

Pure tungsten is widely used in small amounts, the pure metal being obtained from the concentrates. The ore is first fused with Na$_2$CO$_3$ to form soluble sodium tungstate.

$$4\ FeWO_4 + \overline{O_2} + 4\ Na_2CO_3 \longrightarrow 4\ Na_2WO_4 + 2\ Fe_2O_3 + \overline{4\ CO_2}$$

Tungstic acid is then precipitated by adding HCl.

$$2\ Na^+ + WO_4^{--} + 2\ H^+ + 2\ Cl^- \longrightarrow 2\ Na^+ + 2\ Cl^- + H_2WO_4$$

These processes are usually repeated several times to obtain pure H$_2$WO$_4$. Tungstic acid is then heated to form the yellow-green oxide, WO$_3$, and this is reduced to the metal by being heated in an electric furnace in the presence of hydrogen. The metal from the furnace is a gray powder.

The development and use of tungsten steel began with the Paris Exposition in 1900, when a tungsten cutting steel was demonstrated that operated at a temperature hot enough to light a cigarette. In manufacturing tungsten steel, the tungsten concentrate is usually put directly into the furnace. Scheelite is preferable for this purpose because the calcium oxide slags readily.

Prior to 1907, tungsten was known as a hard, brittle metal that could not be worked, but ductile tungsten was finally prepared. The metal powder is pressed into bars by hydraulic presses, and the bars are sintered by a high amperage current. The bars are then heated in the presence of hydrogen and the hot ends of the bars are drawn through swaging machines. The size of the bars is gradually reduced until a heavy wire is formed, and the wire is made thinner by being pulled through at least a hundred progressively smaller dies. This is the process by which the fine tungsten wire used as light bulb filaments is prepared. Four tons of tungsten concentrates will supply wires for over 100,000,000 bulbs. The total radiation emitted by incandescent tungsten metal varies as the fourth power of the temperature, and a tungsten filament is about 4.5 times as efficient as the carbon filaments once used, because it can be operated at a higher temperature. (This also results in a whiter light.) Illumination costs in the United States run to nearly a billion dollars annually. Tungsten saves us nearly $3,000,000,000 per year in light bills.

Tungsten contact points are replacing the more expensive platinum-iridium alloys on telegraph keys, spark plug coils, etc. Tungsten buttons are used as anticathodes in X-ray tubes. Tungsten wire coated with barium oxide is used in various vacuum tubes because it is a good electron emitter. The "tungar" rectifier of an alternating current contains a tungsten filament. Airplane motor valves which contain tungsten can operate when red hot. The metal can be electroplated, and its use as a corrosion-resistant coating is being developed. Modern machinery could not be made without alloying elements like tungsten.

"Carboloy" is a tungsten carbide, W_2C, which is cemented together with nickel. No other substance cuts chilled castings, manganese steel, porcelain, quartz, etc., as efficiently as carboloy.

The reserve of tungsten trioxide, WO_3, in the known deposits of the world is estimated to be about 1,000,000 tons. Of the 15,000 tons of tungsten we use each year, only about one-third is produced in the United States.

Physical and Chemical Properties

Next to carbon, tungsten has the highest melting point of all known substances. It is not oxidized when heated to a temperature lower than red heat. It is extremely resistant to acids, even aqua regia attacking it very slowly. Tungsten is soluble in fused alkalis; a mixture of HF and HNO_3 is the best solvent. The physical properties of tungsten sheet or wire, which is dull white, vary with the amount of swaging or drawing.

Compounds of Tungsten

The compounds of tungsten are in general similar to those of molybdenum. Phospho-tungstic acid, $H_3PO_4 \cdot 12\ WO_3$, is used in organic chemistry to precipitate proteins and alkaloids. Sodium tungstate, Na_2WO_4, is used in making X-ray screens, as a mordant, in fireproofing cloth, and in weighting silk. The oxides are used in coloring glass and porcelain. Gold tungsten salts are used in making stained paper.

Chromium, molybdenum, and tungsten constitute Subgroup B in Group VI. When they display their maximum valence, +6, all three elements have considerable resemblance to sulfur in the same valence (i.e., to SO_3, H_2SO_4, and SO_4^{--}, and to $H_2S_2O_7$ and $S_2O_7^{--}$).

VANADIUM (At. No. 23)

Vanadium, columbium, and tantalum in Group V B of the periodic table are difficult to reduce from their compounds. Vanadium is the lightest of the three and is therefore the least basic.

In 1801 Professor A. M. del Rio of Mexico announced the discovery of "erythronium" so named because its salts become red when heated with acids; but he later became convinced that this new substance was only a mixture of lead oxide and chromic acid. In 1830 Sefström of Sweden announced the discovery of vanadium, and Wöhler proved that same year that vanadium and del Rio's "erythronium" were identical.

Occurrence

Deposits of vanadium ore are found high in the mountains of Peru, and at Rifle, Colorado. The metal generally occurs as vanadates; the principal ores are vanadinite, $Pb_5(VO_4)_3Cl$ (note the analogy to apatite, $Ca_5(PO_4)_3F$); descloizite, $(Pb, Zn)_2VO_4OH$; and carnotite, $(KUO_2VO_4)_2 \cdot 3 H_2O$.

Metallurgy and Uses

Vanadium is extracted from the ore either by the acid method which produces soluble vanadyl compounds, or by an alkaline method which produces soluble vanadates. Uranium and radium are also recovered from carnotite.

Pure metallic vanadium can be prepared by the action of hydrogen on vanadium chlorides, reduction of V_2O_5 with carbon in an electric furnace, reduction with Misch metal and silicon, thermite reduction, and electrolysis of fused V_2O_5 and $Ca(VO_3)_2$. Most of the V_2O_5 is reduced in the presence of iron. The alloys thus produced contain from 25 to 50 per cent vanadium and are used in making vanadium steels. These steels withstand strain, shock, and vibration, and can be given an extremely hard cutting edge. Ferrovanadium is added to steel as a scavenger to remove oxygen. High-speed tools contain only between 0.3 and 0.5 of 1 per cent vanadium. There is little demand for pure metallic vanadium.

Physical and Chemical Properties

The metal obtained by reduction with hydrogen is a gray powder which can be fused into a silver-white mass. The metal is non-magnetic and is harder than quartz. It is soluble in HF, HNO_3, and H_2SO_4.

Nearly 5000 tons of V_2O_5 are contained in the vanadium ore concentrates produced annually throughout the world. At one time Peru produced over 70 per cent of the world's vanadium concentrates, but at present the United States produces about two-thirds. According to the Vanadium Corporation of America, about 20 tons of vanadium pentoxide are recovered each year from the boiler and stack soot of ships that burn Mexican and Venezuelan oil. Vanadium ore concentrates sell at about 25 cents per pound of contained V_2O_5.

Compounds of Vanadium

Almost any color can be obtained by mixing together the various oxides of vanadium. V_2O_5 is red, and V_2O_4 is blue. Vanadium salts give a green color to bromide photographic prints. They are used to fix aniline dyes to silk, and to produce a multitude of colors in the ceramic and glass industries. The use of intimate mixtures of vanadates and silicates with such promoters as copper, calcium, and iron in the contact process for the manufacture of sulfuric acid has converted over 98 per cent SO_2 to SO_3.

COLUMBIUM (At. No. 41)

Columbium compounds were discovered in 1801 by Charles Hatchett, an English chemist. Because the metal itself is always found associated with tantalum, the two were considered to be the same element until 1864, when Blomstrand succeeded in preparing columbium. The first pure columbium was prepared in America by Dr. Balke in 1929; prior to this time there had been only one small specimen in existence, and this was in Germany.

Occurrence

The chief ore is columbite, which contains traces of columbium, tantalum, iron, manganese, tungsten, tin, etc. A simplified formula for columbite is $Fe(CbO_3)_2$. Ore rich in tantalum is called tantalite.

Metallurgy and Uses

Columbium (or niobium, as it is called in some countries) is prepared by the electrolysis of a fused bath of the double fluoride and columbium oxide, the metal forming as flakes on the electrodes. The flakes are not fused, but are converted into ingots by being pressed into bars and heat-treated in a vacuum furnace. These bars can be rolled into sheets, or swaged and drawn into wire. Because columbium combines with all the common gases at high temperatures, the ingots must be processed at a low temperature.

Columbium is no longer merely a laboratory curiosity. The free metal is used in power and vacuum tubes because of its great efficiency as an electron emitter; it is also used to a limited extent in expensive jewelry. As far as can be learned, only one company at present produces the pure metal; it is quoted at $500–$560 per kilogram. Some 40 tons of ferro-columbium are used annually in making weldable high-speed tools. This Fe–Cb alloy contains 56 per cent Cb and sells for about $2.50 per pound of contained columbium. Columbium carbides are used for cutting tools. As an addition agent to stainless steels columbium enhances corrosion resistance by suppressing the formation of harmful chromium carbide. This is of particular value in airplane engine parts exposed to high temperatures, and in rocket construction.

Physical and Chemical Properties; Compounds

Columbium in large pieces is steel gray. It is malleable, is as hard as wrought iron, and can be welded. It combines with hydrogen to form CbH_3,

METALS USED IN THE STEEL INDUSTRY

and at high temperatures reacts with oxygen, nitrogen, and most of the non-metals. The pure metal is insoluble in all acids except HF.

All columbium salts are hydrolyzed on being boiled in acid solutions, and yield a precipitate of columbic acid. Only the pentoxide forms salts. With the halogens it forms a series of oxy-salts, such as $CbOCl_3$. The salts are of no commercial importance. Columbates are prepared by fusing the metal with alkali carbonates.

TANTALUM (At. No. 73)

In 1802 the Swedish chemist, Ekeberg, discovered tantalum in a mineral which he called yttrotantalite, which came from Ytterby. He characterized the task of purifying the element as tantalizing, wherefore he called it tantalum. Tantalum metal was isolated in 1903. By 1908, Dr. Clarence W. Balke had determined the atomic weights of columbium and tantalum. The

FIG. 36.1. Tantalum metal being pressed into bars. (Courtesy, Fansteel Metallurgical Corporation, North Chicago, Ill.)

separation of these two elements is based on the insolubility of potassium fluotantalate, whereas the fluo-oxycolumbate is soluble.

Occurrence

The only tantalum mines known prior to 1937 were located in a desert region in Australia; the lack of water made it impossible to operate them for more than a few months each year. However, new deposits are now being discovered every year. A mine in the Black Hills of South Dakota which is now being operated yields about one pound of metal from every 2.5 tons of ore. Brazil is the world's premier producer (280 tons of ore in 1944), but Russia may soon surpass her.

Metallurgy and Uses

The metal cannot be obtained by simple smelting processes. The ore is treated chemically and the pure salts are electrolytically reduced to powdered metal. This is pressed into bars and sintered in vacuum furnaces, and can then be rolled or drawn.

Tantalum coils, heat exchangers, HCl absorption equipment, and many tantalum-coated metal products are on the market. Rayon spinnerets are made of tantalum, and the metal is used in radar and other electronic equipment. The metal is extensively used in the production of direct from alternating current. If tantalum and lead electrodes are dipped in a sulfuric acid solution, the tantalum, when acting as the anode, forms a thin protective oxide film which does not break down until 200 volts are applied; thus the current can flow only in the opposite direction. More than 75,000 Balkite rectifying sets have been manufactured for railroad signal service.

Physical and Chemical Properties

The hardness of the metal depends upon its metallurgical treatment; the pure metal is soft. It can be machined with ordinary steel tools if carbon tetrachloride is used as the lubricant. A cubic foot of tantalum weighs 1034 pounds.

The metal is attacked by HF, H_2SO_4, H_3PO_4, and all alkalis. Fluorine and hydrogen attack it rapidly at high temperatures.

About 140 tons of tantalum were imported in 1944. The metal sells for about $150.00 per kilogram.

Compounds of Tantalum

Tantalum is usually pentavalent in its compounds. The fluoride is used as a catalyst in synthetic rubber manufacture. The halides hydrolyze readily. The common salts are formed from the insoluble metatantalic acid, $HTaO_3$. Tantalum carbide is used as an extremely hard cutting tool. Vanadium, columbium, and tantalum constitute the subgroup in the nitrogen family.

When their oxidation number is +5 they show some resemblance to the phosphates.

TITANIUM (At. No. 22)

Titanium in Group IV B has both the properties of silicon and some properties of the metals. Like silicon in Group IV A, titanium is widely distributed in nature; thus 784 out of 800 igneous rocks analyzed by the U. S. Geological Survey showed its presence. The element is more abundant than lead, copper, and zinc, but the deposits are rarely rich enough in titanium to make its extraction economical.

William Gregor, an English clergyman who chose geology as his hobby, discovered titanium in 1791 in a black sand found in the county of Cornwall, England. The metal was finally isolated in 1887 by Nilson and Pettersson.

Occurrence

Ilmenite, $FeTiO_3$, is the most important source of titanium. About 280,000 tons of it were mined in the United States in 1944, together with 7000 tons of rutile, TiO_2. In 1936 the total world production of titanium ores was only 200,000 tons.

Metallurgy and Uses

After a slow start the titanium industry has grown at an astonishing rate during the past twenty years. Ninety per cent of the titanium mined goes into pigments; the rest is used for metallurgical purposes.

The pure metal, which melts at about 1800° C., has much less use than its alloys, four of which—Fe–Ti, Fe–C–Ti, Cu–Ti, Mn–Ti— are in common use. Carbon-free ferrotitanium is prepared by reducing ilmenite with aluminum. The ferro-carbon-titanium alloy is made by reducing ilmenite with coke in an electric furnace, or by heating together rutile, carbon, and steel borings. This alloy usually contains 15 to 22 per cent Ti, 4 to 8 per cent C, 1.5 per cent Si; the remainder is iron. Cuprotitanium is made by reducing a rutile-copper mixture with aluminum.

Titanium is used to prevent blowholes in steel and to remove iron oxides and nitrogen from it. It is the best element available for this last, for it will burn in an atmosphere of pure nitrogen. Titanium is used in steel primarily as a deoxidizer and scavenger, not because of any specific quality that it imparts.

Physical and Chemical Properties

Titanium resembles zirconium and cerium in many of its properties. As usually prepared, titanium is an amorphous gray powder; but it can be fused and polished and in this form it will scratch quartz. It is paramagnetic. It emits bright sparks when rubbed against steel. It oxidizes in air at 120° C., and above 700° it decomposes steam. If heated with red lead, it oxidizes explosively. Boron and silicon combine with it; the compounds formed are nearly as hard as diamond. The metal is soluble in dilute acids, hydrogen being liberated.

In its lower valences of $+2$ and $+3$ titanium behaves as a transition metal, forming colored salts. In its tetravalent state it is amphoteric, but is well over on the acidic side. $Ti(SO_4)_2$ is a salt, but $TiCl_4$ is not. $TiCl_4$ is a liquid which hydrolyzes in moist air, producing dense white clouds useful as smoke screens. The metatitanates (such as ilmenite) and fluotitanates are similar to the corresponding silicon compounds. Tetravalent titanium compounds are colorless because there are no electrons in incomplete subshells.

Titanium Compounds and Their Uses

Titanium dioxide, TiO_2, is the most opaque of all white pigments. It is unaffected by chemicals and has such great covering power that considerable of the solid content of a paint containing it can be made up of inexpensive "fillers" (non-opaque white pigments) such as $BaSO_4$, $CaSO_4$, $MgSiO_3$, etc.; lithopone can also be used. Other uses include the whitening of paper, linoleum, and rubber, and the delustering of rayon. Plastic molding powder, white shoe polishes, and face powders are likely to contain TiO_2. Lead titanate, $PbTiO_3$, is another valuable pigment. Its extreme opacity to ultraviolet light prevents the deterioration of paint films that is usually produced by sunlight. Paints containing titanium pigments last so long that they become unsightly because of dirt. A certain amount of zinc oxide may be added to make a paint self-cleaning. Since ZnO is basic, it reacts with the oil of the paint to some extent, forming zinc soap which can be washed away by the rain.

The double sulfate, $Na_2Ti_2(SO_4)_4 \cdot 5\ H_2O$ (containing Ti^{+++}), is used as a mordant in dyeing leather and yarn. The beautiful yellow glaze on pottery is obtained with titanium compounds. Titanium nitride, Ti_2N_2, is so hard that it is used to polish diamonds. A titanium-containing coating is indispensable in certain types of welding rods.

ZIRCONIUM (At. No. 40)

In 1789 Klaproth, a German chemist, realized that a new element was present in an ore called zirconia; and in 1808 Davy tried unsuccessfully to decompose this ore with an electric current. Berzelius finally obtained the impure metal in 1824 by reducing potassium zirconium fluoride with metallic potassium. Fairly pure zirconium can be prepared by heating $ZrCl_4$ and sodium together in a bomb. Zirconium remained a laboratory curiosity for years, and its compounds had few uses. Only since the First World War has it become important, largely as the result of research carried on by the

Foote Mineral Co., the Titanium Alloy Mfg. Co., and the American Zirconium Co. which resulted in new uses for the element and its compounds.

Occurrence

Deposits of the ore have been found in 32 states, but only Florida and North Carolina now produce the ore. Brazil is the largest exporter of zirconium ores, the most important of which are baddeleyite, ZrO_2; brazilite, ZrO_2; and zircon, $ZrSiO_4$. In 1944 we imported 24,000 tons of ore from Brazil and Australia, about one-quarter of which was used for the production of metallic zirconium.

Uses

Germany used zirconium during the First World War in signal flares and gun barrels; an efficient flashlight powder contains 60 per cent zirconium and 40 per cent magnesium. Zirconium wire is used in radio tubes, and the sheet metal is used in making spinneret cups in the rayon industry. The metal in the form of zirconium-silicon or zirconium ferrosilicon is added to steel, for it is very effective in removing oxygen, nitrogen, and sulfur, and in controlling grain size. Zirconium and copper produce a hard alloy, but its electrical conductivity is so low that it is of little use. The metal is quoted at about $6 per pound. About 1000 pounds of ductile zirconium are made each year by decomposing volatilized ZrI_4 by means of an electrically heated wire.

Physical and Chemical Properties

Zirconium is such an active metal that the black powdered form combines readily with the non-metals and must be shipped wet; when dry, it is dangerously explosive. Zirconium hydride, ZrH_2, can be used safely instead of zirconium in powder metallurgy. Once the metal is in massive form it can be made malleable. Below titanium in Group IV B, zirconium is therefore considerably more metallic than titanium. One good indication of this is the formation of the hydride just mentioned; this is a true, salt-like hydride, like those formed by the metals of Groups I A and II A. Another evidence is the fact that it reacts with acids, forming many tetravalent salts.

Compounds of Zirconium

Zirconium dioxide, the most important compound, has a high melting point (2700° C.) and a small coefficient of expansion; it is also resistant to acids. It is non-toxic and is taken internally as "Kontrastin" before the stomach is X-rayed. Zirconia cements and zirconia bricks are used as furnace linings. Zirconia crucibles are used instead of porcelain crucibles for many purposes; platinum alloys can be fused in them. Zirconia pottery glazes are extremely durable. Prior to the First World War about the only use of zirconium compounds was in incandescent gas mantles. Transparent crystals of zircon, ZrSiO$_4$, make one of the most attractive of the semi-precious stones. They occur commonly in a dark topaz color which may be changed by heat to a striking electric blue—or the stone may be ruined. A white zircon is almost as brilliant as a diamond. Unfortunately it is a little softer than quartz; hence its polish is gradually dulled by friction against clothing, for all street dust contains some quartz (sand) particles.

QUESTIONS AND PROBLEMS

1. Plot the atomic weights of the elements discussed in this chapter against their densities.
2. Which of these elements show amphoteric properties?
3. Which are usually multivalent?
4. As found in nature, are these elements usually in their higher valence form? What valences may each of them have?
5. List one important use of each element in the steel industry. List one other use of each one.
6. Compare the acidity of manganese and chromium compounds with change in valence.
7. Show by equations that KMnO$_4$ and K$_2$Cr$_2$O$_7$ are both good oxidizing agents.
8. How could you distinguish between cobalt and nickel? Chromium and manganese?
9. List as many similarities of molybdenum and tungsten as you can.
10. If the supply of tungsten were suddenly exhausted, what would you suggest as a substitute for it in light bulbs?
11. Compare vanadium, columbium, and tantalum in physical and chemical properties, uses, and method of production.
12. Why is there very little demand for metallic vanadium in the steel industry?
13. What method is used in making columbium wire?
14. Why is titanium added to steel?
15. What weight of titanium tetrachloride can be made from 1 kg. of TiO$_2$? Name an interesting property of TiCl$_4$.
16. List some uses of zirconium.
17. Compare the stabilities of the metals listed in this chapter. Would they all serve equally well as protective coatings for iron?
18. Using any laboratory tests which you consider necessary, identify unknowns containing the following substances:

$\begin{cases} KMnO_4 \\ MnO_2 \\ MnSO_4 \end{cases}$ $\begin{cases} K_2Cr_2O_7 \\ CrO_3 \\ (NH_4)_2Cr_2O_7 \end{cases}$ $\begin{cases} ZrO_2 \\ Ti \\ Zr \end{cases}$ $\begin{cases} V_2O_5 \\ KVO_3 \\ V \end{cases}$ $\begin{cases} CoS \\ Ni(CO)_4 \\ Ni \end{cases}$

19. What volume of oxygen at S.T.P. is required to oxidize one molecular weight of MnSO$_4$ to MnO(OH)$_2$?
20. How many of the metals in this chapter can you identify by appearance?

21. Are any of the compounds mentioned in this chapter colored? If so, make a list of the colors and valences of each.

REFERENCES
Books

Titanium. Thornton, W. M. A.C.S. Monograph No. 33. Chem. Catalog Co.
Molybdenum Cerium and Related Alloy Steels. Gillet, H. W. A.C.S. Monograph No. 22. Chem. Catalog Co.
Chemistry in Industry. Howe, H. E. Vol. II, 279–291, 346–359. The Chemical Foundation.

Articles

"Metal Carbonyls." Trout, W. E., Jr. *J. Chem. Ed.* **15,** 113–121 (1938).
"Tungsten." Fink, C. G. *Foote Prints* **2,** 3 (1929). Foote Mineral Co., Philadelphia.
"Chromium Plating." Killeffer, D. H. *Ind. and Eng. Chem.* **19,** 773–776 (1927).
"Uses of Manganese Dioxide." Phalen, W. C. *Chem. and Met. Eng.* **21,** 196–199 (1919).
"Ferro-Alloys." Becket, F. M. *Ind. and Eng. Chem.* **16,** 197–205 (1924).
"Uses of Cobalt." Mason, F. H. *Chem. and Met. Eng.* **29,** 1135–1137 (1923).
"Vanadium." Saklatwalla, B. D. *Ind. and Eng. Chem.* **14,** 968–972 (1922).
"Columbium and Tantalum." Balke, C. W. *Ind. and Eng. Chem.* **27,** 1166–1169 (1935).
"Story of Nickel." Baldwin, W. H. *J. Chem. Ed.* **8,** 1749–1761, 1954–1968, 2325–2340 (1931).
"Sources of Ores of the Ferro-Alloy Metals." Burchard, E. F. *J. Chem. Ed.* **10,** 359–368 (1933).
"Columbium." Critchett, J. H. *Trans. Am. Electro. Soc.* **69,** 62–65 (1936).
"Economics of the Less Familiar Elements." Meyer, H. C. *Ind. and Eng. Chem.* **30,** 431 (1938).
"Recent Developments in Tantalum and Columbium." Balke, C. W. *Ind. and Eng. Chem.* **30,** 251 (1938).
"Zirconium, an Abundant 'Rare' Metal." Raynor, W. M. *Foote Prints* **15,** 3, 6–8 (1943).

» 37 «

THE LESS FAMILIAR METALS

The metals to be discussed in this chapter have been studied in detail by several chemists, and much is known about them; but because of their extremely limited use in industry they are unfamiliar to most people. They will be considered in the following order:

1. The rare earth metals, scandium (At. No. 21), yttrium (At. No. 39), and lanthanum (At. No. 57) in Group III B. See Table 7.2.
2. Gallium (At. No. 31), indium (At. No. 49), and thallium (At. No. 81), in Group III A.
3. Germanium (At. No. 32) in Group IV A and hafnium (At. No. 72) in Group IV B.
4. Thorium (At. No. 90) and uranium (At. No. 92) in Group III B.
5. Technetium (At. No. 43) and rhenium (At. No. 75) in Group VII B.

THE RARE EARTH METALS; SCANDIUM, YTTRIUM, LANTHANUM

In Group III B of the periodic table there appears a single item, "Rare Earths," which includes the elements with atomic numbers 58–71. Little has been done with this group in most chemical laboratories, but they are becoming increasingly important, and it is possible that this whole group will take on new significance in the future. The individual elements of this group in order of increasing atomic weight are shown in Table 37.1.

Because of their great resemblance to lanthanum the rare earth elements are sometimes called the *lanthanides*.

These elements are extremely difficult to separate from each other; even to obtain a compound of one of them in a *pure* state requires great labor. In fact, the discovery of most of them resulted from attempts further to purify a compound.[1] The elements with even atomic numbers are always

[1] Only artificially prepared radioactive isotopes of the elements 43, 61, 85, and 87 are unquestioned. They occur in nature, if at all, only in infinitesimal traces. Of these four, only element 61 is in the rare earth group.

more abundant than those with odd numbers; this is believed to be due to the nuclear structure of the atoms which in turn determines their stability.

Of the many rare earth minerals known, monazite sand is the most important. It contains phosphates of these metals (20 to 60 per cent mixed rare earths and 6 to 9 per cent thoria) and is found in many states in the United States, and in Australia, Brazil, Ceylon, China, India, and Norway.

TABLE 37.1. RARE EARTH ELEMENTS

Element	Symbol	At. No.	At. Wt.	Color	S. G.	M.P.
Cerium	Ce	58	140.13	tin white	6.9	640
Praseodymium	Pr	59	140.92	pale yellow	6.47	940
Neodymium	Nd	60	144.27	pale yellow	6.95	840
Samarium	Sm	62	150.43	pale gray	7.7	1300–1400
Europium	Eu	63	152.0			
Gadolinium	Gd	64	156.9			
Terbium	Tb	65	159.2			
Dysprosium	Dy	66	162.46			
Holmium	Ho	67	164.94			
Erbium	Er	68	167.2	dark gray	4.77	
Thulium	Tm	69	169.4			
Ytterbium	Yb	70	173.04			
Lutecium	Lu	71	174.99			

The separation of the monazite ore from the sand is usually based upon the magnetic properties of the minerals; for example, the Wetherill electroseparator used for this purpose is based on the principle that not only iron minerals, but a large number of others, can be attracted by a sufficiently strong magnetic field. By using magnetic fields of different intensities, the sand can be separated into fractions, one of which is rich in monazite. Monazite is then separated into its various constituents, nearly a dozen steps being required in the purification process before the rare earths are precipitated as the oxalates. Spectrum analysis is used in following and controlling the separation process from this point on. Fractional crystallization of the bromates, oxidation to the tetravalent state, reduction to the divalent state, and electrolytic reduction are among the many processes used in separating one rare earth from another; other processes for this purpose are based on differences in basicity and in magnetic susceptibilities.

The rare earth metals are used commercially, but in only very small quantities. "Misch metal" is an alloy which, when scratched, gives off sparks capable of igniting inflammable gases; it is used in automatic gas-lighting devices, miners' safety lamps, and cigar and cigarette lighters. Its approximate analysis is Ce, 50 to 75 per cent; La, Nd, Pr, 25 to 45 per cent; Fe, 0.5 to 1.0 per cent.

Thorium and cerium oxides are used in Welsbach incandescent gas mantles. Cerium fluoride is used in the carbons of arc-lamp electrodes.

The beautiful golden-yellow, yellowish-green, and purple glassware contains the oxides of cerium, neodymium, and praseodymium respectively. Patents have been granted for mothproofing fabrics with aqueous solutions of casein and thorium or a salt of a rare earth metal such as cerium or lanthanum. Canvas like that used in fire hose can be protected from dampness and mildew by means of rare earth mixtures. Aluminum is purified and magnesium alloys are hardened by the addition of a low percentage of cerium. However, the use of the rare earth metals in alloys is still in its infancy.

Cerium can be separated easily from the other rare earth metals because it *can* have a valence of +4. In that valence it is a strong oxidizing agent and shows chemical properties quite different from those of the other lanthanides or, indeed, of +3 cerium.

Cerium salts are employed in weighting silk, treating seasickness, reducing columbium and tantalum, and manufacturing aniline black; they are also used as mordants in dyeing cotton, as gas purifiers or "getters" in neon lamps, and as catalysts in the Haber process.

The octahydrate of gadolinium sulfate, $Gd_2(SO_4)_3 \cdot 8 H_2O$, is used in the production of very low temperatures because, when in a magnetic field, it transforms some of the magnetic energy into heat and becomes warm. Thus, if a tube of the salt in a container filled with helium gas at low pressure and surrounded by liquid helium is subjected to a powerful magnetic field, it becomes warm and imparts some of its heat to the helium gas. Pumping off some of the gas and removing the magnetic field produces a temperature as low as 0.01° A.

Cerium oxalate is quoted at 70 cents per pound, lanthanum nitrate at $20 per pound, and samarium nitrate at $2.50 per gram. Misch metal costs from $6 to $10 per pound; about 10 tons are produced annually. Practically no rare earth alloys or compounds other than monazite sand are imported at the present time.

Scandium and *yttrium* are similar to the rare earth group in physical and chemical properties. These elements are metallic in character and so nearly alike in their chemical properties that even a qualitative separation is difficult.

GALLIUM, INDIUM, AND THALLIUM

Gallium

Mendeléeff's prediction of the discovery of eka-aluminum, eka-silicon, and eka-boron stimulated the search for hitherto unknown elements. The first of these, eka-aluminum, was discovered in France in 1875 and named gallium in honor of the classical name for France.

Gallium is frequently associated with zinc, aluminum, and copper ores and has been identified spectroscopically in many iron ores. Small amounts of it have been recovered from the residue obtained by redistilling zinc at

THE LESS FAMILIAR METALS

the Bartlesville Zinc Co. plant in Oklahoma. English chemists have discovered that flue dusts from industrial coal burners contain up to 1.5 per cent gallium, and it is estimated that 1000 tons of metal could be obtained from this source each year in Great Britain. However, a process for the recovery of gallium from molybdenum ores which was patented in Germany gave that country control of the market.

The metal is grayish-white with a brilliant luster, but it tarnishes rapidly. Its most interesting property is its low melting point (30° C.) and its high boiling point (about 1700° C.). In the molten state it looks like mercury but is not nearly as dense (s.g. 5.9 to 6.01). It remains a liquid over a longer temperature range than any other known substance.

The use of quartz containers filled with pure gallium as thermometers for temperatures up to 1700° C. is being developed. Gallium has been recommended for optical mirrors, and aluminum-gallium alloys are used in mono-chromatic lamps. The metal sells for about $3 per gram.

In compounds it has valences of two and three, more commonly the latter. The trivalent compounds are quite similar to those of aluminum.

FIG. 37.1. William S. Murray, and more than 250 ounces of indium metal.

Indium

Fairly pure compounds of indium were first prepared by Professor Reich in Germany in 1863, and soon afterward the characteristic indigo-blue spectral lines which give this new element its name were observed. Although the element itself was isolated shortly thereafter, less than one gram of the metal had been prepared as late as 1924. However, William S. Murray became interested in metals while a student at Colgate University, and later organized the Indium Corporation of America, located in Utica, New York. Under his guidance, the company developed methods of obtaining indium, and tons have now been prepared.

Rich indium ores are located in the deserts of Arizona; the 35,000 tons of ore which have been blocked out there will probably yield about two ounces of indium per ton. The ore is concentrated by the flotation process, and the concentrate is then mixed with sodium chloride and roasted in a rotary furnace. The volatile indium chloride is distilled out and precipitated with a Cottrell precipitator. The chloride is further purified, and the pure metal is obtained by electrolysis from a double cyanide solution. Indium is also obtained as a by-product from zinc, lead, and copper smelters. The price fell rapidly, from $30 per ounce in 1935 to $2 per ounce in 1945, as by-product indium became abundant.

The white lustrous metal is soft and ductile, melts at 155° C. and boils at 1450°. It has great surface stability at ordinary temperatures. The metal can be electroplated on other metals; its diffusion into the surface hardens the surface.

One of the most promising uses of indium is in protecting the cadmium alloys used in bearings from the corrosive action of organic acids in the lubricants. When a thin film of indium is electroplated on the bearing and heated to about 200° C., the coating diffuses into the alloy.

Other suggested uses for the metal are in thermometers and dental alloys, in spot-welding spectacle rims, and increasing the efficiency of ultraviolet lamps.

The compounds of indium resemble those of aluminum in solubility. Two oxides, In_2O_3 and In_3O_4, are known. The hydroxide is amphoteric.

Thallium

By means of spectrographic tests, Sir William Crookes discovered thallium in 1861 in some residues from a sulfuric acid plant. He gave it its name because of its characteristic beautiful green line in the spectroscope. Crookes first thought that it was a non-metal similar to sulfur; but he realized his error by 1862, when he showed samples of the metal at the International Exhibition.

Of the several thallium ores in nature, most are mixed metal sulfides, selenides, and arsenides. The metal is obtained as a by-product, most of it in this country coming from cadmium ores. It sells for $12.50 a pound.

Metallic thallium can be cut with a knife. It melts at 303° C. and boils at 1650°. It is a heavy metal (s.g. 11.86) with an appreciable vapor pressure at 174° C. It burns with a green flame. The metal is soluble in acids; the salts that are formed are extremely toxic. The thallous compounds are monovalent and the thallic are trivalent.

One thallium alloy (10 per cent Tl, 20 per cent Sn, and 70 per cent Pb) resists the action of even mixed oxidizing acids and is used as electrodes in the electrodeposition of copper. A liquid amalgam (8.5 per cent Tl, 91.5 per cent Hg) has been used in low-temperature thermometers reading to −60° C.

Thallium compounds were formerly used in depilatories, but several deaths resulting from the absorption of the toxic compounds into the body led to their sale being prohibited. The salts are used in rat poisons, fungicides, insecticides, and mothproofing agents. (In Russia thallium compounds were used to make sheep molt, but this was soon discontinued because too many sheep died.) Small quantities of thallium compounds are used in photoelectric cells, optical glass, and medicine.

GERMANIUM AND HAFNIUM

Germanium

Germanium is below silicon in Group IV A and its compounds resemble those of silicon and carbon. It is like carbon in that it forms two oxides, GeO and GeO_2, but differs in that the oxides are amphoteric.

This grayish-white metal was discovered in 1886 by Winkler, who thought at first that it belonged in Group V; but it was soon proved to be the ekasilicon predicted by Mendeléeff. The ore, argyrodite, contains about 7 per cent germanium, together with silver, sulfur, iron, zinc, mercury, and oxygen. Germanium is found in small quantities in most zinc ores and is a by-product in cadmium recovery. The metal sells at $200 per pound (in 1940 it cost $10 per gram); its principal use is in radionic devices, although many alloys are being found to have desirable properties.

Germanium dioxide, GeO_2, is substituted for SiO_2 in making one type of optical glass, with a high refractive index.

Hafnium

Hafnium is just below zirconium in the periodic table; the two metals are so alike that any separation is extremely difficult. Dozens of fractional crystallizations were necessary before any reasonably pure hafnium compounds were obtained. It was only when the Hungarian chemist, Hevesy, and Dr. Coster of the University of Groningen were advised, in 1923, to use zirconium ores instead of rare earth metal ores that element 72 was discovered. Hafnium is not like the rare earths. It is more common than either silver or gold; in fact, so much is present with zirconium that the latter's atomic weight had to be redetermined after hafnium was discovered.

THORIUM

Thorium, in Group III B, is found in monazite sand; it is separated from the rare earths. Metallic thorium is stable, soft, and malleable, and has a high thermionic emissivity. It sells for about $75 per pound. Thorium is radioactive.[2] Mesothorium, the first disintegration product of thorium, was used for many years as a substitute for radium in therapeutic work, illuminated watch dials, etc. Mesothorium costs about $35 per milligram and is now more expensive than radium.

[2] See Chapter 38.

Thorium dioxide, ThO_2, is one of the most refractory oxides known; crucibles of it can stand temperatures up to 2300° C. The oxides used in the manufacture of incandescent gas mantles are produced by igniting cloth soaked in cerium and thorium nitrate solutions.

URANIUM

In 1789, the German chemist Klaproth produced a yellow precipitate when he added KOH to a nitric acid extraction from pitchblende; this precipitate dissolved in an excess of KOH. Although he thought that it contained a new element, uranium, he was unable to reduce the yellow powder with charcoal. All attempts failed until Peligot, a French scientist, heated some uranous chloride and potassium together; fortunately he was unhurt during the vigorous exothermic reaction that followed. The silver-gray metal has been used in the steel industry as a substitute for vanadium, but other substances have been found cheaper and equally satisfactory.

When really pure uranium metal was desired for the atomic bomb project, it was found that only a few grams were available. The difficult technical problems of large-scale output were solved in 1942, and for some years, at least, a ton or more of metal was produced per day.

In chemical reactions uranium compounds are similar to chromium compounds and are used as catalysts. Sodium uranate, the most common salt, sells for a little over $1 per pound. Uranyl nitrate, $UO_2(NO_3)_2$, is used as a glaze on fine pottery and for red-brown colors in photography. About 100 tons of uranium compounds are used in the United States each year.

Although thorium and uranium were formerly put into Groups IV B and VI B respectively, and justify these placings by their valences of $+4$ and $+6$, they are actually members of a transition group bearing the same relation to actinium that the rare earth elements do to lanthanum (see page 658).

TECHNETIUM AND RHENIUM

The discovery of the elements now called technetium and rhenium, in the manganese subgroup, was announced in 1925. The two metals are similar to manganese in physical and chemical properties. The story of the race to discover these elements on the part of the Noddacks in Germany, a group of Czechs, and two Englishmen is extremely interesting. The Noddacks proposed the names masurium and rhenium, for the eastern and western boundaries of Germany, but only the latter name was accepted, because their discovery of element number 43 could not be confirmed. The explanation of the present name, technetium, is given in the next chapter (page 657).

Rhenium is an extremely heavy metal that melts at about 3400° C.; it can be purchased for about $1 per gram. Although it has been used in several electroplating experiments in this country, no particular uses have as yet been found for it. Several Russian chemists have used rhenium compounds as catalysts, but without startling results.

QUESTIONS AND PROBLEMS

1. With which of the metals discussed in this chapter were you previously familiar?
2. Try to find one commodity in which at least one of these elements is used. Can you suggest other uses for these elements? Substitutes for products containing the elements?
3. Secure present price quotations for each of these elements.

REFERENCES

Books

Chemistry of the Rarer Elements. Hopkins, B. S. D. C. Heath & Co., Boston.

Articles

"Rare Earths. Discovery of the Rare Earths." Weeks, M. E. *J. Chem. Ed.* **9,** 1751–1773 (1932).

"Recently Discovered Elements." Weeks, M. E. *J. Chem. Ed.* **10,** 161–170 (1933).

"Story of Indium." French, S. J. *J. Chem. Ed.* **11,** 270–272 (1934).

"Indium, Occurrence, Recovery, and Uses." Lawrence, R., and Westbrook, L. R. *Ind. and Eng. Chem.* **30,** 611 (1938).

» 38 «

NUCLEAR CHEMISTRY

Throughout this book you have seen how chemical changes can be interpreted in terms of the transfer and rearrangement of the planetary electrons of the atoms which are involved. In all the chemical changes that have been described it has been tacitly assumed that the nuclei of the atoms remained unchanged. But you have been told that atomic nuclei are composed of parts, namely, protons and neutrons; this implies that parts can be added to or taken from them. Is it really true that atomic nuclei can change? And if they can, is it a chemical change? If not, what is it? Yes, nuclear changes can and do take place, both in nature and artificially. Nuclei can either gain or lose either charge or mass, or both. Then what about our definitions of "atom" and "element"? For if the charge of a nucleus changes, it can no longer be the nucleus of an atom of the original element.

Energy of Nuclear Changes

Any change in the nucleus of an atom involves an amount of energy of an entirely different order of magnitude from that involved in even the most energetic of ordinary chemical changes. Most nuclear changes absorb or produce hundreds of millions of times as much energy as do familiar chemical reactions. It can be seen that chemical changes have no chance whatever of inducing any nuclear change; there is no danger of one element turning into another because of a vigorous chemical reaction that does things to its outer electrons. It is therefore easy to put nuclear reactions in a class by themselves and exclude them from any discussion of ordinary chemical reactions. This is what we do when we say that an element is a substance which cannot be decomposed into simpler substances by any chemical reaction, or that atoms are the smallest chemical units of matter.

It might be thought that if any nuclear changes took place in nature the enormous amount of energy emitted would render them very spectacular;

but this is not necessarily true. The energy of the sun is produced entirely by such changes, and this is spectacular enough because such a large proportion of the sun's atoms are involved; but the interior heat of the earth is also produced by nuclear changes, but this is quite unnoticeable because so few of its atoms are unstable under terrestrial conditions. It was only a little over fifty years ago, in fact, that the results of nuclear changes were first observed in a laboratory and given the name *radioactivity*.

Natural Radioactivity

By natural radioactivity is meant the fact that certain elements found in nature undergo spontaneous nuclear decomposition without the intervention of man. The nuclei of element 92, uranium, are unstable. When one of them happens to "let go," a particle having a weight of 4 atomic weight units and a charge of $+2$ (i.e., an He nucleus) is ejected. What is left behind has been reduced in charge from 92 to 90; hence it is now one of the isotopes of thorium. This may be expressed by the equation:

$$U^{238} \longrightarrow Th^{234} + He^4 \quad (\alpha \text{ ray})$$

The superscript numbers are the mass numbers of the particular isotopes involved. It is necessary to specify them because different isotopes of an element show different radioactive behavior.

The new thorium nucleus is still not stable; it presently ejects an electron and turns itself into a protactinium (91) nucleus, in accordance with the equation:

$$Th^{234} \longrightarrow Pa^{234} + \ominus \quad (\beta \text{ ray})$$

The protactinium nucleus in turn ejects an electron and becomes another isotope of uranium. More disintegrations follow, some of one type, some of the other, until finally a stable isotope of lead is produced. It can be seen that any specimen of a uranium compound, unless just purified, will contain small quantities of several other unstable elements.

Vigorous chemical reactions usually release energy in two ways: as kinetic energy of the molecules leaving the site of the reaction (i.e., heat), and as radiant energy (i.e., light). Exactly the same statement is true about the nuclear decomposition reactions mentioned in the preceding paragraph; but the amounts of energy released are so enormous that the results *seem* different. The particles which are ejected have kinetic energies that correspond to temperatures of millions of degrees. It is not surprising that when they were first observed (by Becquerel and the Curies) they were not recognized as incredibly "hot" material particles. Because they radiated in all directions from the speck of material which was producing them, and because they went right through solid objects, they were called, noncommittally, *rays*. As differences between the various kinds of rays were recognized, the rays were designated by the first letters of the Greek alphabet; this served until their nature could be determined. Thus α rays eventually proved to be the nuclei of helium atoms, β rays to be electrons, and γ rays to be an electromagnetic radiation of the same general nature as light. The γ radiation which accompanies most nuclear changes was as difficult to recognize for what it was as were the particle rays; the energy of each quantum was unprecedentedly large and the wave length correspondingly small, rendering ordinary optical methods of studying them inapplicable. γ rays may, in fact, be considered "ultra X rays."

The very excess of energy which at first made it difficult to identify the radiations accompanying nuclear changes made them extremely easy to observe. The use of the Wilson cloud chamber and the Geiger counter for this purpose was described on pages 19 and 20; the extreme sensitivity of the method was mentioned in connection with the application of Paneth's tracer technique to the production of BiH_3 (page 450). Because their emission of these radiations set them off so strikingly from ordinary materials, substances in which unstable atoms are undergoing nuclear changes are called *radioactive*, and spontaneous nuclear disintegrations are called *radioactivity*.

The Rate of Radioactive Disintegration

Unstable nuclei of a given kind do not all disintegrate at the same time, nor does each nucleus exist for a certain length of time and then blow up. It is entirely unpredictable whether a particular nucleus will explode in the next second, or last a million years. It is nevertheless true that the more unstable nuclei experience more disintegrations in proportion to their numbers than do the more stable ones. The situation is the same as in the case of evaporating liquids. It is entirely a matter of chance how long a particular molecule will lie on the surface before it happens to accumulate enough extra energy to evaporate; but the rate of evaporation will be greater from the liquids in which the required amount of energy for evaporation is less.

The volatility of liquids is measured by means of their vapor pressures; this is possible because the process of evaporation is reversible. Radioactivity is not reversible; therefore we must measure the actual rate of decay. We find that in all cases it is proportional to the number of radioactive atoms present. This means that when half of the original atoms have undergone change, the intensity of the radiations will have fallen to half the original value, and so on indefinitely. Obviously it will take an infinite time for the radiation intensity to fall to an infinitesimal value. The full life of any sample of radioactive material is therefore infinite; but the *rate* at which the activity decreases is proportional to the instability and therefore characteristic of the individual isotope. This is expressed by the statement that each radioactive isotope has a characteristic *half life*, or time during which half of the atoms present decay.

Radioactive elements are generally useful on account of their radiations, either for what they can do to substances or organisms, or because the element can be traced by means of them. The half-life period thus determines the usefulness of the isotope to a large extent. If the period is very short, the substance may be practically all gone before the experiment can be completed; if it is too long, the rate of decay will be so slow that small quantities cannot be detected.

Uses of Radioactive Elements

The use of radioactives in medicine depends upon the fact that the radiations can alter or kill cells. The use of radium with cancer of the skin is well known. The treatment is successful because the cancer cells can be killed by an amount of radiation that does not kill healthy cells. Radium can be used only in locations from which it can afterward be removed. It cannot be taken into the system; since it is in the calcium family it is deposited in the bones. The half life is fairly long (1690 years); consequently it continues to radiate, and a slow and painful death results.

Radioactive isotopes can be synthesized which can be used internally, either because a short half life soon renders them innocuous, or because they are promptly excreted. The present problem is to direct them to where they are wanted in the body. A few inorganic ions are promptly concentrated in certain bodily structures—iodide ion in the thyroid gland and the phosphate ion in the bones, for example. Radio-phosphorus and radio-iodine have now been used against overactive bone marrow and hyperthyroidism, with partial success. Many other uses of radio elements will develop when organic molecules are discovered which are taken up preferentially by the diseased organ or the disease-producing organism. The discovery of such compounds is now a far brighter hope than ever before.

Radioactive Tracers. If even a tiny amount of a radioactive isotope is mixed with a quantity of the ordinary element in a compound, it furnishes a "label" that cannot be removed because all the chemical properties of the various isotopes are the same. The "label" can be "read" with a Geiger counter, whose clicking tells not merely where the material is, but how much of it there is. This affords an easy method of determining the solubility of an extremely insoluble salt such as mercuric sulfide. The HgS can be precipitated with H_2S that contains a trace of radio-sulfur, washed free of the adhering solution, and tested to establish its degree of radioactivity. If it is then shaken with pure water at the desired temperature, the water will acquire a degree of radioactivity proportional to the amount of HgS dissolved, and it can be "analyzed" instantly by means of the counter.

The tracer technique is proving invaluable to the physiologist. For example, by means of it the teeth were proved to be much more actively alive than had been suspected. When a rat was fed a meal containing labeled Na_2HPO_4, its teeth became radioactive within four hours. By injecting a solution containing radio-sodium (such as NaCl), other investigators have determined the rate of circulation of the blood, both in normal people and in patients in whom it was feared that an injury had stopped it and that an amputation would be necessary to prevent gangrene. Labeled atoms provide chemists with otherwise unobtainable evidence concerning the mechanism of reactions. It was by means of acid containing O^{17} that the nature of the esterification reaction (pages 701 and 702) was clarified, to name only one of many examples.

Source of Radioactive Elements in Nature

Ordinary lead contains only 23.6 per cent of the 206 isotopes produced as the end product of the radioactive decay of uranium. By applying the mass spectrograph to the lead found in a sample of uranium ore and thus determining how much *extra* Pb^{206} is present, it is possible to calculate, from the known rate of decay of uranium, how old the mineral is. From such experiments it has been estimated that the crust of the earth has been solid for some three billion years. None of the short-lived radioactive isotopes now found in minerals could have persisted for any such period of time; a mass of polonium (half life, 136 days) the size of the earth would have decayed to a single atom in less than 60 years. Only a few radioactive isotopes have half lives of from one to ten billion years, thus enabling our present supply to be merely the residue of the original amount. These are: K^{40}, Re^{187}, Rb^{87}, Sm^{148}, Lu^{176}, Th^{232}, U^{235}, and U^{238}.

Our natural supply of all the others is derived from the radioactive decay of uranium and thorium. For instance, the "radium series" stems from U^{238} by the following steps: Uranium 1 (92) → Uranium X1 (90) → Uranium X2 (91) → Ionium (90) → Radium (88) → Radon (86) → Radium A (84) →Radium B (82) →Radium C (83) ↗Radium C′ (84)↘ ↘Radium C″ (81)↗ Radium D (82) → Radium E (83) → Radium F (84) → Radium G (82). The isotope names used in this list were employed before anyone knew what elements they really were. (Identify the elements by means of the atomic numbers in the parentheses.) Similarly, the "actinium series" comes from the less common isotope of uranium, U^{235}. The remaining heavy naturally radioactive elements belonging to the "thorium series" may have come from a now vanished U^{236}. In all these series the successive disintegrations continue until the atomic number has fallen below 84 *and* the mass number below 210; no nucleus seems to be stable unless both these conditions are met.

TRANSMUTATION OF ELEMENTS

The alchemists dreamed for a thousand years of being able to transmute one element into another. When Pierre and Marie Curie discovered polonium and radium in 1898, they discovered elements which had actually been produced by the transmutation of another element. Natural radioactivity, however, is completely beyond the control of man because nothing man has done has ever changed the *rate* of natural radioactive decay; therefore it was not felt that the problem of the alchemists had been solved. But if an unstable atomic nucleus could change into a stable one by ejecting a particle, or γ rays, it was logical to hope that a stable nucleus could be changed into an unstable one by bombarding it with sufficiently energetic particles or electromagnetic radiation. This was actually first accomplished in 1919 when Lord Rutherford bombarded atoms of some of the lighter elements with α particles (helium nuclei of 10,000 miles per second velocity) and transmuted them into unstable isotopes of the elements two units higher in atomic number. Hundreds of other transmutations have since been performed by the same and other methods. Other projectiles, such as protons, neutrons, and the nuclei of H^2 and H^3, have proved more efficient than α particles; transmutations have also been effected by means of γ rays. Transmutation by bombardment may produce new atoms in several different ways:

Fig. 38.1. Marie Curie. (Courtesy, *Journal of Chemical Education.*)

1. An isotope of the original element may be formed, e.g.,

$$U^{238} + \text{neutron} \longrightarrow U^{239} + \gamma \text{ rays}$$

In other cases γ rays can knock a neutron out of a nucleus.

2. An isotope of the element next higher in atomic number may be formed, e.g.,

$$S^{33} + \text{proton} \longrightarrow Cl^{34}$$

If H^2 or H^3 had been used instead of the proton, a different isotope of the same element would have been produced; i.e., the mass number would have been one or two units higher, but the atomic number would have been the same.

3. An isotope of the element two units higher in atomic number may be formed, e.g.,

$$Pu^{239} + He^4 \longrightarrow Cm^{243}$$

The symbol He^4 will be recognized as standing for the α particle.

4. An isotope of the element next lower in atomic number may be formed, e.g.,

$$Mg^{26} + \gamma \text{ rays} \longrightarrow Na^{25} + \text{proton}$$

Artificial Radioactivity

When a nucleus has been rendered unstable by having absorbed one of the particles just mentioned, or having had a neutron or proton knocked out of it by means of a γ ray, it may decompose instantly or the decomposition may be delayed for any length of time from a fraction of a second to thousands of years. In the latter case the material is said to be artificially radioactive.

Artificial radioactivity produces the same three kinds of radiation as natural radioactivity does, and, in addition, one new kind. In many cases the radiation is similar to β rays except that it is *oppositely charged*. The individual particles have the same weight as electrons, but the charge, although of the same magnitude, is positive; the particles are called *positrons*. Positrons were discovered by C. D. Anderson of the California Institute of Technology in 1932. The life of a positron is always terminated in a small fraction of a second by one of the following reactions:

$$\text{positron} + \text{electron} \rightleftarrows \text{cosmic rays}$$
$$\text{positron} + \text{neutron} \rightleftarrows \text{proton} + \text{energy}$$

The positron is thought not to be a constituent of matter but to be formed at the moment of its ejection from a nucleus by the reverse of the second reaction above. The energy is not necessarily radiant energy; it may be potential energy from force fields within a nucleus, or kinetic energy from a colliding high-velocity particle. Similarly it is believed that the electrons of β rays are not part of the nucleus from which they are ejected, but are created at that moment by means of the reversible reaction:

$$\text{neutron} + \text{energy} \rightleftarrows \text{proton} + \text{electron}$$

The nuclei mentioned at the beginning of this section, which decompose as soon as formed, radiate γ rays or particle rays in decomposing, but the radiation ceases when the bombardment ceases. Neither positrons nor electrons have yet been detected in this class of radiation, but among the particles produced are neutrons, protons, H^3 nuclei, and α particles. In a limited number of cases, namely Th^{232}, U^{235}, Np^{237}, and Pu^{239}, the absorption of a neutron produces a nucleus which, instead of ejecting a small particle, flies into two nearly equal parts and a number of smaller ones, including several neutrons. This process is called *fission*.

Atomic Projectiles

Relatively little was accomplished in the way of nuclear reactions as long as α particles were the only projectiles available for causing them. This was partly because the intensity of α radiation produced by any reasonable quantity of radium is low, and partly because the repulsion between the double positive charge of the α particle and the large positive nuclear charge of the target atom causes most of the projectiles to be deflected

NUCLEAR CHEMISTRY 653

(scattered) without accomplishing anything. Protons, deuterons (i.e., H^2 nuclei), and particularly neutrons, artificially accelerated to extreme velocities, have proved far more successful. The machines used to accelerate these particles, popularly called "atom smashers," operate on two general principles. A charged particle, such as a proton or a deuteron, responds to either an electric field or a *changing* magnetic field.

FIG. 38.2. Workmen beginning the modernization of the Westinghouse Van de Graaff electrostatic generator. (Courtesy, *Chemical and Engineering News*.)

In order to impart sufficient energy to a particle to make it effective in nuclear synthesis it is necessary, if electrical means are employed, to use extremely high voltages obtainable only by extraordinary means. Perhaps the most spectacular of these was devised by Van de Graaff at the Massachusetts Institute of Technology. The Van de Graaff machine at the Westinghouse Research Laboratories is 65 feet high (Fig. 38.2). Electrons are sprayed onto a motor-driven belt made of non-conducting material and carried up into a great insulated sphere from which a collector extends to the belt. The potential of the sphere can be brought to 5,000,000 volts above ground, and using a similar system to pull electrons *out* of another sphere makes a potential difference of 10,000,000 volts available. An α particle which has fallen through such a potential drop has twice as much energy as a proton or an electron, for the amount of energy which a particle acquires depends only upon the charge of the particle and the voltage through which it falls. Energies of atomic projectiles are therefore conveniently expressed in *electron-volts*. The energy emitted per atom of carbon, when it burns to CO_2, is about 4 electron-volts; a temperature of 3,000,000° C. would be required to give gas molecules an average kinetic energy of 10,000,000 electron-volts.

On the night of November 1, 1946, a beam of 200,000,000 electron-volt deuterons, the most powerful atomic projectiles yet produced by man, was obtained from the newest and largest *cyclotron* in the world, at the University of California. In this machine, an electromagnet with pole pieces over 15 feet

FIG. 38.3. E. O. Lawrence's 220-ton cyclotron at the University of California. The pole pieces are 5 feet in diameter; it produces 16,000,000 electron-volt deuterons.

in diameter is used to hold the particles in a circular path in an evacuated chamber while they are given accelerating taps from an electric field that alternates 10,000 times in a thousandth of a second. With each alternation of the field, a particle makes one revolution in the chamber and receives one ten-thousand-volt push and one ten-thousand-volt pull. It is predicted that when the staff is thoroughly familiar with the operation of this colossus (it weighs more than 4000 tons) it will be possible to produce protons of 350,-000,000 electron-volts energy. The cyclotron reproduced in Fig. 38.3 is a prewar model; the later one is too large to be shown plainly in a single photograph.

The General Electric Company's *betatron*, which has produced 100,000,000 electron-volt electrons, operates on the principle of a transformer. Instead of having a secondary consisting of a few thousand turns of wire, it has a doughnut-shaped vacuum tube in which the electrons can make a million revolutions without any resistance. These electrons, when fed into a super-X-ray tube, produce γ rays capable of disintegrating atomic nuclei.

The *synchrotron* combines the action of the betatron with a variation of that of the cyclotron made necessary by the fact that as the speed of an electron approaches that of light, it accelerates much more slowly under the action of a given force. Synchrotrons now under construction at the University of Michigan and at the University of California may well have produced 300,000,000 electron-volt electrons before this book comes from the press. Theoretically it should be possible to build a synchrotron capable of producing particles of at least a billion electron-volt energy.

The most radical in design and perhaps the most potentially important of the accelerators now being built is the Alvarez *linear accelerator*. Protons fed into it from a 4,000,000-volt Van de Graaff machine are swept down its long, straight vacuum tube by the electromagnetic waves produced by a battery of powerful radar transmitters. Properly spaced sections of copper tube protect the particles from the field when it is in its opposite phase. The energy of the moving particles increases at the rate of about a million electron-volts per foot of tube; a 1000-foot tube is considered practical.

Neutrons, the most effective of all projectiles in producing transmutations, cannot be accelerated by electrical or magnetic means because of their lack of charge. Instead, the decomposition of unstable nuclei must be relied upon. The bombardment of beryllium by α particles is a convenient small source of neutrons; an immensely more powerful source is nuclear fission.

The Atomic Bomb

In mentioning nuclear fission (on page 652), we said that it was set off by the absorption of a neutron, and that it produced several neutrons. If each of these new neutrons is absorbed by a neighboring nucleus and produces fission, a branching chain reaction will take place, producing a practically instantaneous explosion. How, then, since there are always a few neutrons wandering around because of cosmic rays, can fissionable substances exist? The answer lies in the fact that the high-speed neutrons produced by fission cannot be absorbed by fissionable nuclei until they have been slowed down to thermal velocities. Ordinarily they all escape before this can happen; but any mass of U^{235} or Pu^{239} above a certain critical size will explode as soon as its component parts are brought together. Ordinary uranium will not do this; it contains 140 times as many non-fissionable U^{238} atoms as it does fissionable atoms, and these U^{238} nuclei absorb *fast* neutrons. Therefore no chain reaction can occur because the fissionable atoms, U^{235}, are so diluted in ordinary uranium that the neutrons they produce are absorbed by the U^{238} or escape before they are sufficiently slowed down.

The fission of plutonium produces about 20,000,000 times as much energy as does the explosion of an equal weight of TNT. Much of this energy is radiated as heat rays, light, X rays, and γ rays; consequently, in addition to the ordinary effects of a terrific explosion, there may be both surface and deep-seated radiation burns. Further damage is done living creatures within a very considerable range by the accompanying blast of neutrons which transmute sodium and phosphorus atoms in the body into radioactive isotopes. In an underwater burst the neutrons are absorbed by the sodium, magnesium, and phosphorus of sea water; hence the water which is sprayed miles into the air is equivalent in radioactivity to thousands of tons of radium. Atomic bombs would render temporarily uninhabitable any city upon which they fell, and a considerable number of such explosions might seriously contaminate the whole earth with radioactivity.

The Uranium Pile

When a U^{238} nucleus absorbs a fast neutron it remains uranium, but its mass number changes to 239 and it becomes radioactive, with a half life of only 23 minutes. The new atom ejects an electron and becomes neptunium, which in turn soon emits another electron and becomes the relatively long-lived element plutonium. The separation of plutonium from uranium is far easier than that of U^{235}, because plutonium is a different element, with different chemical properties, whereas the separation of isotopes is extremely tedious. The scientists of the Manhattan Project therefore undertook to prepare plutonium in quantity from U^{238}, by means of fast neutrons from the fission of U^{235}. To do this it was necessary to slow down one neutron from each fission and use it to produce fission in another U^{235} nucleus.

Graphite can slow down fast neutrons without absorbing them. When bars of uranium and blocks of graphite are alternated in a great cubical pile, the fast neutrons (from U^{235} fission) which escape from each bar of uranium immediately enter graphite. By the time they emerge from the graphite and enter another uranium bar, they have been so slowed down that they are safe from capture by U^{238}. But whenever one of these slow neutrons, in its wanderings, encounters a U^{235} nucleus it is absorbed and produces fission, whereupon several new fast neutrons shoot out. Some of them are absorbed by U^{238}, producing the desired plutonium, and the rest escape into the graphite and the process is repeated. The proportion of the fast neutrons which are caught in the uranium is governed by the thickness of the bars. In order to control the number of slow neutrons and thus prevent explosion, the pile also includes rods of cadmium, a very good absorber of neutrons. The cadmium rods are gradually withdrawn from the pile, whereupon the number of available neutrons increases and the rate of nuclear fissions rises correspondingly. Most of the energy liberated is transformed into heat within the pile, but enough escape as γ rays to make such a pile more dangerous than all the radium ever purified, if it were collected together. A tremendous mass of shielding material is necessary to protect the operators of the pile from this radiation and the swarms of escaping neutrons. As a source of usable energy, the pile is the equivalent of a boiler fire that does not need refueling.

It can be operated at any desired temperature to produce steam for conventional turbines. The cost of uranium is less than the cost of a comparable amount of coal, but the cost of the necessarily large installation is so great as to raise the over-all cost of power a great deal. Such a pile offers a solution for situations in which the major problem is the transportation of fuel.

The Uranium Pile as an Element Factory

The neutron concentration in a uranium pile is several orders of magnitude higher than that produced by the most powerful cyclotron ever thought of. Where earlier syntheses of radioactive elements produced a few atoms, or at most micrograms, the uranium pile can produce them by the gram or kilogram. During World War II the only purpose of the great piles operated by the Manhattan Project was the production of plutonium, which was periodically extracted from the uranium. But many other elements were being produced at the same time, for when a U^{235} nucleus disintegrates it does not always do so in the same way and the weights of the product nuclei may be anywhere between about 85 and 160. Thus over 40 different elements have been found in the wastes at Oak Ridge, all of them intensely radioactive. Radioactive isotopes of nearly all the other elements can be manufactured by inserting some of the stable isotope into the pile and letting it absorb neutrons. These radioactives are expected to prove invaluable not only in the direct treatment of cancer, but in the acquisition of fundamental chemical and physiological knowledge through the tracer technique.

New Elements

Before 1937 no specimens of the elements with atomic numbers 43, 61, 85, or 87 had ever been prepared, although there had been numerous claims to their discovery. Nor was any element known which had an atomic number above 92. The above-mentioned gaps in the periodic system have all been filled by the synthesis of one or several isotopes by means of the cyclotron or the uranium pile. The first new element produced artificially was number 43, in 1937; accordingly the name *technetium* (from the Greek word meaning artificial) has been proposed for it. All the isotopes of the elements thus far prepared are radioactive and have rather short half lives, which suggests strongly that no stable nuclei with these atomic numbers can exist. The new names proposed for elements number 85 and 87 are, respectively, *astatine* (from the Greek word meaning unstable) and *francium* (from France); no new name has yet been suggested for number 61.

As this is written, a total of four new elements beyond number 92 have been synthesized. *Neptunium* (93) and *plutonium* (94) were mentioned above; the other two are *americium* (95) and *curium* (96). The first two of these transuranium elements, as they are called, were named after the two transuranic planets, Neptune and Pluto, just as uranium was named for Uranus. When Herschel discovered the planet Uranus in 1781, he found that it was farther from the sun than any of the previously known planets. In 1789

Klaproth discovered a new metal. In those days the alchemical custom of associating each metal with a heavenly body (see page 14) was still familiar. When this one proved to have the highest known atomic weight, Klaproth thought it appropriate to name the new heaviest element *uranium* after the new farthest planet.

The Actinide Transition Series

By analogy with the series of elements beginning with xenon, the elements beginning with radon should contain a transition series of trivalent elements in which the O shell is filled from 18 to 32 electrons. Xenon has the structure 2, 8, 18, 18, 8; the next two electrons go to the sixth (P) layer, and one electron is added to the octet in the O layer before the transition begins. Lanthanum, with the structure 2, 8, 18, 18, 9, 2, is the typical element; cerium is 2, 8, 18, 19, 9, 2; in the other elements of the lanthanide transition the two outer layers continue to be 9, 2, while the N layer is built up to 32. Actinium, then, should be the typical member of the corresponding transition in the radon series, which should continue with thorium 2, 8, 18, 32, 19, 9, 2, and so on.

As long as only the first three elements in the actinide transition were known, what chemical evidence there was seemed opposed to the idea of the existence of an actinide series. Thorium shows only a valence of $+4$; little is known about the rare element protactinium, but it definitely prefers the valence of $+5$. A $+3$ valence of uranium exists but liberates hydrogen from water; the $+4$ and $+6$ valences are stable. With the discovery of neptunium and plutonium the pattern became clearer, for these elements showed no indication of belonging to Groups VII and VIII respectively; they display valences of $+3$, $+4$, $+5$, and $+6$, the lower oxidation states becoming increasingly more stable as compared with uranium. Americium will probably be difficult or impossible to oxidize above the $+3$ state. Thus it is concluded that the most recently added electrons in the actinides are merely more loosely held than those in the corresponding elements of the lanthanides, although similarly placed. The display of valences above $+3$ is limited to the first two members of the lanthanides, namely, $+4$ for cerium and $+5$ for praseodymium; and in both cases the group valence of $+3$ is stable.

The names that have been proposed for elements 95 and 96 were selected with a view to emphasizing the correspondence between the lanthanides and the actinides. These elements occupy the same relative position in the actinide series as do europium and gadolinium in the lanthanides. The analogy between the names europium and americium is obvious; Gadolin was a famous Swedish chemist who first worked on the rare earths, hence the appropriateness of a reference to the Curies in the *radioactive* actinide series.

Students of science who are capable of understanding and appreciating the significance of atom-splitting have an added responsibility to mankind, for they must be the future leaders if the human race is to survive. Diplomats of the various nations cannot hope to create world peace by attempting to outlaw the use of atomic energy in future wars and at the same time sanctioning national armies or any implements of war such as submarines, battleships, tanks, bombers, and war gases. Scientists will lead the world to peace or pieces, and may each of us do our part to see that it is peace.

QUESTIONS AND PROBLEMS

1. Einstein theorized—and it has been experimentally proved—that energy has weight; conversely, matter can be converted into energy. One gram of mass is equivalent to 25,000,000 kilowatt-hours of energy. Calculate the weight of the energy lost when 12.7 g. of carbon burns and produces 100,000 calories of heat.
2. The fission products of 1 kg. of U^{235} weigh only 999 g. Calculate the amount of energy released.
3. Compute the mass numbers of the isotopes in the "radium series" of radioactive disintegration products from U^{238}.
4. The half life of Np^{239} is 2.3 days. What fraction of this isotope which is present in a bar of uranium at the moment it is withdrawn from a chain-reacting pile will be present 23 days later?
5. Another isotope of neptunium has a half life of 225,000 years. It is formed by the emission of a β particle from the uranium isotope produced when one neutron displaces another from the most common uranium isotope. What is the mass number of this isotope of neptunium?

REFERENCES

Books

The Atomic Story. Campbell, John W., Jr. Henry Holt & Co.

Articles

"The Impact of Nuclear Chemistry." Seaborg, Glen T. *Chem. and Eng. News* **24**, 1192 (1946).
"Elements 43, 85 and 87 Receive Names." *Chem. and Eng. News* **25**, 431 (1947).
"Charts of Isotopes and of Disintegration and Transmutation Reactions." Spencer, Hugh M. *J. Chem. Ed.* **24**, 19 (1947).
"Nonmilitary Uses of Atomic Energy." Thomas, Charles A. *Chem. and Eng. News* **24**, 2481 (1946).
"Accelerators Under Construction at Berkeley." Kastens, M. L. *Chem. and Eng. News* **25**, 224 (1947).
"Fractionation of Isotopes." Squires, A. M. *J. Chem. Ed.* **23**, 538 (1946).

» 39 «

CARBON AND ITS COMPOUNDS

INTRODUCTION

For convenience in studying general chemistry, chemical compounds may be divided into inorganic and organic, the latter being those derived from carbon and carbonaceous material. At one time only plants and animals were thought capable of producing organic compounds, for not a single carbon compound of the type found in plant and animal tissue had been made in a chemical laboratory prior to 1828. That year, when the German chemist Wöhler converted the inorganic salt, ammonium cyanate, NH_4CNO, into urea, $CO(NH_2)_2$, marks the turning point in the history of chemistry. This compound is excreted in the urine as one end product of the oxidation of nitrogenous compounds in the body. Although there are the same number of atoms in NH_4CNO and $CO(NH_2)_2$, the two compounds have entirely different physical and chemical properties; in other words, the same number of atoms held together in various arrangements constitute individual substances. Chemists immediately began the task of synthesizing or creating in the laboratory other compounds which heretofore had been obtained only as products of nature. The results are too amazing to be described adequately by words. How many organic compounds have been isolated from plant and animal tissue or synthesized in the laboratory is unknown because new ones are being discovered or synthesized each day. There are approximately 300,000 carbon compounds, or about ten times the number of compounds of all other elements combined. In so broad a field it is impossible even to remember the names and formulas of so many compounds. Organic chemists soon become specialists in some branch of chemistry such as cellulose, petroleum, vitamins, fats, sugars, etc. They must have a general knowledge of organic compounds and be able to apply it to specific problems, but they make no attempt to know all there is to be known regarding organic chemistry.

The position of carbon in the periodic table accounts for the large number of different fats, carbohydrates, alcohols, hydrocarbons, etc. Carbon, the first element in Group IVA, has four electrons in the outer or valence electron layer of the atom. Such an atom could satisfy the octet rule by gaining, losing, or sharing four electrons. Elements below carbon in this group have a marked tendency to give up electrons. Silicon, just below carbon, resembles it in that it also tends to share electrons. The carbon atom does not form ionic compounds but tends to share its electrons with other carbon atoms or atoms of other elements. Thus if the four electrons are shared with four hydrogen atoms, the molecule CH_4 (methane) is formed; if with four chlorine atoms, the molecule is carbon tetrachloride (CCl_4). Carbon atoms also tend to share electrons with each other; such molecules contain carbon-to-carbon linkages.

—C—	—C—C—	—C—C—C—···n	C=C	—C≡C—
Carbon atom	Two carbon atoms linked together	n carbon atoms linked together	Two electron bonds shared	Three electron bonds shared

Each line extending outward from the carbon atom indicates that other atoms may be shared with it through these covalent electron linkages. From the structural formulas of inorganic compounds it is clear that iron, calcium, phosphorus, etc., atoms do not form such linkages.

The nomenclature of organic compounds has evolved gradually. Even now, however, some phase of it becomes periodically so chaotic that the specialists in this field have to come to agreement even on how a compound is to be named. The products of nature may be divided into large groups such as those obtained from coal, petroleum, living plant and animal tissue, etc.; but the fact that the same organic compounds can be obtained from all these sources makes useless a nomenclature based on source. A much simpler system is based on the fact that certain organic compounds have common groups, just as all sulfates have the SO_4^{--} group, chlorates the ClO_3^- group, etc. The nomenclature will be developed throughout the following pages.

THE ELEMENT CARBON

Although carbon accounts for only 0.08 of 1 per cent of the earth's crust, it is the easiest element to obtain because organic compounds are formed wherever there are soil, water, and sunshine. In addition to these "growing organic compounds," plant and animal tissue ages old, which is found in the earth as coal, oil, petroleum, gas, and deposits of carbonates, can also be utilized. Pure carbon is found in crystalline forms as diamond and graphite; it is amorphous in the various forms of coal.

Diamond

References to the diamond, a gem found by the ancients in Borneo and India, date back to Biblical days. The Latins called it "adamas," a name which progressed through "adamant," "diamaunt," "diamant," finally to diamond. Attempts were made in the past to use the diamond to convert base metals into gold, avert insanity, render poisons harmless, and repel the evil eye; gradually the brilliant stone became known as "the peacemaker" between man and wife.

The large diamond fields of Brazil were discovered in 1727, and these deposits furnished most of the diamonds for the world until still larger fields were found in South Africa in 1867. Diamonds are believed to have been brought to the surface during the eruption of volcanoes, or crystallized out by the heat and pressure developed during the formation of igneous rocks. In 1796, Tennant and Wollaston in England proved that the diamond is pure carbon.

Diamond, the hardest substance known, has a density of 3.52. It burns at 850° C., forming carbon dioxide. Most chemicals have no action on it; however, a mixture of sulfuric acid and potassium dichromate is an exception. If exposed to either sunlight or radium, a diamond becomes luminous in the dark. Direct exposure to radium turns the stone green, but the color disappears when the diamond is heated to a dull red heat. The fact that diamonds are transparent to X rays, whereas paste and glass imitations are not, affords a good test for real stones. Amorphous forms of carbon are good conductors of both heat and electricity; but the diamond, although a good conductor of heat, is a very poor electrical conductor.

Diamonds are usually clear and colorless; rarely are they blue, green, or red. Their brilliance is due to their high index of refraction and the method of cutting. To bring out their display of color, diamonds are usually cut along cleavage lines parallel to their octahedral faces, a process discovered in the 15th century. The weights of diamonds are expressed in carats, a carat being 200 milligrams. The Cullinan diamond, the largest ever found, weighed 3024 carats before it was cut. The price is fairly well controlled by international agreement; a one-carat diamond sells for about $1000.00. Many famous diamonds have been handed down from one generation to another, and fascinating stories have grown up around some of them; for example, the blue Hope diamond is supposed to bring misfortune to its owners.

In 1894 Professor Moissan succeeded in preparing very small diamonds by adding pure sugar carbon to molten steel and suddenly cooling the metal. He reasoned that since iron expands on solidifying, it should exert sufficient pressure on carbon to convert it into diamond.

Graphite

Graphite, a black crystalline form of carbon, differs in many respects from diamond. Its density is only 2.25 and it is among the softest substances known. It is inert to chemicals and burns only at a high temperature. Even though the amount of artificial graphite is increasing, the mining of graphite is still an important industry. Most of the graphite used in pencils comes from Mexico; other large deposits are located in Siberia, Austria, and Ceylon. Although there are some deposits in the United States, the quality of graphite and its cost of production make them of minor importance.

Artificial graphite is made by volatilizing carbon in electric furnaces at about 4000° C.; upon condensing, it becomes crystalline. Graphite electrodes, crucibles, and other such products are indispensable to many electrical processes. About 25,000 tons of graphite are imported annually by the United States. The Acheson Graphite Corporation of Niagara Falls is the principal manufacturer of artificial graphite, although some is produced as a by-product of the silicon carbide industry.

Amorphous Carbon

Many of the impure forms of amorphous carbon such as lampblack, soot, charcoal, coal, and coke are familiar to everyone. Their use as fuels and sources of other compounds will be discussed in later paragraphs.

Wood charcoal is prepared by distilling the volatile constituents from wood in the absence of air. At one time charcoal was used in metallurgy, but it has been supplanted by coke except in the manufacture of certain special steels. Several useful chemicals such as wood alcohol, acetone, etc., are obtained as by-products from the destructive distillation of wood. Some charcoal is burned in fireplaces, etc., and charcoal-burning automobiles have been used in Europe. The ability of charcoal to adsorb gases was mentioned in the chapter on colloids. Charcoal made from coconuts is one of the most efficient gas adsorbers known and is invaluable for gas masks.

Bone black or bone charcoal is used in sugar refining to remove color and impurities from the crude syrup.

Most of the *carbon black* on the market today is prepared by burning waste natural gas from the Texas oil fields in enough oxygen to combine with the hydrogen of the natural gas molecules; under these conditions fluffy black soot or carbon black forms. This substance increases the tensile strength and abrasive resistance of rubber; the small particles of it really constitute the wearing surface of tires. In 1939–1940, when only natural rubber was used, an average of 460 pounds of carbon black was used for each ton of rubber, and a total of about 150,000 tons of it was used in a year. Synthetic rubber, however, requires much more carbon black than does natural rubber, an average of 950 pounds per ton of rubber. For this reason and because of the tremendously expanded use of rubber for military purposes, our consumption of carbon black in 1944 was 469,000 tons. That year's production, with all plants running at capacity, was only 401,000 tons; fortunately, the stock on hand was sufficient to provide the balance. By the end of 1945 production capacity of carbon black in private hands amounted to 625,000 tons, in addition to which there were government plants with 100,000 tons' annual capacity. Ninety-five per cent of the carbon black is used in tires; the balance of it goes into printers' ink, paints, shoe polishes, carbon paper, etc.

OXIDES OF CARBON

Carbon forms two common oxides: CO or carbon monoxide, which is unstable, and CO_2 or carbon dioxide, which is very stable. The suboxide, C_3O_2, is of no importance. The electronic formula of CO is $:C:::O:$; that of CO_2 is $:O::C::O:$.

Carbon Dioxide

Carbon dioxide, a colorless odorless gas, is always produced when carbon is burned in the presence of an excess of oxygen. It is a product of many fermentation reactions and is exhaled in the breath of animals. You can quickly demonstrate its presence in your breath by exhaling into lime water.

Commercial carbon dioxide is obtained chiefly from the burning of coke, the heating of $CaCO_3$, fermentation reactions, and the CO_2 gas wells of the Southwest and Mexico. The recovery of carbon dioxide from burning coke would be simple were it not for the scrubbers required to remove traces of organic compounds. The carbon dioxide also contains nitrogen and oxygen, but these are removed by forcing the mixture of gases under pressure into towers filled with coke over which cold concentrated Na_2CO_3 drips. The CO_2 is taken up, but the oxygen and nitrogen are not absorbed.

In the preparation of $NaHCO_3$ (page 353), carbon dioxide reacts with water to form carbonic acid which in turn reacts with sodium carbonate to yield $NaHCO_3$

$$CO_2 + H_2O \rightleftharpoons H_2CO_3$$
$$2\ Na^+ + CO_3^{--} + H_2CO_3 \rightleftharpoons 2\ Na^+ + 2\ HCO_3^-$$

Increased pressure and a high concentration of CO_2 force the equilibria from left to right. After considerable sodium bicarbonate is formed, it is drained off and heated. This releases the carbon dioxide, which is then dried and compressed in steel cylinders for shipment.

Carbon dioxide is produced when carbonates are heated; this source of CO_2 is used in the Solvay soda process.

The fermentation of sugar constitutes an increasingly important source of CO_2; one-third of the carbon in sugar is liberated as carbon dioxide in these reactions. Should alcohol be used as an automobile fuel to any great extent in this country, more CO_2 will be produced than can be used.

$$C_6H_{12}O_6 \xrightarrow{\text{enzymes}} 2\ C_2H_5OH + 2\ \overline{CO_2}$$
Sugar   Alcohol

In drilling for oil it is not uncommon to strike a pocket or even a gas well of carbon dioxide. Some of these wells are used in the production of solid carbon dioxide, or "dry ice."

Physical and Chemical Properties of Carbon Dioxide. Table 39.1 lists properties of both carbon dioxide and carbon monoxide. CO_2 is not very soluble in water. Although the higher oxides of the halogens, nitrogen, and sulfur are good oxidizing agents, carbon dioxide is a very poor one, showing a resemblance (page 428) to phosphorus in this respect. It will oxidize only such strong reducing agents as hot carbon, and the active metals such as potassium and magnesium; the latter are converted into their corresponding oxides.

$$\overline{CO_2} + C \xrightarrow{\Delta} \overline{2\ CO}$$
$$\overline{CO_2} + 2\ Mg \xrightarrow{\Delta} 2\ MgO + C$$

That carbon dioxide is not toxic is proved by the fact that people can live for some time if they breathe a mixture of 10 per cent oxygen and 90 per cent nitrogen and carbon dioxide. Carbon dioxide is mixed with oxygen and used in artificial respirators because CO_2 stimulates respiration.

TABLE 39.1. PROPERTIES OF CARBON DIOXIDE AND CARBON MONOXIDE

	Melting Point	Boiling Point	Critical Temperature	Critical Pressure	Solubility in Water in cc./cc.
Carbon dioxide	−56.6°[a]	−78.5°	31.1°	73 atm.	1.79 at 0°
Carbon monoxide	−207°	−192°	−139°	35 atm.	0.035 at 0°

[a] at 5.3 atm.

Carbonic Acid. The very slightly acid taste of carbonated beverages is due to carbonic acid, H_2CO_3. This acid is extremely weak and the equilibrium is easily shifted from right to left by the application of heat. The dissociation into the carbonate radical (CO_3^{--}) is nearly negligible in an acid solution.

$$CO_2 + H_2O \rightleftarrows H_2CO_3 \rightleftarrows H^+ + HCO_3^- \rightleftarrows 2\ H^+ + CO_3^{--}$$

The salts of carbonic acid have been discussed in connection with the corresponding metals.

Uses of Carbon Dioxide. Joseph Priestley, the discoverer of oxygen, is usually credited with founding the carbonated beverage industry, for, noticing that water charged with "fixed air" had a pleasant taste, he recommended it to his friends. When sufficient sugar was available, nearly 30,000 tons of carbon dioxide were used each year in the United States for carbonated beverages. Prior to the development of suitable machinery for the liquefaction of gases, these beverages were made by mixing acid and soda (sodium bicarbonate) together, whereas today the liquid carbon dioxide is compressed in steel cylinders.

If liquid carbon dioxide is allowed to escape rapidly from a cylinder, the heat some of it takes up during the vaporization process is sufficient to freeze the rest of it into fluffy snow-white flakes which are called "carbon dioxide snow." A sack of CO_2 can be obtained by putting a cloth sack over the valve of a tank of carbon dioxide and opening the valve. This snow compressed into blocks is a widely used refrigerant and is sold under the name of "dry ice." It has three decided advantages over ice: the temperature of the solid CO_2 is much lower than that of ice, it sublimes and therefore leaves no residue, and one pound of it produces a cooling effect equivalent to that of about fifteen pounds of ice.

Carbon dioxide gas, though not as efficient as SO_2 or NH_3, is used in some mechanical refrigerators. In fact, British ships which carry foodstuffs specify this refrigeration, for there is no danger of spoilage from the gas if the unit breaks. Food is often stored in an atmosphere of CO_2 to lessen spoilage.

Since carbon dioxide is a product of combustion it can be used in fighting fires. Several brands of fire extinguishers on the market can be so adjusted that carbon dioxide will be released. A carbon dioxide gas fire extinguisher system, in which cylinders of CO_2 gas serve as the extinguishers, is used in plants such as telephone companies where thousands of contact points might be ruined by acid or water. Large fire extinguishers usually contain a bottle of acid and a solution of sodium bicarbonate. When the cylinder is inverted, the acid runs out of the bottle and reacts with the bicarbonate solution; the carbon dioxide thus released forces the mixture out of the container. "Foamite" extinguishers contain $NaHCO_3$ and $Al_2(SO_4)_3$. These salts hydrolyze and liberate carbon dioxide; the colloidal alumina forced out with the gas produces a froth.

$$6\ Na^+ + 6\ HCO_3^- + 2\ Al^{+++} + 3\ SO_4^{--} \longrightarrow$$
$$6\ Na^+ + 3\ SO_4^{--} + \underline{2\ Al(OH)_3} + 6\ \overline{CO_2}$$

Licorice, saponin, and other foam and froth stabilizers are also used. These foamite extinguishers are efficient in smothering oil fires, for water poured on an oil fire sinks to the bottom and the fire continues to burn.

The chemical industry is by far the greatest user of carbon dioxide. The baking soda, washing soda, lead paint industries, etc., require thousands of tons of this gas each year. Many important compounds containing carbon dioxide are discussed in detail in other chapters.

Carbon Monoxide

Carbon monoxide is always produced when carbonaceous material burns in an insufficient supply of oxygen. The gas burns with its characteristic blue flame at the surface of coal in a furnace. Many people have lost their lives because of faulty furnaces which allowed this gas to escape into the dwelling. Hot carbon easily reduces carbon dioxide to carbon monoxide.

$$\underline{C} + \overline{CO_2} \longrightarrow 2\,\overline{CO}$$

Carbon monoxide is always produced during the reduction of iron ore.

A small volume of carbon monoxide can be prepared by adding sulfuric acid to formic acid, as shown in Fig. 39.1. When these are heated to 100° C., formic acid is dehydrated.

$$HCOOH \xrightarrow{H_2SO_4} H_2O + \overline{CO}$$

Another method often used is to heat oxalic and sulfuric acids together.

$$H_2C_2O_4 \xrightarrow{H_2SO_4} H_2O + \overline{CO_2} + \overline{CO}$$

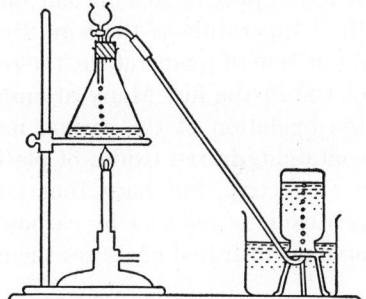

Fig. 39.1. Preparation of carbon monoxide.

The latter again serves as a dehydrating agent, but in this case both CO_2 and CO are produced. The mixture of gases is bubbled through a solution of NaOH which reacts with the carbon dioxide.

Carbon monoxide is a colorless, odorless gas which is almost insoluble in water. Being a lower oxide of carbon, it is a good reducing agent, a property which is used in the steel industry. If carbon monoxide is passed over hot copper oxide, the two react rapidly, with the formation of shiny copper and carbon dioxide. Carbon monoxide is a good fuel. Water gas, which is prepared by passing steam over hot carbon, is a mixture of hydrogen and carbon monoxide. Carbonyls such as nickel carbonyl, $Ni(CO)_4$, are produced by the direct union of metals with carbon monoxide (page 616). In the presence of suitable catalysts carbon monoxide and chlorine react to form the poisonous war gas, phosgene.

$$\overline{Cl_2} + \overline{CO} \longrightarrow \overline{COCl_2}$$

Carbon monoxide is a deadly poison that may be produced in furnaces and garages, and wherever motor traffic is extremely heavy. Physiological chemists have given us an explanation for the toxic action of this gas. When carbon monoxide is taken into the lungs it diffuses through the lung tissue and into the blood stream, where it reacts with the hemoglobin, forming a stable compound which is no longer capable of picking up oxygen. Thus its effect is the same as shutting off the supply of oxygen to the body—the individual becomes dizzy, loses muscular control, and soon becomes unconscious. Breathing air containing 1 cc. of carbon monoxide per liter is fatal in about half an hour. H_2S and HCN are about equally toxic but far less dangerous because they have warning odors, whereas CO has none.

Several tests are used to detect the presence of carbon monoxide. Canaries, which are particularly susceptible to it, are frequently kept in garages. Tomato plants wilt in concentrations of the gas below the lethal amount for human beings. The amount of carbon monoxide in the exhaust gas from automobiles can be determined by passing the gas around a heated wire. If CO is present in sufficient quantity to burn, the heat liberated increases the temperature of the wire. Because resistance to the flow of electricity is a function of temperature, the resistance is plotted against the concentration of CO in the air. Many attempts have been made to catalyze completely the oxidation of the carbon monoxide gas from exhaust pipes. Catalysts containing mixed oxides of platinum, cobalt, nickel, manganese, and silver are effective, but have thus far proved unsuitable for use in cars. Iodine pentoxide is reduced by carbon monoxide and free iodine is liberated; the amount liberated measures the carbon monoxide in the air.

$$I_2O_5 + 5\ \overline{CO} \longrightarrow 5\ \overline{CO_2} + \underline{I_2}$$

Palladium chloride can also be used to detect CO because the gas reduces the chloride to black metallic palladium.

CARBIDES, SULFIDES, AND HALIDES

The carbides of boron, silicon, tungsten, and tantalum are of commercial importance as abrasive agents and have been discussed in connection with the respective elements.

The preparation and properties of carbon disulfide are discussed on page 372.

Carbon tetrachloride is the only important carbon halide. This colorless liquid (B.P. 76.8° C., s.g. 1.59) is prepared by bubbling dry chlorine gas into carbon disulfide in the presence of dissolved iodine which acts as a catalyst.

$$CS_2 + 3\ \overline{Cl_2} \longrightarrow CCl_4 + S_2Cl_2$$

Because the boiling point of sulfur monochloride, S_2Cl_2, is about 50° higher than that of CCl_4, the two products can be separated by fractional distillation. For the properties and uses of S_2Cl_2, see page 372. CCl_4 can be prepared from methane and chlorine.

Carbon tetrachloride is sold under the trade name of "Pyrene." In the gaseous state, CCl_4 is about five times as heavy as air and non-inflammable,

CARBON AND ITS COMPOUNDS

and hence is used as a fire extinguisher; the liquid when sprayed on the fire vaporizes and smothers it. The only objection to this use is that at high temperatures it reacts with steam to form the deadly gas phosgene.

$$\overline{CCl_4} + \overline{H_2O} \longrightarrow \overline{2\ HCl} + \overline{COCl_2}$$

However, there are on record only few cases of difficulty in this respect.

Fused metallic halides are good conductors of electricity; but CCl_4, like $SiCl_4$, $SnCl_4$, $GeCl_4$, PCl_3, and other naturally liquid halides, is not. It is moderately toxic but is used internally for hookworm and other parasites of the intestinal tract. It has a limited use as a fungicide.

Carbon tetrachloride is sold as a cleaning fluid under the trade name of "Carbona" (a mixture of carbon tetrachloride and gasoline, benzol, or naphtha). A mixture containing 40 per cent CCl_4 will not ignite, but it is safer to use at least 50 per cent of CCl_4. Fats, greases, and oils are soluble in this dry-cleaning fluid and hence such spots can be removed from clothes with it.

HYDROCARBONS

The term hydrocarbon denotes a compound composed of the two elements hydrogen and carbon. Hundreds of these compounds are produced either directly or indirectly by plants and animals. Our supplies of coal and petroleum are degradation products of the plants and animals which inhabited the earth centuries ago. Dozens of hydrocarbons can be separated from petroleum. For years it was impossible to make even the low molecular-weight hydrocarbons in the laboratory, but chemical research has now made it possible to prepare many hydrocarbons from carbon and water and other chemicals such as acids, bases, halogens, etc.

If each organic compound had to be considered as an individual which differed vastly from all the others, organic chemistry would be impossible to comprehend. Fortunately, however, these compounds can be classified into groups, and we can study the characteristic of a group as we did in the case of the alkali metals, halogens, alkaline-earth metals, etc.

The groups of hydrocarbons are known as the *methane, ethylene, acetylene,* and *benzene series.* In other words, one group of compounds is similar to methane, another is like ethylene, etc. Each member in a series differs in weight from the preceding member of the series by a constant amount, namely, a (CH_2) group. If x represents one compound in a series, the molecular weight of the next member is $(x+CH_2)$, the next member has a weight of $(x+CH_2+CH_2)$, etc. *Any such series of compounds is called a homologous series and the members of such a series are called homologs.* In discussing the structural formulas of inorganic compounds emphasis was placed on the fact that these formulas could be written in only one way; that is, the atoms which make up molecules can have only one stable arrangement. (There are a few exceptions, but they are of minor importance in general chemistry.) Organic compounds differ in this respect from inorganic compounds, for there are hundreds of cases in which two compounds have the same molecular formula but different structural formulas. These compounds are called *isomers* and this characteristic is called *isomerism*.

Methane and the Methane Series

Although formulas can be written for the compounds CH, CH_2, CH_3, and CH_4, the first three are unknown or unstable. CH_3 is known, but its half life is only 10^{-3} to 10^{-4} second. The simplest hydrocarbon is therefore one in which each valence bond of the carbon atom is shared with one hydrogen atom, $H:\overset{..}{\underset{..}{C}}:H$. Fishermen call this substance "marsh gas"; and they know
       H
that if the gas bubbles which rise to the surface of a pond will ignite, the chances are that they will find only carp and bullheads, fish that can live in water with a low oxygen content. Coal miners call this compound "fire damp"; its ease of combustion makes it one of the greatest fire hazards in the mines. (CH_4 is the principal constituent of natural gas and pockets of it are frequently found in mines.)

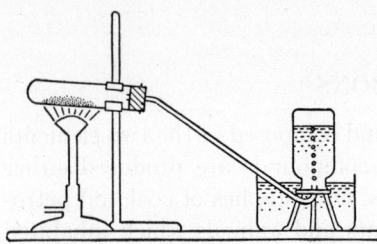

FIG. 39.2. Preparation of methane.

The chemical name for this gas is methane. It can be prepared in the laboratory by the destructive distillation of coal or wood, or more conveniently by heating together solid sodium acetate and sodium hydroxide, as shown in Fig. 39.2.

$$\underline{NaC_2H_3O_2} + \underline{NaOH} \overset{\Delta}{\longrightarrow} \underline{Na_2CO_3} + \overline{CH_4}$$

It can also be prepared by adding aluminum carbide to water.

$$\underline{Al_4C_3} + 12\ H_2O \longrightarrow 4\ \underline{Al(OH)_3} + \overline{3\ CH_4}$$

Pure methane is colorless, odorless, tasteless, insoluble in water, and inert to the action of most chemicals at room temperatures. As natural gas, it is one of our important fuels. Mixtures of oxygen and methane burn explosively. Methane is a product of anaerobic fermentation and is recovered from sewage-disposal plants. The considerable research now in progress may result in its commercial production from many fermentable materials, such as cornstalks, etc.

Chlorine attacks methane slowly in the dark and explosively in bright light, forming substitution products.

CARBON AND ITS COMPOUNDS

$$CH_4 + Cl_2 \longrightarrow CH_3Cl + HCl$$
$$CH_4 + 2\ Cl_2 \longrightarrow CH_2Cl_2 + 2\ HCl$$
$$CH_4 + 3\ Cl_2 \longrightarrow CHCl_3 + 3\ HCl$$
$$CH_4 + 4\ Cl_2 \longrightarrow CCl_4 + 4\ HCl$$

When chlorine and methane are mixed, several of these reactions occur simultaneously. The commercial preparation of CH_3Cl, *methyl chloride*, and $CHCl_3$, *chloroform*, is based on this principle. See page 668 for the preparation of carbon tetrachloride. CH_2Cl_2, dichlormethane, although used in some refrigerators, is not an important compound.

Other members of the methane series may be considered as being built up from methane, although they are obtained on a commercial scale by the fractional distillation of paraffin-like compounds such as petroleum. This is why this series is also called the paraffin series. To show how the series is built up, let us consider the reaction between methyl chloride and metallic sodium which results in the two methyl groups combining to form a molecule of ethane; salt is the other product formed.

$$H-\underset{\underset{H}{|}}{\overset{\overset{H}{|}}{C}}-\boxed{Cl + Na + Na + Cl}-\underset{\underset{H}{|}}{\overset{\overset{H}{|}}{C}}-H \longrightarrow H-\underset{\underset{H}{|}}{\overset{\overset{H}{|}}{C}}-\underset{\underset{H}{|}}{\overset{\overset{H}{|}}{C}}-H + 2\ NaCl$$

Note that ethane differs from methane by a $-\underset{\underset{H}{|}}{\overset{\overset{H}{|}}{C}}-$ group.

$$H-\underset{\underset{H}{|}}{\overset{\overset{H}{|}}{C}}-H \qquad H-\underset{\underset{H}{|}}{\overset{\overset{H}{|}}{C}}-\left[\underset{\underset{H}{|}}{\overset{\overset{H}{|}}{C}}\right]-H$$

If methyl chloride, ethyl chloride, and sodium react together, the next member of the series, C_3H_8 (propane), is formed.

$$C_2H_5Cl + 2\ Na + CH_3Cl \longrightarrow H-\underset{\underset{H}{|}}{\overset{\overset{H}{|}}{C}}-\underset{\underset{H}{|}}{\overset{\overset{H}{|}}{C}}-\underset{\underset{H}{|}}{\overset{\overset{H}{|}}{C}}-H + 2\ NaCl$$

The fourth member of the series, butane, has a boiling point of 0.6° C.; hence it is a liquid in winter and a gas in summer. Mixtures of propane and butane are sold in cylinders as fuel for gas ranges in farm homes.

As the molecular weights of organic compounds increase, the melting and boiling points also increase, as shown in Table 39.2. We realize that petroleum is a complicated mixture from the fact that all the compounds in this table can be obtained by the fractional distillation of crude petroleum. There is a general formula for each hydrocarbon series. The formula for the methane series is C_nH_{2n+2}. If $n=1$, the compound is methane; if $n=2$, the compound is $C_2H_{2\times2+2}$, or C_2H_6, ethane. Hexane contains six carbon atoms, so its formula is $C_6H_{2\times6+2}$, or C_6H_{14}. The name of the compound indicates the number of carbon atoms and the series to which it belongs. Note that the names of the members of the meth*ane* series end in *-ane*.

TABLE 39.2. METHANE OR PARAFFIN SERIES—GENERAL FORMULA, C_nH_{2n+2}

Name	Formula	Melting Point °C.	Boiling Point °C.	Use
Methane	CH_4	—	−161	Natural gas fuel
Ethane	C_2H_6	—	−93	Gas fuel
Propane	C_3H_8	—	−44	Gas fuel
Butane	C_4H_{10}	—	0.6	Gas fuel
Pentane	C_5H_{12}	−131	36	Refinery gases liquefied and added to gasoline
Hexane	C_6H_{14}	−94	69	
Heptane	C_7H_{16}	−90	98	Motor fuel
Octane	C_8H_{18}	−56	125	Motor fuel
Nonane	C_9H_{20}	−51	150	Motor fuel
Decane	$C_{10}H_{22}$	−32	173	Motor fuel
Pentadecane	$C_{15}H_{32}$	10	270	Kerosene
Hexadecane	$C_{16}H_{34}$	19	287	Lubricant
Nondecane	$C_{19}H_{40}$	32	330	Lubricant
Pentatriacontane	$C_{35}H_{72}$	75	331 at 15 mm.	Pitch-heavy grease

Isomerism is so complicated that only one example will be given; the others are left for more advanced courses in chemistry. The valence bonds for butane might be satisfied by writing the structural formula in either of two ways:

```
    H H H H                         H H H
    | | | |                         | | |
H—C—C—C—C—H         or      H—C—C—C—H
    | | | |                         |   |
    H H H H                         H   H
                                        |
                                    H—C—H
                                        |
                                        H
    Normal butane                   Isobutane
```

That these two isomeric compounds are entirely different is shown by the boiling point of normal butane (0.6° C.) and of isobutane (−10° C.).

Ethylene Series. Double-Bond Unsaturated Compounds. General Formula, C_nH_{2n}

The luminous flame of coal gas is due to a small amount of a colorless gas called ethylene, C_2H_4. Since the compound (CH_2) apparently does not exist, the first member of the series is C_2H_4. Ethane has the same number of carbons and two more hydrogens than does ethylene; therefore ethylene, C_2H_4, is said to be unsaturated. Double bonds (=) are used in organic chemistry to indicate that two pairs of valence electrons are shared. Note the formulas of C_2H_6 and C_2H_4.

$$\begin{array}{cc} \text{H H} & \text{H H} \\ | \; | & | \; | \\ \text{H—C—C—H} & \text{H—C=C—H} \\ | \; | & \\ \text{H H} & \end{array}$$

Ethylene is found among the gases produced when petroleum is "cracked."

If ethyl alcohol, C_2H_5OH, and concentrated sulfuric acid are mixed in the ratios of 1:6 and heated, ethylene gas is liberated. Sulfuric acid acts as a dehydrating agent.

$$C_2H_5OH \xrightarrow{H_2SO_4} \overline{C_2H_4} + H_2O$$

Alcohol can also be dehydrated by passing it over bauxite.

Ethylene is used as an illuminating gas because it decomposes easily, liberating finely divided carbon which glows when heated. Cylinders of ethylene are used for blowtorch welding, cutting, etc. For many years a mixture of ethylene gas and oxygen has been used as an anesthetic. Although it does not nauseate most people, the fact that it must be mixed with oxygen presents the chief objection to its use—one spark, and the mixture ignites. Some years ago it was discovered that green citrus fruits ripen quickly when exposed to ethylene; and it is now common practice to pick green fruit, ship it to the market, and ripen it in large storage rooms containing about one part of ethylene per 5000 parts of air. Similarly, newly dug potatoes do not grow until after their winter dormant period; exposing them to ethylene greatly shortens this period. (Ethylene dichloride is also used for this purpose.) The double bond or unsaturated nature of the ethylene molecule makes it readily attacked by many chemicals, and other useful commodities are thus produced. Bromine and chlorine add on directly to the molecule, thus breaking the double bond.

$$\begin{array}{ccc} \text{H H} & & \text{H H} \\ | \; | & & | \; | \\ \text{C=C} + Br_2 & \longrightarrow & \text{H—C—C—H} \\ | \; | & & | \; | \\ \text{H H} & & \text{Br Br} \end{array}$$

Ethylene dibromide is used in anti-knock gasoline, the bromine in $C_2H_4Br_2$ reacting with the lead of lead tetraethyl, $Pb(C_2H_5)_4$, after the latter has served its purpose as an anti-knock compound. Ethylene is used in making mustard gas for chemical warfare. The radiator anti-freeze, glycol, is made from ethylene (page 697).

All members of the ethylene series end in *-ylene*, as Table 39.3 shows. As with members of the methane series, an increase in molecular weight increases the probability of the compound being a solid. Propylene, the second member of the series, differs from ethylene by a $\begin{bmatrix} H \\ | \\ -C- \\ | \\ H \end{bmatrix}$ group.

$$\begin{array}{cc} \underset{\text{Ethylene}}{\text{H}\ \text{H} \\ |\ \ | \\ \text{H—C=C—H}} & \underset{\text{Propylene}}{\text{H}\ \text{H}\ \begin{bmatrix} \text{H} \\ | \\ \text{C} \\ | \\ \text{H} \end{bmatrix} \\ |\ \ |\ \ \ \ \ \ \\ \text{H—C=C—}\ \ \ \ \text{—H}} \end{array}$$

Acetylene Series. Triple-Bond Unsaturated Compounds. General Formula, C_nH_{2n-2}

The first member of the acetylene series is C_2H_2 or, written structurally, $H-C\equiv C-H$. In this compound, carbon has the greatest possible degree of unsaturation. The importance of acetylene is evident from the fact that it is prepared from coal and therefore constitutes an economical method of converting coal into a gaseous fuel. Calcium carbide is prepared by heating lime and coal together.

$$CaO + 3\ C \longrightarrow CaC_2 + \overline{CO}$$

If CaC_2 is added to water, acetylene is produced.

$$CaC_2 + 2\ HOH \longrightarrow \overline{C_2H_2} + Ca(OH)_2$$

The gas burns with a very smoky flame, for it is nearly all carbon. In oxyacetylene and other special burners where combustion is complete, its flame is extremely hot. This is to be expected, because acetylene is produced by an endothermic reaction and therefore decomposes with the liberation of heat ($C_2H_2 \longrightarrow H_2 + 2\ C + 53{,}800$ cal.). This heat together with that liberated during the combustion of carbon and hydrogen produces a high temperature. When acetylene is compressed in cylinders it becomes either a liquid or a solid. The large amount of energy stored up in compressed acetylene makes it dangerously explosive. This danger is overcome by adding acetone to the

CARBON AND ITS COMPOUNDS

cylinders, Because acetone is a good solvent for acetylene and is not explosive, it is used in cylinders for lighting and welding purposes. Prest-O-Lite cylinders contain acetylene dissolved in acetone.

Acetylene is more readily attacked by chemical agents than is ethylene, and twice as much chlorine may be added per molecule because it has twice as much unsaturation.

$$H-C\equiv C-H + Cl_2 \longrightarrow \underset{\underset{Cl}{|}}{H-C}=\underset{\underset{Cl}{|}}{C-H} \quad \text{(Dichloroethylene)}$$

$$H-C\equiv C-H + 2\,Cl_2 \longrightarrow \underset{\underset{Cl}{|}}{\overset{\overset{Cl}{|}}{H-C}}-\underset{\underset{Cl}{|}}{\overset{\overset{Cl}{|}}{C-H}} \quad \text{(Tetrachloroethane)}$$

The hydrocarbons mentioned in the preceding paragraphs are known as *aliphatic hydrocarbons* because fats and oils contain compounds of this type. They are frequently called straight-chain hydrocarbons because the end

TABLE 39.3. UNSATURATED HYDROCARBONS
Aliphatic Hydrocarbons

Ethylene Series, C_nH_{2n}			Acetylene Series, C_nH_{2n-2}		
Name[a]	Formula	Boiling Point °C.	Name	Formula	Boiling Point °C.
Ethylene	C_2H_4	−104	Acetylene (ethine)	C_2H_2	−84
Propylene	C_3H_6	−48	Propine[b]	C_3H_4	−25
Butylene	C_4H_8	−5	Butine	C_4H_6	18.5
Amylene	C_5H_{10}	39 to 40	Pentine	C_5H_8	48
Hexylene	C_6H_{12}	64	Hexine	C_6H_{10}	71.5

Aromatic Hydrocarbons

Benzene Series C_nH_{2n-6}

Name	Formula	Boiling Point °C.
Benzene	C_6H_6	79.6
Toluene[c]	C_7H_8	110.8
Xylene[c]	C_8H_{10}	139
Mesitylene[c]	C_9H_{12}	164

[a] These compounds are also named *ethene, propene, butene, pentene*, etc.
[b] Except for the old name, acetylene, for the first member of the series, all the names end in *-ine*.
[c] The naming of these is complicated. Only four members of the series are listed.

carbon atoms are not linked together. The fourth series of hydrocarbons differs from the other three in that all the carbon atoms are linked together in a ring structure. This series is known as the benzene or aromatic series (the compounds have an aromatic odor).

Benzene or Aromatic Series. General Formula, C_nH_{2n-6}

When Faraday described the properties of benzene in 1825, he opened up a new and startling field of chemistry. When the formula of benzene was found to be C_6H_6, many attempts were made to write a structural formula that would explain its properties. Every effort to write a straight-chain formula resulted in putting in two triple bonds or a triple bond and two double bonds for each molecule. (Try it yourself. Put six carbons in a row, link them together, place the six hydrogens any way you want, and see if you don't have a rather peculiar-looking molecule.) The formula for the structure of benzene which, with minor changes, is used today, was evolved by Kekulé.[1]

Benzene or benzol, from which hundreds of organic compounds are made, is obtained by heating coal and separating the products by fractional distillation. When this source became insufficient, a way was found to prepare it from petroleum. Benzene reacts with nitric acid to form nitrobenzene.

$$C_6H_6 + HNO_3 \longrightarrow C_6H_5NO_2 + H_2O$$

Reducing the oxygen in nitrobenzene with hydrogen produces the compound *aniline*, $C_6H_5NH_2$, from which the beautiful aniline dyes are made. Because of its high anti-knock value, several million gallons of benzene are used in the automotive fuel industry each year.

Phenol, or *carbolic acid*, is benzene in which one hydrogen is replaced by an (—OH) group. If phenol is treated with nitric acid, three (—NO_2) groups substitute for three hydrogens and *trinitrophenol* ($C_6H_2OH(NO_2)_3$), or *picric acid*, is formed. This compound is used as an explosive.

Toluene, the second member of the benzene series, is benzene in which a (—CH_3) group has been substituted for one hydrogen. (This is equivalent to increasing the weight of benzene by a (—CH_2) group.) Toluene is always obtained with benzene when coal is heated. Although toluene has some value as a fuel, it is more important because it can be nitrated to form the powerful explosive, *trinitrotoluene*, or "TNT."

[1] He is said to have been dreaming of wriggling snakes when the picture of carbon atoms chasing each other around and around came to his mind. He awoke suddenly and wrote down a ring structure for benzene with a double bond between every other carbon atom.

CARBON AND ITS COMPOUNDS

$$C_6H_5CH_3 + 3\ HNO_3 \xrightarrow{H_2SO_4} 3\ H_2O + C_6H_2(CH_3)(NO_2)_3$$
Toluene   Trinitrotoluene

The structural formulas for some of these compounds are as follows:

Aniline   Phenol   Trinitrophenol

Toluene   Trinitrotoluene

In some organic compounds, rings are attached to rings. One of the simple two-ring compounds is *naphthalene* (moth balls); a three-ring compound *anthracene*, is used in making many beautiful red dyes. Both of these compounds are coal-tar products.

Naphthalene   Anthracene

FUELS

No single factor is more essential to modern civilization than energy. Satisfying our needs requires other sources of energy than the physical exertion of animals and human beings. A train is useless without an engine to pull it; no one wants a skyscraper office unless elevators are available; an automobile without gasoline means a walk home. Because the wheels of industry would stop without some source of energy, therefore, the question of where energy comes from is extremely important.

At present, in addition to energy from the heat of the earth and direct solar energy, we obtain energy from coal and oil, from gas, water power, wood, tides, wind, peat, oil shale, and alcohol. The sun is the primary source of energy, for without it there would be no coal, oil, gas, peat, oil shale, wood, or alcohol. Whereas, during Pilgrim times in this country, any work done was at the expense of labor by either man or animal, this source of labor now amounts to only about 5 per cent of the energy utilized each year. The total energy consumed in the United States is derived from seven sources; the following figures indicate the approximate percentage from each source: coal, 34; oil, 36.7; water power, 8; natural gas, 8; wood, 7; man and animal, 5; and wind, 1.3.

Many ingenious projects have been devised to guard against the loss of a source of energy, as in the possible depletion of the vast reserves of oil and coal. Experiments are under way with towers 2000 feet high which will operate wind rotators. The steam which operates the air-conditioning units in Cairo, Egypt, is generated by a series of mirrors which focus the sun's rays on the boilers. At present, only about one-third of our potential water power is being used in the United States. This does not include projects for harnessing the tide, such as the uncompleted $36,000,000 project at Passamaquoddy, Maine. Dr. George Claude, a Frenchman, has shown that energy can be generated by passing the warm top layer of ocean water into a vacuum where it evaporates, and using cool deep-sea water for condensing purposes. The utilization of atomic energy is another possibility, but at the present time only the rather scarce element uranium is available as "fuel."

Fuels are classified on the basis of physical state; thus wood and coal are solid fuels; oil, alcohol, and gasoline are liquid fuels; and there are several gaseous fuels. Innumerable by-products are made from all three forms of fuel.

Solid Fuels

Wood. At one time *wood* was the only important solid fuel; it was used so extensively during the 13th and 14th centuries that the European forests were threatened with depletion. Gradually "stones which burned" began to be used as fuel, and the great coal industry was founded. The utilization of coal, together with forest conservation policies, has saved the forests so that wood is available for lumber and other useful products. Enormous amounts of other fuel can be produced from wood. For example, it is possible to "crack" or heat one ton of wood and obtain 40 gallons of tar, from which 10 gallons of gasoline, 8 gallons of diesel oil, coke, and fuel gas can be produced. Cellulose products will be discussed later.

Coal. Large deposits of bituminous, semi-bituminous, lignite, and anthracite *coal* are distributed throughout the world. At the present rate of consumption, the 7400 billion tons of reserve coal will last about 6000 years. That the efficiency of coal consumption has been greatly improved is evident from the fact that in 1920 four pounds of coal were required for one horsepower, whereas today about one pound is average.

The time may come when people who live in cities will have to go to a museum to see a piece of coal. Much misdirected energy is expended in hoisting coal to the surface of the ground, loading it on cars, hauling it to cities, unloading it in storage bins, reloading it into trucks, unloading it into basements, shoveling it into furnaces, and shoveling out the ashes. A more efficient procedure would be to heat the coal in or at the mines to produce gas and coke, and to heat the coke in turn with steam to produce carbon monoxide and hydrogen, and to pipe the gaseous fuels from the mines to the furnaces. This procedure is used in the Ruhr Valley in Germany, and in Russia.

$$\text{Coal} \xrightarrow{\Delta} \text{gaseous fuel} + \text{coke} \xrightarrow[\Delta]{\text{steam}} \overline{CO} + \overline{H_2} + \text{ash}$$

A process for the hydrogenation of coal, developed by the German chemist, Bergius, was the source of much of Germany's gasoline during World War II. Hydrogen and coal are heated together at a suitable temperature and pressure to convert it into hydrocarbons; as much as five barrels of gasoline or oil can be obtained from one ton of coal.

$$1 \text{ ton of coal } + H_2 \xrightarrow[\substack{\text{catalyst} \\ 500°}]{4000 \text{ lbs./sq. in.}} 5 \text{ barrels of oil or gasoline}$$

Furthermore, with this process gasoline, kerosene, gas oil, wax, lubricating oil, and hundreds of other compounds can be produced by the reaction of carbon monoxide and hydrogen. At present, gasoline produced from coal costs about four times as much as that from petroleum. If all the coal were converted into petroleum by the hydrogenation process, the petroleum would last about 24,000 years.

The relative importance of anthracite or hard coal and bituminous or soft coal as sources of energy is shown in Fig. 39.3. (The heat value of coal is often expressed in British thermal units [B.T.U.]. One B.T.U. is the heat required to raise one pound of water one degree Fahrenheit and is equal to 252 calories. Coal averages about 12,000 B.T.U. per pound.) Well over half a billion tons of coal are mined per year in this country. The six most important states of the thirty-two now producing coal are listed in Table 39.4, together with the tons produced by each.

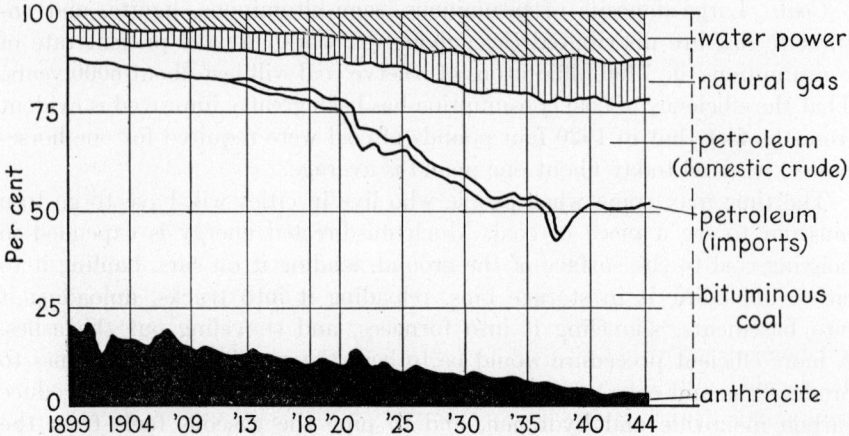

Fig. 39.3. "Per cent of total B.T.U. equivalent contributed by the several sources of energy, counting water power at constant fuel equivalent, 1899–1944." (Courtesy, *Minerals Year Book*, 1945.)

TABLE 39.4. COAL PRODUCTION IN TONS, 1944 (APPROX.)

State	Tons of Coal
West Virginia	164,000,000
Pennsylvania (Bituminous)	148,000,000
Pennsylvania (Anthracite)	64,000,000
Illinois	77,000,000
Kentucky	68,000,000
Ohio	34,000,000
Indiana	28,000,000

Bituminous coal costs around $2 per ton at the mine, and anthracite twice as much. The characteristics of hard, soft, and cannel coal and of lignite are given in Table 39.5.

TABLE 39.5. CHARACTERISTICS OF COAL

	Hard Coal	Soft Coal	Cannel Coal	Lignite
Type of flame	Blue	Luminous	Smoky	Smoky
Percentage volatile matter[a]	3–5	12–26	30–40	28
Percentage carbon	90–93	75–90	60	60–75
Percentage hydrogen	2–4	4–5	6	6
Percentage oxygen and nitrogen	3–5	6–15	14	20–30
Percentage moisture	2–7	2–12	2	6–20
Heat value in calories per gram	8000	7700	6700	4000–6000

[a] All percentage values are approximate.

Products from Coal. When coke was produced by heating coal in ovens, all the volatile matter driven off was considered only a nuisance and was wasted. At present, however, the ash is the only waste product from coal.

CARBON AND ITS COMPOUNDS

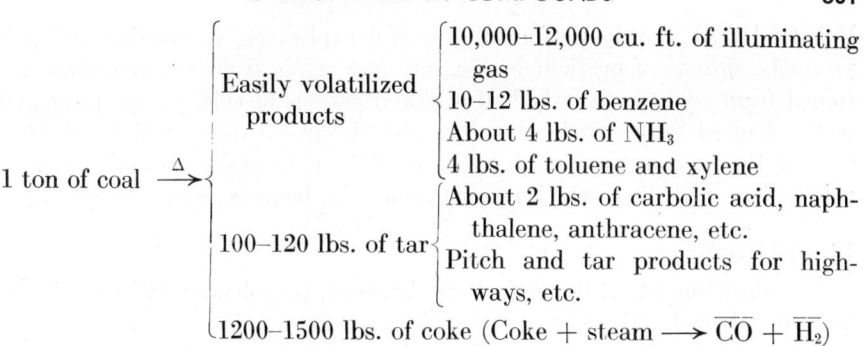

1 ton of coal $\xrightarrow{\Delta}$ Easily volatilized products
- 10,000–12,000 cu. ft. of illuminating gas
- 10–12 lbs. of benzene
- About 4 lbs. of NH_3
- 4 lbs. of toluene and xylene

100–120 lbs. of tar
- About 2 lbs. of carbolic acid, naphthalene, anthracene, etc.
- Pitch and tar products for highways, etc.

1200–1500 lbs. of coke (Coke + steam $\longrightarrow \overline{CO} + \overline{H_2}$)

Chemists have found many uses for *coal tar*, formerly a waste material. Its decided and disagreeable odor is due to sulfur compounds and to organic compounds with high molecular weights. The discovery that the crude coal tar could be fractionally distilled into many portions made it possible to separate benzene, toluene, phenol, anthracene, etc., from one another.

Fig. 39.4. Modern by-product coke ovens; top of battery. (Courtesy, Philadelphia Coke Co.)

Beautiful dyes, lovely perfumes, powerful explosives, economical bakelite products, dozens of medicinals, etc., are now made from raw materials obtained from coal tar. Nearly half a billion gallons of coal tar are produced in the United States each year. The old "beehive" ovens which collected none of the gaseous products have been replaced by the modern by-product coke ovens (Fig. 39.4) which recover ammonia, benzene, etc.

Liquid Fuels

The most important liquid fuels are benzene, petroleum and its products, and the alcohols (the last will be discussed later). Benzene or benzol is blended with gasoline to increase its anti-knock rating, and in some localities pure benzene is used as a fuel.

Petroleum. Oil is found within the arctic circle, in the equatorial jungles of Colombia and Borneo, in the temperate zone of the United States, 13,000 feet above sea level in the Andes Mountains in Peru, below the ocean floor along the coast of California, and in the deserts of Asia. The *Minerals Yearbook* figures on the production of petroleum in 1944 are given in Table 39.6.

TABLE 39.6. WORLD PRODUCTION OF PETROLEUM, 1944, IN MILLIONS OF BARRELS (42 gal./bbl.)

Country	Millions of Barrels	Country	Millions of Barrels
United States	1678	British India	3
U.S.S.R.	275	British Borneo	6
Venezuela	257	Poland	3
Rumania	26	Germany	8
Saudi Arabia	8	Japan	3
Netherlands Indies	40	Sakhalin	5
Mexico	38	Ecuador	3
Hungary	10	Canada	10
Colombia	22	Egypt	9
Peru	14	Austria	10
Argentina	24	Other countries	3
Trinidad	22		
Iran, Iraq and Bahrein Is., (est.)	140	Total	2617

Texas, California, Louisiana, and Oklahoma, the four big producing states in this country, produce about 78 per cent of our annual output; Texas produces 45 per cent; California, 18 per cent; and Louisiana and Oklahoma each about $7\frac{1}{2}$ per cent. Next in order of importance are Kansas, Illinois, New Mexico, Wyoming, Arkansas and Michigan. From 1859 to 1894 Pennsylvania was the most important producer.

Of the nearly 20,000 new oil wells drilled each year, about 70 per cent yield oil. Wells range in depth from a few hundred feet to a mile or more. It has been estimated that our present methods of obtaining oil from the ground will exhaust this country's supply in another fifteen years, but that the life of our oil wells may be extended another sixty years if all the methods now known are used. However, new oil wells may be discovered and untapped sources like the 1,500,000,000 barrels under the city of Chicago may be used. Blowing oxygen into old oil wells might possibly turn the earth into a giant still and we might thus obtain many billion barrels of oil from wells that are now dry. When all our oil is consumed, another 75 years' supply can be obtained from the 14,000,000,000 tons of peat in this country, and a further 400 years' supply from the oil shale in the world.

Refining of Petroleum. The petroleum industry has been equal to the task of separating crude petroleum into dozens of individual products, such as the particular type of fuel required for automobiles, airplanes, tractors, furnaces, and steamships. Crude petroleum may be almost as clear as water and free from offensive odors, or black and thick, with a skunk odor. It consists of many hydrocarbons and traces of nitrogen, sulfur, and oxygen. Sulfur compounds are particularly undesirable in gasoline because they burn to form SO_2 and SO_3, which, in the presence of moisture, corrode the bearings of motors. These sulfur compounds are removed with an alkaline plumbite solution ("Doctor solution"), chlorites, special filter media, solvents, etc. Excessively unsaturated fractions, which polymerize into "gum," are removed by oxidizing them with sulfuric acid or by selective solution in liquid SO_2.

The "cracking" of petroleum has greatly increased the volume of the gasoline fraction obtained from the crude material. There are many patented cracking units such as the "Burton," "Dubbs," etc., and new ones are developed each year. The gasoline fraction is so valuable that even the volatile gases which distill off at low temperatures are polymerized, and the fractions with high molecular weights are heated under pressure until they "crack" or break down into molecular aggregates of about C_8H_{18}.

The high-boiling fractions are separated into lubrication oils, waxes, and asphalt, tar, and pitch. Lubrication oils are further refined to remove waxes, etc. Tar and asphalt would also be "cracked" further except for their use in highway construction, etc. There are some natural deposits of asphalt which are thought to have resulted from the surface evaporation of large volumes of petroleum. The famous lake of pitch or asphalt on the island of Trinidad has an area of 99.3 acres and a depth of over 100 feet. An even larger lake has been discovered in Venezuela, and there are dozens of smaller ones throughout the world.

Gaseous Fuels

Natural, coal, water, producer, and *blast furnace* gases are among our present day fuels. Their approximate composition is given in Table 39.7. Many factors, such as location, type of gas required, and cost, determine which of these fuels will be used. In some localities where the amount of natural gas is insufficient to meet the needs, a mixture of natural and water gas must be used; in other places water gas is used because it is the cheapest.

TABLE 39.7. APPROXIMATE PERCENTAGE COMPOSITION OF GASEOUS FUELS

	Natural	Coal	Water	Producer	Blast Furnace
CH_4, C_2H_6, C_3H_8	99	34	—	3	—
Ethylene series	—	6	—	0.5	—
CO	—	9	44	22.5	26
CO_2	—	1	3	6	13
H_2	—	48	52	10	3
N_2	1	2	1	59	58
B.T.U./cu. ft.	1000–2000	600	300	130	92

Natural Gas. Deposits of natural gas are always associated with petroleum deposits. The composition of natural gas varies greatly. Some wells contain considerable ethane and propane, and others almost none; some contain a fairly large percentage of CO_2, H_2, and N_2, and in others the CO_2 and N_2 are nearly pure. Over 100,000 miles of petroleum and gas lines extend from the oil fields of the United States, and we use annually about 2000 billion cubic feet of natural gas, valued at half a billion dollars. The supply of natural gas in Texas will meet that locality's needs for 200 years; gas lines extend from Texas to the eastern states. The waste of natural gas at present is tremendous—in one oil field in Persia a billion cubic feet of gas, or more than enough to supply the ten largest cities of the United States, is allowed to go to waste each day.

Illuminating gas is usually natural gas to which are added unsaturated hydrocarbons so that the mixture will produce light while burning. Coal gas is a good illuminating gas because it contains about 6 per cent ethylene.

Coal Gas. The destructive distillation of coal results in the production of large volumes of methane and hydrogen. Heavy liquids, or coal tar, are condensed by means of a series of coils. The ammonia is next removed with water and acid scrubbers, the gas being forced upward and countercurrent to a stream of water or acid which trickles downward over acid-resistant rocks. The next unit contains scrap iron or iron oxide which reacts with and removes H_2S.

$$Fe_2O_3 + 3\ \overline{H_2S} \longrightarrow 2\ \underline{FeS} + \underline{S} + 3\ H_2O$$

When the iron oxide has been exhausted, it is regenerated by exposing the ferrous sulfide to moist air.

$$4\ FeS + 3\ O_2 \xrightarrow{H_2O} 2\ Fe_2O_3 + 4\ S$$

The purified gas is stored in the large round tanks which are to be seen near a gas plant.

Water Gas. When steam is passed over white-hot coke, carbon acts as a reducing agent and two gaseous products are obtained.

$$\Delta + C + \overline{H_2O} \longrightarrow \overline{CO} + \overline{H_2}$$

The equation shows that the reaction is endothermic; therefore, as soon as the temperature drops, oxygen or air is blown in to react with carbon and raise the temperature.

$$2 C + \overline{O_2} \longrightarrow \overline{2 CO} + \Delta$$

FIG. 39.5. The U.G.I. mechanical generator carburetted water gas apparatus. (Courtesy, United Engineers and Constructors, Inc., Philadelphia.)

Besides being used as a fuel for cooking and heating, water gas is of industrial importance. The hydrogen can be separated very economically by oxidizing CO to CO_2 in the presence of catalysts and then absorbing the CO_2. An important use of water gas which promises to be of great significance in the future is the conversion of carbon monoxide and hydrogen into synthetic gasoline.

Producer Gas. Many industries require a gaseous fuel. When the composition of the gas is of secondary importance, a combination of water and coal gas provides the cheapest fuel possible. When a deep bed of coal is heated, carbon dioxide forms at the lower level and is reduced to carbon monoxide as it goes upward. When the lower level of coal is hot, steam is forced in and water gas is produced. The cycle is alternated. A big saving is possible if the gas is burned *while still hot*, for otherwise all the nitrogen which dilutes the gas must be reheated.

Blast Furnace Gas. The carbon monoxide always present in blast furnace gas has fuel value if the gas is used while hot; otherwise most of the energy from the CO would be dissipated in warming the nitrogen and carbon dioxide which comprise about 70 per cent of the mixture. Blast furnace gas is a poor fuel, but many plants cannot afford to waste it.

Safety Cautions in the Use of Fuels

Solid fuels are of course the least dangerous, although dust explosions may be caused by powdered fuels. To eliminate this hazard on ships using this type of fuel, the powder is mixed with thick oil; this produces a semi-emulsion which is heavier than water and is protected from accidentally igniting by a layer of water.

Many liquid fuel fires are caused by the use of gasoline as a cleaning fluid. Pure gasoline should never be used indoors for cleaning because a friction spark is sufficient to ignite the vapor from the volatile fluid. The danger from liquid fuels is proportional to the volatility of the liquid.

Numerous sewer gas explosions occur when mixtures of methane and hydrogen are produced by the anaerobic decomposition of organic matter. Gas burners accidentally turned on are responsible for many explosions in the home.

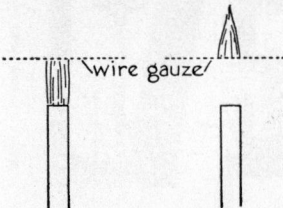

FIG. 39.6. Principle of the Davy safety lamp. The wire gauze conducts heat away. If the gas is ignited above the gauze, the flame burns only above the wire.

The safety lamp developed by Sir Humphry Davy in 1815 has saved the lives of thousands of miners. The principle of the Davy lamp is shown in Fig. 39.6. Note from this figure that the metal gauze radiates the heat so rapidly that there is no flame above it; similarly, the gas may be ignited *above* the gauze without burning below it. The metal gauze with which the lamp is lined cools the flame so that the gas burns *only inside the lamp.* A flame appearing inside this gauze warns the miner of "fire damp."

RUBBER, A HYDROCARBON; THE RUBBER INDUSTRY

No so many years ago, the only rubber trees grew wild in several tropical countries, and rubber was used to a very limited extent; by 1939, millions of rubber trees were cultivated on large plantations, and rubber had become an essential commodity—the automobile industry could not have developed without it.

When rubber trees are six years old, they begin to yield a white liquid, called latex; this continues for the next forty years, during which time the trees grow to the size of maples. The latex, which is an emulsion of rubber particles in water, is collected every four years by natives who tap the trees,

CARBON AND ITS COMPOUNDS

that is, cut through the bark. The colloidal rubber in the latex is stabilized by nitrogenous or protein substances in the water. The rubber can be coagulated by heat and fermentation, the natives stirring the latex with wooden paddles which have been held in a fire (the acid compounds in the wood smoke cause coagulation). However, acetic or formic acid is preferable for this purpose, and is used commercially, the latex being poured into a bath of the acid.

Pure rubber is soluble in carbon disulfide and several organic solvents. Nitric acid and ozone destroy it rapidly. It is brittle at $-20°$ F.; and if cooled in liquid air and then removed, it shatters like glass. Since it becomes soft at $100°$ F., it would be very unsatisfactory for automobile tires.

In 1839, Charles Goodyear made the important discovery that heating raw rubber and sulfur together produced a more elastic, stronger product that is flexible at low temperatures and not sticky at high ones. Crude rubber is now softened with steam, rolled, dried; mixed with a vulcanizer, coloring matter, wearing agents such as carbon and zinc oxide, and accelerators; and then placed in a mold and "heated," "vulcanized," or "cured" at $140°$ C. In preparing rubber for automobile tires and such products, cotton fabrics are added before molding to give increased strength. Before it was discovered that such compounds as PbO and diphenylguanidine, $(C_6H_5NH)_2$-CNH, would accelerate vulcanization, the process required several hours; but now it takes only a few minutes.

The price of rubber during the past twenty years ranged from $.05 to $1 per pound; during the immediate prewar years it was $.15 to $.18 per pound. Table 39.8 shows the world production of rubber over the past century. About 400,000 tons were consumed annually in the United States before the war.

TABLE 39.8. WORLD PRODUCTION OF RUBBER IN TONS PER YEAR

1839	10,000	1912	100,000
1859	30,000	1920	343,000
1900	54,000	1938	1,000,000

The Nature of Rubber

Early researchers found that when rubber was purified as much as possible from natural proteins and added materials, what remained was a hydrocarbon with the empirical formula C_5H_8. When rubber is subjected to destructive distillation in the absence of air, the main product is a volatile liquid with the same empirical formula as that of rubber, but in this case the empirical and molecular formulas have been shown to be the same. The product was identified as *isoprene*. The systematic name of isoprene is 2-methylbutadiene; its structural formula is:

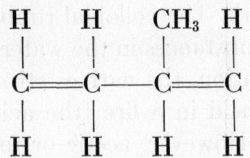

The name indicates that it is derived from butadiene by replacing a hydrogen on the second carbon with a methyl group. (In the parent compound the "di-ene" refers to the two double bonds in what would otherwise be butane.) Since the molecular weight of rubber was from 800 to 2500 times that of isoprene (depending upon how it had been treated) it was concluded that rubber was a polymer of isoprene. It is now known that when a diene polymerizes, the electrons shift from the arrangement indicated above, which may be written (as far as concerns the bonds in the chain itself) $C::C:C::C$, to the following arrangement: $\cdot C:C::C:C\cdot$; the addition of one unit to another can take place indefinitely. In the case of isoprene the following pattern results:

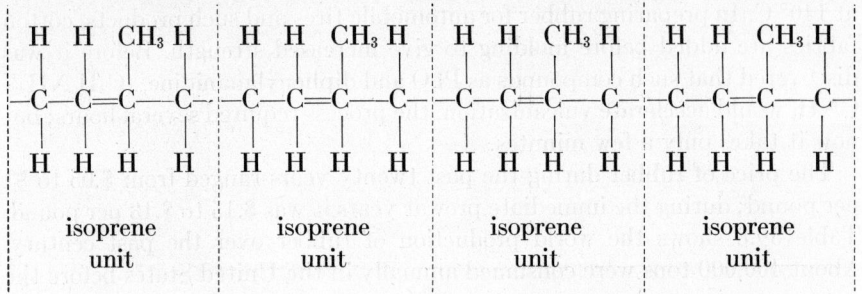

The section of the rubber molecule just shown was drawn stretched out flat on the paper to make it easier to see, and hence there was no explanation of the most characteristic property of rubber, its stretchiness. Actually, the molecule is all kinked up. It is possible for a carbon chain to kink because of its ability to rotate freely around each *single* bond, although the angles between the bonds of any one atom remain constant. The forces that draw the molecule into kinks are the same as those which hold molecules together in a liquid—the van der Waals forces, the small stray fields of magnetic force which surround each covalent bond because of the not quite perfect coupling of the shared electrons. The forces at the double bonds are particularly strong and tend to kink the molecule in such a way that the double bonds lie alongside each other. The existence of the double bonds in rubber is the main reason why it is more rubbery than plastic sulfur, which has an otherwise similar structure. When rubber is stretched, the molecules are straightened out. Vulcanization makes rubber tougher and firmer and harder to "melt" by establishing cross links between the chains. Carried to an extreme, it produces *hard rubber*, or ebonite.

CARBON AND ITS COMPOUNDS

Synthetic Rubber

Early attempts to synthesize rubber from isoprene failed because, as we now know, of the lack of a proper technique for effecting the polymerization. The first successful attempts in that line, with metallic sodium as a catalyst, were made in Germany when that country was cut off from supplies of natural rubber during World War I. By that time the theory of the nature of rubber had progressed to the point where it was plain that the essential factor in producing a synthetic rubber was the physical nature of the molecule, not its exact chemical composition. The Germans therefore used two related substances instead of isoprene, which happened to be much more difficult to prepare. These were butadiene itself and 2,3-dimethylbutadiene. The rubber made from the latter proved more successful and

FIG. 39.7. J. A. Nieuwland. (From French's *The Drama of Chemistry*, courtesy of the author and The University Society.)

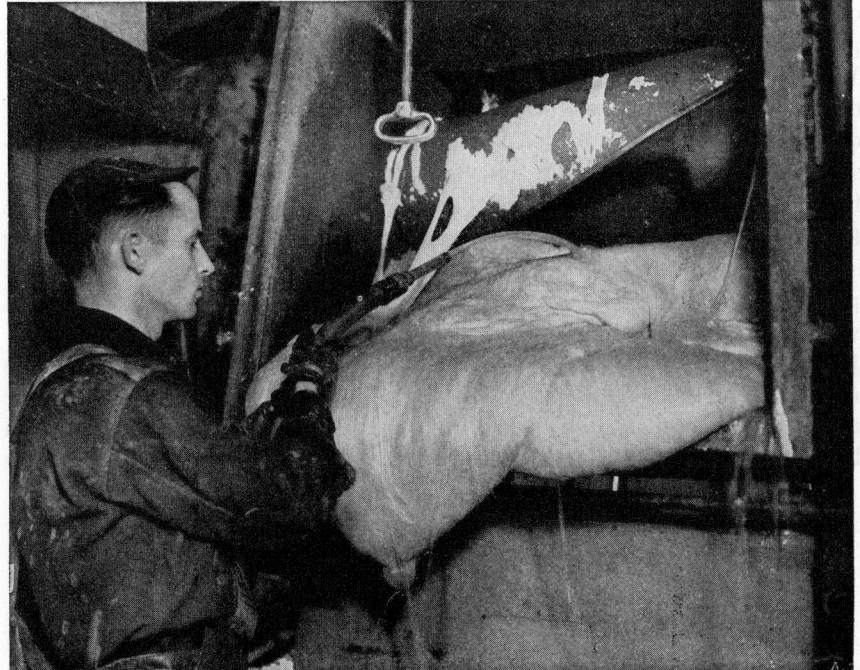

FIG. 39.8. Neoprene is an intermediate stage of processing. (Courtesy, E. I. du Pont de Nemours & Company.)

about 4,000,000 tons of it were manufactured in Germany during that war. The name Buna was given to the whole class of *bu*tadiene rubbers polymerized by *Na*, but this particular synthetic is better known as methyl rubber, because its structure differs from that of natural rubber (page 688) in having an additional methyl group on the *other* side of each double bond.

In 1927, J. A. Nieuwland of Notre Dame University converted acetylene gas into divinyl acetylene. By modifying this process, du Pont chemists produced monovinyl acetylene which reacts with HCl gas and forms chloroprene, CH_2=CH—CCl=CH_2; this has a Cl in the same place where isoprene has a CH_3— group. This they *emulsified* and polymerized into a rubber that has been named neoprene. (The more familiar "Duprene" is a trade name for the du Pont product.) It proved to be as good as or better than natural rubber in most respects and immensely superior in one: it is completely resistant to gasoline, oil, and grease, which quickly soften and ruin natural rubber. It costs several times as much as the natural product ordinarily does, but it is well worth it for special uses.

Emulsion polymerization was a great advance in the art of making rubber. It made it possible to hold the extent of polymerization constant throughout the material, and to stop it at any desired point.

Synthetic rubber research, although not attractive from a financial point of view during the depression of the thirties, was pursued by rubber companies which had the vision to foresee the possibility of war with Japan. With the aid of information from Germany, immensely superior new types of general-purpose rubbers had gone through most of the laboratory stage of development by the time World War II broke out. Under ordinary circumstances it might have taken ten years to move these materials from the laboratory to full-scale commercial production. It is little short of a miracle that our chemists and chemical engineers were able to do this before our stock-pile of natural rubber was exhausted. Furthermore, the scale of production actually achieved was sufficient to provide for our war needs which were more than double our prewar requirements.

The main form produced was the type called GR-S ("general-purpose rubber, styrene") which was a *copolymer* of butadiene and styrene. The latter may be considered as ethylene in which one hydrogen has been replaced by a benzene ring; it is indicated by the formula

$$\langle \bigcirc \rangle\text{—CH}=CH_2$$

An emulsion is made of 3 parts of butadiene, 1 part of styrene, and 7 parts of soapy water, and polymerized by a suitable catalyst. A hypothetical section of the molecule is shown on the opposite page.

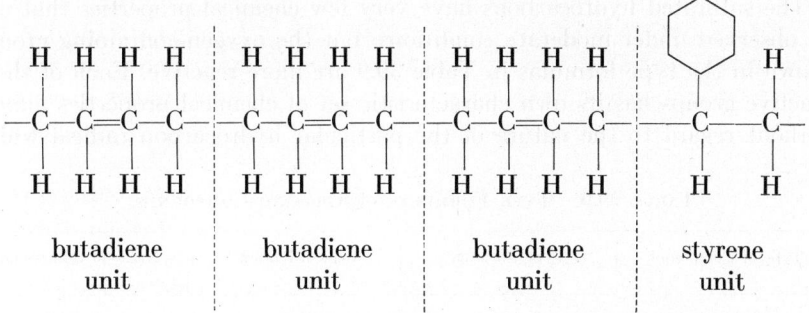

Styrene is manufactured from benzene and ethylene. Butadiene is obtained most cheaply from the butane and butylene present in refinery gases, but during the war emergency large quantities were prepared from ethyl alcohol. GR-S rubber can probably be produced in peacetime about as cheaply as natural rubber, except that from the most efficient plantations.

There is no limit to the number of different synthetic elastic polymers that can be prepared. The term *elastomer* has been suggested for these substances, which are not really synthetic rubber because they differ from it in composition. One other elastomer which is worth mentioning is the oil-resistant Buna-N, in which the styrene is replaced by acrylonitrile. Acrylonitrile is ethylene in which one hydrogen has been replaced by a CN— grouping, CN—CH=CH$_2$.

ORGANIC COMPOUNDS CONTAINING OXYGEN AND OTHER ELEMENTS

The compounds discussed in the preceding paragraphs are quite simple structurally as compared to those which contain oxygen in addition to carbon and hydrogen. Thousands of these compounds are known, but only a few of them have sufficient everyday use for us to know even their trade names. Among these compounds are alcohol, formaldehyde, vinegar, ether, banana oil, acetone, soap, fat, sugar, protein, and cellulose. Still other organic compounds contain nitrogen, sulfur, phosphorus, etc.; a few of them will also be considered.

Compounds which contain carbon, hydrogen, and oxygen are often referred to as derivatives of the hydrocarbons, for their molecule contains a hydrocarbon group. If one hydrogen is removed from methane, the residue is (CH$_3$—) and is called the *methyl group*. Ethane minus one hydrogen leaves the *ethyl group* (C$_2$H$_5$—); propane minus one hydrogen, the *propyl group* (C$_3$H$_7$—), etc. These groups are called the *alkyl radicals*.

The saturated hydrocarbons have very few chemical properties that can be observed under moderate conditions, but the oxygen-containing groups shown in the type formulas in Table 39.9 are more reactive. Each of these reactive groups has its own characteristic set of chemical properties almost without regard to the nature of the particular hydrocarbon radical which

TABLE 39.9. TYPE FORMULAS OF ORGANIC COMPOUNDS

Type of Compound	Type Formula	Typical Example	Name of Compound
Alcohol	R—OH	C_2H_5OH	Ethyl alcohol
Aldehyde	$R-C\overset{O}{\underset{H}{\diagdown}}$	$CH_3-C\overset{O}{\underset{H}{\diagdown}}$	Acetaldehyde
Acid	$R-C\overset{O}{\underset{OH}{\diagdown}}$	$CH_3-C\overset{O}{\underset{OH}{\diagdown}}$	Acetic acid
Ketone	$R-C\overset{O}{\underset{R'}{\diagdown}}$	$CH_3-C\overset{O}{\underset{CH_3}{\diagdown}}$	Acetone
Ester	$R-C\overset{O}{\underset{OR'}{\diagdown}}$	$CH_3-C\overset{O}{\underset{O-C_2H_5}{\diagdown}}$	Ethyl acetate
Ether	R—O—R'	$CH_3-O-C_2H_5$	Methyl ethyl ether

takes the place of the R in the type formula. Thus, even though the alkyl radicals are covalently bound to, say, the hydroxyl group which characterizes an alcohol, the properties which this group shows in methyl alcohol and in ethyl alcohol are practically identical. We may therefore make a class of alcohols just as in inorganic chemistry we made a class of sulfates. Just as the sulfate ion has its own characteristic set of properties, no matter what cation it is paired with, so the —OH radical has its own characteristic set of properties with no (or at least little) regard to what alkyl radical is attached to it. Learn the type formulas of the several classes of organic compounds listed in Table 39.9.

Alcohols

Methyl Alcohol. Methyl alcohol, also known as methanol, is formed when methyl chloride is hydrolyzed.

$$\text{H:}\overset{\text{H}}{\underset{\text{H}}{\text{C}}}\text{:}\ddot{\text{Cl}}\text{:} + \text{H:}\ddot{\text{O}}\text{:} \longrightarrow \text{H:}\overset{\text{H}}{\underset{\text{H}}{\text{C}}}\text{:}\ddot{\text{O}}\text{:H} + \text{H:}\ddot{\text{Cl}}\text{:}$$

This hydrolysis does not proceed as readily as does that of the chloride of a more electrophilic element than carbon; in fact, some acid or base must be present as a catalyst. Because carbon is so weakly electrophilic it is to be expected that methanol will be a weak acid. Actually, the alcohols are slightly less acid than water; the alkali metals liberate hydrogen from them more slowly than from water. Inorganic chemists ordinarily write even weakly acidic hydrogen first in a formula; methanol would thus be written $HOCH_3$ analogous to HOCl, etc. Do not be deceived, because of the organic chemists' habit of writing the formula for methanol CH_3OH, into thinking that there is any analogy between this substance and NaOH. Methanol yields no OH^- ions.

Methyl alcohol, or methanol, is often called wood alcohol, for at one time most of it was produced by the destructive distillation of wood. It is a colorless liquid which boils at 64.7° C. and burns readily with a colorless flame. It is toxic when either breathed into the lungs or drunk; if taken into the body in quantity, it produces blindness, followed by paralysis and death.

The demand for CH_3OH—about 15,000,000 gallons—as a solvent in the shellac and varnish industry, a radiator anti-freeze, a raw material from which formaldehyde and many resins are made, and a denaturant for ethyl alcohol, led to attempts to synthesize it. Since only about 40 gallons of methyl alcohol can be obtained from the destructive distillation of a cord of dry wood, its price was necessarily high, nor was it kept down sufficiently by the sale of the by-products—about half a ton of charcoal, 800 pounds of tar, 700 pounds of gases, and 500 pounds of acetic acid. In 1923 the problem of satisfying the demand was solved, and methyl alcohol produced from wood no longer competes with the synthetic product.[2] When carbon monoxide and hydrogen gas react at a suitable pressure and temperature and in the presence of a catalyst, methanol is produced.

$$CO + 2\ H_2 \xrightarrow[ZnO,\ Cr_2O_3]{200°,\ 1000\ atm.} CH_3OH + \Delta \quad (93\text{ per cent conversion})$$

[2] In that year Germany shipped methanol to the United States, paid the import duty on it, and sold it for 40 cents per gallon, or half the price of alcohol made from wood.

It is more economical to operate at lower pressures and recirculate the gases over the catalyst; hence pressures as low as 150 atm. are used.

Ethyl Alcohol. Ethyl alcohol, C_2H_5OH, is also known as grain alcohol; its chemical name is ethanol, and its structural formula is

$$\begin{array}{c} H\ \ H \\ |\ \ \ | \\ H-C-C-O-H \\ |\ \ \ | \\ H\ \ H \end{array}$$

It can be made from petroleum, by means of C_2H_4 and C_2H_5Cl, but an important method of preparing it still depends upon fermentation reactions. It is produced from glucose, black strap molasses, and other carbohydrates.

$$C_6H_{12}O_6 \longrightarrow 2\ C_2H_5OH + \overline{2\ CO_2}$$

In these fermentation reactions, one-third of the carbon in the glucose molecule goes to produce the practically worthless carbon dioxide. (A few breweries do make "dry ice" from the CO_2.) Many organic substances can be fermented, but corn, molasses, barley, and grapes are the ones most generally used. Yeast cells produces the enzyme or catalyst that is responsible for the decomposition of glucose. Enzymes are usually quite specific in their action; for example, no one enzyme would produce the changes: cellulose $\longrightarrow$ glucose $\longrightarrow$ alcohol. Cellulose can be broken down or hydrolyzed to glucose with acid. Cane sugar, $C_{12}H_{22}O_{11}$, is easily hydrolyzed by being boiled with dilute hydrochloric acid. That glucose when boiled does not decompose into alcohol clearly shows our dependence upon enzymes.

Since alcohol is a germicide, it is impossible to produce a concentration greater than 15 or 18 per cent by fermentation; for any concentration greater than this the fermented product must be fractionally distilled. Beer contains less than 4 per cent alcohol, reinforced wine about 20, and rum and whisky approximately 50 per cent. The alcohol content of solutions is usually expressed as "proof"; the percentage proof spirit multiplied by the factor 0.5 gives the percentage by volume. The human body can oxidize only about 15 ml. of alcohol an hour. Small quantities appear to act as a stimulant by inactivating inhibitory mechanisms, but alcohol in excess acts as a poison that numbs mental and physical processes. Perhaps its greatest harmful effect is the fact that it is habit-forming.

Absolutely pure alcohol cannot be prepared by simple fractional distillation because it forms with H_2O a constant-boiling solution of 97.2 per cent alcohol. Nearly 100 per cent alcohol can be prepared by adding a dehydrating agent such as CaO before distilling; anhydrous $CuSO_4$ is also used. A few years ago another method of preparing pure alcohol for industrial purposes was devised. If benzene is added to an alcohol-water mixture and

CARBON AND ITS COMPOUNDS

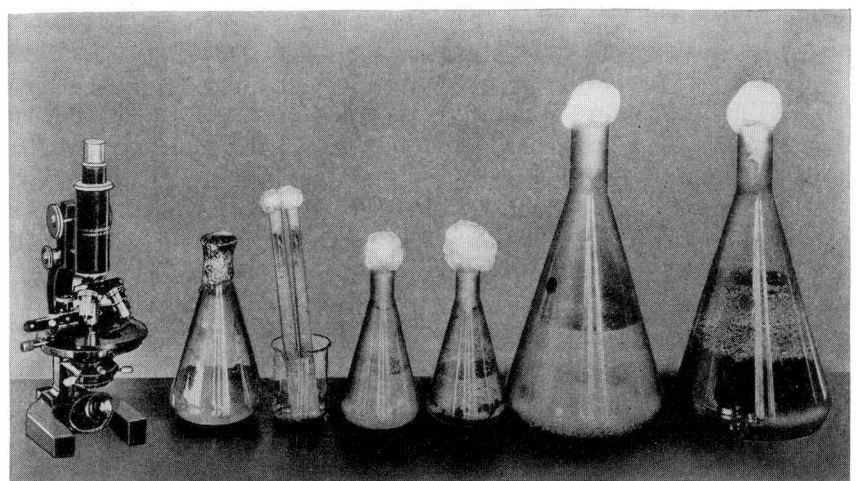

FIG. 39.9. Bacteria propagation, early stages. (Courtesy, Commercial Solvents Corporation.)

the triple mixture is distilled, the first portion of the distillate contains the benzene and water plus a little alcohol, and the residue consists of 100 per cent C_2H_5OH.

Pure ethyl alcohol freezes at $-117°$ C., boils at $78.3°$, and has a density of 0.785 at $20°$. About 100 million gallons of alcohol are used each year in the United States, exclusive of that consumed by the alcoholic beverage industry. It ranks next to water as a solvent, the commercial product being about 95 per cent alcohol; it is an ideal solvent for the essential oils, flavoring

FIG. 39.10. Bacteria propagation in 800-gallon tanks. (Courtesy, Commercial Solvents Corporation.)

extracts like vanilla, lacquers, celluloid, smokeless powder, etc. It is used in preparing chloroform, ether, ethylene, ethylene dibromide, medicinals, etc. Solid alcohol or "canned heat" contains 10 to 15 per cent saturated calcium acetate solution, 85 to 90 per cent alcohol, and 1 per cent stearic acid. Many thousands of gallons of denatured alcohol are used as radiator antifreeze in the northern states.

Butyl Alcohol. Butyl alcohol, C_4H_9OH, and acetone are produced by fermenting corn with bacteria known as "butylic bacillus of Fitz," "bacillus macearans," and other bacteria. One part of acetone is obtained for every two of butyl alcohol. Both are important as solvents.

FIG. 39.11. Lower level of fermentation tanks (50,000-gallon capacity). (Courtesy, Commercial Solvents Corporation.)

Phenol. Phenol, C_6H_5OH (hydroxy-benzene or *carbolic acid*), M.P. 42–3° C., is not considered an alcohol because it is so much more acidic than the compounds which have just been described. It is definitely an acid, although a very weak one; its sodium salt is only partly hydrolyzed in water solution. The acidity of phenol is due to the shortage of electrons in the benzene ring. Three double bonds are necessary to complete the octets; this makes the *phenyl* group, C_6H_5—, very electrophilic. The effect on the oxygen is the same as though a chlorine atom were sharing electrons with it; the oxygen becomes less willing to share electrons with hydrogen and the compound is a stronger acid than water. Phenol is obtained from coal tar by fractional distillation and can also be prepared from benzene. It is a powerful poison and an excellent germicide even when diluted to one part per thousand. Phenol is the active ingredient in the coal tar dips used for domestic animals. Traces of phenol give water a disagreeable taste; chlorinated phenol can be tasted even though present in only one part per billion. Most of the phenol is consumed in the resin industry; 2000 tons are used annually for dyes and pharmaceuticals. Phenol hardens and burns the flesh; the burns heal very slowly.

Glycol. Ethylene, C_2H_4, the compound from which many derivatives are made, is for the most part produced by the vapor phase cracking of petroleum. Glycol or ethylene glycol is prepared by treating ethylene with a solution of hypochlorous acid; the ethylene chlorohydrin which forms is in turn treated with sodium bicarbonate.

$$\begin{array}{c} H\ H \\ |\ \ | \\ C{=}C \\ |\ \ | \\ H\ H \end{array} + HOCl \longrightarrow \begin{array}{c} H\ H \\ |\ \ | \\ HO{-}C{-}C{-}Cl \\ |\ \ | \\ H\ H \end{array} \quad \text{(ethylene chlorohydrin)}$$

$$HO \cdot C_2H_4Cl + NaHCO_3 \longrightarrow HO \cdot C_2H_4 \cdot OH + NaCl + \overline{CO_2}$$

Glycol is frequently written $C_2H_4(OH)_2$; its structural formula

$$\begin{array}{c} H \\ | \\ H{-}C{-}OH \\ | \\ H{-}C{-}OH \\ | \\ H \end{array}$$

shows it to be a dihydric alcohol. It is completely miscible with water and is used as a radiator anti-freeze and in the preparation of many glycol esters.

Glycerol. Glycerol, $C_3H_5(OH)_3$, the most important trihydroxyl alcohol, is obtained from fat (page 702). This colorless, viscous, sweet liquid is non-toxic, and is used in toilet preparations, as a deliquescent substance to keep tobacco moist, as a radiator anti-freeze, and in the manufacture of nitroglycerin, etc. Glycerol has recently been obtained in large quantities from petroleum products (propylene).

Aldehydes

Formaldehyde, $H{-}\overset{\overset{\displaystyle O}{\|}}{C}{-}H$, is the simplest of the aldehydes. This gas is prepared by the partial oxidation of methyl alcohol in the presence of such catalysts as copper gauze, iron and molybdenum oxide, and vanadium pentoxide. Although there are undoubtedly intermediate reactions, the equation for the final reaction is:

698 TEXTBOOK OF CHEMISTRY

$$2 \text{ CH}_3\text{OH} + \text{O}_2 \xrightarrow{600°} 2 \text{ HCHO} + 2 \text{ H}_2\text{O}$$

Formaldehyde is an excellent reducing agent and disinfectant. The 40 per cent solution known as *formalin* is used in embalming, in preserving museum specimens, and as a mild germicide. The development of the plastic industry created a new market for many tons of formaldehyde in phenol-formaldehyde resins.

Acetaldehyde, $\text{CH}_3\overset{\overset{\text{O}}{\|}}{\text{C}}\!\!-\!\!\text{H}$, which is prepared by the gentle oxidation of ethyl alcohol (the preparation of HCHO from CH$_3$OH is similar), is a clear colorless liquid, B.P. 20° C. It is important commercially as an intermediate product in many reactions, among which are the preparation of acetic acid, acetic anhydride, acetone, ethyl acetate, and several medicinals. It is prepared commercially by the reaction of acetylene with H$_2$O in the presence of a catalyst (HgSO$_4$).

$$\text{H}\!-\!\text{C}\!\equiv\!\text{C}\!-\!\text{H} + 2\text{ HOH} \longrightarrow \text{H}\!-\!\overset{\overset{\text{H}}{|}}{\underset{\underset{\text{H}}{|}}{\text{C}}}\!-\!\overset{\overset{\text{H}}{|}}{\underset{\underset{\text{OH}}{|}}{\text{C}}}\!-\!\text{O}\boxed{\text{H}} \longrightarrow \text{CH}_3\text{CHO}$$

A rather complex aldehyde, *furfuraldehyde*, is made from such waste products as oat hulls and corn cobs, and is cheap enough to be used in making resins and in the solvent refining of petroleum (p. 683).

Acids

Organic acids can be prepared for all series of hydrocarbons, those of the methane series being very important. The "fatty acids" or acids obtained from fat are used in the manufacture of soap.

Formic acid, $\text{H}\!-\!\overset{\overset{\text{O}}{\|}}{\text{C}}\!-\!\text{O}\!-\!\text{H}$, the acid of the first member of the methane series, can be prepared by the mild oxidation of formaldehyde.

$$2 \text{ HCHO} + \text{O}_2 \longrightarrow 2 \text{ HCOOH}$$

It was originally obtained by distilling a species of ants, for this acid is present in the "sting" of bees, ants, and the nettle plants. Small quantities of it are used in the dye industry, and in coagulating rubber latex.

The characteristic part of formic acid and its numerous homologues is the *carboxyl* group, —COOH. Compounds containing this group may be referred to as carboxylic acids. The electronic formula of this group is $\cdot\text{C}::\ddot{\text{O}}:$, and
$:\!\ddot{\text{O}}\!:\!\text{H}$

the $\cdot\text{C}::\ddot{\text{O}}:$ part of it (called the *carbonyl* group) enhances the acidity of the proton attached to oxygen just as the phenyl (C_6H_5—) group did in phenol. It is much more effective, in fact, because of the reluctance of oxygen to share two pairs of electrons.

Acetic acid, or vinegar, CH_3COOH or $HC_2H_3O_2$, is an extremely important organic acid which can be obtained by the mild oxidation of ethyl alcohol. (Complete or vigorous oxidation of alcohols produces carbon dioxide and water.) The mild fermentation of apple juice or cider, caused by a mixed culture of organisms, produces "hard cider"; if fermentation is carried too far, acetic acid results. Apple vinegar contains about 4 to 5 per cent acetic acid. Alcohol from any source is turned into acetic acid by the culture of "mother of vinegar."

$$C_2H_5OH + O_2 \xrightarrow{\text{Bacterium aceti}} CH_3COOH + H_2O$$

A nearly colorless vinegar is produced by dripping alcohol which contains certain nutrient materials over beechwood shavings, etc., inoculated with mother of vinegar. Acetic acid is also produced by blowing air through acetaldehyde containing a little manganous sulfate. A "batch" of about 1000 gallons of acetaldehyde can be oxidized to acetic acid every eight hours. (The $MnSO_4$ aids in decomposing an explosive compound that is called peracetic acid.) Pure or glacial acetic acid contains no free water; it is a solid that melts at 16.6° C.

Acetic acid has several important metallic salts. Lead acetate is used in testing for sulfides. Many organic derivatives of acetic acid—amyl acetate and cellulose acetate, for example—are well known. Acetic anhydride, a good solvent for cellulose, is obtained by the further dehydration of acetic acid.

$$2\ HC_2H_3O_2 \longrightarrow H_2O + CH_3C\overset{O}{\diagup}\!\!-\!O\!-\!\overset{O}{\overset{\|}{C}}\!-\!CH_3$$

Oxalic acid, $H_2C_2O_4$, is dibasic, because both hydrogens in its structural formula,

$$\begin{array}{c} \overset{O}{\diagup} \\ C\!-\!O\!-\!H \\ | \\ \overset{O}{\diagup} \\ C\!-\!O\!-\!H \end{array}$$

are replaceable. The oxalates of the alkaline earth metals are insoluble. Calcium is determined quantitatively by precipitating CaC_2O_4; the sour taste of rhubarb is due to potassium acid oxalate. The free acid, which is poisonous, is used in polishing brass rails, cleaning straw hats, etc.

Tartaric acid is another dibasic acid. The formula for tartaric acid is $H_2C_4H_4O_6$; its structural formula is:

$$\begin{array}{c} OH \\ | \\ C=O \\ | \\ H-C-OH \\ | \\ H-C-OH \\ | \\ C(=O)-OH \end{array}$$

The hydrogens of the carboxyl groups $\left[-C(=O)-OH\right]$ ionize and may be replaced by metallic ions. Crystals of potassium acid tartrate frequently form in the bottom of bottles of wine and of grape juice. This salt, when recrystallized, is the cream of tartar used in baking powder. The formula of Rochelle salt is $KNaC_4H_4O_6$.

Citric acid, $H_3(C_6H_5O_7\text{---})$, is a tribasic acid that is found in citrus fruits; it is used in flavoring many carbonated beverages.

Lactic or sour milk acid, $CH_3 \cdot CHOH \cdot C(=O)-OH$, is produced when milk sugar is fermented by the lactic acid bacillus. This acid has the (—OH) group of an alcohol and the carboxyl group $\left[-C(=O)-OH\right]$ of an acid. Cottage cheese is made at home by allowing milk to sour. The lactic acid plus heat coagulates the protein (cottage cheese) which is then filtered on cloth.

Benzoic acid, the simplest acid derived from benzene, is found in cranberries. Its formula, $C_6H_5C(=O)-O-H$, shows that it has one replaceable hydrogen atom. For many years benzoic acid was widely used as a preservative in such foods as tomato ketchup. Food laws now require that labels indicate its presence.

The fatty acids with high molecular weights will be discussed in the section on soaps.

Ketones

Acetone, $CH_3-C(=O)-CH_3$, the most important ketone, is easily prepared by heating calcium acetate.

$$\begin{array}{c}\text{CH}_3-\text{C}\diagup\!\!\!\diagdown\text{O}\\ \phantom{\text{CH}_3-\text{C}}\diagdown\text{O}\\ \phantom{\text{CH}_3-\text{C}}\text{O}\\ \text{CH}_3-\text{C}\diagup\!\!\!\diagup\text{O}\end{array}\text{Ca} \xrightarrow{\Delta} \text{CH}_3-\overset{\overset{\text{O}}{\|}}{\text{C}}-\text{CH}_3 + \text{CaCO}_3$$

Some of this liquid is obtained by the destructive distillation of wood, fermentation reactions, and catalytic decomposition of acetic acid. It is a valuable organic solvent in the varnish, resin, and explosive industries, and in the manufacture of other organic compounds. Its use as a solvent for acetylene was discussed above (page 674).

Esters

Esters are produced by the condensation of an alcohol with an acid which contains oxygen. The slightly acidic proton of the alcohol and an HO— group of the acid are eliminated as water. For example:

$$\underset{\text{acetic acid + ethyl alcohol}}{\text{H}-\overset{\overset{\text{H}}{|}}{\underset{\underset{\text{H}}{|}}{\text{C}}}-\text{C}\diagup\!\!\!\diagup\text{O}\,\boxed{\text{O}-\text{H} + \text{H}}-\text{O}-\overset{\overset{\text{H}}{|}}{\underset{\underset{\text{H}}{|}}{\text{C}}}-\overset{\overset{\text{H}}{|}}{\underset{\underset{\text{H}}{|}}{\text{C}}}-\text{H}} \rightleftarrows \underset{\text{ethyl acetate} \quad + \quad \text{water}}{\text{CH}_3\cdot\text{COO}\cdot\text{C}_2\text{H}_5 + \text{H}_2\text{O}}$$

The reaction is similar to nitration (page 705) but does not require as strong a dehydrating agent because the proton removed by the HO— group of the acid is not so tightly held. Esters of inorganic acids are similar to the organic esters. Thus amyl nitrite, an important remedy in heart disease (angina pectoris), $\text{C}_5\text{H}_{11}\cdot\text{NO}_2$, is formed:

$$\underset{\text{amyl alcohol}}{\text{CH}_3\cdot\text{CH}_2\cdot\text{CH}_2\cdot\text{CH}_2\cdot\text{CH}_2\cdot\text{O}}\,\boxed{\text{H} + \text{HO}}\cdot\underset{\text{nitrous acid}}{\text{NO}} \longrightarrow$$

$$\underset{\text{amyl nitrite}}{\text{CH}_3\cdot\text{CH}_2\cdot\text{CH}_2\cdot\text{CH}_2\cdot\text{CH}_2\cdot\text{O}\cdot\text{NO}} + \underset{\text{water}}{\text{H}_2\text{O}}$$

Esters are named in imitation of salts, partly to show the relationship to the acid from which they are formed, and partly because it was not known until recently that the oxygen of the eliminated water came from the acid (page 650). They must not on any account be confused with salts, for their nature is entirely different; they are purely covalent compounds and form no ions.

Esters of moderate molecular weight are usually pleasant-smelling liquids; many fruit flavors and perfumes are esters. Nitric acid esters are explosive. Glycol dinitrate and glycerol trinitrate (the latter commonly miscalled "nitroglycerine") are the active ingredients of regular dynamites.

Fats. Fats are esters. Animal fats and vegetable oils are made from acids with high molecular weights and the trihydroxyl alcohol, glycerol. Most of these fats and oils are mixtures of several esters; their melting points depend upon the ratio of esters. Animal fats and vegetable oils can be synthesized in the laboratory; the following equation illustrates the reactions:

$$\text{glycerol} + \text{stearic acid} \longrightarrow \text{glycerol stearate (fat)} + \text{water}$$

$$\begin{array}{c} H \\ | \\ H-C-O\,|\,H\ +\ H-O\,|\,-C-C_{17}H_{35} \\ | \\ \\ H-C-O\,|\,H\ +\ H-O\,|\,-C-C_{17}H_{35} \longrightarrow (C_{17}H_{35}COO)_3C_3H_5 + 3\,H_2O \\ | \\ \\ H-C-O\,|\,H\ +\ H-O\,|\,-C-C_{17}H_{35} \\ | \\ H \end{array}$$

If other organic acids are substituted for stearic acid, the corresponding glycerol esters are formed. The formulas for a few of the more common esters are as follows:

Name	Formula	M. P. °C.	Substances Rich in These Esters
Glycerol stearate	$(C_{17}H_{35}COO)_3 \cdot C_3H_5$	70	Beef suet > 75 per cent
Glycerol palmitate	$(C_{15}H_{31}COO)_3 \cdot C_3H_5$	65	Coconut oil
Glycerol oleate	$(C_{17}H_{33}COO)_3 \cdot C_3H_5$	−4	Olive oil and cotton-seed oil > 75 per cent
Glycerol butyrate	$(C_3H_7COO)_3 \cdot C_3H_5$	−75	Butter
Glycerol trinitrate	$(NO_3)_3 \cdot C_3H_5$	13	Dynamite

The melting point of the first ester in the list explains why steak and lamb chops should be eaten while hot. Beef fat contains about 75 per cent stearin ("stearin" is the common name for glycerol stearate), and mutton tallow does not contain much of the low-melting olein; therefore both solidify at a high temperature. Lard, on the other hand, contains about 60 per cent olein; hence bacon grease is a liquid at a much lower temperature than beef suet. Such fats as cottonseed and olive oils are liquids at room temperature because they contain about 75 per cent olein. Both stearin and olein have the same number of carbon atoms, but stearin has two more hydrogen

CARBON AND ITS COMPOUNDS

atoms. Olein has a double bond in the middle of the long hydrocarbon chain and this bond is responsible for the low melting point of olein.

Butter contains several fats. The disagreeable taste and odor of rancid butter are due to the butyric acid produced from glycerol butyrate. Several substitutes for butter are on the market, the most important one being oleomargarine. This is beef fat from which considerable stearin has been removed; low-melting vegetable oils are added to it to give the product the consistency of butter. It is usually "churned" in milk to give it a butter flavor. It is low in vitamins, but has about the same food value as butter, and is much cheaper.

The housewife of today has a wide assortment of cooking oils from which to choose. Sunflower seed, cottonseed, peanuts, corn, soy beans, and olives are all sources of oil. Several fish oils are used as a source of vitamins; and whale oil, although used only in soap making in the United States, is a food in many countries.

Until recently, lard was the only cheap solid fat available for making piecrust, etc. However, organic chemists discovered that liquid vegetable oils, in spite of being rich in the low-melting olein, could be solidified by being heated under pressure with hydrogen and suitable catalysts. (The double bond of olein molecules opens up and two hydrogen atoms add on, one to each carbon. There is one (—C═C—) linkage in each molecule of oleic acid, or three per molecule of glycerol oleate. Finely divided nickel is one of the best catalysts for this reaction.)

Soaps. All soaps were prepared from fats until recently, when it was discovered that soap-like substances could be produced from petroleum. Esters can be hydrolyzed with hot water, as shown by the following equation:

$$CH_3 \cdot COO \cdot C_2H_5 + H \cdot OH \longrightarrow CH_3 \cdot COOH + C_2H_5 \cdot OH$$

Glycerol esters hydrolyze much more slowly than do those of low molecular weight, but this difficulty is easily overcome by adding a base to the water. *Alkaline hydrolysis of a glycerol ester* is called *saponification*; the products are glycerol and the salt of an acid. The salts of fatty acids with high molecular weights are called *soaps*.

$$\begin{array}{c}
\text{H} \quad\quad \text{O} \\
| \quad\quad\quad \| \\
\text{H}-\text{C}-\text{O}-\text{C}-\text{C}_{17}\text{H}_{35} \quad\quad \text{Na}^+ + \text{OH}^- \\
| \quad\quad\quad \text{O} \\
| \quad\quad\quad \| \\
\text{H}-\text{C}-\text{O}-\text{C}-\text{C}_{17}\text{H}_{35} + \text{Na}^+ + \text{OH}^- \longrightarrow \text{C}_3\text{H}_5(\text{OH})_3 + 3\ \text{C}_{17}\text{H}_{35}\ \text{COO}^- + 3\ \text{Na}^+ \\
| \\
\text{H}-\text{C}-\text{O}-\text{C}-\text{C}_{17}\text{H}_{35} \quad\quad \text{Na}^+ + \text{OH}^- \\
| \quad\quad\quad \| \\
\text{H} \quad\quad \text{O}
\end{array}$$

glycerol stearate	+	sodium hydroxide	→	glycerol	+	sodium stearate
Fat	+	Base	→	Glycerol	+	Soap

Soft soaps are prepared by saponifying with KOH or K_2CO_3; hard soaps, with NaOH or Na_2CO_3. Soaps are much less soluble in salt solutions than in water, so that addition of salt causes the soap to "salt out." A good soap should not turn phenolphthalein pink and should be free of fillers. During the past few years satisfactory soaps have been synthesized from petroleum hydrocarbons containing eight to fourteen carbon atoms per molecule. These hydrocarbons are carefully oxidized to the corresponding fatty acids and then converted into soaps. The demand for the free fatty acids in making candles, shaving creams, etc., is sufficient so that it is profitable to hydrolyze fats with steam and suitable catalysts. Glycerol is also used in making explosives and as a radiator anti-freeze.

Ethers

Diethyl ether, $C_2H_5 \cdot O \cdot C_2H_5$, the most common ether, is a liquid that is used as an anesthetic. It is prepared by heating ethyl alcohol and sulfuric acid.

$$2\ C_2H_5OH \xrightarrow[140°\ C.]{H_2SO_4} C_2H_5 \cdot O \cdot C_2H_5 + H_2O$$

We have seen above (page 673) that ethylene can be prepared by changing the concentration of sulfuric acid and the temperature used. Ether has a high vapor pressure (B.P. 34.5° C.) and the vapor is very inflammable; therefore the liquid must be used with great caution. Mixed ethers can be prepared by treating two different alcohols in a similar manner, but it is difficult to prepare a single pure mixed ether. The formula for methyl-ethyl ether would be $CH_3 \cdot O \cdot C_2H_5$. The empirical formulas for dimethyl ether and ethyl alcohol are the same, C_2H_6O, but their structural formulas differ.

$$\begin{array}{cc} \begin{array}{c} \text{H} \quad\quad \text{H} \\ | \quad\quad\ | \\ \text{H—C—O—C—H} \\ | \quad\quad\ | \\ \text{H} \quad\quad \text{H} \\ \text{Dimethyl ether} \end{array} & \begin{array}{c} \text{H} \quad \text{H} \\ | \quad\ | \\ \text{H—C—C—O—H} \\ | \quad\ | \\ \text{H} \quad \text{H} \\ \text{Ethyl alcohol} \end{array} \end{array}$$

Many organic compounds have the same molecular weights but different structural formulas; the above example is typical of this form of isomerism.

Ethers with low molecular weights are good solvents for fats, waxes, resins, and gums.

Derivatives of Benzene

Many thousand compounds can be made from benzene; several of them are familiar under common trade names. A discussion of even the more common derivatives is impossible in a book on general chemistry.

Nitrobenzene is prepared by reacting benzene and nitric acid together in the presence of a dehydrating agent.

$$C_6H_5 \cdot H + HO \cdot NO_2 \longrightarrow C_6H_5NO_2 + H_2O$$

This can be reduced with hydrogen to produce aminobenzene or aniline.

$$C_6H_5NO_2 + 3\ H_2 \longrightarrow C_6H_5NH_2 + 2\ H_2O$$

This compound is the initial material from which many dyes are made.

Phenol is produced from benzene although it is usually obtained from coal tar. Salicylic acid, acetyl salicylic acid (aspirin), and oil of wintergreen are three common substances made from phenol.

$$C_6H_5OH \longrightarrow \underset{\text{Salicylic acid}}{C_6H_4 \cdot OH \cdot COOH} \longrightarrow \underset{\substack{\text{Oil of wintergreen or}\\ \text{methyl salicylate}}}{C_6H_4 \cdot OH \cdot COO \cdot CH_3}$$

$$\longrightarrow \underset{\text{Aspirin}}{C_6H_4 \overset{COOH}{\underset{OOCCH_3}{\diagup}}}$$

In 1919, paraaminobenzenesulfonamide, or sulfanilamide,

$$H_2N-\underset{\underset{O}{\|}}{\overset{\overset{O}{\|}}{S}}-C_6H_4-NH_2$$

was synthesized as a dye intermediate. Nearly ten years later, prontosil, a dye made from it was found to have remarkable germicidal properties. Further investigation showed that these were due to the decomposition of the dye in the body, releasing sulfanilamide. Sulfanilamide is particularly effective against germs of the streptococcus type, which cause a wide variety of vicious diseases. Various minor modifications of the molecule have improved its activity against other diseases; these new drugs have been given names beginning with the prefix "sulfa-" to suggest the common relationship, and are called the *sulfa drugs*. They should never be taken except under the direction of a competent physician, for unless the dose is almost large enough to be dangerous to the patient, a few of the more resistant germs may survive and establish a new strain that can withstand more of the drug than the patient can.

The common indicators, methyl orange and phenolphthalein, are extremely complicated organic compounds which are synthesized from benzene. Even saccharin, $C_6H_4 \cdot CO \cdot SO_2 \cdot NH$, which is over 500 times sweeter than sugar, requires benzene for its preparation.

Cellulose and Other Fibers

In no field of chemistry has greater progress been made than in the field of cellulose and other fibers. Dozens of products are now made from these raw materials which were unheard of twenty years ago. Colleges of Forestry and Agriculture have been responsible for many of these spectacular developments.

Cellulose is the wood-like portion of all plant structure and is present in all plant cells. Cotton is nearly pure cellulose, but wood contains about 20 per cent lignin or binding material, 20 per cent complicated cellulose-like compounds, and 8 per cent mineral salts, etc. At present, cotton and wood are the two important sources of cellulose. Chemists know that the empirical formula of cellulose is $(C_6H_{10}O_5)_n$. They are fairly sure of the atomic linkages, and they can make what they believe is a good guess as to the number of $C_6H_{10}O_5$ groups that are linked together in the molecule.

Some of the larger forms of animal life (including man) are unable to utilize cellulose as a food, because the body contains no substances capable of splitting the large cellulose molecule into smaller units. Within the past few years, however, chemists have demonstrated that it may be profitable to treat cellulose so that a food material can be obtained from it; for example, in several European countries, glucose, a food sugar, is now produced from cellulose that has been hydrolyzed with HCl and H_2SO_4.

$$\text{Wood } (C_6H_{10}O_5)_n + H_2O \xrightarrow{\text{acid}} {}_nC_6H_{12}O_6 \text{ (glucose)}$$

Paper. Paper products consume most of the cellulose in this country. Almost any fibrous material—wood, cotton, rags, straw, and even cornstalks—can be used in making paper. The process depends upon the raw material and the type of paper being manufactured. The wood is ground into a pulp and the lignin is separated from the cellulose with calcium bisulfite or other chemicals, such as Na_2SO_4 and Na_2CO_3; large pressure kettles are used for this "cooking process." After the lignin has been filtered out, the cellulose fiber is bleached, weighted, sized, and rolled into sheets of paper. Paper may be treated with starch, glue, casein, dextrin, dyes, pigments, rosin, aluminum silicate, clay, etc. It is no easy task to process two batches of paper so that they will have the same strength, color, opacity, and texture; the earlier "rule of thumb" tests have been replaced in many mills by scientific testing done by trained men. A new technique has made possible the use of young pine trees in making paper; and the utilization of southern pine promises to make the paper industry one of the future leading industries of the South. High-grade paper is made from rags. The finest materials are blended together in making the paper used for money because it must withstand considerable handling.

"Solutions" of Cellulose. There are several chemicals which will dis-

perse cellulose into such a finely divided state that these colloidal solutions are often confused with true solutions. Soon after glycerol trinitrate, $C_3H_5(NO_3)_3$ (often incorrectly called "nitroglycerin"), was prepared, many other organic compounds were treated with nitric acid and a dehydrating agent (H_2SO_4), and it was discovered that cellulose could be nitrated. The number of nitrate groups added per $C_6H_{10}O_5$ group varies with the temperature and concentration of acid; the degree of nitration may be followed by analyzing for the nitrogen content. All the cellulose nitrate compounds

FIG. 39.12. Paper is made by students at the N. Y. State College of Forestry. (Courtesy, N. Y. State College of Forestry, Syracuse.)

ignite readily; if burned in a closed space, they are explosive. *Guncotton* contains about 13.5 per cent nitrogen, and is used in producing smokeless powder, gelatin dynamite, cordite, etc. *Pyroxylin* contains about 10 per cent nitrogen, and hence is less highly nitrated than guncotton. Many lacquers, artificial leather, celluloid, and collodion contain pyroxylin. Artificial leather is cloth impregnated with pyroxylin. Celluloid is prepared by heating together camphor, alcohol, and cellulose nitrate under pressure and then cooling the substance. It burns very readily. Collodion, the base of some nail polishes, contains pyroxylin dissolved in alcohol and ether; the colors are produced by alcohol and ether-soluble dyes. Collodion is also used to cover cuts and wounds, stop "runs" in stockings, etc. Waterproof lacquer is pyroxylin dissolved in amyl acetate. Pyroxylin was formerly used for photographic films, but has been replaced by cellulose acetate, which does not burn as readily. The better X-ray films are made of cellulose nitrate.

Cellulose can be "dissolved" in several metal salts. Vulcanized fiber is made by heating cellulose in concentrated zinc chloride, pressing the mixture into the desired shape, and removing the salt by washing. The dried product is so hard that it can be sawed like wood; it is used in making paper baskets, trunks, and even gears and washers. (Mixtures of ice-cold HCl and H_2SO_4 will also disperse cellulose.)

Natural Cloth and Substitutes for It. For many years nearly all clothing was made of linen, cotton, wool, and silk. Linen cloth is made from the fiber of flax; cotton, of course, is also plant or cellulose fiber, whereas wool and silk are animal fibers and consist in part of nitrogenous organic compounds. *Mercerized cotton* is made by treating cotton cloth with a solution of sodium hydroxide which partially hydrates the fibers and makes them smooth and round instead of flat and twisted. This is easily seen by looking at mercerized and unmercerized fibers with a microscope. Mercerization increases the strength and durability of the cotton.

A substitute for silk that would be both attractive and cheap was sought for many years before it was found. Now the various substitutes are of such excellent quality and appearance that the silk industry is hard pressed to compete with their manufacturers. The raw material from which artificial silk, or *rayon*, is made is cheap cotton linters, formerly a waste product. These linters are steeped in NaOH to remove the hull particles, bleached with hypochlorite, washed, dried, and packed into bales or rolled into sheets.

There are four general processes for the manufacture of rayon: the *viscose, acetate, cuprammonium,* and *nitrocellulose*. About 95 per cent of the 300,000 tons of rayon produced in the United States annually is made by the viscose and acetate processes; the nitrocellulose process is not used here.

In the *viscose process* sheets of purified cellulose from either cotton or spruce are first treated with alkali to produce alkali cellulose. The sheets are then shredded and aged under controlled temperature and humidity conditions. The addition of carbon disulfide forms orange cellulose xanthate. This when dissolved in NaOH solution becomes a thick honey-like liquid, called *viscose*, and is the spinning solution which is forced through tiny holes in a spinneret into an acid bath. Cellulose is thus regenerated from viscose and forms continuous filaments of rayon which are given a slight twist to produce a continuous filament of *rayon yarn*.

$$\text{Cellulose} + \text{NaOH} \longrightarrow \text{Alkali cellulose}$$
$$\text{Alkali cellulose} + CS_2 \longrightarrow \text{Cellulose xanthate}$$
$$\text{Cellulose xanthate} + \text{acid} \longrightarrow \text{regenerated cellulose}$$

Cellophane is made by the same process, the only difference being that the regenerated cellulose is passed between a series of rollers which convert it into sheets. Rayon and cellophane may be dyed any color.

In the *acetate process,* cellulose is soaked in acetic acid and allowed to age or mature. The pulp is then mixed with acetic anhydride which produces cellulose acetate. After further aging, this clear thick liquid is added to water. The flakes of cellulose acetate which precipitate are dried and dissolved in acetone, forming a thick liquid. This is forced through the holes of the spinneret into warm humid air, filaments of *acetate rayon* (the acetate ester of the polyhydric alcohol, cellulose) being produced as the acetone evaporates. *Celanese* is artificial silk made from cellulose acetate; the celanese fibers have excellent luster. *Note that acetate rayon is a chemical compound of*

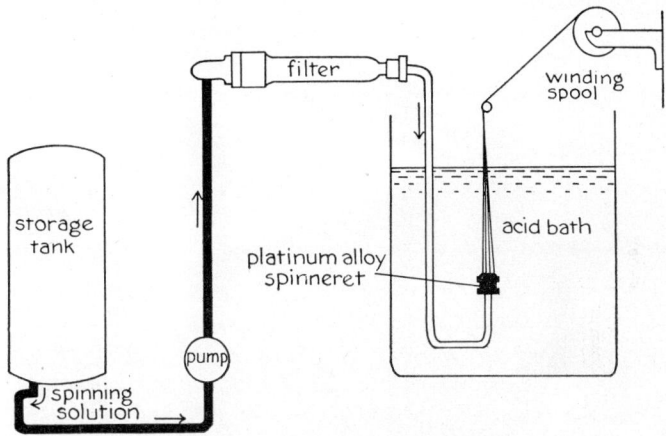

Fig. 39.13. Spinning process used in making viscose rayon.

cellulose (cellulose acetate), whereas rayon is pure regenerated cellulose. There are two simple tests for identifying acetate rayon: (1) when ignited, it leaves a hard metallic bead, and (2) it is soluble in acetone.

In the *cuprammonium process*, pure cellulose is dissolved in an ammoniacal solution of a copper salt. The alkali cellulose thus formed is added to an acid bath, thereby regenerating cellulose.

In the *nitrocellulose process*, a pyroxylin solution is forced through a spinneret, partly dried, and then washed in a denitrating bath. The fibers thus produced have a more brilliant luster than silk and can be dyed in many beautiful colors. This process, however, is unimportant in making rayon.

Nylon. Textile fibers owe their properties to the size and shape as well as the chemical nature of their molecules. They all have two-dimensional giant molecules, like that described for asbestos (page 462). Since this was true of the natural fibers—cellulose, wool, silk, and asbestos—it seemed reasonable to expect that *any* indefinitely long, flexible molecule was a potential raw material for a textile fiber. The first of these new materials to be built up from small molecules was *nylon.* (Rayon and celanese are made by merely working over the natural giant molecules of cellulose.) The spectacular

Fig. 39.14. The first step in the manufacture of "cellophane" cellulose film involves treating sheets of wood pulp, which look like heavy blotting paper, with a solution of caustic soda. The resulting "alkali cellulose" is next shredded to facilitate subsequent operations. This photograph shows a shredding machine at the Richmond, Virginia, plant being unloaded. (Courtesy, E. I. du Pont de Nemours & Company.)

success of nylon has opened the way to an endless variety of new synthetic fibers, each with its own special points of excellence, just as neoprene did in the field of elastomers. The trade names of such products are already numerous.

Nylon itself is made by condensing hexamethylene diamine with adipic acid (both of which are prepared from benzene). The first step in the condensation is:

CARBON AND ITS COMPOUNDS

$$\text{NH}_2\cdot\text{CH}_2\cdot\text{CH}_2\cdot\text{CH}_2\cdot\text{CH}_2\cdot\text{CH}_2\cdot\text{CH}_2\cdot\overset{H}{\underset{|}{N}}\boxed{\text{H}+\text{HO}\cdot}\overset{O}{\underset{\|}{C}}\cdot\text{CH}_2\cdot\text{CH}_2\cdot\text{CH}_2\cdot\text{CH}_2\cdot\text{COOH} \longrightarrow$$

hexamethylene diamine ・・・ adipic acid

$$\text{NH}_2(\text{CH}_2)_6\text{NH}\cdot\text{CO}(\text{CH}_2)_4\text{COOH}$$
nylon monomer

But this product still has one of the active groups at one end of the molecule and the other active group at the other end; therefore any amount of further condensation can take place. The —CO·NH— linkage is called the *amide* (or *peptide*) linkage.

Carbohydrates Used as Food

The carbohydrates (including cellulose) contain carbon, hydrogen, and oxygen; the latter two are in the same ratio as they are in water, but they are not present as water molecules. Oxygen is present in carbohydrates in the aldehyde, ketone, and hydroxyl groups; hydrogen may be linked directly to carbon atoms or be present in the hydroxyl radical. Starches and sugars are the important carbohydrate foods.

Starches. Starch and dextrin both have the formula $(C_6H_{10}O_5)_n$ but the value of n is smaller in dextrin. There are many types of starch, the granules in potatoes, corn, arrowroot, etc., differing from each other in appearance. Cornstarch is the cheapest starch in the United States, but in many European countries potato starch is more common. Heating breaks down the starch molecule and the starch granules burst; therefore cooked starches are digested more readily than uncooked starches. Besides its use as a food, starch is fermented to produce ethyl alcohol, etc. The starch in grains of corn, etc., serves as a source of energy for young plants. *Dextrin*, which has a sweet taste, is obtained by carefully heating dry starch. Because of its sticky nature it is used on postage stamps, envelopes, etc.

Sugars. The two simplest groups of sugars are the monosaccharides and the disaccharides; the former have the empirical formula $C_6H_{12}O_6$, and the latter $C_{12}H_{22}O_{11}$. Each group has many isomers; therefore only a few of the more common sugars will be discussed.

Three important disaccharides are *maltose, lactose,* and *sucrose.*

Maltose, $C_{12}H_{22}O_{11}$, is produced by the action of diastase, an enzyme, on starch. This enzyme is produced when barley, etc., germinates. The sprouted grain is dried and sold as "malt."

$$(C_6H_{10}O_5)_n + H_2O \xrightarrow{\text{diastase}} C_{12}H_{22}O_{11} + \text{dextrin}$$
Starch ・・・ Maltose

Lactose, $C_{12}H_{22}O_{11}$, or milk sugar, is present to the extent of about 5 per cent in cow's milk and over 7 per cent in human milk. It is about one-sixth as sweet as cane sugar. A few thousand tons of lactose recovered from cow's milk are put on the market each year. Cow's milk is made a better food for babies by the addition of lactose to bring the lactose content up to that of human milk. When milk sours, lactose is converted into lactic acid.

Sucrose, $C_{12}H_{22}O_{11}$, the most important sugar, is obtained from sugar beets and sugar cane. (The characteristic flavor of maple sugar is due to impurities, but it is the same as beet and cane sugar when sufficiently purified.) Sugar beets and sugar cane are grown in several states. About one-sixth of the sugar we produce at present is beet sugar; but many thousand tons of sugar must be imported each year from Cuba and other countries to satisfy our annual per capita consumption of 80 pounds. To produce all the sugar consumed in this country would undoubtedly increase its cost.

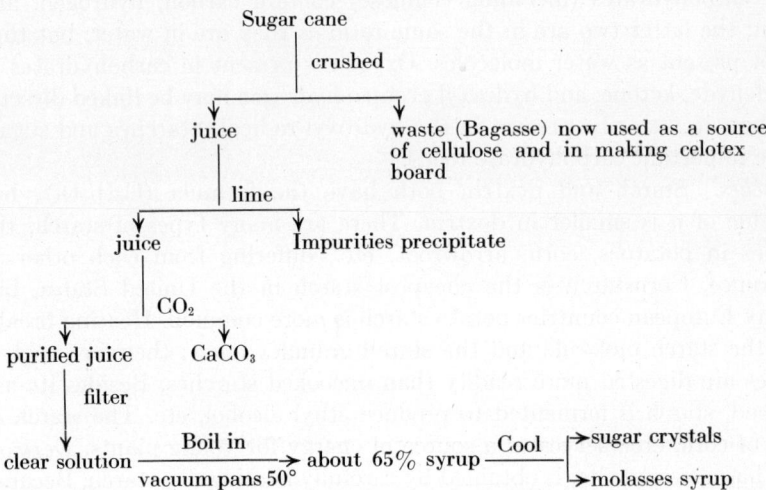

Sucrose, unlike the other sugars mentioned, does not reduce Fehling's solution. If Sucrose is heated with dilute hydrochloric acid, the two monosaccharides glucose and fructose are formed; this mixture, which is called invert sugar, reduces Fehling's solution.

$$C_{12}H_{22}O_{11} + H_2O \xrightarrow{HCl} C_6H_{12}O_6 + C_6H_{12}O_6$$

Diabetic patients are able to decompose sucrose, but the glucose produced is not assimilated; it is excreted in the urine. The Fehling's test for sugar in the urine measures the quantity of reducing sugars that the body cannot utilize.

Rock candy consists of large monoclinic crystals of cane sugar. It melts at about 160° C. and chars at a higher temperature. Caramel is made by partially charring sugar.

Two important monosaccharides are *glucose* (dextrose), or grape sugar, and *fructose* (levulose), or fruit sugar. *These two sugars have the same empiri-*

cal formula but different structural formulas. The molecule of glucose has one aldehyde group and that of levulose has a ketone group.

Glucose, $C_6H_{12}O_6$, the most important monosaccharide, is a constituent of grapes and many other fruits. Over one billion pounds of it are produced each year in this country from hydrolyzed cornstarch.

$$(C_6H_{10}O_5)_n + H_2O \xrightarrow[\text{pressure}]{\text{acid}} nC_6H_{12}O_6$$

The syrup obtained by hydrolyzing starch with acid as a catalyst is a mixture of dextrin, maltose, and glucose; it is used in the confectionery trade

FIG. 39.15. Partially crystallized crude corn sugar being sliced into slabs, after which it is "aged" and shipped for use in the rayon, brewing, tanning, and fermentation industries.

as a sweetening agent, and is sold for home consumption as corn syrup. By using acid under pressure, starch can be converted almost completely into glucose. This concentrated solution (80 per cent glucose) is poured into molds where it solidifies; it is then sold as corn or "grape" sugar (Fig. 39.15). It is possible to crystallize pure dextrose monohydrate in needle-shaped white crystals. This product, about three-fifths as sweet as sugar, is sold under the trade name "Dyno." In the Bergius process developed in Germany in 1935, glucose is produced by the hydrolysis of cellulose.

In the production of alcohol from corn, starch goes through the intermediate compound glucose, and this is in turn fermented.

The Jerusalem artichoke, dahlia bulbs, and several other tubers contain the starch-like substance called *inulin*. This when hydrolyzed forms fructose (levulose) or fruit sugar.

Carbohydrates are converted into fat and stored in the muscle and liver tissues of the body. Sugar is stored as *glycogen* $(C_6H_{10}O_5)_n$, which corresponds to starch in plants. During physical exertion glycogen is converted into lactic acid and energy. The energy required to convert this lactic acid back into glycogen is obtained by the oxidation of some of the lactic acid to carbon dioxide and water at a body temperature of 37° to 38° C. Fatigue is due to an accumulation of lactic acid in the body tissues.

Proteins

Although we could live for a long time on a diet deficient in fat or carbohydrates, our daily diet must contain a minimum of nitrogen compounds, or muscle tissue will be destroyed more rapidly than it is built up. (Some "reducing diets" are entirely too low in these compounds.)

Nitrogen is the key element in proteins, the most complex of the organic food compounds; hydrogen, carbon, and oxygen are also present, and often phosphorus and sulfur. Proteins break down through a series of disintegration products—proteoses, peptones, polypeptides, dipeptides, and amino acids. Glycine, the simplest amino acid, is acetic acid in which one of the hydrogens linked to a carbon is replaced by an (—NH₂) group. The active groups are the same as those of the nylon monomer.

$$\begin{array}{ccc} H & H & O \\ | & | & \parallel \\ N\!-\!C\!-\!C\!-\!OH \\ | & | \\ H & C \end{array}$$

A great variety of amino acids are connected together by amide linkages to form large molecular aggregates in proteins. All attempts to synthesize protein have failed; egg albumen, milk casein, and flour gluten are three common proteins. The end product of most of the nitrogen metabolism in the body is ammonia, which is excreted as urea, $NH_2 \cdot CO \cdot NH_2$. This compound is easily hydrolyzed in the presence of the enzyme urease.

$$\begin{array}{ccc} NH_2 & H & NH_3 \\ | & | & + \\ C\!=\!O \;+\; O & \rightarrow & CO_2 \\ | & | & + \\ NH_2 & H & NH_3 \end{array}$$

Food Accessories

A diet consisting only of *pure* fats, carbohydrates, and proteins would be entirely inadequate, for several other substances are known to be essential for well-being; the list is growing each year. Certain *mineral salts* are essential; *enzymes* break down large molecules into smaller ones which can be digested; *vitamins* in foods function in regulating well-being. The true significance of the many new discoveries now being made each year in these fields cannot be known for years to come.

Enzymes. Living organisms produce organic compounds, called enzymes, which catalyze organic reactions. There are both intracellular and extracellular enzymes; in other words, enzymatic reactions may occur either within or outside of the cells that produce them. Enzymes are similar to catalysts in that only small quantities are necessary to induce chemical reactions, and the reactions are specific because a particular enzyme can produce only one type of reaction.

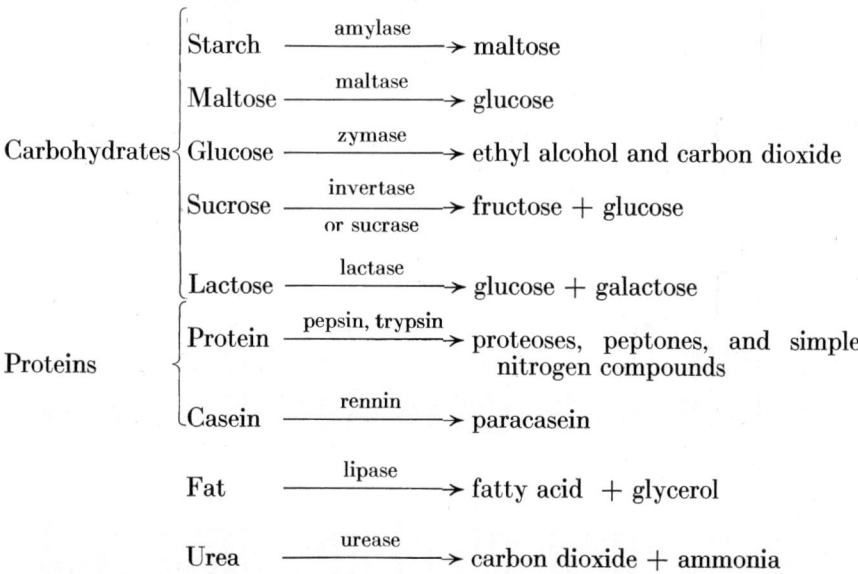

Bacteria and molds contain many enzymes which are responsible for chemical reactions, and many chemicals—alcohol, acetic acid, butyric acid, glycerol, and acetone—are now produced commercially by the enzymatic action of bacteria. Several enzymes are present in grain. After nine years of work Dr. Sumner, of Cornell, isolated and *crystallized* the enzyme urease. One enzyme that has received publicity is obtained from an edible tropical fruit (the *carica papaya*). This enzyme has the astonishing power of breaking down connective tissue. For example, *tough* steak left in contact with it for thirty minutes is tender when cooked. Hence "Tendra," the trade name of this enzyme.

VITAMINS[1]

Characteristics	Physiological Action	Sources
Vitamin A: A high molecular weight alcohol. Stable to heat, acids, and bases, but not to light or oxidation. Soluble in fats and oils, not in water. The yellow pigments of most fruits and vegetables (carotenes, etc.) are called "provitamin A" because they are converted to vitamin A in the animal body.	Promotes growth; essential for skin vitality, normal night vision, pregnancy and lactation; aids in maintaining resistance to infection, normal glandular functions. Increases life span.	Fish liver oils, green leafy vegetables, orange and yellow vegetables, fruits and dairy products, liver, beef fat, kidney, fish roe, prunes.
Vitamin B₁, Thiamine: Sold as the salt thiamine chloride. Comparatively stable toward dry heat but destroyed by autoclaving and by sulfides. Soluble in water (especially when slightly acid) but not in fats and oils.	Promotes growth, stimulates appetite, aids digestion and assimilation. Essential for pregnancy, lactation, and normal functioning of nerve tissue.	Fish, lean meat, liver, eggs, milk, legumes, bran, wheat, nuts, grains, corn, yeast, potatoes, prunes, asparagus, brussels sprouts, dried whey.
Vitamin B₂ (G), Riboflavin: Soluble in water. Stable to heat and fairly stable to oxidation, acids, and bases. Sensitive to light.	Improves growth; essential to cell respiration, reproduction and lactation, nerve tissues. Prolongs active life span and promotes general health.	Green leafy vegetables, dairy products, tomatoes, cauliflower, legumes, bananas, cherries, raisins, wheat, yeast, liver, heart, lean meat, fish.
Vitamin B₆, Pyridoxine: Soluble in water and alcohol, slightly so in ether and other fat solvents. Stable toward conc. HCl, heat, HNO₂. Unstable toward light, ultraviolet radiation and oxidizing agents.	Significance in human nutrition not yet established. It may play role in protein metabolism.	Cabbage, legumes, rice polishings, whole grains, wheat germ, yeast, egg yolk, milk, fish, kidney, meat, liver.
Nicotinic Acid: Usually administered as nicotinamide (niacin) to avoid flushing and tingling of the skin and other symptoms ascribable to the administration of the acid itself. Soluble in hot water and alcohol. Stable to heat, acids and bases.	Promotes health and growth, maintains normal function of skin and gastrointestinal tract. Prevents pellagra (with eventual insanity and death).	Wheat, dried figs, dates, prunes, milk, legumes, spinach, turnip greens, squash, turnips, potatoes, broccoli, rice, peaches, fish, oysters, vital organs, and lean meat.
Vitamin C, Ascorbic Acid: Soluble in water, insoluble in oils. Very sensitive to bases and oxidation, especially with copper catalysis. Fairly stable in weak acid solutions. Generally destroyed by cooking exposed to air, but not by cooking in steam. Strong reducing agent.	Favors good teeth, improves appetite, helps growth. Essential for glandular functions and normal condition of endothelial cells. Prevents scurvy and aids defense against bacterial toxins.	Green and leafy vegetables, citrus fruits, cauliflower, peppers, potatoes, squash, tomatoes, turnips, corn, bananas, raspberries, strawberries, liver, and clams.
Vitamin D, Calciferol (D₂) Irradiated 7-dehydrocholesterol (D₃): Stable to heat, bases, acids, and oxidation. Soluble in fats and oils but not in water. Not made synthetically, but formed on irradiation of ergosterol and other sterols, both in the skin and in foods.	Regulates metabolism of calcium and phosphorus, essential to normal bone growth and tooth development, aids in controlling blood calcium level.	Irradiated food and milk, sea food, enriched flour and bread, egg yolk, butter, cream, chocolate, cocoa, coconut.
Vitamin E, α-Tocopherol: Insoluble in water, soluble in oils and fats. Stable to heat, acids, and bases. Destroyed by rancid fats. Stable to ordinary methods of cooking.	Promotes fertility, growth, and muscular strength. Specific deficiency difficult to produce in human beings.	Meat, dairy products, eggs, nearly all green leaves and whole grains, vegetable oils. Very widely distributed in foods.
Vitamin K, Menadione: Fat-soluble. Destroyed by oxidizing agents, strong acids, and light. Stable to heat and reducing agents.	Essential for production of prothrombin. Aids in prevention of hemorrhage in new-born infants.	Cauliflower, cabbage, leafy green vegetables, tomatoes, cheese, liver, and egg yolk.

[1] Condensed by permission from *Nutritional Charts*, H. J. Heinz Co.

CARBON AND ITS COMPOUNDS

Vitamin A

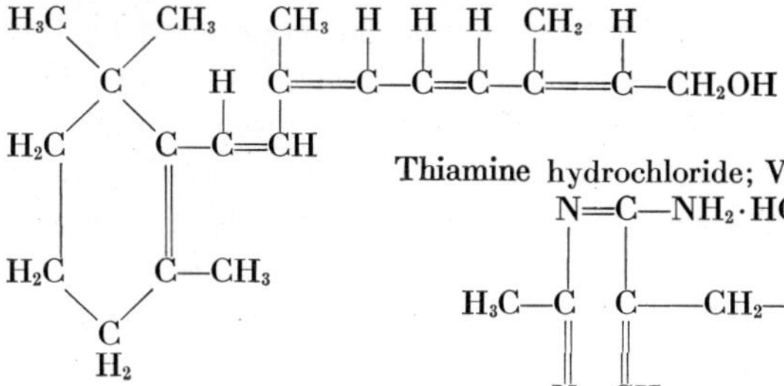

Thiamine hydrochloride; Vitamin B_1

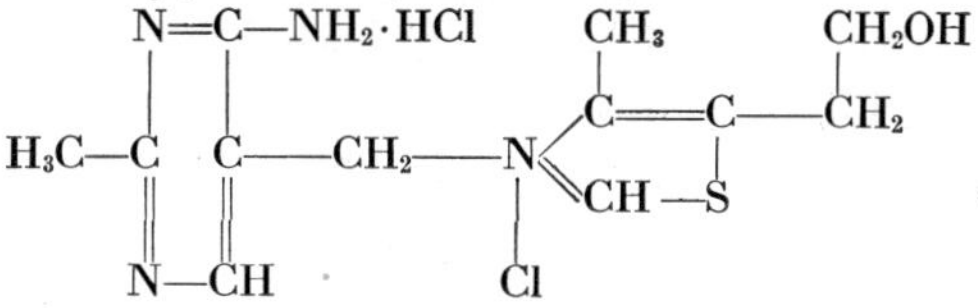

Riboflavin; Vitamin B_2 (G)

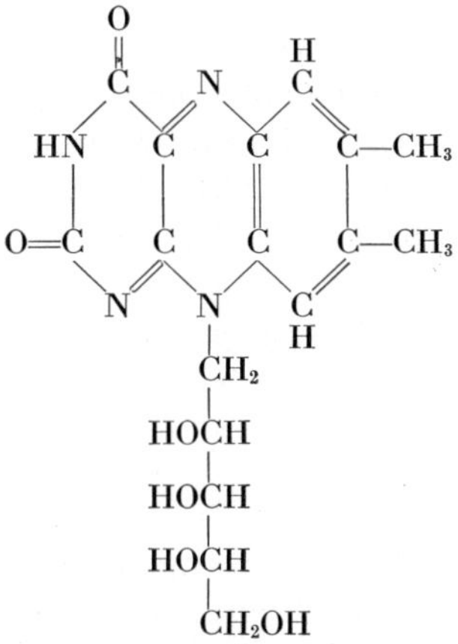

Pyridoxine; Vitamin B_6

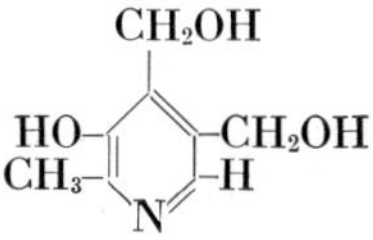

Nicotinic Acid

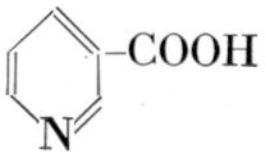

Ascorbic Acid; Vitamin C

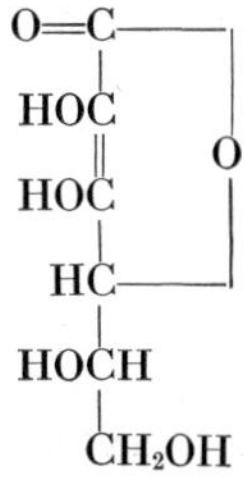

Vitamin K; (Menadione if R = H)

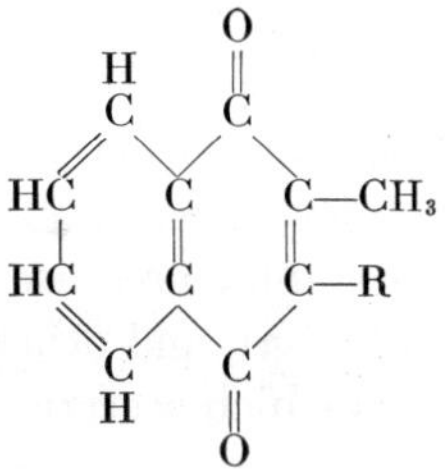

Vitamin D

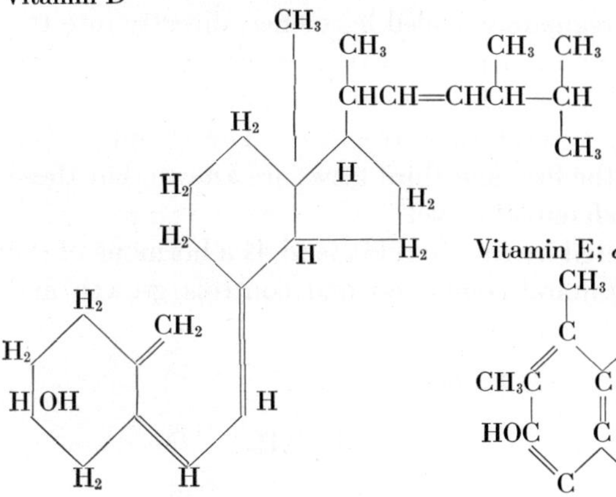

Vitamin E; α-Tocopherol

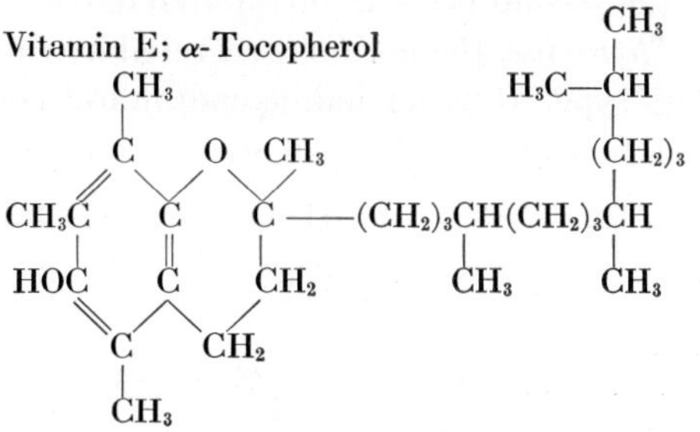

Vitamins. Vitamins are substances traces of which are present in foods and on which depend our growth, health, and vigor throughout life. One of the early experiments on the value of vitamins was that conducted by the Dutch physician, Eijkman, who, while in charge of a hospital in Java, fed table scraps of polished rice to chickens. They developed a disease similar to beriberi which he erroneously thought was due to toxin in the polished rice; however, the chickens recovered when he fed them rice polishing. Scurvy, a disease long common to seamen, was finally overcome by adding fruit juices, sauerkraut, etc., to their diet. At present both experiments on animals and chemical tests are used in determining the potency of vitamin concentrates; and the vitamin content of such substances as cod-liver oil is now expressed in "units" based upon the concentration of the vitamin in the standard.

Vitamin A can be stored in the body for some time, but vitamin C cannot be stored in any great quantity. Except for chemically manufactured ones, all the vitamins except D must be synthesized by plants; vitamin D can be synthesized by the human body with the aid of ultraviolet rays. In spite of this, vitamin D is most frequently deficient in the people of the United States.

The table on page 716 summarizes some of our knowledge regarding the best-known vitamins. The structural formulas of these vitamins are shown on the preceding page.

Hormones

The integration of bodily functions is brought about by two means, one involving nerves and the other involving chemistry. Quick adjustments to outside influences are taken care of by the nervous system. Bodily growth, metabolism, and other functions are controlled by the endocrine or ductless glands which secrete chemical regulators, called hormones, directly into the blood stream. Chemically, these hormones are of three general types: amines or amino acids, complex peptides related to the proteins, and sterols or fat-soluble compounds containing several ring structures. The chemical constituents of many hormones of the first and third types are known, but those of the second type are little understood as yet.

Thyroxine, the hormone secreted by the thyroid gland, is a hormone of the first type. It is an iodine-containing compound and controls growth and metabolism. Its chemical structure is as follows:

CARBON AND ITS COMPOUNDS 719

Adrenalin, another example of this type of hormone, is produced by the suprarenal, a small gland situated above each kidney. The suprarenal gland consists of two parts, the cortex and the medulla; the latter secretes adrenalin. Its structure is:

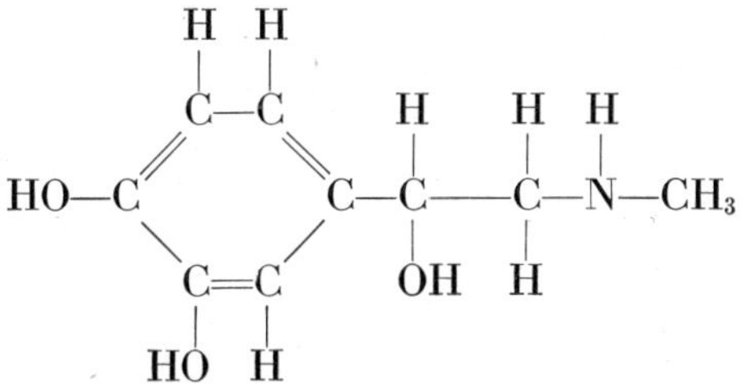

This hormone has a strong stimulating action on the heart and the sympathetic nervous system, and, by releasing glucose from the glycogen stores of the liver, helps the body adjust itself to sudden demands for energy. Adrenalin was the first hormone to be synthesized.

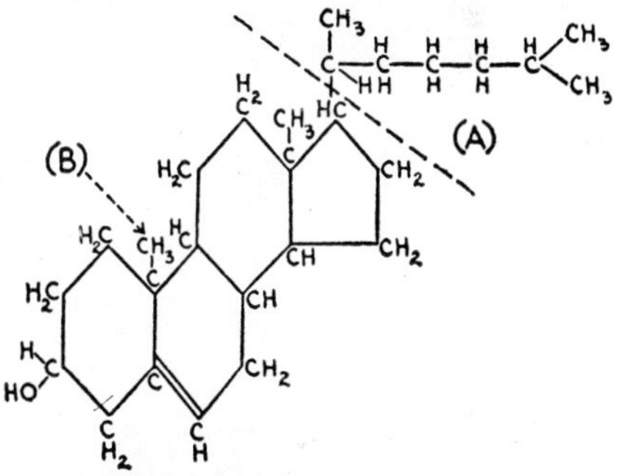

Cortin, a vitally important hormone mixture of the third type, is secreted by the cortex of the suprarenal gland. Among their many functions these hormones control the water and electrolyte (e.g., sodium) balance of the body.

FIG. 39.16. Structure of cholesterol.

Insulin, a hormone of the second type, is secreted by the pancreas. On hydrolysis this hormone produces a number of amino acids and controls the sugar metabolism of the body.

Another peptide hormone which controls the calcium balance of the body is secreted by the parathyroids, small glands embedded in the thyroid gland. The pituitary gland secretes several important peptide hormones.

Hormone research has made most rapid progress in the field of the sex hormones, which are vitally important for the normal development and functioning of the body. All these hormones are of the third or sterol type and are closely related to cholesterol which occurs in the brain and the bile, and in gall stones. The structure of cholesterol shown in Fig. 39.16 was finally determined in 1932 after twenty-four years of research.

The male sex hormones, or androstanes, contain nineteen carbon atoms, and may be considered to be derived from cholesterol by the removal of the long chain at (A) in the figure. The basic structure of the female sex hormones, or oestranes, is similar, except that the methyl group at (B) is absent. A special group of female hormones, called pregnanes, is secreted during pregnancy. They contain twenty-one carbon atoms, group (A) in the cholesterol molecule being replaced with an acetyl $\left[-\overset{O}{\overset{\|}{C}}-CH_3\right]$ group. A large number of hormones have been found to be formed in the body. They differ in the substitution of various reactive groups in the same basic molecule. Some of these compounds are physiologically inactive and as such are

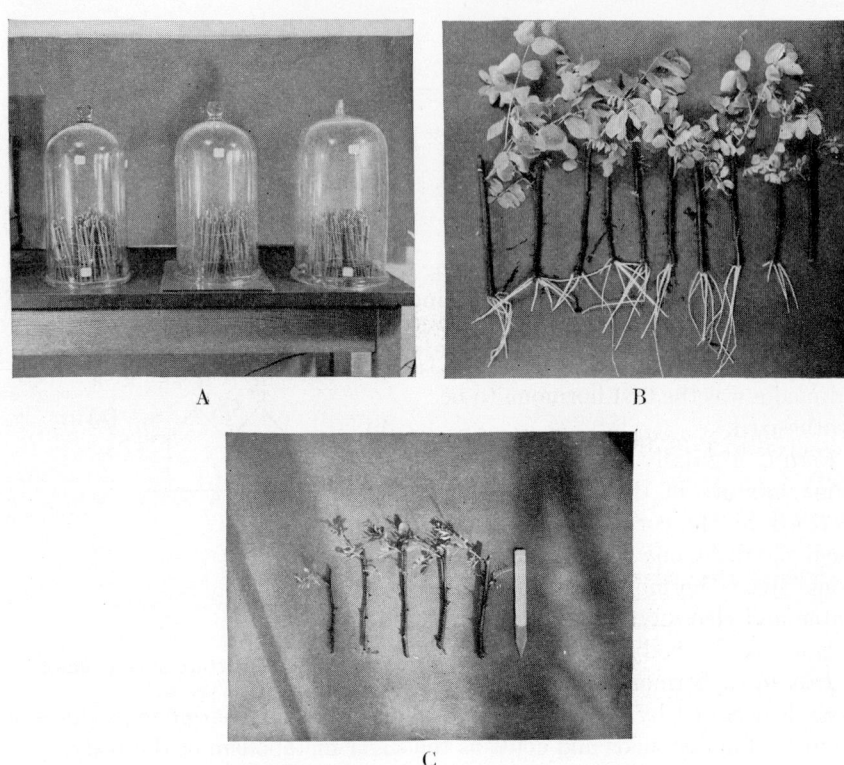

Fig. 39.17. Root growth stimulated by hormone-like substances. For explanation, see text.

excreted in the urine. Several of the sex hormones have been prepared in the laboratory from cholesterol, and it has been found that the inactive types can often be converted into active ones by simple chemical reactions. Small amounts of the active forms are also excreted, presumably because they are produced in excess of bodily needs.

The use of hormone-like substances to stimulate the growth of roots on stems cut from branches of trees promises to increase the number of young trees available for planting. For example, stems from a black locust tree which are treated with a solution of potassium alpha-naphthyl acetate produce roots when planted in sand. Fig. 39.17 A shows how the stems are held in the chemical; B shows the growth produced. Note that both roots and leaves have formed, whereas in C, the control plant, the stem has leaves but no roots. Over 85 chemicals have been found which produce this response in plants, and experiments of this type are becoming a hobby among horticulturists.

Antibiotics

It has long been known that certain microorganisms have the power of inhibiting the growth of bacteria. Thus the British bacteriologist Fleming reported in 1929 that a colony of the mold *Penicillium notatum*, which had accidentally infected an agar bacterial culture, prevented the growth of the bacteria for a considerable distance. It was evident that the inhibiting substance, which he called *penicillin*, was soluble and diffused through the agar. However, no attempt was made to use this substance or to identify similar products from other organisms until 1939, when Dubos of the Rockefeller Institute isolated *tyrothricin* and showed that it had a remarkable curative action on certain bacterial infections in man. The following year the English scientists Chain and Florey reported that partially purified penicillin which they had prepared was effective against a wide variety of bacteria and was almost without any toxic effect on the patient. Furthermore, these bacteria belonged to a class of pathogenic agents which were not susceptible to the sulfa drugs, which were still a new sensation. Stimulated by World War II, research teams in both England and the United States pooled their efforts and, in one of the finest examples of cooperative research ever known, developed methods for the large-scale production and purification of penicillin. Penicillin G, the most important of the five or more individuals present in the natural mixture, is represented by the formula:

$$\underset{}{\text{C}_6\text{H}_5}-\text{CH}_2-\text{CO}-\text{NH}-\text{CH}-\overset{\overset{\displaystyle S}{\diagup\diagdown}}{\text{CH}}\text{C}(\text{CH}_3)_2$$
$$\text{CO}-\text{N}--\text{CH}-\text{COOH}$$

Other penicillins differ in the part of the molecule at the left of the dotted line, and in their effectiveness.

Other important antibiotics are *streptomycin* and *gramicidin*. It now seems probable that all of these natural products, and sulfanilamide as well, are able to stop the growth of bacteria because they resemble (in size, shape, and charge distribution) various substances which are essential to the formation or functioning of vitamins, hormones, or enzymes in the organism's metabolic system. The antibiotics are enough like these substances so that the organism takes them up, but different enough so that they do not work properly.

Plastics

In the modern use of the term, a plastic is not a substance which *is* plastic, but a substance which can be *made* plastic by heating and which, after cooling, will hold any shape into which it has been forced while hot. By implication, at least, a plastic is a relatively new, synthetic material; thus glass and the natural resins (rosin, shellac, damar, etc.) are not usually called plastics, although they fit the above definition.

Plastics are substances whose molecules are too large to crystallize readily. They are therefore *amorphous* like glass, and like glass they soften gradually when heated; they have no definite melting point. They may, in fact, be regarded as supercooled liquids. The problem of synthesizing a plastic is one which we have met before (elastomers, page 689, and synthetic fibers, page 709), namely, the making of giant molecules. It can therefore be solved by the same two chemical expedients: (1) the condensation method, as in nylon; and (2) the polymerization of unsaturated compounds, as in neoprene. (Both nylon and neoprene are, in reality, special cases of plastics.) Certain limitations as to the chemical composition of the reactants in those special cases of the elastomers do not apply to the plastics; because the substance does not need to be elastic the molecule does not have to be kinky, and because the substance does not have to be drawn into fibers the giant molecule does not need to be two-dimensional. A two-dimensional molecule can be formed only if the original reactants have two and only two coupling points. If there is no objection to the giant molecule being a tangled, three-dimensional mass, the original reactants can have three (or more) active groups.

Classes of Plastics. It can be seen from the foregoing discussion that the range of chemical composition for plastics is practically unlimited. Pages would be required merely to list them. Two examples will be given here, so chosen as to illustrate the two great classes into which plastics fall.

Thermoplastic plastics can be softened again by heating, any number of times. They are distinguished by *linear* molecules. *Lucite* (or *Plexiglas*) is such a material. It is formed by the polymerization of the methyl ester of an unsaturated acid, methacrylic acid, that is prepared from acetone, hydrogen cyanide, and methanol. The formula of methyl methacrylate is

$$CH_2{=}C\genfrac{}{}{0pt}{}{\displaystyle CH_3}{\displaystyle COOCH_3}$$

and under the influence of a catalyst the double bond opens thus:

$$-CH_2-C\genfrac{}{}{0pt}{}{\displaystyle CH_3}{\displaystyle COOCH_3}-$$

CARBON AND ITS COMPOUNDS

Polymerization then joins neighbor to neighbor in a chain thousands of units long.

Thermosetting plastics, after they have once been softened and forced into shape, cannot be softened again. All plastics of this type have three-dimensional molecules. They are plastic only while the molecules are of moderate size. The interlacing connections grow rapidly in all directions at the molding temperature; hence by the time the object is removed from the mold it is to all intents and purposes a single molecule. *Bakelite* belongs to this class. Bakelite is a condensation polymer, water being split off from between phenol and formaldehyde as the polymerization progresses. The hydrogens come, in the first stage of the reaction, from the positions on the benzene ring which are adjacent to the HO— group, forming a fusible chain polymer.

This material is powdered and mixed with more formaldehyde and a different catalyst. The powder is molded under a pressure of a ton or more per square inch at about 150° C. It melts, flows together, and then polymerizes further. This time it is the hydrogen opposite the HO— group which condenses with the O= of the formaldehyde; thus the tangled chains are linked together at every point of contact and the substance becomes a solid again, even while hot.

The two most common methods for fabricating plastic parts are compression molding and injection molding. The chemicals used are called the "charge," and may be in either powder or pill form. In compression molding, the mold is heated and pressure is applied until the object has the desired shape. Both types of plastic can be molded with this process, whereas only thermoplastic materials can be used in the injection molding process. In injection molding, the plastic is heated and softened first, and is then forced into the cool mold. This process is more rapid than compression molding and is similar to the die-casting process used with metals.

In 1939 thirty-eight establishments produced $78,000,000 worth of plastics. They paid some 7000 workmen nearly $10,000,000 in wages. Postwar figures are expected to be much higher.

Fig. 39.18. Injection molding of Ethocel (Dow Ethylcellulose). (Courtesy, Dow Chemical Co.)

Farm Chemurgy

During the depression of the thirties the National Farm Chemurgic Council was formed to find and stimulate industrial uses for raw materials that can be grown on farms. (At that time the problem was to find uses for surplus farm products, not to produce a sufficient supply of food.) Since 1935 this organization has done valuable work and has obtained considerable publicity along this line. In the discussion which follows, however, no attempt will be made to distinguish its work from earlier or independent work.

Fig. 39.19 gives some idea of the number of industrial uses that can be found for a single farm crop. Some of these uses are old, others are still in their infancy. When farm products are sold for food, minor differences in flavor and texture are important, and prices are relatively high. But as industrial raw material, only the fundamental chemical nature of a substance is important and the price must compete with that of similar materials from whatever source, including the products of low-priced labor in the Pacific and Asiatic regions. Success for American farmers in meeting this

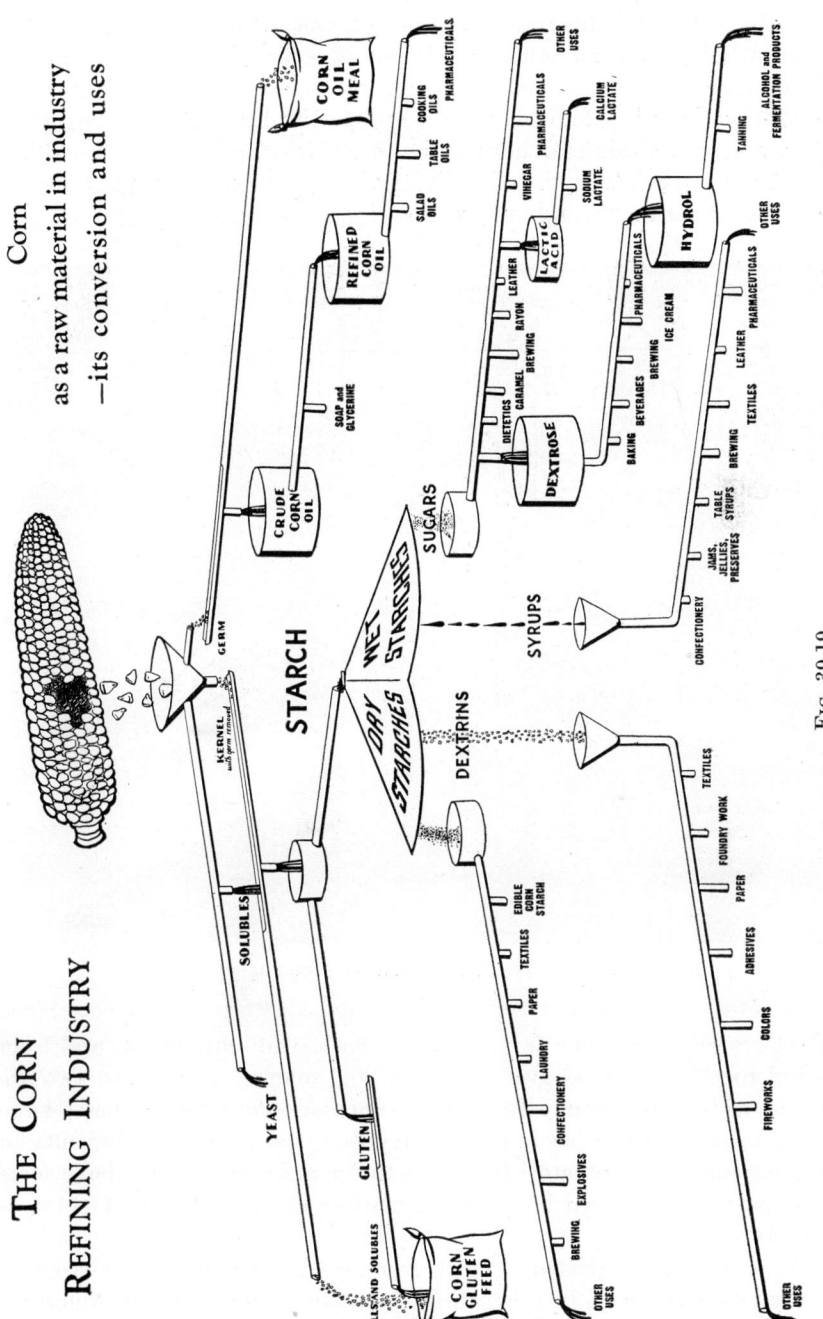

Fig. 39.19.

competition will depend in many cases on increased mechanization. If the farm is to enter the industrial field, it must adopt industrial methods.

The chemical raw materials which can be grown on farms are mainly starch, sugars, protein, oil, and cellulose. All starches have the same chemical composition, but they differ in physical properties because of the structure of the molecule. Grain starches constitute one class, root starches another.

Most of the world's supply of grain starch is produced by the wet milling process from corn and sorghum grown in the temperate zone.

Fig. 39.20. Chemists at work in a corn-refining laboratory.

Root starches are made from potatoes, both white and sweet, and from tropical roots such as cassava, mandioca, and manioc. (These last two are varieties of the same plant. Tapioca is a familiar form.) Europe has a large potato starch industry, but in our country there has been some difficulty in obtaining enough cull potatoes to operate the plants. Only recently have some of the problems involved in obtaining a white starch from sweet potatoes been solved.

The obtaining of dextrose sugar from cornstarch and, in Germany, from cellulose, has been mentioned. In the production of sucrose, American growers of sugar cane in the South and sugar beets in the West must meet the competition of low-paid labor in Cuba and Java.

Ethyl alcohol is an important product with many sources. In general, the fermentation of blackstrap molasses, a by-product of the sugar cane industry, has been the cheapest source. The fermentation of grain is not normally economical except for beverage purposes, where certain flavors are important. Potatoes are fermented in Europe. A practicable process for making alcohol from waste refinery gases (ethylene) is now in operation and seems likely to displace fermentation as the source of industrial alcohol, except where the material fermented is a waste product that has almost no other value. This is an interesting reversal of the idea farm chemurgists once had that alcohol could to some extent replace gasoline as an automobile fuel. From an engineering standpoint, it is perfectly possible to run automobiles both with and *on* alcohol (synthetic rubber tires), but is not economically practical except in emergencies.

Proteins can be used for plastics and fibers as well as for food, but in industrial uses they must compete with petroleum and coal products. The price is therefore low. However, uses have been developed for proteins which are by-products of a more important industry. Examples are: casein from excess skim milk, used to make buttons, glue, and textile fiber ("Aralac"); zein, from corn gluten, used as a plastic; and soybean protein, from the press cake left after the extraction of soy oil, used for similar purposes.

Vegetable oils fall into two classes, non-drying and drying. The former usually contain one double bond in the molecule and are used for food purposes. Food oils can be used as liquids in the crude state (olive, peanut) or after they have been purified to a bland state (cottonseed, corn). Food oils and others not usually classed as food oils (whale, coconut) can be hydrogenated into solid fats which compete with butter and lard. The drying oils contain two or more double bonds and are used in paint and linoleum because of their ability to polymerize into a sort of plastic. Linseed oil is the only one of these which has any long history in the United States, but others are being increasingly grown here. The most important of the newcomers, from the dollars-and-cents point of view, is soybean oil. Tung oil (or China wood oil) is a drying oil with exceptionally fine properties. Our output of it, produced from groves in the Gulf states, has been of a higher grade than that imported from China and may eventually lower the price. Perilla oil is obtained from the tiny seeds of a plant of the mint family which can be grown in the South. About 150 million pounds were imported from Japan in 1937. Chia oil is imported from Mexico, but the plant can be grown in the South.

Cellulose is obtained mainly from wood, cotton, and a number of woody or fibrous stalks. In order for farm-grown cotton to compete with forest-grown wood as a source of industrial cellulose, cotton culture must be mechanized to a high degree. Chemistry has aided progress in this direction by providing a spray which causes the cotton plant to drop all its leaves at once at the end of the season. This permits the lower bolls to ripen and makes easier the task of the mechanical cotton picker.

Paper can be made from flax, hemp, cotton stalks, corn stalks, and other quick-growing crops. The difficulty is in having a sufficient supply of these light materials within trucking distance of a paper mill of economical size. A much more hopeful enterprise is the growing of wood as a farm crop. As the result of the work of Dr. Charles Herty at the Savannah Pulp and Paper Laboratory, $100,000,000 has been invested in the land, labor, and equipment needed to convert southern slash pine into paper. Idle land to the extent of 200,000,000 acres can be made available to this industry. The trees reach cordwood size in ten years. The oil from pine wood is known as "tall" oil, and has been used for years in Europe. As more pine is consumed in the paper industry in the United States, more tall oil will be produced. At present it is being recovered and refined at the Kraft paper mill at Bogalusa, Louisiana. It can be used as an emulsifying agent in the soap industry, and, when sulfonated, as a cutting oil and in mineral ore flotation.

QUESTIONS AND PROBLEMS

1. What are the natural sources of the fuel hydrocarbons?
2. Can the fuel hydrocarbons be synthesized in the laboratory?
3. How do gasoline, kerosene, and lubricating oils differ in composition?
4. What is "cracking"?
5. Calculate the densities of methane, acetylene, and ethane from their formulas.
6. The wax in a candle weighing 45 g. consists of 85 per cent carbon and 15 per cent hydrogen. What weights of CO_2 and H_2O will be formed when 40 per cent of the candle burns?
7. How many liters of gases are formed in the complete combustion of 1 l. of C_2H_2? What is the change in volume?
8. How many grams of CaC_2 are necessary to prepare 44.8 l. of acetylene?
9. How many liters of ethylene can be prepared from 150 g. of C_2H_5OH, 95 per cent pure, assuming an 80 per cent conversion? How many grams of ethylene dibromide can be prepared from this ethylene?
10. Does the double bond in the unsaturated hydrocarbons have the same significance in the aromatic and the aliphatic series? Give examples to illustrate your answer.
11. How much CCl_4 can be prepared by the exhaustive chlorination of the methane produced from 40 g. of Al_4C_3?
12. How much glyceryl oleate must be saponified to give 50 g. of sodium oleate soap, assuming a 90 per cent yield?
13. How much glyceryl trinitrate can be prepared from the glycerin produced in Question 12?
14. How much ethyl alcohol can be produced from the hydrolysis of 120 g. of

CARBON AND ITS COMPOUNDS 729

ethyl acetate? How much acetic acid will be produced? How much N/10 NaOH solution could be neutralized with this amount of acid?

15. How much acetone can be produced from heating 157 g. of $Ca(C_2H_3O_2)_2$?
16. Show by step equations how you can prepare acetone from ethyl alcohol. CH_4 from ethyl alcohol. HCHO from CH_3CHO.
17. How many grams of glucose must be used to prepare 800 g. of alcohol, assuming a 90 per cent yield? How many liters of CO_2 at S.T.P. are produced?
18. Ten grams of a carbohydrate give 15.43 g. of CO_2 and 5.79 g. of H_2O on complete combustion. What is its formula?
19. Can starch be converted to sucrose? To glucose? To ethyl alcohol? Will cellulose undergo these conversions?
20. To what class of organic compounds do each of the following belong: fats, soaps, nitroglycerin, gasoline, kerosene, paraffin?
21. How do C_2H_5OH and C_6H_5OH differ in chemical properties?
22. Using structural formulas, explain the difference in the action of HNO_3 on C_6H_6 and on $C_3H_5(OH)_3$.
23. How many liters of H_2 (S.T.P.) are needed to reduce 40 g. of nitrobenzene to aniline, assuming a quantitative reaction?
24. What is the chemical constitution of the following: pyroxylin, cellulose nitrate rayon, cellulose acetate rayon, viscose rayon, cuprammonium rayon, and cellophane?
25. What are the group characteristics of each of the following types of compounds: alcohols, ethers, aldehydes, organic acids, esters, ketones?
26. Name three methods of preparing CH_3OH, and mention the advantages or disadvantages of each.
27. How can dimethyl ether be prepared in two ways?
28. Given a compound C_2H_6O, how could you tell which of the two possible isomers it was?
29. Why is cellulose acetate film preferable to cellulose nitrate film for most purposes?
30. What is meant by "90 proof" spirits?
31. Why is it difficult to prepare 100 per cent ethyl alcohol from H_2O solutions even though the boiling points of ethyl alcohol and of H_2O are several degrees apart?
32. How is acetone prepared commercially? Of what importance is it to chemical industry?
33. Name two important uses of CCl_4 in the home.
34. Who invented dynamite and what is its chemical nature?
35. Assuming that TNT decomposes in the presence of oxygen to give CO, H_2O, and N_2, calculate the volume change for 10 g. of TNT.
36. How would you distinguish between the following:

$\begin{cases} CH_3CHO \\ C_2H_5OH \\ C_2H_5OC_2H_5 \end{cases}$ $\begin{cases} CH_3COOH \\ C_2H_5OH \\ HCOOH \end{cases}$ $\begin{cases} \text{Cellulose acetate} \\ \text{Cellulose nitrate} \\ \text{Cellophane} \end{cases}$

REFERENCES
Books

Chemistry of Organic Compounds. Conant, J. B. The Macmillan Company.
Chemistry in Industry. Howe, H. E. Chemical Foundation. Vols. I, II.
Industrial Chemistry. Rogers, Allen. D. Van Nostrand & Company, Inc.
Creative Chemistry. Slosson, E. E. D. Appleton-Century Company, Inc.
Chemistry in Medicine. Stieglitz, J. O. Chemical Foundation.
Carbon Dioxide. Quinn, E. L., and Jones, C. L. A.C.S. Monograph No. 72.
Have You Had Your Vitamins? Holmes, H. N. Farrar and Rinehart, Inc.
Carbon Monoxide. Noxious Gases. Henderson, Y., and Haggard, H. W. A.C.S. Monograph No. 35.
Nutritional Charts, Twelfth Edition. H. J. Heinz Co. Pittsburgh, Pa.

Articles

"Carbon Monoxide." Kuentzel, W. E. *J.A.C.S.* **52,** 437–445 (1930).
"Carbon Disulfide." Kobe, K. A. *J. Chem. Ed.* **8,** 867–874 (1931).
"Amorphous Carbon." Day, J. E. *Ind. and Eng. Chem.* **28,** 234–238 (1936).
"Synthetic Gasoline. Hydrogenation of Coal." Wright, C. C., and Gauger, A. W. *Ind. and Eng. Chem.* **26,** 164–169 (1934).
"Hydrogenation of Coal." Pier, M. *Ind. and Eng. Chem.* **29,** 140–145 (1937).
"Gasoline-Alcohol Blends in Internal Engines." Lichty, L. C., and Phelps, C. W. *Ind. and Eng. Chem.* **30,** 222 (1938).
"Man-Made Molecules." Midgley, Thomas. *Ind. and Eng. Chem.* **30,** 120 (1938).
"Motor Fuel Economy in Europe." Egloff, Gustav. *Ind. and Eng. Chem.* **30,** 1091 (1938).
"New Rubber Products." Raynolds, J. W. *J. Chem. Ed.* **16,** 486–491 (1939).
"Centenary of Rubber Vulcanization." *Ind. and Eng. Chem.* **31,** 934–964, 1189–1215 (1939).
"Synthetic Rubber." Bridgwater, E. R. *Ind. and Eng. Chem.* **28,** 394–398 (1936).
"Outlook for Synthetic Rubber." Brauer, O. L. *J. Chem. Ed.* **6,** 1286–1292 (1929).
"Conversion of Wood to Carbohydrates." Bergius, F. *Ind. and Eng. Chem.* **29,** 247–254 (1937).
"Manufacture and Uses of Corn Products." Cathcart, W. R. *J. Chem. Ed.* **4,** 574–582, 758–765 (1927).
"Starch." Shane, R. S. *J. Chem. Ed.* **14,** 460–463 (1937).
"Plant Poisons." Couch, J. F. *J. Chem. Ed.* **14,** 16–30 (1937).
"Glycerol." Guillaudeu, A. *Ind. and Eng. Chem.* **29,** 729–733 (1937).
"Acetone" Cooley, L. C. *Ind. and Eng. Chem.* **29,** 1399–1407 (1937).
"Sugar from Beets." Nees, A. R. *J. Chem. Ed.* **3,** 390–395 (1926).
"History of Cane Sugar." Brown, C. A. *J. Chem. Ed.* **10,** 323–330 (1933).
"Levulose." McGlumphy, J. H., and Eichinger, J. W., Jr. *J. Chem. Ed.* **10,** 453–463 (1933).

"Cellulose in Industry." Scherer, P. C., Jr. *J. Chem. Ed.* **10,** 131–140 (1933).
"Newer Things About Cellulose." Esselen, G. J. *J. Chem. Ed.* **10,** 585–589 (1933).
"Blasting Explosives." Gillie, B. A. *J. Chem. Ed.* **5,** 1213–1223 (1928).
"Chemists in the Explosives Industry." Pearsall, D. E. *J. Chem. Ed.* **16,** 121–128 (1939).
"Textile Fibers." Alexander, J. *Ind. and Eng. Chem.* **31,** 630–642 (1939).
"Industrial Utilization of Agricultural Products." Several authors. *Ind. and Eng. Chem.* **31,** 141–178 (1939).
"Plastics from Wood." Jahn, E. C. *Chem. and Met. Eng.* **46,** 206–207 (1939).
"Bakelite." Bakelite Corp., N. Y. *J. Chem. Ed.* **2,** 1153–1155 (1925).
"Soy Bean Plastics." Taylor, R. L. *Chem. and Met. Eng.* **43,** 172–176 (1936).
"Acrylic Resins." Neher, H. T. *Ind. and Eng. Chem.* **28,** 267–271 (1936).
"Phenol Resins." Mory, A. V. H. *J. Chem. Ed.* **6,** 607–621 (1929).
"Growth of the Dye Industry." Rose, R. E. *J. Chem. Ed.* **3,** 973–1008 (1926).
"Outline of the Dye Industry." Shreve, R. N. *J. Chem. Ed.* **3,** 1259–1270 (1926).
"Soap Industry." Preston, W. C. *J. Chem. Ed.* **2,** 1035–1044, 1130–1139 (1925).
"Detergent Action of Soaps." Rhodes, F. H., and Brainard, S. W. *Ind. and Eng. Chem.* **21,** 60–68 (1929).
"Artificial Silk." Luft, M. G. *Ind. and Eng. Chem.* **17,** 1037–1042 (1925).
"Rayon. Today and Tomorrow." Hussey, R. E., and Scherer, P. I., Jr. *J. Chem. Ed.* **7,** 2543–2570 (1930).
"Viscose Rayon." Shoemaker, M. J. *J. Chem. Ed.* **4,** 1260–1268 (1927).
"Male Hormones." Harrow, B., and Funk, C. *J. Chem. Ed.* **10,** 338–341 (1933).
"Female Hormones." Fevold, H. W. *J. Chem. Ed.* **10,** 175–179 (1933).
"Carotene in Oranges." Taylor, A. L., and Witte, P. J. *Ind. and Eng. Chem.* **30,** 110 (1938).
"Root Stimulus." Zimmermen, *et al.* *Boyce Thompson Institute for Plant Research* **8,** 63–80 (1936).

APPENDIX

THE METRIC SYSTEM
Units
Meter—Liter—Gram

Prefixes	Meaning
kilo	1000
hecto	100
deka	10
deci	0.1
centi	0.01
milli	0.001

MOH'S SCALE OF HARDNESS

1. Talc
2. Gypsum
3. Calcite
4. Fluorite
5. Apatite
6. Feldspar
7. Quartz
8. Topaz
9. Corundum
10. Diamond

(1. Scratch with fingernail. 2. Soft. 3. Scratch with pin. 4. Cut with knife. 5. Barely scratch with knife. 6. Hard to scratch with file. 7. Will scratch glass.)

APPENDIX

CONVERSION TABLES

The units to be converted are arranged alphabetically.

Multiply	By	To Obtain
Atmospheres	76.0	Centimeters of mercury
Atmospheres	29.92	Inches of mercury
Atmospheres	14.7	Pounds per square inch
British thermal units	0.252	Kilogram-Calories
Centimeters	0.3937	Inches
Cubic centimeter	1×10^{-6}	Cubic meters
Cubic centimeter	1×10^{-3}	Liters
Cubic centimeter	1.057×10^{-3}	Quarts
Cubic centimeter	3.531×10^{-5}	Cubic feet
Cubic feet	1728.	Cubic inches
Cubic feet	28.32	Liters
Cubic feet	29.92	Quarts
Cubic inches	16.39	Cubic centimeters
Feet	30.48	Centimeters
Gallons	3785.	Cubic centimeters
Gallons	3.785	Liters
Grains (troy)	0.0648	Grams
Grains (troy)	2.0833×10^{-3}	Ounces (troy)
Grains per gallon	17.12	Parts per million
Grams	980.7	Dynes
Grams	2.205×10^{-3}	Pounds
Horsepower	0.7457	Kilowatts
Inches	2.54	Centimeters
Kilograms	2.205	Pounds
Kilometer	3281.	Feet
Kilometer	0.6214	Miles
Liters	61.02	Cubic inches
Liters	1.0567	Quarts
Liters	0.2642	Gallons
Meters	39.37	Inches
Microns	1×10^{-6}	Meters
Miles	5280.	Feet
Pounds	453.6	Grams
Square centimeters	0.155	Square inches
Square feet	929.	Square centimeters
Square inches	6.452	Square centimeters
Watt-Hours	3.415	British thermal units
Watt-Hours	1×10^{-3}	Kilowatt-Hours

$$°C. = \tfrac{5}{9}(°F. + 40) - 40$$
$$°F. = \tfrac{9}{5}(°C. + 40) - 40$$
$$°A. = °C. + 273$$

APPENDIX

IONIZATION CONSTANTS[1] (25° C.)

Compound	Formula	Ionization Constant
Acetic acid	$H \cdot C_2H_3O_2$	1.8×10^{-5}
Arsenic acid	H_3AsO_4	5×10^{-3}
Arsenious acid	H_3AsO_3	6×10^{-10}
Boric acid	H_3BO_3	6.4×10^{-10}
Carbonic acid	H_2CO_3	3×10^{-7}
Hydrosulfuric acid	H_2S	9.1×10^{-8}
Hypobromous acid	$HBrO$	2×10^{-9}
Hypochlorous acid	$HClO$	3.7×10^{-8}
Hypoiodous acid	HIO	1×10^{-11}
Stannic acid	H_2SnO_3	4×10^{-10}
Ammonium hydroxide	NH_4OH	1.8×10^{-5}
Beryllium hydroxide	$Be(OH)_2$	5×10^{-11}
Lead hydroxide	$Pb(OH)_2$	3×10^{-8}
Silver hydroxide	$AgOH$	1.1×10^{-4}
Zinc hydroxide	$Zn(OH)_2$	1.5×10^{-9}

[1] For primary ionization of polybasic acids and complete dissociation for polyacid bases.

WATER VAPOR PRESSURE AT VARIOUS TEMPERATURES

° C.	Pressure, mm.	° C.	Pressure, mm.	° C.	Pressure, mm.
0	4.6	20	17.5	28	28.3
5	6.5	21	18.6	29	30.0
10	9.2	22	19.8	30	31.8
15	12.8	23	21.0	40	55.3
16	13.6	24	22.4	50	92.5
17	14.5	25	23.8	60	149.4
18	15.5	26	25.2	70	233.7
19	16.5	27	26.7	80	355.1
				90	525.8
				100	760

INDEX

A and B subgroups of elements, 85–86
 comparison, 88
Abnormal properties of electrolytes, 202
Abrasives
 alundum, 530
 boron carbide, 481
 carborundum, 458
 emery, 530
 rouge, jewelers', 609
Absolute temperature scale, 3
Absolute zero, 33
Absorption, 307
Abundance of elements, 13
A.C., 252
Accelerator, linear, 655
Acetaldehyde, 698
Acetate ion, 233, 239
Acetate rayon, 708
Acetic acid, 699
 ionization of, 206
Acetone, 700–701
Acetylene, 674–675
Acheson, 458
Acid, 102, 192–199
 anhydride, 336
 anion, 209
 cation, 211
 salt, 336
 strong, 193
 weak, 206
Acidic elements, 124
Acidic oxides, 123
Acidity, pH, 236
 of various substances, 237
Acrylonitrile, 691
Actinides, 658
Activation energy, 225, 231–232
Activity series, 108, 142–143
Adipic acid, 710–711
Adrenalin, 719
Adsorption, 307
Aerosol, 299, 303
Afridol, 558
Agate, 459

Age of minerals, 650
Air, 270–283
Air conditioning, 272–273
Airships, 281
Alabaster, 525
Alberene, 519
Albumen, 431, 714
Alchemical symbols, 14
Alchemists, 650
Alclad, 517
Alcohol, ethyl, 694
 determination of formula, 95
Alcohols, 673, 693–697
 amyl, 701
 trihydric (glycerol), 697
Aldehydes, 697–698
Algae, 277, 285, 384, 579
Aliphatic hydrocarbons, 669–675
Alkali metals, 84, 310–316
 halides of, 330
 preparation, 313
 properties, 314
 uses, 315
Alkaline earth metals, 502–534
Alkalinity, see pH
Alkyl radicals, 691
Allotropism, 131
Alloys, 496–500
 fusible, 451, 500
 See also individual metals
Alnico, 615
Alpha particles (rays), 20, 651
 nature of, 648
 scattering of, 55
Alternating current, 252
Alum, 531
 chrome, 623
 sodium, 355
Alumina (Al_2O_3), activated, 530
 as drying agent, 274
 sorption by, 308
Aluminum
 analysis for, 532–534

INDEX

Aluminum, (Continued)
  compounds of, 529–532
    hydroxide (in water purification), 286; amphoteric behavior of, 447; acid behavior of, 144
  occurrence, 503–504
  preparation, 507–512
  properties, 502, 513
  uses, 516–518
  welding of, 286
Alundum, 530
Alunite, 504
Alvarez, 655
Amalgam, 545
Amalgamation, 582, 590
Americium, 657
Amethyst, 459
Amino acids, 714
Ammonia, 396
  complexes, 399
  diffusion of, 39
  from coal, 414
  liquid, 402
  nitrogen from, 395
  synthesis of, 416
Ammonia-soda process, 353
Ammonium
  arsenomolybdate, 443
  chloride, 339, 401
  chloroplatinate, 595
  cyanate, 660
  hydroxide, ionization of, 204
  nitrate, 401
  nitrite, 394
  phosphomolybdate, 431
  sulfate from coal, 414
Ampere, 259
Amphoterism, 88, 447
Amyl nitrite, 701
Anderson, 652
Anglesite, 537
Anhydride, acid, 336
  mixed, 343
Aniline, 676, 705
Anions, acid-base properties, 193–194, 209–211
  definition and nomenclature, 92
  table of, 98–99
Anode, 92
  in electrolysis, 247
  in voltaic cells, 254
Anode mud, 251, 389, 544, 576, 582, 616
Anthracene, 677
Antibiotics, 721
Antichlor, 386
Anti-fouling paint, 556
Antifreeze, 693, 696, 697
Antimony, 445–449

Antimony sulfide in matches, 425
Antimonyl compounds, 448
Antiseptics, 329, 347, 375, 558, 585, 694
Apatite, 317, 503
Aqua fortis, 408
Aqua regia, 337
Aqueous tension, 165
Aragonite, 521
Arc process (nitric acid), 418
Argentite, 381
Argillaceous, 472
Argon, 279–280
  in air, 271
Argyrodite, 643
Argyrol, 585
Aromatic hydrocarbons, 675–677
Arrhenius, 195, 201–204, 402
Arsenates, 440, 443
Arsenic, 437–445
  acids, 442
  halides, 443
  occurrence, 438
  oxides, 442
  preparation and properties, 439
  sulfides, 443
  thioacids, 444
  uses, 440
  white, 439, 442
Arsenicals, 441
Arsenites, 440, 442
Arsenopyrites, 439
Arsine, 441, 442
Arsphenamine, 441
Asbestine, 565
Asbestos, 462, 503, 519
  diaphragms, 324
Ascorbic acid, 376, 715–718
Ash, black (soda), 352
Aspdin, 472
Aspirin, 705
Astatine, 325, 657
Astringent, 555
Atacamite, 572
Atmosphere, 270–283
  dust in, 270, 274–276
  pressure unit, 4
Atmospheric pressure, effect on boiling point, 168
Atom, 47, 646
  bomb, 655
  electrical nature, 51
  smashers, 653
Atomic heat, 154
Atomic number, 54, 84
Atomic size, 60
  and chemical nature, 73, 75–77

Atomic structure, 51–68
  research on, 52–61
  table, 56
Atomic weight determination, 151–154
  unit, 43
Attraction, intermolecular, 37–38, 191, 488
Auric and aurous, *see* Gold
Aurocyanide ion, 590
Avogadro's law, 40–46, 153
  number, 43
Azide ion, 403
Azurite, 572

B.T.U., 679
Bacteria, nitrifying, 277
  in water, 285
  sulfur forming, 362
Bacterial fermentation, 670, 695–696, 701
  prevention of, 375
Baddeleyite, 635
Bakelite, 723
Baking powder, 355
Baking soda, 351
Balancing equations, 104, 320
Balke, 630, 631
Balkite rectifiers, 632
Bancroft, 298
Barilla, 352
Barite, 503
Barium
  analysis, 532–534
  compounds, 527–529
    oxide, electron emitter, 628
    perchlorate, drying agent, 274, 349
    peroxide, for H_2O_2, 133
  occurrence, 503
  preparation, 507
  properties, 502, 512–513
  uses, 513–514
Barometer, 4
Baryta (water), 528
Barytes, 384
Base, 102, 123, 192–199
  anion, 210
Base exchange, 291
Basic elements, 124
Basic oxides, 123
Basic salts, 212
Basic slag, 434
Battery
  dry cell, 253
  Edison, 258
  storage, 256
Baumé scale, 382
Bauxite, 503, 509, 512
Bayer process, 509
Bearing metal, 448, 551
Becquerel, 647

Beehive coke ovens, 682
Benzene, 676
  derivatives, 705
Benzoic acid, 700
Bergius process, coal, 157, 679
  glucose, 713
Beryl, 502
Beryllium
  analysis, 532–534
  compounds, 518
  occurrence, 502
  preparation, 504
  properties, 502, 512–513
  uses, 514–515
Berzelius, 389, 453, 634
Bessemer, 604
Beta particles (rays), 648
Betatron, 654
Betts process, 543
Bi-, 210
Bicarbonate ion, 210, 237, 354–356
Bichloride of mercury, 557
Birkeland-Eyde process, 418
Bismuth, 449–452
Bismuthine, 450
Bismuthyl compounds, 450
Bisulfate ion, 193, 207, 209–210, 382
Bisulfite ion, 375, 526
Black ash, 352
Black powder, 367
Blanc-fixe, 384, 527
Blast furnace, 601
Bleach, 339
Bleaching
  by chlorine, 329
  by chlorine dioxides, 342
  by hypochlorites, 346
  by sulfur dioxide, 361, 376
Bleaching powder, 346
Blende, 536
Blimps, 281
Blister copper, 575
Blomstrand, 630
Blood, pH, 238
Bloodstone, 459
Blowpipe
  oxyacetylene, 129
  oxyhydrogen, 156
Blue lead, 411, 565
Blueprints, 611
Blue vitriol, 183, 384
Bluing, 611
Bohr, 54–58
Boiling points
  effect of pressure on, 168
  of liquids, 168–169
  of metals, 26
  of solutions, 184–185, 208

INDEX

Bomb, atomic, 655
Bone black, 663
Borax, 478–480, 482–483
Borax bead tests, 483
Bordeaux mixture, 578
Boric (boracic) acid, 482
Bornite, 572
Boron, 478–485
Boron trifluoride, argon compounds, 280
Borosilicate glass, 467
Boyle, 6, 422
Boyle's law, 30–32
Bragg, 61
Brandt, 422
Brass, 500, 577
   selenium, 390
Braunite, 618
Brazilite, 635
Bredig arc, 302
Bricks, 475, 528
Bridge, potassium chloride, 264
Brimstone, 361
British thermal unit, 679
Brochantite, 572
Bromine
   and potassium, 102
   diffusion of, 29
   discovery, 317
   hydrogen bromide, 333–337
   in sea water, 296, 319
   oxygen compounds of, 350
   preparation, 318–319
   properties, 325–328
   uses, 329
      See also Halogens
Bronsted theory, 123, 194, 212, 403
Bronze, 577
   aluminum, 577
   beryllium, 514–515, 577
   cadmium, 546, 577
   manganese, 619
Brownian movement, 41, 306
Brucite, 503
Buffer solutions, 240
Bullion, lead, 543
   doré, 583
Buna rubber, 690–691
Bunsen, 23, 311
Burette, 196
Butadiene, 689, 691
Butane, 37, 672
Butter, 702, 703
Butter of antimony, 448–449
By-product coke ovens, 682

Cadmium
   analysis, 566
   compounds, 552

Cadmium, (*Continued*)
   neutron absorption by, 656
   occurrence, 536
   preparation, 541
   properties, 544
   uses, 546
Cady, 281
Calamine, 536
Calcareous, 472
Calciferol, 521
Calcination, 494
Calcite, 521
Calcium
   analysis, 532–534
   compounds, 520–526
      aluminate, 474
      arsenate, 440
      bisulfite, 375, 526
      carbide, 674
      carbonate, 277
      chloride, 274, 354
      phosphates, 434
      phosphide, 426
   occurrence, 503
   preparation, 507
   properties, 502, 512–513
   uses, 514
Calgon, 292, 433
Calomel, 557
Calorie, 154
Calorific value, of coals, 680
   of fuel gases, 684
Calutron, 58
Camphor, 707
Canned heat, 696
Carat, 662
Carbohydrates, 711–715
Carbolic acid (phenol), 676–677, 696, 705
Carboloy, 628
Carbon (organic chemistry), 660–728
   amorphous, 663–664
   black, 308, 663
   crystalline, 662–663
   cycle, 276–278
   dioxide, 664–666
      in air, 270–271, 276
      in plant growth, 277
   disulfide, 371
   monoxide, 665–668
      analysis, 579, 685–686
   oxides of, 664–668
   tetrachloride, 668–669
   valence behavior, 661
Carbona, 669
Carbonates, 193, 210, 237, 354–356
Carbonic acid, 665
Carbonyl (group), 698
Carbonyls, 667

INDEX

Carborundum, 458
Carboxyl (group), 698
Carlsbad deposits, 311
Carnallite, 310, 503
Carnotite, 629
Carter process, 565
Casale process, 417
Casein, 714
Cassius, purple of, 591
Cassiterite, 537
Cast iron, 602
Castner process
  for HCN, 411
  for sodium, 313
Catalysis, 226
Catalysts, 104, 119
  nickel, 703
  poisoning of, 381
  platinum and vanadium, 381
Cataphoresis, 306
Cathode, 52
  in voltaic cells, 254
Cathode rays, 53
Cation, 92, 98–99
  acids, 212
Cation-exchange, 290
Caustic soda, 323, 355, 357
Cavendish, 138, 270
Celanese, 709
Celestite, 503
Cell
  Daniell, 255
  dry, 254
  Edison, 258
  electrolytic, 253
  gravity, 256
  lead, 256
  Leclanché, 254
  Nelson, 323
  potential, 261
  sign convention, 264
  storage, 256
  voltaic, 253
Cellophane, 708
Celluloid, 707
Cellulose, 706–710, 727–728
  hydrolysis of, 706, 713
  vulcanized, 555
Cement
  chrome, 623
  Portland, 471
  zinc oxychloride, 555
  zirconia, 635
Cementation, 607
Centigrade, 2
  temperature scale, 3
Ceramics, 475, 483
Cerargyrite, 581

Cerium, 639
Cerussite, 637
Cesium, 311
Chadwick, 53
Chain reactions, 327
Chalcanthite, 572
Chalcocite, 572
Chalcopyrite, 572
Chalk (crayons), 525
Chamber crystals, 379
Charcoal, 663
  activated, 281, 308
Charles' Law, 32–33
Chemical change, 9
  types of, 101–110
Chemical equations, 101–110
Chemical reactions, completion of, 110
Chemistry, definition, 1
Chemurgy, 724–728
Chili saltpeter, 310, 413
China clay, 475
Chinese scarlet, 566
Chinese white, 554
Chlorates, 73, 348
Chloraurate, 337, 409
Chlorauric acid, 592
Chloric acid, 348
Chloride of lime, 346
Chlorinated hydrocarbons, 329
Chlorination of gold ores, 589
Chlorine, 316–352
  available, 286
  chain reaction of, 327
  diatomic nature, 47
  dioxide, 342
  discovery, 317
  electronic structure, 65
  from fused NaCl, 247
  hydrate, 324, 328
  in preparation of oxy-compounds, 343–348
  in water purification, 286
  oxy-acids and salts, 343–351
  preparation, 319, 323
  properties, 324
  uses, 329
  water, 230
  See also Halogens
Chlorites, 73, 343
Chloroform, 671
Chlorophenols, 285
Chlorophyll, 276
Chloroplatinate, 337, 340, 595, 598
Chloroplatinic acid, 594, 598
Chloroprene, 690
Chlorous acid, 347, 388
Chlorozincate ion, 219
Cholesterol, 719

742 INDEX

Chrome alum, 623
Chrome green, 623
Chrome red, 624
Chrome yellow, 566, 623
Chromel, 500
Chromite (ore), 621
Chromium, 613, 621
   plating, 252
Chromosphere, sun's, 138
Chrysocolla, 572
Cinnabar, 11, 537
Citric acid, 700
Clad metal
   Alclad, 517
   nickel-clad, 617
Claude process, 417
Clay, 475, 529
Cleaning solution, 624
Clinker, 472
Cloud chamber, 19, 40
Coagulation
   of colloids, 306
   water purification, 286
Coal, 679–682
   heat values, 680
   hydrogenation, 679
   products, 680–682
   tar, 681
Cobalt, 613–616
Cobalt chloride as moisture indicator, 274
Coconut oil, 702
Coke, 602, 679, 681–682
Colemanite, 478–480
Collision rate, formula, 223
Collodion, 470, 707
Colloidal particle, 41
Colloids, 298–309
   protective, 307
Color of ions, 212
Columbium, 613, 630, 640
Combined gas law, 34–35
Combining volumes, 41–44, 46–47
Combustion, 125–127
Common ion effect, 239
Complex, collision, 231
Complex ions, 74–75, 219, 399
Composition of earth's crust, 13
Composition, percentages from formulas, 96
Compounds, 6, 91–96
   complex, 74–75
Compressibility of gases, 28
Concentrate, ore, 494
Concentration, 176–179
   law, 224
Concrete, 471, 474
Conductivity of electrolytes, 205

Conductors, electric
   metallic, 489
   types, 246
Conservation of mass, 101
Constant, equilibrium, 227
Constant boiling mixtures, 335
Constantan, 617
Contact process, 380
Conversion tables, 733
Converter, Bessemer, 604
Copolymer, 690
Copper, 570–580
   compounds, 578
      ammonia ion, 399
      arsenite, 442
      cyanide ion, 399
   occurrence, 571
   preparation, 572
   properties, 576, 581
   uses, 577
Copperas, 384, 610
   chlorinated, 286, 293, 328
Corn oil, 725
Corn starch, 711, 725
Corn sugar, 713
Corrosion prevention, 547
Corrosive sublimate, 557
Cortin, 719
Corundum, 530
Cosmic rays and gaseous ions, 132
Coster, 643
Cotton, mercerized, 708
Cotton linters, 708
Cottonseed oil, 702
Cottrell precipitator, 275, 307, 494, 642
Coulomb, 259
Coupling of electrons, 66
Covalence, 70–73
   coordinate or dative, 72–73
Covellite, 572
Cracking,
   coal, 679
   petroleum, 145, 339, 532, 683
   wood, 678
Cream of tartar, 355, 357
Critical temperature
   and critical pressure, 38
   and surface tension, 161–162
Crocoite, 621
Crookes, 642
Crucible steel, 607
Cryogenic research, 640
Cryolite, 310, 504, 508, 512
Crystal structure, 60–61
Crystallization, fractional, 215
   water of, 183
Crystals, ionic, 202
Cupellation, 583

INDEX

Cupola furnace, 602
Cuprammonium rayon, 709
Cupric and cuprous, see Copper
Cuprotitanium, 633
Curie, 650–651, 658
Curium, 657
Current, electric, 246
    alternating, 252
    direct, 253
    production of, 252
Cyanamide, 414
Cyanates, 411
Cyanide ion, 410
    complexes, 411
Cyanogen, 411
Cyclotron, 654

D. C., 253
Dalton, 50
Dalton's Law, 164–165, 228
Daniell cell, 255
Daniels, 418
Dative covalence, 72–73
Davy, 10, 201, 254, 312, 317, 405, 453, 504, 634, 686
Deacon process, 323
Dead Sea, 311
Debye-Hückel theory, 203, 243
Decomposition, 102, 105–106
    double, 108
De-electronation, 124–125
Definite proportions, law of, 7
Degasifier, 316, 605
    See also Getters
de Graaff, Van, 653
Degreaser, 329
De-ionization, 292
Deliquescent salts, 525, 553
del Rio, 629
de Luyartes, 626
Density, 4
    of gases, 39
De-oxidizer, 316
Depilatory, 642
Depolarizer, 254
Descloizite, 629
Desiccants, 274, 383, 526, 528
Desulfurizer, 316
Detergents, 287
Detinning, 542
Detonators, 557
Deuterium (H^2), 59, 651
Developers, photographic, 376, 589
Dextrin, 711
Dextrose, 712–713, 725
Diacid bases, 213
Diagonal relationship, 478, 665
Dialysis, 304

Diamond, 662
Diastase, 711
Diatomaceous earth, 460
Diatomic molecules (elements), 48
Dibasic acids, 212
Dichloroethylene, 675
Die casting, 547
Dielectric constant, 174
Diffraction, 61
Diffusion, 27
    Graham's law of, 38
    of liquids, 187
Dihydrol, 191
Dilution law, 234
Dimethylglyoxime, 618
Diphenyl and diphenyl oxide, 165
Dipoles, 173–174, 191
Diprotic acids, 213
Direct current, 253
Direct union reactions, 102–106
Disaccharides, 711
Disintegration, radioactive, 648
Displacement, 102, 106–108, 144–146, 261
Disproportionation, 348
Distillation, 26
    destructive, 414
    fractional, 181–182
Döbereiner's triads, 79–80
Doctor solution, 562
Dolomite, 503
Double bond, 661, 673
Double decomposition (or displacement), 108
Dow, 316
Dowmetal, 515
Downs process, 313
Dowtherm, 166
Dried milk, 166–167
Driers, paint, 564, 615
Driller's mud, 433, 527
Drummond light, 156
Dry cell, 254
Dry ice, 666
Drying agents, 274, 383, 526, 528
Drying of gases, 273–274
Dulong and Petit, law of, 154–155, 163
Duprene, 690
Duralumin, 517
Duriron, 455, 500
Dust in atmosphere, 41, 270, 274–276
Dutch process, 565
Dynamite, 702
Dynamo, 252
Dyno, 713
Dysprosium, 639

E.C.S., See Electrochemical series
Earth, 502

Earth, (*Continued*)
  fuller's, 529
  rare, 529
Earth's crust, composition of, 13
Edison cell, 258, 617
Ehrlich, 441
Eka-aluminum, 640
Eka-silicon, 81, 640, 643
Ekeberg, 631
Elastomer, 691
Electrochemical series
  metals, 143
  non-metals, 108
  relation to electrolysis, 248
Electrode, 70, 92
  glass, 266
  hydrogen, 262
  potential, 262, 264
  reactions, 248
Electrodialysis, 305
Electrodotic, 266
Electrolysis, 247
  fused salts, 248
  metallurgical, 496, 506, 512, 538, 549, 575, 629
Electrolytes, 253
  boiling and freezing points of, 208
  effect of on colloids, 306–307
  weak, 204
Electrolytic cells, 253
Electrolytic dissociation, 201
Electrolytic refining, 250, 512, 575, 583, 590
Electrometallurgy, 495
Electrometric titrations, 267
Electromotive force, 259, 261
Electron
  arrangement in atoms, 64–65
  configuration and periodic table, 85–86
  coupling (pairing), 66
  nature of, 50–53, 652
  orbits, 51
  research, 52–53
  shells or layers, 51
  transfer, 68–70, 73, 97–100, 124–125
  valence behavior of, 68–77
  wave nature of, 51
Electronegative elements, 266
Electronegativity, 73
Electronic formulas, 69–70
Electronic heating (tin plate), 550
Electrophilic, 266
  atoms, 73
  in oxidizing agents, 124
Electrophoresis, 306
Electroplating, 251
  cyanide baths for, 411
Electropositive, 266

Electrotypes, 252
Electrovalence, 70
Elektron (alloy), 515
Elements
  abundance and distribution of, 13
  definition of, 6, 646
  radioactive, 649
  rare earth, 639
  transition, 74
  transmutation of, 650
  transuranium, 657
Emery, 530
E. M. F., 261
Empedocles, 10
Empirical formulas, 94–96
Emulsification of dirt, 288
Emulsions, 300
Emulsoid, 305
Enamel, mottling of tooth, 287, 331
Enamel, vitreous, 476, 528
Enargite, 572
End point, 196
Endothermic reaction, 231
Energy
  activation, 225, 232
  nuclear, 646, 655
  solar, 647
Energy levels, 64–68
Enzymes, 715
Epsom salts (epsomite), 384, 518
Equations, chemical, 101–110
  calculations from, 110–112
Equilibrium, chemical, 140–141
  constant, 227
  disturbing, 229
  effect of pressure on, 232
  effect of temperature on, 231
Equivalent weight, 152, 173, 197–198
Erbium, 639
Ergosterol, 716
Error implied in data, 46
Erythrite, 614
Erythronium, 629
Esters, 701–702
  See also Fats
Etching glass, 338
Ethane, 671
Ethers, 704
Ethyl
  acetate, 701
  alcohol, 673, 694–696, 727
  chloride, 671
  fluid, 318
  gasoline, 564
Ethylene, 673–674
  chlorohydrin, 697
  dibromide, 564, 673
Europium, 639

INDEX

Eutectic, 536
Evaporation, 162
Exhaustibility of gases, 28
Exothermic reaction, 232
Expansion on freezing, 191–192
Explosions, 126–127, 327
Explosives, 348–350, 367, 403, 557, 702, 707

F. (Fahrenheit) temperature scale, 2
Fahrenheit zero, 33
Families of elements, 84
Faraday, 10, 201, 676
    unit of electricity, 260
Faraday's laws, 259
Farm chemurgy, 724, 728
Fats (glyceryl esters), 702, 704
    hydrogenation of, 150
Fehling's solution, 578
Feldspar, 463, 475
Ferberite, 627
Fermentation, 375, 670, 694–696, 699, 701
Ferric and ferrous, see Iron
Ferric hydroxide, colloidal, 301
    in water purification, 286
Ferricyanide ion, 611
Ferrochromium, 622
Ferrocolumbium, 630
Ferromanganese, 619
Ferromolybdenum, 625
Ferrosilicon, 145
Ferrotitanium, 633
Ferrous and ferric, see Iron
Ferrovanadium, 629
Fertilizers, 277, 311, 412–419, 433
Fiberglass, 471
Filler, paint, 564, 634
Filter alum, 531
Filtration, 286
Fink, 517
Fire damp, 686
Fire extinguisher, 355
Fission, nuclear, 652, 655
Fixation of nitrogen by bacteria, 277
Fixed nitrogen, 277, 412–419
Fixing, photographic, 386, 587
Flask, mercury, 549
Flint glass, 466, 469
Flotation, 494
Flumerin, 558
Fluorides in drinking water, 287, 331
Fluorine, 317, 435
    See also Halogens
Fluorite, 317
Fluorspar, 503
Fluosilicate ion, 338
Fluosilicic acid, 339, 458, 542, 544
Fluotitanates, 634

Flux, 282, 287, 402, 467, 483, 495, 602
Fog, 41
Fool's gold, 599
Forces, van der Waals, 191, 488
Formaldehyde, 157, 697
Formic acid, 667, 698
Formula weight, 95
Formulas, chemical, 94–96
    determination of, 95–96
    electronic, 69–70
    empirical, 94
    ionic, use of, 108
    structural, 396
Fractional crystallization, 215
Fractional distillation, 181–182
Francium, 313, 657
Franklin, 402
Franklinite, 536
Frary metal, 514
Frasch process, 363
Fraunhofer lines, plate facing p. 342
Freezing point lowering, 209
Freezing points, of liquids, 169
    of solutions, 184–185, 208
Frequency and energy of light, 54
Frit, 476
Fructose, 712–713
Fuels, 677–686
    gaseous, 683
    liquid, 682
    solid, 678
Fulminate, 557
Fundamental particles, 50, 52–54, 652
    location of in atom, 55, 58
Furfuraldehyde, 698
Furnace
    blast, 601
    cupola, 602
    electric
        for calcium carbide, 458
        for phosphoric acid, 435
        for steel, 607
    open hearth, 605
Fused salts, electrolysis of, 248
Fusible alloys, 451
Fusion, heats of, 163

Gadolin, 658
Gadolinium, 639
Gahn, 618
Galena, 537, 565
Gallium, 640
Galvanizing, 547
Gamma rays, 648
Gangue, 495
Garnet, 462
Garnierite, 616

INDEX

Gas
  ideal, 38
  fuel, *see* Gaseous fuels
  laughing, 405
  law
    Avogadro's, 40
    Boyle's (pressure-volume), 29
    Charles' (temperature-volume), 32
    combined (PVT), 34
    Dalton's (partial pressures), 180
    deviations from, 36
    Gay-Lussac's (combining volumes), 41
    Gay-Lussac's (temperature-pressure), 32
    Graham's (diffusion), 38
    Henry's (solubilities), 179
    van der Waals' (real gases), 38
  mantles (Welsbach), 636, 639, 644
  masks, 308, 663
  mustard, 372
Gaseous fuels, 683–686
Gases, 26–48
  behavior of real, 36–38
  density of, 39
  diffusion of, 38
  drying of, 273
  liquefaction of, 44
  perfect, 38
  rare, noble or inert, 66–67, 271, 278–282
  solutions of, in liquids, 179
Gasoline, 683
Gay-Lussac, 362, 480
  gas law (temperature-pressure), 32
  law of combining volumes, 41
  tower, 379
Geiger counter, 19, 649
Gel, 304, 461
Gelatin, 304
Gems, artificial, 530
Generator
  A.C., 252
  Kipp (hydrogen), 146
  Van de Graaff, 653
German silver, 500, 617
Germanium, 643
Getters, 315, 513, 514, 640
Glass, 465–472
  borosilicate, 467
  germanium, 643
  Jena, 465
  low silica, 471
  optical, 467, 528
  Pyrex, 465
  ruby, 300, 465
  safety, 470
  selenium, 389
  water, 464
  wire, 470

Glass electrode, 266
Glauber's salt, 373, 384
Glazes, 476, 554, 560, 562, 579, 615, 626, 634, 635
Glover tower, 379
Glucinum, *see* Beryllium
Glucose, 706, 712–713
Gluten, 714, 725
Glycerol (glycerine), 697
  trinitrate, 702
Glyceryl esters, *see* Fats
Glycine, 714
Glycogen, 714
Glycol, 697
  dinitrate, 702
Goiter, 330
Gold
  colloidal, 296
  compounds, 592
  in sea water, 300
  occurrence and preparation, 588
  properties, 581, 590
  uses, 591
Goldschmidt process, 517, 622, 629
Goodyear, 687
Graham, 304
Graham's law, 38–39
Graham's salt (Calgon), 433
Gram atomic heat capacity, 154
Gram atomic weight, 151–154
Gram molecule, 43–44
Gram molecular volume, 44
Gram molecular weight, 43–44
Gramicidin, 721
Graphite, 663
  neutron slowing by, 656
Grating, diffraction, 61
Gravity cell, 256
Greenockite, 537
Ground water, 285
Groups, periodic system, 84
  and valence, 86
Guano, 433
Guldberg and Waage, 224
Guncotton, 707
Gunpowder, black, 367
Gypsum, 384, 525

Haber process, 416
Hafnium, 643
Half life, 648
Halides
  alkali, 330
  hydrogen, 333
  phosphorus, 334
  sulfur, 372
Hall, 508

INDEX

Halogens, 312, 316–330
  discovery, 317
  interhalogen compounds, 326
  oxides, 342
  oxy-acids, 343–351
  preparation, 318
  properties, 324
  uses, 329
Hansgirg process, 506
Hard water, 289
Harkins, 20, 21
Hartshorn, 400
Heat capacity, 154
Heat pump, 273
Heats
  of fusion, 163
  of neutralization, 198
  of reaction, 231
  of solution, 182
  of vaporization, 162
  specific, 154–155, 163
Heavy hydrogen, 59–60
Heavy water, 59–60
Helium
  critical pressure, 38
  discovery, 278
  from radium, 18
  in air, 271
Hematite, 600
Henry's law, 179–180
Hevesy, 643
Hexametaphosphate, 433
Hexamethylenediamine, 710–711
Hillebrand, 278
Hjelm, 624
Holmium, 639
Homogeneity of gases, 28
Homogenizer, 302
Homologous series, 669
Hoopes process, 512, 517
Hormones, 718–721
Hubnerite, 627
Humidity of air, 271–274
  effects of, 272
Hydralo, 274
Hydrated lime, 523–524
Hydrates, 183
Hydration of ions, 182
Hydrazine, 403
Hydrazoic acid, 403
Hydrides of metals, 149–150, 315, 635
Hydriodic acid, 337
Hydrocarbons, 669–677
  chlorinated, 329
Hydrochloric acid, 336
Hydrocyanic acid, 411
Hydrofluoric acid, 337, 458
  as pickling agent, 549

Hydrofluosilicic acid, 339, 458, 542, 544
Hydrogen, 138–158
  absorption by metals, 147, 596
  atomic, 150
  bonding, 191–192, 338
  chloride, diffusion, 39
  electrode, 262
  equivalent, 178, 197
  halides, 333
  heavy, 59–60
  ion, 194–195
  peroxide, 133–136, 388
  preparation, 139–146
  properties, 147–150
  spectrum, plate opposite p. 342
  sulfide, 367
    in air, 270
  uses, 156–158
Hydrogenation, 150, 157
Hydrolite, 521
Hydrolysis
  chlorine, 230
  fats, 703–704
  phosphorus halides, 428
  salts, 216
  urea, 714
Hydrometallurgy, 495
Hydrometer, 257
Hydrone, 139
Hydronium
  bisulfate, 382
  chloride, 196, 336
  ion, 192, 194–195, 206, 403
  perchlorate, 350
Hydroponics, 294
Hydrosilicons, 455
Hydrosulfite ion, 388
Hydroxide ion, 192
Hydroxides, amphoteric, 447
Hydroxylamine, 403
Hypernik, 617
Hypo, 385
Hypochlorites, 73, 345
Hypochlorous acid, 230, 287, 339, 343
  in water purification, 287
Hypophosphorous acid, 429
Hyposulfurous acid, 387

Ice
  dry, 666
  expansion on freezing, 190–193
  vapor pressure of, 185
Illinium, 639
Ilmenite, 599, 633
Incandescent lamp, 280
Indicators, 196–197
Indium, 641

Inert gases, 271, 278–282
  chemical compounds of, 280
  electron configurations of, 66, 67
Ink, 610
Insecticides, 440, 442
Insulin, 719
Inter-halogen compounds, 326
Intermolecular attraction, 37–38
Inulin, 714
Invar, 617
Iodides in drinking water, 287
Iodimetry, 328
Iodine
  number, 329
  radio-, 649
  tincture of, 316, 329
  See also Halogens
Iodomercurate ion, 219
Ion effect, common, 239
Ionic crystals, 202
Ionization, 201–204
  constant, 233
  of strong acids, 204
  of water, 192, 234
  of weak acids, 204, 233
  potentials, 6
  and the periodic system, 87
Ions, 18, 19, 21, 201–219
  acid-base properties of, 209–211
  color of, 212
  complex, 74, 399
  equilibrium with molecules, 233–236
  formation of, from elements, 68–70, 96–99
  hydration of, 182
  in crystals, 202
  non-rare gas-type, 212, 219
  rare gas-type, 211
  reactions of, 109–110
  size, 61
Iridium, 595
Iron (and steel), 599, 612
  carbonyl, 608
  cast, 602
  compounds, ferric and ferrous, 609
  galvanized, 547
  in water, 287
  occurrence, 599
  pig, 602
  preparation, 601
  properties, 608
  pure, 251
  pyrites, 362, 373, 599, 610
  sherardized, 549
  wrought, 603
Isobutane, 672
Isoelectric point, 306
Isomers, 670, 672

Isomorphism, 531
Isoprene, 687–688
Isotopes, mass numbers of, 56–60

Jasper, 459
Javelle water, 347
Jena glass, 465
Joule, 261

K layer of electrons, 64–66
Kaolin, 476
Kekulé, 676
Kelp, 318
Kelly, 604
Kelvin temperature scale, 3, 33
Kernel, atomic, 69
Kieselguhr, 460
Kieserite, 518
Kiln, vertical, 523
  rotary, 473, 511
Kilowatt hour, 261
Kindling point, 125
Kinetic molecular theory, 29–48
King, 507
Kipp generator, 146
Kirchhoff, 23, 311
Klaproth, 634, 644, 658
Klaus, 595
Knietsch, 380
Konel, 615
Kontrastin, 635
Kraft paper, 373
Krypton in air, 271
  discovery, 279

L layer of electrons, 64–66
Labeled molecules, 649
Lactic acid, 700, 714, 725
Lactose, 711
Lakes, color, 530
Lamp
  Davy safety, 686
  incandescent, 280
Lampblack, 663
Langmuir, 150
Lanthanides, 638
Larvex, 339
Latex, 686
Laue, von, 61
Laughing gas, 405
Laundry sour, 339
Lavoisier, 117, 138–270
Layers of electrons, 51, 54, 64–69
Leaching, 539
Lead
  alloys, 449, 452, 500
  analysis, 566

INDEX

Lead, (Continued)
  compounds, 561
    arsenate, 440
    azide, 403, 557
  occurrence, 537
  preparation, 542
  properties, 544
  radio-, 647
  red, 562, 566
  uses, 551
Lead chamber process, 377
Lead glass, 467
Lead storage cells, 256
Leaded zinc oxide, 554
Leather, 529, 624
  artificial, 707
Leblanc, 352
Le Chatelier's principle, 229, 231
Leclanché cells, 254
Legumes, 277
Lepidolite, 310
Leucite, 311
Levels, energy, 51, 64
Levulose, 712–714
Lewis electronic formulas, 69–70
Lifting power, 281
Lignin, 706
Lime, 522–525
Lime and soda ash process, 290
Lime, chloride of, 346
Lime glass, 467
Limelight, 156
Limestone, 503, 519
Limonite, 600
Linnaeite, 614
Linseed oil, 564
Liquefaction, 26
  of coal, 157, 679
  of gases, 37, 162–163
Liquid air, 120
Liquids, 37, 44
  boiling point and freezing point, 168, 184–185
  critical temperature and pressure, 38, 45
  polar and non-polar, 173–174
  properties of, 161–169
  solutions of in liquids, 181
Liquor, mother, 318
Litharge, 562
Lithia water, 287
Lithium, 310
Lithopone, 527, 554, 555, 564, 634
Litmus, 196, 237
Lixiviation, 582, 589
Lockyer, 278
Lucite (plexiglas), 722
Lunar caustic, 581
Luster, metallic, 488

Lutecium, 639
  radio-, 650
Lye, soda, 356

M layer of electrons, 64–66
M, *see* Molarity
Magnalium, 500
Magnesia, black, 618
  milk of, 519
Magnesia mixture, 520
Magnesite, 503
Magnesium
  analysis, 532–534
  compounds, 518–520
    ammonium phosphate, 431, 520
    nitride, 427
    perchlorate, 274, 349
  in sea water, 296
  occurrence, 503
  preparation, 504–507
  properties, 502, 512–513
  radio-, 656
  selenium coated, 390
  uses, 515
Magnetic fields
  coupling of electronic, 66, 67
  of ions, 74
  stray, 66
Magnetite, 600, 610
Magneto, 252
Malachite, 572
Malachite green, 237
Malleability, 483
Malt, 711
Maltose, 711
Manganese, 613, 618
Manganese dioxide in dry cells, 254
Manganin, 617, 619
Mantles, incandescent, 636, 639, 644
Marble, 521
Margarine, 703
Marggraf, 537
Marl, 472
Marsh gas, 670
Marsh test, 441, 446
Martin, 605
Masks, gas, 308, 663
Mass
  action, law of, 224
  conservation of, 101
  numbers (table), 56–57
  spectrometer, 23
Masurium, 644
Matches, 425, 503
Matte, 543, 573
Mayerne, 138
Melaconite, 572
Melting, 26, 169–170

INDEX

Mendeléeff, 80–84, 640, 643
Mercerized cotton, 708
Mercurials, organic, 558
Mercurochrome, 558
Mercury
  analysis, 556
  compounds, 555
  occurrence, 537
  preparation, 537
  properties, 544
  still, old, 12
  uses, 549
Mercury vapor lamp, 460, 549
Meson, 54
Mesothorium, 643
Mesotron, 54
Metacinnabarite, 537
Metallic conductivity, 489
Metallic luster, 488
Metallizing, 548–549
Metallurgy, 491–496
Metals, 487–501
  alkali, 84, 310–316
  classification, 490
  electrolytic production and refining, 250
  nature of, 73–77
  occurrence, 489
  rare earth; 638
  transition, 74, 83, 212
Metaphosphoric acid, 430
Metathesis, 102, 108–110
Methane, 670
  derivatives of, 671–673, 693
Methyl alcohol (methanol), 157, 693
Methyl chloride, 456, 671
Methyl orange, 237
Methyl red, 237
Metol developer, 587
Metric system, 2
Meyer, 80
Mica, 463
Milk of lime, 286
Milk of magnesia, 519
Millikan, 52
Minerals, plant nutrition, 294
Mineral water, 287
Mining, 492
Minium, 562
Mirrors, 440, 468–470, 517, 584
Misch metal, 629, 639
Miscibility, 181
Mispickel, 439
Mixtures, nature and detection of, 7
Mohr's salt, 610
Moissan, 318, 662
Mol, 43–44
  of a salt, 95
Molar volume, 44

Molarity, 176–178
Molasses, 694
Molecular velocities, 40
Molecular volume in gas laws, 36–37
Molecular weight determination
  from boiling and freezing points, 184–186
  from gas density, 45
  from mass spectrometer, 23
Molecules, 17
  detection of, 18
  giant, 191
  kinetic energy of, 29
  odd, 342
  of elements, 48
  shapes of, 18, 462
  weight, 23, 45, 184–186
Molybdenum, 613, 624
Monatomic molecules, 48
Monazite, 639, 643
Mond process, 614, 616
Monel, 500, 617
Monoacid bases, 213
Monobasic acids, 212
Monoprotic acids, 213
Monosaccharides, 711
Mordant, 384, 440, 449, 555, 560, 579, 623, 628, 630
  definition, 530
Mortars (plasters), 384, 518, 519, 524, 525
Moseley, 54, 84
Mother liquor, 318
Mother of vinegar, 699
Mud
  driller's, 433, 527
  anode, 251, 389, 511, 544, 576, 582, 616
  red (Bayer process), 510
Multiple proportions, law of, 7
Muriatic acid, 205
Murray, 641
Mustard gas, 372

N (Avogadro's Number), 43–44
  See also Shells of electrons; Normality
N layer of electrons, 64–66
Names of compounds, 91–94
Naphthalene, 677
Natron, 352
Natural gas, 670
Negative elements, 266
Nelson cell, 323
Neodymium, 639
  glass, 471
Neon
  discovery, 279
  in air, 271
  signs, 281
Neoprene, 690

Neosalvarsan, 441
Neptunium, 658
Nessler's reagent, 400, 558
Neutralization, 109–110, 195–199
Neutrino, 54
Neutrons, 50–51, 53
 in transmutations, 651, 655
Newlands, 79–80
Nichrome, 617
Nickel, 613, 616, 703
Nickel carbonyl, 614
Nickel silver, 577
Nieuwland, 689
Niobium, 630
Niter, 270
Niton, See Radon
Nitrates, 409–410
Nitration, 384, 705
Nitric acid, 408
Nitric oxide, 418
Nitride ion, 396
Nitrided steel, 607
Nitrifying bacteria, 277, 413
Nitrobenzene, 676, 705
Nitrocellulose rayon, 709
Nitrogen, 394–421
 cycle, 276–278
 fixed, 277, 412–419
 in air, 270
 oxides, 404
 tri-iodide, 329
Nitroglycerine, 702
Nitroprusside ion, 219
Nitrosyl chloride, 337
Nitrosylferrous ion, 406
Nitrosylsulfuric acid, 379
Nitrous acid, 407
Nitrous oxide, 404
Noble gases, see Inert gases
Noddack, 644
Nomenclature, chemical, 91–94
Non-metals, characteristics, 487, 489
 electronegativity, 73
Non-polar solvents, 173–174
Non-rare gas-type ions, 212
Normality, 178–179
 use in titrations, 197–198
Nuclear chemistry, 646–659
Nucleus, atomic, 51, 55, 58
Number, Avogadro's, 43–44
Nylon, 709–711

Occlusion of hydrogen, 147
Ocean, minerals in, 296
Ochre, cobalt, 614
Octet, valence, 71, 74
Ohm, 259
Oil-drop experiment, 52

Oil of wintergreen, 705
Oils, vegetable, 702–703
Oleo (olein), 703
Olivine, 462
Onyx, 459, 521
Oölite, 599
Opal, 459
Open-hearth process, 605
Optical glass, 467
Orange mineral, 565
Orbital energies, 64–68
Orbits, electronic, 51, 52, 54, 55, 58, 68
Ores, 489
 preliminary treatment of, 493–494
 smelting of, 495–496
Organic chemistry, 660–728
"Oriental" gems, 530
Orpiment, 439, 444
Orthophosphoric acid, 430
Osann, 595
Osmium, 595
Osmosis, 187
Ostwald process, 417
Oxalic acid, 667, 699–700
Oxford process, 616
Oxidation, 124–125
 and reduction, 70, 103
 numbers, 75, 103, 105, 320
Oxides, acid-basic properties of, 123–124
Oxidizing agents, 124–125
 copper oxide, 394
 halogens, 325
 nitric acid, 408
 oxy-halogen compounds, 343
 ozone, 131
 peroxysulfuric acids, 387
 polysulfides, 371
 sulfuric acid, 382
Oxyacetylene torch (blowpipe), 129
Oxygen, 116–135
 cycle, 276
 in air, 270
 O^{17} as tracer, 650
 preparation, 118
 properties, 120
 uses, 127
Oxygen derivatives, organic, 691–704
 acids, 698–700
 alcohols, 693–697
 aldehydes, 697–698
 esters, 701–704
 ethers, 704
 ketones, 700–701
Oxy-halogen acids, 343–351
Oxyhydrogen torch (blowpipe), 156
Ozone, 120, 131–133
 in air, 270
 in water purification, 287

Paint, 564, 634
Pairing of electrons, 66
Palau, 597
Palladium, 594
   absorption of hydrogen, 147
Palmitate ion in soap, 288
Paneth, 450, 649
Paper, 373, 706, 728
Paracelsus, 6
Paraffin series, 671
Paris green, 442
Parkes process, 543, 582
Partial pressures, in mass law, 228
Partial pressures, law of, 164–165
Particle size, 299
Passivity, 609
Paste glass, 466
Pasteurization, 166, 169
Pauling, 191
Pearl white, 450
Pectin, 308
Penicillin, 168, 721
Pentlandite, 616
Pepsin, 715
Peptides, 714
Peptization, 303
Perchlorates, 73, 349
Perchloric acid, 349
Perfect gas, 38
Period, periodic system, 84
Periodic acid, 351
Periodic system chart, 78–89
Permalloy, 617
Permutit, 291
Peroxides, 118–119, 133–136
Peroxysulfuric acids, 133–134, 387
Pervaporation, 305
Petalite, 311
Petit, Dulong and, 154–155
Petroleum, 682–683
Pewter, 500
pH, 236
   control, 239
   meter, 267
   tables, 237
Pharaoh's serpents, 557
Phenol, 285, 676, 677, 696, 705
Phenolphthalein, 237
Phenylmercuric nitrate, 558
Phosgene, 328, 667
Phosphate buffers, 242
Phosphate fertilizers, 433
Phosphate rock, 434
Phosphates, tests for, 431
Phosphine, 426
Phosphonium ion, 427
Phosphoric acids, 412, 429, 435
Phosphorous acid, 429

Phosphorus, 422–436
   compounds, 426–435
      halides, 326, 334, 428
      hydrogen, 426
      oxides, 274, 383, 428, 435
      sulfide, 426
   fertilizers, 433
   occurrence, 422
   preparation and properties, 423
   radio-, 649, 656
Phosphotungstic acid, 628
Photoelectric cells, 315
Photography, 585
   sodium sulfite in, 376, 386
Photon, 54
Physical change, 9
Pickling (metals), 339, 549
Picric acid, 676–677
Pigments, paint, 527, 564, 634
Pile, uranium, 656
Pitchblende, 644
Placer mining, 588
Plants, mineral requirements, 294
Plasma, 168
Plaster
   land, 525
   of Paris, 384, 525
      See also Mortar
Plastics, 707, 721–724
Platinum-black, 263
Platinum metals, 594–598
Plexiglas, 722
Plumbic and plumbous, *see* Lead compounds
Plutonium, 655–657
Polar solvents, 173–174
Polarization, 254
Polonium, 650
Polyatomic molecules (elements), 48
Polymerization, 120, 338, 688–690
Polysulfides, 371
Porcelain, 476, 560
Portland cement, 471
Positive elements, 266
Positive rays, 51
Positron, 54, 652
Potash, 310, 313
   in fertilizer, 311, 412
Potassium, 310
   compounds, 357
      cobaltinitrite, 348
      cyanide, 495
      chlorate, 348
      silver cyanide, 584, 650
   radio-, 650
Potassium chloride bridge, 264
Potato starch, 726

INDEX

Potential
  cell, 261
  electrode, 263
  sign convention, 264
  solution, 261
Powder, black, 367
Powder metallurgy, 627, 631, 635
Praseodymium, 639
Precipitation, 109
  colloids, 301, 306
Pressure, 27, 29–33
  critical, 38
  effect on boiling point of, 168
  effect on equilibrium, 232
  measurement and units, 4
  partial, 164, 228
Pressure cookers, 168–169
Pressures, partial, in mass law, 228
Priestley, 116
Printing, photographic, 587
Producer gas, 685
Projectiles, atomic, 652
Proof spirits, 694
Propane, 671
Propylene, 674
Protactinium, 647
Protargol, 585
Protective coatings, 547
Protective colloids, 307
Proteins, 714–715
Protons
  in transmutations, 651
  nature of, 50, 53
  role in acids, 102, 206
  transfer of, 109–110, 193–196
Proust, 7
Prout's hypothesis, 53
Prussian blue, 566, 611, 623
Prussiates and prussic acid, 411
Pseudo-halides, 411, 412
Psilomelane, 618
Puddling furnace, 603
Pulp, wood, 329
Pure substances, 7, 215
Purple of Cassius, 591
Pyrene, 668
Pyrex glass, 465
Pyrites, 362, 373, 599, 610
Pyro developer, 587
Pyrofax, 37
Pyrolusite, 574, 618
Pyrometallurgy, 495
Pyrophosphoric acid, 430
Pyrosulfuric acid, 381, 387
Pyrotechnics, 529
Pyroxylin, 707
Pyrrhotite, 616

Quartz, 459
Quenching, 499
Quicklime, 522–525

Radicals, nomenclature, 92–93
Radioactive water, 287
Radioactivity, 53, 59
  artificial, 652
  natural, 647
Radium, 649
  A, B, C, C′, C″, D, E, F, G, 650
Radium bromide, 19
Radon, 279
Ramsay, 279, 281
Raoult's law, 184
Rare earth metals, 638
Rare (inert) gas, 278–282
Rare gas-type ion, 68
Ray track, 20, 40
Rayleigh, 279
Rayon, 708–710
Rays, alpha, 20, 55, 648, 651
  beta, 648
  canal, positive, 53
  Roentgen (X rays), 54
Reactants, 101
Reactions, electrode, 248
  speed of, 223
  types of chemical, 101–110
Realgar, 439, 444
Red lead, 562
Redox reactions in cells, 253
Redox equations, 320
Reducing agents, 124–125
  alkali metals, 315, 545, 622
  aluminum, 517, 619, 622, 629, 633
  ammonia, 395
  bacteria, 407
  calcium, 514
  carbon, 423, 540, 629, 633
  carbon monoxide, 602
  chromous ion, 622
  ferrous ion, 622
  hydrogen, 148, 609, 627, 629
  hydrogen iodide, 334
  hydrogen sulfide, 369
  hydrosulfite ion, 388
  hydroxylamine, 404
  magnesium, 520, 622
  manganous ion, 622
  misch metal, 629
  nitrite ion, 408
  oxalate ion, 611
  photographic developers, 376, 587
  silicon, 629
  stannite ion, 451, 559
  stannous ion, 591
  sulfur dioxide, 374

INDEX

Reducing agents, (Continued)
  thiosulfate ion, 386
  tin, 403
  zinc, 387, 622
Reduction, 70, 124–125
Refining, 496
Refractory
  beryllium oxide, 518
  magnesium carbonate, 519
  magnesium oxide, 519
  silicon carbide, 459, 540
  thorium dioxide, 644
  zirconium dioxide, 635
Refrigerant, ammonia as, 397
  sulfur dioxide as, 375
Refrigeration, reversal of, 273
Reich, 641
Relative humidity, 271
Replacement, 102, 106–108, 144–146, 261
Resin, 722
Revere, 570
Reversible reactions, 106, 140–141
Rhenium, 644
Rhodebush, 191
Rhodium, 595
Rhodochrosite, 574, 618
Richards, 59
Ring test, 410
Roasting, 494
Rochelle salt, 578, 584, 700
Rock salt, 316
Rock wool, 460
Roentgen rays (X rays), 54, 61
Rondelles, cobalt, 615
Rouge, jeweler's, 609
Rubber, 24, 401, 686–691
Rubidium, 311
  radio-, 650
Ruby, 530
Ruby glass, 300, 465
Ruthenium, 595
Rutherford, 53, 55–58, 270
Rutile, 633

S.A.S., 356
S.T.P. (standard conditions), 36, 44
Safety glass, 470
Salicylic acid, 705
Salt cake, 352
Saltpeter, 412
  Chile, 310
Salts, 92, 94–95
  electrolysis of fused, 248
  hydrolysis of, 216
  nomenclature, 99
  preparation, 212–216
  solubility, 216
  types, 212

Salvarsan, 441
Samarium, 639
  radio-, 650
Saponification, 703–704
Sapphire, 530
Satin spar, 525
Saturated solutions, 174–176, 242
Scheele, 117, 270, 317, 618, 624, 626
Scheele's green, 442
Scheelite, 627
Sea water, mineral value, 296
Searles Lake deposits, 311
Sedimentation, 286
Sefström, 629
Selenite, 525
Selenium, 361, 388
Semi-permeable membrane, 187
Separation, ore, 494
Series (period), 84
Serpek process, 418
Serpentine, 503, 519
Sewage, 293
Sheep dip, 440
Shells of electrons, 51, 64–69
Sherardizing, 549
Short-stop bath, 587
Shot, lead, 440
Siderite, 599
Siemens, 605
Sign convention, 264
Significant figures, 46
Silent discharge, 132
Silica, 459
  gel, 274, 308, 418, 461
Silicates, 462–464
Silicic acid, 461
Silicofluoride, 339
Silicon, 453–477, 629
  carbide, 458, 540
  dioxide, 459
  halides, 457
  tetrafluoride, 338
Silicones, 456
Silicosis, 275–276
Silver, 581–584
  compounds, 584
    silver ammonia ion, 342, 399
  German, 617
"606," 441
Size of particles, 299
Slag, 495, 602
  basic, 434
Slaked lime, 523
Slaking, 523
Sludge, activated, 293
  See also Mud
Smalt, 615
Smaltite, 614

INDEX

Smashers, atom, 653
Smeaton, 472
Smelting, 495
Smithsonite, 536
Smoke, 41
  control, 274
Soaps, 287, 703–704
  sodium silicate in, 464
Soapstone, 519
Soda, baking, 351
  caustic, 356
  modified, 355
  washing, 351
Soda ash, 351
  electrolytic, 354
Sodium, 310–316
  lamps, 316
  preparation, 313
  radio-, 649, 656
  salts
    aluminate, 532
    amide (sodamide), 314
    arsenate, 440
    arsenite, 440, 442
    bicarbonate, 351
    carbonate, 351
    chloride, 332; chlorine from, 323; electrolysis, 247; precipitation, 244; sodium from, 313
    chlorite, 347
    cyanide, 538
    ethylate, 314
    fluoaluminate, 532
    fluosilicate, 435
    halides, 330–333
    hexametaphosphate, 292
    hydride, 149–150, 315
    hydroxide; from soda ash, 355; electrolytic, 323, 357
    iodate, 317
    magnesium uranyl acetate, 341
    phosphates, 432; buffers, 242
    plumbite, 562
    pyroantimonate, 341
    silicate, 464
    stannite, 451
    sulfide, 373
    thiosulfate, 327, 385
    zincate, 553
Sodium arc lamp, 316
Softening (water), 288
Sol, 299
Solar energy, 647
Solder, 500
Solidification, 27, 196
Solids, 169–170
  solutions of, in liquids, 182–183
Solids in mass law, 224–225, 243

Solubility
  gases, 179
  salts, 216
  dependence on temperature, 174, 176
Solubility product, 242
Solution potential, 261
Solutions, 172, 187
  boiling and freezing points, 184–185, 208
  buffer, 240
  concentration, 176, 179
  constant boiling, 335
  definition, 172
  determination of molecular weights in, 185–186
  electrical conductivity of, 205
  equilibrium with solute, 174–176
  kinds, 172
  molal, 179
  molar, 176
  normal, 178
  of electrolytes, 233–244
  osmosis in, 187, 202
  pH of, 236–239
  Raoult's law of, 184
  saturated and supersaturated, 174–176, 242–244
  standard, 176–179
  vapor pressure of, 184–185
Solution tension, 261
Solvay process, 353
Solvents, 172–174, 284–285
  organic, 329, 695–696, 701, 704
  polar and non-polar, 173–174
Soot, 663
Sörensen, 236
Sorption, 307
Space (crystal) lattice, 60
Specific gravity, 171, 257
Specific heats, 163–164
Spectra, facing, 341
  mass, 23
Spectrograph, 340
  mass, 22
Speculum metal, 440
Spelter, 540
Sphalerite, 536
Spiegeleisen, 618
Spiess, 614
Spinthariscope, 18
Sprinklers, 451
Stability of compounds, 88–89, 335
Stable electron configurations, 66–67
Stainless steel
  selenium, 390
  welding of, 282
Stalactites and stalagmites, 521–522
Standard conditions, 36
Standard pressure, 4

INDEX

Standard solutions, 176–179
Stannic chloride, 330
Stannic and stannous compounds, *see* Tin compounds
Starch, 711, 725–726
   in iodimetry, 328
Stassfurt deposits, 310
Steam, hydrogen from, 140–142
Stearic acid, 702
Steatite, 519
Steel
   alloy, 613
   Bessemer, 604
   crucible, 607
   electric furnace, 607
   open hearth, 605
Stellite, 615
Stibine, 446
Still, alchemical, 12
Stope, mine, 574
Storage batteries, 256, 258
Stratosphere, 270
Stray field, 7, 66
Strength of acids and bases, 194, 205
Streptomycin, 721
Stress, 229
Strohmeyer, 537
Strong acids and bases, 193, 194
Strontianite, 503
Strontium
   analysis, 532–534
   compounds, 526–527
   occurrence, 503
   preparation, 507
   properties, 502, 512–513
   uses, 514
Styrene, 401, 690
Subgroups, periodic system, 84
Sublimation, 170
Substances, 1
Substitution, 261
     See also Displacement
Sucrose, 712
Sugar of lead, 563
Sugars, 711, 714
Sulfanilamide, 705
Sulfates, 362, 384
Sulfides, 367
Sulfite process, 375
Sulfonates, 288
Sulfonation, 288, 384
Sulfur, 361–393
   allotropism, 365
   compounds, 367–388
      halides, 326, 372
      with metals, 367
      with oxygen, 373
   family comparisons, 361

Sulfur, (*Continued*)
   flowers of, 366
   mining of, 363
   occurrence, 362
   properties, 364
   radio-, 649
   springs, 368
   uses, 366
Sulfuric acid, 377
   fuming, 381
Sulfurous acid, 374
Sumner, 715
Supercooling, 169
Superheating, 168
Superphosphate, 434
Supersaturation, 176
Surface tension, 161
Suspensoid, 305
Sylvanite, 588
Sylvite, 310
Symbols of elements, derivation, 14
Synchrotron, 655
Syphilis, 441

Tailings, 494
Talc, 463, 503, 519
Tannic acid, 610
Tantalite, 630
Tantalum, 613, 631, 640
Tapioca, 726
Tar, coal, 681
Tartar, cream of, 355, 357
Tartar emetic, 448
Tartaric acid, 700
Technetium, 644, 657
Tellurium, 361, 388
Temperature, 2
   absolute, 33
   critical, 38
   effect on chemical equilibrium, 231
   effect on reaction rate, 225
   effect on solubility, 174–176
   eutectic, 536
   extreme low, 640
   kindling, 125
   nature of, 29
   standard, 36
Tempering steel, 607
Tennant, 595
Tension
   aqueous, 165
   solution, 261
   vapor, 165
Terbium, 639
Tetrachlorethane, 675
Tetraethyl lead, 564
Tetrahedrite, 572
Tetrahydrol, 191

INDEX

Tetrathionate, 386
Thallium, 642
Thermal decomposition, 335
Thermionic electron emission, 513, 628
Thermite process, 517, 622, 629
Thermometers
  gallium, 641
  thallium, 642
Thinner, paint, 564
Thio-, 385
Thiocyanate test for Fe^{+++}, 612
Thiocyanates, 412
Thomson, 23, 53
Thoria, 639
Thorium, 643, 647, 650
Thulium, 639
Thyroid, 330
Thyroxine, 330, 718
Tin
  analysis, 566
  compounds, 559
  "cry", 545
  disease, 545
  occurrence, 537
  plate, 550
  preparation, 541
  properties, 544, 545
  uses, 550
Tincture of iodine, 316, 329
Titanium, 613, 633
Titanium dioxide, in paints, 564
Titration, 196–198
  electrometric, 267
Toluene, 676–677
Toning, photographic, 587, 630
Torch, welding and cutting, 129, 150, 156
Toricelli, 4
Toxic gases (in smoke), 275
Tracers, 450, 649
Transite, 519
Transition elements, 74–75, 82–83, 212
Transition point, 176
Transmutation, 650, 657
Triacid bases, 213
Triads, Döbereiner's, 79–80
Tribasic acids, 212
Trihydrol, 191–192
Tri-iodide ion, 327
Trinitrophenol, 676, 677
Trinitrotoluene, 676–677
Triple bond, 661, 674–675
Triprotic acids, 213
Trisodium phosphate, 432
Tritium (H^3), 651
Trona deposits, 311
Trona from Solvay process, 355
Tung oil, in paint, 564
Tungar rectifiers, 628

Tungsten, 613, 626
Turnbull's blue, 611
Turpentine, 328, 565
Tyndall effect, 305
Type metal, 449
Typhoid fever, 286
Tyrothricin, 721

Ultra-filtration, 304
Ultramicroscope, 41, 306
Ultra-violet lamp, 460, 549
Ultra-violet light and ozone, 131
Union, direct, 102–106, 214
Unsaturation, 150, 673
Unslaked lime, 522–525
Uranium, 644, 647, 657
  1, X1, X2, 650
  electronic structure, 64, 65
Urea, 396, 412, 415, 660, 714
  phosphate, 435
Urease, 714
Urey, 59

Vacuum evaporation, 166–167
Vacuum tube, 52
Valence
  change of, as oxidation-reduction, 103
  coordinate, or dative, 72–74, 212, 219
  determination of, 151–153
  electrons and, 68–77
  group numbers and, 86
  number, 73, 103, 105, 320
  octet, 71, 74
  periodic classification and, 86
  positive and negative, 70
  shell or layer, 70
  table of, 98
  variable, 76–77
    See also Covalence and Electrovalence
Van de Graaff generator, 653
Van der Waals' law, 38
Van der Waals' forces, 191–192, 488
Vanadium, 613, 628
Van't Hoff's law, 231
Vapor, 165
Vapor pressure, 164–167
  and boiling point, 168, 184–185
  and freezing point, 169, 184–185
Vapor tension, 165
Vaporization, 26
Vat dyes, development of, 134, 388
Vegetable oil, 703, 727
  hydrogenation, 703
Vehicle, paint, 564, 566
Velocity, molecular, 40
Venetian red, 609
Verdigris, 576

INDEX

Vermilion
  American, 624
  Chinese, 537
Vinegar, 699
Viscose rayon, 708
Vitallium, 615
Vitamin C, 376
Vitamins, 715–718
  chart, 716
  structural formulas, 717
Vitreous glazes and enamels, 476
Vitriol, 384
  blue, 183
  green, 183, 610
  oil of, 380
  white, 555
Volt, 259
Volta, 253
Voltaic cells, 253
  anode and cathode, 254
Volume, gram molecular, 44
Volumes, law of combining, 41–44, 46–47
Volumetric analysis, 196
von Hevesy, 643
von Laue, 61
Vulcanization of rubber, 687
Vulcanized fiber, 555
Vycor glass, 471

Washing soda, 351
Water, 190–195, 197–199, 284–297
  acid-base properties, 194
  association of, 191–192
  baryta, 528
  bromine, 325
  carbonated, 665
  density, 191–192
  dipoles of, 173–174
  drinking, 285
  expansion of, on freezing, 190, 191–192
  gas, 141–142, 685
  glass, 464
  hard, 289
  heat of fusion, 190
  heavy, 59–60
  ionization of, 234
  Javelle, 347
  lithia, 287
  mineral, 285, 287
  molecular state, 191
  of crystallization, 183
  purification, 285–292
    by ozone, 132, 133
  radioactive, 287
  softening, 288
  vapor in atmosphere, 271

Watt, 261, 590
Wave mechanics, 51, 58
Weak acids and bases, 193–195
Weathering of rocks, 190
Weight, 2
  formula, 95
  gram atomic, 151–154
  gram molecular, 43–44
Welding of aluminum and stainless steel, 282
Wells, salt, 285, 317, 318
Welsbach mantles, 636, 639, 644
White lead, 564
Willemite, 536
Wilson cloud chamber, 40
Winkler, 84, 643
Winthrop, 570
Wire glass, 470
Withering, 503
Wöhler, 412, 629, 660
Wolframite, 626
Wollaston, 594
Wood, 678
  cracking, 678
  pulp, 329
  See also Cellulose
Wood's metal, 500
Wrought iron, 603
Wulfenite, 625
Wurtzite, 536

X rays, 54–55
  beryllium windows for, 514
Xenon
  in air, 271
  discovery, 279

Yeast, 694
Ytterbium, 639

Zaffre, 615
Zeolite, 290, 463
Zeros of temperature scales, 3, 33
Zinc
  analysis, 566
  compounds, 553
    chloride, hydrolysis, 554
    sulfide, in spinthariscope, 19
  occurrence, 536
  preparation, 538
  properties, 544
  uses, 547
Zircon, 462, 635, 636
Zirconium, 613, 634–636

PERIODIC CLASSIFICATION

PERIODS	GROUP 0	GROUP I	GROUP II	GROUP III
1		1 H-1.0080		
2	2 He-4.003	3 Li-6.940	4 Be-9.02	5 B-10.82
3	10 Ne-20.183	11 Na-22.997	12 Mg-24.32	13 Al-26.97
4	18 A-39.944	19 K-39.096	20 Ca-40.08	21 Sc-45.10
		29 Cu-63.54	30 Zn-65.38	31 Ga-69.72
5	36 Kr-83.7	37 Rb-85.48	38 Sr-87.63	39 Y-88.92
		47 Ag-107.88	48 Cd-112.41	49 In-114.76
6	54 Xe-131.3	55 Cs-132.91	56 Ba-137.36	57 La-138.92
		79 Au-197.2	80 Hg-200.61	81 Tl-204.39
7	86 Rn-222	87 Fr	88 Ra-226.05	89 Ac-229
RARE EARTHS	58 Ce-140.13	59 Pr-140.92	60 Nd-144.27	61 ———
		66 Dy-162.46	67 Ho-164.94	68 Er-167.2
ACTINIDES	90 Th-232.12	91 Pa-231	92 U-238.07	93 Np